D0142249

Frequency response from difference equation, $\quad H(e^{j\theta}) = \dfrac{\displaystyle\sum_{k=0}^{L} b_k e^{-jk\theta}}{1 - \displaystyle\sum_{k=1}^{N} a_k e^{-jk\theta}}$

Sinusoidal steady-state formula, $\quad y_{ss}(n) = X|H(e^{j\theta})| \cos\left(n\theta + \angle H(e^{j\theta})\right)$

$$\text{for } x(n) = X \cos(n\theta)$$

Ideal filter in the frequency domain, $\quad H(e^{j\theta}) = \begin{cases} Ke^{-j\ell\theta}, & \text{in the passband} \\ 0, & \text{otherwise.} \end{cases}$

z-transform definition, $\quad \mathfrak{z}[x(n)] = \displaystyle\sum_{n=-\infty}^{n=+\infty} x(n)z^{-n}$

Linear convolution, $\quad \mathfrak{z}[p(n) = q(n) * r(n)] = P(z) = Q(z) \cdot R(z)$

System transfer function, $\quad H(z) = \mathfrak{z}[h(n)]$

$$= Y(z)/X(z)$$

Discrete Fourier Transform (DFT) pair

$$X(k) = \sum_{n=0}^{N-1} x(n)e^{-j(2\pi/N)nk}, \quad \longleftrightarrow \quad x(n) = \frac{1}{N}\sum_{k=0}^{N-1} X(k)e^{j(2\pi/N)nk},$$

$$k = 0, 1, \ldots, N-1 \qquad\qquad n = 0, 1, \ldots, N-1$$

DFT as a sampled version of the Fourier Transform, $\quad X(k) = X(e^{j\theta})\Big|_{\theta=2\pi k/N}$

DFT pair for a sampled signal

$$X(k\Delta f) = \sum_{n=0}^{N-1} x(nT)e^{-j(2\pi/N)nk}, \quad k = 0, 1, \ldots, N-1$$

$$x(nT) = \frac{1}{N}\sum_{k=0}^{N-1} X(k\Delta f)e^{j(2\pi/N)nk}, \quad n = 0, 1, \ldots, N-1$$

Frequency resolution, $\quad \Delta f = 1/NT = 1/T_0$

(continued)

First Principles of Discrete Systems and Digital Signal Processing

Robert D. Strum
Naval Postgraduate School

Donald E. Kirk
Naval Postgraduate School

 ADDISON-WESLEY PUBLISHING COMPANY

Reading, Massachusetts • Menlo Park, California • New York
Don Mills, Ontario • Wokingham, England • Amsterdam • Bonn
Sydney • Singapore • Tokyo • Madrid • Bogotá • Santiago • San Juan

This book is in the **Addison-Wesley Series in Electrical Engineering: Digital Signal Processing**

Sponsoring Editor: *Tom Robbins*
Production Supervisor: *Laura Skinger*
Production Administrator: *Helen Wythe*
Production: *York Production Services*
Manufacturing Supervisor: *Hugh Crawford*
Text Designer: *Vanessa Piñeiro-Robbins*
Cover Designer: *Richard Hannus*

To

Families

Ione, Sarah, and Arthur   Judy, Kara, Valerie, and Dana

and Mentors
Mac Van Valkenburg
Carvel Wheeler

Library of Congress Cataloging-in-Publication Data

Strum, Robert D.
    First principles of discrete systems and digital
signal processing.

    Includes bibliographies and index.
    1. Signal processing—Digital techniques. I. Kirk,
Donald E., 1937–   . II. Title.
TK5102.5.S774   1988   621.38′043   86-26542
ISBN 0-201-09518-1

Copyright © 1988 by Addison-Wesley Publishing Company, Inc.

All rights reserved. No part of this publication may be reproduced, stored in a retrieval system, or transmitted, in any form or by any means electronic, mechanical, photocopying, recording, or otherwise, without the prior written permission of the publisher. Printed in the United States of America. Published simultaneously in Canada.

CDEFGHIJ-DO-898

Preface

WHY YOU SHOULD READ THIS PREFACE

Several views of a preface are

- A statement or essay, usually by the author, introducing a book and explaining its scope, intention, or background (dictionary)
- Obligatory (publisher)
- The last item provided when your energy and patience are almost exhausted (author)
- Something to be skipped (reader)
- Advertising, subject to the usual attempts to appeal by overstatement, innuendo, etc. (instructor)

At this point you already know when and why we wrote this preface, but why should you read it? Primarily because we think you will know quickly what our approach has been, what we consider the book's strong points to be, and whether these are a good match to your teaching (instructor)/learning (student) style.

WHY WE WROTE THE BOOK

We wrote this book because we were, and are, convinced that there is a need for an introductory level text on discrete systems and digital signal processing. All of us find it easier to understand and manipulate sums and differences rather than integrals and derivatives, and thus it makes sense to learn first about discrete systems. In addition, the rapid swing to digital technology and algorithms makes discrete systems and digital signal processing of fundamental importance in applications. We were also encouraged by the views of others who seem to be on the same "wavelength," for example, M. E. Van Valkenburg who stated in 1974: "It appears that the discrete case is the natural one to the uninhibited mind, but special and somewhat mysterious after a thorough grounding in continuous-time concepts."[†]

We also believe it is better not to cover discrete-time and continuous-time systems in the same course. Van Valkenburg observes " . . . Having taught such a course recently, I conclude that we were right in 1974: mixing the two concepts may give the instructor great satisfaction at the unity of it all, but it thoroughly confuses the students!"[‡]

Among the most satisfying experiences for a teacher is putting ideas together in ways that help students learn. This has been our primary goal in writing the book, and we hope you feel that we've succeeded.

PHILOSOPHY

This is a book about fundamentals. We have attempted to do a thorough job on the basic principles because our experience has been that these are the most difficult for students to master. Once the fundamentals are mastered, an understanding of advanced concepts can be readily obtained. This is also a book about problem solving, seeing interrelationships and connections, and integrating one's knowledge. How do we do this? By reviewing pertinent concepts and relating them to new principles as they are introduced. Extensive examples are included and the results obtained are checked against results developed by alternative approaches. We also summarize the important ideas at the conclusion of each chapter and provide Integrated Review problems in later chapters that require the student to draw on previous knowledge and determine relationships to current topics. Finally, we include Extension and Generalization problems for the student to expand on the results contained in the text.

We believe that students learn by doing. Thus, we typically assign many problems for students to work. We also feel that an important result of the learning process is to develop the ability to learn on your own. In pursuit of this goal we have attempted to gradually place more of a burden on the student as the book proceeds. Consequently, the student

---

[†] From the foreword to the text: *An Introduction to Discrete Systems*, K. Steiglitz, New York: John Wiley and Sons, Inc., 1974.
[‡] From the column "Curriculum Trends," *Newsletter, IEEE Education Society/EE Division of ASEE*, September, 1984.

will find the need to fill in more of the details in Chapter 10 than in Chapter 3, for example.

The conversational writing style in the book reflects our objective of getting the reader involved with the material as a participant in the development, rather than as an observer. We have also attempted not to "culturally bias" the material toward electrical engineering in the belief that people from several other disciplines may find the book to be a good introduction to the field of digital signal processing.

Although, the book is longer than originally envisioned, we have not, of course, covered all the possible topics of interest in discrete systems and digital signal processing. We have, however, attempted to treat the fundamental principles carefully and have provided unusually detailed examples both as illustrations of concepts previously developed and as a vehicle for introducing a new concept that is then developed in more generality. We hope that the result will provide effective leverage for the student in his or her learning process.

FEATURES

We have incorporated many features in this book to aid both the student and instructor. The most important of these are

- A self-contained presentation of both discrete systems and digital signal processing that requires only a minimum amount of calculus and facility with complex numbers as prerequisites.

- Seven Appendices that cover background information and related topics.

- A Vocabulary and Important Relations section at the end of each chapter that gathers together the key terminology, topics, and equations.

- A Preview at the beginning of each chapter and a Review at the end. These are included in the spirit of the teacher's old adage: "Tell them what you're going to tell them; tell them; tell them what you told them."

- Extensive use of examples (approximately 150 of them) with detailed solutions to introduce, amplify, and illustrate the concepts.

- Emphasis on computer-based methods to solve problems, with pseudocode provided for eight computer subroutines/programs. For the convenience of the instructor and student, end of chapter problems that require the use of a computer are indicated with the logo   .

- A large number of figures (approximately 350) illustrate the important concepts.

- Organized procedures for digital filter design.

- An early discussion of the sampling theorem and frequency response methods that allows meaningful filter design problems to be solved before acquiring a complete repertoire of discrete systems techniques.

- More than 350 problems at the end of the chapters, subdivided into the categories: Reinforcement, Extension and Generalization, and Integrated Review.

- A complete solutions manual, written by the authors, that contains solutions to all text problems, listings for several computer programs, and transparency masters for approximately 125 text figures.

- Answers to approximately one-third of the text problems provided at the end of the book.

ORGANIZATION

The presentation in Chapter 1 of several digital signal processing applications is intended to provide motivation for the reader to learn the material that follows. The remainder of the book is divided into the two principal areas:

Discrete Systems—Chapters 2–6

Digital Signal Processing—Chapters 7–11

Chapter 2 introduces the basic concepts of signals and discrete systems including the important sampling theorem. Several models for linear time-invariant systems and analysis techniques are presented in Chapter 3. The important concept of sinusoidal steady-state analysis of discrete systems is discussed in Chapter 4, which also introduces the frequency response model and some fundamental principles of digital filters. Chapter 5 introduces a graphical method for obtaining approximate values of a system's frequency response. (This relatively short chapter may be viewed as optional. We included it because in this age of the ubiquitous computer, it often helps to have fast and easy methods to get approximate answers as a way to get a rough check on computer results, or in explaining (or refuting) unexpected computer output.) The coverage of discrete systems theory concludes with Chapter 6, which presents the theory of z transforms and shows how they can be used to solve difference equations.

Chapter 7 begins the discussion of techniques for digital signal processing. This extensive chapter is concerned mainly with the Discrete Fourier Transform (DFT), its properties, and applications to the evaluation of convolution, correlation, and the determination of spectrum estimates. The radix-2 Fast Fourier Transform (FFT), which makes real-time signal processing possible in many applications, is presented in Chapter 8 as an efficient algorithm for computing Discrete Fourier Transforms. Chapters 9 and 10 introduce digital filter design methods; nonrecursive filter design is the subject of Chapter 9 and Chapter 10 is concerned with the design of recursive filters. Chapter 11 presents several structures for implementing discrete systems and also introduces the state equation model for discrete systems.

PREREQUISITES

The primary prerequisites are a basic background in calculus and the ability to manipulate complex numbers, although a concise presentation of the latter subject is given in Appendix A. Familiarity with fundamental concepts of infinite series, Fourier series, and matrix manipulations may be helpful, but is not required because the necessary material is self-contained.

USE OF THE BOOK

For students with some background in discrete systems theory, the book can be used as the text for an introduction to digital signal processing. This requires review of the important concepts of Chapters 2 through 6 and concentration on the material in Chapters 7 through 11. For those without a background in discrete systems theory, the book can be used to support a two-course sequence. This is the approach we have followed at the Naval Postgraduate School by using the class notes that led to the book as the text for a two-quarter sequence in discrete systems and digital signal processing. The discrete systems course is at the sophomore/junior level and covers the material in Chapters 2–6. The material in Chapters 7–11 is presented in the digital signal processing course, which is at the senior/graduate level. Chapter 11 may also be covered before Chapters 7–10, but our experience has been that additional motivation is provided by presenting this material last.

The book could also be used for a one-semester course in discrete systems and signal processing, although the pace would quicken and/or some material would probably have to be omitted.

Finally, we also believe that the extensive examples and complete discussions make the text suitable for self-study by practicing engineers and scientists.

NOTES TO STUDENTS

We've invested a lot of time to try to help you understand the material in this book, but your active involvement is the key ingredient in the learning process. There are many examples in the text and you are encouraged to try to solve some of these as problems and use the solutions provided to check your work. We have also tried to emphasize techniques for checking answers to problems by using alternative techniques whenever possible. Finally, we encourage you to be skeptical about your problem solutions, especially those involving the use of a computer: always ask "Is the answer reasonable?"

ACKNOWLEDGMENTS

It's hard for us to imagine how any textbook can be written without feedback from students and other faculty members. We have been especially fortunate in this regard by having several classes of students use the versions of the notes that eventually led to the book. We especially wish to acknowledge the helpful comments of Thomas DeMars, Jr., Janine England, Frank Hudik, Sarfraz Hussain, Eva and Manuel Malagon, Antoniou Marquess, Timothy Merrill, Edward Siomacco, and Paulo Sousa. We also thank Paul Montgomery who conceived the cover design and James Harmon who provided the computer logo used throughout the book.

Several faculty colleagues have also contributed significantly to the book. Valuable comments were offered by Richard W. Hamming, Paul H. Moose, Charles W. Therrien, and Michael A. Morgan, and we sincerely thank them. We also acknowledge the helpful suggestions of those who reviewed the manuscript: Artice M. Davis, K. R. Dunipace, John A. Fleming, L. E. Franks, David C. Munson, Jr., Banu Onaral, Richard A. Roberts, and Ferrel G. Stremler.

Our editor Tom Robbins provided many creative ideas and much encouragement. In addition, he even seemed to enjoy being the victim of our numerous, often feeble, and probably futile attempts at humor. Mary Jo Gregory of York Production Services did a superb job in all aspects of supervising the production. During several years filled with promises to begin work on the book, Roger Vaughan continually encouraged us to really begin the project, and once we started, Larry Ziomek provided weekend exhortations to keep at it.

Finally, we had the help of several excellent typists in creating the notes and subsequent revisions that eventually became this book. We appreciate the efforts of Linda Bloom, Darlene Kelley, Maureen Kasputis, Carolyn Meyers, Pat Allen, and Anu Tummala.

R.D.S.
D.E.K.

Carmel, California

Contents

CHAPTER 3

LINEAR TIME-INVARIANT SYSTEMS   77

CHAPTER 4

FREQUENCY RESPONSE AND FILTERS   165

CHAPTER 5

FREQUENCY RESPONSE—A GRAPHICAL METHOD   243

CHAPTER 6

z-TRANSFORMS   281

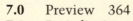

CHAPTER 7

DISCRETE FOURIER TRANSFORM   363

CHAPTER 8

THE FAST FOURIER TRANSFORM   493

CHAPTER 9

NONRECURSIVE FILTER DESIGN   529

CHAPTER 10

RECURSIVE FILTER DESIGN   611

Introduction

1.0 ▬▬ PREVIEW

During the last two decades the availability of small, powerful, and relatively inexpensive digital computers has increased dramatically the applications of digital signal processing. This trend has been reinforced by the concurrent development of efficient numerical procedures (algorithms) for digital signal processing. Now digital signal processing has become a primary application for modern integrated circuit technology with high speed programmable chips capable of performing the operations required. So it is natural to find digital signal processing applied in many diverse areas, several of which we will briefly consider in this chapter.

The discussion is intended to provide motivation to learn the "tools of the trade," presented in the chapters that follow. These tools— concepts, procedures, and techniques—provide the foundation for further study in a number of exciting and fast-paced areas of signal processing.

Finally, the description of the several application areas that were chosen is intended to be strictly descriptive and somewhat superficial. You won't become, for instance, expert in speech processing by merely studying the next section. So, with this said, let's proceed.

1.1 ▬▬ PROCESSING OF SPEECH SIGNALS

Digital processing of speech signals is practical for the following purposes (Rabiner and Schafer, 1978):

a) *storing* and *transmitting* speech signals

b) *enhancing* speech signals to *improve* their overall quality and intelligibility

c) *generating* or *synthesizing* waveforms that closely resemble human speech

d) *verifying* a speaker's *identity* from vocal input

e) *recognizing* a speaker's words and *providing* the equivalent of a written version of them

f) *modifying* speech information into a more *suitable* form for those with visual or auditory handicaps

Now let's consider a brief description of each of these before taking a more detailed look at digital transmission of speech.

A primary goal of *digital speech transmission systems* is to lower the amount of data that needs to be sent, or transmitted, in order to reconstruct the original speech waveform at a receiver. One possible technique is to sample the speech signal at an appropriate rate and then transmit information from which these sample values can be reconstructed at the receiver. An alternate procedure, which requires the transmission of less information (a savings of a factor of 10 to 50 is typical), is to determine a set of parameters using a speech analysis system that characterizes the speech process itself rather than the speech samples. This approach, which is the basis of vocoder (short for voice coder) systems, will be discussed later in more detail.

Speech enhancement has the objective of improving the quality of speech that has been diminished by background noise. For example, the speech of a pilot in the noisy cockpit of an aircraft may be difficult to understand without signal processing designed to suppress the noise and confusion of the cockpit environment.

Speech synthesis systems are intended to generate waveforms that closely resemble human speech. This is accomplished by exciting a model of the human speech mechanism having parameter values that produce the desired speech signals. Applications include automatic information response systems, which are already familiar to many of us who use direct dialing for long distance calls and receive responses telling us, for example, to enter our credit card numbers, or to make a deposit for the first three minutes.

The purpose of *speech verification and identification systems* is to attempt to verify a speaker's identity from her or his speech input. This could be used to control access to a speaker-queried data base, which we might expect in automated bank tellers of the future.

In *speech recognition systems* the objective is to obtain the equivalent of a written version of a speaker's words. Such capability is needed in systems for voice input to a computer, for example, where a limited vocabulary of words is used and there may be a "training" period required for the system to adapt to the speaking characteristics of a user of the system.

Speech modification systems may be used to present speech information in a more readily used form than that available without processing. One example is a system where speed can be varied to enable a blind person to proceed at a comfortable pace while listening to speech.

Now let us further consider an application of both speech analysis and speech synthesis systems as they might be used in a vocoder. A model that can generally provide a good representation of the human speech-producing mechanism is shown in Fig. 1.1. If this model is stimulated by receiving appropriate values for the pitch period, the position of the voiced/unvoiced speech switch, the vocal tract parameters, and the amplitude values A_V and A_N, it will generally produce a good approximation to the actual pressure at the lips of a speaker. In this configuration the impulse train generator and glottal pulse model generate signals that represent voiced sounds such as several vowel sounds. The random noise generator is used to form unvoiced sounds such as "sh" in "shall." The vocal tract parameters are changed at intervals of approximately 10–20 milliseconds. This model is then the basis for a speech synthesizing sys-

FIGURE 1.1 A model for speech processing

Source: Rabiner, L. R., and R. W. Schafer, *Digital Processing of Speech Signals,* © 1978, p. 105. Reprinted by permission of Prentice-Hall, Inc., Englewood Cliffs, New Jersey.

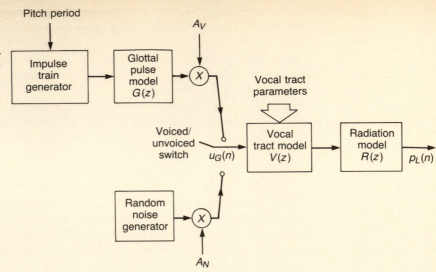

tem and would be found in the receiver portion of a vocoder. At the transmitting end there is a speech analyzer that is subjected to inputs from a speaker and estimates the model parameters that are updated every 10 to 20 ms, and then transmitted. The receiver, which may be close by or far away, receives these parameters and uses them to excite the model of Fig. 1.1 thereby reconstructing the speech at the receiver. A much-simplified block diagram of this process is shown in Fig. 1.2. Details of how the speech analysis process is performed are available in Rabiner and Schafer, 1978, and Rabiner and Gold, 1975.

1.2 ▬ PROCESSING OF SEISMIC SIGNALS

Drilling for oil is expensive and time consuming and so it is naturally of great interest to maximize the potential success of any drilling operations. An effective way to do this is to use signal processing to gain information about the structure of the rock and soil in potential drilling areas.

An effective procedure is to use acoustic sounding data together with other information to discover and define the boundaries of a reservoir that holds oil and gas in porous formations. The field exploration arrange-

FIGURE 1.2 Block diagram representation of a vocoder

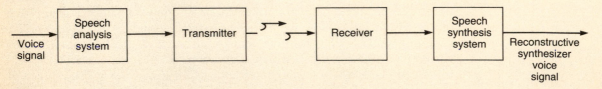

FIGURE 1.3 An arrangement for seismic sounding

Source: Wason, C. B., J. L.
Black, and G. A. King, "Seismic Modeling and Inversion,"
Proceedings of the IEEE Vol.
72, No. 10, p. 1386 (Fig. 2),
© 1984.

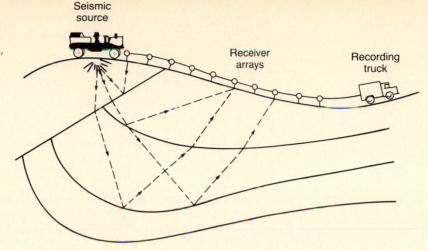

ment shown in Fig. 1.3 (Wason, Black, and King, 1984) includes a source
of seismic energy, an array of receivers for measuring the reflected energy
at several locations, and a truck for recording the received signal histo-
ries.

We can represent the relationship between the transmitted seismic
source and the received signal by the diagram shown in Fig. 1.4. The
objective of the signal processing performed on s(t) is to obtain a good
estimate of the reflection characteristic of subsurface layers. This estimate can then be interpreted to reveal promising and unpromising geo-
graphical structures. The determination of the reflection characteristic
estimate is performed by a procedure known as *deconvolution.* The geologic model corresponding to the reflection characteristic of the subsurface layers may be determined by the process illustrated in Fig. 1.5
(Wason, Black, and King, 1984). The geologic model is used to generate
synthetic data which is then compared with the actual measurement
data. If the actual and synthesized data are approximately the same as one
another, the geologic model is accepted as a good estimate of the true
geology. If the synthesized and actual measurement data differ significantly, the difference is used to compute a perturbation to the geologic
model. After using the perturbation to change the geologic model the
process is repeated and it continues until an acceptable match is found
between synthesized and measured data.

FIGURE 1.4 Model of the
relationship between seismic source and received
signal

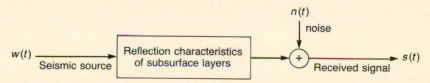

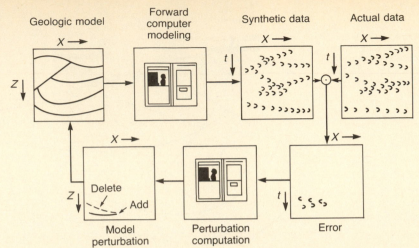

FIGURE 1.5 System used to determine the geologic model from the computer adjustment of the model to match the data

Source: Wason, C. B., J. L. Black, and G. A. King, "Seismic Modeling and Inversion," *Proceedings of the IEEE* Vol. 72, No. 10, p. 1386 (Fig. 2) © (1984) IEEE.

Geologic model

Forward computer modeling

Synthetic data

Actual data

Delete

Add

Model perturbation

Perturbation computation

Error

Additional applications of seismic signal processing are detection, measurement, and prediction of earthquakes; and detection of underground nuclear explosions.

1.3 ▬ RADAR SIGNAL PROCESSING

Many of the recent advances made in radar detection and tracking have been due to the power and feasibility of digital signal processing. A block diagram of a typical radar system is shown in Fig. 1.6 (Oppenheim et al., 1978) where we see that the basic idea is quite simple even though the details of implementation are sophisticated.

A pulse of electromagnetic energy is transmitted and directed by an antenna as a beam that passes through a region of space. If a portion of this energy strikes an object, some of the energy is reflected back to the antenna, which can receive signals as well as transmit them. The time (Δt) taken for the roundtrip of the electromagnetic wave is related to the distance (R) of the target from the transmit/receive antenna by

$$R = c \, \Delta t / 2 \qquad (1.1)$$

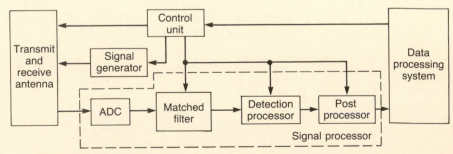

FIGURE 1.6 Block diagram of a large modern radar system

Source: McClellan/Purdy, "Applications of Digital Signal Processing to Radar" in *Applications of Digital Signal Processing,* Alan V. Oppenheim ed., © 1978, p. 241. Reprinted by permission of Prentice-Hall, Inc., Englewood Cliffs, New Jersey.

Control unit

Transmit and receive antenna

Signal generator

Data processing system

ADC

Matched filter

Detection processor

Post processor

Signal processor

where

R = range in meters

c = velocity of light = 3×10^8 meters/second

Δt = roundtrip travel time of the electromagnetic energy in seconds

In this way the range can be computed. Additionally, by knowing the bearing angle and angle of elevation from horizontal of the antenna beam along with the range, an estimated location of the reflecting object can be obtained. It is also possible to extract velocity information by measuring the doppler frequency shift of the received pulse.

In an ideal environment the signal reflected to the radar receiver would be simply a delayed and attenuated replica of the transmitted pulse. Unfortunately, noise effects of the atmosphere, sources of radiation, and the electronic equipment itself degrade the shape of the pulse. Thus, it is not practical to simply look for a received signal that resembles the transmitted signal and determine by measurement the delay between transmitting the pulse and receiving its reflection. In addition, to make the radiated energy large to achieve long-range capability it is desirable to use relatively long pulses rather than short, large pulses and this conflicts with a desire to be able to differentiate between (resolve) two targets that have small range differences. Digital signal processing can be used to alleviate these conflicting requirements by using a technique known as pulse compression by matched filtering. A long duration pulse whose frequency is linearly increased is used to obtain a high energy level for long-range capability. By sweeping the frequency and processing the return pulse with a digital matched filter it is possible to obtain range resolution inversely proportional to the frequency bandwidth of the pulse. Thus, by sweeping the frequency through a large range and doing the necessary matched filtering both long-range capability and the ability to resolve close targets can be achieved. The term "matched filtering" is used because the filter characteristic is matched to the signal transmitted. The process of matched filtering maximizes the probability of detecting a target in the presence of noise.

There are many applications of radar signal processing including air traffic control, weather monitoring, ground mapping, and radar astronomy, as well as the obvious military applications to search and detection of airborne targets.

1.4 ■■■ IMAGE PROCESSING

Examples of image processing are very familiar to us. We've all seen reproductions of images of the earth, moon, and distant planets obtained from voyages of spacecraft, and satellite photos of weather patterns are a daily occurrence on most local television news programs. Images obtained from x-rays and ultrasound are used more and more in the diagnosis and treatment of illnesses, and satellite images are commonly used for mineral exploration, monitoring of agricultural crops, and to explore the surface of the ocean floor.

Prior to processing an image the visual source must be converted into digital form suitable for the input to a computer and is then recorded, or stored. This process is accomplished by an *image acquisition system* (Green, 1983) which introduces distortions, both predictable and random, into the stored image. It is to this acquired digital representation that a variety of image processing algorithms may be applied for the purpose of improving the utility of the information in the image.

One general class of such algorithms seeks to accomplish *image restoration*, that is, to recover the original image by removing the distortions introduced by the acquisition process. Thus, the expected output from an image restoration procedure is an image that more closely resembles the original image than does the acquired, or recorded image. We can visualize this process, as shown in Fig. 1.7, where x and y denote the spatial coordinates of the image plane. Notice that the acquired image is defined only for the discrete set of points x_i, $i = 1, 2, \ldots, N$ and y_j, $j = 1, 2, \ldots, M$. The goal of the restoration process is to make $\hat{f}(x_i, y_j)$ a more accurate representation of $f(x, y)$ than $g(x_i, y_j)$, and there are several algorithms designed to accomplish this objective (Gonzalez and Wintz, 1987; Hunt, 1984).

Another group of image processing algorithms is aimed at improving the usefulness of the processed image. These algorithms are known collectively as *image enhancement* procedures. This application may not result in a representation that is closer to the original image than the image before processing. Indeed, the enhancement techniques that are used depend very much on the application—what works well in one case may be ineffective in another. As a result, there is considerable subjectivity in the use of image enhancement algorithms, and trial and error may be required to obtain a satisfactory result. A graphic example of image enhancement is provided by the three images of Saturn obtained by Voyager 2 and shown in Fig. 1.8. The image in Fig. 1.8(a) contains little discernible information. After the process of contrast enhancement the image appears as in Fig. 1.8(b) where several terrain features are evident. The result of using an alternative enhancement procedure, highpass filtering and contrast enhancement, is shown in Fig. 1.8(c) where we see the additional detail. Contrast enhancement and spatial filtering are only two

FIGURE 1.7 The image restoration process

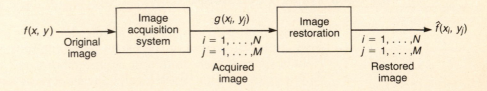

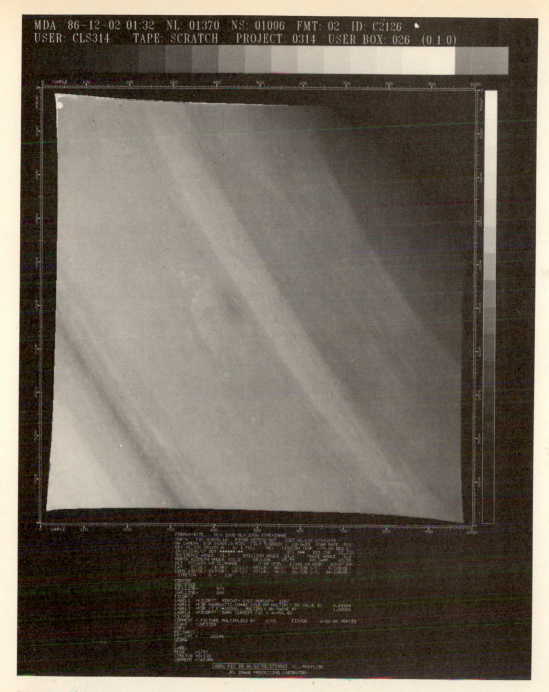

FIGURE 1.8(a) Radiometrically corrected Voyager 2 image of Saturn—little discernible information

Source: Courtesy of Jet Propulsion Laboratory, Pasadena, California.

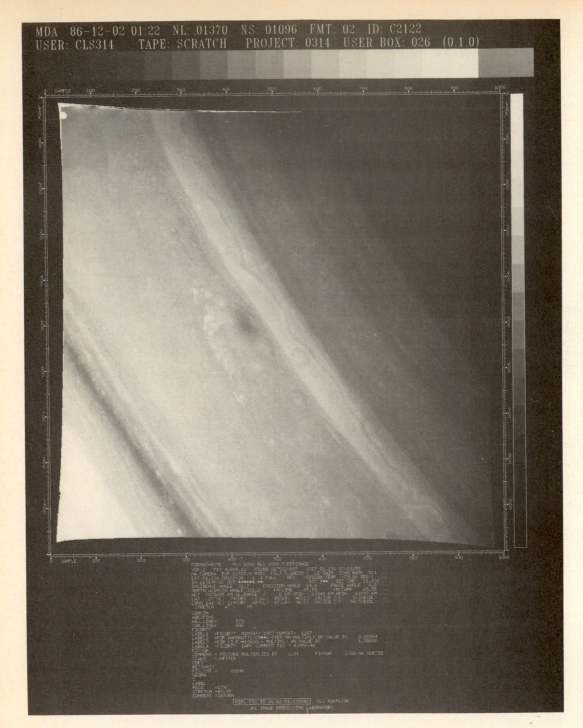

FIGURE 1.8(b) Several terrain features are evident following linear contrast enhancement

Source: Courtesy of Jet Propulsion Laboratory, Pasadena, California.

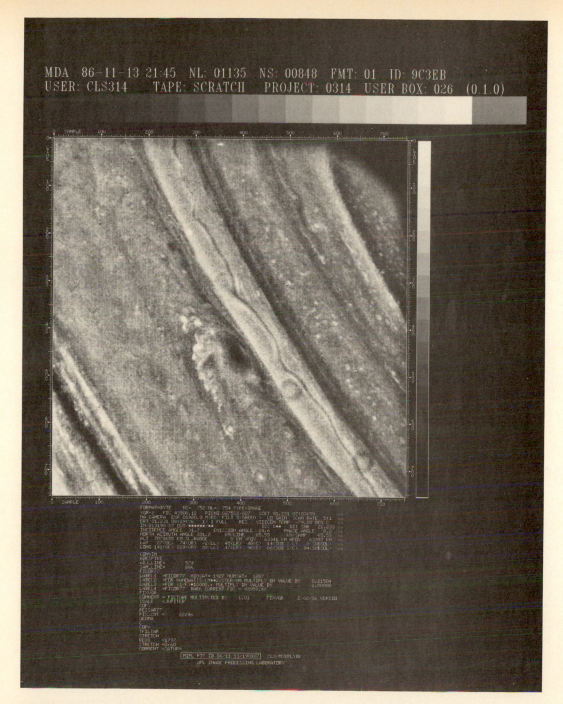

FIGURE 1.8(c) Additional detail is available after application of a high pass filter and linear contrast enhancement

Source: Courtesy of Jet Propulsion Laboratory, Pasadena, California.

of many algorithms used for enhancement; the others include image contouring, bit slicing, color enhancement methods, geometric transformation, image registration, radiometric correction, and color manipulation (Green, 1983; Lim, 1984).

To use computers to extract information about the objects in an image for automatic source analysis and pattern recognition requires another group of processing algorithms. Among them are segmentation, determination of regional and relational descriptions, and establishment of measures of similarity between different regions or different images (Gonzalez and Wintz, 1987).

The final category of image processing techniques we shall survey concerns the reconstruction of images from projections. One field where this has been extensively used is in medicine where the goal is to obtain the internal structure of portions of a person's body by using several projections from radiation of ultrasound, or x-rays, for example. This technique is known as *computerized tomography* (CT). An example is illustrated in Fig. 1.9 where a cardiovascular computerized tomographic (CVCT) scanner is pictured (Boyd and Lipton, 1983). This scanner features magnetic deflection of an electron beam to obtain more rapid scanning than is attainable with mechanical beam scanning. A relatively high scanning speed is essential in studying the cardiovascular system because of blurring and streak artifacts that are caused by cardiac motion. In general, CT scanning is used to identify and locate abnormal structures in the body, e.g. tumors, for the purposes of surgical planning and/or radiation therapy. An introduction to this subject is presented in Herman, 1983.

1.5 ▬ KALMAN FILTERING AND ESTIMATORS

Another type of signal processing problem requires estimating the values of system signals, which generally vary with time, or system parameters, which are often constant, from noisy measurement of system outputs. In such situations we may use a model of the system as shown in Fig. 1.10 where $\mathbf{x}(n)$ is a vector (column matrix) that represents the state of the system at time $t = nT$ (T is the period between sample values), $\mathbf{w}(n)$ is a vector of random inputs to the system, $\mathbf{v}(n)$ represents random measurement errors, and $\mathbf{y}(n)$ is a vector that represents noisy, or inaccurate, measurements. The equations that characterize the plant and the measurement process are known and the objective is to obtain an accurate estimate $\hat{\mathbf{x}}(n)$ of the system state $\mathbf{x}(n)$ by processing the noisy measurements $\mathbf{y}(n)$. One approach for obtaining the estimate $\hat{\mathbf{x}}(n)$ is to use a Kalman filter (Kalman, 1960) as pictured in Fig. 1.11. Under certain assumptions concerning the plant and measurement processes and the statistics of the random processes $\mathbf{v}(n)$ and $\mathbf{w}(n)$, the Kalman filter is the optimal estimator.

FIGURE 1.9 A cardiovascular computed tomographic (CVCT) scanner

Source: Boyd, D. P., and M. J. Lipton, "Cardiac Computed Tomography," *Proceedings of the IEEE*, Vol. 71, No. 3, p. 305 (Figs. 7 and 8) © (1983) IEEE.

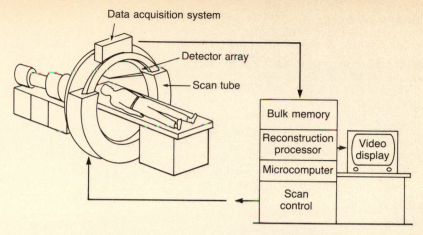

(a) Schematic design of the CVCT scanner system

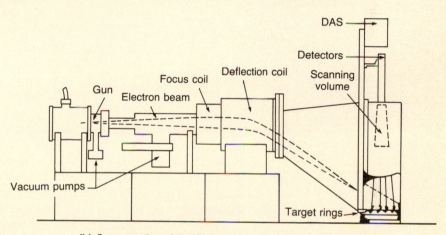

(b) Cross section of the CVCT scan tube indicating the beam focusing and steering method and the target configuration

As an example of this kind of situation, let us consider the tracking of an aircraft by a radar system. We assume that the radar provides measurements of the position and velocity of the aircraft. Unfortunately, these measurements are subject to errors (represented by $\mathbf{v}(n)$ in Fig. 1.10). The goal is to improve the accuracy provided by these measurements and to predict future positions of the aircraft in order to track it and control the location of the radar antenna. The random input $\mathbf{w}(n)$ might represent truly random effects such as wind gusts and turbulence, as well as other effects which we may be forced to treat as if they were random, such as modeling inaccuracies and pilot inputs. The equations that describe the Kalman filter are very similar to those of the actual system. The signals that drive the filter, however, are formed from the error between the

FIGURE 1.10 Model of a
system

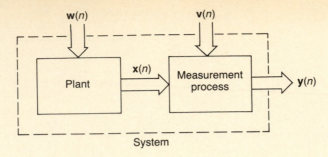

FIGURE 1.11 System with
Kalman filter

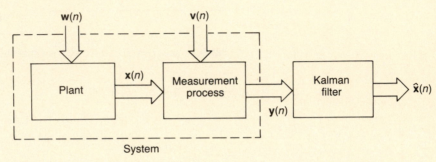

measurement $\mathbf{y}(n)$ and an estimate of the measurement generated by the Kalman filter.

Other applications of Kalman filters include the resetting of the position and correcting biases in inertial navigation systems (Bona and Smay, 1966), telephone load forecasting (Szelag, 1982), orbit determination for satellites (Jazwinski, 1970), tracking of spacecraft (Green, 1983), postflight smoothing of tracking data, and real-time estimation of system parameters.

1.6 ▬ REVIEW

In this chapter we have sampled some of the applications of discrete systems and signal processing. Our goal has been to motivate the reader to acquire the techniques and basic concepts needed to investigate one or more of these application areas. Each of the areas discussed can be the subject of considerable study. Indeed, many volumes exist on each of these topics. Nevertheless, certain fundamentals are central to most applications, and many of these basic concepts are discussed in the chapters that follow. Thus, mastery of the material in this book should prepare you for either advanced courses or for self-study on a variety of signal processing topics.

REFERENCES AND OTHER SOURCES OF INFORMATION

Boyd, D. P., and M. J. Lipton. 1983. "Cardiac Computed Tomography." *Proc. of the IEEE* 71(3): 298–307.

Bona, B. E., and R. J. Smay. 1966. "Optimum Reset of Ship's Inertial Navigation System." *IEEE Trans. on Aerospace and Electronic Systems.* AES-2 (July): 409–414.

Gonzalez, R. C., and P. Wintz. 1987. *Digital Image Processing.* 2d ed., Reading, Massachusetts: Addison-Wesley.

Green, W. B. 1983. *Digital Image Processing, A Systems Approach.* New York: Van Nostrand Reinhold Co.

Gelb, A., ed. 1974. *Applied Optimal Estimation.* Cambridge, Massachusetts: MIT Press.

Hunt, B. R. 1984. "Image Restoration." In *Digital Image Processing Techniques.* M. P. Ekstrom, ed. Orlando, Florida: Academic Press, Inc., pp. 53–76.

Herman, G. T., ed. 1983. *Proc. of the IEEE.* Special issue on computerized tomography 71(3).

Jazwinski, A. H. 1970. *Stochastic Processes and Filtering Theory.* New York: Academic Press.

Kalman, R. E. 1960. "A New Approach to Linear Filtering and Prediction Problems." *Trans. of the ASME—Journal of Basic Engineering:* 35–45.

Lim, J. S. 1984. "Image Enhancement." In *Digital Image Processing Techniques.* M. P. Ekstrom, ed. Orlando, Florida: Academic Press, Inc., pp. 1–52.

Oppenheim, A. V., ed. 1978. *Applications of Digital Signal Processing.* Englewood Cliffs, New Jersey: Prentice-Hall, Inc.

O'Shaughnessy, D. 1987. *Speech Communication,* Reading, Massachusetts: Addison-Wesley.

Rabiner, L. R., and R. W. Schafer. 1978. *Digital Processing of Speech Signals.* Englewood Cliffs, New Jersey: Prentice-Hall, Inc.

Rabiner, L. R., and B. Gold. 1975. *Theory and Application of Digital Signal Processing.* Englewood Cliffs, New Jersey: Prentice-Hall, Inc.

Szelag, C. R. 1982. "A Short-Term Forecasting Algorithm for Trunk Demand Servicing." *The Bell System Technical Journal* 61(1): 67–96.

Wason, C. B., J. L. Black, and G. A. King. 1984. "Seismic Modeling and Inversion." *Proc. of the IEEE* 72(10): 1385–1393.

CHAPTER 2

Signals and Systems

2.6 REVIEW
VOCABULARY AND IMPORTANT RELATIONS
PROBLEMS
REFERENCES AND OTHER SOURCES OF INFORMATION

2.0 ▬ PREVIEW

In this chapter we begin our study of the principles of discrete systems and signal processing. Our first task is to define five different types of signals that are frequently encountered in the analysis and design of signal processing systems. The most important of these signal types for our purposes is a *sequence* that may be thought of as an ordered collection of real or complex numbers. Such sequences may be denoted by $\{x(n)\}$ where n is an integer and the values of the sequence are . . . , $x(-3)$, $x(-2)$, $x(-1)$, $x(0)$, $x(1)$, ... For example, the sequence might represent the amount of money (updated monthly) owed on a loan, in which case we have

$$\{x(n)\} = \{\$1250, \$1135.40, \$1015.30, \$890.15, . . .\}$$
$$\underbrace{\hspace{1cm}}_{x(0)} \quad x(1) \quad\quad x(2) \quad\quad x(3)$$

Initial amount of loan

Another notation commonly used is $x(nT)$ when the sequence values result from sampling a continuously varying function of time, such as a person's blood pressure, at discrete time points separated by T seconds.

Several sequences are common as inputs to digital filtering and signal processing systems. Among the important sequences are the unit sample sequence, the unit step sequence, the family of exponential sequences and, of course, sinusoidal sequences. We shall study all of these in detail in this chapter.

Since many sequences arise by sampling continuously varying signals it is important to understand the limitations of the sampling process. We will give a plausibility argument to show that if the sampling interval is sufficiently small (the sampling frequency is high enough), a signal can be unambiguously represented by its samples. This assumes that the signal contains frequencies only up to a known limiting value. It is also shown that if a high enough sampling frequency isn't used, signals of different frequencies may not be distinguishable from one another.

We then turn to system properties and explore the concepts of linearity, time-invariance, stability, and causality. These properties all play an important, though often implicit, role in the remainder of the book.

The chapter concludes with two examples of how continuous-time processes such as integration and differentiation can be approximated by discrete system models.

2.1 ▬▬ TYPES OF SIGNALS

Before beginning a detailed description of some widely used sequences, a short discussion of five varieties of signals that often appear in signal processing systems is in order. We will use time as the independent variable although distance is also common.

a) *Continuous time* and *continuous amplitude*—This is usually called an *analog signal* and its concept is intuitive for we often encounter a physical phenomenon that can assume any of a continuous range of values in both time and amplitude as in Fig. 2.1(a). Analog signals occur in many different fields such as engineering, science, medicine, economics, and geophysics, to name only a few.

b) *Discrete time* and *continuous amplitude*—This is often called a *sampled signal*. The time steps are uniformly spaced, but the signal can have any level. Fig. 2.1(b) illustrates this where the sampling interval of T seconds is indicated. The whole process of sampling will be treated in more detail later in the chapter.

c) *Discrete time* and *discrete amplitude*—Such a signal is quantized in amplitude with uniform time steps. Thus, we can say that both amplitude and time are quantized. An analog-to-digital converter (A/D) generates this type of signal which is known as a *digital signal* and is portrayed in Fig. 2.1(c) with an amplitude quantization level of one fourth of a unit.

d) *Continuous time* and *continuous amplitude with uniform time steps*—This is known as a sampled-analog or *sampled-data signal* and is characteristic of the output of a *sample and hold* (S/H) device. The signal can have a continuous range of amplitudes that result from sampling an analog signal every T seconds as shown in Fig. 2.1(d). This sampled value is held constant over a sufficient period of time for the A/D converter (Fitchen, 1970), that normally follows the S/H, to make the analog-to-digital conversion. During the intervals when the signal is zero in Fig. 2.1(d), the S/H device is tracking the analog input in preparation for the next sampling instant.

e) *Continuous time* and *discrete amplitude with uniform time steps*—This is similar to the digital signal described in item (c), but here the signal holds its value between time samples. This signal, shown in Fig. 2.1(e), is characteristic of the output of a digital-to-analog (D/A) converter.

In this book, we will be most interested in discrete-time and continuous-amplitude signals (item b) and ways in which they are processed.

Figure 2.2 shows a commonly encountered system configuration wherein an analog signal input, $x_a(t)$, such as in Fig. 2.1(a) is converted into digital form to provide a digital input for a digital signal processor.

FIGURE 2.1 Types of signals

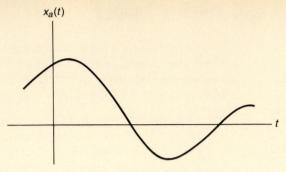

(a) Analog signal (continuous-time)

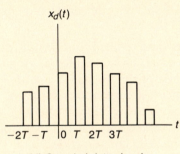

(b) Sampled signal (discrete-time)

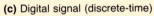
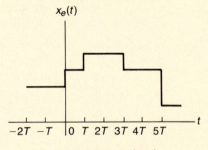

(c) Digital signal (discrete-time)

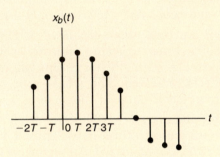

(d) Sampled-data signal
(continuous-time)

(e) D/A output signal
(continuous-time)

FIGURE 2.2 Processing
an analog signal

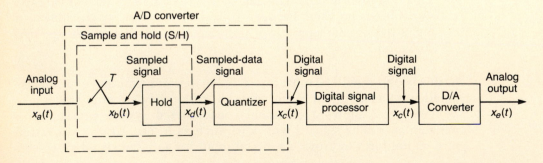

The digital output of the processor may in turn be converted to a continuous-time, discrete-amplitude signal that changes only at uniformly spaced intervals. This process of converting an analog signal into a digital signal appropriate for the input to a signal processor, or computer, is accomplished by an analog-to-digital (A/D) converter. Certain appropriate filters, which will be discussed in later chapters, need to be added to make this a usable and practical system.

2.2 ▪▪▪ SEQUENCES

As described in the previous section (Figs. 2.1(b) and (c)) a discrete-time signal (Cadzow, 1973; Oppenheim and Schafer, 1975; Robinson and Silvia, 1978) is defined only for discrete values of the independent variable at uniform intervals $t = nT$ where T is the interval between time samples and n is an integer. This signal, which is a sequence of numbers, may be obtained by sampling a continuous-time signal, such as blood pressure, for example, at equal intervals of time as indicated in Fig. 2.3(a). The *values* of this sequence are denoted as

$$x(nT) = x(t)\bigg|_{t=nT}, \qquad 0 \leq n \leq \infty \tag{2.1}$$

FIGURE 2.3 The sampling process

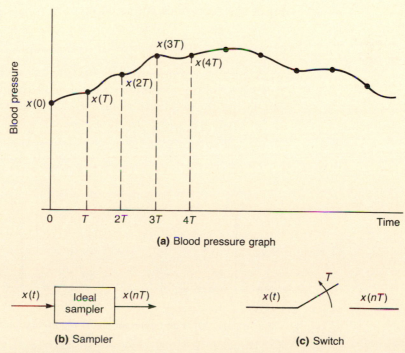

(a) Blood pressure graph

(b) Sampler

(c) Switch

and the sequence may be written as

$$\{x(nT)\} = \{x(0), \ x(T), \ x(2T), \ . \ . \ .\}$$
$$= \{133, \ 147, \ 153, \ . \ . \ .\}. \tag{2.2}$$

The process of generating the values in Fig. 2.3(a) may be viewed as in Fig. 2.3(b) where we assume that the output of the sampling device is the exact value of the input at the sampling instant. The switch in Fig. 2.3(c) samples $x(t)$ every T seconds to give $x(nT)$, hence we are assuming infinite precision with this viewpoint.

It is common practice to write simply $x(n)$ for the sequence value $x(nT)$ and a *sampled* analog signal is denoted as the sequence

$$\{x(n)\} = \{. \ . \ . \ , \ x(-203), \ . \ . \ . \ , \ x(-1), \ x(0), \ x(1), \ . \ . \ . \ , \ x(159), \ . \ . \ .\} \tag{2.3}$$

where $x(n)$ describes the value at $t = nT$ and n is an integer. Sequences may also be obtained naturally such as stock market prices or the temperature in a city measured at hourly intervals where the spacing of the numbers in the sequence is understood. Although stock prices are usually quantized to 1/8 of a dollar levels and temperatures to 1-degree levels, we will generally let $x(n)$ take on any value as we did with the sampled analog signal $x(nT)$.

2.2.1 Some Basic Sequences

a) *Unit sample or unit impulse sequence*—This is the most fundamental of the sequences and is defined by

$$\delta(n) = \begin{cases} 1, \ n = 0 \\ 0, \ n \neq 0 \end{cases} \tag{2.4}$$

with the two common representations as shown in Fig. 2.4.[†] Sometimes a solid line is drawn to emphasize the presence of a unit sample. Using the sequence notation of Eq. 2.3 we write

$$\{\delta(n)\} = \{. \ . \ . \ , \ 0, \ . \ . \ . \ , \ 0, \ 1, \ 0, \ . \ . \ . \ , \ 0, \ . \ . \ .\} \tag{2.5}$$
$$\underset{n \ = \ 0}{\uparrow}$$

FIGURE 2.4 Unit sample (unit impulse)

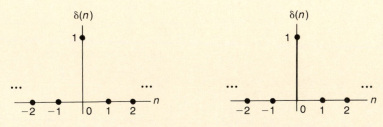

[†]The unit impulse $\delta(t)$ is an important signal representation used in continuous-system theory.

FIGURE 2.5 A constant
sequence

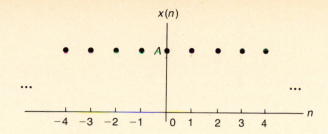

$x(n)$

b) *Constant sequence*—This sequence has the same real value for all
values of n, namely

$$x(n) = A, \qquad -\infty \le n \le \infty \qquad (2.6)$$

or in the form of Eq. 2.3 as

$$\{x(n)\} = \{\ldots, A, \ldots, A, A, A, \ldots, A, \ldots\} \qquad (2.7)$$
$$\underset{n = 0}{\uparrow}$$

with the graphical description in Fig. 2.5.

c) *Unit step sequence*—A widely used variation of the constant sequence is

$$u(n) = \begin{cases} 1, & n \ge 0 \\ 0, & n < 0 \end{cases} \qquad (2.8)$$

or

$$\{u(n)\} = \{\ldots, 0, 0, 1, 1, 1, 1, \ldots, 1, \ldots\} \qquad (2.9)$$
$$\underset{n = 0}{\uparrow}$$

which is called the *unit step sequence*, seen in Fig. 2.6, and commonly denoted by $u(n)$.[†] This sequence has some very useful properties that will be explained later.

FIGURE 2.6 Unit step
sequence and analog
counterpart

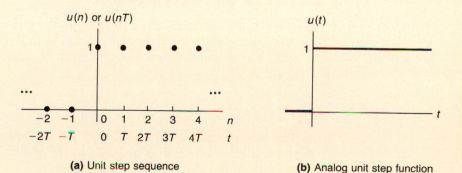

(a) Unit step sequence

(b) Analog unit step function

[†]The counterpart of $u(n)$ in continuous-system theory is the unit step function $u(t)$
shown in Fig. 2.6(b).

FIGURE 2.7 A linear sequence

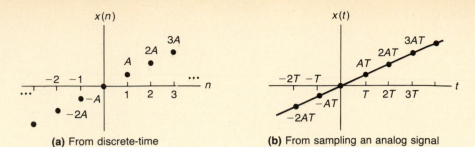

(a) From discrete-time   **(b)** From sampling an analog signal

A *step sequence* follows the pattern of a unit step sequence with the nonzero values of the sequence equal to A rather than 1.

d) *Linear sequence*—This sequence, shown in Fig. 2.7(a), changes in a linear way with the sample number and is described by

$$x(n) = An, \qquad -\infty \le n \le \infty, \qquad A = \text{a constant} \qquad (2.10)$$

or

$$\{x(n)\} = \{\ldots, -2A, -A, 0, A, 2A, \ldots\}. \qquad (2.11)$$
$$\underset{n = 0}{\uparrow}$$

If an analog signal $x(t) = At$ is sampled every T seconds we have the sequence of Fig. 2.7(b), namely,

$$x(nT) = At\Big|_{t=nT} = AnT, \qquad -\infty \le n \le \infty \qquad (2.12)$$

or

$$\{x(nT)\} = \{\ldots, -2AT, -AT, 0, AT, 2AT, \ldots\}. \qquad (2.13)$$
$$\underset{n = 0}{\uparrow}$$

2.2.2 Shifted and Special Sequences

a) *Shifted sample and step sequences*—The ability to describe mathematically certain *shifted sequences* is required for analysis and design. The general definition of a shifted unit sample sequence is given by

$$\delta(n - n_0) = \begin{cases} 1, n = n_0 \\ 0, n \ne n_0 \end{cases}. \qquad (2.14)$$

The shifted sample sequence $3\delta(n + 4)$ is shown in Fig. 2.8(a) while the sequence $3\delta(n - 4)$ is pictured in Fig. 2.8(b). In a similar way the definition of a shifted unit step sequence is

$$u(n - n_0) = \begin{cases} 1, n \ge n_0 \\ 0, n < n_0 \end{cases} \qquad (2.15)$$

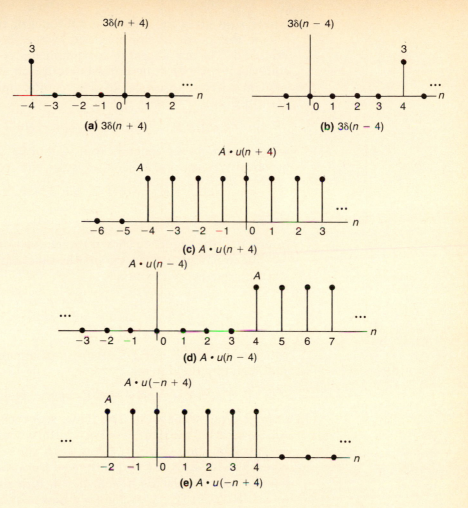

FIGURE 2.8 Some shifted sequences

(a) $3\delta(n + 4)$

(b) $3\delta(n - 4)$

(c) $A \cdot u(n + 4)$

(d) $A \cdot u(n - 4)$

(e) $A \cdot u(-n + 4)$

and the shifted step sequences $Au(n + 4)$, $Au(n - 4)$, and $Au(-n + 4)$ are given in Fig. 2.8(c)–(e). From these examples, we see that the non-zero value of a sample sequence is located where the argument of $\delta(\ )$ is zero and a unit step sequence is "on" (nonzero) whenever the argument of $u(\ )$ is zero or positive.

b) *General description of any sequence*—Consider the sample sequence $A\delta(n)$ and a shifted version $A\delta(n - m)$ as in Fig. 2.9(a). This suggests that any sequence can be described as a weighted sum of shifted unit samples. In particular the relationship is

$$x(n) = \sum_{m=-\infty}^{m=+\infty} x(m)\delta(n - m) \tag{2.16}$$

where $x(m)$ gives the *weight* (amplitude) of the sample *located* at $n = m$, the location being specified by the *shifted* sample $\delta(n - m)$. While Eq. 2.16 may appear to be complicated it can be thought of as a compact notation for the general description of the *nth value* of any sequence. The sequence of Fig. 2.9(b), for example, may be described as

$$x(n) = 2\delta(n + 2) - 2\delta(n + 1) + 3\delta(n) - \delta(n - 1) + 2\delta(n - 2) \quad (2.17)$$

which is simply the general expression of Eq. 2.16 written out term by term. We can, of course, always use the sequence notation

$$\{x(n)\} = \{. . . , 0, 0, 2, -2, 3, -1, 2, 0, 0, . . .\} \quad (2.18)$$
$$\underset{n = 0}{\uparrow}$$

to describe the sequence shown in Fig. 2.9(b).

The important sequences $\delta(n)$, the unit sample, and $u(n)$, the unit step, are related by the sum[†]

$$u(n) = \sum_{m=-\infty}^{m=n} \delta(m) \quad (2.19)$$

which is illustrated in Fig. 2.10 for three different values of n, -3, 0, and 3, and by the difference

$$\delta(n) = u(n) - u(n - 1). \quad (2.20)$$

c) *Other shifted sequences*—The linear sequence of Fig. 2.11(a), $x(n) = An$, is shifted to the right as in Fig. 2.11(b) where the shifted version is described by $y(n) = x(n - 4)$. Thus, with $x(n) = An$, $y(n) = A \cdot (n - 4)$ where the equation for $y(n)$ is derived from the equation for $x(n)$ of Fig. 2.11(a) by replacing n with $n - 4$. In a similar fashion, a shift to the left as in Fig. 2.11(c) gives a new sequence $z(n) = x(n + 4) = (n + 4) \cdot A$. You should recognize the straight-line equation $y = mx + b$ where $y(n)$ replaces y, n replaces x, the slope m is A and the $n = 0$ intercept $-4A$ is equivalent to b. In general, the shifted version $y(n)$ of a sequence $x(n)$ is given by

$$y(n) = x(n - n_0) \quad (2.21)$$

where $n_0 > 0$ produces a right shift (or delay) and $n_0 < 0$ a left shift (or advance) of the original sequence $x(n)$.

d) *Off-on properties of the unit step sequence*—The unit step sequence $u(n)$ may be used to turn another sequence *off* or *on* over a certain

---

[†] In continuous-system theory, the unit step function $u(t)$ is often defined in terms of the unit impulse $\delta(t)$ as

$$u(t) = \int_{-\infty}^{t} \delta(\tau)d\tau$$

FIGURE 2.9(a) Sample and shifted sample sequences

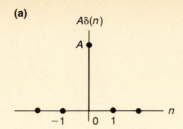
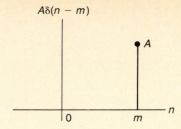

FIGURE 2.9(b) Weighted, shifted unit samples used to describe a sequence

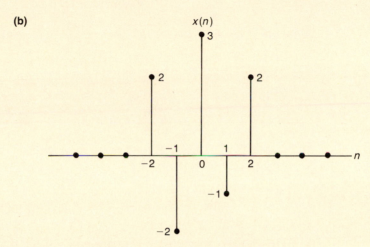

FIGURE 2.10 Generating the unit step sequence by summing the values of unit sample sequence

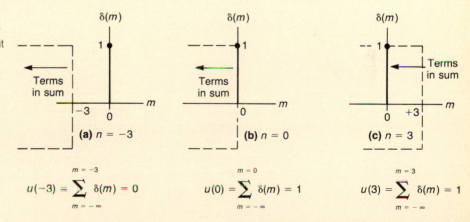

$$u(-3) = \sum_{m=-\infty}^{m=-3} \delta(m) = 0 \qquad u(0) = \sum_{m=-\infty}^{m=0} \delta(m) = 1 \qquad u(3) = \sum_{m=-\infty}^{m=3} \delta(m) = 1$$

range of the sample index n. For instance, with $x(n) = An$ for $-\infty \leq n \leq \infty$, a new sequence can be generated as

$$q(n) = x(n)u(n) \qquad (2.22)$$

where

$$\{u(n)\} = \{\ldots, 0, 0, \ldots, 0, \underset{\underset{n=0}{\uparrow}}{1}, 1, \ldots, 1, \ldots\}. \qquad (2.23)$$

FIGURE 2.11 A shifted linear sequence

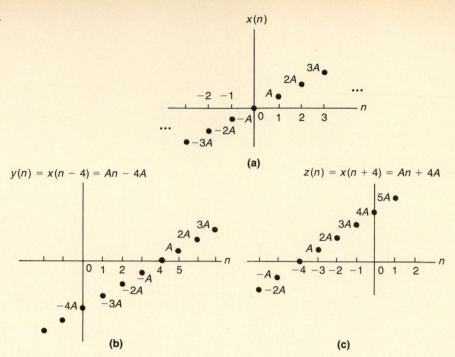

(a)

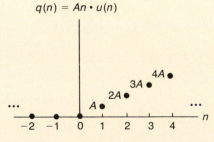

(b)

(c)

This means that $x(n)$ is multiplied by 0 for $n < 0$ and by 1 for $n \geq 0$ and the step sequence $u(n)$, in effect, shuts off $x(n)$ for negative n. Consequently, we have

$$q(n) = \begin{cases} An, & n \geq 0 \\ 0, & n < 0 \end{cases} \quad \text{or} \quad \{q(n)\} = \{\ldots, 0, 0, \ldots, 0, \underset{\underset{n\,=\,0}{\uparrow}}{A}, 2A, \ldots\}$$

$$(2.24)$$

and this so-called "ramp" sequence is shown in Fig. 2.12.

It is common to encounter a sequence that has a non-zero constant value for a finite number of samples and is zero otherwise. This burst or *pulse* of data can be conveniently constructed from step and shifted step sequences. In Fig. 2.13(a), a pulse sequence N samples wide is shown where it should be noticed that the *last* nonzero sam-

FIGURE 2.12 A handy use of the unit step as an on-off sequence

$$q(n) = An \cdot u(n)$$

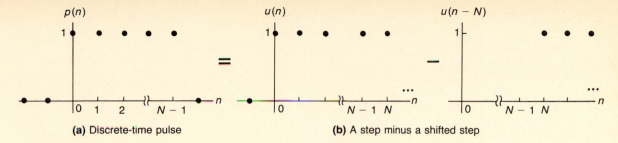

(a) Discrete-time pulse   **(b)** A step minus a shifted step

FIGURE 2.13 Synthesis of a pulse sequence

ple number is $n = N - 1$ because we start counting the nonzero values with $n = 0$ and not 1. This pulse sequence, $p(n)$, can be constructed as in Fig. 2.13(b) from a unit step and a shifted unit step sequence giving

$$p(n) = u(n) - u(n - N) \tag{2.25}$$

where we note that $u(n - N)$ is off (equals 0) for $n < N$ and is on (equals 1) for $n \geq N$. Shifted unit step sequences provide the capability to describe many other sequences in analytical form. This is often a useful alternative to a graphical representation or the use of shifted weighted sample sequences as in Eq. 2.16.

Example 2.1. This example illustrates the use of shifted sequences and the synthesis of some common sequences.

a) Sketch the sequence $x(n) = u(n + N) - u(n - N - 1)$.

b) Given the plot of $x(n) = |n|$ in Fig. 2.14(a), sketch $y(n) = |n|\{u(n + N) - u(n - N - 1)\}$.

c) Sketch the sequences $x_1(n) = An\,u(n)$, $x_2(n) = A(n - N)u(n - N)$ and finally $x_3(n) = x_1(n) - x_2(n)$.

d) A rectangular pulse sequence $p(n) = u(n) - u(n - N)$ was portrayed in Fig. 2.13. Given the triangular pulse sequence $z(n)$ of Fig. 2.14(b), synthesize (describe by an equation) $z(n)$ from appropriate ramp (Fig. 2.12) and shifted ramp sequences.

e) A different version of a triangular pulse is given in Fig. 2.14(c). Synthesize this sequence as the sum of three simpler sequences.

Solution:

a) Figure 2.15(a) shows $x_1(n) = u(n + N)$, $x_2(n) = u(n - N - 1)$ and $x(n) = x_1(n) - x_2(n)$.

b) The result of multiplying $|n|$ by the pulse $u(n + N) - u(n - N - 1)$ is shown in Fig. 2.15(b). Notice that the pulse turns the sequence $|n|$ *on* for $-N \leq n \leq N$ and *off* for all other values of n.

c) See Fig. 2.15(c) for $x_1(n)$, $x_2(n)$, and $x_3(n)$. Note that $x_2(n)$ is simply $x_1(n)$ delayed by N and that the resultant sequence $x_3(n)$ could be called a satu-

FIGURE 2.14 Sequences
for Example 2.1

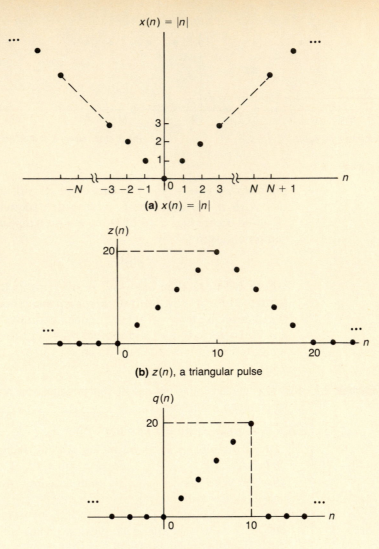

(a) $x(n) = |n|$

(b) $z(n)$, a triangular pulse

(c) $q(n)$, a different triangular pulse

rated ramp because it reaches a certain level, $x_3(n) = AN$ at $n = N$, and remains (is saturated) there.

d) From Fig. 2.14(b) we can read off or calculate the slope of $z(n)$ in the various ranges. Then, starting at $n = 0$, we add ramp or shifted ramp sequences together to obtain a composite sequence that has the desired slope. We need a slope of 0 for $n < 0$, a slope of $20/10 = 2$ for $0 < n < 10$, a slope of $-20/10 = -2$ for $10 < n < 20$, and again a zero slope for $n > 20$. We satisfy these requirements with

$$z(n) = z_1(n) - z_2(n) + z_3(n)$$

$$= 2nu(n) - 4(n - 10)u(n - 10) + 2(n - 20)u(n - 20) \qquad (2.26)$$

as shown in Fig. 2.15(d). We should check this by first verifying that the slopes are correct in the ranges $n < 0$, $0 \le n < 10$, $10 \le n < 20$ and $20 < n$. This is done by setting each unit step sequence to 0 or 1 as appropriate. So, for $n < 0$ we see that all unit step sequences are zero, so the resulting $z(n)$ is zero as required. For $0 \le n < 10$ we have

$$z(n) = 2nu(n) - 4(n - 10)u(n - 10) + 2(n - 20)u(n - 20)$$
$$= 2n \tag{2.27}$$

which has the desired slope of 2. For $10 \le n < 20$,

$$z(n) = 2nu(n) - 4(n - 10)u(n - 10) + 2(n - 20)u(n - 20) \tag{2.28}$$

which has the correct slope of -2. Following a similar approach for the range $20 \le n$ gives $z(n) = 0$ which is correct. We can also check by using Eq. 2.26 by substituting a few values for n which gives

$$z(5) = 2 \cdot 5u(5) - 4(5 - 10)u(-5) + 2(5 - 20)u(-15) = 10$$

$$z(15) = 2 \cdot 15u(15) - 4(15 - 10)u(5) + 2(15 - 20)u(-5) = 10 \tag{2.29}$$

$$z(25) = 2 \cdot 25u(25) - 4(25 - 10)u(15) + 2(25 - 20)u(5) = 0.$$

These results all agree with Fig. 2.14(b).

An alternative way of describing the triangular pulse is to write an equation that describes the pulse over each range of n and then use the appropriate pulse sequence to turn the description on and off. For example, over the range $0 \le n < 10$, $z(n) = 2n$, and to describe the pertinent range we write

$$z(n) = 2n[u(n) - u(n - 10)]. \tag{2.30}$$

For $10 \le n < 20$, $z(n) = -2n + 40 = -2(n - 20)$ and a proper description is

$$z(n) = -2(n - 20)[u(n - 10) - u(n - 20)]. \tag{2.31}$$

Putting this together for all n we have

$$z(n) = 2n[u(n) - u(n - 10)] - 2(n - 20)[u(n - 10) - u(n - 20)]$$
$$= 2nu(n) - 4(n - 10)u(n - 10) + 2(n - 20)u(n - 20) \tag{2.32}$$

as previously.

e) Synthesis of this waveform requires zero slope for $n < 0$, a slope of 2 between $n = 0$ and $n = 10$, and zero slope for $n > 10$. We can build this sequence as in Fig. 2.15(e) from

$$q(n) = q_1(n) - q_2(n) + q_3(n)$$
$$= 2nu(n) - 2(n - 10)u(n - 11) - 20u(n - 11) \tag{2.33}$$

where the third term is needed to keep $q(n) = 0$ for $n > 10$. Checking once

FIGURE 2.15

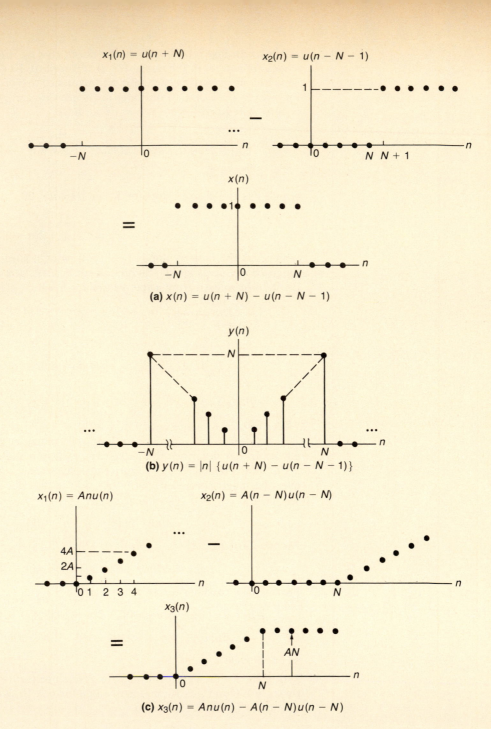

(a) $x(n) = u(n + N) - u(n - N - 1)$

(b) $y(n) = |n| \{u(n + N) - u(n - N - 1)\}$

(c) $x_3(n) = Anu(n) - A(n - N)u(n - N)$

FIGURE 2.15

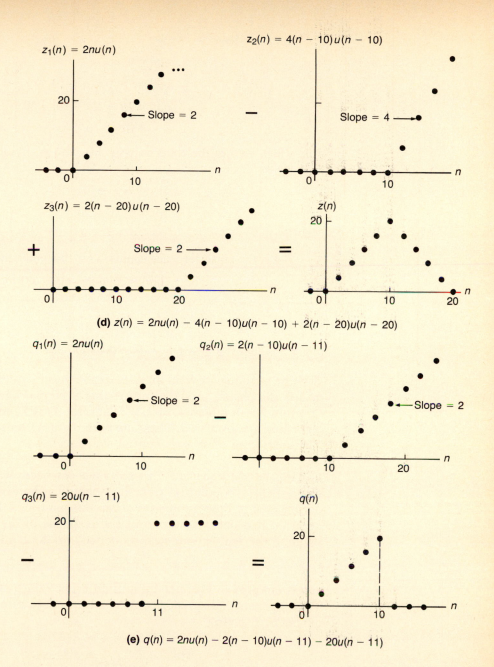

(d) $z(n) = 2nu(n) - 4(n - 10)u(n - 10) + 2(n - 20)u(n - 20)$

(e) $q(n) = 2nu(n) - 2(n - 10)u(n - 11) - 20u(n - 11)$

more, we have

$$q(n) = 0, \ n < 0$$
$$q(n) = 2n, \ 0 \le n \le 10$$
$$q(n) = 2n - 2(n - 10) - 20$$
$$= 0 \cdot n + 0, \ 11 \le n$$

$$(2.34)$$

which verifies the correct slopes. In addition, trying a few values for n yields

$$q(5) \ = 2 \cdot 5 \ = 10$$
$$q(10) = 2 \cdot 10 = 20$$
$$q(15) = 2 \cdot 15 - 2(5) - 20 = 0 \ .$$

$$(2.35)$$

Using the pulse sequence approach for this problem gives us

$$q(n) = 2n[u(n) - u(n - 11)] \qquad (2.36)$$

2.2.3 Exponential and Sinusoidal Sequences

We now introduce several kinds of exponential sequences that are central to any discussion of signal processing systems. Later in the book, the Discrete Fourier Transform (DFT) and the Fast Fourier Transform (FFT) algorithm are discussed. These are both topics that depend heavily upon a particular kind of an exponential sequence.

Real exponential sequence. This sequence can occur in many diverse situations such as population growth, a chemical half-life, or in radioactive dating used to detect forgeries of famous paintings. Real exponential sequences also occur as terms in the response of digital filters. The nth value of the real exponential sequence $x(n)$ is defined by

$$x(n) = a^n, \qquad -\infty \le n \le \infty \qquad (2.37)$$

and is pictured in Fig. 2.16 for four different values of the real constant a. This exponential sequence could result from sampling a continuous-time exponential giving

$$x(nT) = e^{\alpha t}\Big|_{t=nT} = e^{\alpha nT} = (e^{\alpha T})^n \qquad (2.38)$$

where $e^{\alpha T} = a$ to relate this to Eq. 2.37. It is common practice to consider this exponential sequence for $n \ge 0$. Then we can write

$$x(n) = a^n u(n) \qquad (2.39)$$

Complex unit exponential sequence (periodic). This sequence, which pro-

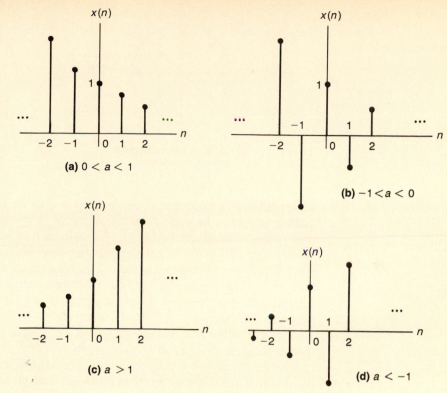

FIGURE 2.16 Real exponential sequences

(a) $0 < a < 1$

(b) $-1 < a < 0$

(c) $a > 1$

(d) $a < -1$

vides the foundation for discrete-time (digital) frequency analysis, is described by

$$p(n) = e^{j(2\pi/N)n} \qquad (2.40)$$

where N is a positive real constant that defines the *period* of the sequence. The values of this complex exponential at sample numbers $n = 0, 1, 2, \ldots$ are

$$p(0) = e^{j0}, \; p(1) = e^{j(2\pi/N)1}, \; p(2) = e^{j(2\pi/N)2}, \; \ldots \qquad (2.41)$$

and at sample numbers $n = N, N + 1, \ldots$, we have

$$p(N) = e^{j(2\pi/N)N}, \; p(N + 1) = e^{j(2\pi/N)(N+1)}, \; \ldots \qquad (2.42)$$

Notice that

$$p(N) = e^{j(2\pi/N)N} = e^{j2\pi} = e^{j0} = p(0) \qquad (2.43)$$

and that

$$p(N + 1) = e^{j(2\pi/N)(N+1)} = e^{j(2\pi/N)N} e^{j(2\pi/N)1} = e^{j(2\pi/N)} = p(1). \qquad (2.44)$$

In general, we indicate this periodic property by the relationship $p(n + N) = p(n)$ for any n. This indicates that the values begin to repeat them-

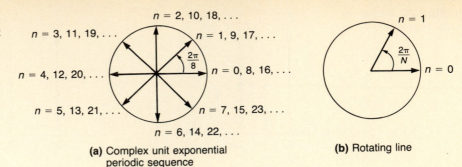

FIGURE 2.17 Graphical representation of complex exponential sequences

$n = 2, 10, 18, \ldots$
$n = 3, 11, 19, \ldots$
$n = 1, 9, 17, \ldots$
$\frac{2\pi}{8}$
$n = 4, 12, 20, \ldots$
$n = 0, 8, 16, \ldots$
$n = 5, 13, 21, \ldots$
$n = 7, 15, 23, \ldots$
$n = 6, 14, 22, \ldots$

(a) Complex unit exponential periodic sequence

$n = 1$
$\frac{2\pi}{N}$
$n = 0$

(b) Rotating line

selves after N samples and consequently this complex exponential sequence is said to be *periodic* with period N. A pictorial representation of this property is given in Fig. 2.17(a) which has been drawn for $N = 8$. Notice that $p(0) = p(8) = p(16) = p(24)$ and so forth, and that $p(1) = p(9) = p(17) = p(25)$ in the same pattern. It is important to notice that, in general, $e^{j(2\pi/N)n}$ is a *complex number* of magnitude 1 (Fig. 2.17(a)) and the sequence $p(n)$ in Eq. 2.40 is often denoted as $\mathbf{p}(n)$ to remind us of this property. We will not follow the practice of writing $\mathbf{p}(n)$ but we must always remember the "complexness" of $e^{j(2\pi/N)n}$. In this vein, it is convenient to think of this sequence as a *line of unit length* rotating in a *counterclockwise* direction with the increasing sample numbers (values of n) providing a rotation of $2\pi/N$ radians per sample. This is illustrated in Fig. 2.17(b) where the rotating line starts at an angle of 0 for $n = 0$ and progresses $2\pi/N$ radians as the sample number goes from 0 to 1.

If we write $e^{-j(2\pi/N)n}$ it will be our convention to think of this as a line rotating in a *clockwise* direction with increasing sample numbers (values of n) providing a rotation of $-2\pi/N$ radians per sample.

Example 2.2. This example illustrates the graphical representation of periodic complex exponential sequences.

a) A periodic complex unit exponential sequence has a period of six. Sketch the rotating line representation for the sample values $n = 0, 1, 2, \ldots$.

b) Repeat part (a) for $e^{-j(2\pi/5)n}$.

Solution:

a) The complex exponential is

$$p(n) = e^{j(2\pi/6)n} \tag{2.45}$$

and the sample values for $n = 0, 1, 2, \ldots$ are shown in Fig. 2.18(a).

b) Because of the negative sign, $e^{-j(2\pi/5)n}$ rotates in a clockwise direction with a period of 5 as shown in Fig. 2.18(b).

CHAPTER 2 SIGNALS AND SYSTEMS

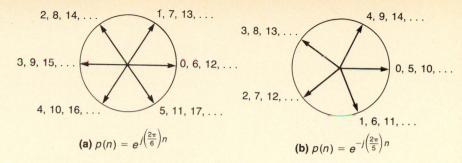

FIGURE 2.18 Results for Example 2.2

(a) $p(n) = e^{j\left(\frac{2\pi}{6}\right)n}$

(b) $p(n) = e^{-j\left(\frac{2\pi}{5}\right)n}$

Cosine or sine sequence (periodic). The Euler identity (see Appendix A on complex numbers)

$$e^{j\alpha} = \cos\,\alpha + j\,\sin\,\alpha \tag{2.46}$$

can be used to generate a cosine or a sine sequence in a very straightforward way. Starting with the periodic complex exponential sequence

$$p(n) = e^{j(2\pi/N)n} = \cos\left(\frac{2\pi}{N}\right)n + j\,\sin\left(\frac{2\pi}{N}\right)n \tag{2.47}$$

we notice that the *real* part of $p(n)$ is a cosine sequence, or

$$x(n) = \mathrm{Re}\,[p(n)] = \mathrm{Re}\,[e^{j(2\pi/N)n}]$$

$$= \cos\left(\frac{2\pi}{N}\right)n \tag{2.48}$$

and, in a similar way, the *imaginary* part of $p(n)$ is a sine sequence namely

$$x(n) = \mathrm{Im}\,[p(n)] = \mathrm{Im}\,[e^{j(2\pi/N)n}]$$

$$= \sin\left(\frac{2\pi}{N}\right)n \tag{2.49}$$

Shown in Fig. 2.19(a) is a plot of the cosine sequence of Eq. 2.48 for $N = 8$ while $x(n) = \sin(2\pi n/8)$ from Eq. 2.49 appears in Fig. 2.19(b). The periodic nature of these sequences is also evident from these plots where we see that $x(-8) = x(0) = x(8) = x(16)\ldots$ or, in general, $x(n) = x(n + 8)$ for all n. It is often necessary to consider sinusoidal sequences such as $x(n) = \cos(2\pi n/N + \phi)$ or $x(n) = \sin(2\pi n/N + \phi)$ where the term ϕ in both expressions is called the phase and is measured in radians. To include this in the rotating line representation that we started with, $p(n)$ is simply multiplied by $e^{j\phi}$ giving

$$p(n) \cdot e^{j\phi} = e^{j(2\pi n/N)} \cdot e^{j\phi}$$

$$= e^{j(2\pi n/N + \phi)}$$

$$= \cos(2\pi n/N + \phi) + j\,\sin(2\pi n/N + \phi). \tag{2.50}$$

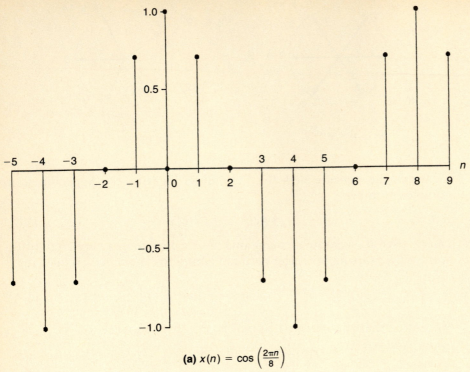

(a) $x(n) = \cos\left(\dfrac{2\pi n}{8}\right)$

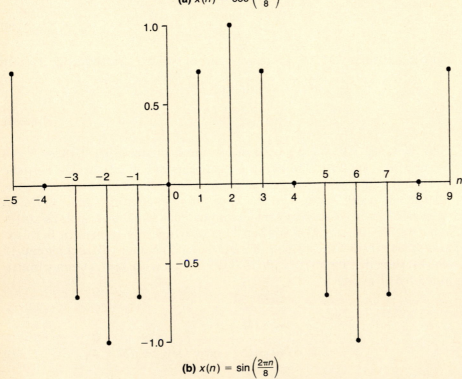

(b) $x(n) = \sin\left(\dfrac{2\pi n}{8}\right)$

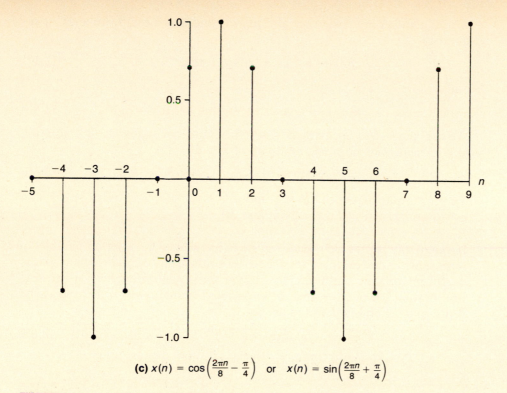

(c) $x(n) = \cos\left(\frac{2\pi n}{8} - \frac{\pi}{4}\right)$ or $x(n) = \sin\left(\frac{2\pi n}{8} + \frac{\pi}{4}\right)$

FIGURE 2.19 Sinusoidal
sequences

For example, the sinusoidal sequence in Fig. 2.19(c) can be described correctly as either

$$x(n) = \cos\left(\frac{2\pi n}{8} - \frac{\pi}{4}\right) \text{ or } x(n) = \sin\left(\frac{2\pi n}{8} + \frac{\pi}{4}\right). \tag{2.51}$$

Californians generally prefer to use cosines so we will describe all sinusoidal sequences as

$$x(n) = A\,\cos\left(\frac{2\pi n}{N} + \phi\right) \tag{2.52}$$

where the positive real number A is called the amplitude or zero-to-peak value of the sequence, ϕ the phase measured in radians and, of course, N is the period, a positive real number. While it is very straightforward to plot a sinusoidal sequence from Eq. 2.52, the reverse problem of finding the equation that describes a given plot can be somewhat more involved. (See Problem 2.29.)

General complex exponential sequence. This sequence is simply a combination of the real and complex exponential sequences and is described by

$$x(n) = Aa^n\, e^{j(2\pi/N)n}\, e^{j\phi} \tag{2.53}$$

where a and A are positive real numbers and ϕ is a real number. Consequently,

$$x(n) \longrightarrow 0 \text{ as } n \longrightarrow \infty \text{ for } 0 < a < 1 \tag{2.54}$$

and

$$x(n) \longrightarrow \infty \text{ as } n \longrightarrow \infty \text{ for } 1 < a < \infty. \tag{2.55}$$

We can generate a decaying $(0 < a < 1)$ sinusoidal sequence or a growing $(a > 1)$ sequence from the real part of $x(n)$ as

$$\text{Re } [Aa^n \, e^{j(2\pi/N)n} \, e^{j\phi}] = Aa^n \cos[(2\pi n/N) + \phi]. \tag{2.56}$$

Two example sequences $(a < 1$ and $a > 1)$ for Eq. 2.56 with $A = 1$ and $\phi = 0$ are shown in Figs. 2.20(a) and (b).

Harmonically related sinusoidal sequences (periodic). In order to be able to represent general periodic sequences by sums of sinusoidal sequences it is useful to consider harmonically related sinusoidal sequences. A rotating line that makes one revolution per period (of N samples) is defined as the *fundamental* and is denoted as

$$p_1(n) = e^{j(1 \cdot 2\pi/N)n} \tag{2.57}$$

and the corresponding fundamental sinusoidal sequence is

$$x_1(n) = \text{Re } [p_1(n)] = \cos\left(\frac{1 \cdot 2\pi n}{N}\right). \tag{2.58}$$

A rotating line that completes 2 revolutions in the period N is called the *2nd-harmonic* and is described by

$$p_2(n) = e^{j(2 \cdot 2\pi/N)n} \tag{2.59}$$

and the corresponding 2nd-harmonic sinusoidal sequence is

$$x_2(n) = \text{Re } [p_2(n)] = \cos\left(\frac{2 \cdot 2\pi n}{N}\right) \tag{2.60}$$

with the fundamental $x_1(n)$ and its 2nd-harmonic plotted in Fig. 2.21. Notice that $x_1(n) = x_1(n + N)$ and that $x_2(n) = x_2(n + N/2)$. The ℓth harmonic is then

$$p_\ell(n) = e^{j(\ell \cdot 2\pi/N)n} \text{ or } x_\ell(n) = \cos\left(\frac{\ell \cdot 2\pi n}{N}\right). \tag{2.61}$$

Example 2.3. This example illustrates the determination of periods and harmonics of periodic sequences.

a) Given $p(n) = e^{j5\pi n/32}$ a harmonic of a sequence whose period is known to be 64. What harmonic is it?

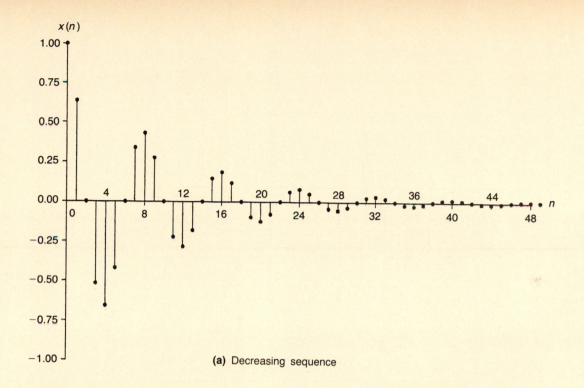

(a) Decreasing sequence

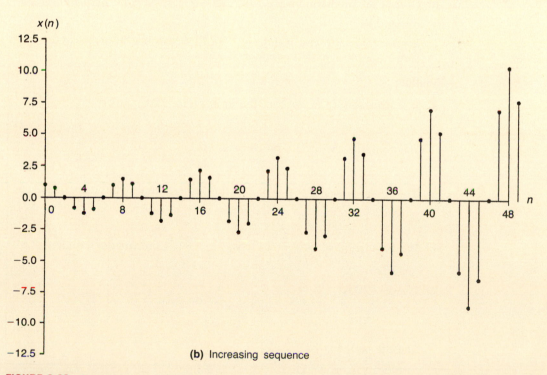

(b) Increasing sequence

FIGURE 2.20 Complex exponential sequences

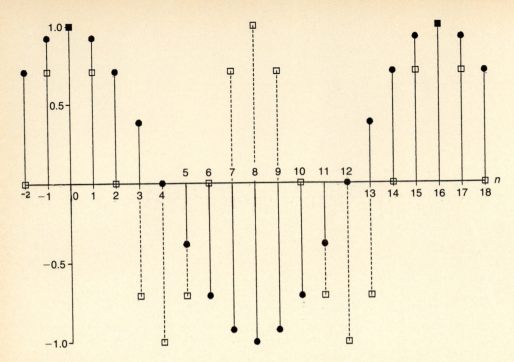

FIGURE 2.21 A fundamental sequence and its second harmonic

b) Given the third harmonic, $x_3(n) = \cos\left(\dfrac{3\pi n}{11}\right)$, what is the period of its fundamental?

c) For the 23rd harmonic, $p_{23}(n) = e^{j(69\pi n/243)}$, determine the period of the fundamental. (Beware of a common factor.)

Solution:

a) It is necessary to put $p(n)$ in the form of Eq. 2.61, namely

$$p_\ell(n) = e^{j(\ell \cdot 2\pi/N)n} \tag{2.62}$$

and doing this with $N = 64$ gives us

$$p(n) = e^{j(5 \cdot 2\pi/64)n}. \tag{2.63}$$

The period is 64 and $p(n) = p_5(n)$ is the 5th harmonic. The cosine sequence is $x(n) = \cos\left(\dfrac{5 \cdot 2\pi}{64}\right)n$.

b) We have $x_3(n) = \cos\left(\dfrac{3\pi n}{11}\right) = \cos\left(\dfrac{3 \cdot 2\pi n}{22}\right)$. Comparison with Eq. 2.61 gives $N = 22$.

c) Now we have

$$p_{23}(n) = e^{j[(3)(23)\pi n/(3)(81)]}$$

$$= e^{j[23 \cdot 2\pi/162]n} \tag{2.64}$$

and the period is 162.

CHAPTER 2 SIGNALS AND SYSTEMS

Other complex exponential sequences. Assume a situation in which a complex exponential is given by $e^{j\alpha n}$ where α is a real constant. What conditions must be met for this complex exponential to be periodic? If a sequence is periodic with period N it must repeat itself every N samples. Thus, for $e^{j\alpha n}$ to be periodic we require that

$$e^{j\alpha n} = e^{j\alpha(n+N)} \qquad (2.65)$$

or

$$e^{j\alpha n} = e^{j\alpha n} e^{j\alpha N}. \qquad (2.66)$$

Thus, we see that for periodicity

$$1 = e^{j\alpha N} \qquad (2.67)$$

which says that

$$\alpha N = \ell \cdot 2\pi \text{ or } \alpha = \frac{\ell \cdot 2\pi}{N}. \qquad (2.68)$$

In other words, α must be a rational multiple of 2π for the complex exponential sequence $e^{j\alpha n}$ to be periodic. In Eq. 2.68 N is the period and ℓ is the order of the harmonic. If α is not a rational multiple of 2π then there are no two values of n for which the values of $e^{j\alpha n}$ are equal and the sequence is nonperiodic.

Example 2.4. This example illustrates the testing of exponentials for periodicity.

Test the following complex exponential sequences for periodicity and find the period where applicable. Assume that any periodic sequences are the fundamental sequences and not harmonics.

a) $x_a(n) = e^{j(0.1)n}$

b) $x_b(n) = e^{j(0.1\pi)n}$

c) $x_c(n) = e^{j\pi n}$.

Solution:

a) For periodicity we must have

$$\alpha = \ell \cdot 2\pi/N \qquad (2.69)$$

and for $x_a(n)$, $\alpha = 0.1$ which is not a rational multiple of 2π so the sequence is not periodic.

b) Here

$$\alpha = 0.1\pi = 2\pi/20 \longrightarrow N = 20. \qquad (2.70)$$

c) In this case,

$$\alpha = \pi = 2\pi/2 \longrightarrow N = 2. \qquad (2.71)$$

Since cosine sequences can be derived from complex exponential sequences, we need to satisfy Eq. 2.68 for the sequence $x(n) = \cos(\alpha n)$ to be periodic. This is quite different from the continuous-time situation because analog signals like

$$x(t) = \cos(\omega_0 t)$$

$$= \cos(2\pi f_0 t)$$

$$= \cos\left(\frac{2\pi t}{T_0}\right) \tag{2.72}$$

are always *periodic* with a period of T_0 second. In Eq. 2.72 ω_0 is the angular frequency measured in rad/s and f_0 the real frequency measured in hertz (cycles/second).

If the discrete cosine sequence is derived from a continuous-time sinusoid sampled every T seconds we have

$$x(nT) = \cos(\omega_0 t)\Big|_{t=nT}$$

$$= \cos(n\omega_0 T) \tag{2.73}$$

and the complex exponential corresponding to this cosine sequence is

$$p(nT) = e^{j(n\omega_0 T)} = e^{j(\omega_0 T)n} = e^{j(2\pi f_0 T)n}. \tag{2.74}$$

Thus, from the argument which led to Eq. 2.68

$$2\pi f_0 T = \frac{\ell \cdot 2\pi}{N} \tag{2.75}$$

therefore, the quantity $f_0 T$ must be a *rational number* for a sequence derived from a sampled continuous sinusoid to be periodic. Thus, surprisingly, sampling a periodic analog signal may produce a nonperiodic sequence.

Example 2.5. This example illustrates the periodicity of a sampled-continuous sinusoid.

Consider a continuous-time sinusoidal voltage

$$v(t) = \cos 20\pi t = \cos(2\pi \cdot 10t) \tag{2.76}$$

that is sampled at intervals of 0.0125 second. Is the resulting sequence periodic?

Solution: The continuous-time frequency is $\omega_0 = 20\pi$ radians and for a sampling interval of $T = 0.0125$ we have

$$(2\pi)(10)(0.0125) = \frac{2\pi}{8}. \tag{2.77}$$

Comparing this with Eq. 2.75 the sampled sinusoid is periodic with period 8 as shown in Fig. 2.22. The discrete-time sequence of period 8 samples is

$$\{v(nT)\} = \{1, 0.707, 0, -0.707, -1, -0.707, 0, 0.707\}$$
$$n = 0 \quad 1 \quad 2 \quad 3 \quad 4 \quad 5 \quad 6 \quad 7 \qquad (2.78)$$

2.2.4 General Periodic Sequences

We have previously considered periodic complex exponential sequences and periodic sinusoidal sequences. These are special cases of general periodic sequences which are defined by the property

$$x(n + N) = x(n) \qquad \text{for all } n \qquad (2.79)$$

where the period N is a positive integer. This equation simply says that if we select an arbitrary sequence member at sample number n, the sequence values begin to repeat N samples later. For a sampled analog signal periodicity is described by

$$x(nT + NT) = x(nT) \qquad (2.80)$$

FIGURE 2.22 Periodic sequence generated by sampling a sinusoid

where T is the sampling interval. Shown in Fig. 2.23 are several different periodic sequences along with their respective periods. Notice that we

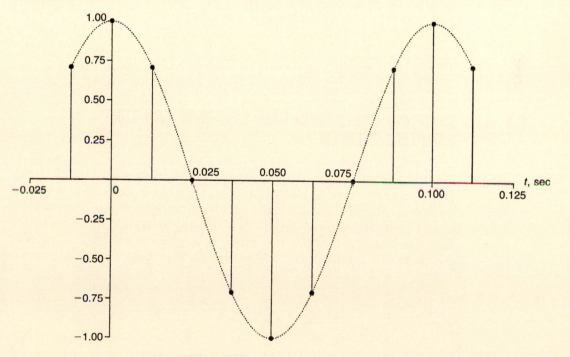

FIGURE 2.23 Periodic
sequences

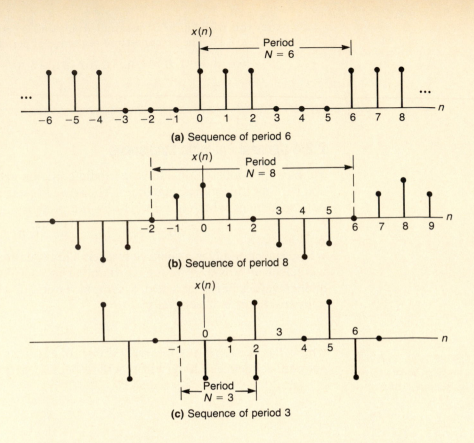

(a) Sequence of period 6

(b) Sequence of period 8

(c) Sequence of period 3

can start at any sample n and that the corresponding sequence value is repeated N samples later.

2.3 ■ SAMPLING CONTINUOUS-TIME SINUSOIDS AND THE SAMPLING THEOREM

The sampling of a continuous-time sinusoid was introduced briefly at the end of the last section. We will now amplify the discussion to focus on some important properties of the sampling procedure for a broader class of signals. Our goal is to determine the conditions that allow an analog signal to be represented by its sample values. As in Section 2.1, we will use the *ideal sampler* of Fig. 2.24 to model the process where the sampler

FIGURE 2.24 Ideal sampling

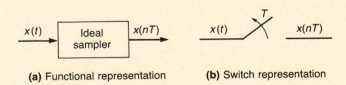

(a) Functional representation

(b) Switch representation

output $x(nT)$ at the sampling point $t = nT$ equals the value of the sampler input $x(t)$ at the same time instant. In practice, the sampler is associated with a hold circuit as part of the A/D converter which supplies a *quantized* input to the digital signal processor as shown earlier in Fig. 2.2. Because of this quantization the amplitude of the A/D output will generally be slightly different than the amplitude of the sampler output. As stated earlier, however, we are assuming infinite precision, in which case the input to the processor has the exact value of the sampled input at the sampling instant.

Consider a sinusoidal input to the ideal sampler of Fig. 2.24

$$x(t) = A \cos(\omega t + \phi) = A \cos(2\pi f t + \phi) \tag{2.81}$$

and the sampled output sequence

$$x(nT) = A \cos(\omega Tn + \phi) = A \cos(2\pi f Tn + \phi) \tag{2.82}$$

or written as a sequence

$$x(n) = A \cos(\theta n + \phi) \tag{2.83}$$

where A is the zero-to-peak amplitude, ϕ is the phase, and $\theta = \omega T = 2\pi f T$ is defined as the *digital frequency of the discrete-time sinusoid*. We will assume that the sampling rate is such that $x(nT)$ and $x(n)$ are periodic sinusoids, which means that

$$\omega T = \frac{\ell \cdot 2\pi}{N} \quad \text{or} \quad 2\pi f T = \frac{\ell \cdot 2\pi}{N}. \tag{2.84}$$

The analog frequency ω can be any value, that is, the range of possible input frequencies is $0 \le \omega < \infty$ if measured in radians per second, or $0 \le f < \infty$ if measured in hertz (cycles per second). Now we need to look at the possible range for the digital frequency θ.

For simplicity and with no lack of generality, consider Eq. 2.83 with $\phi = 0$, which gives

$$x(n) = A \cos(\theta n) = \frac{A}{2} [e^{j\theta n} + e^{-j\theta n}]. \tag{2.85}$$

Since $A/2$ is simply a scale factor we will concentrate on the complex exponentials, namely

$$e^{j\theta n} + e^{-j\theta n}. \tag{2.86}$$

We know that the analog frequency (ω or f) can be anything from 0 to ∞. What about the range of values for the digital frequency θ? We show that only digital frequencies in the range 0 to π can be distinguished from one another.

To do this, we consider the sample values that result from the sequence $x(n) = e^{j\theta n} + e^{-j\theta n}$. First, we show that if θ is in the range $0 \le \theta <$

$\pi^{\dagger}$ then the sample values for two sequences with $\theta = \theta_1$ and $\theta = \theta_2$ ($\theta_1 \neq \theta_2$) *cannot* be equal for all n. Thus, all frequencies (values of θ) in the range $0 \leq \theta < \pi$ are distinguishable from one another. Let's start with two sequences of frequencies θ_1 and θ_2,

$$x_1(n) = e^{j\theta_1 n} + e^{-j\theta_1 n} \tag{2.87}$$

and

$$x_2(n) = e^{j\theta_2 n} + e^{-j\theta_2 n}. \tag{2.88}$$

Can these be equal for all n? There are only two possible ways in which these two sequences can be equal (having excluded the trivial case, $\theta_1 = \theta_2$). They are equal if $\theta_2 = -\theta_1$ or if

$$\theta_2 = \theta_1 + m2\pi, \, m = \pm 1, \, \pm 2, \, \pm 3, \, \ldots. \tag{2.89}$$

Now, if we assume that θ_1 is a frequency in the range $0 \leq \theta < \pi$, what other frequencies yield sample values that are distinguishable (distinct)? The only ones that *are not* are

$$\theta_2 = -\theta_1 \tag{2.90}$$

and

$$\theta_2 = \theta_1 + m2\pi, \, m = \pm 1, \, \pm 2, \, \ldots. \tag{2.91}$$

Since $0 \leq \theta_1 < \pi$, we can write $-\pi < -\theta_1 \leq 0$, so for $\theta_2 \neq \theta_1$, $\theta_2 = -\theta_1$ is not a frequency in the range $0 \leq \theta < \pi$. The other *indistinguishable* frequencies are $\theta_1 + 2\pi$, $\theta_1 + 4\pi$, ... and $\theta_1 - 2\pi$, $\theta_1 - 4\pi$, ... and these also lie outside the range $0 \leq \theta < \pi$.

Let's look at a graphical representation to further illustrate this explanation. Shown in Fig. 2.25 are the samples that result from the complex exponentials $e^{j\theta n}$ and $e^{-j\theta n}$ with $\theta = \pi/4$. If $\theta_2 = -\theta_1$ and we draw the rotating lines the sample values are shown in Fig. 2.26. In comparing Figs. 2.25

FIGURE 2.25 The rotating lines $e^{j\theta n}$ and $e^{-j\theta n}$ with $\theta = \pi/4$

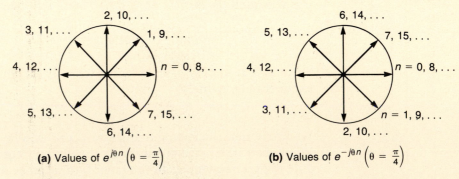

(a) Values of $e^{j\theta n}\left(\theta = \frac{\pi}{4}\right)$ **(b)** Values of $e^{-j\theta n}\left(\theta = \frac{\pi}{4}\right)$

---

†The value $\theta = \pi$ is excluded because a sinusoidal sequence of this frequency would be zero for all n if $x(n) = A \cos(\pi n + \pi/2)$. This sequence of zeros clearly could not be used to reconstruct the original cosine signal from which the sequence was derived.

CHAPTER 2   SIGNALS AND SYSTEMS

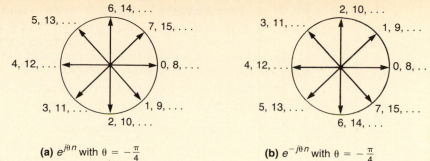

FIGURE 2.26 The rotating lines $e^{j\theta n}$ and $e^{-j\theta n}$ with $\theta = -\pi/4$

(a) $e^{j\theta n}$ with $\theta = -\dfrac{\pi}{4}$

(b) $e^{-j\theta n}$ with $\theta = -\dfrac{\pi}{4}$

and 2.26 and keeping in mind that we must add $(x(n) = e^{j\theta n} + e^{-j\theta n})$ the sample values at each value of n, we see that the same sum will result because the same sample values are added. And if we were to draw the comparable diagrams for $\theta = \pi/4 + 2\pi$, or $\pi/4 + 4\pi$, or $\pi/4 - 2\pi$, or $\pi/4 - 4\pi$, we would see that they would be exactly the same as Figs. 2.25 and 2.26.

What about frequencies outside the range of $0 \le \theta < \pi$? It is not difficult to show that for any frequency outside this range, there is a frequency inside the range $0 \le \theta < \pi$ that has exactly the same sample values. For example, suppose $\theta_1 = 7\pi/3$. If we let $\theta_2 = \theta_1 - 2\pi$, we have $\theta_2 = 7\pi/3 - 2\pi = \pi/3$. In other words the samples of the sequences

$$x_a(n) = e^{j7\pi n/3} + e^{-j7\pi n/3} \text{ and } x_b(n) = e^{j\pi n/3} + e^{-j\pi n/3} \qquad (2.92)$$

are exactly the same. Equivalently,

$$\cos\left(\frac{7\pi n}{3}\right) = \cos\left(2\pi n + \frac{\pi n}{3}\right) = \cos\left(\frac{\pi n}{3}\right). \qquad (2.93)$$

The importance of all of this is that *only* those digital frequencies in the range of 0 to π are distinguishable from one another.

Remember that this discussion began by considering the sampling of analog sinusoids. To what range of analog frequencies does the digital frequency range of 0 to π correspond? We have

$$\theta = \omega T = 2\pi f T = 2\pi f/f_s \qquad (2.94)$$

where $f_s = 1/T$ is the sampling frequency. So we have the range of digital frequencies

$$0 \le 2\pi f/f_s < \pi \qquad (2.95)$$

which becomes in terms of analog frequencies

$$0 \leq f < f_s/2. \tag{2.96}$$

In other words, for unambiguous representation, the analog frequencies must be restricted to the range 0 to $f_s/2$.

Let's recapitulate for a moment and review the situation. We have been working with three sinusoids, namely

$$x(t) = A \cos(\omega t + \phi) \quad \text{analog signal}$$

$$= A \cos(2\pi f t + \phi) \tag{2.97}$$

$$x(nT) = A \cos(\omega T n + \phi) \quad \text{sequence from sampled analog signal}$$

$$= A \cos(2\pi f T n + \phi) \tag{2.98}$$

$$x(n) = A \cos(\theta n + \phi) \quad \text{sequence in terms of } \theta \tag{2.99}$$

where the digital frequency θ, the analog frequency ω or f, the sampling interval T, and the sampling frequency f_s are related by

$$\theta = \omega T = \frac{\omega}{f_s}, \text{ or } \theta = 2\pi f T = \frac{2\pi f}{f_s}. \tag{2.100}$$

Digital frequencies that are distinguishable from one another lie in the range

$$\boxed{0 \leq \theta < \pi} \tag{2.101}$$

which for analog frequencies corresponds to

$$\boxed{0 \leq f < \frac{f_s}{2}}. \tag{2.102}$$

Example 2.6. This example illustrates the potential for ambiguity in the sampling process.

An analog sinusoidal signal $x(t) = \cos(2500\pi t)$ is sampled at a frequency $f_s = 1kHz(T = 1ms = 10^{-3}s)$. Determine the discrete-time sequence $x(n)$ that will be the input to the digital signal processor of Fig. 2.27.

Solution: The input frequency is $f = 1250$ Hz which is beyond the limit of $f_s/2$ or 500 Hz, so we expect the digital frequency to be beyond the range of $\theta = \pi$. This frequency is

$$\theta = \omega T$$

$$= 2500\pi(10^{-3}) = 2.5\pi \tag{2.103}$$

and subtracting 2π to get this into the range of $0 \le \theta < \pi$ we get

$$\theta = 0.5\pi = \pi/2. \qquad (2.104)$$

This gives the discrete-time sequence

$$x(n) = \mathrm{Re}[e^{j(\pi n/2)}]$$

$$= \cos(\pi n/2). \qquad (2.105)$$

Comment: Notice that with the analog frequency $\omega = f_s\theta$, the following signals would all produce the same sequence as Eq. 2.105 assuming samples are taken at $\ldots$, $-3T$, $-2T$, $-T$, 0, T, $2T$, $3T$, $\ldots$

$$x_1(t) = \cos(\omega_1 t), \; \omega_1 = 10^3(0.5\pi) \qquad = 500\pi \text{ or } f_1 = 250$$

$$x_2(t) = \cos(\omega_2 t), \; \omega_2 = 10^3(2\pi + 0.5\pi) = 2500\pi \text{ or } f_2 = 1250$$

$$x_3(t) = \cos(\omega_3 t), \; \omega_3 = 10^3(4\pi + 0.5\pi) = 4500\pi \text{ or } f_3 = 2250 \qquad (2.106)$$

and so forth.

FIGURE 2.27 Processing an analog signal

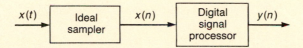

These three analog signals and their samples when $T = 1\text{ms}$ are shown in Fig. 2.28. Thus, all three of these signals have the same sample values.

As an example of why this is undesirable, consider the situation in which a digital signal processor is to determine whether or not the frequency 250 Hz is present in an analog signal, as in a sonar system, for example. If the 250 Hz signal is not present, but either or both the 1250 Hz or 2250 Hz signals are present, the processor would incorrectly conclude from the samples that the 250 Hz signal was present.

Another example of the potential difficulty is the situation where an analog signal consists of the sum of $x_1(t)$, $x_2(t)$, and $x_3(t)$ in Example 2.6. If samples were taken at a frequency $f_s = 1$ kHz, any subsequent processing would treat the frequency 250 Hz as if its amplitude were 3 rather than 1.

How do we avoid the potential difficulties? If we select a high enough sampling frequency, the signal samples will be unambiguous. Furthermore, a result due to Nyquist and Shannon tells us the minimum acceptable value of the sampling frequency. Let us consider the two analog signals in Fig. 2.29(a)

$$x_1(t) = \cos(2\pi \cdot 10^3 t) \qquad \text{solid curve} \qquad (2.107)$$

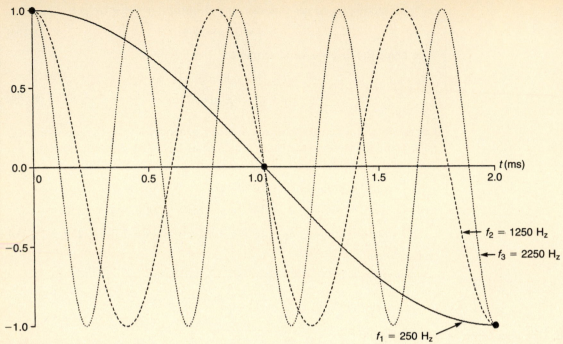

FIGURE 2.28 Illustration of ambiguity in undersampled signals

and

$$x_2(t) = \cos\left(2\pi \cdot \frac{10^3}{4}t\right) \qquad \text{dotted curve} \qquad (2.108)$$

which are sampled at an interval of $T = 1.33(10^{-3})$ second or at a frequency of $f_s = 750$ hertz. Notice that the samples ($\square$ and $\bullet$) occur at the same values for $x_1(t)$ and for $x_2(t)$ and it is impossible to distinguish between them. Thus, at this sampling rate the output of the sampler would be the same if either of these two analog signals were the inputs. This is also easily seen by computing the digital frequencies associated with each, namely

$$\theta_1 = (2\pi f_1)/f_s = (2\pi \cdot 10^3)/750 = 8\pi/3 \text{ or } 8\pi/3 - 2\pi = 2\pi/3 \quad (2.109)$$

$$\theta_2 = (2\pi f_2)/f_s = \left(2\pi \cdot \frac{10^3}{4}\right)/750 = 2\pi/3 \qquad (2.110)$$

where the digital frequencies of $8\pi/3$ and $2\pi/3$ are ambiguous. It is also apparent from Fig. 2.29(a) that the sequence is

$$x(n) = \cos(2\pi n/3) \qquad (2.111)$$

where $N = 3$ and $\theta = 2\pi/3$ were as we found for both θ_1 and θ_2. A similar situation occurs in Fig. 2.29(b) where the sampling frequency has been

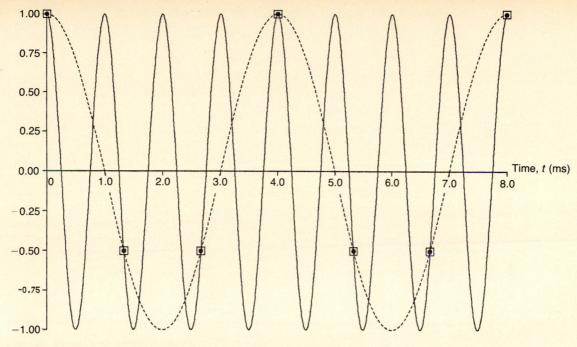

FIGURE 2.29(a)   Result of under sampling, $f_s = 750$ Hz or $T = 1.33$ ms

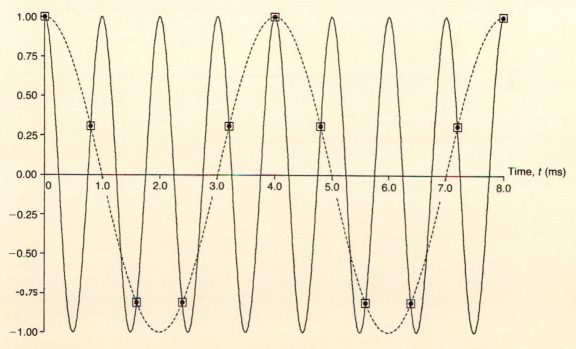

FIGURE 2.29(b)   Result of under sampling, $f_s = 1250$ Hz or $T = 0.8$ ms

increased to $f_s = 1250$ hertz or $T = 0.8$ms, which gives

$$\theta_1 = 2\pi \cdot 10^3/1250 = 8\pi/5 \text{ or } 8\pi/5 - 2\pi = -2\pi/5 \qquad (2.112)$$

and

$$\theta_2 = \left(2\pi \cdot \frac{10^3}{4}\right)/1250 = 2\pi/5 \qquad (2.113)$$

which are indistinguishable. Also, from Fig. 2.29(b) we see that the sequence has a period of 5, giving

$$x(n) = \cos(2\pi n/5). \qquad (2.114)$$

The situation illustrated in Fig. 2.29(a) and (b) where two signals have the same sample values is known as *aliasing*. Thus, even though the two signals are quite different, the sample values could not be used to distinguish between them. Clearly, this is undesirable and it can be avoided by making the sampling frequency high enough. But how high is high enough? Nyquist, 1928, and Shannon, 1949 have shown that

> If a signal contains no frequency components above a frequency f_{max} the signal can be uniquely represented by equally spaced samples if the sampling frequency f_s is greater than twice f_{max}. That is, the sampling frequency must satisfy the inequality $f_s > 2f_{max}$. The other aspect of the Sampling Theorem is that the original analog signal can be recovered by performing the appropriate operations (digital-to-analog conversion and lowpass filtering) on the sample values.[†]

In other words, we must sample at a frequency greater than twice the highest frequency present in the signal that is being sampled. The frequency $2f_{max}$ is known as the Nyquist frequency. In Fig. 2.29(c) the highest frequency is $f_{max} = 10^3$ hertz so for the samples to be unambiguous the sampling frequency must be greater than $f_s = 2 \cdot 10^3$ hertz. Fig. 2.29(c) and (d) illustrate that when a sampling rate of more than the Nyquist rate is used, the samples unambiguously represent the analog signals—there is no aliasing.

In practice we seldom know what range of frequencies is contained in an analog signal. We often know, however, the range of frequencies that is of interest for signal processing. Thus, we simply filter the signal with an analog filter before the sampling process to remove frequency components outside the range of interest. It is impossible to build an analog

---

[†]A lowpass filter passes low frequencies and attenuates higher frequencies. We will consider lowpass and other types of filters in Chapter Four.

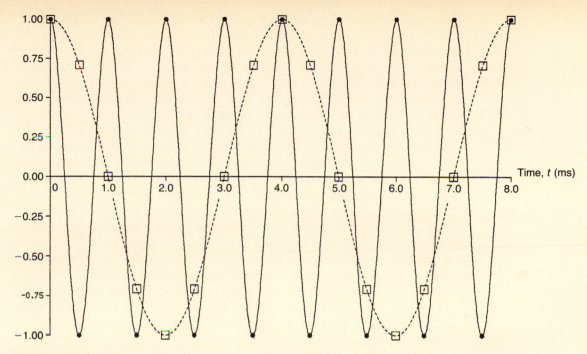

FIGURE 2.29(c) Result of sampling at Nyquist rate: sampling period of $T = 0.5$ ms or $f_s = 2000$ Hz

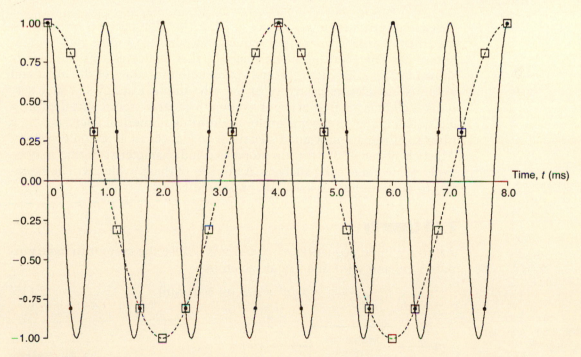

FIGURE 2.29(d) Result of sampling above Nyquist rate: sampling period of $T = 0.4$ ms or $f_s = 2500$ Hz

filter that eliminates all frequencies beyond $2f_{max}$. However, analog filters that sharply attenuate these higher frequencies can be designed and the adverse effects of any remaining frequencies beyond the desired frequency range can be minimized by an appropriate increase in the sampling frequency.

In looking at Fig. 2.29(a) and (b) it might appear that the ambiguity could be avoided by changing the times at which the samples are taken (using the same sample period), or by changing the sampling frequency slightly in order to avoid the coincidence of samples. Although this is true, it does not address the fundamental requirement which is to *guarantee* that the samples of *all frequencies* would be distinct. For example, if the same sampling period were used and the sample times were displaced, we could not be sure that the displacement would be preserved. Similarly, if we changed the sampling frequency slightly, the signals shown in Fig. 2.29(a) and (b) would have different sample values, but there are other signals of different frequencies that could not be distinguished from one another. The point is that we're not willing to leave it to chance whether or not a signal can be uniquely represented by its samples, so we rely on *the Sampling Theorem* which provides a guarantee of no aliasing if we sample at a frequency above the Nyquist frequency.

2.4 ▬ SYSTEMS AND THEIR PROPERTIES

A discrete-time *system* is a *device* or *algorithm* that operates on an input sequence to produce an output sequence according to some rule or computational procedure. A block diagram that indicates this concept is shown in Fig. 2.30 where $x(n)$ and $y(n)$ denote the values of the input and output sequences, respectively, at the nth sample. Examples of such systems include a savings account system, a radar system controlled by a digital computer, an algorithm for performing numerical analysis, and a filter to eliminate unwanted signals or sequences in an avionic system. All such systems have certain properties and characteristics that may be exploited to aid in their analysis. A number of these, which will be essential to our later discussions, are presented below.

2.4.1 Linearity

Arbitrary input sequences $x_1(n)$ and $x_2(n)$ cause the system to have outputs $y_1(n)$ and $y_2(n)$. If an input given by

$$x_3(n) = \alpha_1 x_1(n) + \alpha_2 x_2(n) \tag{2.115}$$

FIGURE 2.30 A system block diagram

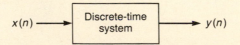

$x(n) \longrightarrow$ [Discrete-time system] $\longrightarrow y(n)$

FIGURE 2.31 Checking a
system for linearity

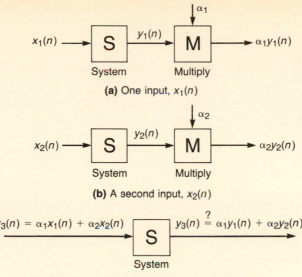

(a) One input, $x_1(n)$

(b) A second input, $x_2(n)$

(c) Both inputs scaled by α_1 and α_2, respectively

where α_1 and α_2 are complex constants, yields an output $y_3(n)$ which is equal to

$$y_3(n) = \alpha_1 y_1(n) + \alpha_2 y_2(n), \qquad (2.116)$$

and this is true for arbitrary values of α_1 and α_2 and for all n, then the system is said to be *linear*. The addition of $\alpha_1 y_1(n)$ and $\alpha_2 y_2(n)$ indicated in Eq. 2.116 is known as the *superposition* property.

It is very useful to draw some diagrams to help visualize the implications of the linearity conditions of Eq. 2.115 and Eq. 2.116. First, consider Fig. 2.31(a) where the system denoted by S operates on the input $x_1(n)$ to produce the output $y_1(n)$. This output then goes to a multiplier denoted by M where $y_1(n)$ is multiplied by the general constant α_1, to give $\alpha_1 y_1(n)$. In Fig. 2.31(b) the same process is applied to the input $x_2(n)$, with the final output after multiplication by α_2 being $\alpha_2 y_2(n)$. Finally, the input $x_3(n) = \alpha_1 x_1(n) + \alpha_2 x_2(n)$ is applied to the same system, and the output $y_3(n)$ is observed, measured or calculated as in Fig. 2.31(c). If $y_3(n) = \alpha_1 y_1(n) + \alpha_2 y_2(n)$ for all n, and with arbitrary $x_1(n)$, $x_2(n)$, α_1, and α_2, then the system is *linear*. It's as simple as that. Let's use the test outlined in Fig. 2.31 on a system that is intuitively nonlinear.

Example 2.7. This example illustrates the linearity test.

Suppose that the system S in Fig. 2.31 is described by

$$y(n) = [x(n)]^2 \qquad (2.117)$$

which says that the output at any sample n is the squared value of the input at that same sample. Show that this is a nonlinear system.

Solution: The test from Fig. 2.31 goes this way. The input $x_1(n)$ produces the output $y_1(n) = [x_1(n)]^2$. Multiplying this output by α_1 gives $\alpha_1 y_1(n) = \alpha_1[x_1(n)]^2$. We use the shorthand notation

$$x_1(n) \xrightarrow{S} y_1(n) = [x_1(n)]^2 \xrightarrow{M} \alpha_1 y_1(n) = \alpha_1[x_1(n)]^2 \qquad (2.118)$$

where $\xrightarrow{S}$ indicates an operation on the input $x_1(n)$; in this case the input is squared to get the output. The M in Eq. 2.118 indicates the multiplication of the output by the arbitrary constant α_1. Similarly,

$$x_2(n) \xrightarrow{S} y_2(n) = [x_2(n)]^2 \xrightarrow{M} \alpha_2 y_2(n) = \alpha_2[x_2(n)]^2 \qquad (2.119)$$

and

$$x_3(n) = \alpha_1 x_1(n) + \alpha_2 x_2(n) \xrightarrow{S} y_3(n) = [x_3(n)]^2 = [\alpha_1 x_1(n) + \alpha_2 x_2(n)]^2$$
$$= \alpha_1^2[x_1(n)]^2 + 2\alpha_1\alpha_2[x_1(n)][x_2(n)] + \alpha_2^2[x_2(n)]^2 \qquad (2.120)$$

The output $y_3(n)$ *does not* equal $\alpha_1 y_1(n) + \alpha_2 y_2(n)$ and the system is *nonlinear*.

To show that a system is nonlinear is a matter of verifying that there is one or more input for which the linearity conditions are not met. To show linearity, however, the linearity conditions must be satisfied for all inputs and for all α_1, and α_2. Thus, it is clearly impractical to verify linearity by enumerating and trying all possible numerical combinations of $x_1(n)$, $x_2(n)$, α_1, and α_2, for there are infinitely many. Rather, we must be able to verify linearity by analytical means. Fortunately, it is possible to identify a class of systems as linear and be able to recognize members of this class by inspection.

On an intuitive level, we can think of a linear system as one which responds to a scaled input by scaling the output by the same scale factor. In addition, a linear system responds to the sum of two inputs by producing the sum of the outputs that result when the inputs are applied separately.

2.4.2 Time-Invariance

An input $x_1(n)$ produces the output $y_1(n)$. Consider a second input $x_2(n)$ which is a shifted version of $x_1(n)$, that is,

$$x_2(n) = x_1(n - n_0). \qquad (2.121)$$

If the output $y_2(n)$ caused by $x_2(n)$ is a delayed replica of $y_1(n)$, i.e.,

$$y_2(n) = y_1(n - n_0) \qquad (2.122)$$

for all n and for arbitrary $x_1(n)$ and n_0, then the system is said to be *time-invariant*. In essence, this property indicates whether or not the system itself is changing with time. A bank account whose rate of inter-

FIGURE 2.32 Definition of a time-invariant system

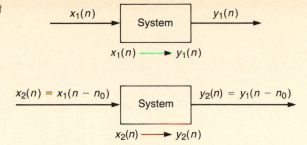

est varies from week to week is not time invariant. For example, $100 invested at the beginning of one month will not generally yield the same amount of money as $100 invested at the beginning of another month. Figure 2.32 gives a pictorial description of time-invariance which is also known as *shift-invariance*.

Loosely speaking, time-invariance means that in responding to the same input applied at different times, the outputs will be identical in shape and size, but may be delayed in time. In other words, the system parameters do not change with time.

2.4.3 Linear Time-Invariant (LTI) Systems

Most of this book will focus on the design and analysis of systems that are both *linear* and *time-invariant*. We will describe this set as LTI (linear time-invariant) systems as represented in Fig. 2.33.

FIGURE 2.33 Linear time-invariant system

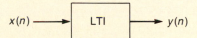

Example 2.8. This example illustrates the tests for linearity and time-invariance.

A system is described by the relationship

$$y(n) = n^2|x(n)|, \ 0 \le n \le \infty \tag{2.123}$$

and we test it for linearity and for time-invariance.

Solution: The test for linearity follows from Fig. 2.31.

a) The input $x_1(n)$ produces the output $y_1(n) = n^2|x_1(n)|$. Then multiplying this output by α_1 gives $\alpha_1 y_1(n) = \alpha_1 n^2|x_1(n)|$.

b) The input $x_2(n)$ produces the output $y_2(n) = n^2|x_2(n)|$. Then multiplying this output by α_2 gives $\alpha_2 y_2(n) = \alpha_2 n^2|x_2(n)|$.

c) Now assume that the input is $x_3(n) = \alpha_1 x_1(n) + \alpha_2 x_2(n)$. The output for this input is $n^2|x_3(n)| = n^2|\alpha_1 x_1(n) + \alpha_2 x_2(n)|$.

d) The test for linearity then is made. Does the sum of the results of (a) and (b) equal that from (c)? In other words, is

$$\alpha_1 n^2 |x_1(n)| + \alpha_2 n^2 |x_2(n)| \text{ equal to } n^2 |\alpha_1 x_1(n) + \alpha_2 x_2(n)|?$$

Clearly these two expressions are not equal for *all* $x_1(n)$, $x_2(n)$, α_1, *and* α_2, which tells us that the system is *nonlinear*. For instance, if $\alpha_1 = \alpha_2 = n = 1$ (just to simplify) we have for $x_1(1) = 2$ and $x_2(1) = -1$, $|2| + |-1| \overset{?}{=} |2 - 1|$. This is not an equality and this verifies the nonlinearity. There are, of course, many other values of α_1, α_2, $x_1(n)$, and $x_2(n)$ that would also show that the system is not linear, but only one failure is enough to reach this conclusion.

Now for the time-invariance test:

a) The shifted input $x_2(n) = x_1(n - n_0)$ produces the output $y_2(n) = n^2 |x_2(n)| = n^2 |x_1(n - n_0)|$.

b) But $y_1(n - n_0) = (n - n_0)^2 |x_1(n - n_0)|$ which in general is not equal to $y_2(n) = n^2 |x_1(n - n_0)|$ and thus the system is time-varying.

2.4.4 Stability

Stability may be defined in terms of the input-output behavior of a system. If the input to a system is bounded (the input magnitude does not grow without bound), and if the system is *stable*, then the output must also be bounded. Suppose that a system input is the bounded sequence (M_1 is the bound) of Fig. 2.34(a) and the output is as in Fig. 2.34(b). The output is bounded in that it never exceeds the value M_2 and so this system appears to be stable. Strictly speaking, we have to consider *all* possible bounded inputs before we can say that the system is stable. Clearly, this is an impractical approach, and we will see in Chapter Three that there are better ways to test for stability. Suppose, on the other hand, that we have the same input of Fig. 2.34(a) applied to a *different* system whose response is shown in Fig. 2.34(c). This new system is *unstable*, for the output grows without bound as $n \to \infty$ even though the input never gets to be larger than M_1. This one test is sufficient to decide that the system is unstable.

Example 2.9. This example illustrates a stability test.

Consider the same system of Example 2.8

$$y(n) = n^2 |x(n)|, \qquad 0 \le n \le \infty \tag{2.124}$$

subjected to the step sequence input of Fig. 2.35(a)

$$x(n) = A \cdot u(n). \tag{2.125}$$

Is this a stable system?

Solution: The input is bounded because it is still of magnitude A as $n \to \infty$. The output $y(n)$ is shown in Fig. 2.35(b) and is unbounded since $y(n) \to \infty$ as $n \to \infty$. Thus, using the definition of stability in this section we have an unstable system.

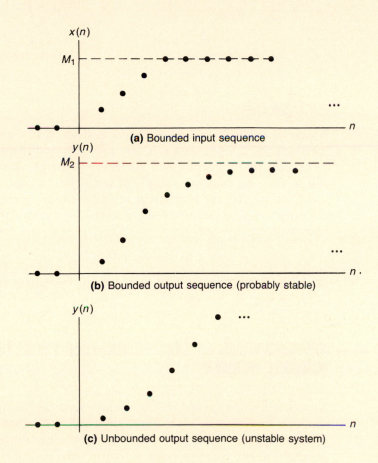

FIGURE 2.34 Stability tests

(a) Bounded input sequence

(b) Bounded output sequence (probably stable)

(c) Unbounded output sequence (unstable system)

FIGURE 2.35 Sequences for Example 2.9

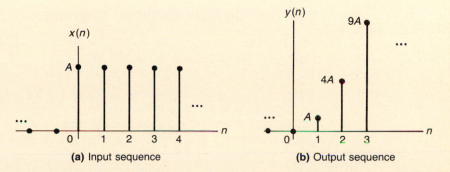

(a) Input sequence

(b) Output sequence

FIGURE 2.36 Noncausal system

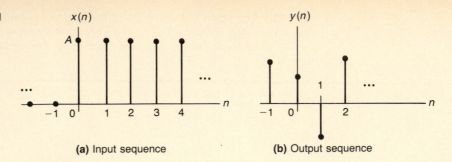

(a) Input sequence   **(b)** Output sequence

2.4.5 Causality

A *causal system* is a *nonpredictive* system in the sense that the output does not precede the input. Thus, the situation displayed in Fig. 2.36 is characteristic of a *noncausal* system because an output occurs $(n = -1)$ before the first nonzero sample of the input is applied to the system at $n = 0$. In stricter mathematical terms, a causal system is one for which the output at any sample N_1 depends only upon the input for $n \leq N_1$. The system

$$y(n) = n^2 x(n + n_0) \tag{2.126}$$

is causal for $n_0 \leq 0$ and noncausal for $n_0 > 0$ as illustrated in Fig. 2.37 for $n_0 = -2$ and $n_0 = 2$, with $x(n) = Au(n)$ a step sequence.

2.5 ■ APPROXIMATION OF CONTINUOUS-TIME PROCESSES BY DISCRETE MODELS

In this section we will introduce some specific examples of discrete systems by showing how the mathematical operations of integration and differentiation, which are typical in continuous-time systems, can be represented in the discrete-time domain.

2.5.1 Discrete Approximation of Integration

The process of *integrating* a continuous-time signal $x(t)$ from an initial time t_0 to the time t is described by

$$y(t) = \int_{t_0}^{t} x(\tau)d\tau + y(t_0) \tag{2.127}$$

where $y(t_0)$ represents the integral at time $t = t_0$ and $y(t)$ represents the integral at time t. Fig. 2.38(a) describes the process and Fig. 2.38(b) shows

FIGURE 2.37 Causal and noncausal systems

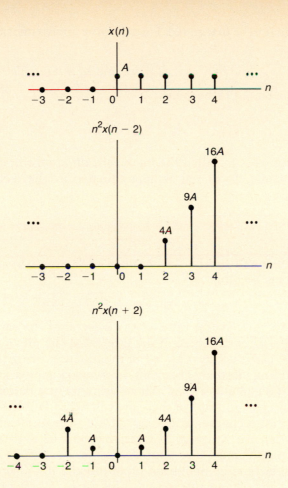

$x(n)$

$n^2x(n-2)$

$16A$

$9A$

$4A$

$n^2x(n+2)$

$16A$

$9A$

$4A$

$4A$

A

A

FIGURE 2.38 Discrete approximation of integration

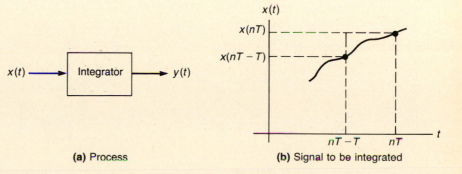

$x(t)$ ——→ | Integrator | ——→ $y(t)$

(a) Process

$x(t)$

$x(nT)$

$x(nT-T)$

$nT-T$ nT

t

(b) Signal to be integrated

a signal to be integrated. For a discrete approximation of Eq. 2.127 we will define

$$t = nT \text{ and } t_0 = nT - T. \tag{2.128}$$

Then Eq. 2.127 becomes

$$y(nT) = \int_{nT-T}^{nT} x(\tau)d\tau + y(nT - T). \tag{2.129}$$

Using what is called the *backward difference method* the definite integral of Eq. 2.129 can be approximated by the rectangular area, $T x(nT)$, giving

$$\int_{nT-T}^{nT} x(\tau)d\tau \approx Tx(nT) \tag{2.130}$$

and using this in Eq. 2.129, the discrete approximation to the integration process becomes

$$y(nT) = T x(nT) + y(nT - T) \tag{2.131}$$

where $y(nT)$ is the value of the integral at the sampling instant $t = nT$, $y(nT - T)$ is the value of the integral at the previous sample $t = nT - T$, $x(nT)$ is the value at $t = nT$ of the function being integrated, and T is the sampling interval. This isn't a very good approximation but it is easy to discuss and understand. There are other and better ways to approximate an integral and two of these are treated in Problems 2.26 and 2.27, at the end of this chapter. Equation 2.131 is an example of a system described by a *difference equation*, a topic that will be discussed in some detail in Chapter Three.

Machine computation of an integral (by discrete approximation) always introduces the potential for errors. We see from Fig. 2.38 that the accuracy of the approximation to integration given by Eq. 2.130 depends upon the sampling interval T. Suppose we want to compute the integral of the ramp-like signal of Fig. 2.39(a) from $t = 0$ to time t. This signal sampled every T seconds is shown in Fig. 2.39(b). The value of $y(nT)$ at $n = 0$ is zero. The discrete approximation of the integral at $t = T$, found from Eq. 2.130, is indicated by the area A_1 in Fig. 2.39(b), and thus the

FIGURE 2.39 Approximate integration of a ramp function

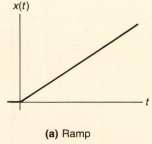

(a) Ramp

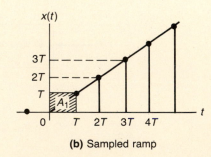

(b) Sampled ramp

CHAPTER 2 SIGNALS AND SYSTEMS

value of the integral at $n = 1$ is

$$y(T) = (T)(T) + 0 = T^2. \tag{2.132}$$

Going to $n = 2$ we have from Eq. 2.131

$$y(2T) = (T)(2T) + T^2 = 3T^2 \tag{2.133}$$

and for $n = 3$ the value of the integral is

$$y(3T) = (T)(3T) + 3T^2 = 6T^2.$$

Suppose that the sampling interval is $T = 0.01s$, then

$$y(0.01) = 10^{-4} + 0 = 10^{-4}$$

$$y(0.02) = (2)10^{-4} + 10^{-4} = 3 \times 10^{-4} \tag{2.134}$$

$$y(0.03) = (3)10^{-4} + (3)10^{-4} = 6 \times 10^{-4}.$$

The true value of the integral is

$$y(t) = \int_0^t \tau d\tau = \frac{t^2}{2} \tag{2.135}$$

and when evaluated at $t = 0.03$ we have

$$y(0.03) = \frac{\tau^2}{2}\bigg|_0^{0.03} = \frac{9 \times 10^{-4}}{2} = 4.5 \times 10^{-4}. \tag{2.136}$$

Thus, even for a relatively small value of T, the error is considerable.

2.5.2 Discrete Approximation of Differentiation

Differential equations are commonly used to model the behavior of continuous-time systems. For example, the height of the water in the leaky tank shown in Fig. 2.40 can be described by the differential equation

$$\frac{dy(t)}{dt} + ay(t) = bx(t) \tag{2.137}$$

where $y(t)$ is the height of the water at time t, $dy(t)/dt$ is the rate of change of the height of water, $x(t)$ is the flow rate of water into the tank, and a

FIGURE 2.40 A leaky tank

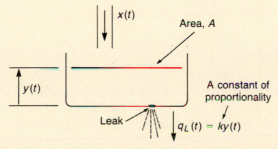

FIGURE 2.41 Approximat-
ing a derivative by a
difference

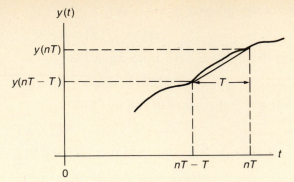

and b are constants that depend on the tank's area and the size of the leak. A graph of a possible $y(t)$ vs. t is shown in Fig. 2.41 and we want to develop a discrete-time representation of Eq. 2.137. From Fig. 2.41 the derivative of $y(t)$ at $t = nT$ can be approximated by

$$\left.\frac{dy(t)}{dt}\right|_{t=nT} \approx \frac{y(nT) - y(nT - T)}{T}. \tag{2.138}$$

Referring to Eq. 2.137 with $t = nT$ we have the approximation

$$\frac{y(nT) - y(nT - T)}{T} + a\, y(nT) = b\, x(nT) \tag{2.139}$$

and solving for $y(nT)$, the system output at $t = nT$, we have

$$y(nT) = \frac{bT}{1 + aT}x(nT) + \frac{1}{1 + aT}y(nT - T). \tag{2.140}$$

If we consider the sampling interval T as understood, the output at the nth sample is

$$y(n) = \frac{bT}{1 + aT}x(n) + \frac{1}{1 + aT}y(n - 1). \tag{2.141}$$

This provides a simple but generally not very accurate way to solve a differential equation by numerical methods (arithmetic). Equations like this one will be solved in Chapter Three.

2.6 ▬ REVIEW

This chapter introduced the types of signals and sequences that occur in discrete systems, along with several properties of such systems. In digital filtering and signal processing discrete-time sequences are frequently encountered, thus we considered several representative sequences in detail. Since sequences often result from sampling a continuous-time signal, it is also important to understand the sampling process. The fundamental result is the Sampling Theorem that states that a signal is represented unambiguously by its samples provided that the sampling frequency is at least twice as large as the *highest* frequency component in the signal. If the sampling frequency is high enough, the resulting digital frequencies all lie in the range $0 \le \theta < \pi$. Furthermore, the signal can be reconstructed from its samples by digital-to-analog conversion and then lowpass filtering.

Digital filtering and signal processing systems receive input sequences and generate corresponding output sequences. While there are many types of such systems that could be considered, those most commonly designed have the properties of linearity, time-invariance, stability, and causality. After defining these properties we illustrated by several examples how one can determine whether or not a system has a specified property.

With this background, we are now ready to consider linear, time-invariant systems in more detail in Chapter Three.

VOCABULARY AND IMPORTANT RELATIONS

a) Continuous-time or analog signal, $x(t)$

   Sequence, $\qquad\qquad \{x(nT)\}$ or $\{x(n)\}$

b) Shifted unit sample sequence $\delta(n - n_0)$

$$\delta(n - n_0) = \begin{cases} 1, n = n_0 \\ 0, n \ne n_0 \end{cases} \qquad (2.14)$$

   which for $n_0 = 0$ becomes the unit sample sequence $\delta(n)$.

c) Shifted unit step sequence $u(n - n_0)$

$$u(n - n_0) = \begin{cases} 1, n \ge n_0 \\ 0, n < n_0 \end{cases} \qquad (2.15)$$

   which for $n_0 = 0$ becomes the unit step sequence $u(n)$.

d) Description for any sequence,

$$x(n) = \sum_{m=-\infty}^{m=+\infty} x(m)\, \delta(n - m) \qquad (2.16)$$

e) A general exponential sequence

$$x(n) = A a^n e^{j\alpha n} e^{j\phi}$$

Special cases:

α and $\phi = 0$, real exponential

$a = 1$, $\alpha = \ell \cdot 2\pi/N$, complex periodic exponential of period N

$a = 1$, $\alpha \neq \ell \cdot 2\pi/N$, complex nonperiodic exponential

f) General cosine sequence, $x(n) = Aa^n\cos(\theta n + \phi)$ where $0 < a < \infty$

$a \neq 1$, oscillatory sequence increasing in magnitude if $a > 1$
decaying in magnitude if $a < 1$

$a = 1$, $\theta = 2\pi/N$, oscillatory periodic sequence which is normally written

$$x(n) = A\cos(2\pi n/N + \phi) \tag{2.52}$$

g) Sampled sinusoids

$$x(t) = A\cos(\omega t + \phi) = A\cos(2\pi f t + \phi) \tag{2.81}$$

$$x(nT) = x(t)\Big|_{t=nT} = A\cos(\omega Tn + \phi) = A\cos(2\pi f Tn + \phi) \tag{2.82}$$

or

$$x(n) = A\cos(\theta n + \phi) \tag{2.83}$$

This establishes the relation

$$\theta = \omega \cdot T = 2\pi f T = 2\pi f/f_s \tag{2.94}$$

which is stated

digital frequency = (analog radian frequency) $\cdot$ (sampling interval)

= (analog radian frequency)/(sampling frequency)

The units of θ are

radians = (radians/second) $\cdot$ (seconds)

h) Sampling Theorem

If a signal contains no frequency components above a frequency f_{max} the signal can be uniquely represented by equally spaced samples if the sampling frequency f_s is greater than twice f_{max}. That is, the sampling frequency must satisfy the inequality $f_s > 2f_{max}$. The other aspect of the Sampling Theorem is that the original analog signal can be recovered by performing the appropriate operations (digital-to-analog conversion and lowpass filtering) on the sample values.

i) Aliasing or ambiguity

j) System properties

$$\left.\begin{array}{l}\text{Linearity}\\\text{Time-invariance}\\\text{Stability}\\\text{Causality}\end{array}\right\} \text{LTI System}$$

k) Difference equation approximations for integration and differentiation

PROBLEMS

Reinforcement

2.1 Given the sequence $x(n) = 2^{-n}$, $-\infty \le n \le \infty$

a) Sketch this sequence as a function of n.

b) Sketch the sequence $x(n)u(n)$ vs. n.

c) Now sketch $x(n)u(-n)$ vs. n.

d) Next, sketch $x(-n)u(-n)$ vs. n.

e) Finally, sketch $x(-n + 2)u(-n + 2)$ vs. n.

2.2 Two sequences $x_1(n)$ and $x_2(n)$ are shown in Fig. P2.2. For each of the following, write an equation for the sequence in terms of shifted sample sequences and sketch the sequence.

a) $[x_1(n) + x_2(n)]$ vs. n

b) $2x_1(n)$ vs. n

c) $-3x_2(n)$ vs. n

d) $[2x_1(n) - 3x_2(n)]$ vs. n

e) $\alpha_1 x_1(n)$ vs. n, $\alpha_1 > 0$

f) $x_1(n)x_2(n)$ vs. n

2.3 A sequence is described by $y(n) = (0.9)^n \cos(2\pi n/8)$. Plot this sequence as a function of n for $-4 \le n \le 7$.

2.4 Given that $x(n) = |n|$, $\quad -\infty \le n \le \infty$

a) Sketch $x(n)$ vs. n.

b) Sketch the sequence $x(n)[u(n + 5) - u(n - 5)]$ vs. n.

2.5 The sequence $y(n)$ is sketched in Fig. P2.5. For each of the following write an equation for the sequence in the form of Eq. 2.16, and sketch the sequence.

a) $y(n - 3)$ vs. n

b) $y(n + 2)$ vs. n

c) $y(-n)$ vs. n

d) $y(3 - n)$ vs. n

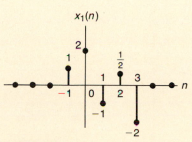

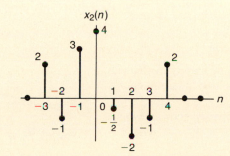

FIGURE P2.2

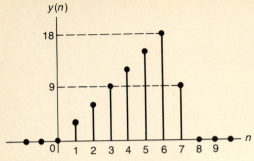

FIGURE P2.5

2.6 Determine if the following sequences are periodic, and if they are find the periods.

a) $x(n) = e^{\cos(\pi n/8)}$ c) $x(n) = \sin(2n + \pi/4)$

b) $x(n) = e^{-n}\cos(\pi n/4)$ d) $x(n) = \cos(6.5n\pi + \pi/3)$

2.7 A continuous-time signal is given by $y(t) = 15.6 \cos(250\pi t - \pi/6)$.

a) Sketch $y(t)$ vs. t.

b) What is the frequency in hertz of $y(t)$?

c) What is the period of $y(t)$?

d) If $y(t)$ is to be represented by its sample values, at what frequency should it be sampled?

e) What is the sample period for the frequency found in part (d)?

f) If $y(t)$ is sampled with a period of $T = 0.001$s, find the expression for the resulting sequence $y(n)$.

g) What is the digital frequency, θ, of $y(n)$ for the value of T given in part (f)?

2.8 An analog signal composed of a sum of four sinusoids is given by

$$y(t) = 2 \cos(100\pi t) + 5 \sin(250\pi t + \pi/6) - 4.5 \cos(375\pi t - \pi/4) + 15.9 \sin(600\pi t + \pi/9)$$

What is the minimum sampling frequency that can be used to produce samples that unambiguously represent $y(t)$?

2.9 An analog signal $y(t) = 10 \cos(500\pi t + \pi/6)$ is sampled at . . . , $-2T$, $-T$, 0, T, $2T$, . . . with $T = 1.0$ millisecond (ms).

a) Sketch $y(t)$ vs. t and show the sample values.

b) Find another sinusoid $v(t)$ which when sampled with $T = 1.0$ ms yields the same values as $y(t)$. Write the equation and sketch $v(t)$ vs. t.

2.10 An analog signal $y(t) = 7 \cos(400\pi t)$ is sampled at . . . , $-2T$, $-T$, 0, T, $2T$, . . . with $T = 1.25$ milliseconds (ms).

a) Sketch $y(t)$ vs. t and show the sample values.

b) Find another sinusoid $r(t)$ which when sampled with $T = 1.25$ ms yields the same sample values as $y(t)$. Write the equation and sketch $r(t)$ vs. t.

c) Repeat parts (a) and (b) if $T = 1$ ms.

2.11 A system is characterized by the input-output relation shown in Fig. P2.11. Determine whether or not the system is

a) Linear

b) Time-invariant

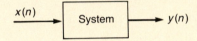

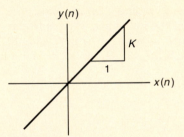

FIGURE P2.11

2.12 Repeat Problem 2.11 for the system whose input-output characteristic is shown in Fig. P2.12.

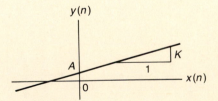

FIGURE P2.12

2.13 Repeat Problem 2.11 for the *saturation* characteristic of Fig. P2.13.

    CHAPTER 2 SIGNALS AND SYSTEMS

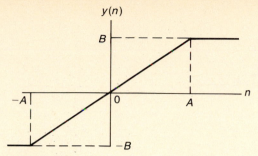

FIGURE P2.13

2.14 The input-output relationship for a system is given by $y(n) = 3nx(n)$.

a) Is the system linear?

b) Is the system time-invariant?

2.15 Repeat Problem 2.14 for the system

$$y(n) = b_0x(n) + b_1x(n-1) + \cdots + b_Lx(n-L)$$

$$= \sum_{k=0}^{L} b_k x(n-k).$$

2.16 A unit delay element is described by the relationship $y(n) = x(n-1)$. Is the unit delay element

a) Linear?

b) Time-invariant?

c) Causal?

d) Stable?

2.17 Determine whether each of the systems given below is causal.

a) $y(n) = 0.25x(n-2) + x(n)$

b) $y(n) = -x(n-1) + 0.25x(n-2) + x(n+1)$

c) $y(n) = x(n+3)$

2.18 Shown in Fig. P2.18 on page 72 are the inputs and outputs for several systems. Which of these systems is causal?

2.19 A system is characterized by the equation $y(n) = 2x(n) + \dfrac{1}{x(n-1)}$. Is the system linear?

2.20 A system is characterized by $y(n) = \dfrac{1}{n}x^2(n-1)$.

a) Is the system linear?

b) Is the system time-invariant?

2.21 Is the system described by $y(n) = 3 - x(n)\cos(n\omega_0 T)$, where T and ω_0 are constants,

a) Linear?

b) Time-invariant?

Extension and Generalization

2.22 One and two cycles of a sawtooth sequence are shown in Fig. P2.22.

a) Write an expression for $x_1(n)$ as a sum of shifted unit sample sequences.

b) Now find an expression for $x_2(n)$ in terms of A, unit step, and shifted unit step sequences.

c) Let $x_N(n)$ be the extension of $x_2(n)$ to N periods. Write an expression for $x_N(n)$ in terms of A and unit step sequences.

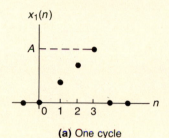

(a) One cycle

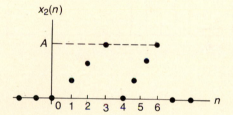

FIGURE P2.22

2.23 The operation of quantization is illustrated in Fig. P2.23 on page 72.

a) Write an input-output equation that describes the operation of the quantizer.

b) Determine whether or not the quantizer is linear.

2.24 The first derivative of $y(t)$ at $t = nT$ is approximated by

$$\left. \frac{dy(t)}{dt} \right|_{t=nT} \approx \frac{y(nT) - y(nT-T)}{T}.$$

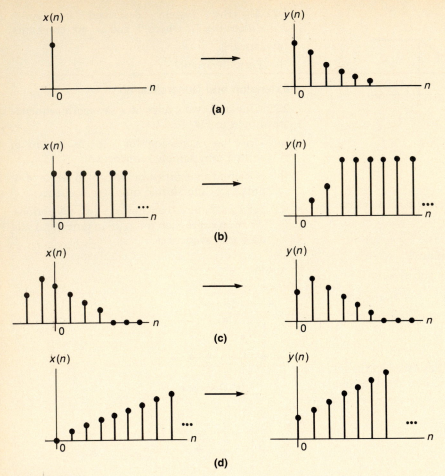

FIGURE P2.18

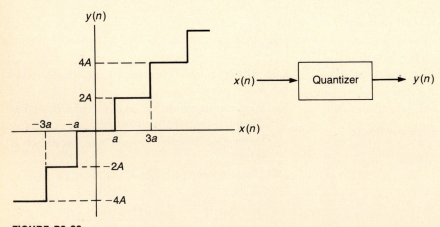

FIGURE P2.23

Show that the second derivative can be approximated by

$$\frac{d^2y(t)}{dt^2}\bigg|_{t=nT} \approx \frac{1}{T^2}[y(nT) - 2y(nT - T) +$$

$$y(nT - 2T)].$$

2.25 Given the differential equation

$$\frac{d^2y(t)}{dt^2} + 5\frac{dy(t)}{dt} + 6y(t) = 7x(t),$$

use the approximations of Problem 2.24 to find the coefficients a_0, a_1, and a_2 in the second-order difference equation $a_0y(nT) + a_1y(nT - T) + a_2y(nT - 2T) = 7x(nT)$ that approximates the continuous-time equation at the sampling instants $t = nT$.

2.26 In Section 2.5 it was shown that the integral

$$y(t) = \int_{t_0}^{t} x(\tau)d\tau + y(t_0)$$

can be approximated by the difference equation $y(nT) = Tx(nT) + y(nT - T)$. Suppose that the *forward difference* approximation is used for the integral, that is

$$\int_{nT-T}^{nT} x(\tau)d\tau \approx x(nT - T) \cdot T.$$

a) Derive the expression for $y(nT)$ using this approximation.

b) Use the relationship determined in part (a) to find the approximate integral of the ramp function described in Section 2.5 and compare the errors for $n = 1, 2, 3$ with those obtained using the backward difference approximation. Let $T = 0.01$ second.

2.27 Repeat Problem 2.26 using the trapezoidal approximation

$$\int_{nT-T}^{nT} x(\tau)d\tau \approx \left[\frac{x(nT) + x(nT - T)}{2}\right] \cdot T.$$

Give a geometric argument that explains the resulting error value. Can you use this geometric argument to find a general class of signals for which this error will be zero?

2.28 The input-output relationship of a system is given by

$$y(n) = \sum_{m=-\infty}^{m=+\infty} h(n - m)\, x(m).$$

a) Is the system linear?

b) Is the system time-invariant?

2.29 The sinusoidal sequences shown in Fig. P2.29(a) and (b) can be described by the equation, $x(n) = A\cos(2\pi n/16 + \phi)$.

a) The data for one period of the sequence of Fig. P2.29(a) are:

$$\{x_a(n)\} = \{\ldots, 9.24, 7.07, 3.83, 0, -3.83, -7.07,$$
$$\underset{n=0}{\uparrow}$$
$$-9.24, -10, -9.24, -2.07, -3.83, 0, 3.83, 7.07,$$
$$9.24, \underset{\substack{\uparrow \\ n=16}}{10, 9.24}, \ldots\}$$

Find the zero-to-peak value A and the phase ϕ. (Hint: You will need two equations in the unknowns A and ϕ.)

b) The data for one period of the sequence of Fig. P2.29(b) are:

$$\{x_b(n)\} = \{\ldots, 8.66, 9.91, 9.66, 7.93, 5.00, 1.31,$$
$$\underset{n=0}{\uparrow}$$
$$-2.59, -6.09, -8.66, -9.91, -9.66, -7.93, -5.00,$$
$$-1.31, 2.59, 6.09, 8.66, \ldots\}$$
$$\underset{n=16}{\uparrow}$$

Find the zero-to-peak amplitude A and the phase ϕ.

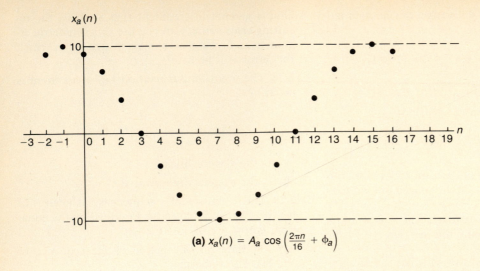

(a) $x_a(n) = A_a \cos\left(\dfrac{2\pi n}{16} + \phi_a\right)$

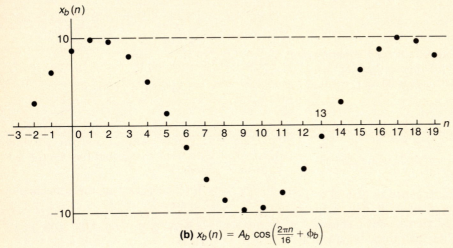

(b) $x_b(n) = A_b \cos\left(\dfrac{2\pi n}{16} + \phi_b\right)$

FIGURE P2.29

REFERENCES AND OTHER SOURCES OF INFORMATION

Cadzow, J. A. 1973. *Discrete-Time Systems.* Englewood Cliffs, New Jersey: Prentice-Hall, Inc.

Childers, D., and A. Durling. 1975. *Digital Filtering and Signal Processing.* St. Paul, Minnesota: West Publishing Co.

Fitchen, F. G. 1970. *Electronic Integrated Circuits and Systems.* New York: Van Nostrand Reinhold Co.

Hamilton, T. D. S. 1977. *Handbook of Linear Integrated Electronics for Research.* London: McGraw-Hill Book Co. Limited.

Nyquist, H. 1928. "Certain Topics in Telegraph Transmission Theory." *Trans. AIEE* 47 (April), 617–644.

Oppenheim, A. V., and R. W. Schafer. 1975. *Digital Signal Processing.* Englewood Cliffs, New Jersey: Prentice-Hall, Inc.

Papoulis, A. 1977. *Signal Analysis.* New York: McGraw-Hill Book Co.

Robinson, E. A., and M. T. Silvia. 1978. *Digital Signal Processing and Time Series Analysis.* San Francisco: Holden-Day, Inc.

Shannon, C. E. 1949. "Communication in the Presence of Noise." *Proc. of the IRE:* 37 (Jan.), 10–21.

Stearns, S. D. 1975. *Digital Signal Analysis.* Rochelle Park, New Jersey: Hayden Book Company.

Steiglitz, K. 1974. *An Introduction to Discrete Systems.* New York: John Wiley & Sons, Inc.

Stremler, F. G. 1982. *Introduction to Communication Systems.* 2nd ed. Reading, Mass.: Addison-Wesley Publishing Co.

CHAPTER 3

Linear Time-Invariant Systems

3.0 ■■■ PREVIEW

The emphasis in this chapter is on various models used to represent discrete systems and on various techniques for finding system response. We begin by describing linear time-invariant (LTI) systems with linear constant-coefficient difference equations using several examples to illustrate the general nature of these systems. We show that the analysis of LTI systems described by difference equations is mostly an exercise in arithmetic with some algebra.

Next, some pictorial ways of representing the structure of discrete systems are presented. These diagrams allow us to obtain a visual interpretation of a system's structure. This useful tool will be discussed further in later chapters.

The unit sample response, which plays a key role in analyzing linear systems, is then presented and used in determining the response of a system to arbitrary inputs through the operation of convolution. By use of the unit sample response, we then consider some basic properties of interconnected systems.

Finally, the initial condition response and the forced response of LTI systems are discussed and a technique is developed for obtaining an analytic expression for the total response. While doing this, another method for determining system stability is brought forth through the concepts of characteristic equations and characteristic roots.

3.1 ■■■ LINEAR CONSTANT-COEFFICIENT DIFFERENCE EQUATIONS

The central theme of this book is the theory and applications of linear time-invariant (LTI) systems in signal processing configurations. These systems need to be modeled and then described in mathematical terms so that their behavior can be understood and modified by design procedures, when desirable. One important way of describing LTI systems is by means of *linear constant-coefficient difference equations*. An example known to most of us is that of the compound-interest calculation, which is described by the difference equation

$$y(nT) = y(nT - T) + \frac{p}{100} y(nT - T) + x(nT) \qquad (3.1)$$

where $y(nT)$ represents the money in a savings account at the time $t = nT$, $y(nT - T)$ represents the money in the account at the previous time sample, p is the "percent" interest paid in a discrete interval of duration T, and $x(nT)$ represents the money deposited at time sample $t = nT$. The time interval T may be measured in days, months, or whatever the policy is of the financial institution. Care needs to be taken to adjust p for the time interval used.

Example 3.1. This example illustrates the response of a savings account system.

Suppose Kate Conrad opens a savings account on her twenty-first birthday and deposits $50 on the first of each month thereafter. Determine the amount of money in the account one year later if the interest rate is 1 percent per month.

Solution: A direct approach is to simply start at $n = 0$ and iterate or solve by recursive methods. Rewriting Eq. 3.1 with T understood to be one month gives us

$$y(n) = y(n - 1) + \frac{1}{100}y(n - 1) + x(n) \tag{3.2}$$

or

$$y(n) = 1.01y(n - 1) + x(n). \tag{3.3}$$

Assuming $y(-1)$ to be zero (the account is opened at $n = 0$) we have

$$y(0) = 0 + 50 = \$50. \tag{3.4}$$

One month later

$$y(1) = 1.01y(0) + x(1) = (1.01)50 + 50 = 50.5 + 50 = \$100.50. \tag{3.5}$$

Another month later

$$y(2) = 1.01y(1) + x(2) = (1.01)(100.50) + 50 = \$151.51. \tag{3.6}$$

In the same way

$y(3) = \$203.02$, $y(4) = \$255.05$, $y(5) = \$307.60$, $y(6) = \$360.68$, $y(7) = \$414.28$,

$y(8) = \$468.43$, $y(9) = \$523.11$, $y(10) = \$578.34$, $y(11) = \$634.13$, and

$$y(12) = \$690.47. \tag{3.7}$$

Comment: The iterative solution above is more or less satisfactory for $n = 12$. But consider the situation for $n = 120$, ten years of savings. In the next section, we develop an important identity that makes long iterations unnecessary.

3.1.1 The Geometric Series—An Important Relationship

The difference equation that describes the savings account situation of Example 3.1 is of the general form,

$$y(n) = \alpha y(n - 1) + \beta x(n) \tag{3.8}$$

where α and β are real constants ($\beta = 1$ in the savings account example). Let us assume that $y(-1)$ is zero and let $x(0) = x(1) = x(2) = \cdots = x(N) = D$, a constant deposit. Starting with $n = 0$ we have

$$y(0) = \beta x(0) = \beta D \tag{3.9}$$

and continuing to $n = 1$ we find

$$
\begin{aligned}
y(1) &= \alpha y(0) + \beta x(1) \\
&= \alpha(\beta D) + \beta D \\
&= \beta D(\alpha + 1).
\end{aligned}
\tag{3.10}
$$

In the same way

$$
\begin{aligned}
y(2) &= \alpha y(1) + \beta x(2) \\
&= \beta D(\alpha^2 + \alpha) + \beta D \\
&= \beta D(\alpha^2 + \alpha + 1)
\end{aligned}
\tag{3.11}
$$

and $y(n)$ at $n = N$ is

$$y(N) = \beta D(\alpha^N + \alpha^{N-1} + \cdots + \alpha + 1). \tag{3.12}$$

Thus, the output at any sample N may be written as

$$y(N) = \beta D \sum_{m=0}^{m=N} \alpha^m \tag{3.13}$$

which we define as

$$y(N) = \beta D S_N \tag{3.14}$$

where S_N is the *finite geometric sum*

$$S_N = \sum_{m=0}^{m=N} \alpha^m. \tag{3.15}$$

To simplify our calculations we can develop a closed-form representation for this finite sum (Cadzow, 1973). Writing out the sum gives

$$S_N = 1 + \alpha + \alpha^2 + \cdots + \alpha^{N-1} + \alpha^N. \tag{3.16}$$

If we multiply by α, we get

$$\alpha S_N = \alpha + \alpha^2 + \alpha^3 + \cdots + \alpha^N + \alpha^{N+1}. \tag{3.17}$$

Now we subtract Eq. 3.17 from Eq. 3.16 to obtain

$$
\begin{aligned}
S_N - \alpha S_N = 1 + \alpha + \alpha^2 + \cdots + \alpha^{N-1} + \alpha^N - \\
(\alpha + \alpha^2 + \cdots + \alpha^N + \alpha^{N+1})
\end{aligned}
\tag{3.18}
$$

or

$$S_N(1 - \alpha) = 1 - \alpha^{N+1}. \tag{3.19}$$

If α is not equal to 1 we can divide both sides by $(1 - \alpha)$, thus, the summation may be written in the closed form

$$\boxed{S_N = \frac{1 - \alpha^{N+1}}{1 - \alpha} \text{ for } \alpha \neq 1} \quad \text{where} \quad \boxed{S_N = \sum_{m=0}^{m=N} \alpha^m} . \quad (3.20)$$

If $\alpha = 1$, the summation S_N has the value $N + 1$. This can be shown either by returning to Eq. 3.15 and substituting $\alpha = 1$, or by applying l'Hôpital's rule[†] to the closed-form expression for S_N in Eq. 3.20. Also, notice that while we have developed the closed form for the finite geometric series with α equal to a real number, the results also apply when α is complex.

This is a good place to turn the expression for the finite geometric sum into the result for the *infinite geometric sum*, i.e., S_N for $N \to \infty$. From the closed form in Eq. 3.20, it is apparent that the magnitude of α must be less than one $(|\alpha| < 1)$ for the sum to be finite for an infinite number of terms $(N \to \infty)$. Thus, the infinite geometric sum is given by

$$\boxed{S_\infty = \frac{1}{1 - \alpha} \text{ provided } |\alpha| < 1} \quad \text{where} \quad \boxed{S_\infty = \sum_{m=0}^{m=\infty} \alpha^m} \quad (3.21)$$

and once again the restriction on the use of the formula for S_∞ must be carefully observed.[†]

Let's return to the formula for the finite geometric sum and use this expression to verify the results found in Example 3.1 by iterative methods. There we found $y(12)$ for the equation

$$y(n) = 1.01y(n - 1) + x(n) \qquad (3.22)$$

with $x(n) = \$50$. Thus, we have $\alpha = 1.01$, $\beta = 1.0$, and $D = 50$. Using Eqs. 3.20 and 3.13 we obtain

$$y(12) = \beta D S_{12} = (1.0)(50)\frac{1 - (1.01)^{13}}{1 - 1.01} = \$690.47 \qquad (3.23)$$

as before.

Example 3.2. This example illustrates the use of the identity for a finite geometric series.

Use Eq. 3.20 to determine the value of the savings account of Example 3.1 on the depositor's 30th birthday assuming a uniform deposit of $50 per month and the same interest rate of 1 percent per month.

Solution: If a deposit is made on the 30th birthday, this would give nine years' use of the account, which is 108 monthly intervals or $N = 108$. From Eq. 3.14

[†]The rule is named after Guillaume François Antoine de l'Hôpital (1661–1704), Marquis de St. Mesme, a French nobleman who wrote the first calculus text, *Analyse des Infiniment Petits*, 1696.
[†]It is easy to see that if $\alpha = 1$, for example, the infinite sum given by Eq. 3.21 does not converge to a finite value.

$$y(N) = \beta DS_N \tag{3.24}$$

and using Eq. 3.20 (since $\alpha \neq 1$) this becomes

$$y(N) = \beta D \cdot \frac{1 - \alpha^{N+1}}{1 - \alpha}. \tag{3.25}$$

With $N = 108$, $\beta = 1$, $D = \$50$, and $\alpha = 1.01$ the value of the account on the 30th birthday is (rounded to the nearest dollar)

$$y(108) = \$50 \cdot \frac{1 - 1.01^{109}}{1 - 1.01}$$

$$= \$50 \cdot \frac{1 - 2.958}{-0.01}$$

$$= \$9791 \tag{3.26}$$

3.1.2 Difference Equations for *N*th-Order Systems

The savings account equation introduced in the previous section is a simple example of difference equations that are often used to describe discrete systems. In general, linear, time-invariant (LTI) systems may be described by difference equations of the form

$$y(n) = a_1 y(n - 1) + a_2 y(n - 2) + \cdots + a_N y(n - N)$$
$$+ b_0 x(n) + b_1 x(n - 1) + \cdots + b_L x(n - L) \tag{3.27}$$

where the a's and b's are real constants and we have accounted for N possible delays of the output $y(n)$, and L possible delays of the input $x(n)$ (Oppenheim and Schafer, 1975). This is called an *Nth-order difference equation* because the output $y(n)$ depends upon the 1st, 2nd, ... and Nth previous values (samples) of the output. This also means that to solve the difference equation starting from any value of n, N previous values of $y(n)$ must be known. Equation 3.27 may be written in a neat, compact way as

$$y(n) = \sum_{k=1}^{k=N} a_k y(n - k) + \sum_{k=0}^{k=L} b_k x(n - k) \tag{3.28}$$

Equation 3.28 represents an important class of discrete systems known as *recursive* systems because the output depends upon previous values of the output as well as the input. An equally important group is described by

$$y(n) = b_0 x(n) + b_1 x(n - 1) + \cdots + b_L x(n - L) \tag{3.29}$$

or

$$y(n) = \sum_{k=0}^{k=L} b_k x(n - k) \tag{3.30}$$

and is known as *nonrecursive*[†] because the previous values of the output don't come into play.

Example 3.3. This example illustrates the iterative solution for a second-order system.

The discrete-time (sampled) version of the rotational motion of a satellite controlled by thrusters is described by the second-order difference equation

$$y(n) = 2y(n-1) - y(n-2) + 0.5x(n) + 0.5x(n-1) \qquad (3.31)$$

where $y(n)$ represents the angular position and $x(n)$ represents the input torque of the thrusters. The two samples of initial angular position preceding $n = 0$ are represented by $y(-1)$ and $y(-2)$. Assume $y(-1) = y(-2) = 1$ and find the output at the first four samples for the following inputs:

a) A unit sample input, $x(n) = \delta(n)$
b) An alternating input, $x(n) = (-1)^n u(n)$

Solution:

a) For the unit sample input, $x(n) = \delta(n) = 1$ for $n = 0$ and the input is zero for all other values of n. The results are presented in tabular form to give an organized way to visualize the solution process

$$y(n) = 2y(n-1) - y(n-2) + 0.5x(n) + 0.5x(n-1)$$

n	$x(n-1)$	$x(n)$	$y(n-2)$	$y(n-1)$	$y(n)$
0	0	1	1 (given)	1 (given)	1.5
1	1	0	1 (given)	1.5	2.5
2	0	0	1.5	2.5	3.5
3	0	0	2.5	3.5	4.5

b) Repeating the above procedure gives the tabular arrangement below.

n	$x(n-1)$	$x(n)$	$y(n-2)$	$y(n-1)$	$y(n)$
0	0	1	1 (given)	1 (given)	1.5
1	1	-1	1 (given)	1.5	2
2	-1	1	1.5	2	2.5
3	1	-1	2	2.5	3

[†]People who are familiar with analog signal processors will recognize this as a transversal filter or tapped delay line.

> *Comment:* This step-by-step (iterative) solution of a difference equation for a known (given) input sequence and for known (given) initial conditions is a straightforward but tedious process if carried out with pencil and paper. Only the simplest problems should be done this way.

3.1.3 Computer Solution of Difference Equations

We see that the step-by-step iterative solution of a difference equation is well suited for a computer procedure. Not only is it easy to obtain numerical answers, but we can use available plotting routines to display these results in graphical form. Let's assume that we are interested in the solution of the difference equation of the general form

$$y(n) = \sum_{k=1}^{N} a_k y(n - k) + \sum_{k=0}^{L} b_k x(n - k). \tag{3.32}$$

The coefficients a_k, $k = 1, 2, \ldots, N$ and b_k, $k = 0, 1, \ldots, L$ are real numbers which are to be provided as input data to the program. It is assumed that the input $x(n)$ is zero for $n < 0$ and that the values of $x(n)$ for $n \geq 0$ are also read as input data to the program. If we have a recursive system $(N > 0)$ we also need to know initial conditions for $n = -1$, $-2, \ldots, -N$ to get the iterative procedure started and these values are also to be provided as input data. For a nonrecursive system, the output depends only on the present and the L past input values and, consequently, no initial conditions are needed.

A first step in developing the computer code for the procedure to solve difference equation is to draw a flowchart, or write pseudocode (Etter, 1987) which represents the algorithm. A pseudocode representation of the main computational portion of the difference equation solution procedure is shown in Fig. 3.1(a). This pseudocode should be self-

FIGURE 3.1(a) Pseudocode for main computational portion of procedure to solve difference equations

```
DO    FOR    NS←—— 0   TO    NSTOP
    Y(NS)←——0.
 (check to see if recursive portion should be skipped)
    IF N ≠ 0 THEN
        (compute the recursive portion)
        DO FOR K←1  TO  N
            Y(NS)←——Y(NS) + A(K)·Y(NS-K)
        END DO
    END IF
     (compute the nonrecursive portion)
    DO FOR K←——0 TO L
        Y(NS)←——Y(NS) + B(K)·X(NS-K)
    END DO
END DO
```

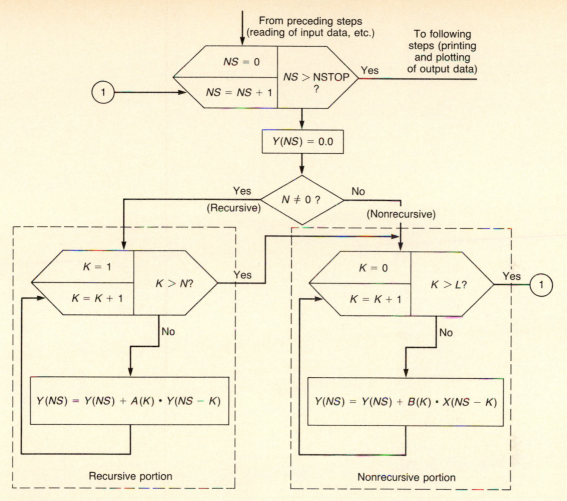

FIGURE 3.1(b) Flowchart for subroutine to solve difference equations

explanatory; however, we observe that the notation $A \leftarrow B$ means that the value of the variable named B is assigned to the variable named A. Of course, as illustrated in Fig. 3.1(a), B may itself be an arithmetic expression. Also, notice that we have used NS in Fig. 3.1(a) for n in Eq. 3.32 and $NSTOP$ is the largest value of NS for which the difference equation is to be solved.

A flowchart representation of the pseudocode is shown in Fig. 3.1(b). The computer code represented by the flowchart or the pseudocode would be a portion of a computer program whose overall structure is illustrated in Fig. 3.2. The flowchart in Fig. 3.2 assumes the availability of a subroutine named PLOTR which provides graphical output of the input and output sequences.

The development of the pseudocode into a program is left as an exercise for the student in Problem 3.20, and Problem 3.21 provides several

FIGURE 3.2 Flowchart of program to solve difference equations

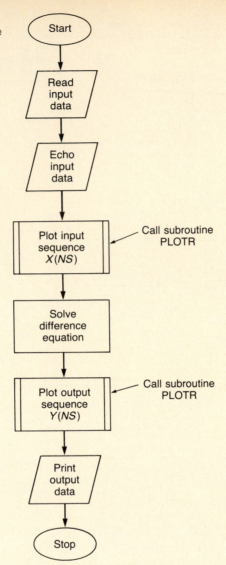

test problems for use in checking the program. These numerical solutions can also serve as a check on the solutions obtained by using methods discussed elsewhere in this chapter.

3.2 ▬ SYSTEM DIAGRAMS OR REALIZATIONS

In the previous section, LTI systems were described, or modeled, by linear, constant-coefficient difference equations and the iterative, or step-by-step, method for solving these equations was discussed. In this section we introduce an alternative model in the form of a system diagram. A system diagram is simply a graphical way of representing the same information contained in difference equations. Such diagrams can provide useful visualizations of system structure. In addition, there are graphical methods for manipulating system diagrams to aid in system analysis.

First, we will define the symbols needed to produce a diagram that represents a linear system (Stearns, 1975). Recall that the general form of the difference equation is

$$y(n) = \sum_{k=1}^{k=N} a_k y(n - k) + \sum_{k=0}^{k=L} b_k x(n - k). \tag{3.33}$$

We note that delays, multiplications, and additions are needed to implement Eq. 3.33. Figure 3.3 shows two sets of commonly used symbols along with the describing relations. The unit delay of Fig. 3.3(a) is described by $x_2(n) = x_1(n - 1)$, which means that the output of the delay D is the same as the input only delayed by one sample interval. The representation of gain in Fig. 3.3(b) is quite straightforward where the output of the gain is simply the input multiplied by a real constant b_0. The building blocks for adding are given in Fig. 3.3(c) where it should be noticed that $x_3(n)$, the sum of $x_1(n)$ and $x_2(n)$, appears at a node in the signal flow graph (SFG) in contrast with appearing at the output of a summing junction represented as $\oplus$ in the block diagram. Normally, the sets of symbols are not mixed and it is strictly a matter of preference as to the use of block diagrams or signal flow graphs. We will use both. System diagrams can

FIGURE 3.3 System diagram building blocks

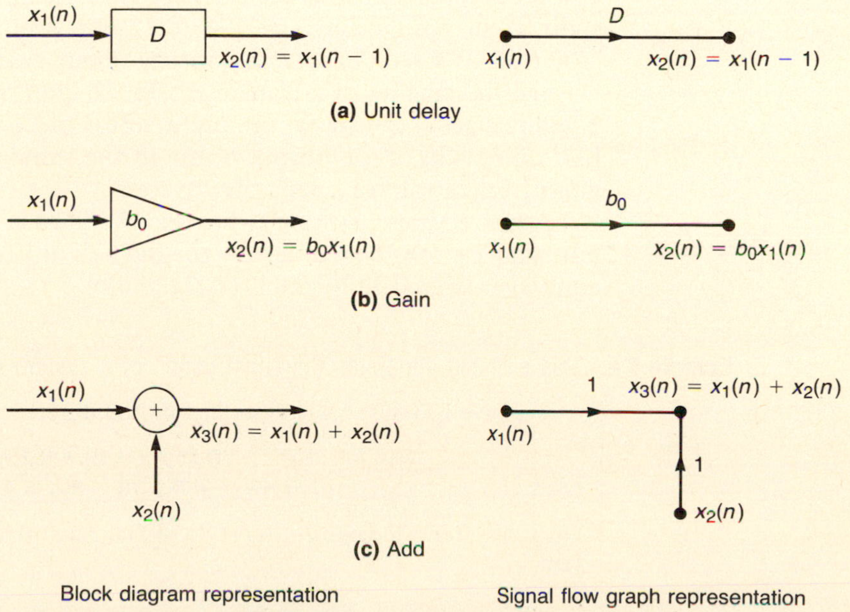

(a) Unit delay

(b) Gain

(c) Add

Block diagram representation   Signal flow graph representation

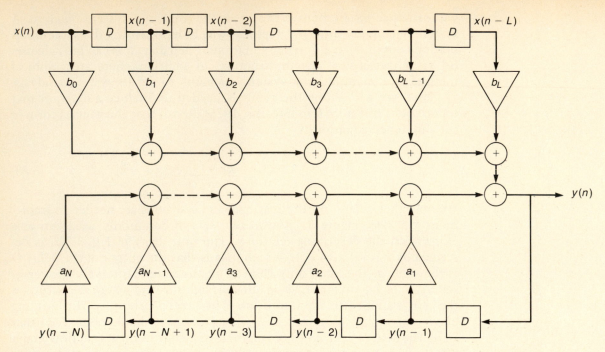

FIGURE 3.4(a) Realization of the general difference equation

represent the hardware implementation of a discrete-time processor or the algorithm to implement the difference equation. In Fig. 3.4(a) a diagram that represents the general difference equation is shown. System realizations are not unique; in fact, in digital filtering applications several different representations for the same system may be drawn to gain insight about which diagram best represents the system for a particular situation. We will have more to say about realizations after we have learned the algebra of z-transforms in Chapter Six. The top half of Fig. 3.4(a) realizes (represents) the input terms of Eq. 3.33 while the bottom half takes care of the output terms in the same equation. This is a diagram (realization) of a recursive system.

A nonrecursive system, where no memory is needed for the past output samples, may be realized by the top half only of Fig. 3.4(a), or as in the equivalent signal flow graph of Fig. 3.4(b).

Example 3.4. This example illustrates the construction of a system diagram.

A recursive LTI system is described by the difference equation

$$y(n) = y(n-1) - 0.75y(n-2) + 0.25y(n-3) - 0.125y(n-4) + x(n) - x(n-4). \tag{3.34}$$

Draw a system diagram in the style of Fig. 3.4(a) that will represent this system.

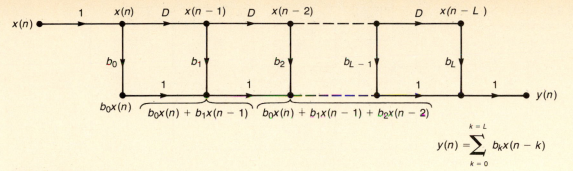

$$y(n) = \sum_{k=0}^{k=L} b_k x(n-k)$$

FIGURE 3.4(b) Realization of a nonrecursive system (signal flow graph)

Solution: The general form of the difference equation is

$$y(n) = a_1 y(n-1) + a_2 y(n-2) + a_3 y(n-3) + a_4 y(n-4) +$$
$$b_0 x(n) + b_1 x(n-1) + b_2 x(n-2) + b_3 x(n-3) + b_4 x(n-4) \quad (3.35)$$

and comparing Eq. 3.34 with Eq. 3.35 yields the gains

$$a_1 = 1, \ a_2 = -0.75, \ a_3 = 0.25, \ a_4 = -0.125,$$

$$b_0 = 1, \ b_1 = b_2 = b_3 = 0 \text{ and } b_4 = -1. \quad (3.36)$$

The system diagram marked with these gains is given in Fig. 3.5. The multipliers showing zero gain could be eliminated, but this is simply a matter of choice.

In the next few chapters we study the principles and applications of a special class of discrete-time systems called digital filters. One important filter that comes from the study of time-series data generated by physical, economic, or biological processes is the moving (sliding) average filter[†] (Robinson, 1982). With this filter, a running average is obtained by accumulating the average over the previous L samples and then as each successive group of samples is taken, adding the new samples into the average and subtracting the oldest samples from the sum. Thus, the accumulated signal is always the average of the L most recent samples. The difference equation description is

$$y(n) = \frac{1}{L}[x(n) + x(n-1) + \cdots + x(n-L+1)]$$

$$= \frac{1}{L} \sum_{k=0}^{k=L-1} x(n-k). \quad (3.37)$$

[†] The name moving average filter comes from H. Wold, *A Study in the Analysis of Stationary Time Series*, Stockholm, Stockholm University, 1938. In this thesis, Wold computed a model of the yearly level of Lake Vaner in Sweden as a moving average of the current and previous years' rainfall.

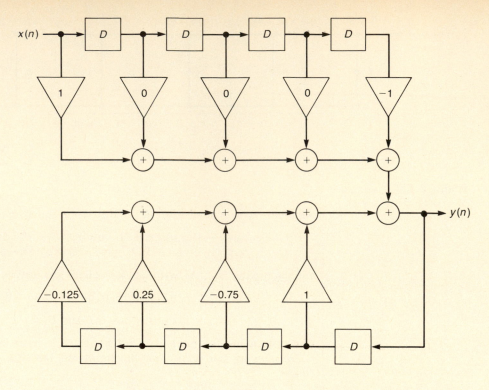

FIGURE 3.5 System diagram for Example 3.4

FIGURE 3.6 Moving average filter $y(n) = \frac{1}{L}\sum_{k=0}^{L-1} x(n-k)$

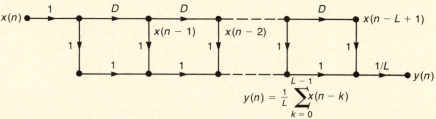

$$y(n) = \frac{1}{L}\sum_{k=0}^{L-1} x(n-k)$$

In a real application L might be a very large number to smooth the data and to get a better measure of the input. A flow graph representation of Eq. 3.37 is given in Fig. 3.6 which is just a special case of Fig. 3.4(b) with all of the b's equal to 1.

3.3 ▬ UNIT SAMPLE RESPONSE

Difference equations and system diagrams are two ways of describing LTI systems that are used in signal processing. A third model is the *unit sample (impulse) response.*[†] The unit sample response is the output se-

---

[†]For those readers who are familiar with the unit impulse response of continuous-time systems, the unit sample response is analogous in discrete systems.

quence produced by applying an input of $x(n) = \delta(n)$ to the system. As we see, if we know a system's unit sample response, we can determine the response to any input sequence. This results in the unit sample response often being used as the basis for implementing a digital signal processing system.

Consider a causal, nonrecursive system described by

$$y(n) = \sum_{k=0}^{k=L} b_k x(n - k) \tag{3.38}$$

subjected to a unit sample input, namely

$$x(n) = \delta(n) = \begin{cases} 1, & n = 0 \\ 0, & n \neq 0. \end{cases} \tag{3.39}$$

When this special input $x(n) = \delta(n)$ is applied to the system, the resulting output is called the unit sample response and is denoted by $h(n)$. That is, $y(n) = h(n)$ if $x(n) = \delta(n)$. Thus, for the nonrecursive system of Eq. 3.38 we find that

$$y(0) = h(0) = b_0 x(0) + b_1 x(-1)^0 + \cdots + b_L x(-L)^0$$
$$= b_0$$

$$y(1) = h(1) = b_0 x(1)^0 + b_1 x(0) + b_2 x(-1)^0 + \cdots + b_L x(1-L)^0$$
$$= b_1$$

$$\vdots$$

$$y(L) = h(L) = b_0 x(L)^0 + b_1 x(L-1)^0 + \cdots + b_L x(0)$$
$$= b_L. \tag{3.40}$$

From this solution of Eq. 3.38, namely Eq. 3.40, it is apparent that

$$y(n) = h(n) = \begin{cases} b_n, & n = 0, 1, 2, \ldots, L \\ 0, & n < 0 \end{cases} \tag{3.41}$$

and the general expression for the unit sample response is

$$h(n) = \sum_{k=0}^{L} b_k \delta(n - k) = \sum_{k=0}^{L} h(k)\delta(n - k) \tag{3.42}$$

or when represented as a sequence

$$\{h(n)\} = \{b_0, b_1, \ldots, b_L\}. \tag{3.43}$$

Example 3.5. This example illustrates the computation of the unit sample response for a nonrecursive system.

Under very special conditions a "digital differentiator" can be approximated by the difference equation

$$y(n) = x(n) - x(n - 1). \qquad (3.44)$$

Find the unit sample response for this system.

Solution: From either Eq. 3.41 or Eq. 3.42

$$h(n) = b_n \qquad (3.45)$$

which gives the sequence $\{h(n)\} = \{1, -1, 0, \ldots\}$. $\qquad (3.46)$

Systems described by the unit sample response of Eq. 3.42 are known as *finite impulse response (FIR) systems* because $h(n)$ has a finite number of terms and with L delays as in Eq. 3.42 we know that for $n \geq L + 1$ the unit sample response is identically zero. It is always possible to represent an FIR system by a difference equation of the form given in Eq. 3.38.

Causal recursive systems, on the other hand, are described by the difference equation

$$y(n) = \sum_{k=1}^{N} a_k y(n - k) + \sum_{k=0}^{L} b_k x(n - k). \qquad (3.47)$$

Let's consider a first-order system described by

$$y(n) = a_1 y(n - 1) + b_0 x(n) \qquad (3.48)$$

subjected to a unit sample input, namely

$$x(n) = \delta(n) = \begin{cases} 1, & n = 0 \\ 0, & n \neq 0. \end{cases} \qquad (3.49)$$

Once again, we want to find the system response caused only by the unit sample input. This implies that all initial conditions, in this case only $y(-1)$, must be set to zero. We weren't concerned about this with nonrecursive systems because their output $y(n)$ depends only upon present and past input values and not upon any previous output value. Consequently, for a unit sample input, the first-order system of Eq. 3.48 has the response

$$y(0) = h(0) = a_1 y(-1)^0 + b_0 x(0)$$
$$= b_0$$

$$y(1) = h(1) = a_1 y(0) + b_0 x(1)^0$$
$$= b_0 a_1$$

$$y(2) = h(2) = b_0 a_1{}^2$$

.
.
.

$$y(n) = h(n) = b_0 a_1{}^n, \qquad n \geq 0. \tag{3.50}$$

We can use the unit step sequence in its off-on application to write

$$y(n) = h(n) = b_0 a_1{}^n \cdot u(n). \tag{3.51}$$

Notice that this first-order system has a unit sample response that is characterized by one real exponential sequence, $b_0(a_1)^n$.

Example 3.6. This example illustrates the unit sample response of a first-order system with one input delay.

Suppose we now have the first-order system

$$y(n) = a_1 y(n-1) + b_0 x(n) + b_1 x(n-1). \tag{3.52}$$

Show that the unit sample response can be put into the form

a) $\quad h(n) = b_0 a_1{}^n \cdot u(n) + b_1 a_1{}^{n-1} \cdot u(n-1) \tag{3.53}$

or alternatively

b) $\quad h(n) = \left(b_0 + \dfrac{b_1}{a_1}\right) a_1{}^n \cdot u(n) - \dfrac{b_1}{a_1} \delta(n). \tag{3.54}$

Solution:

a) The iterative solution of Eq. 3.52 with $x(n) = \delta(n)$ and $x(n-1) = \delta(n-1)$ is

$$y(0) = h(0) = b_0$$

$$y(1) = h(1) = a_1 y(0) + b_1 = a_1 b_0 + b_1$$

$$y(2) = h(2) = a_1 y(1) = a_1{}^2 b_0 + a_1 b_1$$

$$y(3) = h(3) = a_1 y(2) = a_1{}^3 b_0 + a_1{}^2 b_1$$

.
.
.

$$y(n) = h(n) = b_0 a_1{}^n + b_1 a_1{}^{n-1} \qquad n \geq 1. \tag{3.55}$$

Thus, we have

$$y(n) = \begin{cases} b_0, & n = 0 \\ b_0 a_1{}^n + b_1 a_1{}^{n-1}, & n \geq 1. \end{cases} \tag{3.56}$$

It is preferable to write $y(n)$ as a single equation valid for $n \geq 0$. We know that $y(0) = b_0$, and recalling that unit step and shifted unit step sequences can be used for off-on purposes, Eq. 3.56 may be written as

$$y(n) = h(n) = b_0 a_1{}^n \cdot u(n) + b_1 a_1{}^{n-1} \cdot u(n - 1) \qquad (3.57)$$

which is the form desired.

b) To get the second form for $h(n)$ we first repeat $h(n)$ for $n \geq 1$, namely

$$h(n) = b_0 a_1{}^n + b_1 a_1{}^{n-1}$$

$$= a_1{}^n (b_0 + b_1/a_1), \qquad n \geq 1. \qquad (3.58)$$

To make this equation "fit" for $n = 0$ also we can add a weighted sample $A_0 \delta(n)$ giving

$$h(n) = a_1{}^n (b_0 + b_1/a_1) + A_0 \delta(n), \qquad n \geq 0. \qquad (3.59)$$

Once again using $h(0) = b_0$, Eq. 3.59 becomes for $n = 0$

$$b_0 = a_1{}^0 (b_0 + b_1/a_1) + A_0 \quad \text{or} \quad A_0 = -b_1/a_1. \qquad (3.60)$$

Thus, the solution for $n \geq 0$ can be written as

$$h(n) = a_1{}^n (b_0 + b_1/a_1) \cdot u(n) - \frac{b_1}{a_1} \delta(n). \qquad (3.61)$$

Comments:

a) The preceding example provides a good opportunity to use some linear systems characteristics to help explain the results and to extend them to other more complex recursive systems. The system equation with a unit sample input is

$$y(n) - a_1 y(n - 1) = b_0 x(n) + b_1 x(n - 1)$$

$$= b_0 \delta(n) + b_1 \delta(n - 1) \qquad (3.62)$$

which can be described as

$$y(n) - a_1 y(n - 1) = b_0 x_1(n) + b_1 x_2(n). \qquad (3.63)$$

We can then use the superposition property of linear systems to consider the two equations

$$y_1(n) - a_1 y_1(n - 1) = b_0 x_1(n)$$
$$y_2(n) - a_1 y_2(n - 1) = b_1 x_2(n). \qquad (3.64)$$

That is, we can find the responses due to $x_1(n)$ and $x_2(n)$ alone. The total response is then the sum of these responses. We have already determined in Eq. 3.51 that for $x_1(n) = b_0 \delta(n)$ and $x_2(n) = 0$ the response is

$$y(n) = h(n) = b_0 a_1{}^n \cdot u(n) \qquad (3.65)$$

or

$$x_1(n) = b_0 \delta(n) \xrightarrow{\text{produces}} y_1(n) = h_1(n) = b_0 a_1{}^n \cdot u(n) \qquad (3.66)$$

where we are using $y_1(n) = h_1(n)$ to denote the response due to $x_1(n)$ alone. This is an LTI system and so the weighted shifted sample $b_1 \delta(n - 1)$ will produce an output similar to that described by Eq. 3.66 but shifted by one (replace n with $n - 1$) and weighted by b_1 rather than b_0. That is,

$$x_2(n) = b_1\delta(n - 1) \xrightarrow{\text{produces}} y_2(n) = h_2(n) = b_1{a_1}^{n-1} \cdot u(n - 1). \quad (3.67)$$

Using superposition, $h_1(n)$ and $h_2(n)$ can be added together to give

$$h(n) = h_1(n) + h_2(n)$$
$$= b_0{a_1}^n \cdot u(n) + b_1{a_1}^{n-1} \cdot u(n - 1) \quad (3.68)$$

as we found before in Eq. 3.57.

b) Let's extend this line of reasoning to a first-order system with two input delays instead of one, that is

$$y(n) - a_1y(n - 1) = b_0x(n) + b_1x(n - 1) + b_2x(n - 2) \quad (3.69)$$

and with a unit sample input we have

$$y(n) - a_1y(n - 1) = b_0\delta(n) + b_1\delta(n - 1) + b_2\delta(n - 2). \quad (3.70)$$

For this LTI system we know that

$$b_0\delta(n) \xrightarrow{\text{produces}} b_0{a_1}^n \cdot u(n) \quad (3.71)$$

and that

$$b_1\delta(n - 1) \xrightarrow{\text{produces}} b_1{a_1}^{n-1} \cdot u(n - 1). \quad (3.72)$$

It follows, therefore, that

$$b_2\delta(n - 2) \xrightarrow{\text{produces}} b_2{a_1}^{n-2} \cdot u(n - 2) \quad (3.73)$$

and the total response (the unit sample response) is

$$h(n) = b_0{a_1}^n \cdot u(n) + b_1{a_1}^{n-1} \cdot u(n - 1) + b_2{a_1}^{n-2} \cdot u(n - 2). \quad (3.74)$$

Although Eq. 3.74 is a perfectly satisfactory answer, it is somewhat more convenient to use the basic exponential sequence, $C_1{a_1}^n \cdot u(n)$ together with additional sample functions as we did in Eq. 3.61 for the single input delay situation. This gives

$$h(n) = C_1{a_1}^n \cdot u(n) + A_0\delta(n) + A_1\delta(n - 1) \quad (3.75)$$

where $C_1 = b_0 + b_1{a_1}^{-1} + b_2{a_1}^{-2}$, $A_0 = -[b_1{a_1}^{-1} + b_2{a_1}^{-2}]$ and $A_1 = -b_2{a_1}^{-1}$. These values for C_1, A_0 and A_1 are found by equating the values of $h(n)$ from Eq. 3.74 for $n = 0, 1, 2$ with those obtained from Eq. 3.75 for $n = 0, 1, 2$. Thus, an alternative form of the solution given in Eq. 3.74 is

$$h(n) = [b_0 + b_1{a_1}^{-1} + b_2{a_1}^{-2}]{a_1}^n u(n) -$$
$$[b_1{a_1}^{-1} + b_2{a_1}^{-2}]\delta(n) - b_2{a_1}^{-1}\delta(n - 1). \quad (3.76)$$

In general, we can describe the unit sample response $h(n)$ of a recursive system of order N with input delay terms of order L by N exponential sequences (real or complex) and with $L - N + 1$ samples located at $n = 0$,

$1, \ldots, L - N$. This can be written as

$$h(n) = \sum_{k=1}^{k=N} C_k(r_k)^n \cdot u(n) + \sum_{k=0}^{k=L-N} A_k \delta(n - k) \qquad (3.77)$$

where the r_k's, which are assumed to be distinct (different from one another), describe the exponential sequences, the $\delta(n - k)$'s are the shifted samples, and the C_k's and A_k's are the associated constants. Notice that the shifted samples appear if L—the largest delay of one input—is equal to or exceeds the order of the system N.

For first- and possibly second-order systems it may be possible to find the exponentials and their constants by starting from the difference equation

$$y(n) = \sum_{k=1}^{N} a_k y(n - k) + \sum_{k=0}^{k=L} b_k x(n - k) \qquad (3.78)$$

and proceeding with an iterative solution with $x(n) = \delta(n)$ and all initial conditions set to zero. For higher-order systems, it is a very difficult task to recognize or pick out the exponentials $(r_k$'s) and their constants $(C_k$'s) in the solution of the difference equation. For instance, a simple representation of a second-order system is

$$y(n) = [2a \cos \alpha]y(n - 1) - [a^2]y(n - 2) + x(n) \qquad (3.79)$$

and the unit sample response is calculated iteratively as

$$y(0) = h(0) = 1 \longleftarrow x(n) = \delta(n) = \delta(0) = 1$$

$$y(1) = h(1) = [2a \cos \alpha]1$$

$$y(2) = h(2) = [2a \cos \alpha][2a \cos \alpha] - [a^2]1$$

$$y(3) = h(3) = [2a \cos \alpha][4a^2 \cos^2\alpha - a^2] - [a^2][2a \cos \alpha] \qquad (3.80)$$

and so forth. A wizard might recognize the general form of

$$y(n) = h(n) = \frac{1}{\sin \alpha} a^n \sin(n\alpha + \alpha) \cdot u(n) \qquad (3.81)$$

while we mortals need the concepts on forced response found in Section 3.7 of this chapter or the z-transform method of Chapter Six to obtain this result. It's worthwhile to use Eq. 3.81 to verify the results of iteration since the two solutions appear to be so different. From Eq. 3.81

$$h(0) = \frac{1}{\sin \alpha}[1][\sin \alpha] = 1 \qquad (3.82)$$

$$h(1) = \frac{1}{\sin \alpha}[a][\sin 2\alpha] = \frac{a}{\sin \alpha}[2 \sin \alpha \cos \alpha] = 2a \cos \alpha \qquad (3.83)$$

$$h(2) = \frac{1}{\sin \alpha}[a]^2[\sin 3\alpha] = \frac{a^2}{\sin \alpha}[3 \sin \alpha - 4 \sin^3 \alpha]$$

$$= a^2[3 - 4 \sin^2 \alpha]$$

$$= a^2[3 - 4(1 - \cos^2 \alpha)]$$

$$= -a^2 + 4a^2 \cos^2 \alpha \tag{3.84}$$

and so far we are getting the same results. The point of all of this, however, is that an analytical expression for $h(n)$ is very difficult to find from the direct solution of the system difference equations for high-order recursive systems. As a result we normally find an analytical expression for $h(n)$ by using the methods of Section 3.7 of this chapter and those found in Chapter Six.

If a system's unit sample response never approaches zero (i.e. is of infinite duration) the system is said to have an *infinite impulse response* (*IIR*). Thus, a system whose unit sample response has the form given in Eq. 3.77 is an IIR system. This is because the exponential terms $(C_k r_k^n)$ never decay to exactly zero even for systems characterized by $|r_k| < 1$, $k = 1, 2, \ldots, N$ even though the weighted sample terms $A_k \delta(n - k)$ vanish very quickly. Although we have just said that the unit sample response of an IIR system "lasts forever," the response may become quite small even for rather small values of n. For instance, using the unit sample response

$$h(n) = b_0 a_1^n \cdot u(n) \tag{3.85}$$

with $b_0 = 3$ and $a_1 = \dfrac{1}{2}$ we have

$$h(n) = 3\left(\frac{1}{2}\right)^n \cdot u(n) \tag{3.86}$$

and

$$h(10) = 3\left(\frac{1}{2}\right)^{10} = 0.00293$$

$$h(20) = 3\left(\frac{1}{2}\right)^{20} = 0.00000286 \tag{3.87}$$

which means we really don't have to wait forever for the response to decay to almost zero.

To summarize, an infinite impulse response system has a unit sample response given by

$$h(n) = \sum_{k=1}^{N} C_k(r_k)^n + \sum_{k=0}^{L-N} A_k \delta(n - k), \tag{3.88}$$

can always be characterized by a difference equation of the form

$$y(n) = \sum_{k=1}^{N} a_k y(n-k) + \sum_{k=0}^{L} b_k x(n-k), \qquad (3.89)$$

and can be described by a system diagram as in Fig. 3.4(a). A finite impulse response system, on the other hand, has a unit sample response given by

$$h(n) = \sum_{k=0}^{L} b_k \delta(n-k), \qquad (3.90)$$

can always be characterized by a difference equation of the form

$$y(n) = \sum_{k=0}^{L} b_k x(n-k) \qquad (3.91)$$

and can be described by a system diagram as in Fig. 3.4(b). It is also possible to represent FIR systems by a recursive form of a difference equation as shown in the following example.

Example 3.7. This example illustrates the recursive representation of a moving average filter.

Given the nonrecursive description of a moving average filter, namely

$$y(n) = \frac{1}{k}x(n) + \frac{1}{k}x(n-1) + \cdots + \frac{1}{k}x(n-[k-1])$$

$$= \frac{1}{k}\sum_{\ell=0}^{k-1} x(n-\ell). \qquad (3.92)$$

Show that Eq. 3.92 may be written in the recursive form

$$y(n) = y(n-1) + \frac{1}{k}[x(n) - x(n-k)]. \qquad (3.93)$$

Solution: Replacing n with $n-1$ in Eq. 3.92 gives

$$y(n-1) = \frac{1}{k}\sum_{\ell=0}^{k-1} x(n-1-\ell)$$

$$= \frac{1}{k}x(n-1) + \frac{1}{k}x(n-2) + \cdots + \frac{1}{k}x(n-[k-1]) + \frac{1}{k}x(n-k).$$

$$(3.94)$$

Subtracting Eq. 3.94 from Eq. 3.92 gives the recursive form

$$y(n) - y(n-1) = \frac{1}{k}x(n) - \frac{1}{k}x(n-k) \qquad (3.95)$$

or the recursive equation of Eq. 3.93

$$y(n) = y(n - 1) + \frac{1}{k}[x(n) - x(n - k)].$$ (3.96)

Comment: Notice that for $x(n) = \delta(n)$ the output (unit sample response) is

$$y(0) = y(-1) + \frac{1}{k}x(0) - \frac{1}{k}x(-k) = 0 + \frac{1}{k} \cdot 1 - \frac{1}{k} \cdot 0 = \frac{1}{k}$$

$$y(1) = y(0) + \frac{1}{k}[x(1) - x(1 - k)] = \frac{1}{k} + \frac{1}{k}[0 - 0] = \frac{1}{k}$$

$$y(2) = \frac{1}{k}$$

.
.
.

$$y(k) = y(k - 1) + \frac{1}{k}[x(k) - x(0)] = \frac{1}{k} + \frac{1}{k}[0 - 1] = 0$$

$$y(k + 1) = y(k + 2) = \cdots = 0.$$ (3.97)

This response is FIR but the difference equation is recursive. The approach of Example 3.7 can also be generalized to other FIR filters, however, we'll generally adhere to the common practice of using interchangeably the terms recursive and IIR and the terms nonrecursive and FIR.

Example 3.8. This example illustrates some nomenclature and descriptions used in discrete systems.

Give a brief description, mathematical or otherwise, of the following:

a) Finite impulse response (FIR) filter
b) Unit sample response, $h(n)$
c) Recursive system
d) Nonrecursive system
e) Infinite impulse response (IIR) filter

The answers may take different forms.

Solution:

a) A finite impulse response (FIR) filter has a unit sample response that has nonzero values for only a finite number of samples. Most commonly, FIR filters are described by a difference equation of the form

$$y(n) = \sum_{k=0}^{k=L} b_k x(n - k).$$ (3.98)

b) The unit sample response $h(n)$ is the output sequence produced by applying an input of $x(n) = \delta(n)$ to the system with all initial conditions set to zero.

c) The output for a recursive system is computed from knowledge of previous outputs as well as the current and previous inputs as described by

$$y(n) = \sum_{k=1}^{N} a_k y(n - k) + \sum_{k=0}^{L} b_k x(n - k). \qquad (3.99)$$

d) The output of a nonrecursive system depends only upon the current and a finite number of previous values of the input. We show in Section 3.6 that such systems are always stable.

e) An infinite impulse response (IIR) filter has a unit sample response that "never" decays to zero; its response continues indefinitely. Most commonly, IIR filters are described by the difference equation

$$y(n) = \sum_{k=1}^{N} a_k y(n - k) + \sum_{k=0}^{L} b_k x(n - k) \qquad (3.100)$$

or by Fig. 3.4(a).

3.4 ■ CONVOLUTION

As a prelude to this section, we show by example how the unit sample response $h(n)$ can be used to determine a system output for any input. This is a very powerful concept. The first step is to calculate the output for an arbitrary input sequence $x(n)$ by iterative methods. For the first-order system characterized by the difference equation

$$y(n) = a_1 y(n - 1) + b_0 x(n) \qquad (3.101)$$

the response to any input sequence $x(n)$ with $y(-1) = 0$ is

$$y(0) = b_0 x(0)$$
$$y(1) = a_1 b_0 x(0) + b_0 x(1)$$
$$y(2) = a_1^2 b_0 x(0) + a_1 b_0 x(1) + b_0 x(2) \qquad (3.102)$$
$$y(3) = a_1^3 b_0 x(0) + a_1^2 b_0 x(1) + a_1 b_0 x(2) + b_0 x(3).$$

The general solution for any sample value n is

$$y(n) = a_1^n b_0 x(0) + a_1^{n-1} b_0 x(1) + \cdots + a_1 b_0 x(n - 1) + b_0 x(n). \qquad (3.103)$$

The unit sample response of this system was determined in the previous section. From Eq. 3.50 the values are

$$h(n) = a_1^n b_0, \; h(n - 1) = a_1^{n-1} b_0, \ldots. \qquad (3.104)$$

Substituting Eq. 3.104 into 3.103 gives

$$y(n) = h(n)x(0) + h(n-1)x(1) + \cdots + h(1)x(n-1) + h(0)x(n) \quad (3.105)$$

which may be written as the finite sum

$$y(n) = \sum_{m=0}^{m=n} h(m)x(n-m). \quad (3.106)$$

Equation 3.106 is known as the *convolution summation* and represents another way of obtaining the system output for an arbitrary input. Note, however, that we produced this summation for a specific first-order system. After another first-order example we will proceed with a general development.

Example 3.9. This example illustrates the step response of a first-order system computed by convolution.

A first-order system described by the difference equation

$$y(n) = a_1 y(n-1) + b_0 x(n), \qquad n \geq 0 \quad (3.107)$$

was shown to have the unit sample response

$$h(n) = \begin{cases} b_0 a_1^n, & n \geq 0 \\ 0, & n < 0. \end{cases} \quad (3.108)$$

This system is subjected to a unit step sequence input, $x(n) = u(n) = 1$ for $n \geq 0$. Find the output using the convolution sum of Eq. 3.106. Assume $y(-1) = 0$.

Solution: From Eq. 3.106 we have

$$y(n) = \sum_{m=0}^{m=n} h(m)x(n-m) \quad (3.109)$$

and substitution of the given data gives us

$$y(n) = \sum_{m=0}^{m=n} b_0 a_1^m \cdot 1$$

$$= b_0 \sum_{m=0}^{m=n} a_1^m. \quad (3.110)$$

Finally, using the formula for the finite geometric sum Eq. 3.20 we find

$$y(n) = b_0 \frac{1 - a_1^{n+1}}{1 - a_1}, \qquad a_1 \neq 1. \quad (3.111)$$

Comment: This response is shown in Fig. 3.7 for $b_0 = 2$ and $a_1 = 0.8$. It is always good practice to verify a few points on the graph of a result, in this case

$y(n)$. From Eq. 3.111 and the given data

$$y(0) = 2\frac{1-0.8}{1-0.8} = 2 \qquad (3.112)$$

and from the expression for an infinite sum, namely Eq. 3.21

$$y(\infty) = 2\,S_\infty = 2\frac{1}{1-\alpha} \qquad |\alpha| < 1 \qquad (3.113)$$

which for $\alpha = 0.8$ gives

$$y(\infty) = 2\frac{1}{1-0.8} = 10. \qquad (3.114)$$

Both results agree with Fig. 3.7.

3.4.1 A General Way to Find System Response

The principle of convolution was introduced in the analysis of a simple first-order system. Now we derive the same result in a general fashion. The system must be linear, and for present purposes, time invariant (shift invariant),[†] but it need not be causal, nor does the input have to be zero

FIGURE 3.7 Step response using convolution

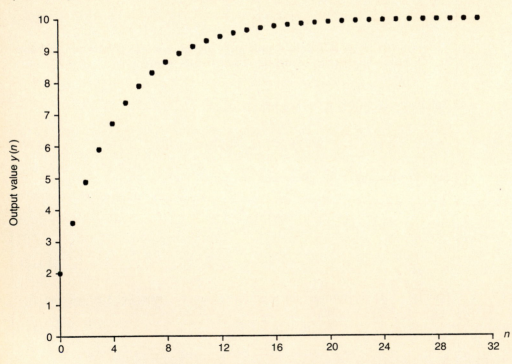

[†] Convolution also applies to time-varying systems but its use with such systems will not be treated in this book.

CHAPTER 3   LINEAR TIME-INVARIANT SYSTEMS

FIGURE 3.8 Linear system

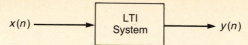

for $n < 0$. Figure 3.8 portrays the block diagram view of the situation. We accompany the general derivation with a graphical description of each step to add insight and to provide a better feel for the procedure. A simple system described by the unit sample response $h(n)$ and a short input sequence $x(n)$ is used to aid the graphical development. We are only interested in the response due to the input $x(n)$ and so all initial conditions are set to zero.

First, we have already defined the unit sample (impulse) response of the system as the sequence $h(n)$. Using symbols,

$$\delta(n) \xrightarrow{\text{produces}} h(n). \tag{3.115}$$

This is illustrated in Fig. 3.9(a) for a specific system with a given $h(n)$.

Second, because the system is time invariant, a shifted input, $\delta(n - m)$, will produce a shifted output, $h(n - m)$.

$$\delta(n - m) \xrightarrow{\text{produces}} h(n - m). \tag{3.116}$$

See Fig. 3.9(b) for the results of this step applied to the specific system.

Third, in Section 2.2.2, we observed that any signal can be described as a sum of weighted shifted samples. That is, the sequence $x(n)$ is

$$x(n) = \sum_{m=-\infty}^{m=\infty} x(m)\delta(n - m). \tag{3.117}$$

In Fig. 3.9(c), an input sequence is shown.

Fourth, using the multiplicative property of linear systems and Eq. 3.116 we find that

$$x(m)\delta(n - m) \xrightarrow{\text{produces}} x(m)h(n - m). \tag{3.118}$$

Figures 3.9(d), (e) and (f) portray this result for each of the three nonzero input samples.

Finally, from the superposition property we can add up all the shifted weighted samples that are the inputs and state that

$$\sum_{m=-\infty}^{m=+\infty} x(m)\delta(n - m) \longrightarrow \sum_{m=-\infty}^{m=+\infty} x(m)h(n - m). \tag{3.119}$$

From Eq. 3.117 we know that the left side of the above operation is $x(n)$. Therefore, since $x(n) \xrightarrow{\text{produces}} y(n)$, where $x(n)$ is the input and $y(n)$ is the

FIGURE 3.9 Graphical description of convolution derivation

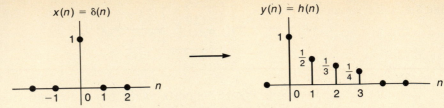

(a) Unit sample response

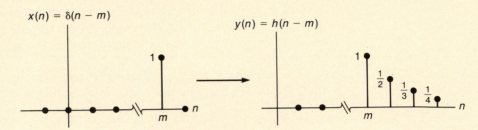

(b) Shifted sample response

$$x(n) = 4\delta(n + 1) + 9\delta(n) - 2\delta(n - 1)$$

(c) Three-sample input sequence

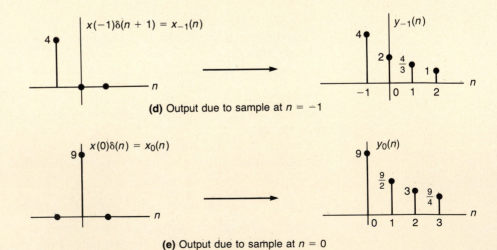

(d) Output due to sample at $n = -1$

(e) Output due to sample at $n = 0$

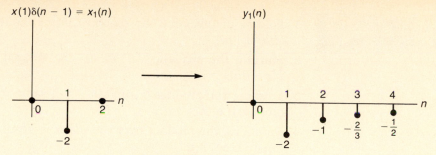

(f) Output due to sample at $n = 1$

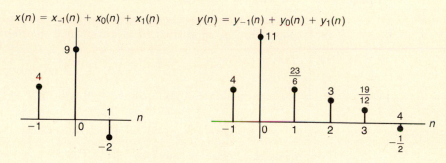

(g) Output due to three-sample input

output, the output is

$$y(n) = \sum_{m=-\infty}^{m=+\infty} x(m)h(n - m) \qquad (3.120)$$

which is defined as the convolution sum. A special form of this summation (limits of 0 and n) was deduced earlier in this section for a specific example. The result of this application of superposition is given in Fig. 3.9(g).

Hence, given the input sequence $x(n)$ to a linear time-invariant (LTI) system with unit sample response $h(n)$, the output may be determined by the convolution sum of Eq. 3.120. This operation is often written in shorthand using a $*$ (star) as

$$y(n) = x(n) * h(n) \qquad (3.121)$$

which is read as $y(n)$ equals the convolution of $x(n)$ and $h(n)$. To evaluate the convolution sum, $x(n) * h(n)$ of Eqs. 3.120 and 3.121, we notice that the sum is carried out over the index m. Evaluating this sum at any sample n consists of four important operations:

1. Folding or reversing the sequence $h(m)$ about the $m = 0$ sample to give $h(-m)$.
2. Shifting the sequence $h(-m)$ to the desired value of n to obtain $h(n - m)$.
3. Forming the product $[x(m)][h(n - m)]$ sample by sample for the desired value of n.
4. Summing the product over the index m resulting in $y(n)$ for the desired value of n.

Example 3.10. This example illustrates the steps in graphical convolution.

In many engineering and scientific applications, a causal system's sample response may be approximated as a truncated first-order exponential, namely

$$h(n) = \begin{cases} r_1^n, & 0 \le n \le M \\ 0, & \text{elsewhere} \end{cases} \tag{3.122}$$

and input data are often in the form of a discrete pulse of the form

$$x(n) = \begin{cases} A, & 0 \le n \le N \\ 0, & \text{elsewhere.} \end{cases} \tag{3.123}$$

These sequences are shown in Fig. 3.10 for $M = 3$, $r_1 = 1/2$, and $N = 4$. Determine the convolution sum $x(n) * h(n)$ using the graphical procedure that was just outlined.

Solution: The convolution sum is repeated for reference.

$$y(n) = \sum_{m=-\infty}^{m=+\infty} x(m)h(n - m) \tag{3.124}$$

1. Folding—The sample response $h(m)$, and the folded version $h(-m)$ are shown in Figs. 3.11(a) and (b).
2. Shifting—The folded sequence $h(-m)$ is shifted for two special values of $n(-1$ and $+8)$ as indicated in Figs. 3.11(c) and (d). For reference, the sequence $x(m)$ is included in Fig. 3.11(e).
3. Multiplying—Next we multiply $x(m)$ by $h(n - m)$ for each specified value of n. Note that Figs. 3.11(c) and (d) are special values of n (-1 and $+8$) because for these limiting values there is no overlap with $x(m)$ vs. m and consequently the results of multiplying $x(m) \cdot h(n - m)$ will be zero for all m. An observation will show the same situation for all $n \le -1$ and all $n \ge 8$. Shown in Fig. 3.12 are the results of the multiplying operation for $n \le -1$, and $n \ge 8$ in Fig. 3.12(a), and for $0 \le n \le 7$ in Figs. 3.12(b)–(i).
4. Summing—With the product $x(m) \cdot h(n - m) = 0$ for all m when $n \le -1$ and $n \ge 8$, the sum is clearly zero in these ranges and hence $y(n) = 0$. The sums for $0 \le n \le 7$ are also indicated in Fig. 3.12 and the result of the convolution, namely $y(n)$, is given in Fig. 3.13.

FIGURE 3.10 Convolution example, input and system unit sample response

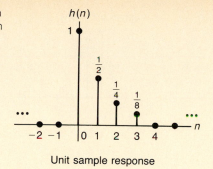

h(n)

Unit sample response

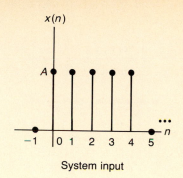

x(n)

System input

FIGURE 3.11 Folding and shifting *h(m)*

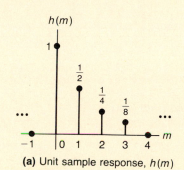

h(m)

(a) Unit sample response, *h(m)*

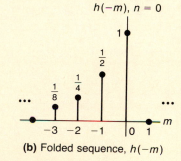

h(−m), n = 0

(b) Folded sequence, *h(−m)*

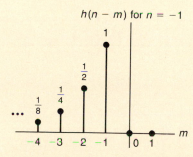

h(n − m) for *n = −1*

(c) Shifted sequence, *h(−1 − m)*

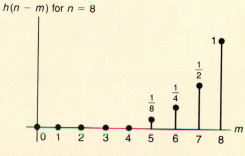

h(n − m) for *n = 8*

(d) Shifted sequence, *h(8 − m)*

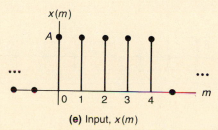

x(m)

(e) Input, *x(m)*

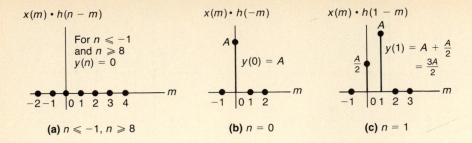

(a) $n \leqslant -1$, $n \geqslant 8$ **(b)** $n = 0$ **(c)** $n = 1$

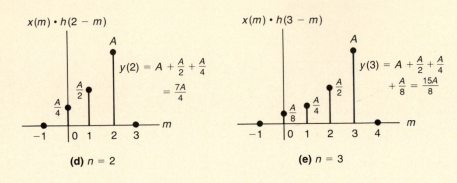

(d) $n = 2$ **(e)** $n = 3$

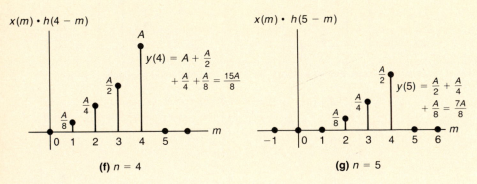

(f) $n = 4$ **(g)** $n = 5$

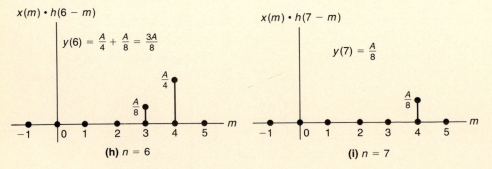

(h) $n = 6$ **(i)** $n = 7$

FIGURE 3.12 The products and sums for evaluation of the convolution

CHAPTER 3   LINEAR TIME-INVARIANT SYSTEMS

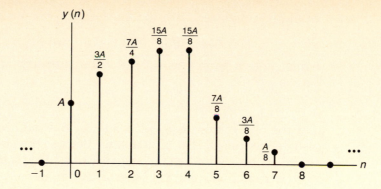

FIGURE 3.13 The resultant convolution

Another convenient way to do these paper and pencil computations is to arrange the sequences to be convolved as below:

$h(-m)$ ...	0	0	0.125	0.250	0.500	1.00	0	0	0	0	0 ··· 0
						$m = 0$ ↑↓					
$x(m)$ ...	0	0	0	0	0	A	A	A	A	A	0 ··· 0

The $h(-m)$ sequence is simply shifted right (for $n > 0$) or left (for $n < 0$) to the desired n, multiplications are done at all values of m and the results added. This process must be carried out once for each desired value of n. For identification purposes, we denote this procedure as the *sliding bar method* of convolution.

We have been using the convolution sum of Eq. 3.120, namely

$$y(n) = \sum_{m=-\infty}^{m=+\infty} x(m)h(n - m).$$

(3.125)

By a change of index, $p = n - m$, we can write the convolution sum as

$$y(n) = \sum_{p=-\infty}^{p=+\infty} x(n - p)h(p)$$

(3.126)

from which the conclusion is

$$\boxed{y(n) = x(n) * h(n) = h(n) * x(n)}.$$

(3.127)

Convolution describes an operation suited for a linear system. Thus, if the input sequence consists of two terms, $x(n) = x_1(n) + x_2(n)$, this sum would be convolved with the unit sample response $h(n)$ to yield

$$[x_1(n) + x_2(n)] * h(n) = x_1(n) * h(n) + x_2(n) * h(n) \qquad (3.128)$$

which comes from the superposition property of linear systems. Of course

$$h(n) * [x_1(n) + x_2(n)] = h(n) * x_1(n) + h(n) * x_2(n) \qquad (3.129)$$

and the results from Eqs. 3.128 and 3.129 would be identical. It should also be mentioned that although we derived the concept of convolution in the context of finding the response of a LTI system, it is a mathematical operation that applies in other situations as well. Thus, we refer to the convolution of any two sequences $f(n)$ and $g(n)$ as

$$f(n) * g(n) = \sum_{m=-\infty}^{m=\infty} f(m)g(n - m) = g(n) * f(n)$$

$$= \sum_{m=-\infty}^{m=\infty} g(m)f(n - m)$$

$$(3.130)$$

Although the summation limits are $m = -\infty$ to $m = +\infty$, typically, either the input sequence $x(n)$ and/or the unit sample response $h(n)$ are zero for some range of values of n and it is often helpful to use such knowledge to alter these limits. The results of doing this are tabulated as follows. (See Problem 3.28.) The range of time index n for which the sequence is nonzero is listed in the columns for $h(n)$ and $x(n)$

$h(n)$	$x(n)$	$y(n)$	
$-\infty \le n \le \infty$	$-\infty \le n \le \infty$	$y(n) = \displaystyle\sum_{m=-\infty}^{m=+\infty} h(m)x(n-m)$	(3.131)
$0 \le n \le \infty$	$-\infty \le n \le \infty$	$y(n) = \displaystyle\sum_{m=0}^{m=+\infty} h(m)x(n-m)$	(3.132)
$0 \le n \le \infty$	$0 \le n \le \infty$	$y(n) = \displaystyle\sum_{m=0}^{m=n} h(m)x(n-m)$	(3.133)

3.4.2 Computer Evaluation of Convolution

Graphical (numerical) convolution is generally feasible for simple problems. With long sequences that usually cannot be readily represented by analytical expressions, however, a computer solution is generally a better way to go. We now develop a description that can easily be converted to computer code for accomplishing convolution.

As a starting point, assume that we want to convolve two sequences as shown in Fig. 3.14(a). The sequences have nonzero values only in the

FIGURE 3.14 Location of nonzero points for the convolution of two sequences

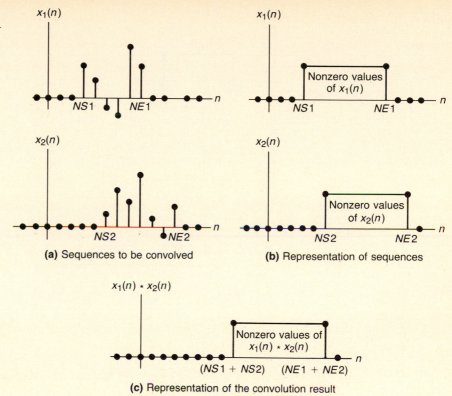

(a) Sequences to be convolved

(b) Representation of sequences

(c) Representation of the convolution result

ranges $NS1 \leq n \leq NE1$ for $x_1(n)$ and $NS2 \leq n \leq NE2$ for $x_2(n)$. To simplify the drawing for figuring out the algorithm, let us represent the sequences as shown in Fig. 3.14(b) where we show rectangles of appropriate lengths to indicate all the nonzero values of $x_1(n)$ and $x_2(n)$. It is important to note that the rectangles include their end points. Thus, the rectangle for $x_1(n)$ includes points in the interval $NS1 \leq n \leq NS2$. Also, it should be kept in mind that $NS1$, $NS2$, $NE1$, and $NE2$ may have positive, negative, or zero values, but $NS1 \leq NE1$ and $NS2 \leq NE2$.

The specific result obtained by convolving two sequences will depend on the numerical values. It can be shown, however (see Problem 3.33), that the interval of nonzero values is as pictured in Fig. 3.14(c).

To facilitate writing an algorithm to do the convolution and to be able to deal with arbitrary values of $NS1$, $NS2$, $NE1$, and $NE2$ it is convenient to recast the convolution of $x_1(n)$ and $x_2(n)$ as shown in Fig. 3.15. We first shift the sequences $x_1(n)$ and $x_2(n)$, giving $XT1(n)$ and $XT2(n)$, which both have their rectangular representations with the left edges at $n - 0$. The next step is to convolve $XT1(n)$ and $XT2(n)$, which gives the rectangular representation shown as $YT(n)$. Finally, $YT(n)$ is shifted right by an amount $NS1 + NS2$ to obtain $y(n) = x_1(n) * x_2(n)$. If $NS1 + NS2 < 0$, the shift turns out to be to the left.

FIGURE 3.15 Shifting operations used in convolution program

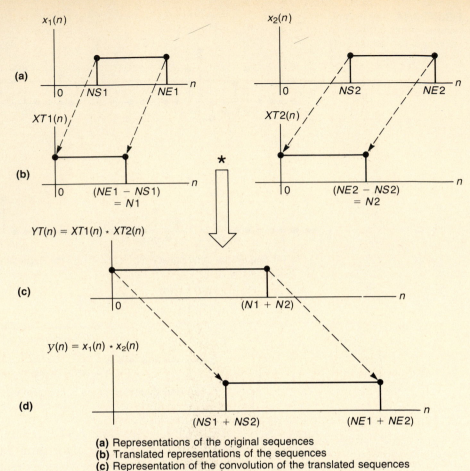

(a) Representations of the original sequences
(b) Translated representations of the sequences
(c) Representation of the convolution of the translated sequences
(d) Representation of convolution of the original sequences

By doing this shifting we can write a procedure or subroutine that convolves two sequences whose nonzero values range from 0 to $N1 = NE1 - NS1$ and from 0 to $N2 = NE2 - NS2$. The sequences $x_1(n)$ and $x_2(n)$ are shifted before entering the convolution procedure and the final shift to obtain $y(n)$ is done after completing the convolution procedure. This allows us to concentrate on the convolution procedure itself which we will now develop.

We can again appeal to pictures to develop the algorithm for evaluating

$$YT(n) = \sum_{m=-\infty}^{\infty} XT1(m)XT2(n-m). \tag{3.134}$$

In Fig. 3.16 we again use the rectangular representations for $XT1(n)$ and

$XT2(n)$. Notice that the rightmost edge of the rectangle representing $XT2(n - m)$ is at the value $m = n$ and the leftmost edge is at $m = n - N2$. Thus, as we slide $XT2(n - m)$ for each different value of n the two rectangles overlap only when $0 \leq n$ and $n - N2 \leq N1$ or for $0 \leq n \leq N1 + N2$. First consider the case where $N1 \geq N2$ as shown in Fig. 3.16(a). Here we will have one of the situations illustrated in Figs. 3.16(b)–(d). In Fig. 3.16(b) we sum the product sequence over the interval $m = 0$ to $m = n$ because all nonzero values of $XT1(m)XT2(n - m)$ lie in this range. For $N2 < n \leq N1$ we have the situation illustrated in Fig. 3.16(c) where the product curve is nonzero for $n - N2 \leq m \leq n$. The other possibility is shown in Fig. 3.16(d) where the product sequence is to be summed over the interval $n - N2 \leq m \leq N1$.

If, on the other hand, $N1 < N2$ as illustrated in Fig. 3.16(e) we have the possibilities shown in Figs. 3.16(f)–(h). For $n \leq N1$ the product sequence is nonzero only for $0 \leq m \leq n$. For $N1 < n \leq N2$, the product sequence is summed over the interval $0 \leq m \leq N1$, and for $N2 < n \leq N1 + N2$ the nonzero values of the product sequence lie in the range $n - N2 \leq m \leq N1$.

A pseudocode representation of a convolution subroutine is given in Fig. 3.17(a) and Fig. 3.17(b) shows a flowchart representation of the same subroutine. To use this subroutine to carry out a convolution, a main program would be developed whose flowchart might look something like the one shown in Fig. 3.18 where subroutines such as CONVOLVE are represented by a single box.

The conversion of the pseudocode to a working subroutine is left as an exercise for the student in Problem 3.38, and some trial problems are contained in Problem 3.39.

3.4.3 Analytical Evaluation of Convolution

Up to this point, we have concentrated our study of convolution on a numerical or graphical point of view. That is, we have not known or cared about an analytical expression for the output. Analytical expressions, however, are preferred for their generality and their usefulness in analyzing LTI systems. To obtain an equation for the output, we need equations for both the sample response and the system input. To keep things simple, let's discuss a system with an exponential sample response subjected to an exponential input, specifically

$$h(n) = \begin{cases} r_1{}^n, & n \geq 0 \\ 0, & n < 0 \end{cases} \quad \text{and} \quad x(n) = \begin{cases} a^n, & n \geq 0 \\ 0, & n < 0 \end{cases} \quad (3.135)$$

where r_1 and a are known constants and $r_1 \neq a$. Because both $h(n)$ and $x(n)$

FIGURE 3.16 Cases that need to be considered in convolution program
(a) Representation of sequences to be convolved, $N1 \geq N2$
(b) $0 \leq n \leq N2$
(c) $N2 < n \leq N1$
(d) $N1 < n \leq N1 + N2$
(e) Representation of sequences for $N1 < N2$
(f) $0 \leq n \leq N1$
(g) $N_1 < n \leq N2$
(h) $N_2 < n \leq N1 + N2$

$N1 \geqslant N2$

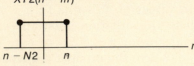
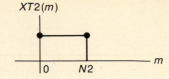

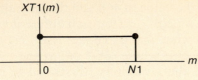
$XT1(m)$ $XT2(m)$

(a)

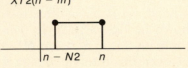
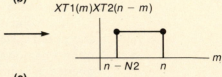

(b)

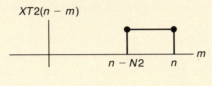
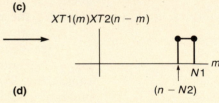

(c)

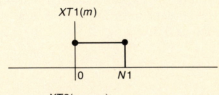
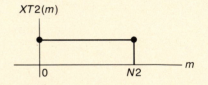

(d)

$N1 < N2$

(e)

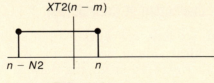
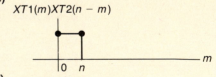

(f)

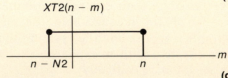
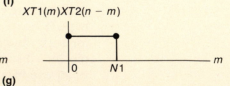

(g)

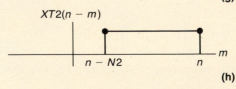
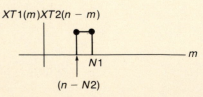

(h)

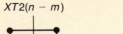

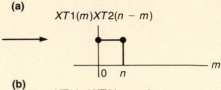

   CHAPTER 3   LINEAR TIME-INVARIANT SYSTEMS

```
SUBROUTINE CONVOLVE(N1, N2, XT1, XT2, YT)

(XT1 AND XT2 are one-dimensional arrays containing the real input
data which are stored in the locations XT1(0), XT1(1), ... , XT1(N1)
and XT2(0), XT2(1), ... , XT2(N2).  The convolution XT1(N)*XT2(N) is
stored in the one-dimensional array YT in the locations YT(0),
YT(1), ... , YT(N1+N2) )

DO FOR N←—0 TO  (N1+N2)
    YT(N)←—0.
    IF  N1 ≥ N2  THEN
        IF  N ≤ N2  THEN
            DO FOR M←—0 TO N
                YT(N)←—YT(N)  + XT1(M)·XT2(N-M)
            END DO
        ELSE IF  N > N2 AND N ≤ N1  THEN
            DO FOR M←—(N-N2) TO N
                YT(N)←—YT(N)  + XT1(M)·XT2(N-M)
            END DO
        ELSE IF  N > N1 AND N ≤ N1 + N2  THEN
            DO FOR M←—(N - N2) TO N1
                YT(N)←—YT(N)  + XT1(M)·XT2(N-M)
            END DO

        END IF
    ELSE IF  N1 < N2  THEN
        IF  N ≤ N1    THEN
            DO FOR M←—0 TO N
                YT(N)←—YT(N)  + XT1(M)·XT2(N-M)
            END DO
        ELSE IF  N > N1 and N ≤ N2  THEN
            DO FOR M←—0 TO N1
                YT(N)←—YT(N)  + XT1(M)·XT2(N-M)
            END DO
        ELSE IF  N > N2 AND N ≤ N1 + N2  THEN
            DO FOR M←—(N - N2) TO N1
                YT(N)←—YT(N)  + XT1(M)·XT2(N-M)
            END DO
        END IF
    END IF
END DO
RETURN
END CONVOLVE
```

(a) Pseudocode for the
subroutine

FIGURE 3.17 Two representations of the convolution subroutine

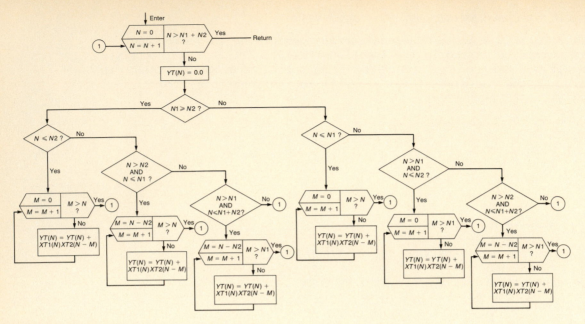

FIGURE 3.17(b) Flowchart
for the subroutine

are zero for $n < 0$ we can use Eq. 3.133 to write the system output as

$$y(n) = \sum_{m=0}^{m=n} h(m)x(n-m)$$

$$= \sum_{m=0}^{m=n} r_1^m a^{n-m}. \tag{3.136}$$

But the sum is on m so we can factor out a^n to give

$$y(n) = a^n \sum_{m=0}^{m=n} (r_1 a^{-1})^m \tag{3.137}$$

and from Eq. 3.20 for a finite geometric sum we have the closed-form
solution

$$y(n) = a^n \left(\frac{1 - (r_1 a^{-1})^{n+1}}{1 - r_1 a^{-1}} \right)$$

$$= a^n \left(\frac{a - r_1^{n+1} a^{-n}}{a - r_1} \right)$$

$$= \frac{a^{n+1} - r_1^{n+1}}{a - r_1}$$

$$= C[a^{n+1} - r_1^{n+1}] = C_a a^n - C_b r_1^n, \qquad n \geq 0 \tag{3.138}$$

FIGURE 3.18 Flowchart of program to evaluate convolution

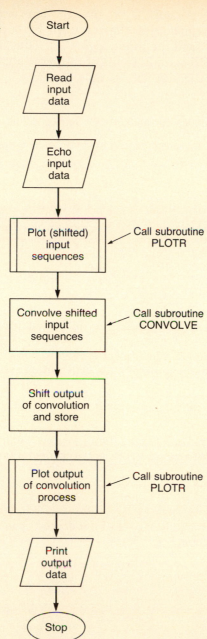

where $C_a = a/(a - r_1)$ and $C_b = r_1/(a - r_1)$. This result points out the fact that the output sequence is characterized by both the unit sample response, $h(n) = r_1{}^n$, and the input, $x(n) = a^n$. Thus, it is generally the case that the output will contain terms of the same algebraic form as terms in the input and in the system's sample response.

Example 3.11. This example illustrates convolution and superposition. _____

Suppose a causal second-order LTI system has the unit sample response

$$h(n) = \begin{cases} \alpha^n + \beta^n, & n \geq 0 \\ 0, & n < 0 \end{cases}$$

$$= [\alpha^n + \beta^n]\, u(n) \tag{3.139}$$

with $\alpha \neq \beta$ and $\alpha \neq 1$ and $\beta \neq 1$. The system is subjected to a step input of amplitude A,

$$x(n) = \begin{cases} A, & n \geq 0 \\ 0, & n < 0 \end{cases}$$

$$= A u(n) \tag{3.140}$$

Determine an analytic expression for the output sequence $y(n)$.

Solution: The output sequence is the convolution of the input sequence and the unit sample response. Using the convolution sum we have

$$y(n) = \sum_{m=-\infty}^{m=\infty} h(m)x(n - m) = \sum_{m=0}^{n} [\alpha^m + \beta^m]A \tag{3.141}$$

where according to Eq. 3.133 the limits are now 0 to n because both sequences are 0 for $n < 0$. Writing Eq. 3.141 as two convolution sums produces

$$y(n) = \sum_{m=0}^{m=n} \alpha^m \cdot A + \sum_{m=0}^{m=n} \beta^m \cdot A. \tag{3.142}$$

The input term A is constant—does not depend upon m—and can be removed from each sum giving

$$y(n) = A \sum_{m=0}^{m=n} \alpha^m + A \sum_{m=0}^{m=n} \beta^m$$

$$= A\left(\frac{1 - \alpha^{n+1}}{1 - \alpha}\right) + A\left(\frac{1 - \beta^{n+1}}{1 - \beta}\right) \tag{3.143}$$

where we have again used the closed-form result for finite geometric series.

To highlight the individual terms in the response, Eq. 3.143 can be rearranged as

$$y(n) = A\left[\frac{1}{1 - \alpha} + \frac{1}{1 - \beta}\right] + A\left[\frac{-1}{1 - \alpha}\right]\alpha^{n+1} + A\left[\frac{-1}{1 - \beta}\right]\beta^{n+1} \tag{3.144}$$

CHAPTER 3 LINEAR TIME-INVARIANT SYSTEMS

or

$$y(n) = C_1 + C_2\alpha^{n+1} + C_3\beta^{n+1}, \qquad n \geq 0 \tag{3.145}$$

where C_1, C_2 and C_3 are constants whose values depend on the input magnitude A and the unit sample response parameters α and β.

Comments:

1. Note again that each term in the output depends on the system characteristics α and β and the input A. See Fig. 3.19(a) for the output sequence for $\alpha = -0.6$ and $\beta = 0.9$ and Fig. 3.19(b) for $\alpha = -0.8$ and $\beta = 0.3$. In both cases, $A = 4$.

2. If we computed the convolution from

$$y(n) = \sum_{m=0}^{m=n} x(m)h(n-m) \tag{3.146}$$

the result is

$$y(n) = \sum_{m=0}^{m=n} A\alpha^{n-m} + \sum_{m=0}^{m=n} A\beta^{n-m}. \tag{3.147}$$

The $A\alpha^n$ in the first sum and $A\beta^n$ in the second do not depend upon m and can be removed giving

$$y(n) = A\alpha^n \sum_{m=0}^{m=n} \alpha^{-m} + A\beta^n \sum_{m=0}^{m=n} \beta^{-m}. \tag{3.148}$$

Using the expression for a finite geometric sum we have

$$y(n) = A\alpha^n \frac{1 - \alpha^{-(n+1)}}{1 - \alpha^{-1}} + A\beta^n \frac{1 - \beta^{-(n+1)}}{1 - \beta^{-1}}$$

$$= A\alpha^{n+1} \frac{1 - \alpha^{-(n+1)}}{\alpha - 1} + A\beta^{n+1} \frac{1 - \beta^{-(n+1)}}{\beta - 1}$$

$$= A\left(\frac{1 - \alpha^{n+1}}{1 - \alpha}\right) + A\left(\frac{1 - \beta^{n+1}}{1 - \beta}\right) \tag{3.149}$$

which now agrees with Eq. 3.143. We stated earlier that

$$y(n) = x(n) * h(n) = h(n) * x(n) \tag{3.150}$$

and the last result specifically illustrates this.

3.4.4 An Application: Stability and the Unit Sample Response

In Chapter Two we defined a stable system as one for which every bounded input produces a bounded output. Let us now show that if a

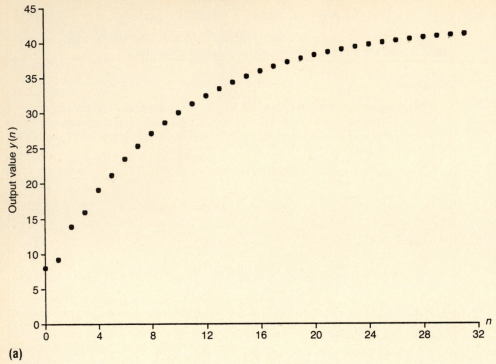

(a)

FIGURE 3.19 Step response using analytical convolution

system's unit sample response satisfies the condition

$$\sum_{n=-\infty}^{n=+\infty} |h(n)| \leq M_1 < \infty \tag{3.151}$$

then the system is stable. M_1 is a positive constant. Assume that we have an input $x(n)$ that is bounded, i.e.,

$$|x(n)| \leq M_2 < \infty. \tag{3.152}$$

From the convolution sum

$$y(n) = \sum_{m=-\infty}^{m=+\infty} x(m)h(n-m)$$

we can take the magnitude of each side which gives

$$|y(n)| = \left| \sum_{m=-\infty}^{m=+\infty} x(m)h(n-m) \right|. \tag{3.153}$$

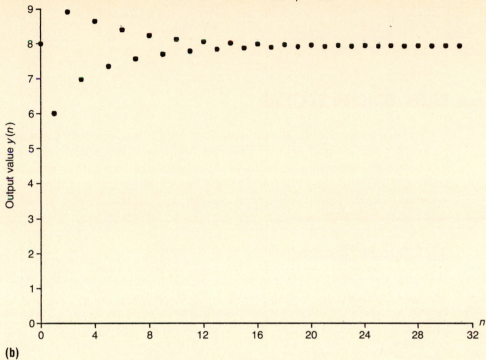

(b)

But we know that

$$\left|\sum_i \alpha_i \beta_i\right| \le \sum_i \left|\alpha_i\right|\left|\beta_i\right| \tag{3.154}$$

consequently

$$|y(n)| \le \sum_{m=-\infty}^{m=+\infty} |x(m)||h(n-m)|. \tag{3.155}$$

Thus, using Eqs. 3.151, 3.152, and 3.155 we have

$$|y(n)| \le M_1 \cdot M_2 < \infty \tag{3.156}$$

so $y(n)$ is a bounded sequence and the system is stable.

The previous development has shown that if the sum of the unit sample response values is bounded the system is stable. (In mathematical language, if $h(n)$ is absolutely summable the system is stable.) It can also be shown that if $h(n)$ is not absolutely summable the system is not stable. Thus, a system is stable if and only if the inequality 3.151 is satisfied.

3.4 CONVOLUTION

121

FIGURE 3.20 Cascade connection

$x(n)$ → DSP 1 $h_1(n)$ → $p(n)$ → DSP 2 $h_2(n)$ → $y(n)$

3.5 ▬ INTERCONNECTED SYSTEMS

Two or more systems can be connected together in various configurations to build a new overall system that can perform a designated task in a more acceptable manner than any of the original systems (subsystems) do individually (Nagle and Nelson, 1981). The interconnection of these subsystems can take various configurations but we concentrate on just two—cascade and parallel.

3.5.1 Cascade Connection

Suppose that two LTI systems are connected in cascade as in Fig. 3.20. Only two systems are shown here but the concepts to be developed will naturally apply with appropriate modification to any number of systems in cascade (series). The first system can be described by the difference equation

$$p(n) = \sum_{k=1}^{k=N_1} a_k p(n-k) + \sum_{k=0}^{k=L_1} b_k x(n-k) \qquad \text{DSP 1} \qquad (3.152)$$

and for the second system we have

$$y(n) = \sum_{k=1}^{k=N_2} c_k y(n-k) + \sum_{k=0}^{k=L_2} d_k p(n-k) \qquad \text{DSP 2.} \qquad (3.153)$$

Although appearing quite complicated, it is straightforward to solve for the $p(n)$ sequence given the sequence $x(n)$ and the starting (initial) values of $p(-1), p(-2), \ldots , p(-N_1)$. Then with the sequence $p(n)$ as the input to the second system, the same procedure is repeated to find $y(n)$ given $y(-1), y(-2), \ldots , y(-N_2)$.

Example 3.12. This example illustrates the cascading of two first-order systems.

Two first-order causal systems are connected in cascade (series) as shown in Fig. 3.21. Their respective difference equations are

$$p(n) = a_1 p(n-1) + b_0 x(n) \qquad y(n) = c_1 y(n-1) + d_0 p(n) + d_1 p(n-1).$$
$$\text{System 1} \qquad\qquad\qquad \text{System 2} \qquad (3.154)$$

Assume zero initial conditions of $p(-1) = 0$ and $y(-1) = 0$ and that $x(n) = 0$ for $n < 0$. Use iterative methods to find $y(0)$ and $y(1)$.

Solution:

First iteration

$$p(0) = b_0x(0) \qquad y(0) = d_0p(0) = d_0b_0x(0) \qquad (3.155)$$

This result for $y(0)$ is reasonable for in Fig. 3.21 we see that the first input sample, $x(0)$, simply goes straight through the gains b_0 and d_0 to the output $y(0)$.

Second iteration

$$p(1) = a_1p(0) + b_0x(1) \qquad y(1) = c_1y(0) + d_0p(1) + d_1p(0)$$
$$= a_1b_0x(0) + b_0x(1) \qquad\qquad = c_1d_0b_0x(0) + d_0a_1b_0x(0)$$
$$+ d_0b_0x(1) + d_1b_0x(0)$$
$$= [c_1d_0b_0 + d_0a_1b_0$$
$$+ d_1b_0]x(0) + d_0b_0x(1) \qquad (3.156)$$

Again this appears to be reasonable for the second input sample, $x(1)$, simply goes straight through the gains b_0 and d_0 to the output $y(1)$. All three terms that multiply $x(0)$ have been through one delay (shift register). For instance the first term, $c_1d_0b_0$, traces $x(0)$ through b_0d_0 and then around the right-hand loop to $y(1)$. The second term $d_0a_1b_0$ traces $x(0)$ through b_0 around the left-hand loop, then through d_0 to $y(1)$. The last term, b_0d_1, follows the path through b_0 then through the delay in the middle loop, then gain d_1 and to $y(1)$. This process could be continued, but a better approach is to use a computer.

Convolution could also be used to obtain $y(n)$ in terms of $x(n)$ for the overall system of Example 3.12. From Fig. 3.20 for DSP 1 we have

$$p(n) = x(n) * h_1(n) \qquad (3.157)$$

and for DSP 2 the corresponding result is

$$y(n) = p(n) * h_2(n). \qquad (3.158)$$

Substituting for $p(n)$ gives

$$y(n) = [x(n) * h_1(n)] * h_2(n) \qquad (3.159)$$

FIGURE 3.21 Cascade example

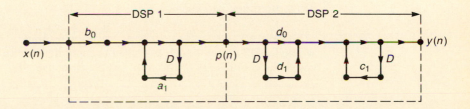

FIGURE 3.22 Resultant system

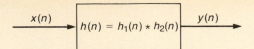

and using the associative property of the convolution operation (see Problem 3.26)

$$y(n) = x(n) * [h_1(n) * h_2(n)] \tag{3.160}$$

which we define as

$$y(n) = x(n) * h(n) \tag{3.161}$$

where $h(n) = h_1(n) * h_2(n)$ and we have the new system of Fig. 3.22.

Example 3.13. This example illustrates the effect of the cascade connection of two nonrecursive systems.

Two identical nonrecursive (FIR) systems are connected in cascade as in Fig. 3.20 with the unit sample response of each given in Fig. 3.23. Find the unit sample response and the difference equation for the cascade connection.

Solution: The unit sample response of the cascaded system is

$$h(n) = h_1(n) * h_2(n)$$
$$= [\delta(n) + \delta(n - 4)] * [\delta(n) + \delta(n - 4)] \tag{3.162}$$

and Fig. 3.24 shows some of the steps needed to obtain the convolution. The system diagram is shown in Fig. 3.25 and the difference equation can be deduced from this as

$$y(n) = x(n) + 2x(n - 4) + x(n - 8) \tag{3.163}$$

because there is one path straight through (no delays), two paths with four delays, and one path with eight delays. The results of Fig. 3.24(c) and Eq. 3.163 are in agreement. We know that the unit sample response $h(n)$ can be deduced from the system difference equation by setting $x(n) = \delta(n)$ with all initial conditions zero. That is,

$$h(n) = y(n) \quad \text{for} \quad x(n) = \delta(n). \tag{3.164}$$

Thus, from Eq. 3.163

$$h(n) = \delta(n) + 2\,\delta(n - 4) + \delta(n - 8) \tag{3.165}$$

where for FIR systems such as these the coefficients of the difference equation equal the coefficients of the unit sample response—$b_n = h(n)$.

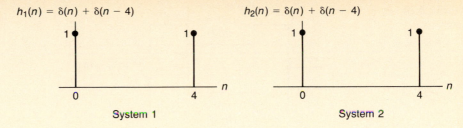

FIGURE 3.23 Sample responses of two cascaded systems

$h_1(n) = \delta(n) + \delta(n - 4)$

$h_2(n) = \delta(n) + \delta(n - 4)$

System 1

System 2

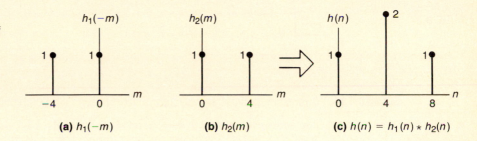

FIGURE 3.24 Resultant unit sample sequence of two cascaded systems

(a) $h_1(-m)$ **(b)** $h_2(m)$ **(c)** $h(n) = h_1(n) * h_2(n)$

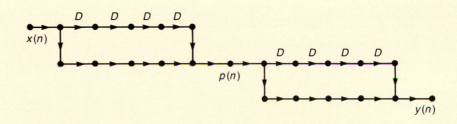

FIGURE 3.25 Cascade system diagram

$x(n)$

$p(n)$

$y(n)$

3.5.2 Parallel Connection

A parallel connection of two digital signal processors is shown in Fig. 3.26. Here from convolution

$$y_1(n) = x(n) * h_1(n) \qquad \text{and} \qquad y_2(n) = x(n) * h_2(n) \qquad (3.166)$$

but

$$y(n) = y_1(n) + y_2(n)$$
$$= x(n) * h_1(n) + x(n) * h_2(n) \qquad (3.167)$$

and, therefore, since convolution is distributive (see Problem 3.26)

$$y(n) = x(n) * [h_1(n) + h_2(n)]$$
$$= x(n) * h(n) \qquad (3.168)$$

where $h(n) = h_1(n) + h_2(n)$ and we have the new system of Fig. 3.27.

FIGURE 3.26 Parallel connection

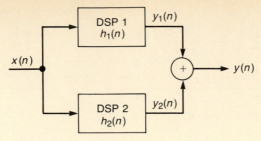

FIGURE 3.27 Resultant system

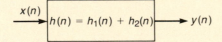

Example 3.14. This example illustrates system design by parallel connection. _____

The same two nonrecursive systems of Example 3.13 are now connected in parallel as in Fig. 3.28. Find the unit sample response and the difference equation for this connection.

Solution: From Fig. 3.28

$$y_1(n) = x(n) + x(n-4) \tag{3.169}$$

and

$$y_2(n) = x(n) + x(n-4), \tag{3.170}$$

thus,

$$y(n) = y_1(n) + y_2(n)$$
$$= 2x(n) + 2x(n-4). \tag{3.171}$$

Again, we have $b_n = h(n)$ which gives the unit sample response

$$h(n) = 2\delta(n) + 2\delta(n-4) \tag{3.172}$$

as shown in Fig. 3.29.

FIGURE 3.28 Parallel example

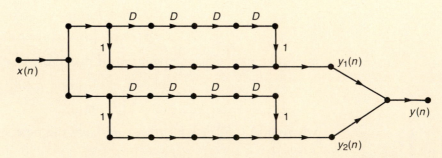

FIGURE 3.29 Resultant unit sample sequence of two parallel systems

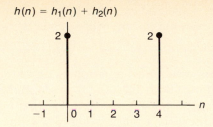

$$h(n) = h_1(n) + h_2(n)$$

As we have seen, the interconnection of subsystems can create interesting and different new overall systems. We have used the most elementary examples; however, in a real signal processing system, things usually will be more complex. Nevertheless, the same basic principles will still apply.

3.6 ▬ INITIAL CONDITION RESPONSE AND STABILITY OF LTI SYSTEMS

As discussed earlier in the chapter, the iterative solution of a difference equation for a particular input and/or set of initial conditions is easy to accomplish with a computer. The result is a numerical solution that is usually sufficient for most applications. However, some rough estimates of the kind of response to expect are often useful and time-saving. One such estimate can be obtained by using the system property of stability, which was introduced in Chapter Two.

We now develop another method for the determination of the stability of an LTI system, and in Chapter Six, stability will be treated again from another viewpoint.

The response, or output, of an LTI system is determined by the system constants, the input and the previous values of the input and output as can be seen from the savings account algorithm of Section 3.1

$$y(n) = \alpha y(n - 1) + \beta x(n) \tag{3.173}$$

or from the equation describing the rotational motion of a satellite

$$y(n) = 2y(n - 1) - y(n - 2) + 0.5x(n) + 0.5x(n - 1). \tag{3.174}$$

The part of the response that is caused by the initial conditions (previous values of the output) is called the *initial condition response*, or the *zero-input response*. This response is determined by setting the input to zero. As a result, the response depends only on the initial conditions and the system coefficients. One reason for wanting to know the initial condition response is the following definition of stability:

If the initial condition response of a system approaches zero as $n \longrightarrow \infty$ for arbitrary initial conditions then the system is stable.

Let's consider a specific example by setting the input to zero in the savings account example (no monthly deposits), we have

$$y(n) = \alpha y(n-1) \qquad \text{or} \qquad y(n) - \alpha y(n-1) = 0. \qquad (3.175)$$

A solution to this difference equation is an expression for $y(n)$ which when substituted into both sides of Eq. 3.175 makes them equal. We can guess the candidates for a solution and test them, therefore, by seeing if they satisfy the difference equation. Let us assume that the response (solution) is an exponential sequence of the form

$$y(n) = Cr^n \qquad (3.176)$$

where C is an arbitrary constant and r describes the exponential that we will determine.[†] Substituting Eq. 3.176 into Eq. 3.175 gives

$$Cr^n - \alpha Cr^{n-1} = 0 \qquad (3.177)$$

or

$$Cr^n - \alpha Cr^n r^{-1} = 0 \qquad (3.178)$$

which yields

$$Cr^n[1 - \alpha r^{-1}] = 0. \qquad (3.179)$$

Since Cr^n cannot be 0 (this would mean that $y(n) = 0$ for all n) it must be that

$$1 - \alpha r^{-1} = 0 \qquad (3.180)$$

or, putting this in terms of positive powers of r,

$$r - \alpha = 0. \qquad (3.181)$$

The value $r = \alpha$ that satisfies this equation is called a *characteristic root* for the system because it "characterizes" the response. Correspondingly, Eq. 3.180, or equivalently Eq. 3.181, is called the *characteristic equation* for the system. Thus, the initial condition response is

$$y(n) = C\alpha^n. \qquad (3.182)$$

This will grow without bound as n increases for $|\alpha| > 1$, it will decay to zero for $|\alpha| < 1$, and will remain at $y(n) = C$ for $\alpha = 1$ or at $y(n) = \pm C$ for $\alpha = -1$. For the first-order system of Eq. 3.173 we define the following conditions for stability:

Characteristic Root	Stability Condition
$|\alpha| \geq 1$	not stable (unstable)
$|\alpha| < 1$	stable

[†] Those readers experienced in continuous systems will recall that the assumed solution for the differential equation $\dfrac{dy(t)}{dt} = \alpha y(t)$ was $y(t) = Ce^{\alpha t}$, an exponential.

We now have three ways of looking at stability: the bounded-input bounded-output definition of Chapter Two, the equivalent statement of Section 3.4.4 in terms of the unit sample response, i.e., $\sum\limits_{n=-\infty}^{\infty} |h(n)| < \infty$, and the initial condition definition just discussed for a first-order system. Let us relate the results obtained from all three approaches for this simple example. It's relatively easy to see the equivalence of the three approaches for $|\alpha| < 1$ and for $|\alpha| > 1$. The case where $|\alpha| = 1$ requires a bit more consideration.

To be specific let $\alpha = 1$ and assume that $\beta > 0$ in which case the system has the difference equation

$$y(n) = y(n - 1) + \beta x(n). \tag{3.183}$$

The initial condition response is simply $y(n) = k$ where k is the initial condition $y(-1)$. So the initial condition response does not approach zero as $n \to \infty$ and we conclude that the system is not stable. To find the unit sample response we let $x(n) = \delta(n)$ with $y(-1) = 0$ and find that

$$h(n) = \beta, \qquad n \geq 0 \tag{3.184}$$

and since $\sum\limits_{n=0}^{\infty} \beta \to \infty$ we again conclude that the system is not stable. For the BIBO approach with $\alpha = 1$ we can select $x(n) = A$, a nonzero constant. Clearly, this input is bounded, but the response of

$$y(n) = y(n - 1) + \beta A \tag{3.185}$$

grows without bound as $n \to \infty$. Thus, the bounded-input, bounded-output viewpoint also indicates that the system isn't stable.

There are many situations in which a stable system is required to meet specifications, but this is not always the case and unstable systems are often useful also. We don't want to think of stable systems as inherently good and unstable ones as bad. For example, if we are trying to accumulate money in the savings account, we want an unstable account with $\alpha > 1$. Such a situation is illustrated in Example 3.1 where $\alpha = 1.01$ which is "barely" unstable, and we see that a little instability is sufficient to cause an appreciable growth over an extended period of time.

Example 3.15. This example illustrates finding the system response caused by the initial conditions.

We go back to the savings account example of Section 3.1 and, instead of making monthly deposits, we examine the growth of the account due to an initial deposit (initial condition) only. To what value would $50 grow from age 21 to age 30 if the interest rate is 1 percent per month?

Solution: The appropriate equation comes from Eq. 3.173 with $x(n) = 0$ and $\alpha = 1.01$, namely

$$y(n) - 1.01y(n-1) = 0. \tag{3.186}$$

From Eq. 3.182 the initial condition solution is

$$y(n) = C(1.01)^n \text{ with } C = \$50 \tag{3.187}$$

and after 9 years $(n = 108)$ the accumulated savings is

$$y(108) = \$50(1.01)^{108} = \$146.45. \tag{3.188}$$

Comment: Although this system is unstable and grows in an exponential fashion, we see from the comparison of accumulating \$9,790 with \$50 monthly deposits with Eq. 3.188 that a monthly deposit is desirable for a large growth in savings.

Earlier we saw that substituting an assumed (correct) form for the solution to the difference equation, $y(n) - \alpha y(n-1) = 0$ led to Eq. 3.180, $1 - \alpha r^{-1} = 0$. This is known as the *characteristic equation*. In general, if we have a recursive difference equation of the form

$$y(n) - \sum_{k=1}^{N} a_k y(n-k) = \sum_{k=0}^{L} b_k x(n-k) \tag{3.189}$$

and substitute $y(n) = Cr^n$ with zero input terms, we obtain the equation

$$Cr^n - \sum_{k=1}^{N} a_k Cr^{n-k} = 0 \tag{3.190}$$

or

$$Cr^n - a_1 Cr^{n-1} - a_2 Cr^{n-2} - \cdots - a_N Cr^{n-N} = 0. \tag{3.191}$$

The assumed solution Cr^n may be factored out giving

$$Cr^n(1 - a_1 r^{-1} - a_2 r^{-2} - \cdots - a_N r^{-N}) = 0. \tag{3.192}$$

Discarding the trivial solution $Cr^n = 0$, the meaningful solutions for r are given by

$$1 - a_1 r^{-1} - a_2 r^{-2} - \cdots - a_N r^{-N} = 0 \tag{3.193}$$

$$\text{or}$$

$$r^N - a_1 r^{N-1} - a_2 r^{N-2} - \cdots - a_N = 0 \quad . \tag{3.194}$$

Hence, Cr^n is a solution for the values of r for which Eq. 3.194—*the characteristic equation*—is satisfied; these values of r are called the *characteristic roots*. Notice that the characteristic equation can be written by inspection from Eq. 3.189 with its right side (input terms) set to zero. The coefficients of the $y(n - k)$'s in Eq. 3.189 are the coefficients of the r's in Eq. 3.194.

Example 3.16. This example illustrates the characteristic equation, characteristic roots and stability for a second-order system.

When some compensatory adjustments are made to the satellite system of Example 3.3, the equation becomes

$$y(n) = -0.3y(n - 1) + 0.4y(n - 2) + 0.5x(n) + 0.5x(n - 1). \quad (3.195)$$

Determine the characteristic equation, the characteristic roots and the stability condition of this system.

Solution: First, by setting the inputs to zero we have

$$y(n) + 0.3y(n - 1) - 0.4y(n - 2) = 0. \quad (3.196)$$

At this point we could use Eq. 3.194 to find the characteristic equation. However, to highlight the procedure we assume, once again, that the solution (response) is an exponential sequence of the form $y(n) = Cr^n$ which gives

$$Cr^n + 0.3Cr^{n-1} - 0.4Cr^{n-2} = 0 \quad \text{or} \quad Cr^n(1 + 0.3r^{-1} - 0.4r^{-2}) = 0. \quad (3.197)$$

Again rejecting $Cr^n = 0$ as a solution because it implies that $y(n) = 0$ for all n gives the characteristic equation

$$1 + 0.3r^{-1} - 0.4r^{-2} = 0 \quad \text{or} \quad r^2 + 0.3r - 0.4 = 0 \quad (3.198)$$

which factors into

$$(1 - 0.5r^{-1})(1 + 0.8r^{-1}) = 0 \quad \text{or} \quad (r - 0.5)(r + 0.8) = 0 \quad (3.199)$$

yielding two characteristic roots

$$r_1 = 0.5 \quad \text{and} \quad r_2 = -0.8. \quad (3.200)$$

This tells us that

$$y_1(n) = C_1(0.5)^n \quad \text{and} \quad y_2(n) = C_2(-0.8)^n \quad (3.201)$$

will satisfy the original difference equation and since the system is linear the sum

$$y(n) = C_1(0.5)^n + C_2(-0.8)^n \quad (3.202)$$

also satisfies Eq. 3.196. To illustrate this we substitute Eq. 3.202 into Eq. 3.196 to obtain

$$C_1(0.5)^n + C_2(-0.8)^n + 0.3[C_1(0.5)^{n-1} + C_2(-0.8)^{n-1}]$$
$$- 0.4[C_1(0.5)^{n-2} + C_2(-0.8)^{n-2}] = 0. \quad (3.203)$$

Using the rules of exponents and collecting like terms on the left produces

$$C_1(0.5)^n[1 + 0.3(2) - 0.4(4)]$$
$$+ C_2(-0.8)^n[1 + 0.3(-1.25)$$
$$- 0.4(1.5625)] = 0. \quad (3.204)$$

We see that the coefficients of C_1 and C_2 are both zero for all n and thus the initial condition solution is

$$y(n) = C_1(0.5)^n + C_2(-0.8)^n \qquad (3.205)$$

and the system is clearly stable because this response will decay to zero as $n \to \infty$, irrespective of the constants C_1 and C_2.

It is useful to carry Example 3.16 a little further to illustrate the calculation of the constants C_1 and C_2 for some given initial conditions. If we use the initial conditions from Example 3.3 of $y(-1) = y(-2) = 1$ we have

$$y(-1) = 1 = C_1(0.5)^{-1} + C_2(-0.8)^{-1}$$

$$y(-2) = 1 = C_1(0.5)^{-2} + C_2(-0.8)^{-2}. \qquad (3.206)$$

There are several methods available for solving simultaneous algebraic equations such as those in Eq. 3.206. Among these are substitution, elimination, determinants, and a matrix solution—we have selected the latter. Thus, in matrix form Eq. 3.206 becomes

$$\begin{bmatrix} 2 & -5/4 \\ 4 & 25/16 \end{bmatrix} \begin{bmatrix} C_1 \\ C_2 \end{bmatrix} = \begin{bmatrix} 1 \\ 1 \end{bmatrix} \qquad (3.207)$$

which has the solution

$$\begin{bmatrix} C_1 \\ C_2 \end{bmatrix} = \frac{1}{130} \begin{bmatrix} 45 \\ -32 \end{bmatrix}. \qquad (3.208)$$

We should check a few values by comparing the analytical solution of

$$y(n) = \frac{1}{130}[45(0.5)^n - 32(-0.8)^n] \qquad (3.209)$$

with the numerical values that result when the original equation with input terms set to zero

$$y(n) = -0.3y(n-1) + 0.4y(n-2) \qquad (3.210)$$

is iteratively solved for the specific initial conditions $y(-1) = y(-2) = 1$. From the solution given in Eq. 3.209 we have

$$y(0) = \frac{1}{130}[45 - 32] = 0.1 \qquad (3.211)$$

and from Eq. 3.210 with $y(-1) = y(-2) = 1$,

$$y(0) = -0.3(1) + 0.4(1) = 0.1. \qquad (3.212)$$

For $n = 1$ the solution gives

$$y(1) = \frac{1}{130}[45(0.5) - 32(-0.8)] = 0.37 \qquad (3.213)$$

and from the difference equation

$$y(1) = -0.3(0.1) + 0.4(1) = 0.37. \qquad (3.214)$$

This is a lengthy procedure so let's look back to review the important steps and conclusions.

1. The characteristic equation is determined by setting the input terms to zero and assuming the exponential solution $y(n) = Cr^n$ to obtain

$$r^2 + 0.3r - 0.4 = 0. \qquad (3.215)$$

2. The characteristic equation is then solved for the characteristic roots and we showed that a valid solution is

$$y(n) = C_1(0.5)^n + C_2(-0.8)^n \qquad (3.216)$$

which indicates a stable system since the magnitudes of both roots, 0.5 and -0.8, are less than one.

3. Using given or known initial conditions the constants C_1 and C_2 are determined by solving two linear algebraic equations.

4. To check we compare numerical results obtained from iteratively solving the original equation with input terms set to zero

$$y(n) = -0.3y(n - 1) + 0.4y(n - 2) \qquad (3.217)$$

with results found by substituting $n = 0, 1, \ldots$ in the analytical solution

$$y(n) = \frac{45}{130}(0.5)^n - \frac{32}{130}(-0.8)^n. \qquad (3.218)$$

The outcome agreed for the first two values of n, which reassured us that the analytical solution is correct.

5. Notice that numerical values of the initial condition response can always be determined by an iterative solution of the modified (inputs set to zero) system equation—a procedure ideally suited for a computer. The solution, for nonrepeated (distinct) roots is of the form

$$y(n) = \sum_{k=1}^{k=N} C_k(r_k)^n \qquad (3.219)$$

and while some effort is required to determine the constants C_k, the analytical form of Eq. 3.219 is more meaningful than just numerical results because it gives insight into the characteristics of the system. It also allows the calculation of, say, $y(100)$ directly without having to first compute the previous 99 values of $y(n)$.

Example 3.17. This example illustrates an oscillatory initial condition response. _____

If the system constants are adjusted again to give a zero-input equation such as

$$y(n) - y(n-1) + 0.5y(n-2) = 0 \qquad (3.220)$$

find the algebraic form of the initial condition response. In the process, decide on the stability situation.

Solution: From Eq. 3.193 or 3.194 the characteristic equation is

$$1 - r^{-1} + 0.5r^{-2} = 0 \qquad \text{or} \qquad r^2 - r + 0.5 = 0 \qquad (3.221)$$

which factors into

$$(r - 0.5 - j0.5)(r - 0.5 + j0.5) = 0 \qquad (3.222)$$

or in terms of the exponential form

$$(r - 0.707e^{j\pi/4})(r - 0.707e^{-j\pi/4}) = 0. \qquad (3.223)$$

Thus, the characteristic roots are

$$r_1 = 0.707e^{j\pi/4} \text{ and } r_2 = 0.707e^{-j\pi/4} \qquad (3.224)$$

and the system is stable because $|r_1| = |r_2| < 1$. The initial condition response is of the form

$$y(n) = C_1(0.707e^{j\pi/4})^n + C_2(0.707e^{-j\pi/4})^n \qquad (3.225)$$

and it can be shown that $C_2 = C_1^*$ where C_1^* denotes the complex conjugate of C_1. This can be simplified by using the Euler relation (see Appendix A) to obtain

$$y(n) = 2|C_1| (0.707)^n \cos(\pi n/4 + \underline{/\,C_1}) \qquad (3.226)$$

Comment: This response is shown in Fig. 3.30 for $C_1 = 2e^{j\pi/6}$. The envelope that establishes the limits for the minimum and maximum values is given by $2|C_1| (0.707)^n$. The complete sequence $y(n)$ is a "damped" (because it eventually goes to zero), oscillatory response.

The following two examples illustrate the special situation of a second-order system with both characteristic roots having magnitude 1. In one case the initial condition response oscillates whereas in the other case it diverges towards infinity.

Example 3.18. This example illustrates the concept of an oscillatory system. _____

Another set of compensatory adjustments is made to the satellite system of Example 3.3 which changes the system equation to

$$y(n) = y(n-1) - y(n-2) + 0.5x(n) + 0.5x(n-1). \qquad (3.227)$$

a) Determine the algebraic form of the initial condition response.

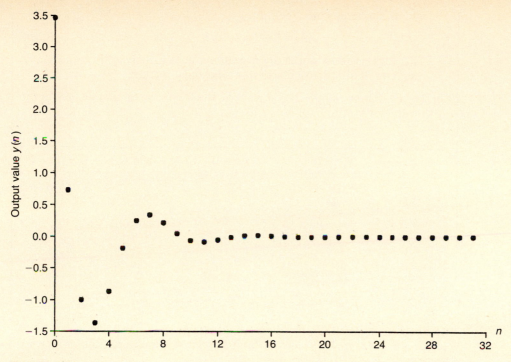

FIGURE 3.30 Damped oscillatory response $y(n) = 4(0.707)^n \cos(n\pi/4 + \pi/6)$

b) Use an iterative solution to find $y(n)$ for $0 \le n \le 6$ for the initial conditions $y(-1) = A$ and $y(-2) = B$.

Solution:

a) With the inputs set to zero we obtain

$$y(n) - y(n-1) + y(n-2) = 0 \qquad (3.228)$$

giving the characteristic equation

$$1 - r^{-1} + r^{-2} = 0 \qquad \text{or} \qquad r^2 - r + 1 = 0 \qquad (3.229)$$

which factors into

$$(r - 0.5 - j0.866)(r - 0.5 + j0.866) = 0 \qquad (3.230)$$

or in the exponential form

$$(r - e^{j\pi/3})(r - e^{-j\pi/3}) = 0 \qquad (3.231)$$

which yields the characteristic roots

$$r_1 = e^{j\pi/3} \text{ and } r_2 = e^{-j\pi/3} \qquad (3.232)$$

with $|r_1| = |r_2| = 1$. The initial condition response is of the form

$$y(n) = C_1(e^{j\pi/3})^n + C_1^*(e^{-j\pi/3})^n \qquad (3.233)$$

which can be put into the form

$$y(n) = 2|C_1| \cos(n\pi/3 + \angle C_1). \qquad (3.234)$$

This response does not decay to zero nor does it increase to infinity as n increases. It simply oscillates in a sinusoidal manner.

b) For $y(-1) = A$ and $y(-2) = B$ we have the following tabular display of the results for $y(n)$.

n	$y(n-2)$	$y(n-1)$	$y(n) = y(n-1) - y(n-2)$
0	B (given)	A (given)	$A - B$
1	A	$A - B$	$-B$
2	$A - B$	$-B$	$-A$
3	$-B$	$-A$	$-A + B$
4	$-A$	$-A + B$	B
5	$-A + B$	B	A
6	B	A	$A - B$

Thus, at $n = 6$ we are back where we started for $n = 0$ and $y(n)$ will clearly repeat for larger n. As predicted from Eq. 3.234 we observe the oscillatory response of Fig. 3.31, where $A = 7$, $B = 5$.

FIGURE 3.31 Output of oscillatory system

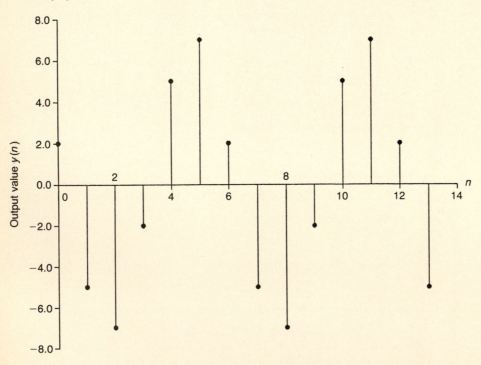

CHAPTER 3 LINEAR TIME-INVARIANT SYSTEMS

Example 3.19. This example illustrates a second-order system with a divergent response.

As our final satellite equation with the inputs set to zero let's consider

$$y(n) - 2y(n-1) + y(n-2) = 0 \qquad (3.235)$$

with the initial conditions $y(-1) = A$ and $y(-2) = 0$. Show that the response is divergent, i.e., $y(n) \to \infty$ as $n \to \infty$.

Solution: The characteristic equation is

$$1 - 2r^{-1} + r^{-2} = 0 \qquad \text{or} \qquad r^2 - 2r + 1 = 0 \qquad (3.236)$$

which factors into

$$(1 - r^{-1})(1 - r^{-1}) = 0 \qquad \text{or} \qquad (r-1)(r-1) = 0 \qquad (3.237)$$

yielding two characteristic roots of $r = 1$.

For the initial conditions $y(-1) = A$ and $y(-2) = 0$, we obtain the following response.

n	$y(n-2)$	$y(n-1)$	$y(n) = 2y(n-1) - y(n-2)$
0	0	A	$2A$
1	A	$2A$	$3A$
2	$2A$	$3A$	$4A$
.	.	.	.
.	.	.	.
.	.	.	.
n	nA	$(n+1)A$	$(n+2)A$

The trend is obvious—the response is definitely diverging, or increasing without bound as n approaches infinity, the characteristic of an unstable system.

From the results above we were able to deduce the general form of the initial condition response, $y(-1) = A$ and $y(-2) = 0$, for any value of n as

$$y(n) = (n+2)A \qquad (3.238)$$

but it is generally not this easy. For two equal real roots, the solution is of the form

$$y(n) = C_1 r^n + n C_2 r^n \qquad (3.239)$$

rather than the usual

$$y(n) = C_1 r^n + C_2 r^n \qquad (3.240)$$

which would not satisfy the original equation. Using Eq. 3.239 with the initial conditions $y(-2) = 0$, $y(-1) = A$, and $r = 1$ we have

$$\begin{aligned} y(-1) &= A = C_1 - C_2 \\ y(-2) &= 0 = C_1 - 2C_2 \end{aligned} \qquad (3.241)$$

which yields $C_1 = 2A$ and $C_2 = A$ and as in Eq. 3.238

$$y(n) = 2A(1)^n + nA(1)^n = (n+2)A. \qquad (3.242)$$

In this section, for reasons of computational convenience, we have considered only first- and second-order recursive systems as examples of the determination of initial condition response and stability. The ideas presented apply also to systems of higher order. For an Nth-order recursive system, the initial condition response is of the form

$$y(n) = C_1 r_1^n + C_2 r_2^n + \cdots + C_N r_N^n \tag{3.243}$$

where $r_1, r_2, \ldots, r_N$ are the N roots (all N roots are assumed to be distinct[†]) of the characteristic equation

$$r^N - a_1 r^{N-1} - a_2 r^{N-2} - \cdots - a_N = 0 \tag{3.244}$$

or

$$r^N - \sum_{k=1}^{N} a_k r^{N-k} = 0. \tag{3.245}$$

Notice that in Eq. 3.243 each of the terms $C_i r_i^n$, $i = 1, \ldots, N$, is a solution of the difference equation with input terms set to zero. Since the system is linear, the sum of these solutions is also a solution. For a stable system the initial condition response must decay to zero as $n \to \infty$ and so for the Nth-order recursive system described by Eq. 3.243 we can generalize our stability rules to the following:

a) $|r_i| < 1$ for all i, the system is stable

b) $|r_i| > 1$ for any i, the system is unstable

c) $|r_i| = 1$ for one or more i and all other characteristic roots have magnitudes less than 1, the system response may have a constant term, an alternating constant, a sinusoidal term, or terms that go to infinity as $n \to \infty$ if there are repeated roots. Each of these cases requires further investigation.

Before we terminate our stability discussion, we must consider the important class of LTI systems called nonrecursive systems (nominally FIR) described by

$$y(n) = b_0 x(n) + b_1 x(n - 1) + \cdots + b_L x(n - L) \tag{3.246}$$

or by the diagram of Fig. 3.32. The filter output $y(n)$ in Eq. 3.246 is the weighted sum of $x(n)$ and its delayed values $x(n - 1)$ through $x(n - L)$, which may be written as the sum

$$y(n) = \sum_{k=0}^{k=L} b_k x(n - k). \tag{3.247}$$

[†]The characteristic equation for an Nth-order system has N roots. If the root r_i is repeated p times the initial condition response is of the form $y(n) = C_1 r_i^n + C_2 n r_i^n + \cdots + C_p n^{p-1} r_i^n +$ the usual terms from nonrepeated roots.

FIGURE 3.32   A nonrecursive system

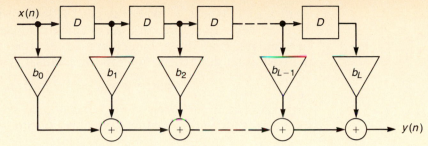

$x(n)$

$y(n)$

From Eq. 3.247 we see that the sum contains only a finite number of terms, and if each element in the input sequence $\{x(n)\} = \{x(0), x(1), \ldots, x(L)\}$ is finite, the weighted sum $y(n)$ will also be finite. Thus, the stability criterion of a bounded input producing a bounded output has been satisfied and we see that all nonrecursive filters are stable. This stability property makes nonrecursive filters very popular and practical for many signal processing applications.

3.7 ▬ FORCED AND TOTAL RESPONSE OF LTI SYSTEMS

We have seen that the convolution summation produces the system output that is caused by the input alone, and any part of the output that is due to initial conditions is not included in the computation. It is, therefore, logical to describe this output that is derived from the input only as the *forced* or *driven output*. We have also seen from convolution that a causal system described by the unit sample response, for example

$$h(n) = [\alpha^n + \beta^n]u(n) \qquad (3.248)$$

when forced or driven by the input $x(n) = A\,u(n)$, yields the output sequence

$$y(n) = C_1 + C_2\alpha^{n+1} + C_3\beta^{n+1}, \qquad n \geq 0. \qquad (3.249)$$

It was noted that the output sequence $y(n)$ contained terms due to both the system parameters and the input. The term C_1 resulted from the constant input $x(n) = A\,u(n)$ and the terms $C_2\alpha^{n+1}$ and $C_3\beta^{n+1}$ are characterized by the system constants α and β. Note that the output $y(n)$ can be written as

$$\begin{aligned} y(n) &= C_1 + C_2\alpha\alpha^n + C_3\beta\beta^n \\ &= \underbrace{C_1}_{\substack{\text{input} \\ \text{term}}} + \underbrace{C_4\alpha^n + C_5\beta^n}_{\text{system terms}}, \qquad n \geq 0. \end{aligned} \qquad (3.250)$$

The result of convolution, in either Eq. 3.249 or Eq. 3.250, depended on knowing the system's unit sample response $h(n)$ and, of course, the

---

input $x(n)$. It is just as likely that an LTI system will be described by a difference equation. The question is how the forced or driven output can be calculated from the system difference equation. Consider, for example, the first-order difference equation for a causal system, namely

$$y(n) = a_1 y(n - 1) + b_0 x(n), \qquad (3.251)$$

with the initial condition $y(-1) = 0$ and $x(n) = a^n u(n)$, an exponential sequence. Calculating $y(n)$ in a recursive fashion gives

$$y(0) = b_0 x(0) = b_0 a^0 = b_0$$

$$y(1) = a_1 y(0) + b_0 x(1) = a_1 b_0 + b_0 a$$

$$y(2) = a_1 y(1) + b_0 x(2) = a_1^2 b_0 + a_1 b_0 a + b_0 a^2$$

$$y(3) = a_1{}^3 b_0 + a_1{}^2 b_0 a + a_1 b_0 a^2 + b_0 a^3 \qquad (3.252)$$

and so forth. In this simple situation, we can find a general expression for $y(n)$ by inspection that is valid for any value of n. Getting an analytical expression for $y(n)$ by this iterative approach is generally impossible for a higher-order system, however. What is the general approach to the problem? From our experience with convolution and the iterative solution of difference equations we have observed that the forced output contains system terms and input terms. In the present simple example, we would expect an output sequence of the form

$$y(n) = \underbrace{C_1 a^n}_{\text{input}} + \underbrace{C_2 a_1{}^n}_{\text{system}}, \qquad n \geq 0. \qquad (3.253)$$

From Eq. 3.253 we notice that the forced response contains a system term of the form $C_2 a_1{}^n$. We also can easily show that the initial condition response for this system has a term of the same form $C_3 a_1{}^n$. The form of these terms can be determined from the original difference equation with the inputs set to zero, generally referred to as the *homogeneous difference equation*

$$y(n) = a_1 y(n - 1). \qquad (3.254)$$

The solution of Eq. 3.254 is called the *complementary solution* and is denoted by

$$y_c(n) = C_2 a_1{}^n. \qquad (3.255)$$

Notice here that if the initial conditions are not zero, $y_c(n)$ represents both the initial condition term and the term of the same form in the forced response.

Next, we turn our attention to the first or input term where $C_1 a^n$ is a "guess," but a good one, since problems like this have been around a long time and lists are available as to what sort of solution to expect. This part of the solution is called the *particular solution*. The total solution is given by

$$y(n) = y_p(n) + y_c(n) \tag{3.256}$$

where $y_p(n)$ represents the particular solution and $y_c(n)$ represents the complementary solution. For this given first-order system, the total solution $y(n)$ is

$$y(n) = C_1 a^n + C_2 a_1{}^n \tag{3.257}$$

and it remains to evaluate C_1 and C_2. We guessed the form of the particular solution and now it must be tested by substitution into the original system equation. At the same time, assuming the guess is valid, the constant C_1 should be evaluated. Rewriting the system equation for the particular solution gives us

$$y_p(n) = a_1 y_p(n-1) + b_0 x(n), \qquad n \geq 0 \tag{3.258}$$

and substituting $y_p(n) = C_1 a^n$ where $x(n) = a^n u(n)$ gives

$$C_1 a^n = a_1 C_1 a^{n-1} + b_0 a^n \tag{3.259}$$

which yields the constant for the input term, namely

$$C_1 = \frac{b_0 a}{a - a_1}. \tag{3.260}$$

The total solution now becomes

$$y(n) = \frac{b_0 a}{a - a_1} a^n + C_2 a_1{}^n, \qquad n \geq 0. \tag{3.261}$$

We proceed as follows to evaluate the remaining constant. We use the known initial condition of $y(-1) = 0$ to compute the value of $y(0)$, which we can then use in Eq. 3.261 to find C_2. The system equation is

$$y(n) = a_1 y(n-1) + b_0 x(n) \tag{3.262}$$

and the solution at $y(0)$ is

$$y(0) = a_1 y(-1) + b_0 x(0)$$

$$= a_1 \cdot 0 + b_0$$

$$= b_0. \tag{3.263}$$

This value is referred to as the *derived initial condition*. Substituting $y(0) = b_0$ into Eq. 3.261 gives us

$$b_0 = \frac{b_0 a}{a - a_1} a^0 + C_2 a_1{}^0 \tag{3.264}$$

which yields the constant for the system term, namely

$$C_2 = -\frac{b_0 a_1}{a - a_1}. \tag{3.265}$$

Thus, the total solution is

$$y(n) = \frac{b_0 a}{a - a_1} \cdot a^n - \frac{b_0 a_1}{a - a_1} \cdot a_1^n, \qquad n \geq 0 \tag{3.266}$$

or, in a more compact form,

$$y(n) = \frac{b_0}{a - a_1}[a^{n+1} - a_1^{n+1}], \qquad n \geq 0. \tag{3.267}$$

We now check a few points to see if they agree with the iterative solution of Eq. 3.252. From Eq. 3.267

$$y(0) = \frac{b_0}{a - a_1}[a - a_1] = b_0 \tag{3.268}$$

which agrees with the previous result and also checks the initial condition. The next value is

$$y(1) = \frac{b_0}{a - a_1}[a^2 - a_1^2] = \frac{b_0}{a - a_1}[(a + a_1)(a - a_1)]$$

$$= b_0(a + a_1) \tag{3.269}$$

which also agrees with our previous work.

In the preceding example the input was an exponential sequence and the particular solution contained the same exponential sequence. Unlike the example, there is usually no need to "guess" the particular solution because lists have been tabulated of particular solutions corresponding to several of the commonly encountered input sequences. Table 3.1 gives a

TABLE 3.1 PARTICULAR SOLUTIONS FOR SEVERAL INPUT SEQUENCES

Term in $x(n)$	Choice of particular solution
C	C_1
Cn	$C_1 n + C_2$
Ca^n	$C_1 a^n$
$C \cos(n\theta)$ or $C \sin(n\theta)$	$C_1 \cos(n\theta + C_2)$ or $C_3 \cos(n\theta) + C_4 \sin(n\theta)$
$Ca^n \cos(n\theta)$ or $Ca^n \sin(n\theta)$	$C_1 a^n \cos(n\theta + C_2)$ or $a^n[C_3 \cos(n\theta) + C_4 \sin(n\theta)]$
$C\, \delta(n)$	no terms due to $C\, \delta(n)$[†]

[†] For the term $C\, \delta(n)$ in $x(n)$, no additional terms appear in $y_p(n)$. We simply assume terms in $y_p(n)$ due to the system and any other inputs, and proceed with the evaluation of the assumed constants.

representative selection. If the input or forcing sequence $x(n)$ is the sum of two or more terms, then the particular solution is the sum formed by taking the corresponding terms from the right-hand column of Table 3.1.

We now generalize the steps to be taken when solving a difference equation for the total response of the system. We assume the most common and simplest situation in which the roots of the characteristic equation are distinct and the input contains no term of the same form as any term in the complementary solution. If the characteristic equation contains any equal roots, or the input contains an exponential sequence that also appears in the complementary solution, we need either an extension of the basic procedure (see Problem 3.34) or the z-transform method explained in Chapter Six.

The given quantities are:

a) The linear equation that describes the system, i.e.,

$$y(n) - \sum_{k=1}^{N} a_k y(n - k) = \sum_{k=0}^{L} b_k x(n - k), \tag{3.270}$$

b) The initial conditions of the output sequence, i.e.,

$$y(-1), \, y(-2), \, \ldots, \, y(-N) \tag{3.271}$$

c) The system input, i.e., $x(n)$ given as an analytic expression.

The required steps are:

PROCEDURE

1. Choose the form for the particular solution $y_p(n)$ from the given input and Table 3.1.

2. Find the constants associated with $y_p(n)$ by substituting the assumed solution for $y_p(n)$ into the given system equation.

3. Find the characteristic roots of the system, i.e., assume $y_c(n) = Cr^n$ as a solution to

$$y(n) - \sum_{k=1}^{N} a_k y(n - k) = 0 \tag{3.272}$$

and find the values of r that satisfy Eq. 3.272. This amounts to finding the roots of the characteristic equation

$$r^N - a_1 r^{N-1} - a_2 r^{N-2} - \cdots - a_N = 0. \tag{3.273}$$

4. The total solution has the form

$$y(n) = y_p(n) + y_c(n) \tag{3.274}$$

where $y_p(n)$ the particular solution comes from item 2 above. Assuming no equal (repeated) roots, $y_c(n)$, the complementary solution, is given by

$$y_c(n) = \sum_{k=1}^{N} C_k (r_k)^n \cdot u(n) + \sum_{k=0}^{L-N} A_k \delta(n - k) \tag{3.275}$$

where the r's come from Eq. 3.273. The weighted unit sample terms occur if $L \geq N$ in the system difference equation. In many situations $L < N$ and the second summation of Eq. 3.275 may be ignored.

5. a) For $L < N$ assume the complementary solution

$$y_c(n) = \sum_{k=1}^{N} C_k(r_k)^n \tag{3.276}$$

and determine the constants associated with $y_c(n)$ by writing N equations that include the N derived initial conditions.

b) For $L \geq N$ assume the complementary solution

$$y_c(n) = \sum_{k=1}^{N} C_k(r_k)^n + \sum_{k=0}^{L-N} A_k \delta(n - k). \tag{3.277}$$

We see that N equations are needed to determine the C_k's and another $L - N + 1$ to find the A_k's. Thus, a total of $N + (L - N + 1) = L + 1$ equations, along with $(L + 1)$ derived initial conditions, are needed.

6. Check a few values produced by letting $n = 0, 1, 2, \ldots$ in the analytical solution of the original difference equation.

We refer to this method as the classical approach for solving linear difference equations with constant coefficients.

Example 3.20. This example illustrates the procedure used to find the total response.

Given a causal LTI system described by

$$y(n) + y(n - 2) = x(n) + x(n - 1) \tag{3.278}$$

with the input a step sequence

$$x(n) = 10 \cdot u(n) \tag{3.279}$$

and the given (known) initial conditions of

$$y(-2) = -10 \text{ and } y(-1) = 0. \tag{3.280}$$

Find the solution $y(n)$ for $n \geq 0$.

Solution: We follow the steps just outlined.

1. From Table 3.1, with $x(n) = 10 \cdot u(n)$, the choice for the particular solution is

$$y_p(n) = C_1, \quad n \geq 0. \tag{3.281}$$

2. Substituting $y_p(n) = C_1$ into the system equation, Eq. 3.278, gives

$$C_1 + C_1 = 10 + 10 \quad \text{or} \quad C_1 = 10 \tag{3.282}$$

hence $y_p(n) = 10$, $n \geq 0$.

3. The characteristic equation is

$$1 + r^{-2} = 0 \qquad (3.283)$$

and the characteristic roots are

$$r_{1,2} = \pm j1 = 1e^{\pm j\pi/2}. \qquad (3.284)$$

4. The total solution is

$$y(n) = y_p(n) + y_c(n)$$
$$= \underbrace{10}_{\text{input}} + \underbrace{C_2 e^{j\pi n/2} + C_3 e^{-j\pi n/2}}_{\text{system}}, \qquad n \geq 0. \qquad (3.285)$$

Here, as is often the case, $L < N$, so we don't have to be concerned about the weighted unit sample terms in Eq. 3.275.

5. The given initial conditions are $y(-2) = -10$, $y(-1) = 0$ and we use these given values and the system equation to find the derived initial conditions $y(0)$ and $y(1)$ which are needed to determine C_2 and C_3. We do this because the solution given in Eq. 3.285 applies only for non-negative values of n. For the system equation

$$y(n) = -y(n-2) + x(n) + x(n-1), \qquad n \geq 0 \qquad (3.286)$$

and $y(-2) = -10$, $y(-1) = 0$ with $x(n) = 10 \cdot u(n)$ we have

$$y(0) = -(-10) + 10 = 20$$
$$y(1) = -0 + 10 + 10 = 20. \qquad (3.287)$$

Now substituting these derived initial conditions into Eq. 3.285 gives us

$$\begin{array}{ll} 20 = 10 + C_2 + C_3 & \text{for } n = 0 \\ 20 = 10 + C_2 e^{j\pi/2} + C_3 e^{-j\pi/2} & \text{for } n = 1 \end{array} \qquad (3.288)$$

which may be written in matrix form as

$$\begin{bmatrix} 1 & 1 \\ e^{j\pi/2} & e^{-j\pi/2} \end{bmatrix} \begin{bmatrix} C_2 \\ C_3 \end{bmatrix} = \begin{bmatrix} 10 \\ 10 \end{bmatrix}. \qquad (3.289)$$

The solution is

$$\begin{bmatrix} C_2 \\ C_3 \end{bmatrix} = \begin{bmatrix} 7.07 e^{-j\pi/4} \\ 7.07 e^{j\pi/4} \end{bmatrix} \qquad (3.290)$$

and putting these values into Eq. 3.285 produces the total solution

$$y(n) = 10 + 7.07 e^{-j\pi/4} e^{j\pi n/2} + 7.07 e^{j\pi/4} e^{-j\pi n/2}$$
$$= 10 + 7.07 e^{j(\pi n/2 - \pi/4)} + 7.07 e^{-j(\pi n/2 - \pi/4)}$$
$$= 10 + 14.14 \cos(n\pi/2 - \pi/4), \qquad n \geq 0^\dagger. \qquad (3.291)$$

---

†Purists may note that the solution for $y(n)$ actually applies for $n \geq -2$ because we have forced this to be the case. Nevertheless, since we are only interested in the solution from $n = 0$ onward we simply restrict the range of n to these values.

Example 3.21. This example illustrates the determination of the unit sample response by the classical method of solving difference equations.

Given the traditional description of a second-order system

$$y(n) = [2a \cos \alpha]y(n-1) - [a^2]y(n-2) + x(n) \qquad (3.292)$$

find the system's response $h(n)$ for $x(n) = \delta(n)$, the unit sample sequence.

Solution: We follow the steps outlined just prior to Example 3.20.

1. With $x(n) = \delta(n)$, we see from Table 3.1 that no terms appear in the total solution due to this input. Thus

$$y_p(n) = 0. \qquad (3.293)$$

2. This step is skipped since $y_p(n) = 0$.

3. The characteristic equation is

$$1 - [2a \cos \alpha]r^{-1} + [a^2]r^{-2} = 0 \qquad \text{or}$$
$$r^2 - [2a \cos \alpha]r + [a^2] = 0. \qquad (3.294)$$

Using the quadratic formula we have

$$r_{1,2} = \frac{2a \cos \alpha \pm \sqrt{4a^2 \cos^2 \alpha - 4a^2}}{2}$$

$$= a \cos \alpha \pm a \sqrt{\cos^2 \alpha - 1}. \qquad (3.295)$$

But $\sin^2 \alpha + \cos^2 \alpha = 1$ or $\cos^2 \alpha - 1 = -\sin^2 \alpha$ which gives the roots

$$r_{1,2} = a \cos \alpha \pm a \sqrt{-\sin^2 \alpha}$$
$$= a \cos \alpha \pm ja \sin \alpha \qquad (3.296)$$

and from the Euler relation, we have the exponential form

$$r_{1,2} = ae^{\pm j\alpha}. \qquad (3.297)$$

4. Therefore, the total solution is

$$y(n) = y_p(n) + y_c(n)$$
$$= 0 + C_1(ae^{j\alpha})^n + C_2(ae^{-j\alpha})^n \qquad (3.298)$$

5. A requirement for finding the unit sample response is that all the initial conditions must be set to zero. Thus, we set

$$y(-2) = y(-1) = 0 \qquad (3.299)$$

for this second-order system and we need to find the derived initial conditions $y(0)$ and $y(1)$. From the system equation of Eq. 3.292

$$y(0) = [2a \cos \alpha] \cdot 0 - [a^2] \cdot 0 + 1 = 1 \qquad (3.300)$$

and

$$y(1) = [2a \cos \alpha] \cdot 1 - [a^2] \cdot 0 + 0 = 2a \cos \alpha. \qquad (3.301)$$

Now we can write two equations in the unknowns C_1 and C_2 in Eq. 3.298.

$$1 = C_1 + C_2 \qquad \text{for } n = 0 \qquad (3.302)$$

$$2a \cos \alpha = C_1 a e^{j\alpha} + C_2 a e^{-j\alpha} \qquad \text{for } n = 1. \tag{3.303}$$

This gives the matrix equation

$$\begin{bmatrix} 1 & 1 \\ ae^{j\alpha} & ae^{-j\alpha} \end{bmatrix} \begin{bmatrix} C_1 \\ C_2 \end{bmatrix} = \begin{bmatrix} 1 \\ 2a \cos \alpha \end{bmatrix} \tag{3.304}$$

which has the solution

$$\begin{bmatrix} C_1 \\ C_2 \end{bmatrix} = \begin{bmatrix} e^{j\alpha}/(2j \sin \alpha) \\ e^{-j\alpha}/(-2j \sin \alpha) \end{bmatrix}. \tag{3.305}$$

Substituting these constants into Eq. 3.298 produces

$$y(n) = \frac{e^{j\alpha}}{2j \sin \alpha}(ae^{j\alpha})^n + \frac{e^{-j\alpha}}{-2j \sin \alpha}(ae^{-j\alpha})^n \tag{3.306}$$

which can be rearranged into the form

$$y(n) = \frac{1}{\sin \alpha} \frac{a^n e^{j(\alpha n + \alpha)} - a^n e^{-j(\alpha n + \alpha)}}{2j}. \tag{3.307}$$

Now recall that $y(n) = h(n)$ for a unit sample input which is the case here, so

$$h(n) = \frac{1}{\sin \alpha} a^n \sin(\alpha n + \alpha), \qquad n \geq 0. \tag{3.308}$$

Comments:

1. We deduced this result by guessing back in Section 3.3 but here we found it in a logical fashion.
2. We could have written C_1^* rather than C_2 in Eq. 3.298 because, with complex conjugate roots, the corresponding coefficient will always be a complex conjugate in order that $y(n)$ be a real function.

Example 3.22. This example illustrates the determination of the unit sample response of a first-order system with input delay.

Given the first-order system

$$y(n) - a_1 y(n - 1) = b_0 x(n) + b_2 x(n - 2) \tag{3.309}$$

use the classical approach to find the unit sample response.

Solution:

1. For a sample input the particular solution is zero. That is, $y_p(n) = 0$.
2. This step is not needed since $y_p(n) = 0$.
3. The characteristic equation is $1 - a_1 r^{-1} = 0$ and the characteristic root is $r_1 = a_1$.
4. The system order is $N = 1$ and the largest delay of the input is $L = 2$. Therefore, using Eq. 3.275 we assume for the total solution

$$y(n) = 0 + C_1 a_1{}^n + A_0 \delta(n) + A_1 \delta(n - 1). \tag{3.310}$$

5. There are three unknowns so we need three derived initial conditions. From Eq. 3.309

$$y(0) = b_0$$

$$y(1) = a_1 b_0$$

$$y(2) = a_1^2 b_0 + b_2. \tag{3.311}$$

Thus, by letting $n = 0, 1$, and 2 in Eq. 3.310 we have three equations in three unknowns, namely

$$b_0 = C_1 + A_0$$

$$a_1 b_0 = C_1 a_1 + A_1$$

$$a_1^2 b_0 + b_2 = C_1 a_1^2. \tag{3.312}$$

Solution of these three equations gives us

$$C_1 = b_0 + b_2 a_1^{-2}, \quad A_0 = -b_2 a_1^{-2} \text{ and } A_1 = -b_2 a_1^{-1} \tag{3.313}$$

with the unit sample response being

$$y(n) = h(n) = (b_0 + b_2 a_1^{-2}) a_1^n \cdot u(n) - [b_2 a_1^{-2}] \delta(n) - [b_2 a_1^{-1}] \delta(n-1). \tag{3.314}$$

In the last two examples we found analytical expressions for the unit sample responses of a first-order and a second-order system. This procedure can be generalized to an Nth-order system described by the difference equation

IMPORTANT COMMENT

$$y(n) - \sum_{k=1}^{N} y_k(n-k) = \sum_{k=0}^{L} b_k x(n-k). \tag{3.315}$$

For a unit sample input and N distinct (unequal) roots the total solution is

$$y(n) = y_p(n) + y_c(n)$$

$$= \begin{cases} \displaystyle\sum_{k=1}^{N} C_k r_k^n \cdot u(n), \text{ if } L < N \\[3ex] \displaystyle\sum_{k=1}^{N} C_k r_k^n \cdot u(n) + \sum_{k=0}^{L-N} A_k \delta(n-k), \text{ if } N \leq L \end{cases} \tag{3.316}$$

where the derived initial conditions are needed to compute the C_k's and the A_k's in Eq. 3.316.

Example 3.23. This example illustrates the total solution with more than one input.

Suppose that we return to the savings account system of Example 3.1 where the system was described at monthly intervals by

$$y(n) = 1.01\, y(n-1) + x(n) \qquad (3.317)$$

with $y(n)$ the amount in the account and $x(n)$ the amount deposited, both at the nth sample. The coefficient 1.01 came from an interest rate of 1 percent per month. In Example 3.1 we used $x(n) = \$50$, a constant. Now let's assume that the amount deposited per month increases in a linear manner as $x(n) = 50 + 5n$, $n \geq 0$. That is, an extra \$5 is deposited each month. Assuming that there is no money in the account before $n = 0$, determine a general expression for $y(n)$ for $n \geq 0$.

Solution: Once again, we follow the steps of the previous examples.

1. From Table 3.1, with $x(n) = 50 + 5n$, the particular solution is

$$y_p(n) = \underbrace{C_1}_{\text{from } 50} + \underbrace{C_2 + C_3 n}_{\text{from } 5n}$$

$$= C_4 + C_3 n. \qquad (3.318)$$

2. Substituting into the system equation of Eq. 3.317 gives

$$C_4 + C_3 n = 1.01[C_4 + C_3(n-1)] + 50 + 5n \qquad (3.319)$$

and for $n = 0$ we have

$$C_4 = 1.01[C_4 - C_3] + 50 \qquad (3.320)$$

and for $n = 1$

$$C_4 + C_3 = 1.01[C_4] + 50 + 5. \qquad (3.321)$$

Rearranging Eqs. 3.320 and 3.321 gives us

$$-0.01 C_4 + 1.01 C_3 = 50$$

$$-0.01 C_4 + C_3 = 55 \qquad (3.322)$$

which has the solution of $C_3 = -500$ and $C_4 = -55{,}500$.

3. The characteristic equation is

$$1 - 1.01 r^{-1} = 0 \qquad (3.323)$$

with the single root of $r = 1.01$.

4. The total solution is

$$y(n) = y_p(n) + y_c(n)$$

$$= C_4 + C_3 n + C_5(1.01)^n$$

$$= -55{,}500 - 500n + C_5(1.01)^n. \qquad (3.324)$$

5. We were given that $y(-1) = 0$, so the derived initial condition is

$$y(0) = (1.01) \cdot 0 + 50 + 5 \cdot 0 = 50 \qquad (3.325)$$

which when substituted into Eq. 3.324 yields

$$50 = -55{,}500 - 0 + C_5 \qquad \text{or} \qquad C_5 = 55{,}550 \qquad (3.326)$$

The amount of money in the account at any month n is given by

$$y(n) = -55{,}500 - 500n + 55{,}550(1.01)^n, \qquad n \geq 0. \qquad (3.327)$$

6. As a check $y(0) = 50$ and $y(1) = 105.5$, which can be computed iteratively from Eq. 3.317, the system equation.

The classical method of solving difference equations gives analytical solutions. Although we have used the method presented only for recursive difference equations, it can also be applied to nonrecursive systems. In Chapter Six we will see that z-transforms can also be used to obtain analytical solutions for difference equations.

3.8 ■ REVIEW

In this chapter we considered three important mathematical models for discrete systems—difference equations, the unit sample response $h(n)$, and system diagrams. In addition, we found that discrete systems are classified as either being recursive—the output is affected by past outputs as well as present and past values of the input—or nonrecursive—the output depends only on present and past values of the input. In either case, the response of a discrete system can be found by iteratively solving its difference equations, usually with aid of a computer program. Such an approach, however, usually leads to numerical values rather than to analytical expressions, which are generally preferred. If a situation occurs, however, where the finite geometric series is present, a closed-form expression results from using Eq. 3.20.

We also found that the response of a linear, time-invariant discrete system can be described in terms of the convolution summation which can be evaluated in three ways—graphically, numerically (using the "sliding bar" method or a computer program), or analytically. The concept of convolution was derived from the consideration of a system's unit sample response. This response, designated as $h(n)$, totally characterizes a system because the system response to any input can be determined if the unit sample response is known. The unit sample (unit impulse) response was also used to classify systems as FIR—having a finite impulse response—or IIR—having an infinite impulse response. Normally, FIR systems are implemented in nonrecursive form and IIR in recursive form.

Diagrams or implementations are used to describe and portray certain properties of LTI systems in a visual manner. Recursive and nonrecursive forms, for instance, are easily seen from a diagram. And by interconnecting systems in cascade or in parallel, new systems can be designed and specified through the unit sample responses of the original systems.

In considering the response of LTI systems we observed that there is a portion of the response caused by the initial conditions, known as the initial condition response, and another component, the forced response, due to system inputs. A method for determining the total response was developed that consists of finding the complementary and particular solutions. The complementary solution is found from the characteristic equation and the particular solution can often be found from a table, such as Table 3.1. To solve an Nth-order difference equation, N initial condition values must be known. We notice that this corresponds to the number of delays of the output in the system diagram.

In studying linear systems, we often use definitions of system characteristics, and one of these, stability, was reintroduced in this chapter and investigated by determining the roots of a system's characteristic equation.

VOCABULARY AND IMPORTANT RELATIONS

a) Difference equations are one form of mathematical model for linear discrete systems. Iterative solution of difference equations—normally done with a computer (Section 3.1.3).

Finite geometric sum

$$S_N = \sum_{m=0}^{m=N} a^m = \frac{1 - a^{N+1}}{1 - a}, \ a \neq 1 \tag{3.20}$$

Infinite geometric sum

$$S_\infty = \sum_{m=0}^{m=\infty} a^m = \frac{1}{1 - a}, \ |a| < 1 \tag{3.21}$$

Difference equation for an Nth-order system

$$y(n) = a_1 y(n-1) + a_2 y(n-2) + a_N y(n-N) + b_0 x(n) + b_1 x(n-1) + \cdots + b_L x(n-L) \tag{3.27}$$

$$y(n) = \sum_{k=1}^{k=N} a_k y(n-k) + \sum_{k=0}^{k=L} b_k x(n-k) \quad \text{recursive (nominally IIR)} \tag{3.28}$$

$$y(n) = \sum_{k=0}^{k=L} b_k x(n-k) \quad \text{nonrecursive (nominally FIR)} \tag{3.30}$$

b) Characteristic equation and initial condition response

$$1 - a_1 r^{-1} - a_2 r^{-2} - \cdots - a_N r^{-N} = 0 \tag{3.193}$$

or

$$r^N - a_1 r^{N-1} - a_2 r^{N-2} - \cdots - a_N = 0 \qquad (3.194)$$

or

$$r^N - \sum_{k=1}^{N} a_k r^{N-k} = 0. \qquad (3.245)$$

The characteristic roots may be distinct, i.e., no two roots are equal, or repeated. Initial condition response or zero-input response (assuming distinct characteristic roots)

$$y(n) = \sum_{k=1}^{N} C_k r_k^{\,n}. \qquad (3.219)$$

c) Stability: System is stable if magnitude of each root of the characteristic equation is less than one.

d) Convolution summation

$$y(n) = x(n) * h(n) = \sum_{m=-\infty}^{m=\infty} x(m)h(n - m) \qquad (3.120)$$

$$y(n) = h(n) * x(n) = \sum_{m=-\infty}^{m=\infty} h(m)x(n - m).$$

Graphical method of convolution: folding, shifting, multiplying sequences, and adding the values of a sequence

Sliding bar method of convolution

Computer evaluation of convolution (Section 3.4.2)

Analytical convolution (Section 3.4.3)

e) Unit sample response

$$x(n) = \delta(n) \xrightarrow{\text{produces}} y(n) = h(n) \quad \text{(assuming zero initial conditions)}$$

f) Total Response

Complementary solution $\quad y_c(n)$

Particular solution $\quad y_p(n)$

Total response $\quad y(n) = y_c(n) + y_p(n)$

Initial Condition Response $\longrightarrow$ Complementary Solution

Forced Response $\begin{cases} \text{System terms} \\ \text{Input terms} \longrightarrow \text{Particular Solution} \end{cases}$

CHAPTER 3   LINEAR TIME-INVARIANT SYSTEMS

g) System Diagrams (see Fig. 3.4(a))

h) Interconnected systems

   Cascade (Fig. 3.20)

   Parallel (Fig. 3.26)

i) Summary of Analysis Procedures

Starting Point	Solution Method	Result Obtained
Difference Equations	Iterative numerical solution (generally by computer)	Total solution in tabular (numerical) form[†]
Difference Equations	Classical Solution	Total solution in analytical form $y(n) = y_p(n) + y_c(n)$
Unit Sample Response, $h(n)$	Convolution graphical sliding bar ⟶ (generally by computer) analytical ⟶	 Forced response in tabular form Forced response in analytical form

[†]Except in simple cases where analytical results may be obtained.

PROBLEMS

Reinforcement

3.1 An operation often performed in digital signal processing is that of removing the average value of a signal prior to other operations. To make this practical, an estimate of the average value is determined by computing the average of the last N sample values of the input sequence. When this is done the system is called a moving average filter. Consider the N-point moving average digital filter

$$y(n) = \frac{1}{N}[x(n) + x(n-1) + \cdots + x(n - [N-1])].$$

a) Suppose $N = 5$ and $x(n)$ is as shown in Fig. P3.1. Find $y(n)$ for $n = 0$ to 8. Assume that $x(n) = 0$ for $n < 0$.

b) Which values of $y(n)$ least accurately represent the average value of the input and why?

3.2 Tom Robbins has received a gift of $10,000 from his rich uncle. Tom invests the money in a municipal bond fund and so pays no income tax on the interest received. He receives interest every 6 months and the annual rate of return is R percent. He may also elect to withdraw from or invest additional funds into the fund at the end of each six-month period.

a) Write a difference equation that describes the

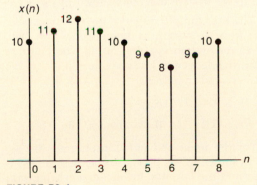

FIGURE P3.1

value of Tom's investment. Let $y(n)$ be the value at the end of the nth six-month period.

b) Suppose the annual rate of return is 9 percent and Tom withdraws $300 every 6 months. How much money will be in the fund at the end of 3 years?

c) Develop a closed-form solution for the difference equation found in part a) from which the value of $y(n)$ for any n could be computed. Assume that a constant amount of money is withdrawn at the end of every six months.

d) Suppose Tom wished to withdraw the same amount of money every six months so that the value of the fund will be zero at the end of the tenth year. How much should he withdraw each six months?

3.3 a) Darlene Kelley opens an IRA on her 30th birthday. She deposits $2,000 at this time and $2,000 on her birthday every year thereafter until and including her 60th birthday. Assume that the IRA account pays 10 percent interest compounded annually, write a difference equation that describes the evolution of her IRA account, and find the amount in Darlene's IRA on her 60th birthday. The income is tax free until she begins to withdraw funds after her 60th birthday.

b) Jane Stanley opens a bank account on her 30th birthday. Like Darlene, she deposits $2,000 each year on her birthday and the account earns 10 percent interest. Jane, however, pays income tax on the interest earned. Assume that the interest is subject to combined federal and state taxes of 25 percent. Write a difference equation that describes the variation of the funds in her account, and determine the amount that will be in Jane's account on her 60th birthday.

3.4 a) For the discrete system whose block diagram is shown in Fig. P3.4, $x(n)$ is the unit alternating sequence, i.e.,

$$x(n) = \begin{cases} 0, & n < 0 \\ (-1)^n, & n \ge 0 \end{cases}$$

At $n = -1$ the outputs of the unit delays are all zero. Sketch the sequences $x(n)$, $p(n)$, $y(n)$, $r(n)$ and $q(n)$ for $n = 0, 1, 2, 3$.

3.5 Draw a system realization for each of the following difference equations

a) $y(n) = 2x(n) - x(n-1) + 5x(n-2)$

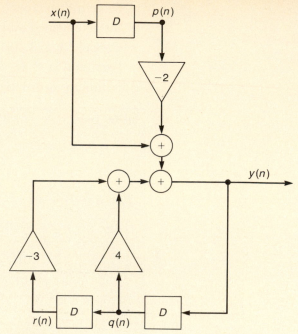

FIGURE P3.4

b) $y(n) = -3y(n-1) - 10y(n-2) + 6y(n-3)$

c) $y(n) = -3y(n-1) - 10y(n-2) + 6y(n-3) + 2x(n) - x(n-1) + 5x(n-2)$

3.6 Draw a system diagram for the systems characterized by the difference equations

a) $y(n) = -2y(n-1) + y(n-2) - x(n-1) + 3x(n-3)$

b) $y(n) = -3y(n-2) + y(n-3) - x(n) + 4x(n-1)$

3.7 Find the difference equations which correspond to the system diagrams shown in Fig. P3.7.

3.8 The unit sample response for a nonrecursive linear discrete system is tabulated below. The input to the system is $x(n) = 5u(n)$, where $u(n)$ is the unit step sequence. Use convolution to find the system response $y(n)$ for $n = 0, 1, 2, 3, 4$.

n	0	1	2	3	4	5	6	...
$h(n)$	0.0	0.0	3.0	0.75	0.56	0.23	0.0	...

3.9 For the input and unit sample response sequences shown in Fig. P3.9, use graphical convolution to find the outputs. In each case, sketch $y(n)$ vs. n.

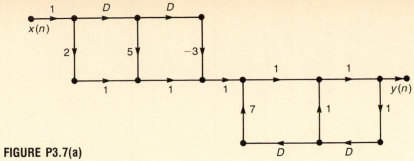

FIGURE P3.7(a)

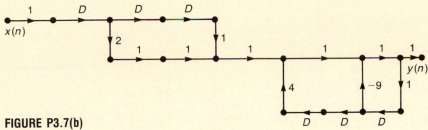

FIGURE P3.7(b)

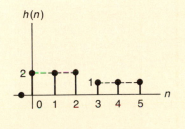
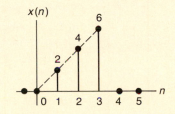

(a)

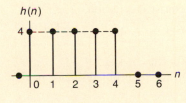
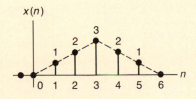

(b)

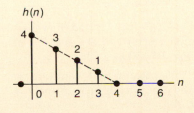
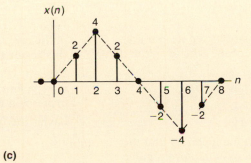

(c)

FIGURE P3.9

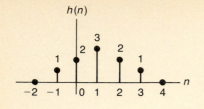

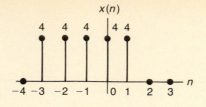

(d)

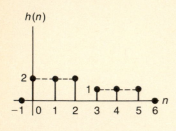

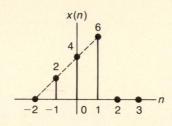

(e)

FIGURE P3.9 (cont.)

3.10 The difference equations describing several LTI discrete systems are given below. Determine whether or not each system is stable.

a) $y(n) = 3x(n) + 2x(n-1) - x(n-3)$

b) $y(n) = -1.5y(n-1) - y(n-2) - 0.25y(n-3)$

c) $y(n) = 1.6y(n-1) + 1.45y(n-2)$

d) $y(n) = 1.6y(n-1) + 1.45y(n-2) + x(n)$

e) $y(n) = 1.6y(n-1) + 1.45y(n-2) + x(n) + 6x(n-1) + 8x(n-2)$

3.11 Given below are the characteristic equations for several LTI discrete systems. Determine whether each system is stable or unstable.

a) $r^2 - 0.25 = 0$

b) $r^2 - 4 = 0$

c) $(r + 0.5)(r - 3.0) = 0$

d) $r^2 + r + 0.5 = 0$

e) $r^2 + 2.25r + 1.12 = 0$

3.12 The characteristic equations for several systems are given below. Determine whether or not each system is stable.

a) $(r - 0.8 - j0.9)(r - 0.8 + j0.9) = 0$

b) $r^3 - r^2 - 1.5r - 1 = 0$ ⎫
c) $r^3 + 1.5r^2 + r + 0.25 = 0$ ⎬

You may want to use a computer to find the roots of these cubic equations. Or, since a cubic always has at least one real root, it can be found by

trial and error and factored out, leaving a quadratic to be solved by the quadratic formula.

d) $(r^2 - r + 0.5)(r^2 + 0.5r + 0.125) = 0$

3.13 A causal LTI system is described below (the parameters a, α, b_0 and b_1 are real).

$$y(n) - [2a \cos \alpha]y(n-1) + a^2 y(n-2) = b_0 x(n) + b_1 x(n-1)$$

a) Mark the appropriate gains on the system diagram in Fig. P3.13(a).

b) Find the characteristic equation.

c) What are the values of b_0, b_1, a and α for a stable system?

d) Find the values of the constants b_0, b_1, a and α to make the initial condition response of the form

$$y(n) = C_1(e^{j\pi/2})^n + C_2(e^{-j\pi/2})^n$$

e) For $a = 1$, $\alpha = \pi/3$, $b_0 = b_1 = 1$, find the values of the unit sample response for $0 \le n \le 7$. Plot this result in Fig. P3.13(b).

f) Explain why this pattern will continue as $n \to \infty$. From the plot in e) deduce an analytic expression for $h(n)$.

g) Given the unit sample response

$$\{h(n)\} = \{\ldots, 0, \ 1, \ 2, 1, -1, -2, -1, 1, 2, 1, \ldots\}$$
$$\uparrow$$
$$n = 0$$

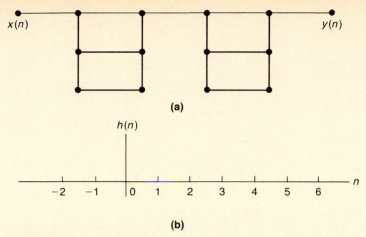

(a)

(b)

FIGURE P3.13

Use the sliding bar technique to find $h(n)*x(n)$ for $x(n) = u(n)$. Generate and plot the values for $-\infty \le n \le 7$.

3.14 A difference equation describing the rotational motion of a spacecraft is given by $y(n) = y(n-1) - 0.5y(n-2) + 0.5x(n) + 0.5x(n-1)$ where $y(n)$ represents the angular position and $x(n)$ represents the input torque of the thrusters.

a) Assuming that $y(-2) = y(-1) = 0$ and $x(n) = \cos(n\pi/3)u(n)$ find an analytical expression for the response $y(n)$ for $n \ge 0$.

b) Compare a few values of $y(n)$ found from the analytical solution of part a) with values found by iteratively solving the difference equation.

3.15 A discrete system is characterized by the difference equation $y(n) = y(n-1) - 0.5y(n-2) + 0.5x(n)$.

a) Find an analytical expression for the unit step response. Assume $y(-1) = y(-2) = 0$.

b) Check the solution found in part a) against the values $y(0)$, $y(1)$, $y(2)$, found by solving the difference equation iteratively.

3.16 A system is characterized by the difference equation $y(n) - 7y(n-1) + 10y(n-2) = 20x(n)$. The input sequence is $x(n) = 3u(n) + 4nu(n)$ and the initial conditions are $y(-1) = y(-2) = 0$.

a) Find an analytical expression for the solution of the difference equation.

b) Verify your solution with a few points found by solving the difference equation iteratively.

3.17 The unit sample response for the system of Problem 3.15 is given by $h(n) = (0.707)^{n+1} \cos(\pi n/4 - \pi/4)$, $n \ge 0$.

a) Use analytical convolution to obtain the unit step response of this system.

b) Check this result with the solution obtained in Problem 3.15.

3.18 Consider, once more, the system of Problem 3.16, namely $y(n) - 7y(n-1) + 10y(n-2) = 20x(n)$ subjected to the unit sample input $x(n) = \delta(n)$. For $y(-1) = y(-2) = 0$, the response $y(n)$ to this input is the unit sample response $h(n)$. Show that the unit sample response is given by $h(n) = (40/3)[-(2)^n + 2.5(5)^n]$, $n \ge 0$. Use the method from Section 3.7 to do this.

3.19 A discrete system is described by the difference equation $y(n) = -2.5y(n-1) - y(n-2) + x(n) - x(n-2)$.

a) Draw a block diagram or signal flow graph that represents the system.

b) Is the system stable?

c) Find an analytical expression for the initial condition response of the system if $y(0) = 4$ and $y(1) = 1$.

d) Find the values of the unit sample response $h(0)$, $h(1)$, $h(2)$, and $h(3)$ by numerical iteration. Do not attempt to find an analytical expression.

e) Using the values of $h(0)$, $h(1)$, $h(2)$, and $h(3)$

from part c), find the forced response of the system for $n = 0, 1, 2, 3$ to the input $x(n) = 2u(n) + (1/2)^n u(n)$.

f) Find an analytical expression for the forced response of the system for $x(n) = 2u(n) + (1/2)^n u(n)$. Compare the values obtained from the analytical expression for $n = 0, 1, 2, 3$ with the results from part (e).

g) Find an analytical expression for the total response of the system for an input of $x(n) = 2u(n) + (1/2)^n u(n)$ with initial conditions $y(0) = 4$ and $y(1) = 1$. How are the values obtained from this expression related to the results obtained in parts (c) and (e)?

Extension and Generalization

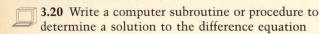 **3.20** Write a computer subroutine or procedure to determine a solution to the difference equation

$$y(n) = \sum_{k=1}^{N} a_k y(n - k) + \sum_{k=0}^{L} b_k x(n - k).$$

Assume that:

a) N and L are in the range $0 \leq N \leq 10$ and $0 \leq L \leq 10$.

b) The initial conditions $y(-1)$, $y(-2)$, . . . , $y(-N)$ are input data.

c) $x(n)$ may be specified either in the form of a table of input values, or as an analytical expression supplied by the user.

d) The input sequence is zero for $n < 0$.

3.21 Use the computer program developed in Problem 3.20 to check the solution obtained in the following problems:

a) Problem 3.2

b) Problem 3.3

c) Problem 3.8

d) Problem 3.13(e), (g)

e) Problem 3.14

f) Problem 3.15

g) Problem 3.16

h) Problem 3.18

3.22 An algorithm for computing the square root of a number X is given by the difference equation

$y(n) = \frac{1}{2}\left[y(n - 1) + \frac{X}{y(n - 1)}\right]$ where $y(n)$ is the nth estimate of $\sqrt{X}$. To begin the calculation, a value of $y(0)$ is guessed (the value must be positive).

a) Let $X = 2$ and $y(0) = 10$. Find $y(6)$ by recursive solution.

b) Repeat part a) for $y(0) = 1000$, and also evaluate $y(13)$.

c) If $y(n - 1) \gg X$, what is the approximate value of $y(n)$?

d) Can the geometric series be used to find a closed form solution for $y(n)$? Explain.

e) If the algorithm converges, $y(n)$ approaches a constant whose value is $\sqrt{X}$. Let the constant which $y(n)$ approaches be denoted by Y and show that $Y = \sqrt{X}$. HINT: If the algorithm converges, what can be said about the values of $y(n)$ and $y(n - 1)$?

3.23 A generalization of the square root algorithm of Problem 3.22 is a method for finding solutions of algebraic equations. Consider the problem of finding the solutions of the algebraic equation $f(y) = 0$. A typical curve of $f(y)$ as a function of y is shown in Fig. P3.23. Suppose that $y(n - 1)$ is as shown; the corresponding value of the function is $f(y(n - 1))$. Let us use this information to obtain a value of $y(n)$ by constructing the tangent at point A and projecting it to the y axis where $f(y)$ would be zero if it were a linear function of y.

a) Denoting the slope of the tangent at point A by

$$f'(y(n - 1)) = \frac{df(y)}{dy}\bigg|_{y = y(n - 1)}$$

determine the equation for $y(n)$ in terms of $y(n - 1)$, $f(y(n - 1))$ and $f'(y(n - 1))$.

b) Let $f(y) = y^2 - X$ and show that the equation found in part a) leads to the square root algorithm $y(n) = \frac{1}{2}\left[y(n - 1) + \frac{X}{y(n - 1)}\right]$.

c) Use the equation found in part a) to devise an algorithm for finding the Kth root of a number X.

d) Apply the algorithm of part (c) to find the following:

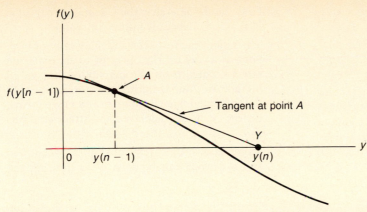

$f(y)$

$f(y[n-1])$

A

Tangent at point A

Y

$y(n)$

0     $y(n-1)$ $y(n)$

y

FIGURE P3.23

i) The 4th root of 87 starting with $y(0) = 5000$.

ii) The 4th root of 87 starting with $y(0) = 1$.

iii) The 5th root of 1024 starting with $y(0) = 1$.

iv) The 5th root of 1024 starting with $y(0) = 8$.

e) What can you say about the dependence of the algorithm's performance on the starting guess, $y(0)$?

3.24 The difference equation for a general LTI discrete system is given by $y(n) = a_1y(n-1) + a_2y(n-2) + \cdots + a_Ny(n-N) + b_0x(n) + b_1x(n-1) + \cdots + b_Lx(n-L)$.

a) What role do the b_k, $k = 0, 1, \ldots, L$, coefficients play in the characteristic equation?

b) If the b_k, $k = 0, 1, \ldots, L$, and the a_k, $k = 1, 2, \ldots, N$, coefficients are fixed and the system is stable, can the system be made unstable by changing the values of the b coefficients? Explain.

c) Suppose the a_k, $k = 1, 2, \ldots, N$, coefficients are all zero. Is the system stable, or unstable, or stable for certain values of the b's and unstable for others? Explain.

3.25 A polynomial in factored form can be written as $P_N(z) = (z - r_1)(z - r_2) \ldots (z - r_N) = z^N + a_1z^{N-1} + a_2z^{N-2} + \cdots + a_N$ where the r_i's are, in general, complex numbers.

a) Show that regardless of the value of N (the degree of the polynomial) $a_1 = -(r_1 + r_2 + \cdots + r_N) = \Sigma$ (negatives of the roots).

b) Show that $a_N = (-r_1)(-r_2) \ldots (-r_N) =$ product of the negatives of the roots.

c) Can you deduce a pattern for expressing the other coefficients in terms of the roots?

3.26 Show that convolution satisfies the following:

a) The distributive property, that is $x(n) * [h_1(n) + h_2(n)] = x(n) * h_1(n) + x(n) * h_2(n)$.

b) The associative property, that is $[x(n) * h_1(n)] * h_2(n) = x(n) * [h_1(n) * h_2(n)]$.

3.27 Starting from the definition, show that convolution is a linear operation, that is $[\alpha h_1(n) + \beta h_2(n)] * x(n) = \alpha h_1(n) * x(n) + \beta h_2(n) * x(n)$ for arbitrary α, β, $h_1(n)$, $h_2(n)$, and $x(n)$.

3.28 Starting from the definition of discrete convolution

$$h(n) * x(n) = \sum_{m=-\infty}^{m=\infty} h(m)x(n-m)$$

show that:

a) If $h(n) = 0$ for $n < 0$

$$h(n) * x(n) = \sum_{m=0}^{m=\infty} h(m)x(n-m).$$

b) If $x(n) = 0$ for $n < 0$

$$h(n) * x(n) = \sum_{m=-\infty}^{m=n} h(m)x(n-m).$$

c) If $x(n) = 0$ for $n < 0$ and $h(n) = 0$ for $n < 0$

$$h(n) * x(n) = \sum_{m=0}^{m=n} h(m)x(n-m).$$

3.29 The sample values of a transmitted radar pulse $s(n)$ are shown in Fig. P3.29(a). If a target is present, the sampled return pulse $x(n)$ is as shown in Fig. P3.29(b). The return pulse is processed by convolving it with the unit sample response $h(n)$ shown in Fig. P3.29(c).

a) Find and sketch the sequence $y(n) = h(n) * x(n)$. Label all numerical values.

b) The radar operator sees a display only of $y(n)$. Suggest a way for the operator to estimate the target's range from the display of $y(n)$ vs. n. Include in your thinking the possibility that the returned signal may be somewhat distorted, i.e., is not a delayed and attenuated version of the transmitted signal $s(n)$.

c) There is a simple relationship between $x(n)$ and $h(n)$ that can be seen by inspecting the

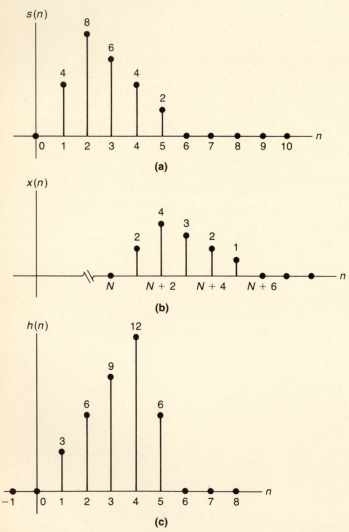

FIGURE P3.29

graphs of the two sequences. Determine the relationship in the form of an equation.

3.30 Consider the system $y(n) = x(n) + \alpha y(n-1) + \beta y(n-2)$.

a) It is desired to determine the unit sample response $h(n)$. Find the expressions for $h(n)$, $n = 0, 1, 2, 3, 4$ in terms of α and β. Simplify the expressions as much as possible.

b) Let $\alpha = -1$, $\beta = 2$, $y(-1) = 0$, $y(-2) = 0$ and

$$x(n) = nu(n) = \begin{cases} n, & n \geq 0 \\ 0, & n < 0. \end{cases}$$

Find the values of $y(0)$, $y(1)$, $y(2)$ and $y(3)$.

3.31 Consider the moving average filter described in Section 3.2 given by

$$y(n) = \frac{1}{L} \sum_{k=0}^{k=L-1} x(n-k) \qquad (3.37)$$

One way to implement this filter in a computer program is to simply evaluate $y(0)$, $y(1)$, ... $y(s)$. For each value of n, this requires $(L-1)$ additions and one division by L (or multiplication by $1/L$). Let's consider an alternative implementation of this filter.

a) Write the expressions for $y(n+1)$ and $y(n)$ and find an equation for $y(n+1) - y(n)$ in the simplest form possible.

b) Determine the number of additions and multiplications for the algorithm based on the equation found in part a) and compare with the number of operations required to evaluate Eq. 3.37 using a brute force approach.

3.32 In planning ahead for his daughter's college expenses, John Thompson decides to save enough in order to provide exactly the amount needed. Mr. Thompson needs to determine the amount required and makes the following simplifying as-

sumptions: Annual tuition and expenses $= E$, paid in two installments, one at the beginning of the school year and the second six months later; A tax-free income of P percent annual rate is generated by the fund. This income is compounded every six months; and the fund is started with a deposit of $\$F_0$ six months before the first tuition payment is due.

a) Let F be the amount of money in the fund at any time during the four-year college period. Write a difference equation that describes the fund's evolution.

b) Use iteration to find an analytical expression for the solution of the equation found in part a) in terms of the initial value of the fund F_0, P and E. Let $n = 0$ correspond to the time when the first payment is made.

c) If P is 10 percent, what must be the initial amount in the fund, expressed in terms of the annual expense E, in order that when the eighth and last payment is made the fund is depleted?

3.33 Two sequences $x(n)$ and $h(n)$ having N and M nonzero samples are shown in Fig. P3.33. Use graphical analysis to determine the range of values of n which contains the nonzero samples of the convolution $y(n) = h(n) * x(n)$.

3.34 Suppose that the savings account system described by $y(n) - 1.01y(n-1) = \beta x(n)$, with $y(-1) = 0$, is subjected to an exponential input of monthly deposits, namely $x(n) = (1.01)^n$, $n \geq 0$. Determine an analytic expression for the money in the account $y(n)$ for $n \geq 0$. Use $\beta = 1$. HINT: Show that $y_p(n) = C_1(1.01)^n$ does not satisfy the system equation and, if necessary, refer to Example 3.19 for help in choosing a suitable $y_p(n)$.

3.35 The repayment of a loan can be described by the difference equation $y(n) = y(n-1) +$

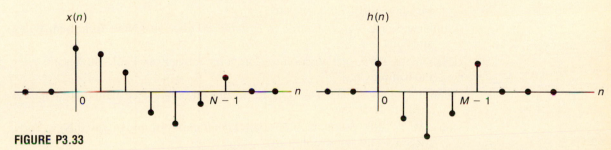

FIGURE P3.33

$(r/100) y(n - 1) - P$ where $y(n)$ = principal owed at time $t = nT$, T = one month, r = the monthly rate of interest in percent, and P = the monthly loan payment. The initial amount of the loan is $y(0) = Y$, and the first payment is made at $n = 1$.

a) Find a closed-form analytical expression (no summations allowed) for the principal owed at the end of the Lth month. Your answer should be in terms of Y, r, L and P.

b) If the loan is to be completely repaid in L months, find an analytical expression (in terms of Y, r, and L) for the required monthly payment P.

c) Using the results of part (b), what is the monthly payment if the loan is for $20,000 at an annual interest rate of 9 percent and it is to be repaid at the end of 10 years?

d) Find an analytical expression in terms of P, Y, and r for the length of time L needed to completely repay the loan.

e) Use the expression found in part (d) to determine how long it will take to repay a loan of $10,000 with a monthly payment of $150 if the annual interest rate is 8 percent.

3.36 Use analytical convolution to obtain an expression for the system response to the input sequence $x(n) = 3u(n) + 4n\,u(n)$ for the system of Problem 3.18 with the initial conditions $y(-1) = y(-2) = 0$. Compare this result with that from Problem 3.16.

3.37 We want to design a digital oscillator to generate the sequence $y(n) = A\cos(2\pi n/N + \varphi)$ from the algorithm $y(n) = a_1 y(n - 1) + a_2 y(n - 2)$.

a) Find the necessary values of a_1 and a_2.

b) Determine the initial conditions $y(-1)$ and $y(-2)$ to make $A = 2$ and $\varphi = -\pi/4$.

3.38 Write and test a computer subroutine to evaluate the convolution of two sequences $XT1(n)$ and $XT2(n)$ where the nonzero values of $XT1(n)$ lie in the interval $0 \le n \le N_1$ and the nonzero values of $XT2(n)$ are in the range $0 \le n \le N_2$. Assume that $N_1 \le 200$ and $N_2 \le 200$.

3.39 Use the computer subroutine of Problem 3.38 in a program to check the solutions of the following:

a) Problem 3.9

b) Problem 3.29

c) Problem 3.36

d) Example 3.9

e) Example 3.11

REFERENCES AND OTHER SOURCES OF INFORMATION

Bozic, S. M. 1979. *Digital and Kalman Filtering.* London: Arnold Publishers, Ltd.

Cadzow, J. A. 1973. *Discrete-Time Systems.* Englewood Cliffs, New Jersey: Prentice-Hall, Inc.

Etter, D.M. 1987. *Structured Fortran 77 for Scientists and Engineers,* 2nd Ed. Menlo Park, California: The Benjamin/Cummings Publishing Company, Inc.

Gold, B., and C. M. Radar. 1969. *Digital Processing of Signals.* New York: McGraw-Hill Book Company.

Goldberg, S. 1958. *Introduction to Difference Equations.* New York: John Wiley and Sons.

Graham, N. 1979. *Introduction to Computer Science,* St. Paul, Minnesota: West Publishing Co.

Hamming, R. W. 1983. *Digital Filters,* 2nd Ed. Englewood Cliffs, New Jersey: Prentice-Hall, Inc.

Jong, M. T. 1982. *Methods of Discrete Signal and System Analysis.* New York: McGraw-Hill Book Company.

Mayhan, R. J. 1984. *Discrete-Time and Continuous-Time Linear Systems.* Reading, Massachusetts: Addison-Wesley Publishing Company.

Nagle, H. T. Jr., and V. P. Nelson. 1981. "Digital Filter Implementation on 16-Bit Microcomputers," *IEEE MICRO* 1 (February): 23–41.

Oppenheim, A. V., and R. W. Schafer. 1975. *Digital Signal Processing.* Englewood Cliffs, New Jersey: Prentice-Hall, Inc.

Oppenheim, A. V., and A. S. Willsky. 1983. *Signals and Systems.* Englewood Cliffs, New Jersey: Prentice-Hall, Inc.

Robinson, E. A., and M. T. Silvia. 1978. *Digital Signal Processing and Time Series Analysis.* San Francisco: Holden-Day, Inc.

Robinson, E. A. 1982. "A Historical Perspective of Spectrum Estimation," *Proc. of the IEEE* 70 (September): 885–907.

Strum, R. D., and J. R. Ward. 1985. *Electric Circuits and Networks*, 2nd Ed. Englewood Cliffs, New Jersey: Prentice-Hall, Inc.

Stearns, S. D. 1975. *Digital Signal Analysis.* Rochelle Park, New Jersey: Hayden Book Company.

CHAPTER 4

Frequency Response and Filters

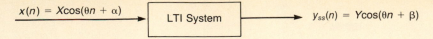

$x(n) = X\cos(\theta n + \alpha)$ → LTI System → $y_{ss}(n) = Y\cos(\theta n + \beta)$

4.0 ■■■ PREVIEW

In the previous chapter, we started our development of the convolution sum by representing the input to a linear time-invariant (LTI) system as a sum of weighted shifted samples. We showed how the forced response of a system to any input can be constructed from the system's response to these weighted shifted samples. We can, therefore, determine the system's forced output to any input if the unit sample response $h(n)$ is known.

Because of superposition, the forced response of an LTI system to any input consisting of a linear combination of sequences is the linear combination of the separate responses to each of these sequences. We show that the steady-state response of a stable LTI system to the complex exponential input $e^{j\theta n}$ has a particularly simple form. This provides us with a very useful method for analyzing LTI systems subjected to a particular kind of input, such as $x(n) = X\cos(\theta n)$, a sinusoidal sequence. The very powerful concept of frequency response is then developed and used to explain the process of filtering. We show that if the input sequence is $x(n) = X\cos(\theta n + \alpha)$ the steady-state output sequence has the form $y_{ss}(n) = Y\cos(\theta n + \beta)$ as indicated in Fig. 4.1.

The basic idea of frequency response is to find the changes in the output amplitude (Y) and the output phase (β) for changes in the input frequency (θ) with the input amplitude (X) and the input phase (α) held constant. This yields the frequency response characteristics of the filter and describes how sinusoidal sequences are affected when processed through the system. In the case of design, we are able to develop a filter with desired frequency characteristics to perform a specified task. For instance, a filter may be required that passes frequencies in a certain band while attenuating the other frequencies. For example, a digital notch filter can be used to suppress 60-Hz noise from a power supply while passing other frequencies.

4.1 ■■■ SINUSOIDAL STEADY-STATE RESPONSE OF LTI SYSTEMS

An important characteristic of an LTI system is its steady-state response to a sinusoidal input sequence. If the input sequence is $x(n) = X\cos(\theta n)$, or the sampled continuous-time input is $x(nT) = X\cos(\omega Tn) = X\cos(2\pi fTn)$, it can be written using complex exponentials and the Euler relation as

$$\cos(\theta n) = \frac{1}{2}[e^{j\theta n} + e^{-j\theta n}] \tag{4.1}$$

or

$$\cos(\omega Tn) = \frac{1}{2}[e^{j\omega Tn} + e^{-j\omega Tn}] \tag{4.2}$$

where n is an integer in the range $-\infty \leq n \leq \infty$. From Chapter Two we recall that a constant sequence can be derived from the cosine sequences of Eqs. 4.1 or 4.2 by setting θ or ω equal to zero, giving for Eq. 4.1

$$\cos(0 \cdot n) = \frac{1}{2}[e^{j0 \cdot n} + e^{-j0 \cdot n}] = \frac{1}{2}[1 + 1] = 1. \tag{4.3}$$

Since a constant or DC sequence $x(n) = 1$ can be constructed from the complex exponential $e^{j\theta n}$ with $\theta = 0$, this allows us to discuss both sinusoidal and constant sequences from the point of view of the complex exponential. This is significant because it is quite easy to find the steady-state response of an LTI system to this exponential input $x_1(n) = e^{j\theta n}$, and it is just as simple to find the steady-state response to its conjugate $x_2(n) = e^{-j\theta n}$. Then, from superposition we can determine the steady-state response to the input

$$x(n) = x_1(n) + x_2(n)$$

$$= e^{j\theta n} + e^{-j\theta n}$$

$$= 2\cos(\theta n), \qquad -\infty \leq n \leq \infty. \tag{4.4}$$

To show how this is done consider the system of Fig. 4.2 with the complex exponential input of $x(n) = e^{j\theta n}$, $-\infty \leq n \leq \infty$, with the linear time-invariant (LTI) system described by its unit sample response $h(n)$. From convolution the output sequence is given by

$$y(n) = \sum_{m=-\infty}^{m=+\infty} h(m)x(n - m) \tag{4.5}$$

and for the input $x(n) = e^{j\theta n}$ we have

$$y(n) = \sum_{m=-\infty}^{m=\infty} h(m)e^{j\theta(n-m)}$$

$$= \sum_{m=-\infty}^{m=\infty} h(m)e^{j\theta n}e^{-j\theta m}. \tag{4.6}$$

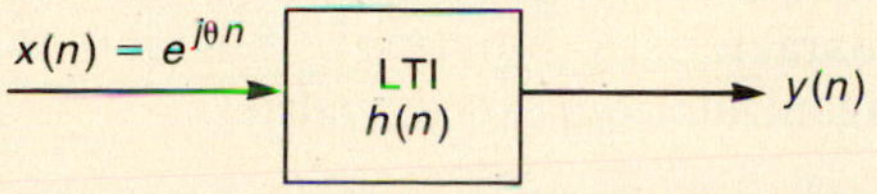

FIGURE 4.2 LTI system with a complex exponential input sequence

$$x(n) = e^{j\theta n} \longrightarrow \boxed{\begin{array}{c} \text{LTI} \\ h(n) \end{array}} \longrightarrow y(n)$$

But we are summing on the index m, so we can take $e^{j\theta n}$ outside the summation and write

$$y(n) = e^{j\theta n} \sum_{m=-\infty}^{m=\infty} h(m)e^{-j\theta m}. \tag{4.7}$$

Recall that the input was defined for $-\infty \le n \le \infty$, which means that this output is the steady-state output that remains after all transients have decayed to zero. Designating this steady-state output as $y_{ss}(n)$ and recognizing the term $e^{j\theta n}$ as the input sequence $x(n)$ we have

$$y_{ss}(n) = x(n) \sum_{m=-\infty}^{m=\infty} h(m)e^{-j\theta m}. \tag{4.8}$$

From Eq. 4.8 we see that the steady-state output sequence $y_{ss}(n)$ is simply the input sequence $x(n) = e^{j\theta n}$ multiplied by the complex constant

$$\sum_{m=-\infty}^{m=\infty} h(m)e^{-j\theta m}. \tag{4.9}$$

The summation of Eq. 4.9 is defined as the *characteristic value* or *eigenvalue* of the system and is denoted by

$$\boxed{H(e^{j\theta}) = \sum_{m=-\infty}^{m=\infty} h(m)e^{-j\theta m}}. \tag{4.10}$$

In the next section we see that $H(e^{j\theta})$ also goes by the name *frequency response*. Thus, using this definition for the system's eigenvalue, the steady-state output given by Eq. 4.8 may be written as

$$\boxed{y_{ss}(n) = x(n)H(e^{j\theta}) \text{ for } x(n) = e^{j\theta n}, \ -\infty \le n \le \infty}. \tag{4.11}$$

The sequence $e^{j\theta n}$ is referred to as the system's *characteristic function* or *eigenfunction*. This result may be depicted as

the input, $x(n) = e^{j\theta n} \xrightarrow{\text{produces}}$

the steady-state output, $y_{ss}(n) = e^{j\theta n}H(e^{j\theta})$. (4.12)

In words we can state that the

(steady-state output due to characteristic function $e^{j\theta n}$)
= (characteristic function) · (characteristic value)
= (eigenfunction) · (eigenvalue) (4.13)

Example 4.1. This example illustrates the use of the eigenvalue method. ——————

Assume that the LTI system of Fig. 4.2 is nonrecursive or FIR with the unit sample response

$$h(n) = \delta(n) + \delta(n - 1) \tag{4.14}$$

and that the input is the complex exponential sequence, $x(n) = e^{j(\pi/2)n}$, $-\infty \leq n \leq \infty$. Determine the steady-state output $y_{ss}(n)$ for this input.

Solution: First, we need to find the eigenvalue $H(e^{j\theta})$ from Eq. 4.10 as

$$H(e^{j\theta}) = \sum_{m=-\infty}^{m=\infty} h(m)e^{-j\theta m}$$

$$= \sum_{m=-\infty}^{m=\infty} [\delta(m) + \delta(m-1)]e^{-j\theta m} \tag{4.15}$$

and using the definitions of $\delta(m)$ and $\delta(m-1)$ this becomes

$$H(e^{j\theta}) = 1e^{j0} + 1e^{-j\theta} = 1 + e^{-j\theta}. \tag{4.16}$$

The next step is to evaluate this system eigenvalue for the specific eigenfunction $e^{j\theta n} = e^{j\pi n/2}$, which gives us

$$H(e^{j\pi/2}) = 1 + e^{-j\pi/2} = 1 - j = 1.41e^{-j\pi/4}. \tag{4.17}$$

Using Eq. 4.11 the steady-state output is

$$y_{ss}(n) = e^{j\theta n}H(e^{j\theta})$$

$$= e^{j(\pi/2)n} \times 1.41e^{-j\pi/4} = 1.41e^{j(\pi n/2 - \pi/4)}, \quad -\infty \leq n \leq \infty. \tag{4.18}$$

Comment: Comparison of the input and output sequences shows that the system has caused an amplitude change from 1 to 1.41 and a phase change of $-\pi/4$ radian. In terms of Chapter Two it is useful to think of both $x(n)$ and $y_{ss}(n)$ as lines rotating counter clockwise at an angular velocity of $\pi/2$ radians per sample n.

It is also possible to interpret eigenfunctions and eigenvalues from a geometric or graphical point of view. Let's consider what the important result of Eq. 4.11

$$x(n) = e^{j\theta n} \longrightarrow y_{ss}(n) = H(e^{j\theta})e^{j\theta n} \tag{4.19}$$

means geometrically. We know that $e^{j\theta}$ is a complex number having a magnitude of 1 and an angle of θ. Similarly, $H(e^{j\theta})$ is a complex number that can be expressed as

$$H(e^{j\theta}) = Me^{jP} \tag{4.20}$$

where the magnitude, or gain, is $M = |H(e^{j\theta})|$ and the angle, or phase, is $P = \angle H(e^{j\theta})$.

FIGURE 4.3 Geometric interpretation of eigenfunctions and eigenvalues

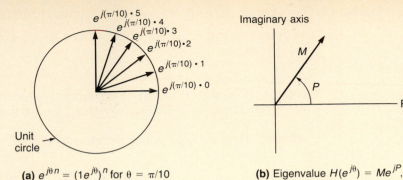

(a) $e^{j\theta n} = (1e^{j\theta})^n$ for $\theta = \pi/10$

(b) Eigenvalue $H(e^{j\theta}) = Me^{jP}$, a complex number (vector)

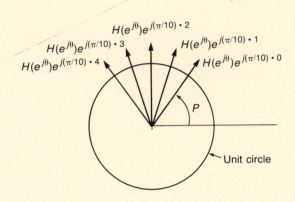

(c) $H(e^{j\theta})e^{j\theta \cdot n}$ for different values of n

The system input is

$$x(n) = e^{j\theta n} \tag{4.21}$$

and as in Chapter Two this can be represented as a vector having length 1 and an angle of θn. This is shown in Fig. 4.3(a) for $\theta = \pi/10$ radian and several different values of n. What happens when this eigenfunction $e^{j\theta n}$ is multiplied by the eigenvalue $H(e^{j\theta}) = Me^{jP}$? The eigenvalue, a complex number, can be represented by the vector in Fig. 4.3(b). When we multiply the eigenvalue by each of the vectors shown in Fig. 4.3(a) the result is as shown in Fig. 4.3(c). The important point is that the system output has the same form as the input, it is simply scaled by the factor M and rotated by the angle P.

If you are conversant with linear algebra this paragraph will be of interest, however, it can be skipped without losing continuity. Similar to the eigenvalue and eigenfunctions of the preceding discussion are the concepts of eigenvalues and eigenvectors from linear algebra. Let **x** and **y** be vectors each having r components related by

$$\mathbf{y} = \mathbf{Tx} \tag{4.22}$$

where $\mathbf{T}$ is an $r \times r$ matrix, that is, a linear transformation. There are r special vectors $\mathbf{x}_i$, $i = 1, 2, \ldots, r$ for which

$$\mathbf{T}\mathbf{x}_i = \lambda_i \mathbf{x}_i, \qquad i = 1, 2, \ldots, r \qquad (4.23)$$

where the λ_i are, in general, complex numbers. The vectors $\mathbf{x}_i$ are called the eigenvectors of $\mathbf{T}$ and the λ_i are the corresponding eigenvalues. We observe that the effect of the linear transformation $\mathbf{T}$ on an eigenvector is to simply scale it by the complex constant λ_i. To visualize the eigenvector/eigenvalue relationship we can use the representation

$$\mathbf{x}_i \xrightarrow[\mathbf{T}]{\text{Linear transformation}} \lambda_i \mathbf{x}_i \qquad (4.24)$$

whereas for a linear discrete system

$$e^{jn\theta} \xrightarrow{\text{Linear discrete system}} H(e^{j\theta}) e^{jn\theta}. \qquad (4.25)$$

Example 4.2. This example illustrates the geometric interpretation of eigenfunctions and their associated eigenvalues.

Suppose we have a system whose eigenvalue is

$$H(e^{j\theta}) = 1 + e^{-j\theta} \qquad (4.26)$$

and the system input is

$$e^{j\theta n} = (e^{j\pi/10})^n = (e^{j0.314})^n. \qquad (4.27)$$

Draw the vectors that represent the eigenfunctions $e^{j\theta n}$ and the respective products $H(e^{j\theta}) \cdot e^{j\theta n}$ for $n = 0, 1, 2,$ and 3.

Solution: Since $\theta = \pi/10$, $H(e^{j\pi/10}) = 1 + e^{-j\pi/10} = 1.98e^{-j0.157}$, and the necessary computations are tabulated below.

n	$e^{j\theta n} = (e^{j\pi/10})^n$	$H(e^{j\pi/10})e^{j\pi n/10}$
0	$(e^{j\theta})^0 = 1e^{j0}$	$(1.98e^{-j0.157})(1e^{j0}) = 1.98e^{-j0.157}$
1	$(e^{j\theta})^1 = 1e^{j\pi/10}$	$(1.98e^{-j0.157})(1e^{j\pi/10}) = 1.98e^{j0.157}$
2	$(e^{j\theta})^2 = 1e^{j2\pi/10}$	$(1.98e^{-j0.157})(1e^{j2\pi/10}) = 1.98e^{j0.471}$
3	$(e^{j\theta})^3 = 1e^{j3\pi/10}$	$(1.98e^{-j0.157})(1e^{j3\pi/10}) = 1.98e^{j0.785}$

These results are drawn in Fig. 4.4 where the scaling and rotation of each eigenfunction is readily apparent.

Suppose we now have a situation in which an input sequence is the sum of three complex exponentials, namely

$$x(n) = C_1 e^{j\theta_1 n} + C_2 e^{j\theta_2 n} + C_3 e^{j\theta_3 n} \qquad (4.28)$$

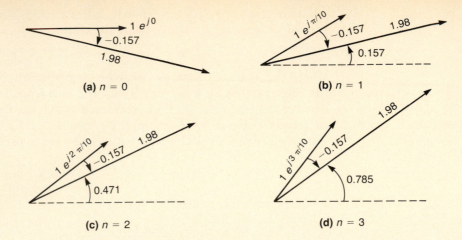

FIGURE 4.4 Results of Example 4.2

(a) $n = 0$

(b) $n = 1$

(c) $n = 2$

(d) $n = 3$

where C_1, C_2, and C_3 are arbitrary constants. Then by superposition we can write the output sequence as

$$y_{ss}(n) = H(e^{j\theta_1})C_1e^{j\theta_1 n} + H(e^{j\theta_2})C_2e^{j\theta_2 n} + H(e^{j\theta_3})C_3e^{j\theta_3 n}. \qquad (4.29)$$

This process is detailed below

Input	Produces	Steady-State Output
$x_1(n) = C_1e^{j\theta_1 n}$	$\longrightarrow$	$y_{1ss}(n) = H(e^{j\theta_1})C_1e^{j\theta_1 n}$
$x_2(n) = C_2e^{j\theta_2 n}$	$\longrightarrow$	$y_{2ss}(n) = H(e^{j\theta_2})C_2e^{j\theta_2 n}$
$x_3(n) = C_3e^{j\theta_3 n}$	$\longrightarrow$	$y_{3ss}(n) = H(e^{j\theta_3})C_3e^{j\theta_3 n}$

$$x(n) = \sum_{k=1}^{k=3} C_k e^{j\theta_k n} \quad \longrightarrow \quad y_{ss}(n) = \sum_{k=1}^{k=3} H(e^{j\theta_k})C_k e^{j\theta_k n}. \qquad (4.30)$$

This can be extended to L inputs in which case we write

$$x(n) = \sum_{k=1}^{k=L} C_k e^{j\theta_k n} \longrightarrow y_{ss}(n) = \sum_{k=1}^{k=L} H(e^{j\theta_k})C_k e^{j\theta_k n}. \qquad (4.31)$$

Thus, if the input to an LTI system is a linear combination of complex exponentials, then the steady-state response can be computed using characteristic values (eigenvalues) as in Eq. 4.31.

Example 4.3. This example illustrates the application of Eq. 4.31 to a nonrecursive LTI system.

Consider the same nonrecursive (FIR) LTI system with the unit sample response

$$h(n) = \delta(n) + \delta(n - 1) \qquad (4.32)$$

with the associated eigenvalue (characteristic value) of this system from Eq. 4.16 given by

$$H(e^{j\theta}) = 1 + e^{-j\theta}. \tag{4.33}$$

For a system input of

$$x(n) = 1 + 10\cos(\pi n/10)$$

$$= 1^n + 10\cos(\pi n/10), \qquad -\infty \le n \le \infty \tag{4.34}$$

use Eq. 4.31 to determine the steady-state output $y_{ss}(n)$.

Solution: With the help of the Euler relation, and the fact that $1^n = e^{(j0)n}$, we can write the input as the linear combination of complex exponentials as

$$x(n) = 1e^{j0n} + 5e^{j\pi n/10} + 5e^{-j\pi n/10}, \qquad -\infty \le n \le \infty$$

$$= x_1(n) + x_2(n) + x_3(n) \tag{4.35}$$

where

$$x_1(n) = 1e^{j0n}, \quad x_2(n) = 5e^{j\pi n/10} \quad \text{and} \quad x_3(n) = 5e^{-j\pi n/10} \tag{4.36}$$

with the eigenfunctions noted to be

$$e^{j\theta_1 n} = e^{j0n}, \quad e^{j\theta_2 n} = e^{j\pi n/10} \quad \text{and} \quad e^{j\theta_3 n} = e^{-j\pi n/10} \tag{4.37}$$

and the three associated multiplicative constants are

$$C_1 = 1, \quad C_2 = 5, \quad \text{and} \quad C_3 = 5. \tag{4.38}$$

When evaluated for the three eigenfunctions $e^{j\theta_1 n} = 1$, $e^{j\theta_2 n} = 1e^{j\pi n/10}$, and $e^{j\theta_3 n} = e^{-j\pi n/10}$ the eigenvalues are

$$H(e^{j\theta_1}) = H(e^{j0}) = 1 + e^{-j0} = 2 \tag{4.39}$$

$$H(e^{j\theta_2}) = H(e^{j\pi/10}) = 1 + e^{-j\pi/10}$$

$$= 1.95 - j0.31 = 1.97e^{-j0.16} \tag{4.40}$$

$$H(e^{j\theta_3}) = H(e^{-j\pi/10}) = 1 + e^{j\pi/10}$$

$$= 1.95 + j0.31 = 1.97e^{+j0.16}. \tag{4.41}$$

Then, from Eq. 4.31 we have

$$y_{ss}(n) = \sum_{k=1}^{k=3} H(e^{j\theta_k})C_k e^{j\theta_k n}$$

$$= H(e^{j\theta_1})C_1 e^{j\theta_1 n} + H(e^{j\theta_2})C_2 e^{j\theta_2 n} + H(e^{j\theta_3})C_3 e^{j\theta_3 n}$$

$$= (2)(1)(e^{j0n}) + (1.97e^{-j0.16})(5)(e^{j\pi/10})^n + (1.97e^{j0.16})(5)(e^{-j\pi/10})^n$$

$$= 2 + 5(1.97)[e^{j(\pi n/10 - 0.16)} + e^{-j(\pi n/10 - 0.16)}]. \tag{4.42}$$

The first term is simply a constant and the last two terms may be combined into a cosine sequence yielding the output

$$y_{ss}(n) = 2 + 19.7\cos(\pi n/10 - 0.16), \qquad -\infty \le n \le \infty \tag{4.43}$$

with the input and output shown in Fig. 4.5. Notice that the input sequence

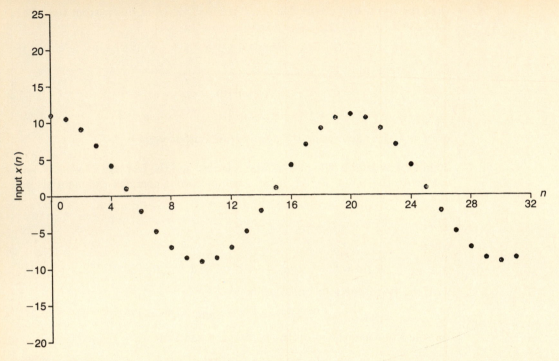

FIGURE 4.5(a) $x(n) = 1 + 10\cos(\pi n/10)$

$x(n)$, a cosine sequence oscillating about the constant value of 1, has been altered by the system to yield the output sequence $y_{ss}(n)$, a cosine sequence of different amplitude and phase oscillating about the constant value of 2.

Two comments are in order at this time to emphasize the significant characteristics of the eigenfunction/eigenvalue approach to linear systems analysis:

IMPORTANT COMMENT

1. For a complex exponential sequence input to an LTI system, $x(n) = e^{j\theta n}$, $-\infty \le n \le \infty$ the output due to this input is given by

   (output due to the eigenfunction $e^{j\theta n}$) = (eigenfunction)(eigenvalue).

   Recall that the magnitude of $e^{j\theta n}$ is always 1. There are other outputs due to the natural characteristics of the system that are not calculated by this approach. (See Section 3.7 on Forced Response).

2. If the system is stable, which is guaranteed if

$$\sum_{n=-\infty}^{n=+\infty} |h(n)| < \infty, \tag{4.44}$$

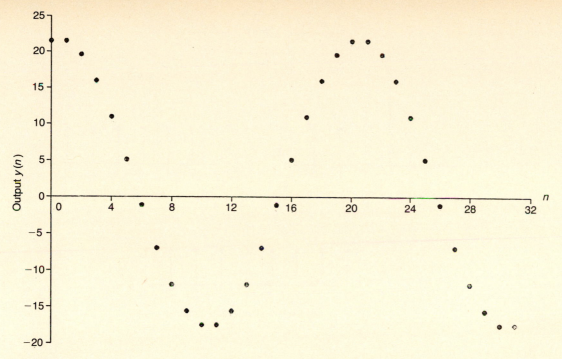

FIGURE 4.5(b) $y(n) = 2 + 19.7 \cos(\pi n/10 - 0.16)$

then the eigenfunction/eigenvalue approach yields the steady-state response of the system. If the system is not stable, a steady-state response usually does not exist.

Example 4.4. This example illustrates eigenfunction/eigenvalue analysis of a recursive system.

Consider the recursive (IIR) system of Fig. 4.6(a) with the unit sample response

$$h(n) = \begin{cases} 0 \, , \, n < 0 \\ a^n, \, n \geq 0 \end{cases} \quad \text{with} \quad 0 < a < 1$$

$$= \quad a^n u(n) \tag{4.45}$$

as in Fig. 4.6(b). The input is the constant sequence $x(n) = 1^n$, $-\infty \leq n \leq \infty$, shown in Fig. 4.6(c). Determine the steady-state system response

$$y_{ss}(n) = H(e^{j\theta})e^{j\theta n}. \tag{4.46}$$

Solution: With a constant input sequence the eigenfunction (characteristic function) is $e^{j\theta n} = e^{j0n} = 1$. The general expression for the system eigenvalue (characteristic value) is

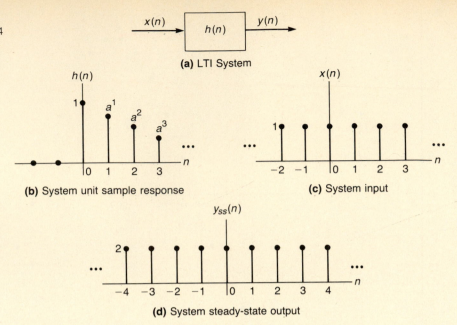

FIGURE 4.6 System and sequences for Example 4.4

$x(n)$ $h(n)$ $y(n)$

(a) LTI System

$h(n)$

(b) System unit sample response

$x(n)$

(c) System input

$y_{ss}(n)$

(d) System steady-state output

$$H(e^{j\theta}) = \sum_{m=-\infty}^{m=\infty} h(m)e^{-j\theta m} \tag{4.47}$$

and for this specific system with $h(n) = a^n u(n)$ we have

$$H(e^{j\theta}) = \sum_{m=0}^{m=\infty} a^m e^{-jm\theta}$$

$$= \sum_{m=0}^{m=\infty} (ae^{-j\theta})^m \tag{4.48}$$

where the lower limit becomes $m = 0$ because $h(m) = 0$ for $m < 0$. Since $|a| < 1$ this is a *convergent infinite geometric series* which (see Eq. 3.21) can be written in a closed form to yield the system eigenvalue

$$H(e^{j\theta}) = \frac{1}{1 - ae^{-j\theta}} \quad \text{because} \quad |ae^{-j\theta}| = |a|\,|e^{-j\theta}| = |a| \cdot 1 < 1. \tag{4.49}$$

The input is $x(n) = e^{j\theta n} = (e^{j0})^n$, so we need to evaluate $H(e^{j\theta})$ for $\theta = 0$ which gives

$$H(1) = H(e^{j\theta})\Big|_{\theta=0}$$

$$= \frac{1}{1 - a}. \tag{4.50}$$

The steady-state output is

$$y_{ss}(n) = 1^n H(1) = (1^n)\left(\frac{1}{1-a}\right) = \frac{1}{1-a}, \qquad -\infty \le n \le \infty \qquad (4.51)$$

and this result is shown in Fig. 4.6(d) for $a = 0.5$.

Now consider a sinusoidal sequence $x(n) = X\cos(\theta_0 n)$ as the input to the system of Example 4.4. We stated in the beginning of the chapter that the steady-state output will also be a sinusoidal sequence modified in amplitude and in phase from that of the input. Let's illustrate this by an example. From Eq. 4.49 the system eigenvalue is

$$H(e^{j\theta}) = \frac{1}{1 - ae^{-j\theta}} \qquad (4.52)$$

which must be evaluated for the complex exponentials (eigenfunctions) of the input sequence $x(n) = X\cos(\theta_0 n)$. The input can be written as

$$x(n) = \frac{X}{2}(e^{j\theta_0 n} + e^{-j\theta_0 n}) \qquad (4.53)$$

revealing the two eigenfunctions $e^{j\theta_0 n}$ and $e^{-j\theta_0 n}$. The eigenvalue for $e^{j\theta_0 n}$ is

$$H(e^{j\theta_0}) = \frac{1}{1 - ae^{-j\theta_0}} \qquad (4.54)$$

and for the exponential $e^{-j\theta_0}$ we have

$$H(e^{-j\theta_0}) = \frac{1}{1 - ae^{j\theta_0}}. \qquad (4.55)$$

Putting both of these complex numbers into rectangular form we get

$$H(e^{j\theta_0}) = \frac{1}{1 - a(\cos\theta_0 - j\sin\theta_0)} \quad \text{and}$$

$$H(e^{-j\theta_0}) = \frac{1}{1 - a(\cos\theta_0 + j\sin\theta_0)}. \qquad (4.56)$$

We observe that these eigenvalues are complex conjugates, because the expressions are identical, except that wherever j appears in one $-j$ appears in the other. Thus, we can write

$$H(e^{-j\theta_0}) = H^*(e^{j\theta_0}) \qquad (4.57)$$

where H^* denotes the complex conjugate of H. Consequently, the eigenvalues of Eq. 4.56 can be represented in terms of magnitude (M) and phase (P) as

$$H(e^{j\theta_0}) = Me^{jP} \quad \text{and} \quad H(e^{-j\theta_0}) = Me^{-jP} \qquad (4.58)$$

where

$$M = \frac{1}{[(1 - a\cos\theta_0)^2 + (a\sin\theta_0)^2]^{1/2}} \quad \text{and}$$

$$P = -(\tan^{-1}\{a\sin\theta_0/(1 - a\cos\theta_0)\}). \qquad (4.59)$$

Calling $y_{1ss}(n)$ the output due to the eigenfunction $e^{j\theta_0 n}$ and $y_{2ss}(n)$ that resulting from $e^{-j\theta_0 n}$ we have, because of superposition,

$$y_{ss}(n) = y_{1ss}(n) + y_{2ss}(n)$$

$$= H(e^{j\theta_0}) \cdot \frac{X}{2} e^{j\theta_0 n} + H(e^{-j\theta_0}) \cdot \frac{X}{2} e^{-j\theta_0 n}. \qquad (4.60)$$

Substituting the definitions of Eq. 4.58 into Eq. 4.60 gives

$$y_{ss}(n) = Me^{jP} \frac{X}{2} e^{j\theta_0 n} + Me^{-jP} \frac{X}{2} e^{-j\theta_0 n}$$

$$= \frac{XMe^{j(\theta_0 n + P)}}{2} + \frac{XMe^{-j(\theta_0 n + P)}}{2}$$

$$= \frac{XM}{2}\left[e^{j(\theta_0 n + P)} + e^{-j(\theta_0 n + P)} \right]. \qquad (4.61)$$

Using the Euler relation we can write the steady-state output as

$$y_{ss}(n) = XM \cos(\theta_0 n + P) \qquad (4.62)$$

and recalling the input to be

$$x(n) = X \cos(\theta_0 n) \qquad (4.63)$$

we note that the amplitude of the real sinusoidal input sequence is X while that of the real sinusoidal output sequence is XM. Thus, the input sequence was altered in magnitude by a factor of M by the system. In a similar fashion, the argument (phase) of the input is 0 while that of the output is P. Thus, the input sequence was altered in phase by P radians by the system.

4.2 ▬ FREQUENCY RESPONSE

If we make the input to a system a unit amplitude sinusoid with zero phase and observe the output magnitude and phase (that is, the eigenvalue) as the frequency of the input varies, the result is called the *frequency response*. Starting with the specific system from the previous section, we extend the results to develop the general theory of frequency response, which is central to the entire field of digital signal processing. In many engineering applications, it is required that a system change the relative amplitudes of frequency components in a sequence to filter out some unwanted components. For example, bandpass filters are used in speech processing systems to reject frequencies outside of a particular frequency range prior to processing to determine signal parameters. Our starting point is to extend the results of Section 4.1 to show that in general, the frequencies in the output sequence are the same as the frequencies of the input sequence, but their magnitudes and phases are altered by the frequency response (eigenvalue).

In the previous section we saw that a system described by the unit sample response $h(n) = a^n \cdot u(n)$ when subjected to the input $x(n) = X \cos(\theta_0 n)$ had the steady-state output $y_{ss}(n) = XM \cos(\theta_0 n + P)$ where $M = |H(e^{j\theta_0})|$ and $P = \angle H(e^{j\theta_0})$. This result is seen in Fig. 4.7 where we are reminded that the system eigenvalue $H(e^{j\theta_0})$ is derived for the eigenfunction (complex exponential) $e^{j\theta_0 n}$. To make this example more specific suppose that the system parameter is $a = 0.5$ and that the input sequence is $x(n) = 2 \cos(\pi n/4)$, $-\infty \le n \le \infty$. From Eq. 4.49 we find that the system eigenvalue for the eigenfunction $e^{j\theta_0 n}$ is

$$H(e^{j\theta_0}) = \frac{1}{1 - ae^{-j\theta_0}} \qquad (4.64)$$

which for $a = 0.5$ and the digital frequency $\theta_0 = \pi/4$ becomes

$$H(e^{j\pi/4}) = \frac{1}{1 - 0.5e^{-j\pi/4}} = \frac{1}{0.646 + j0.354} = 1.357e^{-j0.5} = Me^{jP} \qquad (4.65)$$

so that $M = 1.357$ and $P = -0.5$ and from Eq. 4.62 we obtain the steady-state output sequence

$$y_{ss}(n) = 2(1.357) \cos(\pi n/4 - 0.5)$$
$$= 2.71 \cos(\pi n/4 - 0.5). \qquad (4.66)$$

Figure 4.8 shows the plots for the input $x(n)$ and the output $y_{ss}(n)$. Note that the output amplitude and phase differ from that of the input but that the frequency $(\theta_0 = \pi/4)$ and the period $(N = 8)$ remain the same.

FIGURE 4.7 General form of the output sequence when the input is a sinusoidal sequence

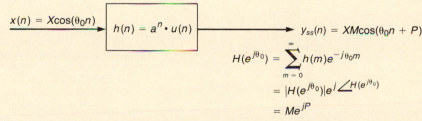

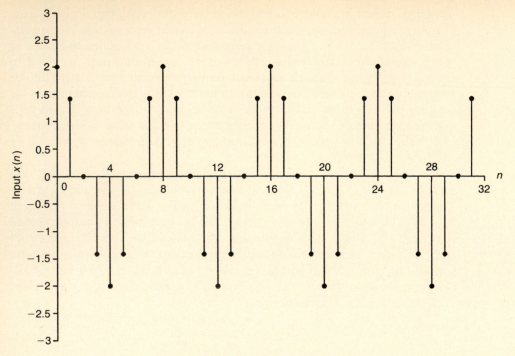

(a) Input sequence $x(n) = 2\cos(\pi n/4)$

FIGURE 4.8 Input/output sequences for a first-order filter

Example 4.5. This example illustrates the effect on the steady-state response of changing the input frequency.

Suppose that in the system of the discussion above the frequency of the input sequence is changed to $\theta_0 = 3\pi/4$ from $\theta_0 = \pi/4$. What is the effect on the output sequence $y_{ss}(n)$?

Solution: We need the eigenvalue for $e^{j\theta n} = e^{(j3\pi/4)n}$, which is

$$H(e^{j3\pi/4}) = \frac{1}{1 - 0.5e^{-j3\pi/4}} = \frac{1}{1.354 + j0.354} = 0.72e^{-j0.26} = Me^{jP} \quad (4.67)$$

so that $M = 0.72$ and $P = -0.26$ and for the input $x(n) = 2\cos(3\pi n/4)$ the output is

$$y_{ss}(n) = 2M\cos(3\pi n/4 + P)$$

$$= 2(0.72)\cos(3\pi n/4 - 0.26)$$

$$= 1.44\cos(3\pi n/4 - 0.26). \quad (4.68)$$

Comment: This is quite different from the earlier result where the input

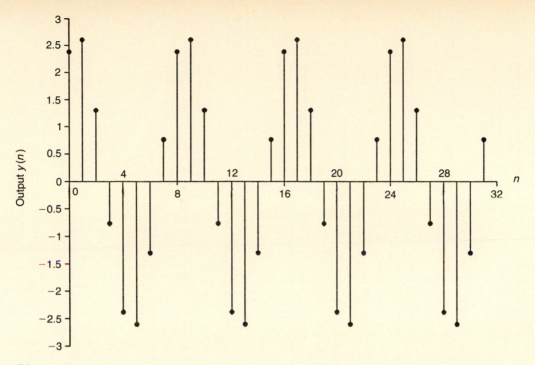

(b) Output sequence
$y(n) = 2.71 \cos(\pi n/4 - 0.500)$

frequency was $\pi/4$ rather than $3\pi/4$. The output magnitude is much lower (1.44 vs. 2.71) for the higher frequency ($3\pi/4$ vs. $\pi/4$) so the system appears to be one that passes lower frequencies more easily than higher ones. (In this case the sequence at the frequency of $\pi/4$ is amplified because the gain is 1.357, whereas the sequence at a frequency of $3\pi/4$ is decreased in magnitude due to a gain of 0.72.) Two other very simple calculations make this conjecture more plausible. The digital frequency $\theta_0 = \pi$ makes the system eigenvalue

$$H(e^{j\pi}) = \frac{1}{1 - 0.5e^{-j\pi}} = 0.67 \qquad (4.69)$$

and for the digital frequency $\theta_0 = 0$ (a constant sequence) we have

$$H(e^{j0}) = \frac{1}{1 - 0.5e^{-j0}} = 2. \qquad (4.70)$$

So for this system we see the following results for M, the magnitude of the eigenvalue $H(e^{j\theta_0})$:

θ_0	0	$\pi/4$	$3\pi/4$	π
M	2	1.36	0.72	0.67

The magnitude of $H(e^{j\theta})$ decreases as the digital frequency increases from 0 to π which means that the amplitude of the output sequence is also decreasing as the frequency increases. This system is called *lowpass*. There is much more to come on this subject later. Figure 4.9 portrays the results of Example 4.5.

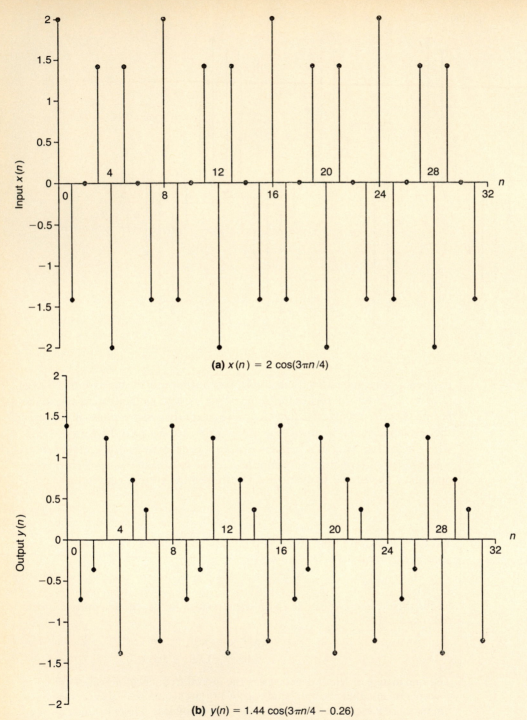

(a) $x(n) = 2\cos(3\pi n/4)$

(b) $y(n) = 1.44\cos(3\pi n/4 - 0.26)$

FIGURE 4.9 Results for Example 4.5

As discussed earlier, a common way in which sequences can arise is when analog (continuous-time) signals are sampled. Such a situation is shown in Fig. 4.10 for an analog sinusoidal input of $x(t) = X \cos \omega t = X \cos 2\pi f t$. (The sampling of continuous-time (analog) sinusoids was discussed in Chapter Two and should be reviewed if necessary.) Let's look at this system to see how it relates to the previous example. First, assume that the frequency of the input sequence is 100 Hz and that its amplitude is $X = 2$. This gives

$$x(t) = 2 \cos 2\pi(100)t = 2 \cos 200\pi t \tag{4.71}$$

and if the sampling interval is $T = 0.00125$ second, which corresponds to a frequency sampling rate of $1/T = f_s = 800$ Hz, the sequence is then

$$x(nT) = x(t)\Big|_{t=nT}$$

$$= 2 \cos(200\pi nT) \tag{4.72}$$

which for $T = 0.00125$ s becomes

$$x(0.00125n) = 2 \cos(\pi n/4). \tag{4.73}$$

It is customary simply to write

$$x(n) = 2 \cos(\pi n/4) \tag{4.74}$$

remembering that $T = 0.00125$ s. We used this input sequence in the first discussion of sinusoidal steady-state response at the beginning of this section. Similarly, if the analog input is tripled in frequency to $f = 300$ Hz with the same sampling frequency of 800 Hz, then $x(t) = 2 \cos(600\pi t)$ and the sampled version is

$$x(nT) = 2 \cos(600\pi nT) \tag{4.75}$$

or

$$x(0.00125n) = 2 \cos(3\pi n/4) \tag{4.76}$$

and in the commonly used notation

$$x(n) = 2 \cos(3\pi n/4) \tag{4.77}$$

as in Example 4.5. Thus, we see that if two input sequences are generated by sampling continuous sinusoids, the sinusoid at frequency 100 Hz passes through the digital filter of Example 4.5 with about half the decrease in amplitude experienced by the samples from the sinusoid whose frequency is 300 Hz.

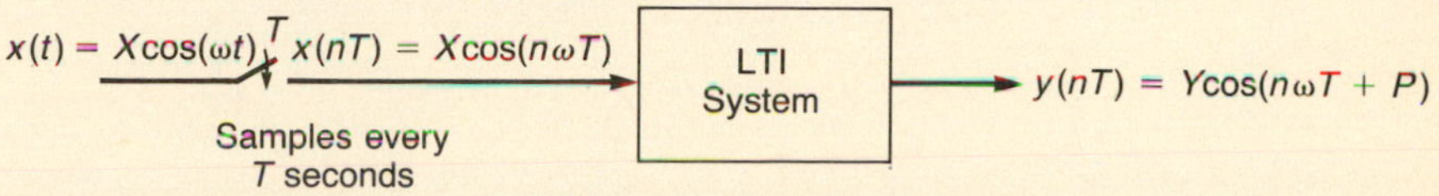

FIGURE 4.10 Sampling a continuous-time system

$$x(t) = X\cos(\omega t) \quad \xrightarrow{T} \quad x(nT) = X\cos(n\omega T) \quad \boxed{\begin{array}{c} \text{LTI} \\ \text{System} \end{array}} \quad \longrightarrow \quad y(nT) = Y\cos(n\omega T + P)$$

Samples every
T seconds

4.2.1 Sinusoidal Steady-State Response—General Statement

Consider the LTI system of Fig. 4.11(a) subjected to the sinusoidal input sequence $x(n) = X \cos(\theta n)$, or in the notation of a sampled analog signal $x(nT) = X \cos(\omega T n)$ where the digital frequency θ and the analog frequency ω are related by $\theta = \omega T$ with T representing the sampling interval. By putting the input in terms of complex exponentials, the steady-state output may be written in terms of eigenfunctions and eigenvalues in the following way. For the input sequence

$$x(n) = X \cos(\theta n) = \frac{X}{2}(e^{j\theta n} + e^{-j\theta n}) \qquad (4.78)$$

the output sequence is

$$y_{ss}(n) = \frac{X}{2}[e^{j\theta n}H(e^{j\theta}) + e^{-j\theta n}H(e^{-j\theta})]. \qquad (4.79)$$

For the specific system considered earlier where $H(e^{j\theta_0}) = 1/(1 - ae^{-j\theta_0})$, we saw that $H(e^{j\theta_0})$ and $H(e^{-j\theta_0})$ were complex conjugates. That is, $H(e^{-j\theta_0}) = H^*(e^{j\theta_0})$ where the star $*$ denotes complex conjugate. But a moment's consideration will show that this is a general result for any linear system where the unit sample response $h(n)$ is a sequence of real numbers, because the notation indicates that $H(e^{-j\theta})$ is simply $H(e^{j\theta})$ with $e^{-j\theta}$ replacing $e^{j\theta}$ everywhere in $H(e^{j\theta})$. Thus, $H(e^{-j\theta})$ is identical in form to $H(e^{+j\theta})$ except that the sign of every term involving j is reversed, so $H(e^{j\theta})$ and $H(e^{-j\theta})$ are complex conjugates of one another. We also know that complex conjugates have the same magnitude and that the phase of one is the negative of the phase of the other. Thus,

$$H(e^{j\theta}) = Me^{jP} \text{ and } H(e^{-j\theta}) = Me^{-jP} \qquad (4.80)$$

FIGURE 4.11(a) LTI system with a sinusoidal input

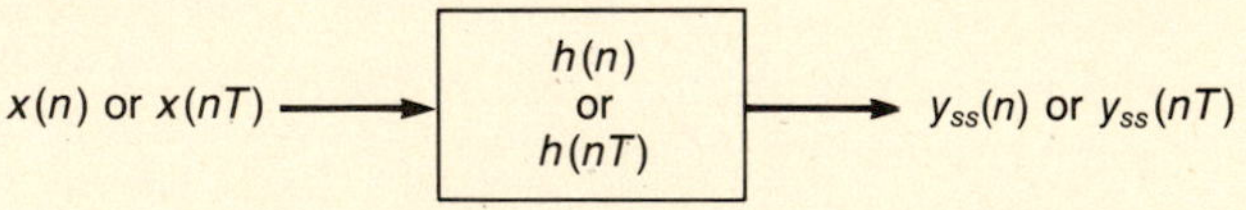

$$x(n) \text{ or } x(nT) \longrightarrow \boxed{\begin{array}{c} h(n) \\ \text{or} \\ h(nT) \end{array}} \longrightarrow y_{ss}(n) \text{ or } y_{ss}(nT)$$

FIGURE 4.11(b) The important result for a sinusoidal input

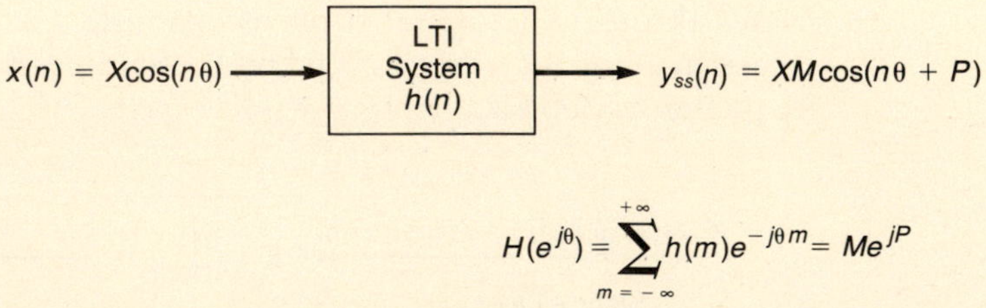

$$x(n) = X\cos(n\theta) \longrightarrow \boxed{\begin{array}{c} \text{LTI} \\ \text{System} \\ h(n) \end{array}} \longrightarrow y_{ss}(n) = XM\cos(n\theta + P)$$

$$H(e^{j\theta}) = \sum_{m=-\infty}^{+\infty} h(m)e^{-j\theta m} = Me^{jP}$$

and we can substitute this result into Eq. 4.79 to obtain

$$y_{ss}(n) = \frac{X}{2}[e^{j\theta n}Me^{jP} + e^{-j\theta n}Me^{-jP}]$$

$$= \frac{XM}{2}[e^{j(\theta n+P)} + e^{-j(\theta n+P)}]$$

$$= XM \cos(\theta n + P). \tag{4.81}$$

This result is summarized in Fig. 4.11(b) where

$$H(e^{j\theta}) = \sum_{m=-\infty}^{m=\infty} h(m)e^{-j\theta m} \tag{4.82}$$

which, when written in terms of magnitude and phase, becomes

$$H(e^{j\theta}) = |H(e^{j\theta})|e^{j\angle H(e^{j\theta})} = Me^{jP}. \tag{4.83}$$

It is common practice to refer to $H(e^{j\theta})$ as the *frequency response function* or simply the frequency response of the LTI system with the magnitude or gain of $H(e^{j\theta})$ denoted by M and its angle or phase given by P.

From Eq. 4.81 we see that the steady-state output is a sinusoid having the same frequency (θ) as the input. The magnitude (XM) of the output sinusoid is the magnitude of the input sinusoid (X) multiplied by the magnitude, or gain, of the frequency response $M = |H(e^{j\theta})|$, associated with the input frequency θ; the phase of the output is shifted from the input phase by the phase of the frequency response at frequency θ, $P = \angle H(e^{j\theta})$.

PROCEDURE

The preceding result can be extended to the more general situation (see Problem 4.21) where the input to a stable linear time-invariant system is given by

$$x(n) = X \cos(\theta n + \alpha) \qquad \text{input} \tag{4.84}$$

and the corresponding output is

$$y_{ss}(n) = X|H(e^{j\theta})| \cos(\theta n + \alpha + \angle H(e^{j\theta})) \qquad \text{output} \tag{4.85}$$

or in an alternative form,

$$y_{ss}(n) = XM \cos(\theta n + \alpha + P) = Y \cos(\theta n + \alpha + P) \qquad \text{output.} \tag{4.86}$$

The result in Eqs. 4.85 or 4.86 makes the evaluation of a stable system's steady-state response to a sinusoidal input very straightforward. As a result, we will give Eq. 4.85 a special name—*the sinusoidal steady-state formula*. It says that when a sinusoidal sequence is applied to an LTI system, then to obtain the steady-state output sequence the amplitude is multiplied by the magnitude of $H(e^{j\theta})$ and the phase is shifted by the angle of $H(e^{j\theta})$. Keep in mind that the system must be stable in order to use the sinusoidal steady-state formula.

Henceforth, rather than using the eigenfunction/eigenvalue method developed in Section 4.1 to obtain the steady-state output due to one or more sinusoidal input sequences, we are able to use the sinusoidal steady-state formula (and superposition as appropriate).

Example 4.6. This example illustrates the frequency response and steady-state response of a digital differentiator. _____

Under special conditions (see Problem 4.19) a *digital differentiator* can be approximated by the unit sample response $h(n) = \delta(n) - \delta(n - 1)$.

a) Find a general expression for the magnitude and phase of the frequency response function $H(e^{j\theta})$.

b) Determine the steady-state response to the input sequence $x(n) = 10 \cos(\theta n)$ for the digital frequencies $\theta = \pi/3$, $\pi/2$, $2\pi/3$, and π.

Solution:

a) This nonrecursive system is stable and the frequency response function is

$$H(e^{j\theta}) = \sum_{m=-\infty}^{m=+\infty} [\delta(m) - \delta(m - 1)]e^{-j\theta m}$$

$$= 1e^{-j\theta \cdot 0} - 1e^{-j\theta \cdot 1}$$

$$= 1 - e^{-j\theta}. \tag{4.87}$$

This is a perfectly good answer, however, to put it more directly in terms of magnitude and phase we use the Euler relation on $e^{-j\theta}$ in Eq. 4.87 to obtain

$$H(e^{j\theta}) = 1 - [\cos\theta - j \sin \theta]$$

$$= \sqrt{(1 - \cos \theta)^2 + (\sin \theta)^2}\, e^{j\tan^{-1} [\sin \theta/(1-\cos \theta)]} \tag{4.88}$$

where

$$M = \sqrt{(1 - \cos \theta)^2 + \sin^2 \theta} \quad \text{and} \quad P = \tan^{-1}\left[\frac{\sin \theta}{1 - \cos \theta}\right]. \tag{4.89}$$

b) We need to evaluate the frequency response function, $H(e^{j\theta}) = 1 - e^{-j\theta}$, at the values of the four given input frequencies and then apply the sinusoidal steady-state formula of Eq. 4.86 for each input. For $\theta = \pi/3$

$$H(e^{j\pi/3}) = 1 - e^{-j\pi/3} = 1 - (\cos \pi/3 - j \sin \pi/3) = 1e^{j\pi/3} \quad (4.90)$$

$$y_{ss}(n) = 10(1) \cos(\pi n/3 + \pi/3) = 10 \cos(\pi n/3 + \pi/3). \quad (4.91)$$

For $\theta = \pi/2$

$$H(e^{j\pi/2}) = 1 - e^{-j\pi/2} = 1 - (-j) = \sqrt{2}e^{j\pi/4} \quad (4.92)$$

$$y_{ss}(n) = 10(\sqrt{2}) \cos(\pi n/2 + \pi/4) = 14.14 \cos(\pi n/2 + \pi/4). \quad (4.93)$$

For $\theta = 2\pi/3$

$$H(e^{j2\pi/3}) = 1 - e^{-j2\pi/3} = 1 - (\cos 2\pi/3 - j \sin 2\pi/3) = \sqrt{3}e^{j\pi/6} \quad (4.94)$$

$$y_{ss}(n) = 10(\sqrt{3}) \cos(2\pi n/3 + \pi/6) = 17.32 \cos(2\pi n/3 + \pi/6). \quad (4.95)$$

For $\theta = \pi$

$$H(e^{j\pi}) = 1 - e^{-j\pi} = 2 \quad (4.96)$$

$$y_{ss}(n) = 20 \cos (\pi n). \quad (4.97)$$

Notice that as the input frequency θ changes from $\theta = \pi/3$ to $\pi/2$, $2\pi/3$, and then π the output sequence increases in amplitude from 10 to 20 which is characteristic of a highpass system.

Comment: A plot of M vs θ and P vs θ is shown in Fig. 4.12 and in this simple situation we can describe both M and P analytically. For

$$H(e^{j\theta}) = 1 - e^{-j\theta} \quad (4.98)$$

with hindsight or previous experience we can factor out $e^{-j\theta/2}$ giving

$$H(e^{j\theta}) = e^{-j\theta/2}(e^{j\theta/2} - e^{-j\theta/2}). \quad (4.99)$$

Then multiplying and dividing by $2j$ produces

$$H(e^{j\theta}) = 2je^{-j\theta/2}\left[\frac{e^{j\theta/2} - e^{-j\theta/2}}{2j}\right] \quad (4.100)$$

which can be written as

$$H(e^{j\theta}) = 2je^{-j\theta/2} \sin(\theta/2) \quad (4.101)$$

or since $j = e^{j\pi/2}$,

$$H(e^{j\theta}) = 2 \sin(\theta/2)e^{j(\pi/2-\theta/2)}. \quad (4.102)$$

The magnitude and phase plots of Fig. 4.12 are easily seen to agree with the magnitude and phase components of Eq. 4.102.

Example 4.7. This example illustrates several applications of the sinusoidal steady-state formula.

The rotational motion of the satellite of Chapter Three in an oscillatory mode is described by the unit sample response

$$h(n) = Ka^n \cos(\alpha n) \cdot u(n), \quad 0 < a < 1 \quad (4.103)$$

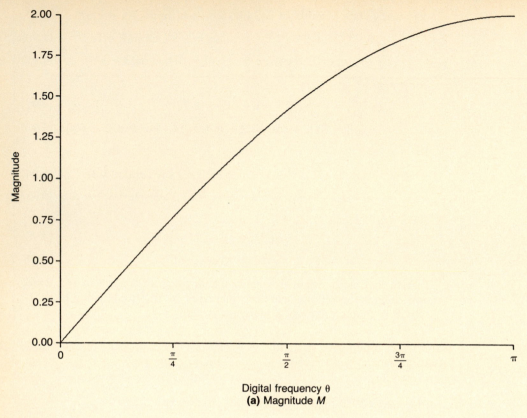

Digital frequency θ
(a) Magnitude M

FIGURE 4.12 Frequency response for $H(e^{j\theta}) = 1 - e^{-j\theta}$

a) Find an analytical expression for the frequency response function $H(e^{j\theta})$.

b) For the system parameters $K = 1$, $a = 0.9$, and $\alpha = \pi/3$, find the steady-state response $y_{ss}(n)$ to the following inputs:

    i) the sequence $x(n) = 2 \cos(\pi n/6 + \pi/12)$

    ii) a 1-kilohertz sampled analog signal, $x(t) = 4 \cos(2000\pi t)$, where the sampling frequency is 6 kilohertz

    iii) the sequence $x(n) = 6 \sin(\pi n/2 - \pi/6)$

    iv) a 3-kilohertz sampled analog signal, $x(t) = 8 \sin(6000\pi t)$, where the sampling frequency is still 6 kilohertz.

Solution:

a) We use the Euler relation to write $h(n)$ in the form

$$h(n) = Ka^n \left[\frac{e^{j\alpha n} + e^{-j\alpha n}}{2} \right] \cdot u(n)$$

$$= \frac{K}{2} \left[(ae^{j\alpha})^n + (ae^{-j\alpha})^n \right] \cdot u(n). \qquad (4.104)$$

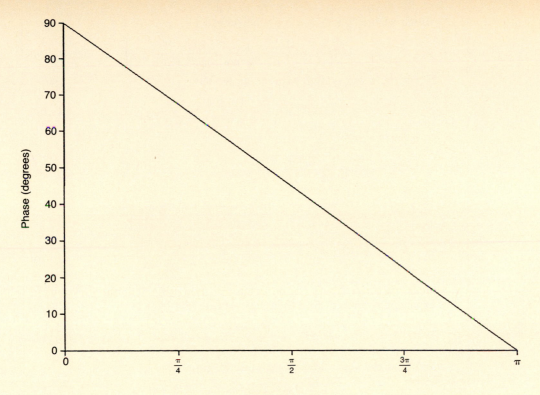

(b) Phase *P*

Since $\sum_{n=0}^{\infty} |h(n)| < \infty$, the frequency response follows as

$$H(e^{j\theta}) = \frac{K}{2} \sum_{m=0}^{\infty} (ae^{j\alpha})^m e^{-j\theta m} + \frac{K}{2} \sum_{m=0}^{\infty} (ae^{-j\alpha})^m e^{-j\theta m}$$

$$= \frac{K}{2} \sum_{m=0}^{\infty} (ae^{j\alpha}e^{-j\theta})^m + \frac{K}{2} \sum_{m=0}^{\infty} (ae^{-j\alpha}e^{-j\theta})^m \quad (4.105)$$

Then using the relationship for an infinite geometric sum in Eq. 3.21 we obtain from Eq. 4.105

$$H(e^{j\theta}) = \frac{K}{2} \left[\frac{1}{1 - ae^{j\alpha}e^{-j\theta}} + \frac{1}{1 - ae^{-j\alpha}e^{-j\theta}} \right]. \quad (4.106)$$

Combining the two parts over a common denominator and collecting terms gives

$$H(e^{j\theta}) = \frac{K}{2} \left[\frac{2 - ae^{-j\theta}(e^{j\alpha} + e^{-j\alpha})}{1 - ae^{-j\theta}(e^{j\alpha} + e^{-j\alpha}) + a^2 e^{-j2\theta}} \right] \quad (4.107)$$

which with $e^{j\alpha} + e^{-j\alpha} = 2\cos\alpha$ becomes

$$H(e^{j\theta}) = K\left[\frac{1 - a(\cos\alpha)e^{-j\theta}}{1 - 2a(\cos\alpha)e^{-j\theta} + a^2 e^{-j2\theta}}\right]. \tag{4.108}$$

b) For the given system parameters we have

$$H(e^{j\theta}) = \frac{1 - 0.45e^{-j\theta}}{1 - 0.90e^{-j\theta} + 0.81e^{-j2\theta}}. \tag{4.109}$$

i) For $\theta = \pi/6$:

$$H(e^{j\pi/6}) = \frac{1 - 0.45e^{-j\pi/6}}{1 - 0.90e^{-j\pi/6} + 0.81e^{-j\pi/3}}$$

$$= \frac{1 - 0.45\cos(\pi/6) + j0.45\sin(\pi/6)}{1 - 0.90\cos(\pi/6) + j0.90\sin(\pi/6) + 0.81\cos(\pi/3) - j0.81\sin(\pi/3)}$$

$$= \frac{0.610 + j0.225}{0.626 - j0.251}. \tag{4.110}$$

Next, we convert both the numerator term and the denominator term to exponential form to find their ratio giving us

$$H(e^{j\pi/6}) = \frac{0.650e^{j0.353}}{0.674e^{-j0.381}} = 0.96e^{j0.73} \tag{4.111}$$

and from the sinusoidal steady-state formula

$$y_{ss}(n) = 2(0.96)\cos(\pi n/6 + \pi/12 + 0.73). \tag{4.112}$$

Remember that the phase of the output is the phase of the input plus the phase of the frequency response. In this case, this is the sum of $\pi/12$ and 0.73 which gives 0.99 radian. Thus,

$$y_{ss}(n) = 1.93\cos(\pi n/6 + 0.99). \tag{4.113}$$

ii) Converting the sampled signal to a sequence by using $\theta = \omega T = \omega/f_s$ gives the digital frequency $\theta = 2000\pi/6000 = \pi/3$ and the input $x(n) = 4\cos(\pi n/3)$. The frequency response is

$$H(e^{j\pi/3}) = \frac{1 - 0.45e^{-j\pi/3}}{1 - 0.90e^{-j\pi/3} + 0.81e^{-j2\pi/3}} \tag{4.114}$$

which needs to be reduced to a single term in exponential form. Following the procedure of Eqs. 4.110 and 4.111 gives us

$$H(e^{j\pi/3}) = 5.25e^{-j0.03}. \tag{4.115}$$

From the sinusoidal steady-state formula

$$y_{ss}(n) = (4)(5.25)\cos(\pi n/3 - 0.03)$$

$$= 21\cos(\pi n/3 - 0.03). \tag{4.116}$$

iii) Although this is a sine sequence the procedure is obviously the same. Thus, we need to find $H(e^{j\pi/2})$ which is

$$H(e^{j\pi/2}) = \frac{1 - 0.45e^{-j\pi/2}}{1 - 0.90e^{-j\pi/2} + 0.81e^{-j\pi}}$$

$$= 1.20e^{-j0.94}. \tag{4.117}$$

We could convert the input sine sequence to a cosine by subtracting $\pi/2$ radians giving $x(n) = 6\cos(n\pi/2 - 2\pi/3)$ and then apply the sinusoidal steady-state formula. It is simpler, however, to work directly with the given sine sequence with the result

$$y_{ss}(n) = (6)(1.20)\sin(n\pi/2 - \pi/6 - 0.94)$$

$$= 7.20\sin(\pi n/2 - 1.46) \tag{4.118}$$

or if cosines are really preferred

$$y_{ss}(n) = 7.20\cos(\pi n/2 - 3.04). \tag{4.119}$$

iv) For $\omega = 6000\pi$ and $f_s = 6000$, $\theta = 6000\pi/6000 = \pi$ rad and the input sequence is $x(n) = 8\sin(\pi n)$. Thus,

$$H(e^{j\pi}) = \frac{1 - 0.45e^{-j\pi}}{1 - 0.90e^{-j\pi} + 0.81e^{-j2\pi}}$$

$$= 0.54e^{j0} \tag{4.120}$$

and the steady-state output sequence is

$$y_{ss}(n) = 8(0.54)\sin(\pi n + 0)$$

$$= 4.32\sin(\pi n). \tag{4.121}$$

Comment: Computer plots of $M = |H(e^{j\theta})|$ and $P = \angle H(e^{j\theta})$ are shown in Fig. 4.13. Notice that M varies from 0.60 to a maximum value of 5.25 at $\theta \approx \pi/3$ and back down to 0.54 at $\theta = \pi$. The system treats different input frequencies in quite different ways with the four frequencies used in this example indicated on the plots.

Example 4.8. This example illustrates superposition and frequency response analysis.

For the LTI system of Fig. 4.14 with the unit sample response $h(n) = \delta(n) + \delta(n-1)$, a stable system, we are given that the input sequence is $x(n) = x_1(n) + x_2(n) + x_3(n)$ where $x_1(n) = 1$, $x_2(n) = 10\cos(\pi n/4)$, and $x_3(n) = 4\cos(\pi n/2)$, $-\infty \leq n \leq \infty$. Determine the steady-state output, $y_{ss}(n)$.

Solution: Here we use Eq. 4.85 three times and then add the results. You may question the inclusion of $x_1(n)$ in this process but earlier in this chapter as well as in Chapter Two we noted that a constant sequence could be thought of as a sinusoid of zero frequency. That is, $(e^{j\theta})^n$ for $\theta = 0$ is clearly $(e^{j0})^n = 1^n = 1 = x_1(n)$. The expression for the system's frequency response is

$$H(e^{j\theta}) = \sum_{m=0}^{m=1} h(m)e^{-j\theta m} = 1 + e^{-j\theta} \tag{4.122}$$

and a tabular arrangement of the results is presented.

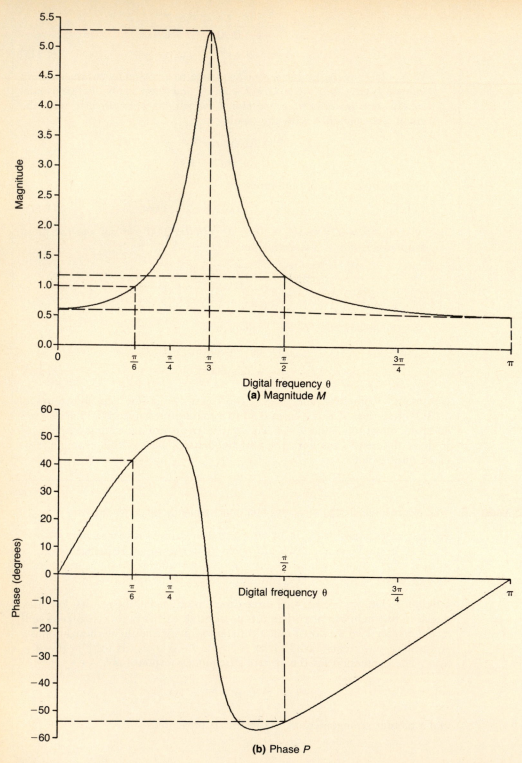

FIGURE 4.13 Frequency response for Example 4.7

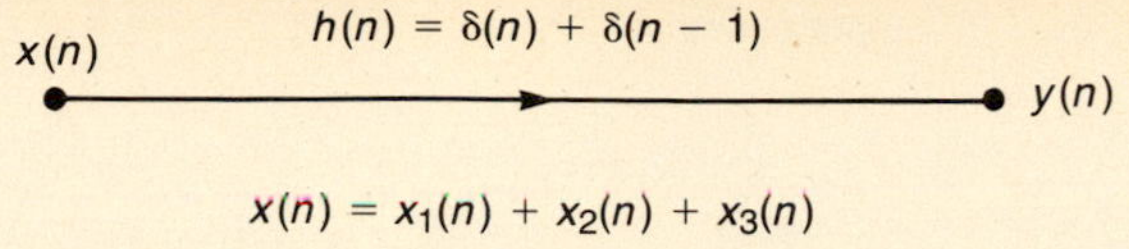

FIGURE 4.14 Configuration for Example 4.8

$$x(n) \qquad h(n) = \delta(n) + \delta(n-1)$$
$$\bullet\!\!\longrightarrow\!\!\longrightarrow\!\!\longrightarrow\!\!\longrightarrow\!\!\longrightarrow\bullet \; y(n)$$

$$x(n) = x_1(n) + x_2(n) + x_3(n)$$

Input $(-\infty \le n \le \infty)$	$H(e^{j\theta}) = 1 + e^{-j\theta}$	Output $(-\infty \le n \le \infty)$
$x_1(n) = e^{j(0)n} = 1$	$H(e^{j0}) = 1 + 1 = 2$	$y_{1ss}(n) = 2(1) = 2$
$x_2(n) = 10\cos(\pi n/4)$	$H(e^{j\pi/4}) = 1 + e^{-j\pi/4}$ $= 1.848 e^{-j\pi/8}$	$y_{2ss}(n) = 18.48\cos(\pi n/4 - \pi/8)$
$x_3(n) = 4\cos(\pi n/2)$	$H(e^{j\pi/2}) = 1 + e^{-j\pi/2}$ $= 1.414 e^{-j\pi/4}$	$y_{3ss}(n) = 5.66\cos(\pi n/2 - \pi/4)$

$$x(n) = x_1(n) + x_2(n) + x_3(n) \qquad y_{ss}(n) = y_{1ss}(n) + y_{2ss}(n) + y_{3ss}(n)$$

Comment: It is instructive to exhibit these results from a graphical point of view. Shown in Fig. 4.15(a) are the input amplitudes X_k, $k = 0$, $\pi/4$, and $\pi/2$, and the input phases, which are all zero. The frequency response of the system is

$$H(e^{j\theta}) = 1 + e^{-j\theta}$$

$$= M e^{jP} \tag{4.123}$$

and the magnitude M and the phase P for the system are shown in Fig. 4.15(b). We know from the sinusoidal steady-state formula that the output amplitude is the input amplitude multiplied by the frequency response magnitude and that the output phase is the input phase plus the frequency response phase. These results are shown in Fig. 4.15(c).

4.2.2 The Nature of $H(e^{j\theta})$

From the previous work and examples we have more than sufficient evidence to state that the system frequency response function $H(e^{j\theta})$ totally determines the steady-state system output sequence for a given sinusoidal input sequence. The basis of many discrete-system design procedures, therefore, is to determine an acceptable frequency response function $H(e^{j\theta})$ that will satisfy both the magnitude and phase criteria of any particular design situation. Let's look at the nature of $H(e^{j\theta})$ in a bit more detail.

Periodicity. We begin by showing that $H(e^{j\theta})$ is a periodic function with a period of 2π. The frequency response function is defined as

$$H(e^{j\theta}) = \sum_{m=-\infty}^{m=+\infty} h(m) e^{-j\theta m} \tag{4.124}$$

Input amplitude X_k

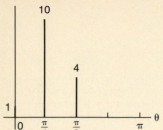

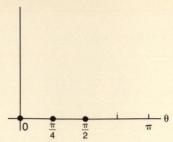

Input phase α_k

(a) Frequency content of input sequence

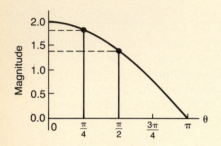

(b) Frequency response for $H(e^{j\theta}) = 1 + e^{-j\theta}$
Magnitude M

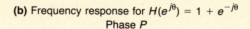

(b) Frequency response for $H(e^{j\theta}) = 1 + e^{-j\theta}$
Phase P

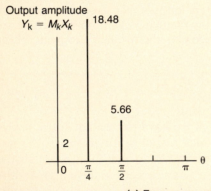

Output amplitude
$Y_k = M_k X_k$

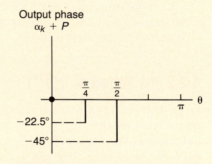

Output phase
$\alpha_k + P$

(c) Frequency content of output sequence

FIGURE 4.15 Data and results for Example 4.8

and if we substitute $(\theta + 2\pi)$ for θ in the expression for $H(e^{j\theta})$ the result is

$$H(e^{j(\theta + 2\pi)}) = \sum_{m=-\infty}^{m=+\infty} h(m)e^{-j(\theta + 2\pi)m}$$

$$= \sum_{m=-\infty}^{m=+\infty} h(m)e^{-j\theta m}e^{-j2\pi m}. \tag{4.125}$$

But $e^{-j2\pi m} = 1$ for all integer values of m so

$$H(e^{j(\theta+2\pi)}) = \sum_{m=-\infty}^{m=+\infty} h(m)e^{-j\theta m}$$

$$= H(e^{j\theta}) \tag{4.126}$$

and the fact that the frequency response function is periodic with period 2π has been established. Figure 4.16 illustrates this periodicity for the filter having the frequency response $H(e^{j\theta}) = 1/(1 - 0.5e^{-j\theta})$.

We've seen from our discussion of the sampling theorem that the useful frequency range of a discrete system is between 0 and π, or, if you prefer, between $-\pi$ and π. Why then are we interested in the periodicity of $H(e^{j\theta})$ which concerns frequencies outside of this useful range? The periodicity property is simply another way of looking at the information provided by the sampling theorem—if a signal is undersampled (i.e., its digital frequency is greater than π) it will be treated by the system as if it were a frequency in the range $-\pi < \theta < \pi$. That is, frequencies in the input signal above $f_s/2$ are aliased to frequencies in the range $-f_s/2 < f < f_s/2$.

Symmetry. For the specific system whose frequency response is shown in Fig. 4.16 we notice that the magnitude M is an even function of θ, that is

$$M = |H(e^{j\theta})| = |H(e^{-j\theta})| \tag{4.127}$$

and that phase P is an odd function, namely

$$P = \angle H(e^{j\theta}) = -\angle H(e^{-j\theta}). \tag{4.128}$$

To show the general nature of the above observations we assume that the unit sample response has real values. Thus, we have

$$H(e^{j\theta}) = \sum_{m=-\infty}^{\infty} h(m)e^{-j\theta m} = \sum_{m=-\infty}^{\infty} h(m)[\cos(\theta m) - j\sin(\theta m)]$$

$$= \sum_{m=-\infty}^{\infty} h(m)\cos(\theta m) - j\sum_{m=-\infty}^{\infty} h(m)\sin(\theta m) \tag{4.129}$$

and similarly

$$H(e^{-j\theta}) = \sum_{m=-\infty}^{\infty} h(m)e^{+j\theta m} = \sum_{m=-\infty}^{\infty} h(m)[\cos(\theta m) + j\sin(\theta m)]$$

$$= \sum_{m=-\infty}^{\infty} h(m)\cos(\theta m) + j\sum_{m=-\infty}^{\infty} h(m)\sin(\theta m). \tag{4.130}$$

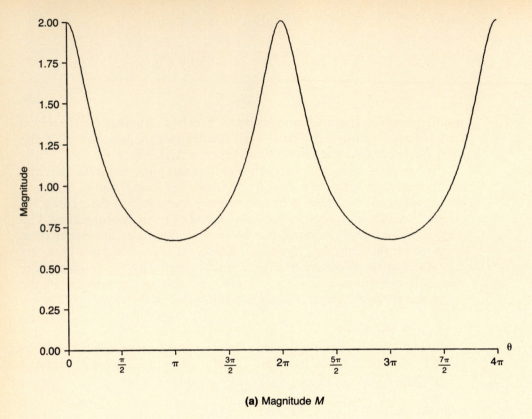

(a) Magnitude M

FIGURE 4.16 The periodic
frequency response of
$H(e^{j\theta}) = 1/(1 - 0.5e^{-j\theta})$

Letting

$$u = \sum_{m=-\infty}^{\infty} h(m) \cos(\theta m) \text{ and } v = \sum_{m=-\infty}^{\infty} h(m) \sin(\theta m)$$

Eq. 4.129 becomes

$$H(e^{j\theta}) = u - jv \qquad (4.131)$$

and Eq. 4.130 follows as

$$H(e^{-j\theta}) = u + jv. \qquad (4.132)$$

Thus, we see that

$$|H(e^{j\theta})| = |H(e^{-j\theta})| = \sqrt{u^2 + v^2} = M \qquad (4.133)$$

which satisfies the definition of an even function.

The phase of $H(e^{j\theta})$ is $\tan^{-1}(-v/u)$, while that of $H(e^{-j\theta})$ is $\tan^{-1}(v/u)$, and consequently

$$\angle H(e^{j\theta}) = -\angle H(e^{-j\theta}) = P \qquad (4.134)$$

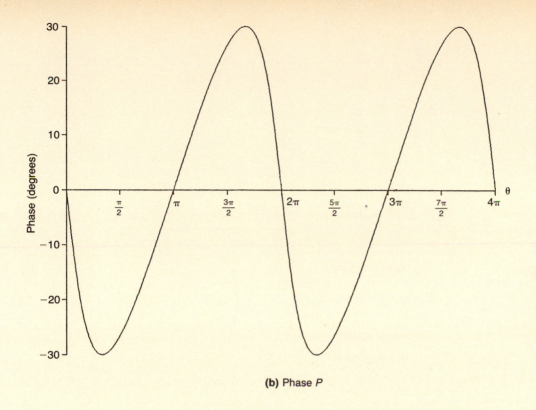

(b) Phase P

which satisfies the definition of an odd function. To summarize,

$$|H(e^{j\theta})| = |H(e^{-j\theta})| \quad \text{and} \quad \angle H(e^{j\theta}) = -\angle H(e^{-j\theta}) \qquad (4.135)$$

so the magnitude is an even function and the phase is an odd function.

Frequency Range   We recall from Chapter Two that $\theta_{\max} = \pi$ is the upper bound of the unambiguous digital frequencies and that this corresponds to a maximum analog frequency of

$$f_{\max} = \frac{f_{\text{sampling}}}{2} = f_s/2. \qquad (4.136)$$

As an example, the magnitude portion of the frequency response for

$$H(e^{j\theta}) = \frac{1}{1 - 0.5e^{-j\theta}} \qquad (4.137)$$

is shown in Fig. 4.17 with three different frequency scales: digital frequency in radians, analog frequency in hertz, and analog frequency in rad/s.

Again from earlier discussions, because of aliasing, it is usually necessary to precede the sampler with a continuous-time analog filter that

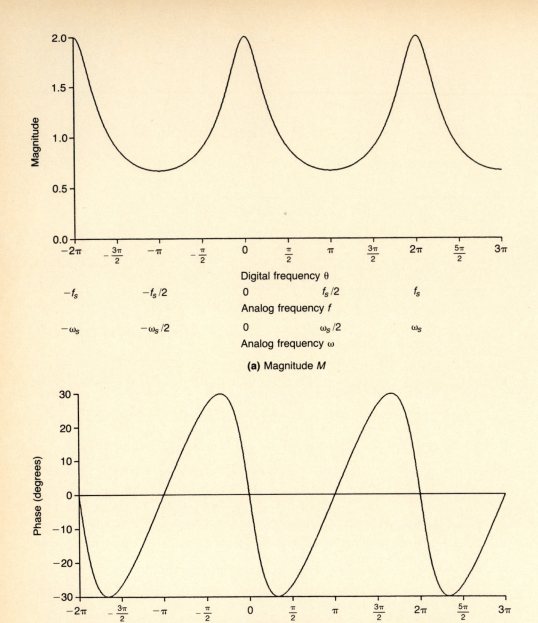

(a) Magnitude M

(b) Phase P

FIGURE 4.17 Three different frequency scales

CHAPTER 4 FREQUENCY RESPONSE AND FILTERS

essentially removes all frequencies above the frequency $f = 1/2T = f_s/2$ hertz which corresponds to $\theta = 2\pi f_s T/2 = \pi$ radians. This filter is called a *prefilter*; the fundamentals of analog filters are discussed in Chapter Ten. A typical arrangement of system components in a digital filter realization is illustrated in Fig. 4.18. Since $H(e^{j\theta})$ is periodic it is customary to use $H(e^{j\theta})$ for $-\pi \le \theta \le \pi$ as the range of interest for the frequency response as is shown in Fig. 4.19(a) and (b). And because of the symmetry properties that were just discussed, we often show $H(e^{j\theta})$ for $0 \le \theta \le \pi$ only and deduce the values for the other half of the period if they are needed.

Decibels. The magnitude, or gain, of the frequency response function $H(e^{j\theta})$ is a real number M in the range $0 \le M \le \infty$. In Fig. 4.19(a), for example for $H(e^{j\theta}) = 1/(1 - 0.5e^{-j\theta})$, M is plotted as a function of θ for $-\pi \le \theta \le \pi$ where the values of M vary from 0.67 to 2.00. In many situations, the range of values of M is much greater than this and it is more informative to define M in decibels as

$$M_{dB} = 20 \log_{10} M. \tag{4.138}$$

Some values of M and the corresponding dB values are given below.

M	0.01	0.10	1.0	10.0	100
M_{dB}	-40	-20	0	20	40

The definition of M_{dB} in Eq. 4.138 is equivalent to

$$M_{dB} = 20 \cdot x \text{ where } M = 10^x. \tag{4.139}$$

A plot of M_{dB} vs. θ is given in Fig. 4.19(c) for $H(e^{j\theta}) = 1/(1 - 0.5e^{-j\theta})$ and we notice the following by comparison with Fig. 4.19(a):

$$M = 0.67 \longrightarrow M_{dB} = -3.48$$
$$M = 1 \longrightarrow M_{dB} = 0$$
$$M = 2 \longrightarrow M_{dB} = 6$$

We use M both as a real number and in decibels throughout the book.

4.2.3 Computer Evaluation of Frequency Response

Since we often need frequency response information it is useful to have a computer program that can provide it. Generally, it is convenient to plot frequency response data, however, here we will concentrate on a procedure to provide only a tabulation of magnitude and phase for a specified frequency range. Our starting point is a discrete system whose frequency

FIGURE 4.18 A typical digital filter system configuration

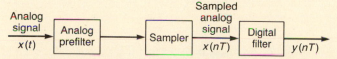

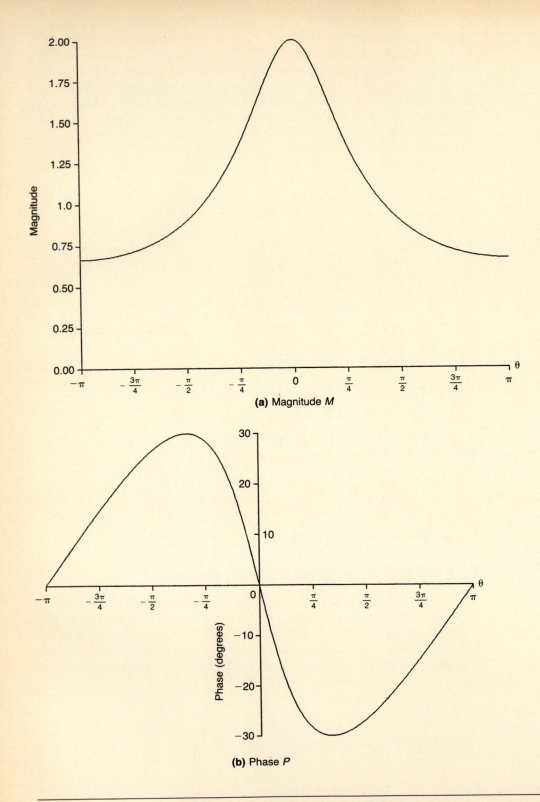

(a) Magnitude M

(b) Phase P

CHAPTER 4 FREQUENCY RESPONSE AND FILTERS

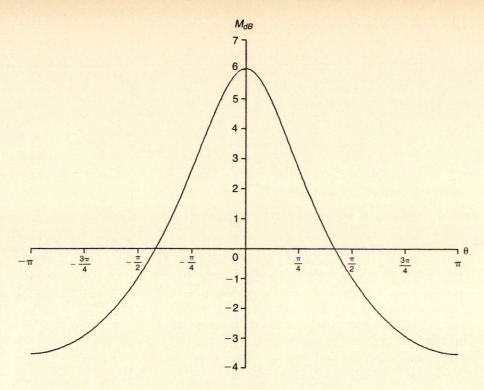

(c) Magnitude M in dB

FIGURE 4.19 One period
of the frequency response
for $H(e^{j\theta}) = 1/(1 - 0.5e^{-j\theta})$

response is assumed to be of the general form

$$H(e^{j\theta}) = \frac{\displaystyle\sum_{k=0}^{L} b_k e^{j(L-k)\theta}}{\displaystyle\sum_{k=0}^{N} c_k e^{j(N-k)\theta}}. \tag{4.140}$$

Notice that we have written $H(e^{j\theta})$ in terms of positive powers of $e^{j\theta}$. For notational convenience we define $z = e^{j\theta}$, which enables us to write

$$H(z) = \frac{\displaystyle\sum_{k=0}^{L} b_k z^{L-k}}{\displaystyle\sum_{k=0}^{N} c_k z^{N-k}}. \tag{4.141}$$

Our computer algorithm is developed on the assumption that we start with an equation of the form of Eq. 4.141. To see that Eq. 4.141 can be used to describe the kinds of systems we've been considering let us look at a system whose frequency response is given by

$$H(e^{j\theta}) = \frac{1}{L+1} \sum_{k=0}^{L} e^{-jk\theta} = \frac{1}{L+1}[1 + e^{-j\theta} + \cdots + e^{-jL\theta}]. \quad (4.142)$$

Multiplying and dividing by $e^{jL\theta}$ gives

$$H(e^{j\theta}) = \frac{e^{jL\theta} + e^{j(L-1)\theta} + \cdots + 1}{(L+1)e^{jL\theta}} = \frac{\displaystyle\sum_{k=0}^{L} e^{j(L-k)\theta}}{(L+1)e^{jL\theta}} \quad (4.143)$$

and replacing $e^{j\theta}$ by z yields

$$H(z) = \frac{\displaystyle\sum_{k=0}^{L} z^{L-k}}{(L+1)z^L} \quad (4.144)$$

which has the same form as Eq. 4.141 with $b_k = 1$, $k = 0, 1, \ldots, L$ and $c_0 = (L+1)$, $c_1 = c_2 = \ldots = c_N = 0$. Also notice that both numerator and the denominator are polynomials of degree L.

Next, let's consider how to evaluate Eq. 4.141 for $z = e^{j\theta}$ with θ taking on a range of values in the interval $0 \le \theta \le \pi$. It should be apparent that both the numerator and the denominator polynomials can be evaluated in the same way. An obvious approach to doing this is to note that

$$\sum_{k=0}^{L} b_k z^{L-k} = b_0 z^L + b_1 z^{L-1} + \cdots + b_L \quad (4.145)$$

and we could proceed to find the various powers of z, multiply by the coefficients and add up the numbers. Complex arithmetic is, of course, required. A more efficient computational procedure is to rewrite Eq. 4.145 in a "nested" form, i.e.

$$\sum_{k=0}^{L} b_k z^{L-k} = (\ldots.(((b_0 z + b_1)z + b_2)z + b_3)z + \ldots) + b_L. \quad (4.146)$$

(To find the savings that result from using Eq. 4.146 see Problem 4.24.) Using this nested form as the basis for the algorithm, the pseudocode for a subroutine to calculate and tabulate frequency response values is shown in Fig. 4.20. It is assumed that the computer language has complex arithmetic intrinsic functions. We assume that the coefficients are real numbers, but the program could easily be written to allow them to be complex. In writing the pseudocode we assume that the following functions are available, either as intrinsic functions of the language, or as user-written procedures:

COMPLEX (U,V)—generates the complex number $U + jV$ from its real part U and its imaginary part V.

```
SUBROUTINE DFRESP (B, A, MH, PH, THETAV, L, N, THETA0, DLTHTA, NUMPTS)
(A and B are the arrays of real coefficients; MH and PH are the
magnitude and phase; L and N are the degrees of numerator and
denominator; THETA0, DLTHTA, and THETAV are the starting value of theta,
the increment of theta, and the array of values of theta — all three are in
radians; NUMPTS is the number of frequency values to be considered)
PI ←——— 3.14159
DO FOR NP ←——— 1 TO NUMPTS

    (initialize numerator and denominator as complex numbers
    whose real parts are B(0) and A(0))

    NUMERATOR ←——— (1+j0)·B(0)
    DENOMINATOR ←——— (1+j0)·A(0)

    (update value of Z)

    THETAV(NP) ←——— THETA0 + (NP-1)·DLTHTA
    Z ←——————— COMPLEX(COSINE(THETAV(NP)), SINE(THETAV(NP)))

    (if L not equal to 0, evaluate rest of numerator)

    IF L ≠ 0 THEN
        DO FOR K ←——— 1 TO L
            NUMERATOR ←——— Z·NUMERATOR + B(K)·(1+j0)
        END DO
    END IF

    (if N not equal to 0, evaluate rest of denominator)

    IF N ≠ 0 THEN
        DO FOR K ←——— 1 TO N
            DENOMINATOR ←——— Z·DENOMINATOR + A(K)·(1+j0)
        END DO
    END IF

    (calculate ratio of numerator to denominator and express as
    magnitude and phase)

    H ←——— NUMERATOR/DENOMINATOR
    MAGNITUDE_H(NP) ←——— COMPLEX_ABSOLUTE_VALUE(H)

    (calculate phase in degrees, being sure to avoid any divide-by-zero
    situations—if the real part of H is smaller in magnitude than some small
    positive number EPSILON, treat it as if it were zero and set the phase
    values depending on the imaginary part of H)

    IF ABSOLUTE_VALUE(REAL_PART(H)) > EPSILON THEN
        PHASE(NP) ←——— (180./PI)· ARC_TANGENT(IMAGINARY_PART(H)/REAL_PART(H))
    END IF
END DO
RETURN
END DFRESP
```

FIGURE 4.20 Pseudocode for discrete frequency response computations

COSINE (X)—computes the cosine of the real argument X.

SINE (X)—computes the sine of the real argument X.

ABSOLUTE_VALUE (Y)—calculates the absolute value of the real argument Y.

COMPLEX_ABSOLUTE_VALUE (H)—calculates the absolute value of the complex argument H.

REAL_PART (H)—calculates the real part of the complex argument H.

IMAGINARY_PART (H)—calculates the imaginary part of the complex argument H.

ARC_TANGENT (Q)—calculates the inverse tangent of the real number Q.

These are available as intrinsic functions in FORTRAN 77, for example.

4.3 ▬ FREQUENCY RESPONSE FUNCTION FROM THE SYSTEM DIFFERENCE EQUATIONS

We know how to get the unit sample response from a system's difference equation by following the procedure outlined in Chapter Three, Section 3.7, on finding the forced and total response of LTI systems. We also know how to obtain a system's frequency response function $H(e^{j\theta})$ from the unit sample response $h(n)$ by using Eq. 4.10, the summation $H(e^{j\theta}) = \sum_{m=-\infty}^{\infty} h(m)e^{-j\theta m}$. We now see that it is possible to go directly from the difference equation to the frequency response as seen in Fig. 4.21. Before looking at the general result, let's consider the example of a stable first-order system described by

$$y(n) - ay(n-1) = x(n), \qquad |a| < 1 \tag{4.147}$$

subjected to the complex exponential input, $x(n) = e^{j\theta n}$. For a stable system ($|a| < 1$) and in the steady state we know that the output sequence is

$$y_{ss}(n) = e^{j\theta n}H(e^{j\theta}) \tag{4.148}$$

where $H(e^{j\theta})$ is the frequency response and it is our aim to find $H(e^{j\theta})$ from the difference equation, Eq. 4.147. Replacing n with $n-1$ in Eq. 4.148 we have

$$y_{ss}(n-1) = e^{j\theta(n-1)}H(e^{j\theta}) \tag{4.149}$$

and substituting Eq. 4.148 and 4.149 into Eq. 4.147 gives

$$e^{j\theta n}H(e^{j\theta}) - ae^{j\theta(n-1)}H(e^{j\theta}) = e^{j\theta n} \tag{4.150}$$

FIGURE 4.21 Ways of obtaining a discrete system's frequency response

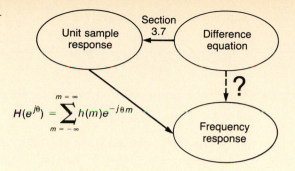

or

$$e^{j\theta n}H(e^{j\theta}) - e^{j\theta n}ae^{-j\theta}H(e^{j\theta}) = e^{j\theta n} \qquad (4.151)$$

and after dividing through by $e^{j\theta n}$,

$$H(e^{j\theta}) - ae^{-j\theta}H(e^{j\theta}) = 1. \qquad (4.152)$$

Solving for $H(e^{j\theta})$ gives the frequency response

$$H(e^{j\theta}) = \frac{1}{1 - ae^{-j\theta}} \qquad (4.153)$$

which is the result obtained in Example 4.4 when we started from a given unit sample response of $h(n) = a^n \cdot u(n)$. The relationships among the unit sample response, the difference equation, the system diagram, and the frequency response for this first-order system are shown in Fig. 4.22.

This same approach can be used to obtain a general result that allows us to obtain the expression for a system's frequency response directly from its difference equation. We start with the Nth-order difference equation, namely

$$y(n) - a_1 y(n-1) - a_2 y(n-2) - \cdots - a_N y(n-N)$$
$$= b_0 x(n) + b_1 x(n-1) + \cdots + b_L x(n-L) \qquad (4.154)$$

FIGURE 4.22 The relationships among the unit sample response, difference equation, system diagram, and frequency response for a first-order system

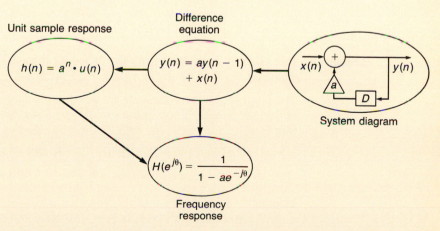

which we can write more compactly as

$$y(n) - \sum_{k=1}^{k=N} a_k y(n-k) = \sum_{k=0}^{k=L} b_k x(n-k). \tag{4.155}$$

With $x(n) = e^{j\theta n}$, the input delayed by k samples is

$$x(n-k) = e^{j\theta(n-k)} = e^{j\theta n} e^{-j\theta k} \tag{4.156}$$

and for $y_{ss}(n) = H(e^{j\theta})e^{j\theta n}$, the output delayed by k samples is

$$y_{ss}(n-k) = H(e^{j\theta})e^{j\theta n}e^{-j\theta k}. \tag{4.157}$$

Substituting Eqs. 4.156 and 4.157 into the general difference equation of Eq. 4.155 gives

$$H(e^{j\theta})e^{j\theta n} - \sum_{k=1}^{N} a_k H(e^{j\theta})e^{j\theta n}e^{-j\theta k} = \sum_{k=0}^{L} b_k e^{j\theta n}e^{-j\theta k} \tag{4.158}$$

which can be put into the form

$$H(e^{j\theta})\left[1 - \sum_{k=1}^{N} a_k e^{-j\theta k}\right]e^{j\theta n} = e^{j\theta n}\left[\sum_{k=0}^{L} b_k e^{-j\theta k}\right]. \tag{4.159}$$

Then solving for the frequency response function $H(e^{j\theta})$ we get

$$H(e^{j\theta}) = \frac{\displaystyle\sum_{k=0}^{L} b_k e^{-j\theta k}}{1 - \displaystyle\sum_{k=1}^{N} a_k e^{-j\theta k}} \tag{4.160}$$

or

$$H(e^{j\theta}) = \frac{b_0 + b_1 e^{-j\theta} + \cdots + b_L e^{-j\theta L}}{1 - a_1 e^{-j\theta} - \cdots - a_N e^{-j\theta N}}. \tag{4.161}$$

Example 4.9. This example illustrates finding the frequency response function from the difference equation of an IIR system.

The satellite system of Example 4.7 was described by the unit sample response $h(n) = Ka^n \cos(\alpha n)$. This system can also be described by the difference equation

$$y(n) - [2a \cos \alpha]y(n-1) + a^2 y(n-2) = K[x(n) - (a \cos \alpha)x(n-1)]. \tag{4.162}$$

Find the frequency response function from the difference equation.

Solution: The coefficients of this equation when compared with Eq. 4.154 are $a_1 = 2a \cos \alpha$, $a_2 = -a^2$, $b_0 = K$, $b_1 = -Ka \cos \alpha$ and so from Eq. 4.161 the frequency response function is:

$$H(e^{j\theta}) = K\frac{1 - a\,(\cos\alpha)e^{-j\theta}}{1 - 2a\,(\cos\alpha)e^{-j\theta} + a^2 e^{-j2\theta}} \qquad (4.163)$$

which is the result obtained in Eq. 4.108. Recall that for stability $0 \leq a < 1$.

Example 4.10. This example illustrates finding the frequency response of an FIR filter from its difference equation.

A moving average (MA) FIR filter is described by

$$y(n) = \frac{1}{L+1}\sum_{k=0}^{k=L} x(n-k). \qquad (4.164)$$

a) Find a closed-form analytical expression for the frequency response function of this filter.

b) Obtain a plot of the magnitude and phase of $H(e^{j\theta})$ for $0 \leq \theta \leq \pi$ with $L = 4$.

c) For $L = 4$ (an average of the current and past four samples), find $y_{ss}(n)$ with $x(n) = 0.50\cos(\pi n/4)$.

Solution:

a) Writing out the sum gives

$$y(n) = \frac{1}{L+1}[x(n) + x(n-1) + \cdots + x(n-L)] \qquad (4.165)$$

where we see that all of the input coefficients are $1/(L+1)$ and there are no delayed outputs, making all the a's in Eq. 4.154 zero and so the frequency response is

$$H(e^{j\theta}) = \frac{1}{L+1}[1 + e^{-j\theta} + \cdots + e^{-j\theta L}]$$

$$= \frac{1}{L+1}\sum_{k=0}^{L} e^{-j\theta k}. \qquad (4.166)$$

The finite geometric sum of Eq. 4.166 can be written in closed form as

$$H(e^{j\theta}) = \left[\frac{1}{L+1}\right]\frac{1 - e^{-j\theta(L+1)}}{1 - e^{-j\theta}}$$

$$= \left[\frac{1}{L+1}\right]\frac{e^{-j(L+1)\theta/2}[e^{j(L+1)\theta/2} - e^{-j(L+1)\theta/2}]}{e^{-j\theta/2}[e^{j\theta/2} - e^{-j\theta/2}]} \qquad (4.167)$$

or

$$H(e^{j\theta}) = \frac{1}{L+1}e^{-j\theta L/2}\left[\frac{\sin\left(\theta\left[\frac{L+1}{2}\right]\right)}{\sin(\theta/2)}\right]. \qquad (4.168)$$

b) Computer-generated magnitude (M) and phase (P) plots for $H(e^{j\theta})$ with $L = 4$ are shown in Fig. 4.23. It is always a wise policy to inspect computer results for reasonableness before using the data or proceeding with the analysis/design problem. Although the abrupt phase changes of 180 degrees at $\theta = \pi/5$ and $\theta = 2\pi/5$ (where $M = 0$) might appear to be incorrect, we will see later in Chapter Nine that phase changes like these are easily explained with the aid of concepts that are developed in Chapter Five. The values of M and P for the input frequency of $\theta = \pi/4$ are marked on the diagrams.

c) For $L = 4$, Eq. 4.168 becomes

$$H(e^{j\theta}) = \frac{1}{5}e^{-j2\theta}\left[\frac{\sin(5\theta/2)}{\sin(\theta/2)}\right] \tag{4.169}$$

and evaluation at the input frequency of $\theta = \pi/4$ produces

$$H(e^{j\pi/4}) = \frac{1}{5}e^{-j\pi/2}\left[\frac{\sin(5\pi/8)}{\sin(\pi/8)}\right]$$

$$= 0.48e^{-j\pi/2} \tag{4.170}$$

and the steady-state response is

$$y_{ss}(n) = 0.24\cos(\pi n/4 - \pi/2). \tag{4.171}$$

Example 4.11. This example shows how to obtain the frequency response from the system diagram.

A second-order system is described by the diagram in Fig. 4.24. Find the frequency response $H(e^{j\theta})$.

Solution: We can write the system difference equation from this diagram. It is

$$y(n) = -0.5y(n-2) + x(n-1) - x(n-3) \tag{4.172}$$

or

$$y(n) + 0.5y(n-2) = x(n-1) - x(n-3). \tag{4.173}$$

The system's characteristic equation is

$$r^2 + 0.5 = 0 \tag{4.174}$$

with the corresponding characteristic roots of

$$r_{1,2} = 0.707e^{\pm j\pi/2} \tag{4.175}$$

and so the system is stable and the frequency response can be determined. The difference equation coefficients when compared with Eq. 4.154 are

$$a_1 = 0, \ a_2 = -0.5, \ b_0 = 0, \ b_1 = 1, \ b_2 = 0, \ b_3 = -1 \tag{4.176}$$

and so using Eq. 4.161 the frequency response function is

$$H(e^{j\theta}) = \frac{e^{-j\theta} - e^{-j3\theta}}{1 + 0.5e^{-j2\theta}} = \frac{e^{j2\theta} - 1}{e^{j3\theta} + 0.5e^{j\theta}}. \tag{4.177}$$

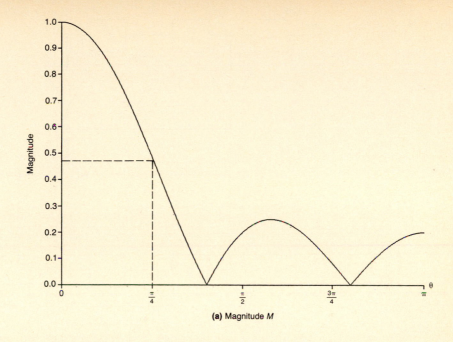

(a) Magnitude *M*

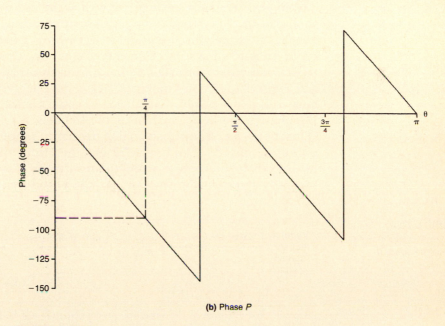

(b) Phase *P*

FIGURE 4.23 Frequency response for moving average filter of Example 4.10

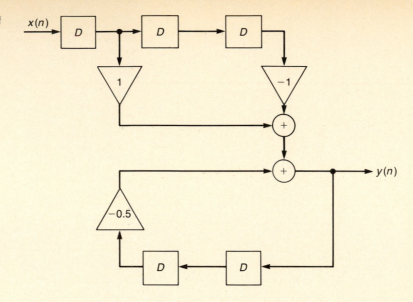

FIGURE 4.24 System of Example 4.11

$x(n)$

$y(n)$

We have used three different models for LTI systems (difference equations, unit sample response, and system diagrams) and have been able to determine the frequency response function from each starting point (see Fig. 4.21). What if a mathematical model such as any of the three discussed is unavailable and yet we still want to know the frequency response of an LTI system? This calls for an experimental determination of $H(e^{j\theta})$. One widely used method is to perform a frequency response test on the unknown system. Consider the set-up illustrated in Fig. 4.25(a) where an oscillator provides a signal of variable frequency that is sampled and applied to the unknown LTI system. The system input is the sequence $x(n) = X\cos(\theta n + \alpha)$ where, for convenience, the amplitude X and the phase α are held constant as the frequency θ is varied from θ to π. (This, of course, requires an analog frequency range of $0 \le f \le 0.5 f_s$.) The output amplitude Y and phase P obtained from the measured data are recorded below.[†] Then, plotting the results for M and P gives the experimentally determined results of Fig. 4.25(b) and we have achieved the de-

FIGURE 4.25(a) Setup for frequency response test for a discrete system

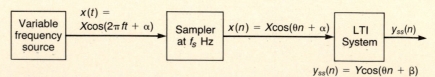

$y_{ss}(n) = Y\cos(\theta n + \beta)$

[†]Because of the timing of the sampling process, it may not be possible to directly measure or observe the amplitude Y and/or the phase β of the output sequence $y_{ss}(n) = Y\cos(\theta n + \beta)$. It is always possible, however, to compute Y and β from the measured or observed data (see Problem 2.29).

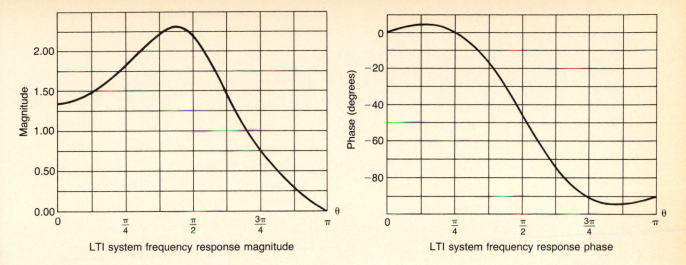

FIGURE 4.25(b) Experimentally determined frequency response plots

LTI system frequency response magnitude

LTI system frequency response phase

sired frequency response where $H(e^{j\theta})$ is known from numerical data (or curves) rather than as an analytical expression.

Frequency	Input Amplitude	Phase	Amplitude	Phase	$M = \dfrac{Y_i}{X}$	$P = \beta_i - \alpha$
θ_1	X	α	Y_1	β_1	Y_1/X	$\beta_1 - \alpha$
θ_2	X	α	Y_2	β_2	Y_2/X	$\beta_2 - \alpha$
θ_3	X	α	Y_3	β_3	Y_3/X	$\beta_3 - \alpha$
.	.	.	.	.	.	.
.	.	.	.	.	.	.
.	.	.	.	.	.	.
θ_k	X	α	Y_k	β_k	Y_k/X	$\beta_k - \alpha$
.	.	.	.	.	.	.
.	.	.	.	.	.	.
.	.	.	.	.	.	.

Example 4.12. This example illustrates a use of the graphical representation of frequency response.

The LTI system that is described by the frequency response plots of Fig. 4.25(b) is subjected to an input that is the sum of several sinusoidal sequences, namely

$$x(n) = 8 \cos(\pi n/8 + 0.28) - 2 \sin(\pi n/2 + \pi/4)$$
$$+ 20 \cos(5\pi n/8 - 0.28) + 16 \cos(3\pi n/4 + \pi/6). \quad (4.178)$$

Determine the steady-state output $y_{ss}(n)$. Accuracy to the precision of information on the graphs is, of course, adequate.

Solution: From the graphs, we read off the following values of $H(e^{j\theta})$

$$H(e^{j\pi/8}) = 1.5e^{j5°} = 1.5e^{j0.09}, \; H(e^{j\pi/2}) = 2.2e^{-j45°} = 2.2e^{-j0.79}$$

$$H(e^{j5\pi/8}) = 1.5e^{-j75°} = 1.5e^{-j1.31}, \; H(e^{j3\pi/4}) = 0.75e^{-j90°} = 0.75e^{-j\pi/2}. \quad (4.179)$$

Then applying the sinusoidal steady-state formula gives the steady-state output sequence

$$y_{ss}(n) = 12 \cos(\pi n/8 + 0.37) - 4.4 \sin(\pi n/2) + 30 \cos(5\pi n/8 - 1.59)$$
$$+ 12 \cos(3\pi n/4 - \pi/3). \quad (4.180)$$

To conclude this subject, let's review the procedure used to solve the central problem of this chapter where we are given a stable, linear time-invariant (LTI) system subjected to a sinusoidal input $x(n) = X \cos(\theta n + \alpha)$ with the objective of determining the steady-state output $y_{ss}(n)$. We proceed as follows:

PROCEDURE

1. Find the system frequency response function

$$H(e^{j\theta}) = |H(e^{j\theta})|e^{j\angle H(e^{j\theta})}$$

$$= Me^{jP}. \quad (4.181)$$

This can be done in four different ways.

a) We can start with the unit sample response $h(n)$ and evaluate

$$H(e^{j\theta}) = \sum_{m=-\infty}^{m=+\infty} h(m)e^{-j\theta m}. \quad (4.182)$$

b) We can start with the difference equation and use the algorithm

$$y(n) - \sum_{k=1}^{N} a_k y(n-k) = \sum_{k=0}^{L} b_k x(n-k) \longrightarrow H(e^{j\theta}) = \frac{\displaystyle\sum_{k=0}^{L} b_k e^{-j\theta k}}{1 - \displaystyle\sum_{k=1}^{N} a_k e^{-j\theta k}}$$

$$(4.183)$$

c) We can start with the system diagram, proceed to find the difference equation, and use the approach in (b).

d) We can determine $H(e^{j\theta})$ by experiment. That is, for each input $x_i(n) = X_i \cos(\theta_i n + \alpha_i)$, the output $y_{kss}(n) = Y_i \cos(\theta_i n + \beta_i)$ is measured. This allows the calculation of the gain and phase at each frequency, namely

$$M = \frac{Y_i}{X_i} \quad \text{and} \quad P_i = \beta_i - \alpha_i. \quad (4.184)$$

Then a smooth plot of M vs θ and P vs θ is made from these data with the result being a graphical display of $H(e^{j\theta})$.

2. From Eqs. 4.85 and 4.86, the sinusoidal steady-state formula, the steady-state output is

$$y_{ss}(n) = X|H(e^{j\theta})| \cos(\theta n + \alpha + \angle H(e^{j\theta}))$$

$$= XM \cos(\theta n + \alpha + P) = XM \cos(\theta n + \beta) \qquad (4.185)$$

where the input is

$$x(n) = X \cos(\theta n + \alpha). \qquad (4.186)$$

In other words, the output is a sinusoid of the same frequency as the input. The amplitude of the output is the input amplitude (X) multiplied by the magnitude (M) of the frequency response at the input frequency (θ); the phase of the output (β) is the phase (P) of the frequency response at the input frequency (θ), added to the input phase (α).

4.4 ▬ FILTERS

According to the Oxford English Dictionary (Oxford University Press, 1971) the primary definition of the filtering process is "To pass (a liquid) through a filter, or some porous medium, for the purpose of removing solid particles or impurities." All of us are familiar with this definition for we have poured cooked pasta into a colander to drain off the cooking water from the pasta; we have changed or had someone else change the oil filter in an automobile where the filter was used to strain out impurities produced by the motor; or have seen a furnace filter covered with lint and dust.

Analog filters for electrical signals began appearing in telephone transmission lines early in this century following the work of Oliver Heaviside. In 1923, Otto Zobel of Bell Telephone Laboratories invented m-derived filter sections making filter design a routine task accomplished in a catalog look-up fashion. Butterworth of the Admiralty Research Laboratory in Great Britain introduced a new concept in 1930 that combined filtering and amplification, and wave filters were first described in 1932 by George Campbell of Bell Laboratories. In 1930, the filter design problem of approximation was addressed simultaneously by Butterworth and Cauer, the result being the maximally flat and Chebyshev approximations that remain in use today. The first electromechanical filter was introduced in 1946 by Robert Adler of Zenith Radio Corp. and was used in broadcast and communications receivers.

Digital filtering traces back several centuries, however, the advent of readily available digital hardware and the publication of the book *System Analysis by Digital Computer,* edited by F. F. Kuo and J. F. Kaiser (John Wiley & Sons, 1966) really started things off in the field of digital signal processing. In that book, J. F. Kaiser presents the first unifying treatment from a modern viewpoint. He defines a digital filter as:

> The term *digital filter* refers to the computational process or algorithm by which a sampled signal or sequence of numbers (acting as an input) is transformed into a second sequence of numbers termed the output signal. The computational process may be that of low-pass filtering (smoothing), bandpass filtering, interpolation, the generation of derivatives, etc.

4.4.1 A Typical Filtering Problem

Consider the following simplified situation. A sinusoidal sequence

$$s(n) = S \cos(\theta n) \tag{4.187}$$

representing information [$s(n)$ is used to remind us that this is a desired signal] is transmitted through a medium to a receiving sensor. Because of the effects of the medium, an unwanted signal, $g(n)$ [we use $g(n)$ to remind us of garbage], is added to the sequence $s(n)$ in the manner indicated in Fig. 4.26. Let us assume that the unwanted signal is

$$g(n) = G \cos(10\theta n + \gamma). \tag{4.188}$$

Notice that the frequency of $g(n)$ is 10 times that of $s(n)$. The received signal $r(n)$ is

$$r(n) = s(n) + g(n) \tag{4.189}$$

or in terms of the given sinusoidal sequences

$$r(n) = S \cos(\theta n) + G \cos(10\theta n + \gamma). \tag{4.190}$$

Plots of the sequences $s(n)$ and the signal plus noise $s(n) + g(n)$ are shown in Fig. 4.27 for $S = 10$, $G = 4$, $\theta = \pi/20$ and $\gamma = \pi/6$.

The received signal $r(n)$ contains both a desired component $s(n)$ and an undesired component $g(n)$. The undesired or unwanted component is often called *noise*. In an attempt to recover the desired signal, we can put the signal received through a filter as in Fig. 4.28. Having some hindsight and/or experience, let's assume that the filter is described by the differ-

FIGURE 4.26 Generation of a noisy signal

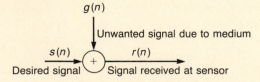

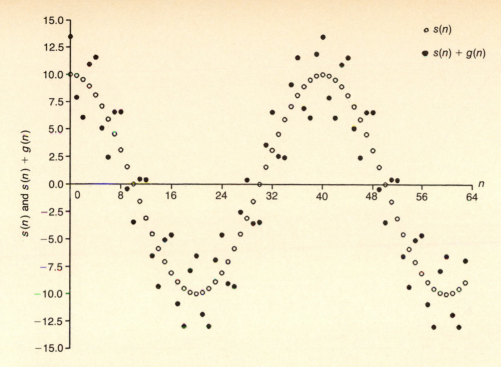

FIGURE 4.27 Signal and signal + noise sequences

ence equation

$$y(n) = r(n) + 0.9r(n - 2) \qquad (4.191)$$

which corresponds to the frequency response

$$H(e^{j\theta}) = 1 + 0.9e^{-j2\theta} \qquad (4.192)$$

with the magnitude and phase plots of Fig. 4.29. The received signal, which is also the input to the filter, is a sum of two sinusoids, namely

$$r(n) = s(n) + g(n)$$

$$= 10\cos(\pi n/20) + 4\cos(\pi n/2 + \pi/6). \qquad (4.193)$$

The response of the filter to the first component (the desired signal) is carried out in the standard way. For $s(n) = 10\cos(\pi n/20)$ we have frequency response function evaluated at $\theta = \pi/20$, as

$$H(e^{j\pi/20}) = 1 + 0.9e^{-j2(\pi/20)}$$

$$= 1.88e^{-j0.15} \qquad (4.194)$$

FIGURE 4.28 Noisy system with filter

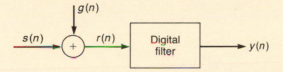

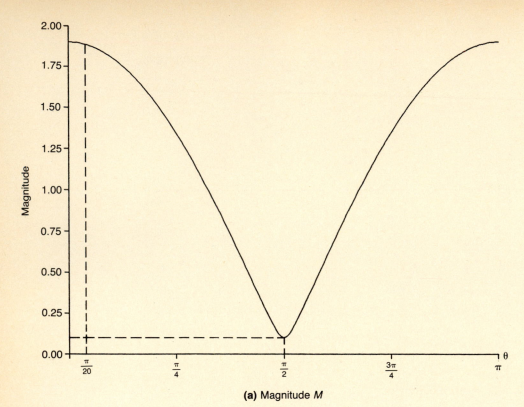

(a) Magnitude *M*

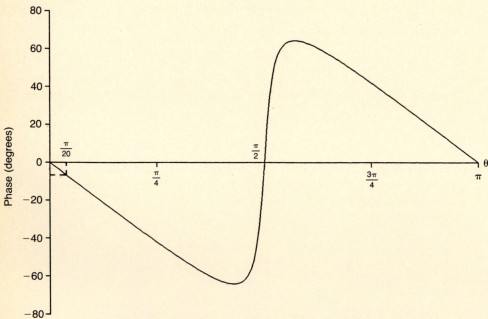

(b) Phase *P*

FIGURE 4.29 Frequency response for $H(e^{j\theta}) = 1 + 0.9e^{-j2\theta}$

and from the sinusoidal steady-state formula of Eq. 4.85 the associated steady-state output is

$$y_{1ss}(n) = 10(1.88)\cos(\pi n/20 - 0.15) = 18.8\cos(\pi n/20 - 0.15). \quad (4.195)$$

Following the same procedure for the second component (the unwanted signal), $g(n) = 4\cos(\pi n/2 + \pi/6)$, the frequency response function is

$$H(e^{j\pi/2}) = 1 + 0.9e^{-j2(\pi/2)}$$

$$= 0.1e^{j0}. \quad (4.196)$$

Relying on the steady-state result of Eq. 4.85 once again, the second component of the output sequence is

$$y_{2ss}(n) = (4)(0.1)\cos(\pi n/2 + \pi/6) = 0.4\cos(\pi n/2 + \pi/6) \quad (4.197)$$

and because of the linearity property, the output is the sum of $y_{1ss}(n)$ and $y_{2ss}(n)$, namely

$$y_{ss}(n) = 18.8\cos(\pi n/20 - 0.15) + 0.4\cos(\pi n/2 + \pi/6) \quad (4.198)$$

which is shown in Fig. 4.30. Also shown is the input $s(n)$ which has been scaled to a maximum value of 18.8 (the maximum value of the signal component of the output) for comparison purposes. We can see that although $y_{ss}(n)$ is not identical to the desired signal $s(n)$, it certainly is a closer match than the noise corrupted signal $r(n)$. We have succeeded in

FIGURE 4.30 Filtered output sequence $y_{ss}(n)$ and scaled input sequence $s(n)$

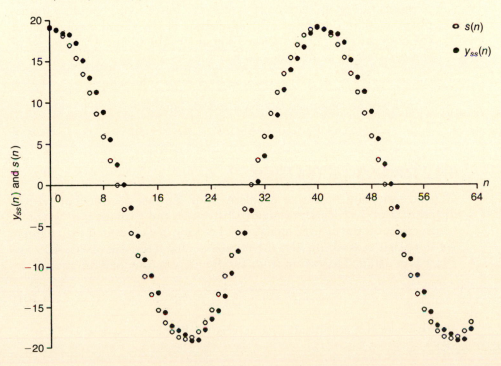

our design problem for we have recovered the profile of the desired signal while managing to significantly reduce the noise contribution.

Comments:

1. The pertinent calculations used in this example are tabulated below.

Input	Filter Characteristic	Output
$s(n) = 10 \cos(\pi n/20)$	$H(e^{j\pi/20}) = 1.88e^{-j0.15}$	$y_{1ss}(n) = 18.8 \cos(\pi n/20 - 0.15)$
$g(n) = 4 \cos(\pi n/2 + \pi/6)$	$H(e^{j\pi/2}) = 0.1e^{j0}$	$y_{2ss}(n) = 0.4 \cos(\pi n/2 + \pi/6)$

We can easily see that the desired signal $s(n)$ is amplified because its amplitude is multiplied by a factor of 1.88 when passed by the filter, while the unwanted signal $g(n)$ is attenuated because its amplitude is multiplied by a factor of 0.1.

2. The filter gains of 1.88 and 0.1 can also be seen on the magnitude frequency response plot of Fig. 4.29(a) at the frequencies $\theta = \pi/20$ and $\theta = \pi/2$, respectively.

3. The insignificant phase shift caused by the filter at these two frequencies is evident in Fig. 4.29(b).

4. If the gain increase of 1.88 (remember that the input signal $s(n)$ was scaled to a maximum value of 18.8 rather than 10 for comparison purposes in Fig. 4.30) is undesirable, the output $y(n)$ could be multiplied by 10/18.8 to return the amplitude of the signal component of the output to that of the desired signal. Or, the frequency response of the filter could be designed to be

$$H'(e^{j\theta}) = (10/18.8)[1 + 0.9e^{-j2\theta}] \tag{4.199}$$

which would make the filter difference equation

$$y'(n) = (10/18.8)[r(n) + 0.9r(n - 2)]. \tag{4.200}$$

4.4.2 Comparison of Two Filters

Consider the same filtering problem from the last section but with a different kind of filter intended to filter out the garbage $g(n)$ without much effect on the desired signal $s(n)$. Looking back through the chapter, we note that something like the recursive characteristic of Fig. 4.19 appears promising. This came from the frequency response function

$$H(e^{j\theta}) = \frac{1}{1 - 0.5e^{-j\theta}} \tag{4.201}$$

and to make the amplitude characteristic sharper we will try

$$H(e^{j\theta}) = \frac{1}{1 - 0.9e^{-j\theta}} \qquad (4.202)$$

which has the magnitude and phase plots given in Fig. 4.31. Notice that the "dc gain" or $|H(e^{j0})|$ for this recursive filter is $1/(1 - 0.9) = 10$ where $|H(e^{j0})|$ for the nonrecursive filter was $1 + 0.9 = 1.9$. As previously mentioned, gain changes are easily accomplished by modifying the input coefficients of the filter difference equation. Recalling that the filter input is

$$r(n) = 10 \cos(\pi n/20) + 4 \cos(\pi n/2 + \pi/6) \qquad (4.203)$$

we read from the plots of Fig. 4.31 the gain and phase at $\theta = \pi/20$ and $\theta = \pi/2$ giving $H(e^{j\pi/20}) \approx 5.6e^{-j52°} = 5.6e^{-j0.91}$ and $H(e^{j\pi/2}) \approx 0.75e^{-j42°} = 0.75e^{-j0.73}$. The filter output, which is shown in Fig. 4.32 is

$$y_{ss}(n) \approx 10(5.6) \cos(\pi n/20 - 0.91)$$
$$+ 4(0.75) \cos(\pi n/2 + \pi/6 - 0.73) \qquad (4.204)$$

or

$$y_{ss}(n) \approx 56 \cos(\pi n/20 - 0.91) + 3 \cos(\pi n/2 - 0.21). \qquad (4.205)$$

(Note that in this case the input has been scaled to the maximum value of the signal component of the output of 56 for comparison purposes.) We could, of course, have computed the frequency response at these two frequencies directly getting

$$H(e^{j\pi/20}) = \frac{1}{1 - 0.9e^{-j\pi/20}}$$

$$= \frac{1}{1 - 0.9(0.988 - j0.156)} = 5.59e^{-j0.90} \qquad (4.206)$$

and

$$H(e^{j\pi/2}) = \frac{1}{1 - 0.9e^{-j\pi/2}} = \frac{1}{1 - 0.9(0 - j)} = 0.74e^{-j0.73}. \qquad (4.207)$$

It is apparent that reading directly from the plots gives sufficient accuracy for most situations.

How do these results compare with those obtained for the previous filter? One measure of comparison is tabulated below.

Filter 1, $H(e^{j\theta}) = 1 + 0.9e^{-j2\theta}$	Filter 2, $H(e^{j\theta}) = 1/(1 - 0.9e^{-j\theta})$
$\|H(e^{j\pi/20})\| = 1.88e^{-j0.15}$	$\|H(e^{j\pi/20})\| = 5.59e^{-j0.90}$
$\|H(e^{j\pi/2})\| = 0.10e^{j0}$	$\|H(e^{j\pi/2})\| = 0.74e^{-j0.73}$
$\dfrac{\|H(e^{j\pi/20})\|}{\|H(e^{j\pi/2})\|} \approx 19$	$\dfrac{\|H(e^{j\pi/20})\|}{\|H(e^{j\pi/2})\|} \approx 7.5$

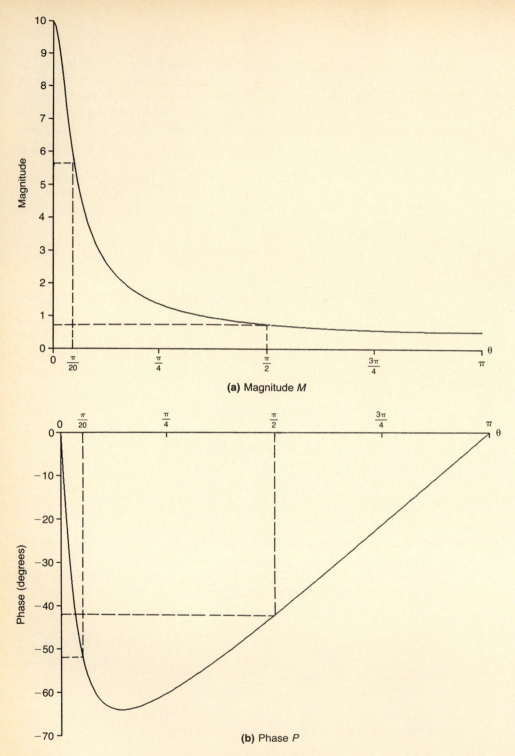

FIGURE 4.31 Frequency response for $H(e^{j\theta}) = 1/(1 - 0.9e^{-j\theta})$

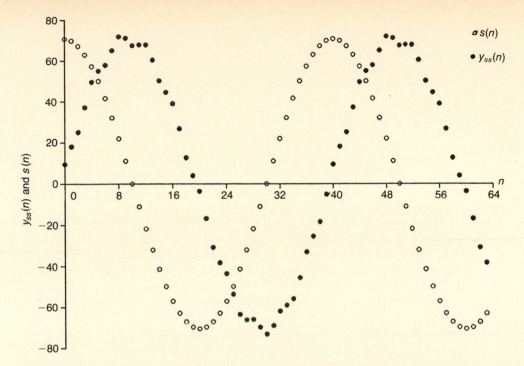

FIGURE 4.32 Filtered output (new filter) $y_{ss}(n)$ and scaled input sequence $s(n)$

Thus, the first filter "passes" the desired frequency of $\theta = \pi/20$ with a gain approximately 19 times that of the undesired frequency of $\theta = \pi/2$. This ratio in decibels is $20 \log_{10} 19$ or 25.6 dB. The corresponding numbers for the second filter are approximately 7.5 or 17.5 dB. On this basis of comparison we would conclude that the relative noise suppression of the first filter is superior to the second one (19 or 25.6 dB versus 7.5 or 17.5 dB).

4.5 ▬ IDEAL FILTERS

We've looked at a few simple filters of various types, now we want to consider filtering from a more general point of view. Suppose we have a signal to be filtered. What is the best, or ideal, filter that could be used? Let's assume that the signal into the filter of Fig. 4.33(a) is made up of two groups of sinusoids,

$$x(n) = s(n) + g(n)$$

$$= \sum_{m=1}^{M_1} S_m \cos(\theta_m n) + \sum_{m=M_1+1}^{M_2} G_m \cos(\theta_m n). \qquad (4.208)$$

Furthermore, assume that the frequencies θ_m, $m = 1, 2, \ldots, M_1$ lie in one range and that the frequencies θ_m, $m = M_1 + 1, \ldots, M_2$ lie in some other range as in Fig. 4.33(b).

FIGURE 4.33 Filtering
problem

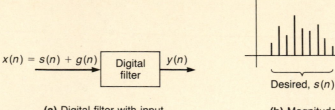

(a) Digital filter with input
consisting of signal and
noise sequences

(b) Magnitudes of the frequency
components in $x(n)$

What is the best that we can do? It would be ideal if we could pass the $s(n)$ portion with all sinusoidal components having the same relative amplitudes and phases to preserve the shape of the $s(n)$ sequence and have the $g(n)$ components obliterated, i.e., reduced to zero amplitude. What kind of filter would do this?

Consider a sequence $s(n)$, a desired signal that is to be separated from the signal $x(n)$, the input to the ideal filter of Fig. 4.34(a). The steady-state output sequence $y_{ss}(n)$ should have the same shape as the desired sequence $s(n)$ and will be delayed because the processing that occurs in the filter will take some amount of time. That is, for an input $x(n)$ the output should be

$$y_{ss}(n) = Ks(n - \ell) \qquad (4.209)$$

where K represents a change in amplitude ($K = 1$ would be satisfactory

FIGURE 4.34 Ideal low-pass filter characteristics

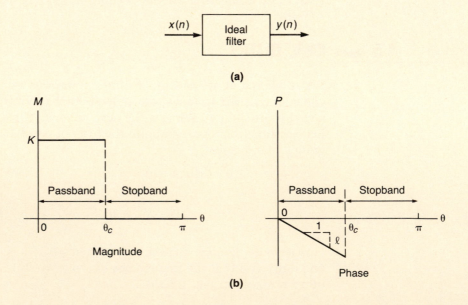

(a)

Magnitude

Phase

(b)

but is not required) and ℓ represents the time lag or shift caused by the system. Let's do some simple mathematics to put all of this on a more solid quantitative footing. We want

$$y_{ss}(n) = Ks(n - \ell) \tag{4.210}$$

where substituting the desired signal $s(n)$ from Eq. 4.208 gives

$$y_{ss}(n) = \sum_{m=1}^{M_1} KS_m \cos(\theta_m[n - \ell])$$

$$= K \sum_{m=1}^{m=M_1} S_m \cos(\theta_m n - \theta_m \ell). \tag{4.211}$$

We know that the desired portion of the input $x(n)$ is given by

$$s(n) = \sum_{m=1}^{M_1} S_m \cos(\theta_m n) \tag{4.212}$$

and we know from the sinusoidal steady-state formula that a single sinusoidal input

$$S \cos(\theta n) \xrightarrow{\text{produces}} y_{ss}(n) = S|H(e^{j\theta})| \cos(\theta n + \underline{/H(e^{j\theta})}). \tag{4.213}$$

Thus, with the help of Eq. 4.213, a comparison of Eq. 4.212 with Eq. 4.211 yields the result for each frequency θ_m which is

$$|H(e^{j\theta_m})| = K \quad \text{and} \quad \underline{/H(e^{j\theta_m})} = -\theta_m \ell, \ m = 1, \ldots, \ M_1 \tag{4.214}$$

and, since we want to get rid of the undesired frequency components

$$|H(e^{j\theta_m})| = 0 \quad , \quad m = M_1 + 1, \ldots, M_2. \tag{4.215}$$

Consequently, the general expression for the frequency response is

$$H(e^{j\theta_m}) = \begin{cases} Ke^{-j\theta_m \ell} = Me^{jP_m} & , \quad m = 1, \ldots, M_1 \\ 0 & , \quad m = M_1 + 1, \ldots, M_2 \end{cases} \tag{4.216}$$

which is described by the magnitude and phase characteristics of Fig. 4.34(b). The frequency range $0 \le \theta \le \theta_c$ is referred to as the filter *passband* and the range $\theta_c \le \theta \le \pi$ is called the *stopband*.

While the concept of ideal filtering has been illustrated for a lowpass situation, similar results apply for highpass, bandpass, and bandstop filters. Figure 4.35 shows the magnitude and phase characteristics for ideal filters of the lowpass, highpass, bandpass, and bandstop varieties. For simplicity, we generally assume that all frequencies in the passband may be present and so the ideal filter characteristic is

$$H(e^{j\theta}) = \begin{cases} Ke^{-j\theta \ell} & , \quad \text{in the passband} \\ 0 & , \quad \text{otherwise.} \end{cases} \tag{4.217}$$

FIGURE 4.35 Frequency response characteristics of ideal filters

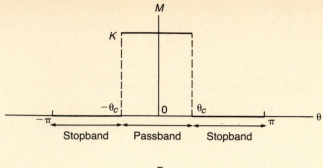

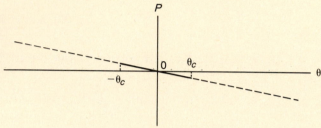

(a) Lowpass filter characteristics

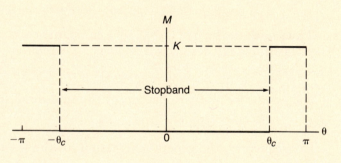

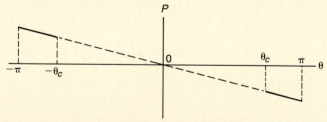

(b) Highpass filter characteristics

CHAPTER 4 FREQUENCY RESPONSE AND FILTERS

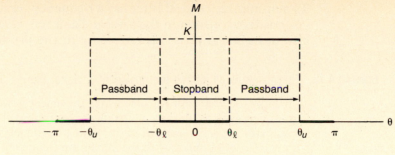

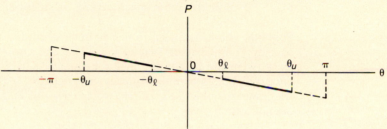

(c) Bandpass filter characteristics

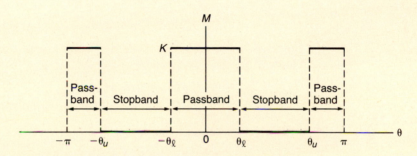

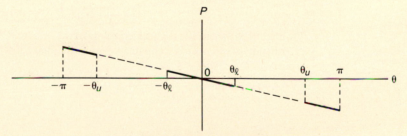

(d) Bandstop filter characteristics

To summarize, an ideal filter has a frequency response whose magnitude is a positive constant in the passband and zero elsewhere. The ideal filter also has a linear phase characteristic in the passband.

Example 4.13. This example illustrates the design of a digital filter.

Consider the system of Fig. 4.36 where the objective is to design a digital filter to implement the filtering of analog or continuous-time signals. We want to pass, with the same gain, all of the analog frequencies in the frequency range from 10 to 20 kilohertz with the maximum frequency in the analog signal $x(t)$ being 50 kilohertz. What specifications are required for the digital filter?

Solution: First, we need to decide upon a minimum sampling rate for this system. From Chapter Two we know that the sampling frequency must be at least twice the maximum analog frequency and that this analog frequency corresponds to a digital frequency of π radians.[†] With the frequency limit of the input signal at 50 kilohertz we can set this at one-half the sampling frequency which gives

$$f_s/2 = (50)10^3 \tag{4.218}$$

or

$$f_s = 2(50)10^3 \text{ Hz} \quad \text{and} \quad T = 1/f_s = 10^{-5} \text{ s}. \tag{4.219}$$

Thus, the desired digital passband frequencies range from the lower passband frequency of

$$\theta_{\text{lower}} = \theta_\ell = \omega_\ell T$$
$$= (2\pi)(10)(10^3)(10^{-5}) = 0.2\pi \tag{4.220}$$

to the upper passband frequency of

$$\theta_{\text{upper}} = \theta_u = \omega_u T$$
$$= (2\pi)(20)(10^3)(10^{-5}) = 0.4\pi. \tag{4.221}$$

This results in the ideal filter characteristic of Fig. 4.37 where the passband magnitude is the positive constant K and the phase has the desired linear characteristic $P = -\theta\ell$.

FIGURE 4.36 Filtering an analog signal

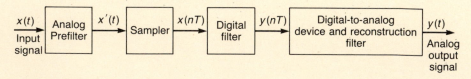

[†]In practice, it may be possible to relax this requirement by selecting a sampling frequency that causes aliased frequencies to lie in the stopband of the digital filter.

CHAPTER 4   FREQUENCY RESPONSE AND FILTERS

FIGURE 4.37 Ideal filter characteristic for Example 4.13

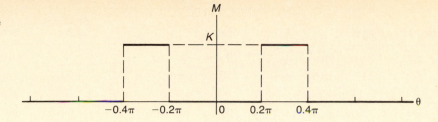

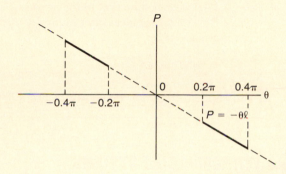

Example 4.14. This example illustrates the steps in determining the desired characteristics of an ideal filter.

The input sequence to a digital filter is

$$x(n) = 35 \cos(\pi n/5) + 21 \cos(\pi n/2 - \pi/4) - 15 \cos(2\pi n/3 + \pi/6)$$
$$+ 7 \cos(3\pi n/4 + \pi/3) \quad (4.222)$$

and the observed or measured output sequence is

$$y_{ss}(n) = 10.5 \cos(\pi n/2 - \pi/2) - 7.5 \cos(2\pi n/3 - \pi/6). \quad (4.223)$$

Sketch a frequency response characteristic which gives this input-output behavior. The answer is, of course, not unique.

Solution: From the sinusoidal steady-state formula, the calculated output sequence is given by

$$y_{ss}(n) = 35|H(e^{j\pi/5})| \cos(\pi n/5 + \angle H(e^{j\pi/5}))$$

$$+ 21|H(e^{j\pi/2})| \cos(\pi n/2 - \pi/4 + \angle H(e^{j\pi/2}))$$

$$- 15|H(e^{j2\pi/3})| \cos(2\pi n/3 + \pi/6 + \angle H(e^{j2\pi/3}))$$

$$+ 7|H(e^{j3\pi/4})| \cos(3\pi n/4 + \pi/3 + \angle H(e^{j3\pi/4})). \quad (4.224)$$

Comparison of Eq. 4.224 with the observed output sequence of Eq. 4.223 allows us to build a suitable frequency response characteristic. The necessary computations are given in the following table.

Frequency	Input	Output	Magnitude scaling	Phase shift	$H(e^{j\theta})$
$\pi/5$	$35\cos(\pi n/5)$	0	0	no meaning	0
$\pi/2$	$21\cos(\pi n/2 - \pi/4)$	$10.5\cos(\pi n/2 - \pi/2)$	0.5	$-\pi/4$	$0.5e^{-j\pi/4}$
$2\pi/3$	$-15\cos(2\pi n/3 + \pi/6)$	$-7.5\cos(2\pi n/3 - \pi/6)$	0.5	$-\pi/3$	$0.5e^{-j\pi/3}$
$3\pi/4$	$7\cos(3\pi n/4 + \pi/3)$	0	0	no meaning	0

Plotting these data we have the magnitude and phase plots of Fig. 4.38(a). From Fig. 4.38(a) we can state that in the passband the gain must be $M = 0.5$ and the phase $P = -\theta/2$. One ideal filter (there are many others) that would meet these criteria is given by

$$H(e^{j\theta}) = \begin{cases} 0.5e^{-j\theta/2}, & \pi/4 \le \theta \le 0.7\pi \\ 0, & \text{elsewhere in the interval } 0 \le \theta \le \pi \end{cases} \qquad (4.225)$$

and its characteristics are shown in Fig. 4.38(b).

4.6 ■ INTERCONNECTED SYSTEMS

In Chapter Three, we connected subsystems together to create a system that had new and desirable characteristics. We obtained the unit sample response of a cascade system by convolving the unit sample responses of the subsystems. For instance, the connection of the two subsystems of Fig. 4.39 produced a new system as described. Now let's look at this situation from the point of view of frequency response.

If we know that the frequency responses of the two systems are given by

$$H_1(e^{j\theta}) = M_1 e^{jP_1} \text{ and } H_2(e^{j\theta}) = M_2 e^{jP_2} \qquad (4.226)$$

and that the input sequence at the digital frequency θ is

$$x(n) = X\cos(\theta n) \qquad (4.227)$$

then the steady-state output of the first system is

$$w_{ss}(n) = XM_1 \cos(\theta n + P_1). \qquad (4.228)$$

But the output of System 1 is the input to System 2 and so

$$y_{ss}(n) = XM_1 M_2 \cos(\theta n + P_1 + P_2). \qquad (4.229)$$

Thus, we can say that the frequency response of the two cascaded subsystems is

$$H(e^{j\theta}) = M_1 M_2 e^{j(P_1 + P_2)} = M_1 e^{jP_1} \cdot M_2 e^{jP_2}$$

$$= Me^{jP} \qquad (4.230)$$

where $M = M_1 M_2$ and $P = P_1 + P_2$. The frequency response of the new

FIGURE 4.38(a) Data for Example 4.14

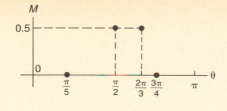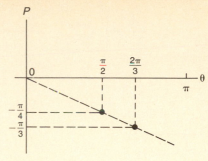

FIGURE 4.38(b) Filter characteristics for Example 4.14

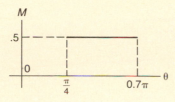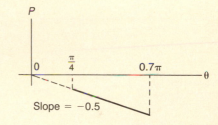

FIGURE 4.39 Cascade connection of systems

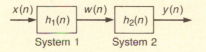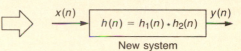

System 1   System 2   New system

system comes from multiplying the frequency response functions, i.e., multiplying the two magnitudes and adding the two phases. It is easily seen that this result can be extended to the situation where several systems are connected in cascade and the overall frequency response is the product of the frequency responses for each system.

Example 4.15. This example illustrates the construction of a bandpass filter from a cascade connection of a lowpass and a highpass filter.

An ideal lowpass filter shown in Fig. 4.40(a) is connected in cascade with an ideal highpass filter, also shown in Fig. 4.40(a). Show that this connection results in an ideal bandpass filter.

Solution: Multiplying the magnitudes and adding the phases gives the frequency response characteristic in Fig. 4.40(b), which is a bandpass characteristic.

A parallel interconnection was also discussed in Chapter Three and this configuration is illustrated in Fig. 4.41. Now in the steady-state, for

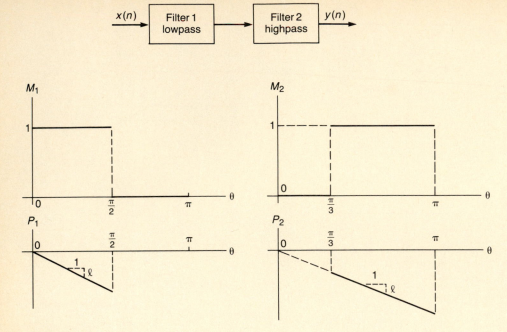

FIGURE 4.40(a) Cascade combination of ideal lowpass and highpass with overlapping passbands

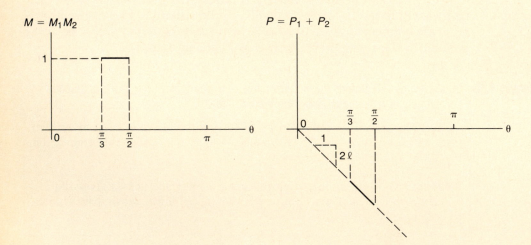

FIGURE 4.40(b) Resultant bandpass filter characteristic

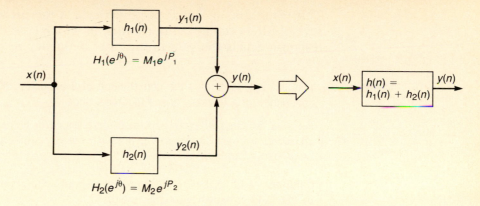

FIGURE 4.41 Parallel combination

$$x(n) = X \cos(\theta n),$$

$$y_{1ss}(n) = XM_1 \cos(\theta n + P_1) \tag{4.231}$$

and

$$y_{2ss}(n) = XM_2 \cos(\theta n + P_2) \tag{4.232}$$

with the output given by

$$
\begin{aligned}
y_{ss}(n) &= y_{1ss}(n) + y_{2ss}(n) \\
&= XM_1 \cos(\theta n + P_1) + XM_2 \cos(\theta n + P_2) \\
&= X[M_1 \cos(\theta n + P_1) + M_2 \cos(\theta n + P_2)].
\end{aligned} \tag{4.233}
$$

We can use the complex exponential representation of sinusoidal sequences to help us simplify the right side of Eq. 4.233. Representing $XM_1 \cos(\theta n + P_1)$ by the complex exponential $XM_1 e^{j(\theta n + P_1)}$ and $XM_2 \cos(\theta n + P_2)$ by the complex exponential $XM_2 e^{j(\theta n + P_2)}$ we can write Eq. 4.233 as

$$
\begin{aligned}
y_{ss}(n) &= Re\{X[M_1 e^{j(\theta n + P_1)} + M_2 e^{j(\theta n + P_2)}]\} \\
&= Re\{X[M_1 e^{j\theta n} e^{jP_1} + M_2 e^{j\theta n} e^{jP_2}]\} \\
&= Re\{Xe^{j\theta n}[M_1 e^{jP_1} + M_2 e^{jP_2}]\}.
\end{aligned} \tag{4.234}
$$

Now defining

$$Me^{jP} = M_1 e^{jP_1} + M_2 e^{jP_2} \tag{4.235}$$

gives

$$
\begin{aligned}
y_{ss}(n) &= Re[Xe^{j\theta n} Me^{jP}] = XM \, Re[e^{j(\theta n + P)}] \\
&= XM \cos(\theta n + P).
\end{aligned} \tag{4.236}
$$

Thus, we can say that the frequency response of the two parallel systems is the sum of the frequency responses, namely

$$H(e^{j\theta}) = H_1(e^{j\theta}) + H_2(e^{j\theta}). \tag{4.237}$$

This result can, of course, be generalized to the situation where there are several filters connected in parallel, in which case the overall frequency response equals the sum of the filter frequency responses.

Example 4.16. This example illustrates the construction of a bandstop filter from the parallel connection of a lowpass and a highpass filter.

An ideal lowpass filter and an ideal highpass filter whose frequency response characteristics are shown in Fig. 4.42 are connected in parallel. Show that this results in a bandstop filter.

Solution: Adding these two frequency response characteristics gives the result in Fig. 4.43, a bandstop characteristic.

4.7 ▬ REVIEW

The main theme of this chapter was the study of the response of linear time-invariant systems to sinusoidal input sequences. To do this, we started with the convolution summation and found the system output for a certain class of inputs—the complex exponential $x(n) = e^{j\theta n}$. The result was the steady-state output $y_{ss}(n) = e^{j\theta n} H(e^{j\theta})$, where the new terms eigenfunction, $e^{j\theta n}$, and eigenvalue, $H(e^{j\theta})$, were introduced. The designations characteristic function and characteristic value were also used to describe $e^{j\theta n}$ and its associated $H(e^{j\theta})$, respectively.

The steady-state response to the input $x(n) = X \cos(n\theta + \alpha)$ was determined by using the newly defined eigenfunctions and eigenvalues and this led to the sinusoidal steady-state formula that we used in several examples. Specifically, the eigenvalue for the eigenfunction $e^{j\theta n}$ is $H(e^{j\theta})$ and was given the special name of frequency response or frequency response function. The system frequency response can be computed from the unit sample response as

$$H(e^{j\theta}) = \sum_{n=-\infty}^{n=+\infty} h(n)e^{-j\theta n} \qquad (4.238)$$

or from the system difference equation by means of an algorithm that was developed in the chapter. The pseudocode for a computer subroutine to evaluate $H(e^{j\theta})$ and an experimental method for determining the plots of the magnitude and phase of $H(e^{j\theta})$ were also introduced.

The emphasis on frequency response in the first part of the chapter set the stage for the introduction of filters in the last half. The concept of an ideal filter was described in the discrete-time domain and then its frequency response was developed. Various kinds of ideal filters were described and then the frequency response characteristics of cascade and parallel connections were considered.

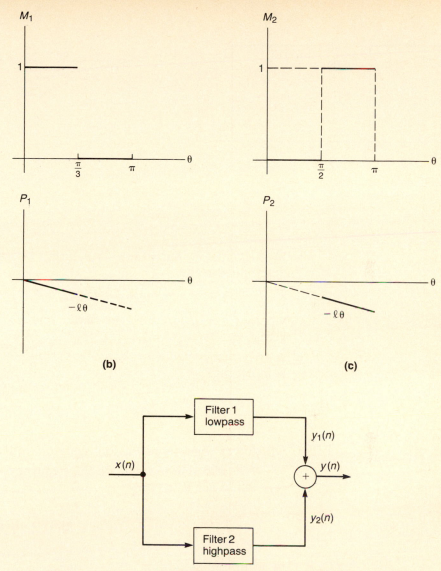

FIGURE 4.42 Parallel combination of ideal low-pass and highpass with nonoverlapping passbands

A new category of problems is introduced in this chapter. These problems are designated Integrated Review and are intended to provide just that.

VOCABULARY AND IMPORTANT RELATIONS

a) The use of complex exponentials was reviewed in this chapter. Complex exponentials, denoted by $e^{j\theta n}$, are defined for all values of n and have unity amplitude.

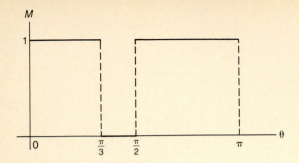

FIGURE 4.43 Bandstop filter of Example 4.16

b) By convolution, the steady-state output of a stable LTI system was determined to be

$$y_{ss}(n) = e^{j\theta n}H(e^{j\theta}), \quad -\infty \leq n \leq \infty \qquad (4.11)$$

where $e^{j\theta n}$ is a system eigenfunction and $H(e^{j\theta})$ is the associated eigenvalue.

c) A system eigenvalue for the system input $e^{j\theta n}$ is calculated from the summation

$$H(e^{j\theta}) = \sum_{m=-\infty}^{m=+\infty} h(m)e^{-j\theta m} \qquad (4.10)$$

which was then defined as the system frequency response.

d) We were also able to calculate the frequency response from the system difference equation,

$$y(n) - \sum_{k=1}^{k=N} a_k y(n-k) = \sum_{k=0}^{L} b_k x(n-k) \qquad (4.155)$$

by using the algorithm

$$H(e^{j\theta}) = \frac{\displaystyle\sum_{k=0}^{L} b_k e^{-jk\theta}}{1 - \displaystyle\sum_{k=1}^{N} a_k e^{-jk\theta}}. \qquad (4.160)$$

e) A stable LTI system with a sinusoidal input is described in the steady-state by Fig. 4.44 where the value of the system's frequency response at the digital frequency θ is $H(e^{j\theta}) = Me^{jP}$, X is the zero-to-peak amplitude of the input sequence, and the input phase is α radians.

CHAPTER 4 FREQUENCY RESPONSE AND FILTERS

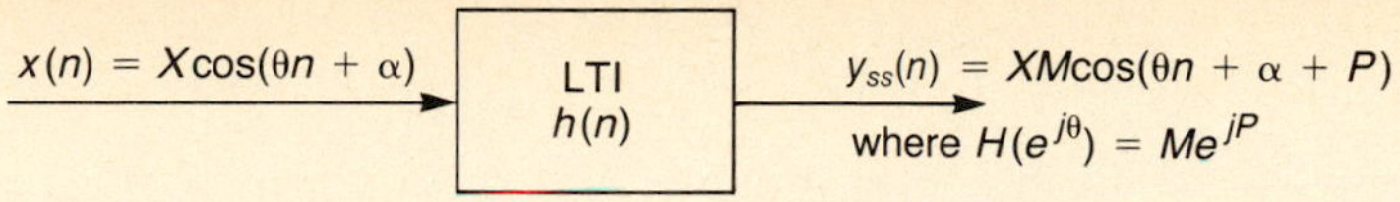

FIGURE 4.44 Sinusoidal steady-state

$$x(n) = X\cos(\theta n + \alpha)$$ → LTI $h(n)$ → $$y_{ss}(n) = XM\cos(\theta n + \alpha + P)$$
where $H(e^{j\theta}) = Me^{jP}$

f) The frequency response function $H(e^{j\theta}) = Me^{jP}$ is periodic—$H(e^{j\theta}) = H(e^{j(\theta \pm 2\pi)})$ and symmetrical—$|H(e^{j\theta})| = |H(e^{-j\theta})| = M$ (even symmetry) or $\angle H(e^{j\theta}) = -\angle H(e^{-j\theta}) = P$ (odd symmetry).

g) An ideal filter is defined in the discrete-time domain by

$$y_{ss}(n) = Ks(n - \ell) \qquad (4.209)$$

where $s(n)$ is the signal of interest in the input sequence $x(n)$. In terms of frequency response this becomes

$$H(e^{j\theta}) = \begin{cases} Ke^{-j\theta\ell} & , \quad \text{in the passband} \\ 0 & , \quad \text{otherwise.} \end{cases} \qquad (4.217)$$

In Eq. 4.217 the filter gain or magnitude is $M = K$ and the phase is $P = -\ell\theta$. Thus, the filter gain is a constant and the phase is a linear function of frequency θ in the passband.

PROBLEMS

Reinforcement

4.1 A discrete system is described by the difference equation $y(n) = x(n) - x(n-1)$.

a) Find the steady-state output for an input of $x(n) = e^{j\pi n/4}$.

b) Repeat part (a) for $x(n) = e^{-j\pi n/4}$.

c) Determine the steady-state output for $x(n) = 10\cos(\pi n/4)$.

 4.2 For the system of Problem 4.1, obtain a plot of the magnitude and phase of the frequency response for $0 \le \theta \le \pi$.

4.3 A continuous-time (analog) sinusoidal signal $x(t) = 0.707\sin(2000\pi t)$ is sampled at a frequency of 4 kHz and is then filtered by an LTI system described by the algorithm $y(n) - y(n-1) + 0.5y(n-2) = x(n)$, where $y(n)$ is the system output and $x(n)$ the input. Find the equation for the steady-state output $y_{ss}(n)$.

4.4 The input to a discrete system is $x(n) = 20\cos(\pi n/10) + 10\cos(\pi n/8 + \pi/2) + 25\cos(\pi n/3 - \pi/12)$. The steady-state output is $y_{ss}(n) = 5\cos(\pi n/10 - \pi/5) + 2.5\cos(\pi n/8 + \pi/4)$.

a) Sketch a frequency response magnitude and phase that would yield this input-output behavior. (The answer is not unique.)

b) Describe your answer above in words, e.g., bandpass filter with cutoff frequencies of $\pi/4$ and $\pi/2$.

4.5 A continuous-time signal is to be filtered to remove frequency components in the range 10 kHz $\le f \le$ 50 kHz. The maximum frequency component present in the signal is 100 kHz. The filtering is to be accomplished by sampling the continuous-time signal and using a digital filter.

a) What is the minimum sampling rate that can be used?

b) For the minimum sampling rate found in (a) what range of digital frequencies should be rejected by the filter?

c) Sketch the magnitude characteristic of an ideal digital filter that will accomplish the desired filtering operation.

4.6 The unit sample response of a linear time-invariant discrete system is

$$h(n) = -\frac{10}{3}\delta(n) + 30(-0.5)^n u(n) - \frac{80}{3}(-0.6)^n u(n).$$

a) Find the eigenvalue of the system that corresponds to the eigenfunction $e^{j\theta n} = (e^{j0})^n = 1^n$.

b) Repeat (a) for $e^{j\theta n} = e^{j\pi n/2}$.

4.7 A system's unit sample response is
$h(n) = 0.5(-0.8)^n u(n) + 0.5(0.8)^n u(n)$.

a) Find the eigenvalue that corresponds to the eigenfunction $e^{j\theta n} = (e^{j0})^n = 1^n$.

b) Determine the eigenvalue for the eigenfunction $e^{-j\pi n/2}$.

c) Determine the eigenvalue for the eigenfunction $e^{j\pi n/4}$.

4.8 An LTI discrete system is characterized by the difference equation
$y(n) = 0.5y(n-2) + x(n) + x(n-2)$.

a) Find the eigenvalue that corresponds to the eigenfunction $e^{j\theta n} = e^{j\pi n/4}$.

b) Repeat part (a) for the eigenfunction $e^{-j\pi n/4}$.

c) Determine the steady-state response for $x(n) = 2.5 \cos(\pi n/4)$.

4.9 An LTI discrete system is characterized by the difference equation $y(n) = \frac{1}{\sqrt{2}}y(n-1) -$

$$\frac{1}{4}y(n-2) + x(n) - \frac{4}{\sqrt{2}}x(n-1) + 4x(n-2).$$

a) Find the eigenvalue that corresponds to the eigenfunction $e^{j\theta n} = 1^n$.

b) Find the eigenvalue that corresponds to the eigenfunction $e^{j\pi n/6}$.

c) Repeat part (b) for $e^{j\theta n} = e^{j\pi n/3}$.

d) What do you observe about the answers to parts (a) through (c)?

4.10 The magnitude and phase characteristics of an ideal filter are shown in Fig. P4.10 for $-\pi \le \theta \le \pi$.

a) Find the steady-state response of the system if the input is $x(n) = 10 \cos(\pi n/8 - \pi/6) + 15 \cos(\pi n/2 + \pi/3) + 25 \cos(6\pi n/10 + \pi/4) - 9 \cos(4\pi n/5 + 3\pi/10)$.

b) What kind of a filter is this?

4.11 The magnitude and phase characteristics for a linear discrete system are given in Fig. P4.11 for $-\pi \le \theta \le \pi$.

a) Find the system's steady-state output if the input is $x(n) = 3 \cos(\pi n/6 + \pi/3) + 7 \cos(\pi n/3 - \pi/6) - 5 \cos(4\pi n/5 - \pi/2) + 3.5 \cos(9\pi n/10 + 3\pi/8)$.

b) What kind of a filter is this system?

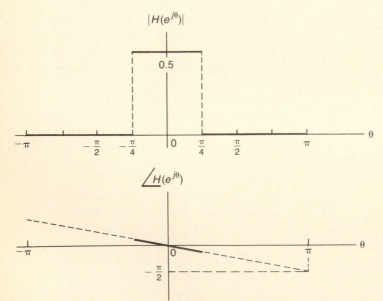

FIGURE P4.10

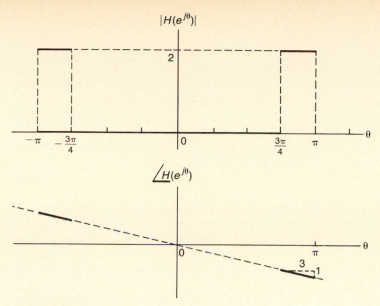

FIGURE P4.11

4.12 The input to a digital filter is given by $x(n) = 2 + 4.5 \cos(\pi n/6) + 12 \cos(\pi n/4) + 9 \cos(3\pi n/8) + 13 \cos(\pi n/2) + 3 \cos(3\pi n/4)$. A plot of the frequency response of this filter is shown in Fig. P4.12.

a) Write the expression for the filter output $y_{ss}(n)$.

b) Sketch the individual sinusoids in the output $y_{ss}(n)$.

c) What kind of filter is this?

4.13 Repeat Problem 4.12 for the filter characteristic shown in Fig. P4.13.

FIGURE P4.13

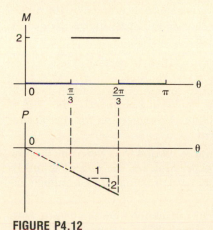

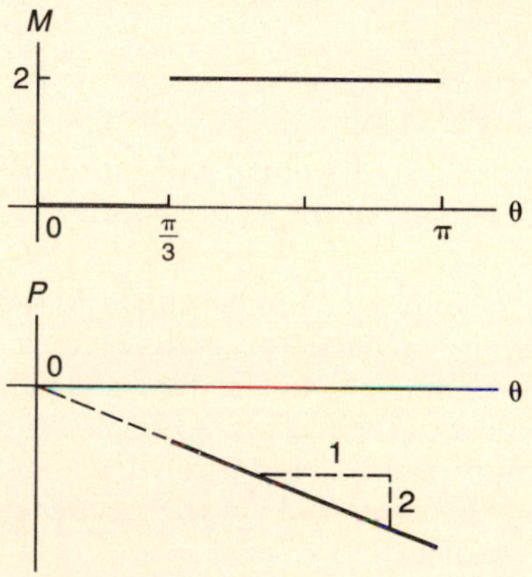

FIGURE P4.12

4.14 Given an LTI system with an input sequence $x(n) = 2 + 4.5 \cos(\pi n/6 - \pi/9) + 12 \cos(\pi n/4 + \pi/12) - 9 \cos(3\pi n/8 - \pi/12) + 13 \sin(\pi n/2) + 3 \cos(3\pi n/4)$.

a) Show a plot of the input amplitudes and a plot of the input phases as functions of θ.

b) If $x(n)$ is the input to a digital filter whose frequency response characteristic is shown in Fig. P4.14, show a plot of the corresponding output amplitudes and phases as functions of θ.

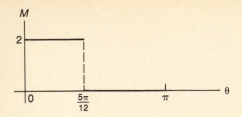

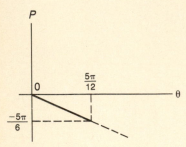

FIGURE P4.14

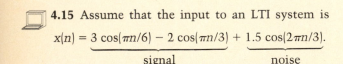

4.15 Assume that the input to an LTI system is

$$x(n) = \underbrace{3\cos(\pi n/6) - 2\cos(\pi n/3)}_{\text{signal}} + \underbrace{1.5\cos(2\pi n/3)}_{\text{noise}}.$$

It is desired to filter out the noise portion of the sequence $x(n)$ while passing the signal portion undistorted.

a) The discrete system to be used is an ideal low-pass filter whose frequency response characteristic is shown in Fig. P4.15(a). Find and plot the steady-state output $y_{ss}(n)$. Also plot the signal portion of $x(n)$ and compare with $y_{ss}(n)$. (Assume that the magnitude of the frequency response is equal to 1.)

b) Now assume that the discrete system has the same magnitude portion as in part (a) but the phase is as given in Fig. P4.15(b). Find and plot the steady-state output $y_{ss}(n)$ and compare with the signal portion of $x(n)$. Let the phase curve be defined by $P = -4\theta^2/\pi$.

c) Assume that the phase characteristic is again the same as in part (a), but that the magnitude part of the frequency response is as shown in Fig. P4.15(c). Find and plot the steady-state output $y_{ss}(n)$ and compare with the signal portion of $x(n)$.

d) What do you conclude by comparing the results of parts (a), (b), and (c)?

4.16 A system's frequency response is

$$H(e^{j\theta}) = \frac{e^{j2\theta}}{e^{j2\theta} + 0.25}.$$

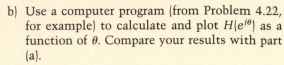

a) Calculate a few values of $H(e^{j\theta})$ and sketch the frequency response for $0 \le \theta \le \pi$.

b) Use a computer program (from Problem 4.22, for example) to calculate and plot $H(e^{j\theta})$ as a function of θ. Compare your results with part (a).

4.17 a) A *noncausal* FIR (finite-impulse response) filter has the unit sample response $h_{nc}(n)$ shown in Fig. P4.17(a). Find an analytical expression for the frequency response function $H_{nc}(e^{j\theta})$.

b) A *causal* FIR filter has the unit sample response $h_c(n)$ shown in Fig. P4.17(b). Find an analytical expression for the frequency response function $H_c(e^{j\theta})$.

c) Find an expression that relates $H_c(e^{j\theta})$ to $H_{nc}(e^{j\theta})$. What can be said about $|H_c(e^{j\theta})|$ and $|H_{nc}(e^{j\theta})|$? What is the relationship between $\angle H_{nc}(e^{j\theta})$ and $\angle H_c(e^{j\theta})$?

4.18 a) The ideal digital filters whose frequency responses are shown in Fig. P4.18(a) are connected in cascade as in Fig. P4.18(b). Find the range of frequencies that can be present in the output $y_{ss}(n)$.

b) The ideal digital filters whose frequency responses are shown in Fig. P4.18(a) on page 240 are connected in parallel as in Fig. P4.18(c). Find the range of frequencies that can be present in the output $y_{ss}(n)$.

Extension and Generalization

4.19 An LTI system's output is given by the difference of the present and the past inputs divided by the sampling period, that is,

$$y(nT) = \frac{1}{T}[x(nT) - x([n-1]T)].$$

a) If the input to the system is a sampled cosine given by $x(nT) = X\cos(n\omega T)$ or $x(n) = X\cos(\theta n)$, find the expression for the steady-state output.

b) If the sampling period T is very small show how the expression for the output found in part (a) may be approximated by a simpler expression.

c) Compare the expression found in part (b) with the input signal. What mathematical opera-

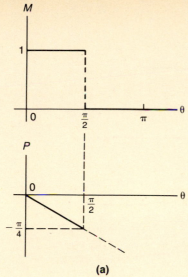

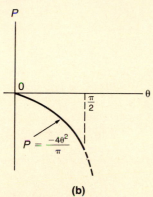

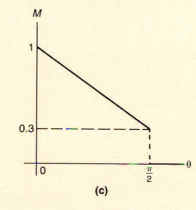

FIGURE P4.15

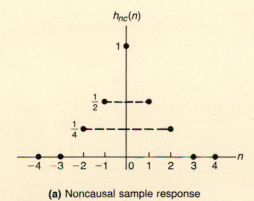

(a) Noncausal sample response   **(b)** Causal sample response

FIGURE P4.17

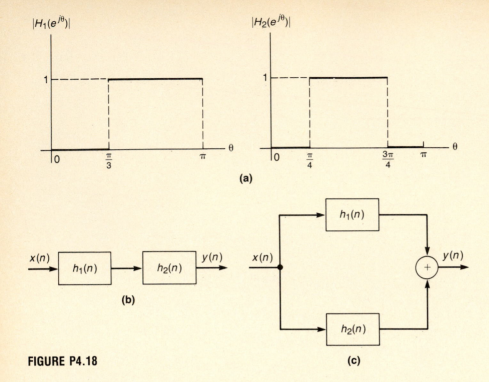

FIGURE P4.18

(a)

(b)

(c)

tion (approximately) does this system perform on the input?

d) Suppose that the input to the system is $x(n) = x_S(n) + x_N(n) = X_S \cos(\theta n) + X_N \cos(10\theta n)$ where $x_S(n)$ is the desired signal and $x_N(n)$ is unwanted noise.

i) Determine the steady-state response of the system. Assume $T << \pi/\omega$.

ii) What is the effect of the filter on the relative magnitudes of the signal and noise sequences?

4.20 It is desired to develop a difference equation that approximates the mathematical operation of integration. Suppose the function to be integrated is $x(t)$ shown in Fig. P4.20. The integral of $x(t)$ can be interpreted as the area under the $x(t)$ vs. t curve. The area under the curve in the interval $(n-1)T$ to nT is approximately equal to, using the formula for the area of a trapezoid, Area $= T\dfrac{x(n) + x(n-1)}{2}$. If $y(n)$ is the total area under the curve in the interval $-\infty$ to nT then

$$y(n) = y(n-1) + \frac{x(n) + x(n-1)}{2}T \qquad (1)$$

where $y(n-1)$ is the area in the interval $-\infty$ to $(n-1)T$. In other words,

$$\left[\begin{array}{c}\text{Area in the interval} \\ -\infty \text{ to } nT\end{array}\right] = \left[\begin{array}{c}\text{Area in the interval} \\ -\infty \text{ to } (n-1)T\end{array}\right]$$
$$+ \left[\begin{array}{c}\text{Area in the interval} \\ (n-1)T \text{ to } nT\end{array}\right].$$

a) Find the expression for the frequency response that corresponds to Eq. 1.

b) Find the steady-state solution for $y(n)$ if

$$x(n) = A \cos(\pi n/4).$$

4.21 The input sequence to an LTI system is $x(n) = X \cos(\theta n + \alpha)$. From first principles, show that the steady-state output is $y_{ss}(n) = XM \cos(\theta n + \alpha + P)$ where $H(e^{j\theta}) = Me^{jP}$.

4.22 Using the algorithmic description given in Section 4.2.3, write a computer subroutine or procedure to calculate the frequency response of a discrete system.

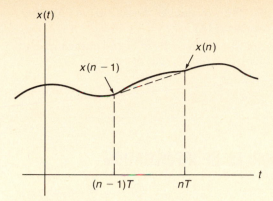

$x(t)$

$x(n)$

$x(n-1)$

$(n-1)T$ nT t

FIGURE P4.20

 4.23 Use the subroutine written in Problem 4.22 to obtain frequency response plots for the systems given in the following problems:

a) 4.16

b) 4.19 (Use $T = 1$)

c) 4.20(a) (Use $T = 1$)

d) 4.28(c)

4.24 Consider the polynomial $P(z) = b_0 z^L + b_1 z^{L-1} + b_2 z^{L-2} + \cdots + b_{L-1} z + b_L$ where b_k, $k = 0, 1, \ldots, L$ are assumed to be complex numbers and z is a complex variable. It is desired to estimate the computational cost of evaluating $P(z)$ for a specified value of z.

a) Determine the number of complex multiplies and adds required to evaluate $P(z)$ if it is done by finding z, multiplying by b_{L-1} and adding to b_L, followed by finding z^2, multiplying by b_{L-2} and adding, etc.

b) Repeat part (a) if the nesting approach is used, that is $P(z) = (\ldots(((b_0 z + b_1)z + b_2)z + b_3)z + \ldots) + b_L$.

4.25 The frequency response $H(e^{j\theta})$ of a discrete system can be written as the sum of an even frequency response function $H_e(e^{j\theta})$ and an odd frequency response function $H_o(e^{j\theta})$, i.e. $H(e^{j\theta}) = H_e(e^{j\theta}) + H_o(e^{j\theta})$ where $H_e(e^{j\theta}) = H_e(e^{-j\theta})$ and $H_o(e^{j\theta}) = -H_o(e^{-j\theta})$. Find expressions for $H_e(e^{j\theta})$ and $H_o(e^{j\theta})$ in terms of $H(e^{j\theta})$ and $H(e^{-j\theta})$.

Integrated Review

4.26 A discrete system has the frequency response $H(e^{j\theta}) = 1 + 4e^{-j\theta} - 3e^{-j2\theta} + 2e^{-j3\theta}$.

a) Find a difference equation that describes this system.

b) Determine this system's unit sample response.

c) Draw a block diagram or signal flow graph for this system.

d) The frequency response of a *different system* is given by

$$H(e^{j\theta}) = \frac{1 - 2.5e^{-j\theta} + 1.5e^{-j2\theta}}{1 + 0.4e^{-j\theta} - 0.05e^{-j2\theta}}.$$

Find a difference equation that describes this system.

e) Construct a block diagram or signal flow graph for the system of part (d).

f) Find an analytical expression for the initial condition response of the system of part (d) if the initial conditions for the output are $y(0) = 0$, $y(1) = 3$.

g) Find an analytical expression for the unit sample response of the system of part (d).

4.27 A discrete system is characterized by the difference equation $y(n) = -0.25y(n-2) + x(n)$.

a) What is the order of this system?

b) Draw a system diagram.

c) Is the system stable? Explain.

d) Find an analytical expression for the system's unit step response.

e) Find a closed form analytical expression (no summations allowed) for the system's frequency response.

f) For a system input of $x(n) = 6 + 15\cos(\pi n/2 + 0.436)$ find an analytical expression for the steady-state output.

4.28 A discrete system has the frequency response $H(e^{j\theta}) = 2 - 3e^{-j\theta} + 4e^{-j2\theta}$.

a) Find the difference equation that describes this system.

b) Determine this system's unit sample response.

c) The frequency response of a *different system* is given by

$$H(e^{j\theta}) = \frac{2 + 0.25e^{-j\theta}}{1 - 1.25e^{-j\theta} + 0.375e^{-j2\theta}}.$$

Find the difference equation that describes this system.

d) Construct a system diagram.

e) Which of the following terms describe the system of part (c)?

lowpass   highpass   bandpass   bandstop

IIR FIR recursive nonrecursive Moving Average (MA)

f) Find the algebraic form of the unit sample response for the system of part (c).

REFERENCES AND OTHER SOURCES OF INFORMATION

Antoniouu, Andreas. 1979. *Digital Filters: Analysis and Design.* New York: McGraw-Hill Book Company.

Bennett, R. J. 1979. *Spatial Time Series.* London: Pion Limited.

Braun, M. 1977. *Differential Equations and Their Applications.* New York: Springer-Verlag.

Hamming, R. W. 1983. *Digital Filters*, 2nd Ed. Englewood Cliffs, New Jersey: Prentice-Hall, Inc.

Oppenheim, A. V., and A. S. Willsky. 1983. *Signals and Systems.* Englewood Cliffs, New Jersey: Prentice-Hall, Inc.

Papoulis, A. 1977. *Signal Analysis.* New York: McGraw-Hill Book Company.

Van Valkenburg, M. E. 1982. *Analog Filter Design.* New York: Holt, Rinehart and Winston.

Zverev, A. I. 1967. *Handbook of Filter Synthesis.* New York: John Wiley and Sons, Inc.

CHAPTER 5

Frequency Response– A Graphical Method

5.0 ▬▬ PREVIEW

In Chapter Four, we began our discussion of digital filters and their frequency response. The concepts of ideal filters were introduced and several examples of filtering were presented, both in the discrete-time domain and by utilizing the associated frequency response characteristics.

It is apparent that the task of obtaining the exact frequency response characteristics of a filter is well-suited for a computer, for only in the simplest of situations are paper and pencil computations feasible. Indeed, if you worked Problem 4.22 you already have such a program available. Nevertheless, although we believe in using the computer, we don't believe results just because they come from a computer. Thus, one goal of this chapter is to develop a means of checking computer output quickly to verify its reasonableness.

A second goal is to use the graphical method for frequency response to design simple filters easily and rapidly with back-of-an-envelope computations. We design several practical filters using this procedure. Concurrently with this approximate design and analysis tool for frequency response, we will reinforce the relationships among several views of a discrete system—implementation diagram, difference equation, unit sample response, and frequency response.

5.1 ▬▬ GRAPHICAL CONCEPTS

We start with the frequency response function

$$H(e^{j\theta}) = \frac{1 + 0.5e^{-j\theta}}{1 - 0.5e^{-j\theta}}$$

$$= \frac{e^{j\theta} + 0.5}{e^{j\theta} - 0.5} \tag{5.1}$$

which is a complex number that may be written as the ratio of a numerator term and a denominator term as

$$H(e^{j\theta}) = \frac{Ne^{j\alpha}}{De^{j\beta}} \tag{5.2}$$

or

$$H(e^{j\theta}) = \frac{N}{D}e^{j(\alpha - \beta)} = Me^{jP} \tag{5.3}$$

where M is the magnitude and P is the phase of the frequency response, and we want to estimate M and P from a graphic or geometric point of view.

FIGURE 5.1 Graphical evaluation of the numerator term

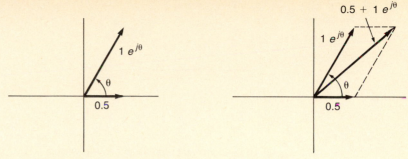

(a) The numerator represented as two vectors   **(b)** Construction of a parallelogram

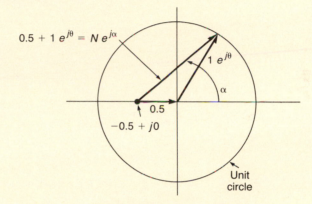

(c) The equivalent head-to-tail addition

First, consider the two terms $e^{j\theta}$ and 0.5 in the numerator of Eq. 5.1 or represented as the vectors $1e^{j\theta}$ and 0.5 in the complex plane of Fig. 5.1(a). We want to evaluate the sum of these two vectors to find $Ne^{j\alpha}$, the numerator of Eq. 5.2. This can be accomplished by using the familiar parallelogram rule for adding two vectors as shown in Fig. 5.1(b). A more convenient, but equivalent, approach is to represent the desired sum as shown in Fig. 5.1(c). Notice that we measure the vector $0.5 + 1e^{j\theta}$ from its origin, the point $-0.5 + j0$, and that the tip of the resultant vector $Ne^{j\alpha}$ lies on the unit circle.

Now consider the two terms in the denominator of Eq. 5.2, $e^{j\theta}$ and -0.5, represented as the vectors $1e^{j\theta}$ and -0.5 in Fig. 5.2(a) with the parallelogram addition rule implemented in Fig. 5.2(b). In Fig. 5.2(c) we see the equivalent approach to the addition of -0.5 to $e^{j\theta}$ where this vector is measured from the point $0.5 + j0$ and the tip of the resultant vector $De^{j\beta}$ lies on the unit circle.

Finally, we need to consider these two complex numbers $Ne^{j\alpha}$ and $De^{j\beta}$ for digital frequencies in the range $0 \leq \theta \leq \pi$. In Fig. 5.3 we have drawn each of these two vectors for four different frequencies, $\theta = 0$, $\pi/2$,

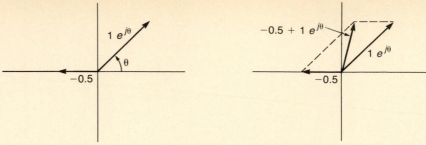

FIGURE 5.2 Graphical evaluation of the denominator term

(a) The denominator represented as two vectors   **(b)** Construction of a parallelogram

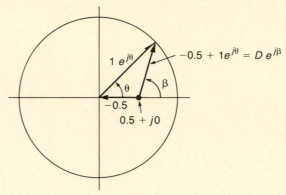

(c) The equivalent head-to-tail addition

FIGURE 5.3 The graphical method for a first-order filter

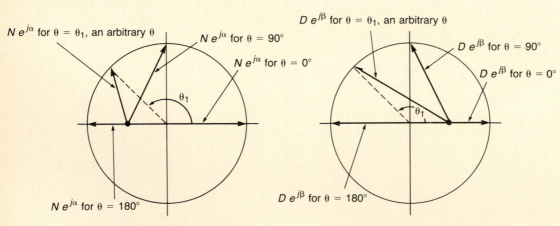

(a) Evaluation of the numerator term for several different frequencies

(b) Evaluation of the denominator term for several different frequencies

π, and θ_1, an arbitrary value of θ. The magnitude of the frequency response is $M = N/D$, the phase is $P = \alpha - \beta$ and it is very easy to make three quick calculations as tabulated below.[†]

Frequency θ	Numerator $Ne^{j\alpha}$	Denominator $De^{j\beta}$	Ratio Me^{jP}
0	$1.5e^{j0°}$	$0.5e^{j0°}$	$3e^{j0°}$
$\pi/2$	$1.12e^{j63.4°}$	$1.12e^{j116.6°}$	$1e^{-j53.2°}$
π	$0.5e^{j180°}$	$1.5e^{j180°}$	$0.33e^{j0°}$

The magnitude M decreases as the frequency increases, and from Fig. 5.3 we see that N decreases in length and D increases in length as θ changes from 0 to π. The phase P is a bit harder to predict but a little study will show that α is smaller than β for all frequencies and hence the phase will be negative for all $0 < \theta < \pi$. Thus, this filter is described as lowpass and negative phase. Engineers might call this a phase lag filter since when the input is a sinusoidal sequence the output sinusoidal sequence always is behind (lags) the input sequence. The exact magnitude and phase plots are given in Fig. 5.4 where we see that the three points that were computed give a reasonable estimate of what to expect.

Example 5.1. This example illustrates the graphical estimation of the frequency response of two first-order systems.

The general form of the unit sample response for a given causal, first-order filter is $h(n) = a^n u(n)$ with $|a| < 1$ to ensure stability. Use the graphical method just discussed to estimate the frequency response for two different values of a, say ± 0.5.

Solution: First, for $a = +0.5$ we have

$$H(e^{j\theta}) = \sum_{m=0}^{m=\infty} (0.5)^m e^{-j\theta m} \tag{5.4}$$

where this infinite geometric sum can be written as

$$H(e^{j\theta}) = \frac{1}{1 - 0.5e^{-j\theta}}, \quad \text{since} \quad |0.5e^{-j\theta}| < 1$$

$$= \frac{e^{j\theta}}{e^{j\theta} - 0.5}. \tag{5.5}$$

This is of the general form

$$H(e^{j\theta}) = \frac{Ne^{j\alpha}}{De^{j\beta}}$$

$$= Me^{jP}. \tag{5.6}$$

[†]For ease of visualization we sometimes express angles in degrees.

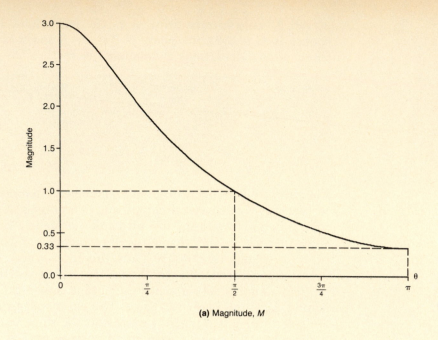

(a) Magnitude, *M*

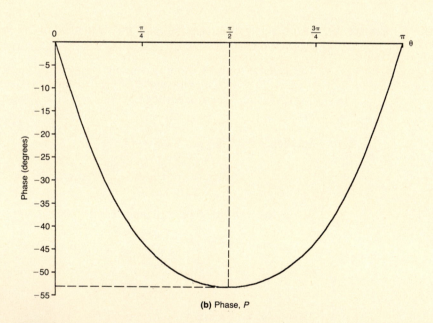

(b) Phase, *P*

FIGURE 5.4 First-order lowpass filter frequency response

The numerator vector is $Ne^{j\alpha} = 1e^{j\theta}$ for all values of θ as in Fig. 5.5(a) and the denominator vector $De^{j\beta}$ starts with $0.5e^{j0°}$ at $\theta = 0$ and increases in length and in phase to $1.5e^{j180°}$ at $\theta = \pi$. Three easy-to-make computations are tabulated below and we note that M decreases monotonically as θ increases from 0 to π while D increases monotonically as shown in Fig. 5.5(b), and that the phase will always be negative because β is always greater than α for $0 < \theta < \pi$. Again this is a lowpass, negative phase (or phase lag) filter where the computer-generated frequency response is as shown in Fig. 5.6.

Frequency θ	Numerator $Ne^{j\alpha}$	Denominator $De^{j\beta}$	Ratio Me^{jP}
0	$1e^{j0°}$	$0.5e^{j0°}$	$2e^{j0°}$
$\pi/2$	$1e^{j90°}$	$1.12e^{j116.6°}$	$0.89e^{-j26.6°}$
π	$1e^{j180°}$	$1.5e^{j180°}$	$0.67e^{j0°}$

Now for the negative value of $a = -0.5$, the frequency response is

$$H(e^{j\theta}) = \frac{1}{1 - ae^{-j\theta}} = \frac{1}{1 + 0.5e^{-j\theta}}$$

$$= \frac{e^{j\theta}}{e^{j\theta} + 0.5}$$

$$= \frac{Ne^{j\alpha}}{De^{j\beta}} = Me^{jP} \qquad (5.7)$$

and shown in Fig. 5.7 is the vector addition that results in the denominator term $De^{j\beta} = 0.5 + 1e^{j\theta}$. The numerator is always $1e^{j\theta}$ which leads to the quick tabulation indicated and we note that M increases monotonically (D decreases monotonically with θ). Here, however, the phase is positive because $\alpha = \theta$ is always greater than β. Figure 5.8 shows the amplitude and phase characteristics of this highpass filter that would be used to filter out sequences composed

FIGURE 5.5 The frequency response function represented by vectors for $H(e^{j\theta}) = e^{j\theta}/(e^{j\theta} - 0.5)$

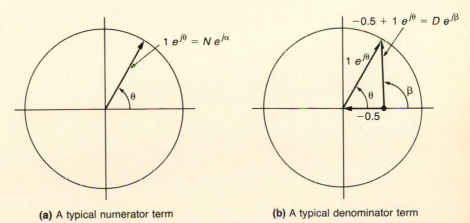

(a) A typical numerator term

(b) A typical denominator term

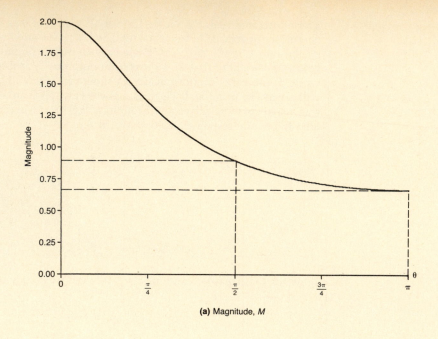

(a) Magnitude, *M*

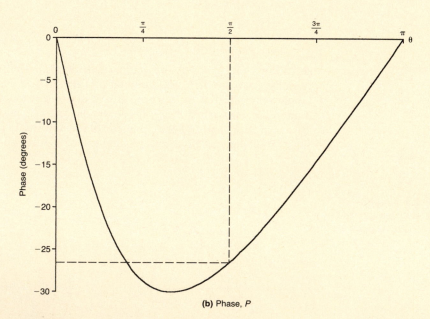

(b) Phase, *P*

FIGURE 5.6   Lowpass filter frequency response

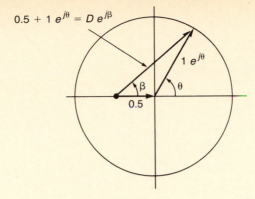

FIGURE 5.7 Illustration of the graphical evaluation of the denominator term for $H(e^{j\theta}) = e^{j\theta}/(e^{j\theta} + 0.5)$

$$0.5 + 1\,e^{j\theta} = D\,e^{j\beta}$$

of low frequency sinusoids and pass more easily those containing higher frequencies.

Frequency θ	Numerator $Ne^{j\alpha}$	Denominator $De^{j\beta}$	Ratio Me^{jP}
0	$1e^{j0°}$	$1.5e^{j0°}$	$0.67e^{j0°}$
$\pi/2$	$1e^{j90°}$	$1.12e^{j63.4°}$	$0.89e^{j26.6°}$
π	$1e^{j180°}$	$0.5e^{j180°}$	$2e^{j0°}$

Comment: To reflect for a moment on this example, we note the simplicity inherent in digital filters. The difference equation that corresponds to the unit sample response of $h(n) = a^n u(n)$ is

$$y(n) = ay(n-1) + x(n) \tag{5.8}$$

and the system diagram for this first-order recursive filter is given in Fig. 5.9. So, merely changing the sign of the filter coefficient a from $+$ to $-$ dramatically alters the filter characteristic: a lowpass becomes a highpass.

5.2 ▬ GEOMETRIC ALGORITHM FOR SKETCHING THE FREQUENCY RESPONSE

We now generalize the approach of the previous section where we estimated the frequency response of three first-order filters from a geometric point of view. Most filters aren't simply first-order, but the graphical method is still helpful and naturally applies to higher-order systems.

The frequency response of an Nth-order system was derived in Chapter Four from the Nth-order difference equation

$$y(n) - \sum_{k=1}^{N} a_k y(n-k) = \sum_{k=0}^{L} b_k x(n-k) \tag{5.9}$$

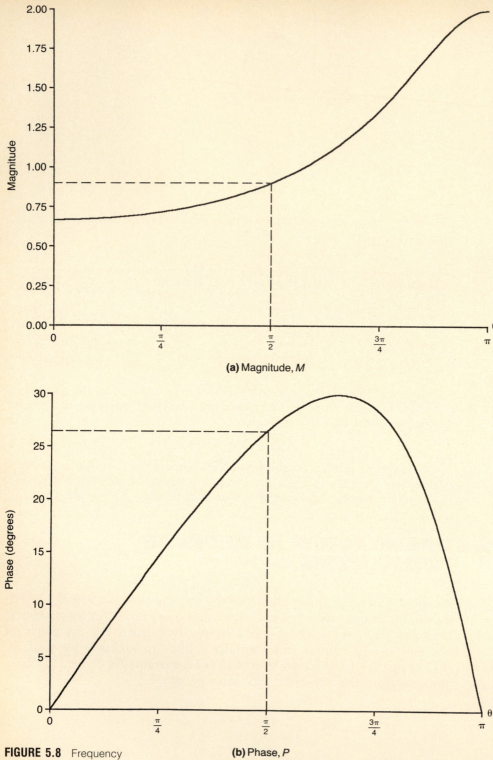

FIGURE 5.8 Frequency response for system with $H(e^{j\theta}) = e^{j\theta}/(e^{j\theta} - 0.5)$

(a) Magnitude, M

(b) Phase, P

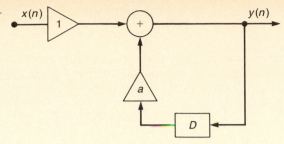

and the result from Eq. 4.161 is repeated below

$$H(e^{j\theta}) = \frac{b_0 + b_1 e^{-j\theta} + b_2 e^{-j2\theta} + \cdots + b_L e^{-jL\theta}}{1 - a_1 e^{-j\theta} - a_2 e^{-j2\theta} - \cdots - a_N e^{-jN\theta}}. \tag{5.10}$$

We must keep in mind that the concept of frequency response is meaningful only for a stable system. Thus, we must ensure that the roots of the characteristic equation all have magnitudes less than one before obtaining $H(e^{j\theta})$ in Eq. 5.10 and proceeding. Putting Eq. 5.10 in terms of powers of $e^{j\theta}$ rather than $e^{-j\theta}$ we have

$$H(e^{j\theta}) = e^{j(N-L)\theta}\left[\frac{b_0 e^{jL\theta} + b_1 e^{j(L-1)\theta} + \cdots + b_L}{e^{jN\theta} - a_1 e^{j(N-1)\theta} - \cdots - a_N}\right]. \tag{5.11}$$

We know that $e^{j\theta}$ is a complex quantity whose magnitude is always 1. For the moment, let's rewrite Eq. 5.11 in terms of a more general complex variable designated as z that can take on any value, that is, let $z = \sigma + j\phi = \gamma e^{j\psi}$, where σ, ϕ, γ, and ψ are real. With this assumption Eq. 5.11 becomes

$$H(z) = \frac{z^{N-L}[b_0 z^L + b_1 z^{L-1} + \cdots + b_L]}{z^N - a_1 z^{N-1} - \cdots - a_N} \tag{5.12}$$

where we have replaced the complex quantity $e^{j\theta}$ with the complex variable z. Equation 5.12 is a generalization of Eq. 5.11 because z can take on any value while $e^{j\theta}$ is restricted to values whose magnitudes are always 1. Factoring the equation for $H(z)$ into first-order terms gives

$$H(z) = b_0 z^{N-L} \frac{(z - n_1)(z - n_2) \cdots (z - n_L)}{(z - d_1)(z - d_2) \cdots (z - d_N)} \tag{5.13}$$

where $n_1, n_2, \ldots, n_L$ are the roots of

$$(z - n_1)(z - n_2) \cdots (z - n_L) = 0 \tag{5.14}$$

and $d_1, d_2, \ldots, d_N$ are the roots of

$$(z - d_1)(z - d_2) \cdots (z - d_N) = 0^\dagger.$$ (5.15)

We are now in a position to use our new complex variable z. In Example 4.11 of the last chapter we developed the frequency response for a second-order filter in Eq. 4.177 to be

$$H(e^{j\theta}) = \frac{e^{-j\theta} - e^{-j3\theta}}{1 + 0.5e^{-j2\theta}}$$

$$= \frac{e^{j2\theta} - 1}{e^{j3\theta} + 0.5e^{j\theta}}.$$ (5.16)

Extending Eq. 5.16 to the more general variable z gives us

$$H(z) = \frac{z^2 - 1}{z^3 + 0.5z}$$ (5.17)

which needs to be in factored form to apply the geometric algorithm. For the numerator we have

$$z^2 - 1 = 0, \text{ with the roots } z_1 = 1 \text{ and } z_2 = -1.$$ (5.18)

The third-order denominator gives

$$z(z^2 + 0.5) = 0 \text{ with the roots } z_1 = 0, z_2 = j\sqrt{0.5}, \text{ and } z_3 = -j\sqrt{0.5}.$$ (5.19)

Putting the complex roots $(z_{2,3} = \pm j\sqrt{0.5})$ into exponential form, Eq. 5.17 can be expressed in factored form as

$$H(z) = \frac{(z - 1)(z + 1)}{z(z - 0.707e^{j\pi/2})(z - 0.707e^{-j\pi/2})}.$$ (5.20)

Comparing Eq. 5.20 with Eq. 5.13 we see that

$$n_1 = 1, n_2 = -1, d_1 = 0, d_2 = 0.707e^{j\pi/2}, \text{ and } d_3 = 0.707e^{-j\pi/2}$$ (5.21)

with the n's marked with zeros and the d's as x's in Fig. 5.10(a). Thus, the n's can naturally be called *zeros* because for these values of z, $H(z)$ is zero. At the values of z defined as the d's the complex function $H(z)$ becomes infinite, and thus we call these the *poles*, signifying a large (tall) value. In summary, $H(z) = 0$ at the zeros and $H(z) \to \infty$ at the poles. These definitions of poles and zeros are quite useful in explaining the graphical procedure for estimation of the frequency response of a filter.

Let's stop for a minute to consider our position and the relationship between z and $e^{j\theta}$ remembering that our ultimate goal is to find the frequency response $H(e^{j\theta})$. We have just factored $H(z)$ into first-order terms

---

†Keep in mind that the roots $n_1, n_2, \ldots, n_L$ and $d_1, d_2, \ldots, d_N$ are complex numbers, in general, and that all complex roots must appear in conjugate pairs because the coefficients in the polynomials are all real numbers.

FIGURE 5.10 Using poles
and zeros to estimate the
frequency response

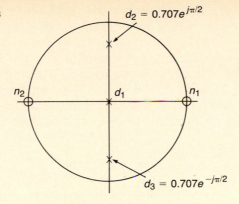

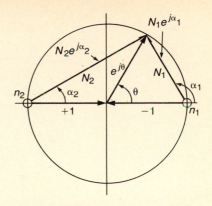

(a) A plot of the poles and zeros

(b) A typical set of numerator vectors

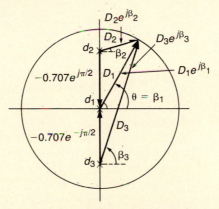

(c) A typical set of denominator vectors

and have described this factorization in terms of poles and zeros. Having done that, we will now get back to the desired $H(e^{j\theta})$ by letting the general complex variable z equal the specific value $e^{j\theta}$. Thus, Eq. 5.20 becomes

$$H(e^{j\theta}) = \frac{(e^{j\theta} - 1)(e^{j\theta} + 1)}{e^{j\theta}(e^{j\theta} - 0.707e^{j\pi/2})(e^{j\theta} - 0.707e^{-j\pi/2})} \tag{5.22}$$

which we will now interpret geometrically.

First, consider the numerator term $e^{j\theta} - 1$, which is more easily visualized as $-1 + e^{j\theta}$. From Fig. 5.10(b) we see that $-1 + e^{j\theta}$ can be drawn as a vector from the zero n_1 to the point on the unit circle that is the tip of $e^{j\theta}$. This vector is $N_1e^{j\alpha_1}$ in Fig. 5.10(b). Likewise, the term $e^{j\theta} + 1$ can be drawn as a vector from the zero n_2 to the point on the unit circle that is the tip of $e^{j\theta}$. This vector is $N_2e^{j\alpha_2}$ in Fig. 5.10(b). In summary, the numerator of $H(e^{j\theta})$ can be described in terms of two vectors drawn from the two zeros, n_1 and n_2, to the point on the unit circle that is the tip of $e^{j\theta}$.

Naturally, the denominator terms invite the same interpretation. The term $D_1 e^{j\beta_1} = D_1 e^{j\theta}$ is simply a vector drawn from the pole d_1 to the point on the unit circle that is the tip of $e^{j\theta}$ as in Fig. 5.10(c). The term $e^{j\theta} - 0.707 e^{j\pi/2}$ is a vector drawn from d_2 to the unit circle and is $D_2 e^{j\beta_2}$ in Fig. 5.10(c). Finally, $e^{j\theta} - 0.707 e^{-j\pi/2} = D_3 e^{j\beta_3}$ and we see that the denominator of $H(e^{j\theta})$ can be described in terms of three vectors drawn from the three poles, d_1, d_2, and d_3, to the point on the unit circle that is the tip of $e^{j\theta}$.

The frequency response is

$$H(e^{j\theta}) = \frac{(N_1 e^{j\alpha_1})(N_2 e^{j\alpha_2})}{(D_1 e^{j\beta_1})(D_2 e^{j\beta_2})(D_3 e^{j\beta_3})} \qquad (5.23)$$

which can be simplified to

$$H(e^{j\theta}) = \frac{N_1 N_2}{(1)D_2 D_3} e^{j(\alpha_1 + \alpha_2 - \theta - \beta_2 - \beta_3)} \qquad (5.24)$$

with $D_1 = 1$ and $\beta_1 = \theta$.

The magnitude is $M = N_1 N_2/(1)D_2 D_3$ and the phase is $P = \alpha_1 + \alpha_2 - (\theta + \beta_2 + \beta_3)$. Now what about an estimate of M vs. θ from this graphical point of view? (We will not concern ourselves with P vs. θ in this example.) All five vectors from Eq. 5.23 are shown in Fig. 5.11 to aid us in the visualization for an arbitrary value of θ. Starting with $\theta = 0$ we see that $N_1 = 0$ at this frequency which also causes M to be zero as seen on the computer-generated frequency response plot in Fig. 5.12. Going to the other extreme of $\theta = \pi$, $N_2 = 0$ and so we have $M = 0$ at both $\theta = 0$ and π.

Now looking at $M = N_1 N_2/D_2 D_3$ as θ goes from 0 to π we note that D_2 becomes relatively short (remember that this is a qualitative method and only approximate or estimated values are required) at $\theta = \pi/2$ where it is $(1 - 0.707)$ or about 0.3. At $\theta = \pi/2$, $N_1 = N_2 = \sqrt{2}$, and $D_3 = 1.707$. Thus, the "gain" at $\theta = \pi/2$ is approximately

FIGURE 5.11 A typical set of vectors used in estimating the frequency response of a bandpass filter

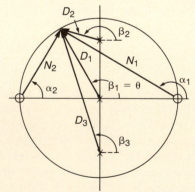

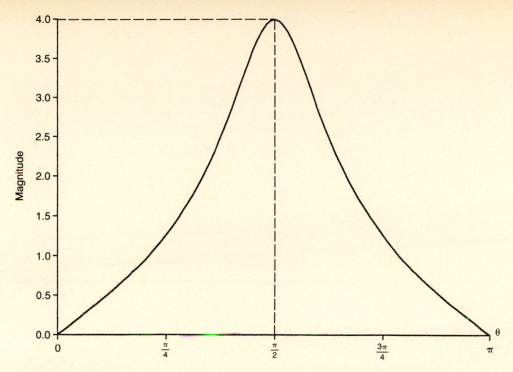

FIGURE 5.12 Bandpass digital filter frequency response magnitude M

$$M_{\theta=\pi/2} = \frac{N_1 N_2}{D_1 D_2} \approx \frac{(\sqrt{2})(\sqrt{2})}{(0.3)(1.707)} \approx 4 \tag{5.25}$$

and this point is also seen on the graph of Fig. 5.12. Remember that this method will yield approximate answers or good guesses and that is all that is intended. For all but the simplest filters, plots of phase P vs. frequency θ are difficult to estimate using this approach and we do not try to do so.

Let us now give a general statement of this geometric algorithm for obtaining a sketch of $H(e^{j\theta})$.

PROCEDURE

We start with the factored form of the frequency response written in terms of the general complex variable z as

$$H(z) = \frac{b_0 z^{N-L}(z - n_1)(z - n_2) \cdots (z - n_L)}{(z - d_1)(z - d_2) \cdots (z - d_N)} \tag{5.26}$$

which in terms of $z = e^{j\theta}$ becomes

$$H(e^{j\theta}) = b_0 e^{j(N-L)\theta} \frac{(e^{j\theta} - n_1)(e^{j\theta} - n_2) \cdots (e^{j\theta} - n_L)}{(e^{j\theta} - d_1)(e^{j\theta} - d_2) \cdots (e^{j\theta} - d_N)}. \tag{5.27}$$

To interpret this graphically, Eq. 5.27 is written in terms of vectors as

$$H(e^{j\theta}) = b_0 e^{j(N-L)\theta} \frac{(N_1 e^{j\alpha_1})(N_2 e^{j\alpha_2}) \cdots (N_L e^{j\alpha_L})}{(D_1 e^{j\beta_1})(D_2 e^{j\beta_2}) \cdots (D_N e^{j\beta_N})} \quad (5.28)$$

where $N_q e^{j\alpha_q}$ is the vector from the zero n_q to the tip of the $e^{j\theta}$ vector, $q = 1,$ $2, \ldots, L$ and $D_p e^{j\beta_p}$ is the vector from the pole d_p to the tip of the $e^{j\theta}$ vector, $p = 1, 2, \ldots, N$. Remember that $z = e^{j\theta}$ where θ is the digital frequency of the input. The magnitude of the frequency response is

$$M = b_0 N_1 N_2 \cdots N_L / D_1 D_2 \cdots D_N \quad (5.29)$$

and the phase is

$$P = (N - L)\theta + \alpha_1 + \alpha_2 + \cdots + \alpha_L - (\beta_1 + \beta_2 + \cdots + \beta_N)$$

$$= (N - L)\theta + \sum_{k=1}^{L} \alpha_k - \sum_{k=1}^{N} \beta_k. \quad (5.30)$$

The N's, D's, α's, and β's can be evaluated as indicated in Fig. 5.13.

5.3 ▪ GRAPHICAL DESIGN OF FILTERS

The design of filters can be viewed as a matter of shaping the frequency response by placing the roots of the numerator and denominator polynomials (the zeros and poles) of $H(z)$ in the appropriate locations in the complex plane. In this section we see how it is possible to do this. Although there are other methods that we consider later that involve structured step-by-step procedures, it is surprising to find that filters with reasonably good performance characteristics can be designed by this simple graphical approach. Before describing the design technique, we focus on a few simple concepts that aid us in formulating this graphical method.

FIGURE 5.13 The general case for the graphical evaluation of the frequency response

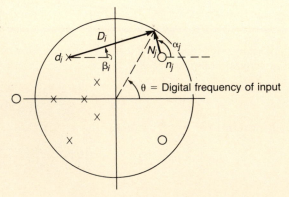

5.3.1 Stability

The frequency response $H(e^{j\theta})$ is valid only for a stable system, so let us now investigate stability in terms of the location of the poles and zeros of the general frequency response function $H(z)$.

First, a causal nonrecursive filter with L delays of the input is described by the difference equation

$$y(n) = b_0 x(n) + b_1 x(n-1) + \cdots + b_L x(n-L) \tag{5.31}$$

and the unit sample response is found by letting $x(n) = \delta(n)$ giving

$$y(n) = b_0 \delta(n) + b_1 \delta(n-1) + \cdots + b_L \delta(n-L). \tag{5.32}$$

Since $x(n) = \delta(n)$, Eq. 5.32 is the unit sample response and we use the notation

$$h(n) = h(0)\delta(n) + h(1)\delta(n-1) + \cdots + h(L)\delta(n-L), \tag{5.33}$$

which is the unit sample response of a stable filter because

$$\sum_{n=0}^{n=+\infty} |h(n)| < \infty. \tag{5.34}$$

The frequency response of this filter is

$$
\begin{aligned}
H(e^{j\theta}) &= \sum_{m=0}^{L} h(m)e^{-j\theta m} \\
&= h(0) + h(1)e^{-j\theta} + \cdots + h(L)e^{-jL\theta} \\
&= \frac{h(0)e^{jL\theta} + h(1)e^{j(L-1)\theta} + \cdots + h(L)}{e^{jL\theta}}.
\end{aligned}
\tag{5.35}
$$

To talk about poles and zeros we need to express Eq. 5.35 in terms of the general complex variable z rather than the special value of $z = e^{j\theta}$. This gives us the *generalized frequency response*[†]

$$H(z) = \frac{h(0)z^L + h(1)z^{L-1} + \cdots + h(L)}{z^L} \tag{5.36}$$

which we look at in terms of its poles and zeros. First, we note that the poles that come from the equation

$$z^L = 0 \tag{5.37}$$

are L in number and all lie at the origin of the complex z-plane. The zeros are the roots of

$$h(0)z^L + h(1)z^{L-1} + \cdots + h(L) = 0 \tag{5.38}$$

[†]In Chapter Six we use $H(z)$ in an even more general way and call it the system transfer function.

and since the coefficients in this equation are the filter weights used to shape the frequency response (magnitude and phase), these zeros are a function of the design and consequently may lie anywhere in the complex plane. So for a nonrecursive filter that is always stable we have established that all L poles are at the origin, and the L zeros can take on any values with complex zeros always occurring in conjugate pairs.

Turning our attention to causal recursive filters, we observed in Section 3.7 that the unit sample response of a causal, Nth order recursive filter with distinct characteristic roots is given by

$$h(n) = \sum_{k=1}^{k=N} C_k r_k{}^n u(n) + \sum_{k=0}^{k=L-N} A_k \delta(n - k)$$

$$= h_1(n) + h_2(n) \tag{5.39}$$

where the r_k's are the system's characteristic roots, the C_k's and A_k's are constants, and $u(n)$ is needed to denote the causal nature of the filter. Let us assume that the system is stable and see what this means in terms of the poles and zeros. The frequency response is given by

$$H(e^{j\theta}) = \sum_{m=0}^{\infty} h_1(m) e^{-j\theta m} + \sum_{m=0}^{\infty} h_2(m) e^{-j\theta m}$$

$$= H_1(e^{j\theta}) + H_2(e^{j\theta}) \tag{5.40}$$

and the contribution to the frequency response for a typical term in $H_1(e^{j\theta})$ in Eq. 5.40 is described by

$$H_{1k}(e^{j\theta}) = \sum_{m=0}^{m=\infty} C_k r_k{}^m e^{-j\theta m}$$

$$= C_k \sum_{m=0}^{m=\infty} (r_k e^{-j\theta})^m. \tag{5.41}$$

Turning once more to the complex variable z, Eq. 5.41 becomes

$$H_{1k}(z) = C_k \sum_{m=0}^{m=\infty} (r_k z^{-1})^m$$

$$= \frac{C_k}{1 - r_k z^{-1}} \quad \text{for} \quad |r_k z^{-1}| < 1. \tag{5.42}$$

Including all of the terms from $h_1(m)$ and, consequently $H_1(e^{j\theta})$, gives

$$H_1(z) = \frac{C_1}{1 - r_1 z^{-1}} + \frac{C_2}{1 - r_2 z^{-1}} + \cdots + \frac{C_N}{1 - r_N z^{-1}}$$

$$= \frac{C_1 z}{z - r_1} + \frac{C_2 z}{z - r_2} + \cdots + \frac{C_N z}{z - r_N}. \tag{5.43}$$

Combining these functions over a common denominator results in

$$H_1(z) = \frac{\text{a polynomial in } z}{(z - r_1)(z - r_2) \cdots (z - r_N)}. \tag{5.44}$$

Returning to Eq. 5.39 to investigate the effect of $h_2(n)$ we have

$$H_2(e^{j\theta}) = \sum_{m=0}^{\infty} [A_0\delta(m) + A_1\delta(m - 1) + \cdots + A_{L-N}\delta(m - [L - N])]e^{-jm\theta}$$

$$\tag{5.45}$$

which can be written as

$$H_2(e^{j\theta}) = A_0 + A_1e^{-j\theta} + \cdots + A_{L-N}e^{-j(L-N)\theta}. \tag{5.46}$$

In terms of z, Eq. 5.46 becomes

$$H_2(z) = A_0 + A_1z^{-1} + \cdots A_{L-N}z^{-(L-N)}$$

$$= \frac{A_0z^{L-N} + A_1z^{L-N-1} + \cdots + A_{L-N}}{z^{L-N}}$$

$$= \frac{\text{a polynomial in } z}{z^{L-N}}. \tag{5.47}$$

Finally, we add $H_1(z)$ from Eq. 5.44 and $H_2(z)$ from Eq. 5.47 to obtain $H(z)$, namely

$$H(z) = H_1(z) + H_2(z)$$

$$= \frac{\text{a polynomial in } z}{(z - r_1)(z - r_2) \cdots (z - r_N)} + \frac{\text{a polynomial in } z}{z^{L-N}} \tag{5.48}$$

or

$$H(z) = \frac{\text{a polynomial in } z}{(z - r_1)(z - r_2) \cdots (z - r_N)z^{L-N}}. \tag{5.49}$$

We assumed this to be a stable system where the magnitudes of all of the r's are less than 1 and, consequently, all of the poles of $H(z)$ lie inside the unit circle since there are also $L - N$ poles at $z = 0$. The zeros come from setting the numerator polynomial to zero and once again are unrestricted as to their location. For a recursive filter we have established two facts concerning stability—the zeros can take on any values provided that complex zeros occur in conjugate pairs, and all of the poles must lie inside the unit circle and any complex poles must occur in conjugate pairs.

Thus, for any causal (recursive or nonrecursive) stable filter with real coefficients, all of the poles of the generalized frequency response function $H(z)$ must lie inside the unit circle. The zeros may be located anywhere. Both poles and zeros may be real or complex, but complex poles or zeros must occur in conjugate pairs.

5.3.2 Effects of Poles and Zeros on the Frequency Response

a) A filter pole close to the unit circle produces a large gain at nearby frequencies. Recalling that the magnitude (gain) of the frequency response is written

$$M = b_0 N_1 N_2 \cdots N_L / D_1 D_2 \cdots D_N \qquad (5.50)$$

we see that a "small" value for any D, say D_ℓ, gives a "large" value for M. (Note again that these are qualitative statements and don't imply the precise and accurate results of a computer program.) Thus, in Fig. 5.14(a), the pole at 0.8 produces a relatively large gain at $\theta = 0$ (the vector from the pole to the unit circle is relatively short). Naturally all the other poles and zeros contribute to the computation of M but for $\theta = 0$, the pole at 0.8 dominates the situation. In a similar manner, the pole at $0.95e^{j\pi/2}$ produces a large gain at frequencies near $\theta = \pi/2$ because the vector from that pole to the unit circle is short, in this case, for points close to $\theta = \pi/2$ the vector lengths are about 0.1. See Fig. 5.14(b) for the magnitude portion of the frequency response of the system represented by Fig. 5.14(a).

b) A filter zero close to the unit circle produces a small gain at nearby frequencies. The vector from the zero at -0.9 to the unit circle is short for frequencies near $\theta = \pi$ and hence controls the gain near this frequency. Likewise, the zero at $0.95e^{j\pi/4}$ produces a small gain for θ close to $\pi/4$ producing a definite "notch" in the frequency response. Of course, putting zeros right on the unit circle gives zero gain at that point and is an effective way to remove an unwanted frequency. It may even be desirable to place zeros outside the unit circle. Problem 5.9 illustrates this situation.

c) The gain scale of the filter may be controlled by the factor b_0. It is common practice to set b_0 at a value that provides a certain gain at a particular frequency.

d) Finally, a legitimate question to ask is, "What about the phase? How can we estimate pertinent phase values from the pole-zero diagram?" Except in the simplest cases, such as some of the examples we've considered previously, it is difficult to learn much about phase from these diagrams without a lot of effort and we do not address this topic in any substantive way.

5.3.3 Correspondence Between Analog and Digital Frequencies

To process analog signals by digital techniques, the analog signal must first be sampled. Consider an analog sinusoid

$$x(t) = X_1 \cos(\omega_1 t) \qquad (5.51)$$

FIGURE 5.14 Showing the effect of the location of the poles and zeros on the frequency response

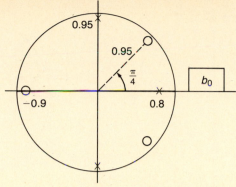

$$H(z) = b_0 \; \frac{(z + 0.9)(z - 0.95e^{j\pi/4})(z - 0.95e^{-j\pi/4})}{(z - 0.8)(z - 0.95e^{j\pi/2})(z - 0.95e^{-j\pi/2})}$$

(a) Pole-zero description

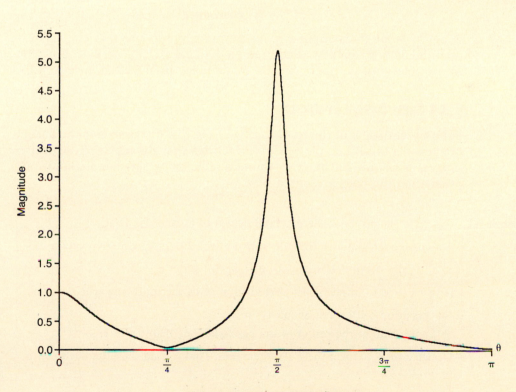

(b) Frequency response magnitude, *M*

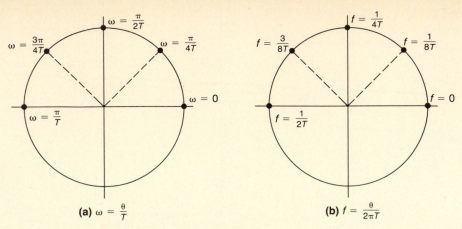

(a) $\omega = \dfrac{\theta}{T}$

(b) $f = \dfrac{\theta}{2\pi T}$

and its sampled version with a sampling interval of T seconds

$$x(nT) = X_1 \cos(\omega_1 nT) \tag{5.52}$$

or in terms of f rather than ω

$$x(nT) = X_1 \cos(2\pi f_1 nT). \tag{5.53}$$

Recalling that the sampling frequency is $f_s = 1/T$ and that the highest unambiguous frequency in the sampled signal is $f_s/2$, we can show the unit circle with pertinent analog frequencies indicated as in Fig. 5.15.

5.3.4 Some Design Problems

Let's try out some of the tools that we have just discussed for the design of a few digital filters. We need to remember that the result of the design process is not unique and that there may be many satisfactory solutions other than the ones presented here.

Example 5.2. This example illustrates the graphical design of a bandpass filter.

A recursive second-order filter described by the difference equation (algorithm)

$$y(n) = a_1 y(n-1) + a_2 y(n-2) + b_0 x(n) + b_1 x(n-1) + b_2 x(n-2) \tag{5.54}$$

is to be used to implement a digital filter with the following specifications:

a) passband centered at about $\theta = \pi/2$.

b) unity gain at the center of the passband, i.e., $|H(e^{j\pi/2})| = 1$.

Design a filter to meet these requirements. That is, find the filter coefficients a_1, a_2, b_0, b_1, and b_2.

Solution: The recursive second-order filter of Eq. 5.54 has a generalized frequency response function of the form

$$H(z) = \frac{b_0 + b_1 z^{-1} + b_2 z^{-2}}{1 - a_1 z^{-1} - a_2 z^{-2}}$$

$$= \frac{b_0 z^2 + b_1 z + b_2}{z^2 - a_1 z - a_2} \tag{5.55}$$

which may be arranged in the factored form

$$H(z) = b_0 \frac{(z - n_1)(z - n_2)}{(z - d_1)(z - d_2)}. \tag{5.56}$$

The corresponding frequency response written as a ratio of vectors is

$$H(e^{j\theta}) = b_0 \frac{N_1 e^{j\alpha_1} N_2 e^{j\alpha_2}}{D_1 e^{j\beta_1} D_2 e^{j\beta_2}}. \tag{5.57}$$

Where should the poles and zeros be located? There are, of course, many solutions to a design problem that is posed as this one—with very general and somewhat unrestricted specifications. Let's proceed, however, with one possible solution.

i) The center of the bandpass is to be located close to $\theta = \pi/2$ radians. This means that the gain is to be "large" in the region of $\theta = \pi/2$ which can be achieved by making D_1 "small" near $\theta = \pi/2$. Thus, let us place a pole at the position d_1 shown in Fig. 5.16(a). Since there must also be a complex conjugate pole we also have one at d_2 as shown. We locate them more specifically in step iii.

ii) The poles d_1 and d_2 have been selected to control the bandpass characteristic of this filter and consequently the zeros n_1 and n_2 can be located in many suitable places, one of which is the origin where we put the two zeros as in Fig. 5.16(b). Now the magnitude of the frequency response is $M = b_0 N_1 N_2 / D_1 D_2 = b_0 / D_1 D_2$ because $N_1 = N_2 = 1$ for all values of θ.

iii) Lastly, to take care of the unity gain requirement at $\theta = \pi/2$ we draw two vectors (the two vectors from the zeros have already been accounted for) from d_1 and d_2 to $\theta = \pi/2$ on the unit circle as in Fig. 5.16(c). The gain at this value of $\theta = \pi/2$ is

$$M_{\pi/2} = 1 = b_0 \frac{1}{D_1 D_2}$$

$$= b_0 \frac{1}{(1 - |d_1|)(1 + |d_2|)}$$

$$= b_0 \frac{1}{1 - |d_1|^2} \quad \text{since } |d_1| = |d_2|. \tag{5.58}$$

We have one equation in two unknowns and if we choose $|d_1| = |d_2| = 0.9$ to get the poles close to the unit circle we have

$$1.0 = b_0/(1 - 0.9^2) \quad \text{or} \quad b_0 = 0.19 \tag{5.59}$$

and the unknown constants in Eq. 5.56 have been determined to be

$$n_1 = n_2 = 0, \ d_1 = 0.9 e^{j\pi/2}, \ d_2 = 0.9 e^{-j\pi/2}, \text{ and } b_0 = 0.19. \tag{5.60}$$

FIGURE 5.16 The design
of a bandpass filter by the
graphical method

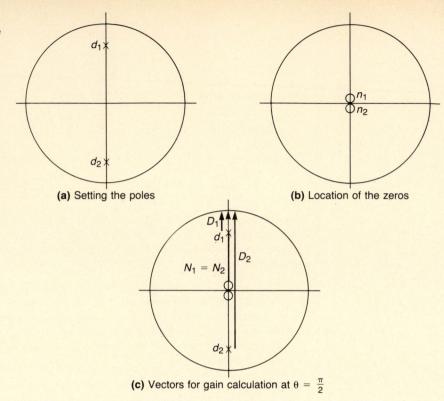

(a) Setting the poles

(b) Location of the zeros

(c) Vectors for gain calculation at $\theta = \frac{\pi}{2}$

Now that we've selected the locations for the poles and zeros we want to find the filter coefficients so we can implement the filter. From Eqs. 5.56 and 5.60 the generalized frequency response is

$$H(z) = \frac{0.19z^2}{(z - 0.9e^{j\pi/2})(z - 0.9e^{-j\pi/2})}$$

$$= \frac{0.19z^2}{z^2 + 0.81}$$

$$= \frac{0.19}{1 + 0.81z^{-2}} \tag{5.61}$$

and comparison with Eq. 5.55 yields the filter coefficients

$$b_0 = 0.19, \ b_1 = b_2 = 0, \ a_1 = 0, \ \text{and} \ a_2 = -0.81. \tag{5.62}$$

The filter realization and algorithm are given in Fig. 5.17(a) and a computer generated magnitude plot in Fig. 5.17(b). Notice the symmetry of the plot, due to the symmetrical poles and zeros, the DC gain of 0.105, and the desired gain of 1.0 at $\theta = \pi/2$.

Comment: The shape of the plot is controlled by N_1N_2/D_1D_2 and the scale

FIGURE 5.17 Results for
Example 5.2

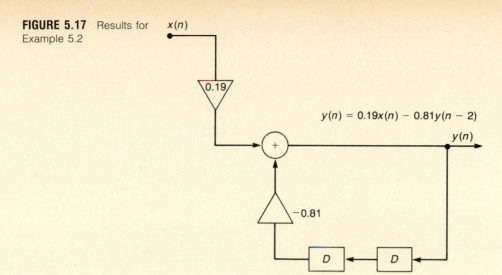

$$y(n) = 0.19x(n) - 0.81y(n - 2)$$

(a) An implementation of the bandpass design

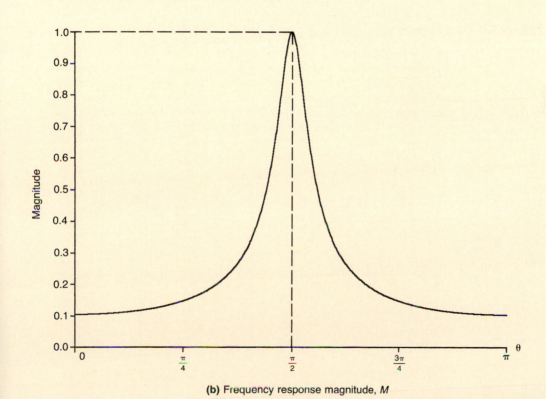

(b) Frequency response magnitude, M

can be altered by adjusting b_0. Suppose we want a "sharper" characteristic than that in Fig. 5.17(b). We can get the magnitudes N_1 and N_2 into the act by placing two zeros at $n_1 = 0.9$ and $n_2 = -0.9$ as in Fig. 5.18(a). Now for the same gain at $\theta = \pi/2$ we have from Fig. 5.18(b)

$$M_{\pi/2} = 1.0 = b_0 N_1 N_2 / D_1 D_2$$

$$= b_0 \frac{(1 + 0.81)^{1/2}(1 + 0.81)^{1/2}}{(0.1)(1.9)} \qquad (5.63)$$

which yields $b_0 = 0.105$. The magnitude plot of Fig. 5.18(c) shows a much more selective bandpass characteristic and the generalized frequency response is

$$H(z) = 0.105 \frac{(z + 0.9)(z - 0.9)}{z^2 + 0.81}$$

$$= \frac{0.105z^2 - 0.085}{z^2 + 0.81} = \frac{0.105 - 0.085z^{-2}}{1 + 0.81z^{-2}}. \qquad (5.64)$$

Comparison with Eq. 5.55 yields the filter coefficients

$$b_0 = 0.105, \ b_1 = 0, \ b_2 = -0.085, \ a_1 = 0, \ \text{and} \ a_2 = -0.81 \qquad (5.65)$$

with the filter implementation in Fig. 5.18(d).

Example 5.3. This example illustrates the graphical design of a notch filter. ____

There is a frequent need for a digital filter that has the characteristic of Fig. 5.19(a) where the intent is to suppress or reject analog frequencies in the region of some frequency ω_c rad/s. One application occurs where signal contamination is present in the control system of a spacecraft because of the body-bending-mode signals that are caused by the structure-borne vibrations. These unwanted signals can cause stability problems for the spacecraft control sys-

FIGURE 5.18 Design of a bandpass filter (a second try)

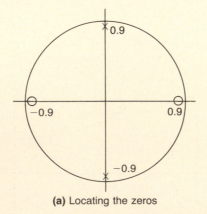

(a) Locating the zeros

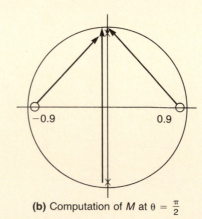

(b) Computation of M at $\theta = \frac{\pi}{2}$

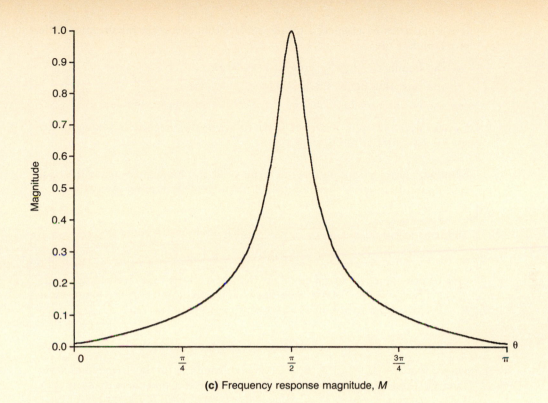

(c) Frequency response magnitude, M

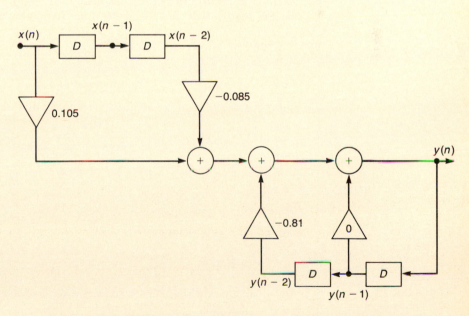

(d) An implementation of $y(n) = -0.81y(n - 2) + 0.105x(n) - 0.085x(n - 2)$

tem. Let's describe a typical filtering problem that occurs in this situation. The problem data are:

a) the frequency range of interest is 0–50 Hz
b) the sampling frequency is 100 Hz
c) the bending-mode frequency that is to be suppressed is 6 Hz.

Design a second-order recursive filter to achieve a magnitude frequency response plot similar to Fig. 5.19(a).

Solution: First, we put our data in terms of digital frequencies using the relation digital frequency = (analog radian frequency) · (sampling interval) or

$$\theta = \omega T \tag{5.66}$$

making the digital frequency to be suppressed

$$\theta_c = (2\pi)(6)(0.01) = 0.12\pi. \tag{5.67}$$

One design approach would be to put the zeros on the unit circle at the angle $\theta_c = 0.12\pi$ as in Fig. 5.19(b). The flat characteristic outside the region near $\theta_c = 0.12\pi$ gives a good hint as to where to put the poles. With the gain given by

$$M = b_0 N_1 N_2 / D_1 D_2 \tag{5.68}$$

we see that if $N_1 N_2 \approx D_1 D_2$ the gain will be simply b_0 for the frequencies other than θ_c. Thus, the poles are placed at the angle $\theta = \theta_c$ and close to, but necessarily inside, the zeros. This makes $N_1 \approx D_1$ and $N_2 \approx D_2$ as in Fig. 5.19(c). Actually, the bandwidth can be adjusted by varying the pole radius R_p, but to avoid the details, let's make $R_p = 0.9$. Summarizing we have

$$n_{1,2} = 1e^{\pm j0.12\pi}$$

$$d_{1,2} = 0.9e^{\pm j0.12\pi}$$

$$b_0 \text{ undetermined} \tag{5.69}$$

which gives the generalized frequency response function

$$H(z) = b_0 \frac{(z - 1e^{j0.12\pi})(z - 1e^{-j0.12\pi})}{(z - 0.9e^{j0.12\pi})(z - 0.9e^{-j0.12\pi})} \tag{5.70}$$

which, by using the Euler equation, becomes

$$H(z) = b_0 \frac{z^2 - 2\cos(0.12\pi)z + 1}{z^2 - 1.8\cos(0.12\pi)z + 0.81}. \tag{5.71}$$

For simplicity we'll make $b_0 = 1$, which gives

$$H(z) = \frac{z^2 - 1.86z + 1}{z^2 - 1.67z + 0.81} = \frac{1 - 1.86z^{-1} + z^{-2}}{1 - 1.67z^{-1} + 0.81z^{-2}} \tag{5.72}$$

and comparison with Eq. 5.55 yields the filter coefficients

$$b_0 = 1, \; b_1 = -1.86, \; b_2 = 1, \; a_1 = 1.67, \text{ and } a_2 = -0.81. \tag{5.73}$$

Figure 5.19(d) gives the realization for this filter and the magnitude plot is in

FIGURE 5.19 Design of a notch filter

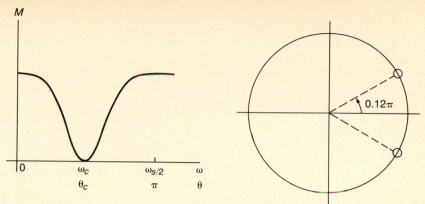

(a) Desired magnitude characteristic with a notch at ω_c **(b)** Locating the zeros on the unit circle

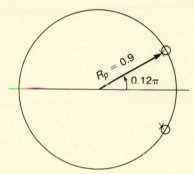

(c) Adding the poles at $z = 0.9e^{\mp j0.12\pi}$

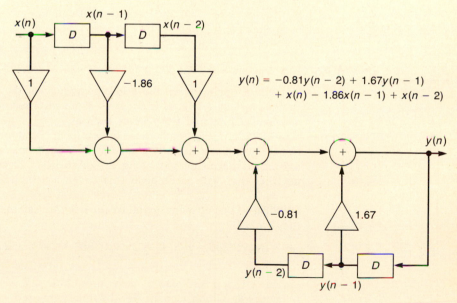

$$y(n) = -0.81y(n-2) + 1.67y(n-1)$$
$$+ x(n) - 1.86x(n-1) + x(n-2)$$

(d) Filter realization

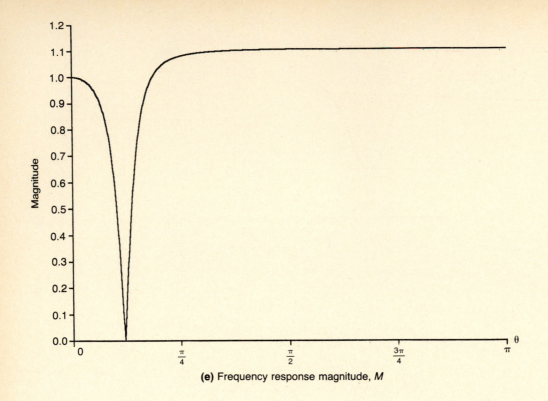

(e) Frequency response magnitude, M

Fig. 5.19(e). Note that the undesirable frequency of $f = 6$ Hz $(\theta = 0.12\pi)$ has been effectively suppressed.

Example 5.4. This example illustrates the graphical design of a comb filter. _____

In medical applications, the 60-Hz frequency of the power supply is often "picked up" by test equipment such as an EKG recorder. At the same time, harmonically related frequencies such as $f_2 = 2 \times 60 = 120$ Hz and $f_3 = 3 \times 60 = 180$ Hz are created because of nonlinear phenomena. To ensure an accurate recording, it is necessary to eliminate or suppress these frequencies as the unfinished magnitude plot of Fig. 5.20(a) suggests. Design a nonrecursive digital filter that will accomplish this, given a sampling frequency of 360 Hz.

Solution: The pertinent digital frequencies are calculated from $\theta = 2\pi f/f_s$ and they are

$$\theta_1 = 2\pi(60)/360 = \pi/3, \; \theta_2 = 2\pi(120)/360 = 2\pi/3, \text{ and } \theta_3 = 2\pi(180)/360 = \pi.$$
$$(5.74)$$

We know that a zero placed on the unit circle at $\theta = \theta_k$ eliminates the digital frequency θ_k, which accounts for the three zeros at $\theta = \pi/3$, $2\pi/3$, and π in Fig. 5.20(b). Remember that complex zeros must occur in conjugate pairs, and this

FIGURE 5.20 Nonrecursive (comb) filter design

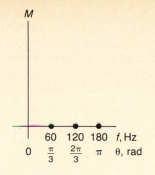

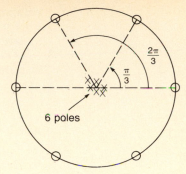

(a) Desired gains of zero at f = 60, 120 and 180 Hertz

6 poles

(b) Locating six zeros

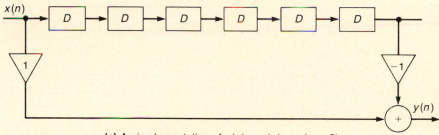

(c) An implementation of $y(n) = x(n) - x(n-6)$

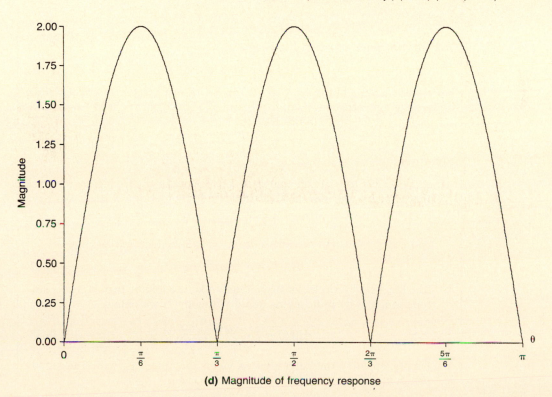

(d) Magnitude of frequency response

requires the addition of the two zeros at $\theta = -\pi/3$ and $-2\pi/3$. The sixth zero at $\theta = 0$ is added to eliminate any DC in the signal and also creates a symmetrical pattern which produces the often desirable property of linear phase.

Our ultimate goal is the algorithm to implement this filter so we first need to form $H(z) = N(z)/D(z)$ and create the difference equation from this frequency response function. From Fig. 5.20(b) the numerator polynomial is

$$N(z) = (z - 1)(z - e^{j\pi/3})(z - e^{j2\pi/3})(z - e^{j\pi})(z - e^{j4\pi/3})(z - e^{j5\pi/3}) \quad (5.75)$$

which when multiplied and simplified yields the expression

$$N(z) = z^6 - 1. \quad (5.76)$$

What about the denominator $D(z)$? For simplicity, we might be tempted to make $D(z) = 1$ which would give

$$H(z) = z^6 - 1 \quad (5.77)$$

and the corresponding difference equation

$$y(n) = x(n + 6) - x(n) \quad (5.78)$$

which describes a noncausal filter because of the requirement for $x(n + 6)$, the sixth future value of the input which is, of course, unknown to all but certain stargazers and several pseudosavants. Instead, by making $D(z) = z^6$ we have

$$H(z) = \frac{z^6 - 1}{z^6}$$

$$= 1 - z^{-6} \quad (5.79)$$

and the difference equation for a causal filter

$$y(n) = x(n) - x(n - 6) \quad (5.80)$$

giving the implementation of Fig. 5.20(c). Because of the symmetrical placing of the zeros, and because all of the poles are at the origin $(z = 0)$, the symmetrical response of Fig. 5.20(d) results.

Comments:

1. It is possible to write an analytical expression for the frequency response that explains the symmetrical magnitude plot of Fig. 5.20(d). We have

$$H(e^{j\theta}) = 1 - e^{-j6\theta} \quad (5.81)$$

and, using hindsight or experience, $e^{-j3\theta}$ can be factored leaving

$$H(e^{j\theta}) = e^{-j3\theta}[e^{j3\theta} - e^{-j3\theta}]. \quad (5.82)$$

The bracketed term looks suspiciously like it could be turned into a sine function, and by multiplying and dividing by $2j$ we obtain

$$H(e^{j\theta}) = 2je^{-j3\theta} \frac{(e^{j3\theta} - e^{-j3\theta})}{2j}. \quad (5.83)$$

Finally, applying the Euler relation yields the more easily interpreted expression

$$H(e^{j\theta}) = 2\sin(3\theta)e^{j(\pi/2 - 3\theta)} \tag{5.84}$$

and it is clear that the magnitude, $M = |2\sin(3\theta)|$ goes to zero at $\theta = \pi/3$, $2\pi/3$, and π as shown.

2. We went through a lengthy argument to show that the denominator of the generalized frequency response function $H(z)$ had to be $D(z) = z^6$ rather than $D(z) = 1$ for a causal filter. However, once we had determined the numerator to be $N(z) = z^6 - 1$ we could have found $D(z)$ directly from Eq. 5.36, namely

$$H(z) = \frac{h(0)z^L + h(1)z^{L-1} + \cdots + h(L)}{z^L} \tag{5.85}$$

which for this specific filter becomes

$$H(z) = \frac{z^6 - 1}{z^6}$$

$$= 1 - z^{-6} \tag{5.86}$$

as before.

5.4 ■ REVIEW

This chapter was mainly an exercise in the use of graphical mathematics with the intent of obtaining a geometric interpretation of frequency response calculations. We weren't looking for exact results but only for approximate ones with the goal of getting quick and easy answers before or while proceeding with more sophisticated methods, including computer-aided design (CAD).

The frequency response function $H(e^{j\theta})$ was generalized to $H(z)$ where the complex variable z can take on any value including, of course, $z = e^{j\theta}$. The poles and zeros of $H(z)$ were defined and a geometric algorithm for obtaining an estimate of the magnitude of frequency response $|H(e^{j\theta})|$ was developed.

Stability criteria for both recursive and nonrecursive filters were derived, the general effects of pole-zero locations on frequency response were considered, and the digital processing of analog signals was, once again, discussed. Three examples of graphical design concluded this short but hopefully useful chapter.

VOCABULARY AND USEFUL RELATIONSHIPS

a) A stable LTI system described by the difference equation

$$y(n) - \sum_{k=1}^{N} a_k y(n-k) = \sum_{k=0}^{L} b_k x(n-k) \tag{5.9}$$

gives the system frequency response

$$H(e^{j\theta}) = \frac{b_0 + b_1 e^{-j\theta} + \cdots + b_L e^{-jL\theta}}{1 - a_1 e^{-j\theta} - a_2 e^{-j2\theta} - \cdots - a_N e^{-jN\theta}}$$

$$= \frac{\displaystyle\sum_{k=0}^{L} b_k e^{-jk\theta}}{1 - \displaystyle\sum_{k=1}^{N} a_k e^{-jk\theta}}. \tag{5.10}$$

b) The specific complex quantity $e^{j\theta}$ may be generalized to z giving

$$H(z) = \frac{b_0 + b_1 z^{-1} + \cdots + b_L z^{-L}}{1 - a_1 z^{-1} - \cdots - a_N z^{-N}}$$

$$= \frac{z^{N-L}[b_0 z^L + b_1 z^{L-1} + \cdots + b_L]}{z^N - a_1 z^{N-1} - \cdots - a_N} \tag{5.12}$$

which can be put into the factored form

$$H(z) = b_0 z^{N-L} \frac{(z - n_1)(z - n_2) \cdots (z - n_L)}{(z - d_1)(z - d_2) \cdots (z - d_N)}. \tag{5.13}$$

In Eq. 5.13 we see that, for $N - L > 0$, there are $N - L$ zeros at the origin ($z = 0$), and for $N - L < 0$, there are $N - L$ poles at the origin. The other poles and zeros are given by $n_1, n_2, \ldots, n_L$—the zeros of $H(z)$—and $d_1, d_2, \ldots, d_N$—the poles of $H(z)$.

c) For stability, the magnitude of all poles must be less than 1, $|d_i| < 1$, $i = 1, 2, \ldots, N$.

d) The frequency response for all values of θ comes from evaluating $H(z)$ at $z = e^{j\theta}$, which gives

$$H(e^{j\theta}) = b_0 e^{j(N-L)\theta} \frac{(N_1 e^{j\alpha_1})(N_2 e^{j\alpha_2}) \cdots (N_L e^{j\alpha_L})}{(D_1 e^{j\beta_1})(D_2 e^{j\beta_2}) \cdots (D_N e^{j\beta_N})} \tag{5.28}$$

where $N_q e^{j\alpha_q}$ is the vector from the zero $z = n_q$ to the tip of the $e^{j\theta}$ vector and $D_p e^{j\beta_p}$ is the vector from the pole $z = d_p$ to the tip of the $e^{j\theta}$ vector. The frequency response magnitude is

$$M = b_0 N_1 N_2 \cdots N_L / D_1 D_2 \cdots D_N \tag{5.29}$$

and the phase is

$$P = (N - L)\theta + \sum_{k=1}^{L} \alpha_k - \sum_{k=1}^{N} \beta_k. \tag{5.30}$$

PROBLEMS

Reinforcement

5.1 An LTI discrete system has a frequency response of the form

$$H(e^{j\theta}) = \frac{A}{1 + Be^{-j\theta} + Ce^{-j2\theta}}.$$

a) Use the graphical method to sketch the magnitude of the frequency response for $0 \le \theta \le \pi$ for

   i) $A = 0.68,$ $B = -0.4,$ $C = 0.08$

   ii) $A = 0.5$, $B = -1.0,$ $C = 0.5$

   iii) $A = 0.82,$ $B = -1.8,$ $C = 1.62$

Hint: Always be sure to check that the system is stable before sketching the frequency response.

b) Can you extrapolate your observations from part (a) to any general concepts?

5.2 An LTI discrete system is characterized by a difference equation of the form

$$y(n) = -By(n-1) - Cy(n-2) + Ax(n).$$

a) Use the graphical method to *sketch* the magnitude of the frequency response in the range $0 \le \theta \le \pi$ for

   i) $A = 0.64,$ $B = -0.4,$ $C = 0.04$

   ii) $A = 0.25,$ $B = -1.0,$ $C = 0.25$

   iii) $A = 0.01,$ $B = -1.8,$ $C = 0.81$

b) Can you extrapolate your observations from part (a) to any general conclusions?

5.3 An analog signal is sampled at a frequency of 1 kilohertz.

a) What is the highest analog frequency that can be represented unambiguously by the sample values?

b) On a sketch of the unit circle show the analog frequencies in Hz that correspond to $\theta = 0$, $\pi/4$, $\pi/2$, $3\pi/4$, π.

5.4 An LTI discrete system has a generalized frequency response of the form

$$H(z) = \frac{A_0 z^2 + A_1 z + A_2}{z^2 + B_1 z + B_2}.$$

Use the graphical approach to sketch the magnitude of the frequency response for

a) $A_0 = 1$ $A_1 = 0$ $A_2 = 0$
   $B_1 = -1.4$ $B_2 = 0.98$

b) $A_0 = 1$ $A_1 = 0.8$ $A_2 = 0.97$
   $B_1 = -1.4$ $B_2 = 0.98$

c) Compare the results of parts (a) and (b) and explain your conclusions.

5.5   a) $H(z) = \dfrac{z^2}{z^2 - 1.8z + 0.81}$

   b) $H(e^{j\theta}) = \dfrac{e^{j2\theta}}{e^{j2\theta} - 1.27e^{j\theta} + 0.81}$

Sketch M versus digital frequency θ.

5.6 The frequency response function of a fourth-order recursive filter is given by

$$H(z) = \frac{z^4 - z^2}{z^4 + 0.25}.$$

a) Find the poles and zeros of $H(z)$.

b) Sketch the magnitude of the frequency response.

c) Describe the filter.

5.7 The frequency response of a second-order LTI digital filter is of the form

$$H(e^{j\theta}) = \frac{b_0 + b_1 e^{-j\theta} + b_2 e^{-j2\theta}}{1 - a_1 e^{-j\theta} - a_2 e^{-j2\theta}}.$$

a) Sketch the magnitude of the frequency responses for $0 \le \theta \le \pi$ for the coefficient values given below. Assume in all cases that $b_0 = 1$, $b_1 = b_2 = 0$. In each case indicate whether the filter is lowpass, highpass, etc.

   i) $a_1 = -1.8,$ $a_2 = -0.81$

   ii) $a_1 = -1.27,$ $a_2 = -0.81$

   iii) $a_1 = 0,$ $a_2 = -0.81$

   iv) $a_1 = 1.27,$ $a_2 = -0.81$

   v) $a_1 = 1.8,$ $a_2 = -0.81$

b) Compare the results obtained in the different parts of (a) and explain your conclusions.

5.8 The frequency response of a second-order finite-impulse response (FIR) digital filter is given by $H(e^{j\theta}) = b_0 + b_1 e^{-j\theta} + b_2 e^{-j2\theta}$.

a) Sketch the magnitude of the frequency responses for $0 \le \theta \le \pi$ for the coefficient values given below. In each case state whether the filter is lowpass, highpass, etc.

  i) $b_0 = 1$, $b_1 = -1.8$, $b_2 = 0.81$

  ii) $b_0 = 1$, $b_1 = -1.27$, $b_2 = 0.81$

  iii) $b_0 = 1$, $b_1 = 0$, $b_2 = 0.81$

b) Compare the results obtained in the different parts of (a) and explain your conclusions.

c) Compare the results obtained in this problem with those of Problem 5.7. Explain your observations.

5.9 An LTI digital filter is characterized by the frequency response

$$H(e^{j\theta}) = \frac{1 - 2e^{-j\theta} + 2e^{-j2\theta}}{1 - e^{-j\theta} + 0.5e^{-j2\theta}}.$$

Sketch the magnitude of the frequency response for $0 \le \theta \le \pi$.

5.10 Use the graphical approach to show that the frequency response of an LTI discrete system has the following characteristics:

a) $|H(e^{j(\pi - \alpha)})| = |H(e^{j(\pi + \alpha)})|$,
   i.e., $|H(e^{j\theta})|$ is an even function about the point $\theta = \pi$.

b) $\angle H(e^{j(\pi - \alpha)}) = -\angle H(e^{j(\pi + \alpha)})$,
   i.e., $\angle H(e^{j\theta})$ is an odd function about the point $\theta = \pi$.

5.11 Use the graphical approach to show that the frequency response of an LTI discrete system is periodic with period 2π.

Integrated Review

5.12 An analog signal whose highest frequency component is at 2000 Hz is to be passed through a digital lowpass filter after having been sampled at a frequency of 10 kHz. The lowpass filter is to have the following characteristics:

$$0.8 \le |H| \le 1.0 \qquad 0 \le f \le 300 \text{ Hz}$$
$$|H| \le 0.707 \qquad 500 \text{ Hz} \le f < 1000 \text{ Hz}$$
$$|H| \le 0.4 \qquad 1000 \text{ Hz} \le f \le 2000 \text{ Hz}$$

Find a frequency response characteristic and the corresponding difference equation for a digital filter that meets these specifications.

Hint: Try to find the simplest possible filter that

meets the requirements and gradually increase the complexity if necessary to achieve the desired response.

5.13 a) An LTI digital filter has the frequency response characteristic

$$H_a(e^{j\theta}) = \frac{K_a e^{j2\theta}}{(e^{j2\theta} + 0.81)}.$$

Sketch $|H_a(e^{j\theta})|$ as a function of θ for $0 \le \theta \le \pi$. For the moment, leave K_a as an unassigned scale factor.

b) Sketch the magnitude of the frequency response of the digital filter characterized by

$$H_b(e^{j\theta}) =$$
$$\frac{K_b e^{j4\theta}}{(e^{j2\theta} - 0.31e^{j\theta} + 0.81)(e^{j2\theta} + 0.31e^{j\theta} + 0.81)}.$$

Temporarily leave K_b as an unassigned scale factor.

c) Adjust K_a and K_b so that $|H_a(e^{j\pi/2})| = |H_b(e^{j\pi/2})| = 1$ and compare the frequency responses found in parts (a) and (b).

5.14 A nonrecursive filter is described by

$$h(n) = \delta(n) - 1.477\delta(n - 8).$$

a) Plot the poles and zeros of the generalized frequency response $H(z)$.

b) For $z = e^{j\theta}$, sketch $|H(e^{j\theta})|$ vs. θ for $-\pi \le \theta \le \pi$.

c) For $x(n) = 10 \cos(3\pi n/8 + 0.30)$, $-\infty \le n \le \infty$, find the steady-state response $y_{ss}(n)$.

d) Write the system difference equation and draw the associated implementation for this filter.

5.15 The pole-zero plots of $H(z)$ for several filters are given in Fig. P5.15. Do the following for each filter:

  i) Describe the type of filter (i.e., lowpass, highpass, bandpass, or bandstop).

  ii) State whether the filter is recursive or nonrecursive.

  iii) Find the system difference equation making $b_0 = 1$ and draw the system diagram.

5.16 An LTI system is described by

$$H(z) = \frac{z^4 + z^2}{z^4 + 0.25}.$$

a) Plot the poles and zeros.

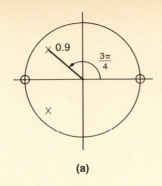

(a)

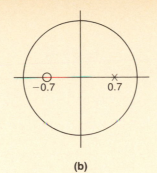

(b)

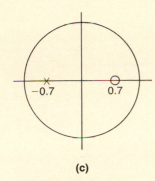

(c)

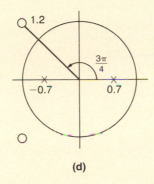

(d)

FIGURE P5.15

b) Sketch the magnitude of the frequency response.

c) If the input to the system is the sequence $x(n) = 0.532 \cos(\pi n/4 + \alpha_1) +$ $1.125 \cos(\pi n/2 + \alpha_2) + 0.170 \cos(\pi n + \alpha_3)$, find the steady-state output sequence $y_{ss}(n)$.

d) Write the difference equation that describes this system and draw the system diagram.

REFERENCES AND OTHER SOURCES OF INFORMATION

Cadzow, J. A. 1973. *Discrete-Time Systems.* Englewood Cliffs, New Jersey: Prentice-Hall, Inc.

Mayhan, R. J. 1984. *Discrete-Time and Continuous-Time Linear Systems.* Reading, Massachusetts: Addison-Wesley Publishing Co.

Oppenheim, A. V., and R. W. Schafer. 1975. *Digital Signal Processing.* Englewood Cliffs, New Jersey: Prentice-Hall, Inc.

Strum, R. D., and J. R. Ward. 1985. *Electric Circuits and Networks.* 2nd Ed. Englewood Cliffs, New Jersey: Prentice-Hall, Inc.

CHAPTER 6

z-Transforms

6.9 SOLUTION OF DIFFERENCE EQUATIONS
6.10 CONNECTIONS BETWEEN THE TIME DOMAIN AND THE z-DOMAIN

6.11 GENERAL RESULTS AND MISCELLANY

6.12 REVIEW
VOCABULARY AND IMPORTANT RELATIONS
TABLES OF TRANSFORMS AND PROPERTIES

PROBLEMS
REFERENCES AND OTHER SOURCES OF INFORMATION

6.0 ▬ PREVIEW

Up to this point we have established a considerable amount of theory about and observed several applications of the analysis of digital signal processing systems. All of this has been accomplished in the discrete-time and frequency domains. It is also common practice, however, to design and analyze discrete systems from the point of view of the z-transform which has the desirable property of converting linear difference equations to linear algebraic equations. This enables us to analyze system response and characteristics using algebraic manipulations that are common to our mathematical repertoire.

In this chapter we introduce the z-transform and illustrate some of its applications in analyzing discrete systems. We begin by establishing the definition and some properties of the z-transform and then develop the transform pairs for several commonly occurring sequences. Next, system characteristics, such as frequency response and stability are investigated from the z-transform point of view. We also establish an important relationship between z-transforms and convolution. Inverse transform techniques are then developed and applied to obtain procedures for solving linear difference equations. Finally, noncausal systems are considered and the importance of the region of convergence (ROC) of the *z*-transform power series becomes apparent.

6.1 ▬ DEFINITIONS

The *z-transform* of the sequence $x(n)$ is defined as

$$\mathfrak{z}[x(n)] = X(z) = \sum_{n=-\infty}^{n=+\infty} x(n)z^{-n} \qquad (6.1)$$

where z is a complex variable. When written out term by term Eq. 6.1 becomes

$$X(z) = \cdots + x(-203)z^{203} + \cdots + x(-1)z + x(0)z^0$$
$$+ x(1)z^{-1} + \cdots + x(159)z^{-159} + \cdots \qquad (6.2)$$

where we see that the exponent of z indicates the location of each sample in the sequence and the coefficient of z indicates the amplitude or weight of each sample. For instance, a sequence consisting of a single sample at $n = 0$ as in Fig. 6.1(a) is described by $x(n) = x(0)\delta(n)$ and consequently from Eq. 6.2 the *z*-transform is

$$\mathfrak{z}[x(0)\delta(n)] = x(0)z^0 = x(0) \qquad (6.3)$$

and a sequence made up of only a sample at $n = m$ as in Fig. 6.1(b), described by $x(n) = x(m)\delta(n - m)$ for $m > 0$, has the transform

$$\mathfrak{z}[x(m)\delta(n - m)] = x(m)z^{-m}. \qquad (6.4)$$

As a particular example the sequence in Fig. 6.1(c) is

$$x(n) = \{\cdots 0, 0, 1, -2, \quad 3, \quad -1, 2, 0, 0, \cdots\} \qquad (6.5)$$
$$\uparrow$$
$$n = 0$$

which may be described in terms of *shifted weighted samples* as

$$x(n) = \delta(n + 2) - 2\delta(n + 1) + 3\delta(n) - \delta(n - 1) + 2\delta(n - 2). \qquad (6.6)$$

This sequence has the *z*-transform from Eq. 6.1 of

$$X(z) = \sum_{n=-\infty}^{n=+\infty} \{\delta(n + 2) - 2\delta(n + 1) + 3\delta(n)$$
$$- \delta(n - 1) + 2\delta(n - 2)\}z^{-n}. \qquad (6.7)$$

Knowing that $A\delta(n - m) = A$ at $n = m$ we can evaluate Eq. 6.7 as

$$X(z) = z^2 - 2z^1 + 3z^0 - z^{-1} + 2z^{-2} \qquad (6.8)$$

or

$$X(z) = z^2 - 2z + 3 - z^{-1} + 2z^{-2}. \qquad (6.9)$$

FIGURE 6.1 Important sequences

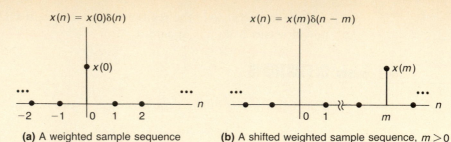

(a) A weighted sample sequence   **(b)** A shifted weighted sample sequence, $m > 0$

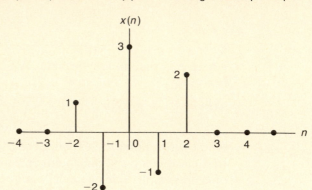

(c) A general sequence of shifted weighted samples

Notice that z^{-1} represents a delay (D) of one sample or of one unit, and z^{+1} represents an advance of one unit. Out of the general definition of Eq. 6.1 comes the specific result for a shifted weighted sample, namely

$$\mathfrak{z}[A\delta(n - m)] = Az^{-m} \tag{6.10}$$

where the real constants A and m represent the weight and amount of shift of the sample. Using Eq. 6.10, we can write by inspection the z-transform of any sequence such as the one in Fig. 6.1(c).

Naturally, this transform process goes both ways, for when $X(z)$ is known or given, then we need to find the sequence $x(n)$. The notation for this *inverse transform* process is

$$\mathfrak{z}^{-1}[X(z)] = x(n) \tag{6.11}$$

where we have taken a transform $X(z)$ back into the discrete-time domain. Then we can write the counterpart to Eq. 6.10, namely

$$\mathfrak{z}^{-1}[Az^{-m}] = A\delta(n - m) \tag{6.12}$$

and in a simple example, if $X(z) = 13z^{-10}$, then $x(n) = 13\delta(n - 10)$. The whole process is shown diagrammatically as

$$x(n) \longleftrightarrow X(z) \tag{6.13}$$

where the double-ended arrow indicates the "goes either way" nature of our new algebraic tool. We discuss several methods of doing this inverse transformation later in the chapter.

Our focus in this chapter will be on sequences that are zero for negative n. We refer to these as right-sided sequences.[†] However, for the adventurous, Section 6.11 of this chapter treats left- and two-sided sequences as well. From Eq. 6.1 the z-transform is seen to have the following important features (Stearns, 1975):

1. $X(z)$ is a polynomial or power series in z and is determined by the complete sequence $\{x(n)\}$.

2. In a sampled system, $X(z)$ is formally independent of the sampling interval T, but the factor z^{-n}, when associated with $x(n)$, corresponds to the time $t = nT$ and in this sense z^{-n} implies a delay of nT seconds from the time $t = 0$.

6.2 ▬ RIGHT-SIDED SEQUENCES—SOME TRANSFORM PAIRS

We now develop the transforms for some important right-sided sequences that are common to discrete-time systems. (Remember these right-sided sequences are zero for $n < 0$.) Other transforms are derived in the end-of-chapter problems and Table 6.1, at the end of the chapter, summarizes these results.

The transform definition and notation are indicated in Eq. 6.1, namely

$$\mathfrak{z}[f(n)] = F(z) \tag{6.14}$$

or in a common notation

$$f(n) \longleftrightarrow F(z) \tag{6.15}$$

where we have used the neutral notation $f(n)$ for the sequence which may be a system input, output, or internal signal. In Eq. 6.15 $f(n)$ and $F(z)$ are called a *z-transform pair*. For the moment, we concentrate on going from $f(n)$ to $F(z)$, but in a later section the inverse transform process of going from $F(z)$ to $f(n)$ will be examined.

6.2.1 Sample (Impulse) Sequence

For $f(n) = A\delta(n)$ and using Eq. 6.1

$$F(z) = \sum_{n=-\infty}^{n=\infty} A\delta(n)z^{-n} = Az^0 = A \tag{6.16}$$

[†] Strictly speaking a right-sided sequence generally is defined as one that has nonzero values only for $n \geq n_0$, however, we find it convenient to assume that $n_0 = 0$.

---

as we found earlier in Eq. 6.3. This is entry number 1 in Table 6.1 on page 352 and is denoted as

$$f(n) = A\delta(n) \longleftrightarrow F(z) = A \qquad (6.17)$$

or, for short

$$\boxed{A\delta(n) \longleftrightarrow A} \; . \qquad (6.18)$$

6.2.2 Step Sequence

For $f(n) = Au(n)$ and using Eq. 6.1,

$$F(z) = \sum_{n=-\infty}^{n=\infty} Au(n)z^{-n} = A\sum_{n=0}^{n=\infty} z^{-n} = A\sum_{n=0}^{n=\infty} (z^{-1})^n = \frac{A}{1 - z^{-1}} \qquad (6.19)$$

where we have used the closed form expression for the infinite geometric series, Eq. 3.21 which requires that $|z^{-1}| < 1$. This series may be written in the closed form, $F(z) = A/(1 - z^{-1})$, for $|z^{-1}| < 1$ or $|z| > 1$. This set of values for z is called the *region of convergence* and becomes very apparent from the infinite series, namely

$$F(z) = A[1 + z^{-1} + z^{-2} + \cdots + z^{-n} + \cdots]$$
$$= A[1 + 1/z + 1/z^2 + \cdots] \qquad (6.20)$$

which converges only for $|z| > 1$. The transform of a step sequence is the second entry in Table 6.1.

6.2.3 Real Exponential Sequence

For $f(n) = Aa^n$, $n \geq 0$ and $f(n) = 0$, $n < 0$, i.e., $f(n) = Aa^n u(n)$, we have

$$F(z) = \sum_{n=-\infty}^{n=\infty} Aa^n u(n)z^{-n} = A\sum_{n=0}^{n=\infty} (az^{-1})^n = \frac{A}{1 - az^{-1}} \quad \text{for} \quad |az^{-1}| < 1$$
$$\text{or} \quad |z| > |a| \qquad (6.21)$$

or, in shorthand notation

$$\boxed{Aa^n \cdot u(n) \longleftrightarrow \frac{A}{1 - az^{-1}}} \; . \qquad (6.22)$$

Notice that the z-transform pair Eq. 6.22 becomes the pair for the step sequence by making $a = 1$. This closed form of the infinite geometric series has a region of convergence (ROC) of $|az^{-1}| < 1$ or $|z| > |a|$ and is the third entry in Table 6.1.

6.2.4 Complex Exponential Sequence

For $f(n) = Aa^n e^{j\theta n}$, $n \geq 0$ and $f(n) = 0$, $n < 0$ we have

$$F(z) = \sum_{n=-\infty}^{n=\infty} Aa^n e^{j\theta n} u(n) z^{-n} = A \sum_{n=0}^{n=\infty} (ae^{j\theta} z^{-1})^n$$

$$= \frac{A}{1 - ae^{j\theta} z^{-1}} \quad \text{for} \quad |ae^{j\theta} z^{-1}| < 1 \tag{6.23}$$

The region of convergence is $|ae^{j\theta} z^{-1}| < 1$ or $|z| > |ae^{j\theta}|$ or $|z| > |a|$ since $|e^{j\theta}| = 1$ and the pair is the fourth entry in Table 6.1. We notice that $Aa^n e^{j\theta n}$ can be written as $A(ae^{j\theta})^n$ or simply $A\alpha^n$ where α is a complex number. The transform is then

$$\boxed{\quad \mathfrak{z}[Aa^n e^{j\theta n} \cdot u(n)] = \frac{A}{1 - \alpha z^{-1}} = \frac{A}{1 - ae^{j\theta} z^{-1}} \quad} . \tag{6.24}$$

This indicates that the third entry is simply a special case of entry number 4. In fact, with some algebraic manipulations, entries 2, 3, 5, 6, 7, and 8 can all be found from pair number 4.

6.2.5 General Oscillatory Sequence

For $f(n) = Aa^n \cos(\theta n)$, $n \geq 0$ and $f(n) = 0$, $n < 0$ we have

$$F(z) = \sum_{n=0}^{n=\infty} Aa^n \cos(\theta n) z^{-n}. \tag{6.25}$$

Factoring out the constant A and using the Euler relation gives

$$F(z) = A \sum_{n=0}^{n=\infty} a^n \left[\frac{e^{j\theta n} + e^{-j\theta n}}{2} \right] z^{-n} \tag{6.26}$$

which can be written as two terms, namely

$$F(z) = \frac{A}{2} \sum_{n=0}^{n=\infty} a^n e^{j\theta n} z^{-n} + \frac{A}{2} \sum_{n=0}^{n=\infty} a^n e^{-j\theta n} z^{-n}. \tag{6.27}$$

Equation 6.27 can be rewritten as

$$F(z) = \frac{A}{2} \sum_{n=0}^{n=\infty} (ae^{j\theta} z^{-1})^n + \frac{A}{2} \sum_{n=0}^{n=\infty} (ae^{-j\theta} z^{-1})^n$$

$$= \frac{A}{2} \left[\frac{1}{1 - ae^{j\theta} z^{-1}} + \frac{1}{1 - ae^{-j\theta} z^{-1}} \right] \quad \text{for} \quad |ae^{\pm j\theta} z^{-1}| < 1. \tag{6.28}$$

The right side of Eq. 6.28 may be combined over a common denominator as

$$F(z) = \frac{A}{2} \left[\frac{2 - az^{-1}(e^{j\theta} + e^{-j\theta})}{(1 - ae^{j\theta}z^{-1})(1 - ae^{-j\theta}z^{-1})} \right]$$

$$= \frac{A(1 - az^{-1}\cos\theta)}{1 - az^{-1}(e^{j\theta} + e^{-j\theta}) + a^2z^{-2}}. \qquad (6.29)$$

Equation 6.29 can be put into the standard quadratic (second-order) form

$$\boxed{\begin{aligned} \mathfrak{z}[Aa^n \cos(\theta n) \cdot u(n)] &= \frac{A(1 - az^{-1}\cos\theta)}{1 - (2a\cos\theta)z^{-1} + a^2z^{-2}} \\ &= \frac{Az(z - a\cos\theta)}{z^2 - (2a\cos\theta)z + a^2} \end{aligned}} . \qquad (6.30)$$

The ROC is $|ae^{\pm j\theta}z^{-1}| < 1$ or $|z| > |a|$ and the pair is entry number 5 in Table 6.1 on page 352.

6.2.6 Cosine Sequence

The previous result can be used to derive the cosine pair by simply making $a = 1$ and we have

$$\boxed{A\cos(\theta n) \cdot u(n) \longleftrightarrow \frac{A(1 - z^{-1}\cos\theta)}{1 - (2\cos\theta)z^{-1} + z^{-2}}, \quad |z| > 1} \qquad (6.31)$$

which is entry number 6 in Table 6.1. Entry number 7, which is derived in Problem 6.16a, gives the results for $A\sin(\theta n)$. Another useful z-transform pair is number 8, which is derived in Problem 6.16b.

6.3 ▬ PROPERTIES AND RELATIONS

Several transform properties and important relations are presented here; a collection of properties is given in Table 6.2. Some of the entries in this table are derived in the chapter problems. Except where noted otherwise, these apply for sequences defined for $-\infty \le n \le \infty$.

6.3.1 Linearity

If $\mathfrak{z}[f_1(n)] = F_1(z)$ and if $\mathfrak{z}[f_2(n)] = F_2(z)$ then

$$\boxed{\mathfrak{z}[af_1(n) + bf_2(n)] = aF_1(z) + bF_2(z)} \qquad (6.32)$$

where $f_1(n)$ and $f_2(n)$ are arbitrary sequences and a and b are arbitrary constants. This is the first entry in Table 6.2. The region of convergence for the right side of Eq. 6.32 is the region where both $F_1(z)$ and $F_2(z)$ converge. Linearity is a very important property because it means that the z-transform of a sequence which can be written as a sum of sequences can be found by evaluating the transform of each constituent sequence and then forming the sum. It is often possible to write sequences as sums of other simpler sequences, and so the linearity property is quite useful. Likewise, if one has a z-transform written as a sum of transforms, that is,

$$F(z) = F_1(z) + F_2(z) + \cdots + F_M(z) \tag{6.33}$$

the linearity property tells us that to find $f(n)$, the inverse transform of $F(z)$, we can find $f_1(n), f_2(n), \ldots, f_M(n)$ separately and then form the sum

$$f(n) = f_1(n) + f_2(n) + \cdots + f_M(n). \tag{6.34}$$

In general,

$$\boxed{\sum_{k=1}^{p} C_k f_k(n) \longleftrightarrow \sum_{k=1}^{p} C_k F_k(z)} \tag{6.35}$$

where the C_k's are arbitrary constants. This observation forms the basis for an often used method, known as the partial fraction expansion technique, for finding inverse z-transforms.

6.3.2 Shifting Property

For the shifted sequence $f(n - m)$ where m is any integer, its z-transform is

$$\mathfrak{z}[f(n - m)] = \sum_{n=-\infty}^{n=+\infty} f(n - m)z^{-n} \tag{6.36}$$

and with $\ell = n - m$ we have

$$\mathfrak{z}[f(n - m)] = \sum_{\ell=-\infty}^{+\infty} f(\ell)z^{-\ell}z^{-m} = z^{-m} \sum_{\ell=-\infty}^{+\infty} f(\ell)z^{-\ell}. \tag{6.37}$$

We recognize the last summation in Eq. 6.37 as the z-transform of $f(n)$ and thus the shifting property is

$$\boxed{\mathfrak{z}[f(n - m)] = z^{-m}F(z)} . \tag{6.38}$$

This is the second entry in Table 6.2.

FIGURE 6.2 Unit pulse
sequence

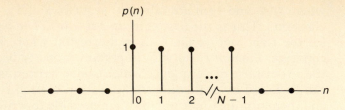

Example 6.1. This example illustrates the use of the shifting property.

The digital pulse of Fig. 6.2 was discussed in earlier chapters. We use linearity and the shift property to obtain its transform.

Solution: The sequence $p(n)$ may be described as

$$p(n) = u(n) - u(n - N) \tag{6.39}$$

where $u(n - N)$ is a shifted unit step sequence. Thus, from linearity

$$\mathfrak{z}[p(n)] = \mathfrak{z}[u(n)] - \mathfrak{z}[u(n - N)] \tag{6.40}$$

and using pair number 2 in Table 6.1 and the shifting property gives

$$P(z) = \frac{1}{1 - z^{-1}} - \frac{z^{-N}}{1 - z^{-1}}$$

$$= \frac{1 - z^{-N}}{1 - z^{-1}}, \qquad |z^{-1}| < 1 \quad \text{or} \quad |z| > 1. \tag{6.41}$$

6.3.3 Multiplication by *n* and Derivatives in *z*

This property can be used for finding transforms of sequences such as a ramp $n \cdot u(n)$, a kind of exponential $na^n \cdot u(n)$, a version of a cosine $n\cos(\theta n) \cdot u(n)$, and so forth. Or, in general, it is useful for finding $\mathfrak{z}[nf(n)]$ with $\mathfrak{z}[f(n)] = F(z)$ known.

Starting with Eq. 6.1 we have

$$F(z) = \sum_{n=-\infty}^{n=\infty} f(n)z^{-n} \tag{6.42}$$

and differentiating both sides with respect to z gives

$$\frac{dF(z)}{dz} = \sum_{n=-\infty}^{n=\infty} -nf(n)z^{-(n+1)}. \tag{6.43}$$

Then multiplying through by $-z$ yields

$$-z\frac{dF(z)}{dz} = \sum_{n=-\infty}^{n=\infty} nf(n)z^{-n}z^{-1}z. \qquad (6.44)$$

Thus, we see that

$$\boxed{\mathfrak{z}[nf(n)] = -z\frac{dF(z)}{dz} \text{ where } \mathfrak{z}[f(n)] = F(z)} \, . \qquad (6.45)$$

This is property number 3 in Table 6.2.

Example 6.2. This example illustrates an application of the derivative in z property.

Use property number 3 in Table 6.2 to develop the z-transform of an important sequence, a digital "ramp" as shown in Fig. 6.3.

Solution: It is seen that $r(n) = nu(n) = nf(n)$ where $f(n) = u(n)$, the unit step. We know, or can look up, the transform of the unit step $u(n)$, which is

$$U(z) = F(z) = \frac{z}{z-1}, \qquad |z| > 1. \qquad (6.46)$$

Applying Eq. 6.45 to find the z-transform of $r(n)$ we have

$$\mathfrak{z}[nf(n)] = -z\frac{dF(z)}{dz}$$

$$= -z\frac{d}{dz}\left[\frac{z}{z-1}\right] \qquad (6.47)$$

and carrying out the derivative operation gives

$$R(z) = -z\frac{(z-1)(1)-(z)(1)}{(z-1)^2}$$

$$= \frac{z}{(z-1)^2}, \qquad |z| > 1. \qquad (6.48)$$

Comment: This is pair number 9 in Table 6.1 where the pair is shown for the ramp $An \cdot u(n)$ rather than simply $n \cdot u(n)$.

FIGURE 6.3 Unit ramp sequence

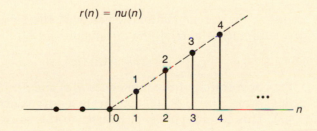

$r(n) = nu(n)$

6.4 ■■■ CONVOLUTION

The forced output of an LTI system can be determined from the convolution sum

$$y(n) = \sum_{m=-\infty}^{m=+\infty} h(m)x(n-m) \tag{6.49}$$

and by taking the z-transform of Eq. 6.49 we have

$$\mathfrak{z}[y(n)] = \mathfrak{z}\left[\sum_{m=-\infty}^{m=\infty} h(m)x(n-m) \right] \tag{6.50}$$

or

$$Y(z) = \sum_{n=-\infty}^{n=\infty} \left[\sum_{m=-\infty}^{m=\infty} h(m)x(n-m) \right] z^{-n}. \tag{6.51}$$

Interchanging the order of summation gives us

$$Y(z) = \sum_{m=-\infty}^{m=\infty} \sum_{n=-\infty}^{n=\infty} h(m)x(n-m)z^{-n} \tag{6.52}$$

or, since $h(m)$ does not depend on n

$$Y(z) = \sum_{m=-\infty}^{m=\infty} h(m) \sum_{n=-\infty}^{n=\infty} x(n-m)z^{-n}. \tag{6.53}$$

Now let $\ell = n - m$, or $-n = -(\ell + m)$ which when substituted into Eq. 6.53 yields

$$Y(z) = \sum_{m=-\infty}^{m=\infty} h(m) \sum_{\ell=-\infty}^{\ell=\infty} x(\ell)z^{-\ell}z^{-m}$$

$$= \sum_{m=-\infty}^{m=\infty} h(m)z^{-m} \sum_{\ell=-\infty}^{\ell=\infty} x(\ell)z^{-\ell}. \tag{6.54}$$

We recognize the second summation as $X(z)$, the z-transform of $x(n)$ and the first summation is $H(z)$, the z-transform of $h(n)$. It follows that

$$Y(z) = H(z)X(z). \tag{6.55}$$

Thus, the convolution of the sequences $h(n)$ and $x(n)$ and the product of the z-transforms $H(z)$ and $X(z)$ constitute a z-transform pair as shown in Fig. 6.4(a). This result applies, of course, to the convolution of any two sequences $x_1(n)$ and $x_2(n)$, as illustrated in Fig. 6.4(b).

FIGURE 6.4 Discrete-time
domain convolution and z-
domain multiplication

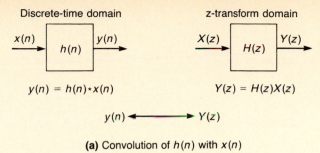

(a) Convolution of $h(n)$ with $x(n)$

$$q(n) = x_1(n) * x_2(n) \qquad\qquad Q(z) = X_1(z)X_2(z)$$

$$q(n) \longleftrightarrow Q(z)$$

(b) Convolution of $x_1(n)$ with $x_2(n)$

The region of convergence (ROC) must be considered in the result of Eq. 6.55. If, for example,

$$h(n) = (0.5)^n u(n) \longrightarrow H(z) = \frac{1}{1 - 0.5z^{-1}}, \qquad |z| > 0.5 \qquad (6.56)$$

and

$$x(n) = (2)^n u(n) \longrightarrow X(z) = \frac{1}{1 - 2z^{-1}}, \qquad |z| > 2 \qquad (6.57)$$

then the only region that satisfies both the ROC of $H(z)$ and that of $X(z)$ is $|z| > 2$ which then is the ROC for $Y(z)$. This result will be generalized later in Section 6.11 where it will be shown that the region of convergence for the z-transform of a right-sided sequence such as

$$F(z) = \sum_{k=1}^{N} \frac{C_k}{1 - d_k z^{-1}}$$

$$= \sum_{k=1}^{N} \frac{C_k z}{z - d_k}$$

$$= \frac{C_1 z}{z - d_1} + \frac{C_2 z}{z - d_2} + \cdots + \frac{C_N z}{z - d_N} \qquad (6.58)$$

is that region greater than the largest value of $|d_k|$. This region is described as *outside a circle of radius* $|d_k|$. If, for example, a right-sided sequence has the transform

$$X(z) = \frac{2z}{z-1} - \frac{3z}{z-2} + \frac{17z}{z+10} \qquad (6.59)$$

the region of convergence for $X(z)$ is outside a circle of radius 10 or for $|z| > 10$.

Example 6.3. This example illustrates convolution by the use of z-transforms.

In Section 3.4 of Chapter Three we found the output of a linear system with the unit sample response

$$h(n) = \begin{cases} (1/2)^n, & 0 \le n \le 3 \\ 0, & \text{elsewhere} \end{cases} \qquad (6.60)$$

that was subjected to the input

$$x(n) = \begin{cases} A, & 0 \le n \le 4 \\ 0, & \text{elsewhere} \end{cases} \qquad (6.61)$$

by using the convolution sum. The output $y(n)$ is portrayed in Fig. 6.5. Now determine the output $y(n)$ by using Eq. 6.55.

Solution: The transform of the output sequence is the transform of $h(n)$ multiplied by the transform of the input, or

$$Y(z) = H(z)X(z) = \left[1 + \frac{1}{2}z^{-1} + \frac{1}{4}z^{-2} + \frac{1}{8}z^{-3}\right] \cdot$$
$$\left[A + Az^{-1} + Az^{-2} + Az^{-3} + Az^{-4}\right], \quad |z| > 0 \quad (6.62)$$

and carrying out the indicated multiplication gives

$$Y(z) = A\left[1 + \frac{3}{2}z^{-1} + \frac{7}{4}z^{-2} + \frac{15}{8}z^{-3} + \frac{15}{8}z^{-4}\right.$$
$$\left. + \frac{7}{8}z^{-5} + \frac{3}{8}z^{-6} + \frac{1}{8}z^{-7}\right]. \quad (6.63)$$

From linearity we know that the transform of the sum of sequences is equal to the sum of the transforms. Also, from Table 6.2, we know that

$$\mathfrak{z}[A\delta(n-m)] = Az^{-m}. \qquad (6.64)$$

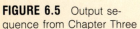 **FIGURE 6.5** Output sequence from Chapter Three

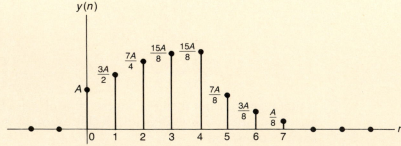

Using Eq. 6.64 on Eq. 6.63 gives

$$y(n) = A\left[\delta(n) + \frac{3}{2}\delta(n-1) + \frac{7}{4}\delta(n-2) + \frac{15}{8}\delta(n-3) + \frac{15}{8}\delta(n-4) \right.$$
$$\left. + \frac{7}{8}\delta(n-5) + \frac{3}{8}\delta(n-6) + \frac{1}{8}\delta(n-7) \right]. \quad (6.65)$$

This agrees with Fig. 6.5, which came from the convolution of Chapter Three.

Example 6.4 This example illustrates another application of z-transforms to evaluate convolution.

In Chapter Three we connected two systems in cascade and derived a new system with the characteristics indicated in Fig. 6.6. In Example 3.13

$$h_1(n) = h_2(n) = \delta(n) + \delta(n-4) \quad (6.66)$$

and

$$h(n) = h_1(n) * h_2(n) = \delta(n) + 2\delta(n-4) + \delta(n-8). \quad (6.67)$$

Determine this same result using the z-transform approach.

Solution: From Fig. 6.6(a) we have

$$p(n) = h_1(n) * x(n) \quad (6.68)$$

and

$$y(n) = h_2(n) * p(n) \quad (6.69)$$

so, using the linear convolution property just developed

$$P(z) = H_1(z)X(z) \quad \text{and} \quad Y(z) = H_2(z)P(z). \quad (6.70)$$

Substituting the expression for $P(z)$ into the second of these equations gives

$$Y(z) = H_2(z)H_1(z)X(z). \quad (6.71)$$

We also know from Fig. 6.6(b) that

$$y(n) = h(n) * x(n). \quad (6.72)$$

Thus, from the convolution property we can write the z-transform of $y(n)$ as

$$Y(z) = H(z)X(z). \quad (6.73)$$

FIGURE 6.6 Equivalent representation ot systems in cascade

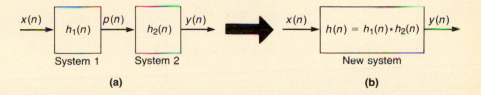

$$(a) \qquad\qquad\qquad (b)$$

Since

$$h(n) = h_1(n) * h_2(n),$$ (6.74)

in terms of z-transforms this becomes

$$\boxed{H(z) = H_1(z)H_2(z)} \quad .$$ (6.75)

Using these results in the present example gives

$$H(z) = \mathfrak{z}[\delta(n) + \delta(n-4)]\mathfrak{z}[\delta(n) + \delta(n-4)]$$ (6.76)

and from the shifting property we have

$$H(z) = [1 + z^{-4}][1 + z^{-4}]$$
$$= 1 + 2z^{-4} + z^{-8}, \qquad |z| > 0.$$ (6.77)

Again from Eq. 6.64 and linearity

$$h(n) = \delta(n) + 2\delta(n-4) + \delta(n-8)$$ (6.78)

as above.

Comment: While we have derived and then illustrated linear convolution with the sample response $h(n)$ and the system input $x(n)$, the property applies, of course, to any pair of discrete sequences. That is, for

$$p(n) = q(n) * r(n)$$ (6.79)

then

$$P(z) = Q(z)R(z).$$ (6.80)

6.5 ▬ TRANSFER FUNCTIONS

This concept was introduced in the previous section but here it will be expanded and used to illustrate some important characteristics of LTI systems. Starting with an input sequence, we consider the resulting output sequence (the forced response). The system transfer function is defined in words by

$$\text{system transfer function} = \frac{z\text{-transform of output sequence}}{z\text{-transform of input sequence}}$$ (6.81)

and we list three procedures that yield a quantitative expression for the transfer function.

1. *System Transfer Function from the Definition*—For the input sequence $x(n)$ we have $\mathfrak{z}[x(n)] = X(z)$, and for the resulting output sequence $y(n)$ we have $\mathfrak{z}[y(n)] = Y(z)$. Thus, the system transfer function is

$$T(z) = \frac{Y(z)}{X(z)} \quad . \tag{6.82}$$

Example 6.5. This example illustrates the determination of the system transfer function from the input/output sequences.

In Example 6.3 the input sequence

$$x(n) = \begin{cases} A, & 0 \le n \le 4 \\ 0, & \text{elsewhere} \end{cases} \tag{6.83}$$

produced the output sequence

$$y(n) = A\left[\delta(n) + \frac{3}{2}\delta(n-1) + \frac{7}{4}\delta(n-2) + \frac{15}{8}\delta(n-3) + \frac{15}{8}\delta(n-4)\right.$$
$$\left. + \frac{7}{8}\delta(n-5) + \frac{3}{8}\delta(n-6) + \frac{1}{8}\delta(n-7)\right]. \tag{6.84}$$

Use these data to find the system transfer function $T(z) = Y(z)/X(z)$.

Solution: From Eqs. 6.82 through 6.84 we have

$$T(z) = \frac{Y(z)}{X(z)}$$

$$= \frac{A\left[1 + \frac{3}{2}z^{-1} + \frac{7}{4}z^{-2} + \frac{15}{8}z^{-3} + \frac{15}{8}z^{-4} + \frac{7}{8}z^{-5} + \frac{3}{8}z^{-6} + \frac{1}{8}z^{-7}\right]}{A[1 + z^{-1} + z^{-2} + z^{-3} + z^{-4}]}$$

$$= \frac{z^7 + \frac{3}{2}z^6 + \frac{7}{4}z^5 + \frac{15}{8}z^4 + \frac{15}{8}z^3 + \frac{7}{8}z^2 + \frac{3}{8}z + \frac{1}{8}}{z^7 + z^6 + z^5 + z^4 + z^3}. \tag{6.85}$$

Comment: By using long division on the result in Eq. 6.85 we get a series that terminates, namely

$$\frac{Y(z)}{X(z)} = 1 + \frac{1}{2}z^{-1} + \frac{1}{4}z^{-2} + \frac{1}{8}z^{-3} \tag{6.86}$$

and we notice that this is the $H(z)$ contained in Eq. 6.62.

2. *System Transfer Function from the Unit Sample Response*—For an LTI system we know that

$$x(n) = \delta(n) \xrightarrow{\text{produces}} y(n) = h(n) \tag{6.87}$$

or in terms of z-transforms Eq. 6.87 becomes

$$X(z) = 1 \xrightarrow{\text{produces}} Y(z) = H(z) \tag{6.88}$$

and using the transfer function definition of Eq. 6.82

$$T(z) = \frac{Y(z)}{X(z)}$$

$$= Y(z) \qquad \text{because } X(z) = 1. \tag{6.89}$$

But with $y(n) = h(n)$, $Y(z) = H(z)$, and so the system transfer function $T(z)$ is actually $H(z)$, the z-transform of the unit sample response. Thus,

$$\boxed{\frac{Y(z)}{X(z)} = H(z) = \mathfrak{z}[h(n)]} \tag{6.90}$$

and, from now on, we will use $H(z)$ to denote the system transfer function.

Example 6.6. This example illustrates the determination of the system transfer function from the unit sample response.

a) A causal first-order IIR filter has the unit sample response

$$h(n) = \beta a^n u(n). \tag{6.91}$$

b) The nonrecursive comb filter from Chapter Five has the unit sample response

$$h(n) = \delta(n) - \delta(n - 8). \tag{6.92}$$

c) Finally, the stable satellite from Chapter Three was described by the unit sample response

$$h(n) = 1.58(0.707)^n \cos(\pi n/4 - 1.25) \, u(n). \tag{6.93}$$

Find the system transfer function for all three of the unit sample responses just given.

Solution:

a) From pair number 3 in Table 6.1

$$H(z) = \mathfrak{z}[\beta a^n u(n)]$$

$$= \frac{\beta}{1 - az^{-1}} = \frac{\beta z}{z - a} \quad \text{for} \quad |z| > |a|. \tag{6.94}$$

b) Using linearity and the shift property

$$H(z) = \mathfrak{z}[\delta(n) - \delta(n - 8)]$$

$$= 1 - z^{-8}$$

$$= \frac{z^8 - 1}{z^8}, \qquad |z| > 0. \tag{6.95}$$

c) From pair number 8 in Table 6.1

$$H(z) = 3[1.58(0.707)^n \cos(\pi n/4 - 1.25)u(n)]$$

$$= \frac{0.5 + 0.5z^{-1}}{1 - z^{-1} + 0.5z^{-2}}$$

$$= \frac{0.5z^2 + 0.5z}{z^2 - z + 0.5}, \qquad |z| > 0.707. \tag{6.96}$$

3. *System Transfer Function from the System Difference Equation—* Starting with the system difference equation for a causal system, namely

$$y(n) - \sum_{k=1}^{N} a_k y(n - k) = \sum_{k=0}^{L} b_k x(n - k) \tag{6.97}$$

we take the z-transform and use the shifting property to find

$$Y(z) - Y(z) \sum_{k=1}^{N} a_k z^{-k} = X(z) \sum_{k=0}^{L} b_k z^{-k}. \tag{6.98}$$

The system transfer function is then

$$H(z) = \frac{Y(z)}{X(z)} = \frac{\displaystyle\sum_{k=0}^{L} b_k z^{-k}}{1 - \displaystyle\sum_{k=1}^{N} a_k z^{-k}}$$

$$= \frac{b_0 + b_1 z^{-1} + b_2 z^{-2} + \cdots + b_L z^{-L}}{1 - a_1 z^{-1} - a_2 z^{-2} - \cdots - a_N z^{-N}}, \qquad |z| > |d_k| \tag{6.99}$$

where the region of convergence is outside a circle of radius $|d_k|$ where d_k is the root having the largest magnitude of

$$1 - a_1 z^{-1} - a_2 z^{-2} - \cdots - a_N z^{-N} = 0. \tag{6.100}$$

Let us now return to the concept of poles and zeros introduced in Chapter 5. A transfer function can be factored into first-order terms in z^{-1} with the result

$$H(z) = \frac{b_0(1 - n_1 z^{-1})(1 - n_2 z^{-1}) \cdots (1 - n_L z^{-1})}{(1 - d_1 z^{-1})(1 - d_2 z^{-1}) \cdots (1 - d_N z^{-1})} \tag{6.101}$$

or

$$H(z) = b_0 z^{N-L} \frac{(z - n_1)(z - n_2) \cdots (z - n_L)}{(z - d_1)(z - d_2) \cdots (z - d_N)} \tag{6.102}$$

where the n's are the system zeros and the d's are the system poles.

These same definitions were used in Chapter Five when we referred to the zeros and poles of the complex function $H(z)$ which was derived from the frequency response $H(e^{j\theta})$. The term z^{N-L} governs the transfer function characteristics at $z = 0$. For $N - L > 0$, there are $N - L$ zeros at $z = 0$ and for $N - L < 0$ there are $N - L$ poles at $z = 0$.

Example 6.7. This example illustrates the determination of the poles and zeros of a system transfer function.

In Chapter Three we described the rotational motion of a satellite by the difference equation

$$y(n) - 2y(n - 1) + y(n - 2) = 0.5x(n) + 0.5x(n - 1) \qquad (6.103)$$

where $y(n)$ represented the angular position (output) and $x(n)$ represented the thrust (input). Find the transfer function $H(z)$ and plot its poles and zeros.

Solution: From Eq. 6.97 we see that $b_0 = 0.5$, $b_1 = 0.5$, $a_1 = 2$, and $a_2 = -1$, which, using Eq. 6.99 gives the transfer function

$$H(z) = \frac{Y(z)}{X(z)} = \frac{0.5 + 0.5z^{-1}}{1 - 2z^{-1} + z^{-2}}$$

$$= \frac{0.5z^2 + 0.5z}{z^2 - 2z + 1}$$

$$= \frac{0.5z(z + 1)}{(z - 1)(z - 1)}, \qquad |z| > 1 \qquad (6.104)$$

and the plot of the poles and zeros is given in Fig. 6.7. Notice that there is a zero at $z = 0$ and that the scale factor of 0.5 is also indicated on the plot.

FIGURE 6.7 $H(z) =$
$\dfrac{0.5z(z + 1)}{(z - 1)(z - 1)}$

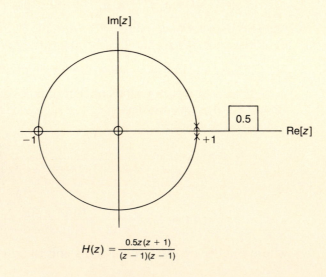

$$H(z) = \frac{0.5z(z + 1)}{(z - 1)(z - 1)}$$

The pole-zero plots for the three filters examined in Example 6.6 are shown in Figs. 6.8 through 6.10. The zeros and poles of the transfer function for the comb filter of Eq. 6.92 as shown in Fig. 6.9 are quite interesting. The transfer function is

$$H(z) = \frac{z^8 - 1}{z^8}, \qquad |z| > 0 \tag{6.105}$$

and we see that all 8 poles are at the origin $(z = 0)$ from the solution of

$$z^8 = 0 \tag{6.106}$$

The zeros come from solving

$$z^8 - 1 = 0 \quad \text{or} \quad z^8 = 1. \tag{6.107}$$

FIGURE 6.8 Pole-zero plot for $H(z) = \dfrac{\beta z}{z - a}$ for a causal recursive filter with $a > 0$

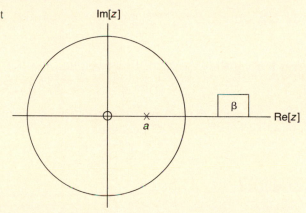

FIGURE 6.9 Pole-zero plot for $H(z) = \dfrac{z^8 - 1}{z^8}$ for a comb filter

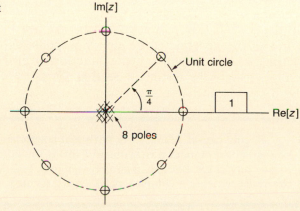

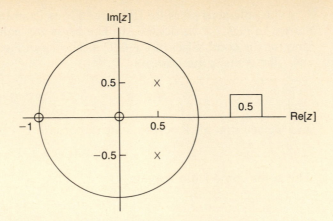

We can write $1 = 1\,e^{jk2\pi}$ where $k = 0, \pm1, \pm2, \ldots$ which gives

$$z^8 = 1\,e^{jk2\pi} \tag{6.108}$$

and finding the 8 roots of this complex number produces

$$z_{1,2,\ldots,8} = (1)^{1/8}\,e^{jk2\pi/8}, \qquad k = 0, 1, 2, \ldots, 7. \tag{6.109}$$

Thus, there are 8 zeros on the unit circle beginning at $z = 1$ and located every $2\pi/8$ radians or 45 degrees.

6.6 ▬ STABILITY

Earlier, system stability was defined in terms of the unit sample response; that is, stability is guaranteed if

$$\sum_{n=-\infty}^{n=+\infty} |h(n)| < \infty. \tag{6.110}$$

In Section 5.3.1 system stability was defined in terms of the poles and zeros of the generalized frequency response $H(z)$ which we now have defined as the system transfer function $H(z)$. Here, therefore, we will simply restate the results of Section 5.3.1.

For any causal, stable filter with real coefficients, all of the poles of the system transfer function $H(z)$ must lie inside the unit circle. The zeros may be located anywhere. Both poles and zeros may be real or complex, but because of the real coefficients complex poles or zeros must occur in conjugate pairs.

A nonrecursive filter is always stable, because all of its poles lie at the origin of the z plane. A typical pole-zero plot for a causal, stable recursive system might look like Fig. 6.11 where the zeros are anywhere, but all of the poles have a magnitude less than one, i.e., they are inside the unit circle. (In Section 6.11 we describe a stable anticausal system that has all of its poles outside the unit circle.)

6.7 ■ FREQUENCY RESPONSE REVISITED

In Chapter Four, we developed the frequency response of a linear system by the use of eigenfunctions and eigenvalues. Specifically, the frequency response was defined in terms of the unit sample response $h(n)$ as

$$H(e^{j\theta}) = \sum_{n=-\infty}^{n=+\infty} h(n)e^{-jn\theta}. \tag{6.111}$$

In Section 6.5 we found that the system transfer function is the z-transform of the unit sample response, i.e.,

$$H(z) = \sum_{n=-\infty}^{n=+\infty} h(n)z^{-n}. \tag{6.112}$$

Comparison of these two equations yields the valuable connection between the frequency response and the system transfer function, namely

$$H(e^{j\theta}) = H(z)\Big|_{z=e^{j\theta}} \tag{6.113}$$

or, in words, the frequency response may be obtained by evaluating the transfer function along the unit circle in the z-plane. This leads naturally

FIGURE 6.11 A typical pole-zero plot for a stable system

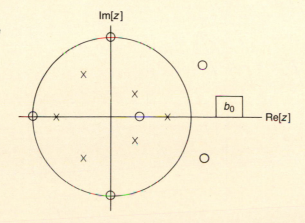

to the graphical procedures of Chapter Five where we had

$$H(e^{j\theta}) = H(z)\Big|_{z=e^{j\theta}} \qquad (6.114)$$

with z the general complex variable. The results of the geometric algorithm for evaluation of the frequency response are given in Eqs. 5.26 through 5.30 and are not restated here.

Example 6.8. This example illustrates a frequency response calculation from a transfer function.

Determine the frequency response of the system whose transfer function is

$$H(z) = \frac{z + 0.5}{z - 0.5}, \qquad |z| > 0.5. \qquad (6.115)$$

Solution: We want the frequency response so we evaluate this transfer function at all values where $|z| = 1$, or $z = e^{j\theta}$, as in Fig. 6.12. Thus, the numerator is $0.5 + e^{j\theta} = Ne^{j\alpha}$ and the denominator is $-0.5 + e^{j\theta} = De^{j\beta}$, and, as in earlier work,

$$H(e^{j\theta}) = \frac{0.5 + e^{j\theta}}{-0.5 + e^{j\theta}}$$

$$= \frac{Ne^{j\alpha}}{De^{j\beta}}$$

$$= Me^{jP} \qquad (6.116)$$

where $M = N/D$ and $P = \alpha - \beta$.

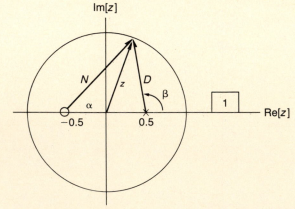

FIGURE 6.12 Graphical evaluation of frequency response for $H(z) = \dfrac{z + 0.5}{z - 0.5}$

▬▬ **THE EVALUATION OF INVERSE TRANSFORMS**

Much of the usefulness of the z-transform in the context of digital signal processing applications is conceptual and simply offers a new way to tackle problems of analysis and design that were encountered earlier. For instance, a unit delay is represented as z^{-1} rather than D and a system output can be computed from $y(n) = \mathfrak{z}^{-1}[H(z) \cdot X(z)]$ rather than from the convolution $y(n) = h(n) * x(n)$.

There are, however, at least two situations in which z-transforms provide quantitative results more easily than other methods:

1. At present, many of the rules and techniques for designing recursive digital filters depend on the use of z-domain properties. We need to know about z-transforms to be able to make use of this large collection of experience and organized (tabulated) procedures. (The design of recursive filters is studied in Chapter Ten.)

2. In certain LTI systems, such as the design and analysis of digital control systems, it is important to have an analytical discrete-time domain expression for the signals (sequences) that appear in the different parts of an often complex configuration. These analytical expressions can be determined by the classical methods of Chapter Three but it has become customary to resort to the algebraic z-transform procedures to find these answers. In other words, there are times when we need to find the inverse transform of $Y(z)$ to obtain an analytical expression for the sequence, $y(n)$[†]. We now formally address this problem.

6.8.1 Inverse Transforms from the Definition

This approach hardly qualifies as a serious method for finding inverse transforms but it offers a very good starting point for the topic. We know from Eq. 6.12 that

$$\mathfrak{z}^{-1}[Az^{-m}] = A\delta(n - m) \qquad (6.117)$$

and so if we have the transform of a sequence $Y(z)$ given by

$$Y(z) = 1 + 2z^{-1} + 3z^{-2} + 2z^{-3} + z^{-4} \qquad (6.118)$$

we can use Eq. 6.12 and linearity to write the sequence $y(n)$ as

$$y(n) = \delta(n) + 2\delta(n - 1) + 3\delta(n - 2) + 2\delta(n - 3) + \delta(n - 4) \qquad (6.119)$$

[†]If we simply want numerical results for $y(n)$, it often makes more sense to solve the system equations by computer iteration rather than resort to transform methods.

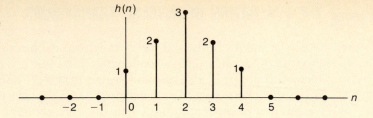

FIGURE 6.13 Output sequence obtained from the z-transform definition

or using the sequence notation

$$y(n) = \{ \ldots 0, 0, 1, 2, 3, 2, 1, 0, 0 \ldots \} \qquad (6.120)$$
$$\uparrow$$
$$n = 0$$

which is shown in Fig. 6.13. This approach is direct and gives inelegant but correct answers. To use this method, however, requires that the transform be in the form of a power series in z^{-1}.

6.8.2 Inverse Transforms from Long Division

This method is most useful if we want the values of only a few samples at the beginning of a sequence. Here we start with a transfer function given as the ratio of two polynomials such as

$$H(z) = \frac{0.5z^2 + 0.5z}{z^2 - z + 0.5}, \qquad |z| > 0.707 \qquad (6.121)$$

which is the transfer function of the stable satellite discussed earlier. Suppose we want to find the unit sample response of this satellite, i.e., the inverse transform of $Y(z) = H(z)X(z)$ with $X(z) = 1$. Using plain old long division we have

$$
\begin{array}{r}
0.5 + 1.0z^{-1} + 0.75z^{-2} \cdots \\
z^2 - z + 0.5 \overline{)0.5z^2 + 0.5z } \\
\underline{0.5z^2 - 0.5z + 0.25} \\
0 \quad + 1.0z - 0.25 \\
\underline{1.0z - 1.00 + 0.50z^{-1}} \\
0 \quad + 0.75 - 0.50z^{-1} \\
\underline{0.75 - 0.75z^{-1} + 0.375} \\
0 \cdots
\end{array}
$$

and so on giving

$$Y(z) = 0.5 + 1.0z^{-1} + 0.75z^{-2} + \cdots. \qquad (6.122)$$

Then using Eq. 6.12, $\mathfrak{z}^{-1}[Az^{-m}] = A\delta(n - m)$, we have the unit sample response

$$y(n) = h(n) = 0.5\delta(n) + 1.0\delta(n - 1) + 0.75\delta(n - 2) + \cdots. \qquad (6.123)$$

Again this is inelegant, but it produces correct values easily. If carried out for many terms, however, it becomes unwieldy and inaccurate due to numerical roundoff. The approach is recommended only for obtaining a few values at the start of a sequence. To apply this method for right-sided sequences as we are doing here, the transform must be written as

$$P(z) = \frac{N(z)}{D(z)} \qquad (6.124)$$

with both $N(z)$ and $D(z)$ written in descending powers of z.

Example 6.9. This example compares discrete-time and transform-domain analysis.

The stable satellite that we have been using is described by the unit sample response

$$h(n) = 1.58(0.707)^n \cos(n\pi/4 - 1.25) \cdot u(n) \qquad (6.125)$$

and by the corresponding transfer function, using pair number 8

$$H(z) = \frac{0.5z^2 + 0.5z}{z^2 - z + 0.5}, \qquad |z| > 0.707. \qquad (6.126)$$

Show that these two expressions yield the same values for $h(n)$ for $0 \le n \le 2$.

Solution: Equation 6.126 is the transform we used to illustrate the long division method. By long division we found the first three terms to be

$$h(0) = 0.50, \quad h(1) = 1.00, \text{ and } h(2) = 0.75. \qquad (6.127)$$

From Eq. 6.125 for $n = 0$, 1, and 2, we obtain

$$h(0) = 1.58(0.707)^0 \cos(0\pi/4 - 1.25) = 0.50$$
$$h(1) = 1.58(0.707)^1 \cos(\pi/4 - 1.25) = 1.00 \qquad (6.128)$$
$$h(2) = 1.58(0.707)^2 \cos(\pi/2 - 1.25) = 0.75$$

The results agree, at least up through $n = 2$.

6.8.3 Inverse Transforms from Partial Fractions and Table Look-Up

Over the many years that z-transforms have been used, the transforms of the most widely used sequences have already been determined. It makes good sense to use these results rather than starting at square one each time we want an inverse transform. The basic idea is to express a given transform as the sum of terms of one or more of the forms given in Table 6.1 and then use linearity to write down the inverse transform by inspection. This method will yield analytical expressions which, as was mentioned earlier, are often quite useful. The procedure is now illustrated using three cases that cover most of the important situations. We start with the simplest and most straightforward of these.

Case 1: Nonrepeated real poles

Given an LTI system that has the transfer function

$$H(z) = \frac{4z^2}{z^2 - 0.25} = \frac{4z^2}{(z - 0.5)(z + 0.5)}, \qquad |z| > 0.5 \qquad (6.129)$$

and we want to find the unit sample response, that is, the system output for an input $x(n) = \delta(n)$. The output transform $Y(z)$ is

$$Y(z) = H(z) \cdot X(z)$$

$$= \frac{4z^2}{z^2 - 0.25} \cdot 1 = \frac{4z^2}{z^2 - 0.25}. \qquad (6.130)$$

The next step is to find the poles and put $Y(z)$ in the form

$$Y(z) = \frac{4z^2}{(z - 0.5)(z + 0.5)} \qquad (6.131)$$

where the poles are clearly distinct or nonrepeated. The idea here is to write

$$Y(z) = \frac{4z^2}{(z - 0.5)(z + 0.5)} \equiv \frac{C_1 z}{z - 0.5} + \frac{C_2 z}{z + 0.5} \qquad (6.132)$$

where this decomposition, which is the reverse of combining terms over a common denominator, is called the *Partial Fraction Expansion* (PFE). The algebraic relation involved, namely

$$\frac{4z^2}{(z - 0.5)(z + 0.5)} \equiv \frac{C_1 z}{z - 0.5} + \frac{C_2 z}{z + 0.5} \qquad (6.133)$$

is an identity which must hold for all values of z. While calculating C_1 and C_2 we are therefore at liberty to choose those particular values of z which simplify the calculation. Thus, if we can find the constants C_1 and C_2, we can use entry number 3 in Table 6.1 and linearity to describe the sequence $y(n)$ that corresponds to this transform $Y(z)$ as

$$y(n) = C_1(0.5)^n u(n) + C_2(-0.5)^n u(n) \qquad (6.134)$$

or

$$y(n) = \begin{cases} C_1(0.5)^n + C_2(-0.5)^n, & n \geq 0 \\ 0, & n < 0. \end{cases} \qquad (6.135)$$

There are several ways to find the partial fraction constants C_1 and C_2 in Eq. 6.132. You may have previously learned one of these methods. We recommend, however, the procedure that is now outlined. After learning this procedure, you could try Problems 6.27 and 6.28 which suggest alternative ways to evaluate C_1 and C_2 so that the pairs of Table 6.1 may be used.

We need the constants C_1 and C_2 in the relation

$$Y(z) = \frac{4z^2}{(z - 0.5)(z + 0.5)} \equiv \frac{C_1 z}{z - 0.5} + \frac{C_2 z}{z + 0.5}. \tag{6.136}$$

Dividing through by z gives

$$\frac{Y(z)}{z} = \frac{4z^2}{z(z - 0.5)(z + 0.5)} \equiv \frac{C_1 z}{z(z - 0.5)} + \frac{C_2 z}{z(z + 0.5)} \tag{6.137}$$

or, cancelling the z terms in numerator and denominator

$$\frac{Y(z)}{z} = \frac{4z}{(z - 0.5)(z + 0.5)} \equiv \frac{C_1}{z - 0.5} + \frac{C_2}{z + 0.5}. \tag{6.138}$$

It is easier and more straightforward to evaluate C_1 and C_2 from the partial fraction expansion of Eq. 6.138 than from that of Eq. 6.136 so our first step will always be to divide through by z. This also guarantees a proper fraction which is necessary for the PFE method. When the constants have been determined we multiply through by z and our partial fractions will be in the form of entry number 3 in Table 6.1.

Starting with the equation for $Y(z)/z$, namely

$$\frac{4z}{(z - 0.5)(z + 0.5)} \equiv \frac{C_1}{z - 0.5} + \frac{C_2}{z + 0.5} \tag{6.139}$$

how might one find C_1? One possibility would be to multiply both sides by the denominator of the term involving C_1 (in this case, $z - 0.5$):

$$\frac{4z(z - 0.5)}{(z - 0.5)(z + 0.5)} \equiv C_1 + \frac{C_2(z - 0.5)}{z + 0.5}. \tag{6.140}$$

If we can select a value of z to make the coefficient of C_2 equal to zero on the right side of the equation, C_1 can be easily determined. This can be achieved by putting $z = 0.5$ on both sides of the equation to give

$$C_1 = \frac{4z}{z + 0.5}\bigg|_{z=0.5} = \frac{4(0.5)}{1} = 2. \tag{6.141}$$

We will find C_2 using the same method. That is, we multiply through the original identity by the denominator of C_2, $z + 0.5$, then set $z = -0.5$ to eliminate the term in C_1. The original identity is

$$\frac{4z}{(z - 0.5)(z + 0.5)} \equiv \frac{C_1}{z - 0.5} + \frac{C_2}{z + 0.5} \tag{6.142}$$

and multiplying both sides by $z + 0.5$ gives us

$$\frac{4z(z + 0.5)}{(z - 0.5)(z + 0.5)} \equiv \frac{C_1(z + 0.5)}{z - 0.5} + C_2 \tag{6.143}$$

where C_2 is found by setting $z = -0.5$ to eliminate the term involving C_1, that is,

$$C_2 = \frac{4z}{z - 0.5}\bigg|_{z=-0.5} = \frac{4(-0.5)}{-1.0} = 2. \qquad (6.144)$$

We can verify this expansion by recombining the two fractions over their common denominator giving

$$\frac{2}{z - 0.5} + \frac{2}{z + 0.5} = \frac{2z + 1 + 2z - 1}{(z - 0.5)(z + 0.5)}$$

$$= \frac{4z}{(z - 0.5)(z + 0.5)} \qquad (6.145)$$

which by comparison with Eq. 6.139 establishes the validity of the expansion. Having found that

$$\frac{Y(z)}{z} = \frac{2}{z - 0.5} + \frac{2}{z + 0.5} \qquad (6.146)$$

we multiply through by z giving

$$Y(z) = \frac{2z}{z - 0.5} + \frac{2z}{z + 0.5}. \qquad (6.147)$$

Using the linearity property (the transform of a sum equals the sum of the transforms) and pair number 3 in Table 6.1, we find that

$$y(n) = h(n) = 2(0.5)^n u(n) + 2(-0.5)^n u(n)$$

$$= \begin{cases} 2(0.5)^n + 2(-0.5)^n, & n \geq 0 \\ 0, & n < 0. \end{cases} \qquad (6.148)$$

This unit sample response is plotted in Fig. 6.14 where the stable response decays to essentially zero in ten samples. The speed of response is often important in digital filter applications.

FIGURE 6.14 $y(n) = h(n) = [2(0.5)^n + 2(-0.5)^n]u(n)$

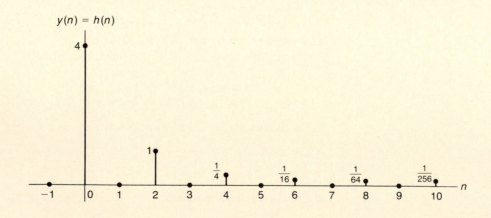

Comment: In this example dividing $Y(z)$ by z simply cancelled a numerator term of z changing the numerator term of the original fraction from $4z^2$ to $4z$. This cancellation does not always happen as we now see. Consider the transform

$$Y(z) = \frac{4(z^2 + z + 1)}{(z - 0.5)(z + 0.5)}, \qquad |z| > 0.5 \qquad (6.149)$$

where we expand $Y(z)/z$ as

$$\frac{Y(z)}{z} = \frac{4(z^2 + z + 1)}{z(z - 0.5)(z + 0.5)}, \qquad |z| > 0.5. \qquad (6.150)$$

Now there is no cancelling of z terms and $Y(z)/z$ has a pole at $z = 0$ giving the PFE expansion

$$\frac{4(z^2 + z + 1)}{z(z - 0.5)(z + 0.5)} \equiv \frac{C_0}{z} + \frac{C_1}{z - 0.5} + \frac{C_2}{z + 0.5} \qquad (6.151)$$

where

$$C_0 = \left. \frac{4(z^2 + z + 1)\cancel{z}}{\cancel{z}(z - 0.5)(z + 0.5)} \right|_{z=0} = -16$$

$$C_1 = \left. \frac{4(z^2 + z + 1)\cancel{(z - 0.5)}}{z\cancel{(z - 0.5)}(z + 0.5)} \right|_{z=0.5} = 14$$

$$C_2 = \left. \frac{4(z^2 + z + 1)\cancel{(z + 0.5)}}{z(z - 0.5)\cancel{(z + 0.5)}} \right|_{z=-0.5} = 6. \qquad (6.152)$$

Then multiplying by z we have

$$Y(z) = -16 + \frac{14z}{z - 0.5} + \frac{6z}{z + 0.5} \qquad (6.153)$$

and

$$y(n) = -16\delta(n) + [14(0.5)^n + 6(-0.5)^n]\, u(n). \qquad (6.154)$$

Problems 6.5 through 6.9 provide basic drill in using the partial fraction expansion method.

Case 2: Nonrepeated complex poles

Consider the system of Eq. 6.129 subjected to the sinusoidal input $x(n) = \sin(n\pi/2)u(n)$. We will find the output sequence $y(n)$ in a closed form after decomposing $Y(z)$ into partial fractions. Using the results of Section 6.5 the transform of the output $y(n)$ is

$$Y(z) = H(z)X(z) \qquad (6.155)$$

and from entry number 7 in Table 6.1 the transform of the input is

$$\mathfrak{z}[\sin(n\pi/2)] = \frac{z^{-1}\sin(\pi/2)}{1 - 2\cos(\pi/2)z^{-1} + z^{-2}}$$

$$= \frac{z}{z^2 + 1}, \qquad |z| > 1 \qquad (6.156)$$

and then from Eq. 6.155 the transform of the output is

$$Y(z) = \frac{4z^2}{z^2 - 0.25} \cdot \frac{z}{z^2 + 1}, \qquad |z| > 0.5. \qquad (6.157)$$

We now proceed to the partial fraction expansion of $Y(z)/z$ by initially factoring the denominator into first-order terms. In the case of the complex roots we write them in exponential form to match entry number 8 in Table 6.1. Thus,

$$\frac{Y(z)}{z} = \frac{4z^2}{(z - 0.5)(z + 0.5)(z - 1e^{j\pi/2})(z - 1e^{-j\pi/2})} \equiv \frac{C_1}{z - 0.5} + \frac{C_2}{z + 0.5}$$
$$+ \frac{C_3}{z - 1e^{j\pi/2}} + \frac{C_4}{z - 1e^{-j\pi/2}} \qquad (6.158)$$

and, as in the previous situation, we calculate the constants in the usual way.

$$C_1 = \frac{4z^2\cancel{(z - 0.5)}}{\cancel{(z - 0.5)}(z + 0.5)(z - 1e^{j\pi/2})(z - 1e^{-j\pi/2})}\Bigg|_{z=0.5} = 0.8 \qquad (6.159)$$

$$C_2 = \frac{4z^2\cancel{(z + 0.5)}}{(z - 0.5)\cancel{(z + 0.5)}(z - 1e^{j\pi/2})(z - 1e^{-j\pi/2})}\Bigg|_{z=-0.5} = -0.8 \qquad (6.160)$$

$$C_3 = \frac{4z^2\cancel{(z - 1e^{j\pi/2})}}{(z - 0.5)(z + 0.5)\cancel{(z - 1e^{j\pi/2})}(z - 1e^{-j\pi/2})}\Bigg|_{z=1e^{j\pi/2}} = 1.6e^{-j\pi/2} \qquad (6.161)$$

$$C_4 = \frac{4z^2\cancel{(z - 1e^{-j\pi/2})}}{(z - 0.5)(z + 0.5)(z - 1e^{j\pi/2})\cancel{(z - 1e^{-j\pi/2})}}\Bigg|_{z=1e^{-j\pi/2}} = 1.6e^{j\pi/2} \qquad (6.162)$$

Notice that $C_4 = C_3{}^*$, which is a good check on our algebra. With all the constants determined we rewrite Eq. 6.158, as $Y(z)$ rather than $Y(z)/z$ which is

$$Y(z) = \frac{0.8z}{z - 0.5} - \frac{0.8z}{z + 0.5} + \frac{1.6e^{-j\pi/2}z}{z - 1e^{j\pi/2}} + \frac{1.6e^{j\pi/2}z}{z - 1e^{-j\pi/2}} \qquad (6.163)$$

and so from pair number 3 and pair number 8 ($a = 1$, $\theta = \pi/2$, $A/2 = 1.6$, and $\alpha = -\pi/2$) we have the output sequence

$$y(n) = 0.8(0.5)^n - 0.8(-0.5)^n + 3.2\cos(n\pi/2 - \pi/2), \qquad n \geq 0. \qquad (6.164)$$

Case 3: Repeated poles
We use the system from the past two examples to determine the output sequence $y(n)$ with the system input a ramp, namely $x(n) = n$ for $n \geq 0$

and $x(n) = 0$, $n < 0$. First,

$$Y(z) = H(z)X(z) \tag{6.165}$$

and from entry number 9 in Table 6.1, the transform of the input is

$$\mathfrak{z}[nu(n)] = \frac{z}{(z-1)^2}, \qquad |z| > 1 \tag{6.166}$$

and the transform of the output is then

$$Y(z) = \frac{4z^2}{z^2 - 0.25} \cdot \frac{z}{(z-1)^2}, \qquad |z| > 1. \tag{6.167}$$

Proceeding to the partial fraction expansion of $Y(z)/z$, we notice that there is a *repeated root* at $z = 1$. If we consider the process of combining terms over a common denominator, we see that the most general possible form of the PFE is

$$\frac{Y(z)}{z} = \frac{4z^2}{(z-0.5)(z+0.5)(z-1)^2}$$

$$= \frac{C_1}{z-0.5} + \frac{C_2}{z+0.5} + \frac{C_3}{(z-1)^2} + \frac{C_4}{z-1}. \tag{6.168}$$

In the usual way

$$C_1 = \left. \frac{Y(z)}{z} \cdot (z-0.5) \right|_{z=0.5} = 4 \tag{6.169}$$

and

$$C_2 = \left. \frac{Y(z)}{z} \cdot (z+0.5) \right|_{z=-0.5} = -4/9 = -0.444 \tag{6.170}$$

with

$$C_3 = \left. \frac{Y(z)}{z} \cdot (z-1)^2 \right|_{z=1} = 16/3 = 5.333. \tag{6.171}$$

If we try to find C_4 in the normal way, we first multiply by $(z-1)$:

$$\frac{4z^2 (z-1)}{(z^2 - 0.25)(z-1)^2} = \frac{C_1(z-1)}{z-0.5} + \frac{C_2(z-1)}{z+0.5}$$

$$+ \frac{C_3(z-1)}{(z-1)^2} + \frac{C_4(z-1)}{z-1}. \tag{6.172}$$

Then, if we put $z = 1$ as usual, we find that the term on the left side of the equation and the third term on the right go to infinity, even though the first two terms go to zero in the normal fashion. We can take a different approach to avoid the problem just encountered with infinity.

Substituting the known constant C_3 and simply indicating the intended substitution of $z = 1$, the three remaining terms of Eq. 6.172 become

$$\left. \frac{4z^2}{(z^2 - 0.25)(z - 1)} \right|_{z=1} = \left. \frac{16/3}{z - 1} \right|_{z=1} + C_4 \qquad (6.173)$$

and solving for the only unknown partial fraction constant gives

$$C_4 = \left\{ \frac{4z^2}{(z^2 - 0.25)(z - 1)} - \frac{(16/3)}{z - 1} \right\}\Bigg|_{z=1}. \qquad (6.174)$$

Combining these two terms over a common denominator yields

$$C_4 = \left. \frac{4z^2 - \dfrac{16}{3}(z^2 - 0.25)}{(z^2 - 0.25)(z - 1)} \right|_{z=1}$$

$$= \left. \frac{\left(4 - \dfrac{16}{3}\right)z^2 + \dfrac{4}{3}}{(z^2 - 0.25)(z - 1)} \right|_{z=1}. \qquad (6.175)$$

In multiple pole (repeated roots) situations like this one, the "misbehaving term" in the denominator, in this case $(z - 1)$, will always be a factor of the numerator. This fact allows us to find C_4 as

$$C_4 = \left. \frac{-\dfrac{4}{3}(z + 1)\cancel{(z - 1)}}{(z^2 - 0.25)\cancel{(z - 1)}} \right|_{z=1} = -32/9. \qquad (6.176)$$

Note that because $(z - 1)$ cancels in the combination of the two terms which individually become infinite as $z \rightarrow 1$, the combination has a finite value $(-32/9)$ for $z = 1$.

Multiplying Eq. 6.168 by z gives

$$Y(z) = \frac{4z}{z - 0.5} - \frac{(4/9)z}{z + 0.5} + \frac{(16/3)z}{(z - 1)^2} - \frac{(32/9)z}{z - 1} \qquad (6.177)$$

and from pair numbers 2, 3, and 9 we have the sequence

$$y(n) = 4(0.5)^n - (4/9)(-0.5)^n + (16/3)n - (32/9), \quad n \geq 0. \qquad (6.178)$$

Comments:

1. Since we've used a lot of algebra here there is always a good possibility of some errors. We saw, however, in Section 6.8.2 that it is quite easy to find the values of the first few samples by long division and then we can use these values to check our analytical results of Eq. 6.178. While not an absolute guarantee, this will provide strong evidence about the correctness of our partial fraction expansion and table-look-up procedures.

First, from Eq. 6.178,

$$y(0) = 4(1) - (4/9)(1) + (16/3)(0) - (32/9) = 0$$

$$y(1) = 4(0.5) - (4/9)(-0.5) + (16/3)(1) - (32/9) = 4$$

$$y(2) = 4(0.25) - (4/9)(+0.25) + (16/3)(2) - (32/9) = 8$$

$$y(3) = 4(0.125) - (4/9)(-0.125) + (16/3)(3) - (32/9) = 13. \quad (6.179)$$

Next, by long division we have for the transform of the output

$$Y(z) = \frac{4z^3}{(z^2 - 0.25)(z^2 - 2z + 1)}$$

$$= \frac{4z^3}{z^4 - 2z^3 + 0.75z^2 + 0.5z - 0.25}. \quad (6.180)$$

The quotient is

$$
\begin{array}{r}
4z^{-1} + 8z^{-2} + 13z^{-3} \cdots \\
z^4 - 2z^3 + 0.75z^2 + 0.5z - 0.25 \overline{)\,4z^3} \\
\underline{4z^3 - 8z^2 + 3z + 2 - z^{-1}} \\
0 \quad 8z^2 - 3z - 2 + z^{-1} \\
\underline{8z^2 - 16z + 6 + 4z^{-1} - 2z^{-2}} \\
0 \quad 13z - 8 - 3z^{-1} + 2z^{-2} \\
\underline{13z - 26 \cdots} \\
0 \quad \cdots
\end{array}
$$

Thus, from long division

$$Y(z) = 0z^0 + 4z^{-1} + 8z^{-2} + 13z^{-3} + \cdots \quad (6.181)$$

and consequently the sequence is

$$y(n) = 4\delta(n - 1) + 8\delta(n - 2) + 13\delta(n - 3) + \cdots. \quad (6.182)$$

This result agrees with that of Eq. 6.179 and we have a reasonable degree of confidence that the analytical expression for $y(n)$ in Eq. 6.178 is correct.

2. The second comment concerns this method for determining the PFE constants for transforms with repeated poles. We needed to exercise some additional care with repeated poles but the expansion was still handled by the normal technique. The only "trick" needed is the requirement that the coefficients corresponding to the repeated roots must be calculated in order, starting with the coefficient of the highest denominator power. That is, for a transform $Y(z)$ with a thrice-repeated pole at $z = p_3$ the usual expansion is

$$\frac{F(z)}{z} = \frac{C_1}{z - p_1} + \frac{C_2}{z - p_2} + \frac{C_3}{(z - p_3)^3} + \frac{C_4}{(z - p_3)^2} + \frac{C_5}{z - p_3} \quad (6.183)$$

and the PFE constants C_1 and C_2 may be calculated at any time and in any order. However, C_3, C_4, and C_5 must be found in the order C_3, C_4, and C_5 using the method that was developed in Case 3.

6.8.4 Partial Fraction Expansion—General Statement

PROCEDURE

Consider the z-transform of a sequence $f(n)$ in the standard form

$$F(z) = b_0 \frac{Q(z)}{(z - p_1)(z - p_2) \cdots (z - p_N)}, \qquad |z| > |p_k| \qquad (6.184)$$

where b_0 is a scale factor, $Q(z)$ is the numerator polynomial, and we assume that all N poles are different.[†] The region of convergence is outside $|p_k|$ where p_k is the pole of $F(z)$ having the largest magnitude. To ensure a *proper fraction* and for convenience, we divide by z to obtain

$$\frac{F(z)}{z} = b_0 \frac{Q(z)}{z(z - p_1)(z - p_2) \cdots (z - p_N)} \qquad (6.185)$$

which is expanded into partial fractions in the manner

$$b_0 \frac{Q(z)}{z(z - p_1)(z - p_2) \cdots (z - p_N)} \equiv \frac{C_0}{z} + \frac{C_1}{z - p_1}$$
$$+ \frac{C_2}{z - p_2} + \cdots + \frac{C_N}{z - p_N} \quad [‡] \qquad (6.186)$$

where

$$C_0 = b_0 \frac{Q(z) \cdot z}{z(z - p_1)(z - p_2) \cdots (z - p_N)} \bigg|_{z=0}$$
$$= b_0 \frac{Q(0)}{(-p_1)(-p_2) \cdots (-p_N)} \qquad (6.187)$$

and for the pole at $z = p_i$ we have

$$C_i = b_0 \frac{Q(z) \cdot (z - p_i)}{z(z - p_1)(z - p_2) \cdots (z - p_i) \cdots (z - p_N)} \bigg|_{z=p_i}$$
$$= b_0 \frac{Q(p_i)}{p_i(p_i - p_1) \cdots (p_i - p_N)}. \qquad (6.188)$$

Then multiplying by z yields

$$F(z) = C_0 + \frac{C_1 z}{z - p_1} + \frac{C_2 z}{z - p_2} + \cdots + \frac{C_N z}{z - p_N}$$
$$= C_0 + \sum_{k=1}^{k=N} \frac{C_k z}{z - p_k} \qquad (6.189)$$

[†] For multiple poles, see Case 3 in Section 6.8.3.
[‡] Notice that if $Q(z)$ is of the form $z^\ell Q(z)$ with $\ell > 0$, then the z in the denominator of the left side will cancel with a factor of z in the numerator. No harm is done if this cancellation is not performed because C_0 will turn out to be zero anyway.

and from pair number 1 and pair number 3 the sequence is

$$f(n) = C_0\delta(n) + \sum_{k=1}^{k=N} C_k(p_k)^n, \quad n \geq 0. \tag{6.190}$$

If there are pairs of complex conjugate poles, each pair should be combined into a general oscillatory sequence as in pair number 8.

6.8.5 Checking Partial Fraction Expansions and Inverse Transforms

We have already used long division to verify results obtained from a partial fraction expansion. There are other ways to check results at various stages in the process. In this section we illustrate some ways of doing this verification.

1. *Comparison of values from long division and partial fraction expansion* (Review)—As mentioned earlier, the long division method, although conceptually simple, does not lead to analytical expressions for inverse transforms. It is a straightforward method, however, for computing numerical values for a few samples. So one method to check an answer for an inverse transform obtained by the partial fraction expansion approach is to evaluate the answer for a few values of n and compare with the results obtained by long division.

2. *"Re-assemblying" the partial fraction expansion*—The algebra required to find partial fraction coefficients can be tedious and error prone. One way to verify that it has been done correctly is to re-assemble the expansion and see if it yields the original transform.

3. *Checking against known or easily-computed initial conditions*—Suppose we start with a difference equation involving an input sequence $x(n)$ and an output $y(n)$. We have seen in Chapter Three that it is easy to solve iteratively for values of $y(n)$ starting with an adequate number of initial conditions. We can do this for a few values of n and then compare the results either with the numerical values found from long division—which checks the correctness of the transform $Y(z)$—or with the values found by substituting for n in the analytical expression for $y(n)$ obtained from the partial fraction expansion. How many values of n are necessary? Assuming that Table 6.1 has been used properly to obtain the correct form of the exponentials, we need a value of n for each PFE coefficient.

4. *Complex conjugate coefficients in partial fraction expansion*—In Problem 6.29 it is shown that complex conjugate roots in a partial fraction expansion lead to complex conjugate coefficients. Knowing that this is true, we can do one of two things: calculate only one of these complex coefficients and obtain the other one by forming the complex conjugate, or calculate both coefficients and check to see

that they are in fact conjugates as a verification of the algebraic manipulations.

6.9 ▬ SOLUTION OF DIFFERENCE EQUATIONS

We have considered several different methods for solving difference equations of the form

$$y(n) - \sum_{k=1}^{N} a_k y(n - k) = \sum_{k=0}^{L} b_k x(n - k) \qquad (6.191)$$

where $x(n)$ is the system input and $y(n)$ is the system output at sample number n (or $t = nT$). Among the approaches used to solve such equations are:

1. Iterative solution—Results in a numerical answer.

2. Classical solution—Results in an analytical expression.

Both of the above methods yield the total solution—that is, the output caused by both the input and the initial conditions. Two other techniques for getting the output under special conditions are:

3. Convolution—Results in the output caused by the input only (the forced response) and the answers may be in either numerical or analytical form.

4. Eigenvalue/eigenfunction or frequency response approach (sinusoidal steady-state formula)—Results in the steady-state response for a stable system only when the input is a sum of sinusoidal sequences.

Now, let us apply z-transform techniques to the solution of difference equations. The result is the complete response, due to input and initial conditions, in an analytical form. While this is a very powerful and useful procedure, its application is normally restricted to systems of relatively low order (N) because of the large amount of algebra involved in these pencil and paper computations. We consider a few examples, however, to illustrate the procedure and to compare the results with those obtained earlier by other approaches.

Unilateral z-transform. In this section, we restrict ourselves to the solution of difference equations that represent causal systems. Typically, we are interested in the response of systems for $n \geq 0$. Thus, in the definition of the z-transform given in Eq. 6.1, the lower limit on the sum becomes zero and the unilateral transform of an arbitrary sequence $f(n)$ is defined as

$$F_u(z) = \sum_{n=0}^{n=\infty} f(n)z^{-n} \qquad (6.192)$$

where the sub u denotes the unilateral transform in contrast with the general transform definition of Eq. 6.1.

The properties given in Table 6.2, properly modified, are valid also for unilateral transforms. Property 2, the shifting property, is particularly important for solving difference equations and we need to see if any modifications are necessary for its application when using the transform definition of Eq. 6.192 (Papoulis, 1977).

Shifting Property for Unilateral Transforms. For

$$F(z) = \sum_{n=-\infty}^{+\infty} f(n)z^{-n} \tag{6.193}$$

we have $\mathfrak{z}[f(n - m)] = z^{-m}F(z)$ for all real integer values of m. Using $F_u(z)$ to denote the unilateral transform of $f(n)$, the corresponding unilateral transform of $f(n - m)$ for $m > 0$ is

$$\mathfrak{z}[f(n - m)] = \sum_{n=0}^{\infty} f(n - m)z^{-n}$$

$$= \sum_{\ell=-m}^{\infty} f(\ell)z^{-(\ell+m)} \qquad \text{where } \ell = n - m$$

$$= f(-m) + f(-m + 1)z^{-1} + \cdots + f(-1)z^{-(-1+m)}$$

$$+ \sum_{\ell=0}^{\infty} f(\ell)z^{-\ell}z^{-m}. \tag{6.194}$$

But the last term on the right side of Eq. 6.194 is simply $z^{-m}F_u(z)$ and so we have the shifting theorem for unilateral transforms, namely

$$\mathfrak{z}[f(n - m)] = f(-m) + f(-m + 1)z^{-1} + \cdots + f(-1)z^{-(m-1)} + z^{-m}F_u(z)$$

$$= \sum_{\ell=-m}^{-1} f(\ell)z^{-(\ell+m)} + z^{-m}F_u(z). \tag{6.195}$$

Notice that Eq. 6.195 clearly includes the needed initial condition terms—the m initial conditions needed to solve a difference equation of mth order.

Example 6.10. This example illustrates the z-transform solution of a first-order difference equation with zero initial condition.

In Chapter Two a savings account was described by

$$y(n) - 1.01y(n - 1) = x(n). \tag{6.196}$$

Find the amount of money in the account $y(n)$ for $n \geq 0$ with $y(-1) = 0$. Let $x(n)$ represent a constant deposit of $50 per month for $n \geq 0$.

Solution: Taking the z-transform of Eq. 6.196 and using the shifting theorem for a unilateral transform yields

$$Y(z) - 1.01[z^{-1}Y(z) + y(-1)z^0] = X(z) \qquad (6.197)$$

or

$$Y(z) = \frac{1}{1 - 1.01z^{-1}} X(z), \qquad |z| > 1.01 \qquad (6.198)$$

where we have dropped the sub u notation. The input $x(n)$ can be described mathematically by the step sequence $x(n) = 50 \cdot u(n)$ which gives

$$Y(z) = \frac{1}{1 - 1.01z^{-1}} \cdot \frac{50}{1 - z^{-1}}, \qquad |z| > 1.01$$

$$= \frac{z}{z - 1.01} \cdot \frac{50z}{z - 1} \qquad (6.199)$$

and expanding $Y(z)/z$ yields

$$Y(z)/z = \frac{50z}{(z - 1.01)(z - 1)} = \frac{C_1}{z - 1.01} + \frac{C_2}{z - 1}. \qquad (6.200)$$

After evaluating C_1 and C_2 as described in Section 6.8.3 and multiplying by z the transform of the output is

$$Y(z) = 50 \left[\frac{101z}{z - 1.01} - \frac{100z}{z - 1} \right] \qquad (6.201)$$

and the amount of money in the account is given by the inverse transform

$$y(n) = 50[101(1.01)^n - 100]u(n). \qquad (6.202)$$

Comment: We should check a few values to compare with the results of Examples 3.1 and 3.2. A random selection gives

$$y(0) \quad = 50[101 - 100] = \$50 \quad \text{as in Eq. 3.4}$$

$$y(12) \quad = 50[101(1.01)^{12} - 100] = \$690.47 \quad \text{as in Eq. 3.7}$$

$$y(108) = 50[101(1.01)^{108} - 100] = \$9791 \quad \text{as in Eq. 3.26.}$$

Example 6.11. This example illustrates the z-transform solution for nonzero initial conditions.

In Example 3.20 the system equation was

$$y(n) + y(n - 2) = x(n) + x(n - 1) \qquad (6.203)$$

with an input sequence of $x(n) = 10 \cdot u(n)$ and initial conditions of $y(-2) = -10$ and $y(-1) = 0$. Find the output sequence $y(n)$ for $n \geq 0$ and compare it with the result of Eq. 3.291.

Solution: Taking the z-transform of Eq. 6.203 and applying the shifting property just developed gives us

$$Y(z) + [z^{-2}Y(z) + z^{-1}y(-1) + y(-2)] = X(z) + z^{-1}X(z) + x(-1) \quad (6.204)$$

and substitution of the given initial conditions yields

$$Y(z) + z^{-2}Y(z) + 0 + (-10) = X(z) + z^{-1}X(z) + 0. \quad (6.205)$$

Now the z-transform of the input $x(n) = 10 \cdot u(n)$ is $X(z) = 10/(1 - z^{-1})$ and when substituted into Eq. 6.205 produces

$$Y(z) + z^{-2}Y(z) - 10 = \frac{10}{1 - z^{-1}} + \frac{10z^{-1}}{1 - z^{-1}}$$

$$= \frac{10(1 + z^{-1})}{1 - z^{-1}}. \quad (6.206)$$

Solving Eq. 6.206 for $Y(z)$ and doing some algebra leaves us with

$$Y(z) = \frac{10 + \dfrac{10(1 + z^{-1})}{1 - z^{-1}}}{1 + z^{-2}}$$

$$= \frac{20}{(1 + z^{-2})(1 - z^{-1})}$$

$$= \frac{20z^3}{(z^2 + 1)(z - 1)}. \quad (6.207)$$

To use the PFE method of Section 6.8.3 we expand $Y(z)/z$ as

$$\frac{Y(z)}{z} = \frac{20z^2}{(z^2 + 1)(z - 1)} = \frac{C_1}{z - 1} + \frac{C_2}{z - 1e^{j\pi/2}} + \frac{C_3}{z - 1e^{-j\pi/2}} \quad (6.208)$$

where

$$C_1 = \left.\frac{20z^2}{z^2 + 1}\right|_{z=1} = 10, \quad C_2 = \left.\frac{20z^2}{(z - 1e^{-j\pi/2})(z - 1)}\right|_{z=1e^{j\pi/2}} = 7.07e^{-j\pi/4}$$

and, of course, $C_3 = C_2{}^* = 7.07e^{j\pi/4}$. This makes the output transform equal to

$$Y(z) = \frac{10z}{z - 1} + \frac{(7.07e^{-j\pi/4})z}{z - 1e^{j\pi/2}} + \frac{(7.07e^{j\pi/4})z}{z - 1e^{-j\pi/2}} \quad (6.209)$$

and the corresponding output sequence is

$$y(n) = 10 + 14.14\cos(\pi n/2 - \pi/4), \quad n \geq 0 \quad (6.210)$$

as found by classical methods in Eq. 3.291.

In Chapter Three we discussed the complementary solution and the particular solution of difference equations. And we also put the solutions into the categories of initial condition response and forced response. We now review these definitions in terms of z-transforms using the system of Example 6.11 to illustrate matters.

Initial Condition and Forced Responses. This is very straightforward; we simply group the terms of the transformed equation according to their origin. Transforming the difference equation for Example 6.11 and assuming that $x(n) = 0$ for $n < 0$ gives

$$Y(z) + z^{-2}Y(z) + z^{-1}y(-1) + y(-2) = X(z) + z^{-1}X(z) \quad (6.211)$$

and arranging the transformed equation into initial conditions and forced components gives

$$Y(z) = \underbrace{\frac{-z^{-1}y(-1) - y(-2)}{1 + z^{-2}}}_{\substack{\text{initial condition} \\ \text{component}}} + \underbrace{\frac{1 + z^{-1}}{1 + z^{-2}}X(z)}_{\substack{\text{forced} \\ \text{component}}} \quad (6.212)$$

where we define the initial condition part as

$$Y_{I.C.}(z) = \frac{-z^{-1}y(-1) - y(-2)}{1 + z^{-2}} \quad (6.213)$$

and the forced part as

$$Y_F(z) = \frac{1 + z^{-1}}{1 + z^{-2}}X(z). \quad (6.214)$$

Inserting the given data from Example 6.11 yields

$$Y_{I.C.}(z) = \frac{10z^2}{z^2 + 1} \quad \text{and} \quad Y_F(z) = \frac{10z^2(z + 1)}{(z^2 + 1)(z - 1)} \quad (6.215)$$

and taking the inverse transforms we get

$$y(n) = y_{I.C.}(n) + y_F(n)$$

$$= \underbrace{10\cos(\pi n/2)}_{\substack{\text{initial condition} \\ \text{solution}}} + \underbrace{10 + 10\cos(\pi n/2 - \pi/2)}_{\text{forced solution}}, \quad n \geq 0. \quad (6.216)$$

Notice that the initial condition response contains system terms only; these are due to the characteristic roots

$$z_{1,2} = 1e^{\pm j\pi/2} \quad (6.217)$$

that came from solving the characteristic equation

$$1 + z^{-2} = 0. \quad (6.218)$$

The forced response contains a term characteristic of the system and a term due to the system input (the pole of $Y_F(z)$ at $z = 1$).

Complementary Solution and Particular Solution. Here, we simply put all terms of Eq. 6.212 together in one fraction giving

$$Y(z) = \frac{-z^{-1}y(-1) - y(-2) + X(z) + z^{-1}X(z)}{1 + z^{-2}} \qquad (6.219)$$

which for the given data becomes

$$Y(z) = \frac{20z^3}{(z^2 + 1)(z - 1)}$$

$$= \underbrace{\frac{C_1 z}{z - 1}}_{\substack{\text{particular} \\ \text{solution component}}} + \underbrace{\frac{C_2 z}{z - 1e^{j\pi/2}} + \frac{C_2{}^* z}{z - 1e^{-j\pi/2}}}_{\substack{\text{complementary} \\ \text{solution component}}} \cdot \qquad (6.220)$$

Evaluating the PFE constants and looking up the pairs gives the output

$$y(n) = \underbrace{10}_{\substack{\text{particular} \\ \text{solution}}} + \underbrace{14.14\cos(\pi n/2 - \pi/4)}_{\substack{\text{complementary} \\ \text{solution}}}. \qquad (6.221)$$

Notice that the complementary solution is the sum of the initial condition solution and that part of the forced solution that is characteristic of the system rather than the input. That is,

$$y_c(n) = \underbrace{10\cos(\pi n/2)}_{\substack{\text{initial condition} \\ \text{response}}} + \underbrace{10\cos(\pi n/2 - \pi/2)}_{\substack{\text{system component of} \\ \text{forced response}}} \qquad (6.222)$$

or as in Eq. 6.221

$$y_c(n) = 14.14\cos(\pi n/2 - \pi/4). \qquad (6.223)$$

The particular solution is that part of the forced solution that is characteristic of the input rather than the system. The forced solution from Eq. 6.216 was

$$y_F(n) = 10 + 10\cos(\pi n/2 - \pi/2) \qquad (6.224)$$

and the part of this due to the input is

$$y_P(n) = 10 \qquad (6.225)$$

as in Eq. 6.221. A diagram of this categorization of the parts of the solution is given in Figure 6.15.

We have worked with several specific difference equations to show how the z-transform method can be used to obtain their solution. In the process we encountered once again such terms as characteristic equation, characteristic roots, complementary and particular solution, and initial condition and forced response. However, to emphasize the main thrust of

FIGURE 6.15 The parts of the solution of a difference equation

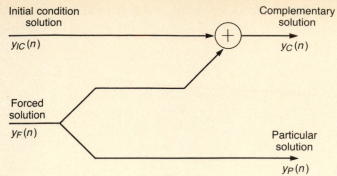

this section, a general method for solving difference equations is now outlined.

Given a system difference equation of the form

$$y(n) - \sum_{k=1}^{N} a_k y(n - k) = \sum_{k=0}^{L} b_k x(n - k) \qquad (6.226)$$

with the known initial conditions $y(-1), \ldots, y(-N)$ and a given input sequence $x(n)$, the procedure for finding the output $y(n)$ is:

PROCEDURE

1. *Transform* the difference equation using the shifting theorem for unilateral transforms, namely

$$\mathfrak{z}[y(n - m)] = z^{-m} Y(z) + z^{-m+1} y(-1) + z^{-m+2} y(-2) + \cdots + y(-m)$$

$$= z^{-m} Y(z) + \sum_{\ell=-m}^{-1} y(\ell) z^{-(\ell+m)} \qquad (6.227)$$

and insert the given initial conditions. Then look up or determine the transform of the input sequence $x(n)$.

2. Solve the transformed version of Eq. 6.226 for $Y(z)$. This requires very careful algebraic manipulations.

3. Expand $Y(z)/z$ in a partial fraction expansion to determine the coefficients.

4. Multiply $Y(z)/z$ by z and then use the z-transform table to find the sequence $y(n)$.

5. Check your results by one of the methods suggested in Section 6.8.5.

Example 6.12. This example illustrates system response computations using the z-transform.

A third-order system is described by

$$y(n) + 0.125y(n - 3) = x(n) + x(n - 1) \qquad (6.228)$$

with $y(-1) = 1$, $y(-2) = 2$, $y(-3) = 3$ and $x(n) = 4n \cdot u(n)$.

a) Transform the system equation and write $Y(z)$ as $Y_{I.C.}(z) + Y_F(z)$.

b) Find the system characteristic equation and its characteristic roots. Is the system stable?

c) Without evaluating the partial fraction constants determine the analytical form for $y_{I.C.}(n)$ and $y_F(n)$.

Solution:

a) Transforming Eq. 6.228 gives us

$$Y(z) + 0.125[z^{-3}Y(z) + y(-1)z^{-2} + y(-2)z^{-1} + y(-3)] = X(z) + z^{-1}X(z) + x(-1) \quad (6.229)$$

and inserting the given initial conditions and the transform of the input yields

$$Y(z) + 0.125[z^{-3}Y(z) + z^{-2} + 2z^{-1} + 3] = \frac{4z}{(z-1)^2} + \frac{z^{-1}4z}{(z-1)^2} + 0. \quad (6.230)$$

Notice that $x(-1) = 0$ because $x(n) = 0$ for $n < 0$. The initial condition part of the transform $Y(z)$ is

$$Y_{I.C.}(z) = 0.125\frac{[-3 - 2z^{-1} - z^{-2}]}{1 + 0.125z^{-3}}$$

$$= 0.125\frac{[-3z^3 - 2z^2 - z]}{z^3 + 0.125}, \qquad |z| > 0.5 \quad (6.231)$$

and the forced part is

$$Y_F(z) = \frac{\dfrac{4z}{(z-1)^2} + \dfrac{4}{(z-1)^2}}{1 + 0.125z^{-3}}$$

$$= \frac{4z^4 + 4z^3}{(z-1)^2(z^3 + 0.125)}, \qquad |z| > 1. \quad (6.232)$$

b) From $Y_{I.C.}(z)$ we find the characteristic equation to be

$$z^3 + 0.125 = 0 \quad (6.233)$$

and the characteristic roots are the three roots of

$$z^3 = -0.125$$

$$= 0.125e^{j(\pi + k2\pi)}, \qquad k = 0, 1, 2 \quad (6.234)$$

which are

$$z_0 = 0.5e^{j\pi/3}, \ z_1 = 0.5e^{j\pi} = -0.5 \quad \text{and} \quad z_2 = 0.5e^{j5\pi/3}. \quad (6.235)$$

The system is clearly stable because we have a causal system and the magnitude of each root is less than one.

c) For the initial condition part of the response we have

$$Y_{I.C.}(z) = \frac{0.125[-3z^3 - 2z^2 - z]}{(z - 0.5e^{j\pi/3})(z + 0.5)(z - 0.5e^{j5\pi/3})} \quad (6.236)$$

and $Y_{I.C.}(z)/z$ becomes

$$\frac{Y_{I.C.}(z)}{z} = \frac{C_1}{z - 0.5e^{j\pi/3}} + \frac{C_1{}^*}{z - 0.5e^{-j\pi/3}} + \frac{C_3}{z + 0.5}. \qquad (6.237)$$

Using Table 6.1 the initial condition response is of the form

$$y_{I.C.}(n) = 2|C_1|(0.5)^n \cos(\pi n/3 + \angle C_1) \cdot u(n) + C_3(-0.5)^n \cdot u(n) \qquad (6.238)$$

which decays to zero as $n \to \infty$. The forced response is found from the partial fraction expansion

$$\frac{Y_F(z)}{z} = \frac{C_4}{z - 0.5e^{j\pi/3}} + \frac{C_4{}^*}{z - 0.5e^{-j\pi/3}} + \frac{C_5}{z + 0.5}$$

$$+ \frac{C_6}{(z - 1)^2} + \frac{C_7}{z - 1} \qquad (6.239)$$

as

$$y_F(n) = 2|C_4|(0.5)^n \cos(\pi n/3 + \angle C_4) \cdot u(n) + C_5(-0.5)^n \cdot u(n)$$
$$+ C_6 n \cdot u(n) + C_7 \cdot u(n). \qquad (6.240)$$

6.10 ■ CONNECTIONS BETWEEN THE TIME DOMAIN AND THE z-DOMAIN

The design and/or analysis of LTI systems is usually carried out with some paper and pencil calculations together with extensive use of computer simulation and computer-aided design (CAD) programs. Estimates made by doing simple calculations and more sophisticated computer computations complement each other and both, with varying degrees of use, are normally required. In this section, we explore several facets of the z-domain (transform domain) that yield time domain characteristics of a system that are useful to the designer. By using the z-domain as much as we can to glean information needed to predict the performance of the system, the sometimes painful process of finding inverse transforms (PFE) can often be avoided—which is a great advantage.

6.10.1 Poles and Zeros and Time Response

The output of an LTI system is affected by the input, the initial conditions, and the system characteristics as portrayed in Fig. 6.16. In the last section, we described the output (response) as

$$y(n) = y_{I.C.}(n) + y_F(n) \qquad (6.241)$$

or in terms of z-transforms as

$$Y(z) = Y_{I.C.}(z) + Y_F(z). \qquad (6.242)$$

FIGURE 6.16 Items that affect the response of an LTI system

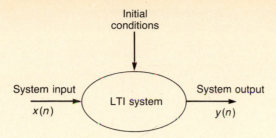

The partial fraction expansion of $Y_{I.C.}(z)$ is

$$Y_{I.C.}(z) = \sum_{k=1}^{N} \frac{C_k z}{z - p_k} \tag{6.243}$$

where the p_k's are the poles (assumed to be distinct) of $Y_{I.C.}(z)$ or the characteristic roots of the system. Thus, the initial condition response

$$y_{I.C.}(n) = \sum_{k=1}^{N} C_k (p_k)^n \tag{6.244}$$

is characterized by the poles (system poles) of $Y_{I.C.}(z)$ and their location in the z-plane determines the nature of the response in the time domain. The partial fraction constants (the C_k's) are simply scale factors, real or complex. The transform of the forced response can be written as

$$Y_F(z) = \frac{C_{N+1} z}{z - p_1} + \frac{C_{N+2} z}{z - p_2} + \cdots + \frac{C_{2N} z}{z - p_N} + \boxed{\begin{array}{c} \text{Input} \\ \text{Terms} \end{array}} \tag{6.245}$$

where there are N system poles and also some poles due to the input sequence.

In any case, it is useful to be able to relate the location of either the system poles or the input poles with the form or characteristic of the sequence associated with each pole. This is really nothing more than having a closer look at a z-transform table such as Table 6.1 with the help of graphical interpretation. The terms are discussed from the point of view of a partial fraction expansion. Notice that the zeros of $Y(z)$ only affect the partial fraction constants—the nature of the response depends only upon the poles.

The first 6 entries in Table 6.3 describe real axis pole locations—see p_0 in Fig. 6.17—along with an algebraic and a graphical description of the corresponding sequences. Entries 7 and 8 describe oscillatory (sinusoidal) sequences—see p and p^* in Fig. 6.17—and entries 9 and 10 consider two common cases of multiple poles.

TABLE 6.3 CONNECTIONS BETWEEN THE TIME DOMAIN AND THE z-DOMAIN

	Term	Pole	Sequence	Graphical Description

For distinct real axis poles we have

1. $\dfrac{Cz}{z-p}$ $0 < p < 1$ Cp^n Decaying exponential

2. $\dfrac{Cz}{z-p}$ $p > 1$ Cp^n Increasing exponential

3. $\dfrac{Cz}{z-p}$ $-1 < p < 0$ Cp^n Decaying (alternating) exponential

4. $\dfrac{Cz}{z-p}$ $p < -1$ Cp^n Increasing (alternating) exponential

5. $\dfrac{Cz}{z-1}$ 1 C Step

6. $\dfrac{Cz}{z+1}$ -1 $C(-1)^n$ Alternating (step)

For distinct complex poles such as

$$p = |p|e^{\pm j\angle p} = ae^{\pm j\theta}$$

we have the following:

7. $\dfrac{Cz}{z - 1e^{j\theta}} + \dfrac{C^*z}{z - 1e^{-j\theta}}$ $\pm 1e^{j\theta}$ $2|C|\cos(n\theta + \angle C)$ Undamped sinusoidal sequence

8. $\dfrac{Cz}{z - ae^{j\theta}} + \dfrac{C^*z}{z - ae^{-j\theta}}$ $ae^{\pm j\theta}$ $2|C|a^n\cos(n\theta + \angle C)$ Damped sinusoidal sequence frequency $= \theta$ and decays to zero as $n \to \infty$. Faster decay as $a \to 0$.

$2|C|a^n\cos(n\theta + \angle C)$ Increasing sinusoidal sequence with frequency $= \theta$ and increases $\to \infty$ as $n \to \infty$.

Finally, for multiple poles, it is best to consider each case on its own although two cases are considered below.

9. $\dfrac{Cz}{(z-1)^2}$ $z_{1,2} = 1$ Cn Ramp

10. $\dfrac{Cz}{(z-a)^2}$ $\begin{aligned}z_{1,2} &= a \\ 0 &< a < 1\end{aligned}$ Cna^n

FIGURE 6.17 Real and
complex pole locations

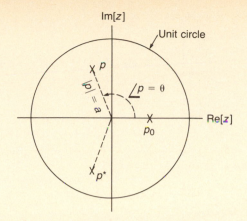

Example 6.13. This example illustrates finding the form of the response $y(n)$ from the pole-zero plot of $Y(z)$.

Given the pole-zero plot of $Y(z)$ as in Fig. 6.18, determine an analytical expression for $y(n)$ without evaluating the PFE constants.

Solution: From Fig. 6.18 we can write

$$Y(z) = \frac{17z^2(z^2 + 3z + 4.5)}{(z^2 + 0.25)(z + 0.9)(z - 0.5)}$$

$$= \frac{C_1 z}{z - 0.5e^{j\pi/2}} + \frac{C_1^* z}{z - 0.5e^{-j\pi/2}} + \frac{C_3 z}{z + 0.9} + \frac{C_4 z}{z - 0.5} \qquad (6.246)$$

and the time-domain sequence is of the form

$$y(n) = 2|C_1|(0.5)^n \cos(\pi n/2 + \angle C_1) + C_3(-0.9)^n + C_4(0.5)^n, \qquad n \geq 0 \quad (6.247)$$

Comment: The term $C_3(-0.9)^n$ "dominates" the response in the sense that it lasts the longest. For instance, at $n = 10$ we have $C_3(-0.9)^{10} = 0.349C_3$, $C_4(-0.5)^{10} = 0.0098C_4$, and $2|C_1|(0.5)^{10} \cos(5\pi + \angle C_1) = 2|C_1|(0.0098) \cos(5\pi + \angle C_1)$ where we see that the effect of the pole at $z = -0.9$ is still very much present while the responses due to the other poles have decayed to essentially zero. To use some jargon, poles close to the unit circle are "slow" poles and those close to the origin are "fast" poles. The values of the partial fraction constants C_1, C_2, and C_3 also influence the dominance of any particular pole. In the analysis above, we have assumed that all three constants are of the same order of magnitude to assert that the pole at $z = -0.9$ dominates the response. While this is probably a good guess, computer simulation is required to be certain.

6.10.2 System Response to Some Special Inputs

The difference equation that describes the rotational motion of a satellite was given in Chapter Three as

$$y(n) - y(n - 1) + 0.5y(n - 2) = 0.5x(n) + 0.5x(n - 1) \qquad (6.248)$$

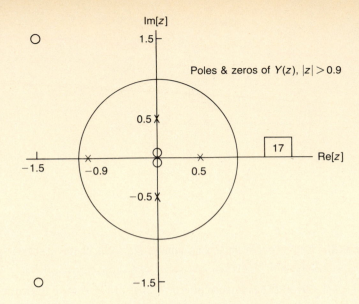

FIGURE 6.18 Pole-zero plot for Example 6.13

Im[z]

1.5

Poles & zeros of $Y(z)$, $|z| > 0.9$

0.5

−1.5

−0.9

0.5

Re[z]

17

−0.5

−1.5

where $y(n)$ represents the angular position and $x(n)$ the input torque of the thrusters. Let's find the response $y(n)$ to several different inputs with all initial conditions set equal to zero.

Unit sample response. Taking the z-transform of Eq. 6.248 gives

$$Y(z) - z^{-1}Y(z) + 0.5z^{-2}Y(z) = 0.5X(z) + 0.5z^{-1}X(z) \qquad (6.249)$$

and solving for the z-transform of the output $y(n)$ yields

$$Y(z) = \frac{0.5 + 0.5z^{-1}}{1 - z^{-1} + 0.5z^{-2}} X(z). \qquad (6.250)$$

We notice that the system transfer function is

$$H(z) = \frac{0.5 + 0.5z^{-1}}{1 - z^{-1} + 0.5z^{-2}} \qquad (6.251)$$

and with the input of $x(n) = \delta(n)$ and consequently $X(z) = 1$, we have

$$Y(z) = H(z) \cdot 1 = \frac{0.5(1 + z^{-1})}{1 - z^{-1} + 0.5z^{-2}}$$

$$= \frac{0.5z(z + 1)}{z^2 - z + 0.5}, \qquad |z| > 0.707. \qquad (6.252)$$

Next, we expand $Y(z)/z$ as

$$\frac{Y(z)}{z} = \frac{0.5(z + 1)}{(z - 0.707e^{j\pi/4})(z - 0.707e^{-j\pi/4})}$$

$$= \frac{0.79e^{-j1.25}}{z - 0.707e^{j\pi/4}} + \frac{0.79e^{j1.25}}{z - 0.707e^{-j\pi/4}}. \qquad (6.253)$$

Multiplying Eq. 6.253 by z gives

$$Y(z) = \frac{0.79e^{-j1.25}z}{z - 0.707e^{j\pi/4}} + \frac{0.79e^{j1.25}z}{z - 0.707e^{-j\pi/4}} \qquad (6.254)$$

and from pair number 8 in Table 6.1 or entry number 8 in Table 6.3 the angular position output for a unit impulse input is given by

$$y(n) = 1.58(0.707)^n \cos(\pi n/4 - 1.25), \qquad n \geq 0 \qquad (6.255)$$

with a plot of the response shown in Fig. 6.19. The plot shows the initial value of this oscillatory response to be 0.5 and it decays to nearly zero in approximately ten samples. The initial-value theorem (see Problem 6.31 and entry 5 in Table 6.2) gives

$$y(0) = \lim_{z \to \infty} Y(z)$$

$$= \lim_{z \to \infty} \left[\frac{0.5z(z + 1)}{z^2 - z + 0.5} \right] = 0.5 \qquad (6.256)$$

which can be checked by long division where we recall that the z^0 term always gives the value at $n = 0$. We can also use Eq. 6.255 to check the initial value as

$$y(0) = 1.58(0.707)^0 \cos(0\pi/4 - 1.25) = 1.58 \cos(-1.25) = 0.5. \quad (6.257)$$

The final value of zero is verified directly from Eq. 6.255 or, for practice, we can use the final-value theorem (FVT) (see Problem 6.32 and

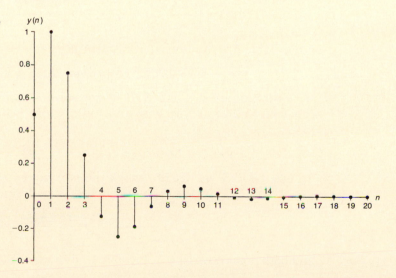

FIGURE 6.19 Unit sample response of the rotational motion of a satellite

entry 6 in Table 6.2), namely

$$y(\infty) = \lim_{z \to 1} (z - 1) \cdot Y(z) \qquad \text{provided all poles of } (z - 1) \cdot Y(z)$$
$$\text{lie inside the unit circle.} \qquad (6.258)$$

To check on this restriction regarding the poles of $(z - 1) \cdot Y(z)$

$$(z - 1) \cdot Y(z) = \frac{(z - 1)0.5z(z + 1)}{(z - 0.707e^{j\pi/4})(z - 0.707e^{-j\pi/4})} \qquad (6.259)$$

and the poles of $(z - 1) \cdot Y(z)$ are the poles of $Y(z)$ which at $z = 0.707e^{\pm j\pi/4}$ lie inside the unit circle. Thus, it is legal to use the FVT which gives

$$y(\infty) = \lim_{z \to 1} \left[\frac{(z - 1)0.5(z + 1)}{z^2 - z + 0.5} \right] = 0. \qquad (6.260)$$

Unit step response. Suppose that the thrusters driving this satellite provide a sampled step input of $x(n) = 1$ for $n \geq 0$. The output transform is now

$$Y(z) = \frac{0.5z(z + 1)}{z^2 - z + 0.5} \cdot \frac{z}{z - 1}, \qquad |z| > 1 \qquad (6.261)$$

and

$$\frac{Y(z)}{z} = \frac{0.5(z + 1)}{z^2 - z + 0.5} \cdot \frac{z}{z - 1}$$

$$= \frac{0.79e^{-j2.82}}{z - 0.707e^{j\pi/4}} + \frac{0.79e^{j2.82}}{z - 0.707e^{-j\pi/4}} + \frac{2}{z - 1} \qquad (6.262)$$

or

$$Y(z) = \frac{0.79e^{-j2.82}z}{z - 0.707e^{j\pi/4}} + \frac{0.79e^{j2.82}z}{z - 0.707e^{-j\pi/4}} + \frac{2z}{z - 1}. \qquad (6.263)$$

From Table 6.1 the inverse transform is

$$y(n) = 1.58(0.707)^n \cos(n\pi/4 - 2.82) + 2, \qquad n \geq 0 \qquad (6.264)$$

with the plot given in Fig. 6.20. Doing some checking from Eq. 6.261 we can verify $y(0) = 0.5$ by long division or from Eq. 6.264 with $n = 0$ we have

$$y(0) = 1.58(0.707)^0 \cos(0\pi/4 - 2.82) + 2 = 0.5. \qquad (6.265)$$

To use the FVT we need to check the proviso on its use. Do the poles of $(z - 1) \cdot Y(z)$ lie inside the unit circle? They do indeed, since

$$(z - 1) \cdot Y(z) = \frac{(z - 1)(0.5z)(z + 1)}{(z - 0.707e^{j\pi/4})(z - 0.707e^{-j\pi/4})(z - 1)} \qquad (6.266)$$

and both poles have $|z| < 1$. Errors are often made by checking the poles of

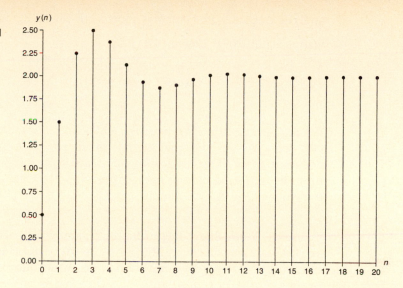

FIGURE 6.20 Unit step response of the rotational motion of a satellite

$Y(z)$ rather than $(z - 1) \cdot Y(z)$. Letting $z = 1$ in Eq. 6.266 we obtain the final value $(n \to \infty)$ of

$$y(\infty) = 2 \qquad (6.267)$$

which agrees with both the plot and Eq. 6.264.

Sinusoidal response. Now consider a sinusoidal input of $x(n) = \cos(n\pi/3)$ to the same second-order system giving the transform

$$Y(z) = \frac{0.5z(z + 1)}{z^2 - z + 0.5} \cdot \frac{z(z - 0.5)}{z^2 - z + 1} \qquad (6.268)$$

for $x(n) = \cos(n\pi/3)$. The partial fraction expansion of $Y(z)/z$ is

$$\frac{Y(z)}{z} = \frac{0.5z(z + 1)(z - 0.5)}{(z - 0.707e^{j\pi/4})(z - 0.707e^{-j\pi/4})(z - e^{j\pi/3})(z - e^{-j\pi/3})}$$

$$= \frac{C_1}{z - 0.707e^{j\pi/4}} + \frac{C_1{}^*}{z - 0.707e^{-j\pi/4}} + \frac{C_3}{z - e^{j\pi/3}}$$

$$+ \frac{C_3{}^*}{z - e^{-j\pi/3}}. \qquad (6.269)$$

The partial fraction constants are evaluated in the usual manner with the transform $Y(z)$ being

$$Y(z) = \frac{0.559e^{j1.11}z}{z - 0.707e^{j\pi/4}} + \frac{0.559e^{-j1.11}z}{z - 0.707e^{-j\pi/4}}$$

$$+ \frac{0.866e^{-j\pi/2}z}{z - e^{j\pi/3}} + \frac{0.866e^{j\pi/2}z}{z - e^{-j\pi/3}} \qquad (6.270)$$

and the output $y(n)$, which is plotted in Fig. 6.21, is

$$y(n) = 1.12(0.707)^n \cos(\pi n/4 + 1.11)$$
$$+ 1.73 \cos(\pi n/3 - \pi/2), \quad n \geq 0. \quad (6.271)$$

By long division or the IVT

$$y(0) = 0.5. \quad (6.272)$$

We cannot use the FVT because when $(z - 1) \cdot Y(z)$ is formed there are two poles, $z = 1e^{\pm j\pi/3}$, that are not inside the unit circle so this theorem does not apply. The final or steady-state solution is sinusoidal like the input as we found using the eigenfunction/eigenvalue approach of Chapter Four.

Sinusoidal Steady-State. Beginning in Chapter Four we have seen that the steady-state response of a linear system to a sinusoidal input is an important result that applies in a variety of situations. We now look at this principle from the viewpoint of z-transforms and then relate it to frequency response, a very familiar concept.

We start with a stable LTI system subjected to a sinusoidal input as in Fig. 6.22(a) and we want to find the expression for the sinusoidal steady-

FIGURE 6.21 Rotational motion of a satellite in response to an input $x(n) = \cos(\pi n/3)$

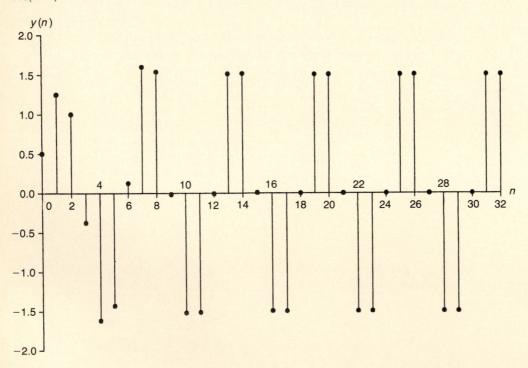

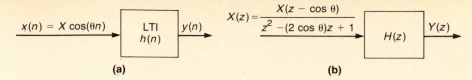

FIGURE 6.22 Stable system with sinusoidal input

(a) $x(n) = X\cos(\theta n)$ → LTI $h(n)$ → $y(n)$

(b) $X(z) = \dfrac{X(z - \cos\theta)}{z^2 - (2\cos\theta)z + 1}$ → $H(z)$ → $Y(z)$

state output $y_{ss}(n)$. We can do this with the sinusoidal steady-state formula in Chapter Four but here let's get the steady-state result by using z-transforms. The transfer function is $H(z) = Y(z)/X(z)$ as in Fig. 6.22(b) from which we can write

$$Y(z) = H(z)X(z)$$

$$= H(z) \cdot \frac{X \cdot z(z - \cos\theta)}{z^2 - (2\cos\theta)z + 1} \tag{6.273}$$

and we expand $Y(z)/z$ by partial fractions giving

$$\frac{Y(z)}{z} = H(z) \cdot \frac{X \cdot [z - \cos\theta]}{z^2 - (2\cos\theta)z + 1} = \frac{C_1}{z - p_1} + \frac{C_2}{z - p_2}$$

$$+ \cdots + \frac{C_N}{z - p_N} + \frac{C_{in}}{z - e^{j\theta}} + \frac{C_{in}{}^*}{z - e^{-j\theta}} \tag{6.274}$$

where $C_1, C_2, \ldots, C_N$ are the partial fraction constants for the system poles which are assumed to be simple (not multiple) and C_{in} and $C_{in}{}^*$ are the PFE constants for the poles due to the sinusoidal input. After multiplying Eq. 6.274 by z, the inverse transform yields the response valid for $n \geq 0$ of

$$y(n) = \underbrace{C_1(p_1)^n + C_2(p_2)^n + \cdots + C_N(p_N)^n}_{\text{terms due to system}} + \underbrace{C_{in}e^{j\theta n} + C_{in}{}^*e^{-j\theta n}}_{\text{terms due to input}}. \tag{6.275}$$

The LTI system was assumed to be stable and consequently all the terms due to the system poles will decay to zero as $n \to \infty$ ($|p_i| < 1$). Thus, the remaining terms make up the sinusoidal steady-state solution

$$y_{ss}(n) = C_{in}(e^{j\theta})^n + C_{in}{}^*(e^{-j\theta})^n \tag{6.276}$$

where we need to determine the constants C_{in} and $C_{in}{}^*$. From Eq. 6.274 we have

$$C_{in} = H(z)\frac{X \cdot [z - \cos\theta][z - e^{j\theta}]}{[z - e^{j\theta}][z - e^{-j\theta}]} \cdot \Bigg|_{z=e^{j\theta}}$$

$$= H(e^{j\theta})\frac{X \cdot [e^{j\theta} - \cos\theta]}{e^{j\theta} - e^{-j\theta}} \tag{6.277}$$

and invoking the Euler relation in two different ways gives us

$$C_{in} = H(e^{j\theta}) \frac{X \cdot [\cos\theta + j \sin\theta - \cos\theta]}{2j(\sin\theta)}$$

$$= \frac{X}{2} H(e^{j\theta}) \qquad (6.278)$$

and, consequently, the complex conjugate is

$$C_{in}{}^* = \frac{X}{2} H(e^{-j\theta}). \qquad (6.279)$$

Putting these constants back into Eq. 6.276 yields

$$y_{ss}(n) = \frac{X}{2}\{H(e^{j\theta})\}\, e^{j\theta n} + \frac{X}{2}\{H(e^{-j\theta})\}\, e^{-j\theta n}. \qquad (6.280)$$

But we can write $H(e^{j\theta})$ and $H(e^{-j\theta})$ in terms of their magnitude and phase which puts Eq. 6.280 into the form

$$y_{ss}(n) = \frac{X}{2}\left|H(e^{j\theta})\right| e^{j\angle H(e^{j\theta})} e^{j\theta n} + \frac{X}{2}\left|H(e^{-j\theta})\right| e^{j\angle H(e^{-j\theta})} e^{-j\theta n}. \qquad (6.281)$$

We know that

$$|H(e^{j\theta})| = |H(e^{-j\theta})| \quad \text{and} \quad \angle H(e^{j\theta}) = -\angle H(e^{-j\theta}) \qquad (6.282)$$

which allows us to express Eq. 6.281 as

$$y_{ss}(n) = \frac{X}{2}\left|H(e^{j\theta})\right| \{e^{j\angle H(e^{j\theta})} e^{j\theta n} + e^{-j\angle H(e^{j\theta})} e^{-j\theta n}\} \qquad (6.283)$$

and finally we get the important result, the sinusoidal steady-state formula once more and as before

$$\boxed{y_{ss}(n) = X|H(e^{j\theta})| \cos(\theta n + \angle H(e^{j\theta})), \text{ where } H(e^{j\theta}) = H(z)\Big|_{z=e^{j\theta}}.}$$

$$(6.284)$$

An enormous effort was used to get to this result but it will not have to be done again for Eq. 6.284 should always be used for the steady-state response of a stable LTI system under sinusoidal excitation. Figure 6.23 summarizes the situation, where $H(e^{j\theta}) = Me^{jP}$ as in earlier chapters.

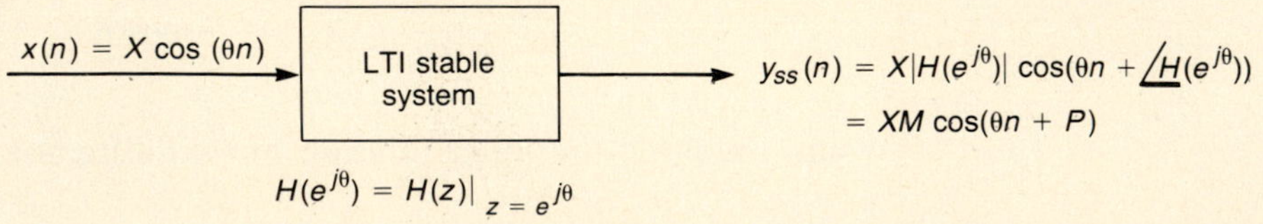

FIGURE 6.23 Summary of sinusoidal steady-state formula

$$x(n) = X \cos(\theta n) \longrightarrow \boxed{\begin{array}{c} \text{LTI stable} \\ \text{system} \end{array}} \longrightarrow$$

$$y_{ss}(n) = X|H(e^{j\theta})| \cos(\theta n + \angle H(e^{j\theta}))$$
$$= XM \cos(\theta n + P)$$

$$H(e^{j\theta}) = H(z)\big|_{z = e^{j\theta}}$$

This procedure is simply an alternative to the eigenfunction/eigenvalue (frequency response) method presented in Chapter Four. The same words of caution should be stated. The LTI system must be stable for the result of Eq. 6.284 and/or Fig. 6.23 to be valid, i.e., all the system poles must lie inside the unit circle.

Example 6.14. This example illustrates the application of the sinusoidal steady-state result.

Use the results summarized in Fig. 6.23 to find the steady-state response for the satellite system in Fig. 6.24 for the input $x(n) = 10 \cos(\pi n/3)$.

Solution: First, we need to check the system poles to see if they lie inside the unit circle. Using the quadratic formula we have

$$z_{1,2} = \frac{1 \pm \sqrt{1 - 2}}{2} = 0.5 \pm j0.5 = 0.707 e^{\pm j\pi/4} \qquad (6.285)$$

showing that the system is stable and consequently we may use Eq. 6.284 to get the steady-state solution. Evaluating the frequency response at $\theta = \pi/3$ gives

$$H(e^{j\pi/3}) = H(z)\Big|_{z=e^{j\pi/3}}$$

$$= \frac{0.5z(z + 1)}{z^2 - z + 0.5}\Big|_{z=e^{j\pi/3}}$$

$$= 1.73 e^{-j\pi/2} \qquad (6.286)$$

and from Fig. 6.23 and/or Eq. 6.284 the steady-state output is

$$y_{ss}(n) = 17.3 \cos(\pi n/3 - \pi/2). \qquad (6.287)$$

Comment: Comparing the input

$$x(n) = 10 \cos(\pi n/3) \qquad (6.288)$$

with the steady-state output of Eq. 6.287 we see that the amplitude of the input has been altered by a factor of 1.73 and the input phase has been shifted from 0 to $-\pi/2$ radians. This, of course, could have been determined from the frequency response of Eq. 6.286

$$H(e^{j\pi/3}) = 1.73 e^{-j\pi/2} \qquad (6.289)$$

without writing the expression for $y_{ss}(n)$.

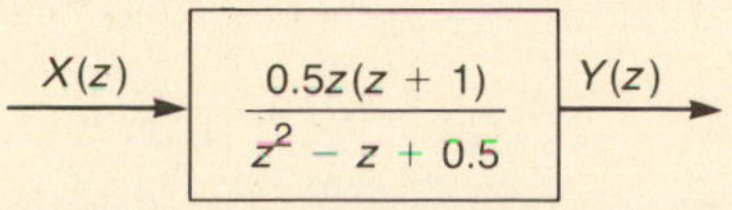

FIGURE 6.24 System for Example 6.14

$$X(z) \longrightarrow \boxed{\frac{0.5z(z + 1)}{z^2 - z + 0.5}} \longrightarrow Y(z)$$

In this final section of the chapter, several concepts introduced earlier are discussed again from a different and somewhat more general point of view. Although this section could be skipped without loss of continuity, we think it will strengthen your comprehension of and appreciation for the z-transform method.

6.11.1 Noncausal Systems

In Chapter Two we introduced the concept of noncausal systems, but to this point we have dealt mainly with causal systems. It is often convenient, however, to design a noncausal system as an intermediate step in developing a causal system. We will see an example of this approach in Chapter Nine where the design of nonrecursive filters is considered.

To begin, let's review the concept of a noncausal system and extend somewhat our previous definitions. We recall from Chapter Two that a noncausal system has a nonzero output before the first nonzero sample of the input is applied to the system. This means that a noncausal system has a unit sample response that has nonzero values for $n < 0$ and possibly also for $n \geq 0$ as shown in Fig. 6.25(a). A causal system has a unit sample response that is zero for $n < 0$ as in Fig. 6.25(b). Finally, we call a system that has $h(n) = 0$ for $n \geq 0$ an *anticausal* system as in Fig. 6.25(c). A typical noncausal filter has the transfer function

$$H(z) = h(-I)z^I + h(-I+1)z^{I-1} + \cdots + h(-1)z^1 + h(0) + h(1)z^{-1} + \cdots$$

$$+ h(I-1)z^{-(I-1)} + h(I)z^{-I} = \sum_{n=-I}^{n=I} h(n)z^{-n}. \quad (6.290)$$

We can view a noncausal system as having causal and anticausal parts. For the transfer function of Eq. 6.290 those terms for $n \geq 0$ are the causal part and the terms for $n < 0$ are the anticausal part. This noncausal filter is made causal by shifting all the terms in the unit sample response $h(n)$ to the right by I samples and the transfer function of the causal filter denoted by $H'(z)$ becomes

$$H'(z) = z^{-I} H(z) \quad (6.291)$$

or

$$H'(z) = h(-I) + h(-I+1)z^{-1} + \cdots + h(-1)z^{-(I-1)} + h(0)z^{-I}$$
$$+ h(1)z^{-(I+1)} + h(I-1)z^{-(2I-1)} + h(I)z^{-2I} \quad (6.292)$$

The filter weights can be reindexed by letting $h'(n) = h(n-I)$ which gives the transfer function of a causal filter, namely

$$H'(z) = \sum_{n=0}^{n=2I} h'(n)z^{-n}. \quad (6.293)$$

FIGURE 6.25 The unit sample response of noncausal, causal, and anticausal systems

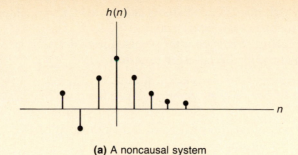

(a) A noncausal system

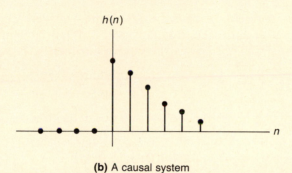

(b) A causal system

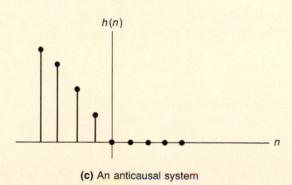

(c) An anticausal system

The frequency response of the noncausal filter of Eq. 6.290 is given by

$$H(e^{j\theta}) = Me^{jP} \qquad (6.294)$$

and from Eq. 6.291 we observe that the frequency response of the causal system is

$$H'(e^{j\theta}) = e^{-jI\theta} H(e^{j\theta})$$
$$= Me^{j(P-I\theta)}. \qquad (6.295)$$

Thus, the magnitude of the frequency response is unaffected by the shift from the noncausal to the causal condition. Now that we've seen one way in which noncausal systems can occur, let's consider in more detail their z-transform characteristics.

Earlier in this chapter we used long division to determine the inverse transform of the transfer function

$$H(z) = \frac{0.5z^2 + 0.5z}{z^2 - z + 0.5} = 0.5 + z^{-1} + 0.75z^{-2} + \cdots \qquad (6.296)$$

and we found the unit sample response to be

$$h(n) = 0.5\,\delta(n) + 1.0\,\delta(n-1) + 0.75\,\delta(n-2) + \cdots. \qquad (6.297)$$

This represents a causal system and we were careful to write $H(z) = N(z)/D(z)$ in descending powers of z. What happens if we use ascending powers? This produces the equivalent form

$$H(z) = \frac{0.5z + 0.5z^2}{0.5 - z + z^2} \qquad (6.298)$$

and using long division on this quotient gives us

$$
\begin{array}{r}
z + 3.0z^2 + 4.0z^3 \cdots \\
0.5 - z + z^2 \overline{)0.5z + 0.5z^2 } \\
\underline{0.5z - 1z^2 + z^3} \\
0 + 1.5z^2 - z^3 \\
\underline{1.5z^2 - 3z^3 + 3z^4} \\
0 + 2z^3 - 3z^4 \\
\underline{2z^3 - 4z^4 + 4z^5} \\
0 \cdots
\end{array}
$$

and so on which produces the series

$$H(z) = z + 3.0z^2 + 4.0z^3 + \cdots. \qquad (6.299)$$

Taking the inverse transform we have

$$h(n) = \delta(n+1) + 3.0\,\delta(n+2) + 4.0\,\delta(n+3) + \cdots \qquad (6.300)$$

which is clearly the unit sample response of an anticausal system. How can this be? We have found two very different unit sample response sequences from the same transfer function by simply carrying out the long division in different ways. The answer to this dilemma lies with the region of convergence of the z-transform.

Consider the unit sample response of Fig. 6.26(a) for a causal system

$$h(n) = \begin{cases} a^n, & n \geq 0 \\ 0, & n < 0 \end{cases}$$

$$= a^n \cdot u(n) \qquad (6.301)$$

which has the z-transform

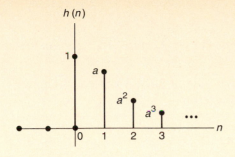

(a) Unit sample response $0 < a < 1$

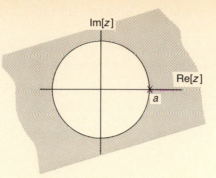

(b) Region of convergence

FIGURE 6.26 A causal system

$$H(z) = \sum_{n=-\infty}^{\infty} a^n z^{-n} \cdot u(n) = \sum_{n=0}^{\infty} (az^{-1})^n$$

$$= \frac{1}{1 - az^{-1}} \quad \text{for} \quad |az^{-1}| < 1 \quad \text{or} \quad |z| > |a| \qquad (6.302)$$

where $|z| > |a|$ is the region of convergence of the infinite series of Eq. 6.302. Notice that the system pole is at $z = a$ and that the series converges outside of this radius as shown in Fig. 6.26(b).

Next, let's consider the unit sample response of Fig. 6.27(a) for an anticausal system described by the unit sample response

$$h(n) = \begin{cases} a^n, & n \leq -1 \\ 0, & n \geq 0 \end{cases}$$

$$= a^n \cdot u(-n - 1). \qquad (6.303)$$

Notice that the shifted unit step function $u(-n - 1) = 0$ for $n \geq 0$ and $u(-n - 1) = 1$ for $n \leq -1$. The unit sample response of this anticausal

FIGURE 6.27 A noncausal system

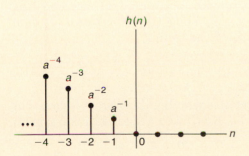

(a) Unit sample response $0 < a < 1$

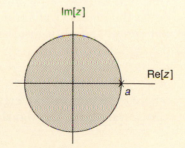

(b) Region of convergence

system has the z-transform

$$H(z) = \sum_{n=-\infty}^{n=\infty} a^n z^{-n} \cdot u(-n-1) = \sum_{n=-\infty}^{n=-1} (az^{-1})^n. \qquad (6.304)$$

By adding and subtracting 1 on the right side of Eq. 6.304 we can change the upper limit to 0 and have the expression

$$H(z) = \sum_{n=-\infty}^{n=0} (az^{-1})^n - 1. \qquad (6.305)$$

The limits on the sum can be changed to 0 to ∞ from $-\infty$ to 0 by changing the sign on n inside the summation giving

$$H(z) = \sum_{n=0}^{n=\infty} (az^{-1})^{-n} - 1 \qquad (6.306)$$

or

$$H(z) = \sum_{n=0}^{\infty} (a^{-1}z)^n - 1. \qquad (6.307)$$

The summation in Eq. 6.307 can be written in closed form and $H(z)$ becomes

$$H(z) = \frac{1}{1 - a^{-1}z} - 1 \qquad \text{for} \quad |za^{-1}| < 1 \quad \text{or} \quad |z| < |a| \qquad (6.308)$$

or

$$H(z) = -\frac{1}{1 - az^{-1}} \qquad \text{for} \quad |z| < |a|. \qquad (6.309)$$

The significant result expressed in Eq. 6.309 is that the region of convergence (ROC) is quite different as shown in Fig. 6.27(b) where it is seen that the series converges inside of the pole at $|z| = a$. The minus sign is simply the result of the algebra but must be accounted for when writing down the inverse transform of Eq. 6.309. Thus, the z-transform for both the causal and anticausal systems is of the form

$$H(z) = \frac{k}{1 - az^{-1}} \qquad \text{for} \quad |z| > |a| \quad \text{or for} \quad |z| < |a| \qquad (6.310)$$

where the region of convergence specifies whether the system is causal or anticausal. Using the transform of Eq. 6.310 we have for a causal system

$$h(n) = \begin{cases} ka^n, & n \geq 0 \\ 0, & n < 0 \end{cases} \qquad \text{for} \quad |z| > |a| \qquad (6.311)$$

and for an anticausal system

$$h(n) = \begin{cases} -ka^n, & n \le -1 \\ 0, & n \ge 0. \end{cases} \quad \text{for} \quad |z| < |a| \tag{6.312}$$

This all amounts to the following. Given a transfer function $H(z)$, we need to know the region of convergence to specify the unit sample response $h(n)$. The results for the first-order systems of Eqs. 6.311 and 6.312 can be extended (Oppenheim and Schafer, 1975) to higher-order systems as follows. For a system with N poles that has a region of convergence $|z| > |p_i|$ where p_i is the pole farthest from $z = 0$, the system is causal. Likewise for a region of convergence of $|z| < |p_j|$ where p_j is the pole closest to $z = 0$, the system is anticausal. Consider, for example, the system transfer function

$$H(z) = \frac{1}{\left(1 - \frac{1}{3}z^{-1}\right)(1 + 3z^{-1})}, \quad |z| > 3 \tag{6.313}$$

with the partial fraction expansion

$$H(z) = \frac{C_1 z}{z - \frac{1}{3}} + \frac{C_2 z}{z + 3}, \quad |z| > 3. \tag{6.314}$$

We see in Fig. 6.28(a) that the region of convergence is outside both poles and consequently we have a causal system with the unit sample response

$$h(n) = \begin{cases} C_1\left(\frac{1}{3}\right)^n + C_2(-3)^n, & n \ge 0 \\ 0, & n < 0 \end{cases} \tag{6.315}$$

If, however, we have

FIGURE 6.28 Regions of convergence

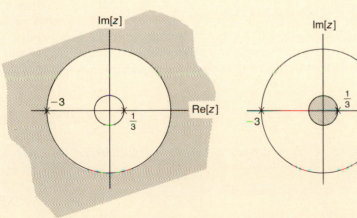

(a) ROC is $|z| > 3$, a causal system   **(b)** ROC is $|z| < \frac{1}{3}$, an anticausal system

$$H(z) = \frac{C_1 z}{z - \dfrac{1}{3}} + \frac{C_2 z}{z + 3}, \qquad |z| < \frac{1}{3} \tag{6.316}$$

we see that the region of convergence in Fig. 6.28(b) is inside both of the poles and consequently the system is anticausal with

$$h(n) = \begin{cases} -C_1 \left(\dfrac{1}{3}\right)^n - C_2(-3)^n, & n \leq -1 \\ 0, & n \geq 0 \end{cases} \tag{6.317}$$

All of the discussion about causal and anticausal sample responses can be extended to right- and left-sided sequences as well. Thus, for a left-sided sequence described by

$$x(n) = \begin{cases} a^n, & n \leq -1 \\ 0, & n \geq 0 \end{cases} \tag{6.318}$$

we use the results of Eq. 6.303 through Eq. 6.309 to write the transform as

$$X(z) = \frac{-1}{1 - az^{-1}}, \qquad |z| < |a|. \tag{6.319}$$

Equations 6.318 and 6.319 constitute the basic exponential pair for left-sided sequences which is similar to pair number 3 in Table 6.1 for right-sided sequences. The pair for the left-sided sequences can be written as

$$x(n) = a^n u(-n-1) \longleftrightarrow X(z) = \frac{-1}{1 - az^{-1}}, \qquad |z| < |a| \tag{6.320}$$

and the pair for $\mathfrak{z}[Aa^n \cdot u(-n-1)]$ is the only entry in Table 6.4.

Suppose that the region of convergence for the transform

$$X(z) = \frac{4z^2}{(z - 0.5)(z - 2)} = \frac{-1.33z}{z - 0.5} + \frac{5.33z}{z - 2} \tag{6.321}$$

is between the poles or where $0.5 < |z| < 2$ as shown in Fig. 6.29. That is, the ROC is inside the pole at $z = 2$ and outside the pole at $z = 0.5$. From the previous discussion we know that a left-sided sequence is represented by

$$\frac{5.33z}{z - 2}, \qquad |z| < 2 \tag{6.322}$$

because the region of convergence is inside the pole at $z = 2$ while a right-sided sequence is represented by

$$\frac{-1.33z}{z - 0.5}, \qquad |z| > 0.5 \tag{6.323}$$

because the region of convergence is outside the pole at $z = 0.5$. Thus, we

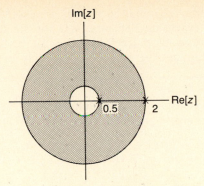

FIGURE 6.29 ROC for a two-sided sequence

Im[z]

Re[z]

0.5   2

ROC is 0.5 < |z| < 2, a two-sided sequence

have a two-sided sequence (left and right), namely

$$x(n) = -5.33(2)^n u(-n-1) - 1.33(0.5)^n u(n). \tag{6.324}$$

Example 6.15. This example illustrates the importance of the region of convergence.

Given the transform

$$Y(z) = 2 + \frac{3z}{z + \frac{1}{2}} + \frac{4z}{z - 3} \tag{6.325}$$

find the inverse transform $y(n)$ for the region of convergence (ROC) specified.

a) $|z| < 1/2$

b) $1/2 < |z| < 3$

c) $|z| > 3$

Solution: For all three parts the inverse transform of 2 is simply $2\delta(n)$. We need to concern ourselves only with the relation of the two poles $(z = -1/2$ and $z = 3)$ to the specified ROCs.

a) The ROC is inside both poles and consequently we have two left-sided sequences as well as $2\delta(n)$. From Eq. 6.320

$$y(n) = 2\delta(n) - 3\left(-\frac{1}{2}\right)^n u(-n-1) - 4(3)^n u(-n-1). \tag{6.326}$$

b) The ROC of $1/2 < |z| < 3$ is inside the pole at $z = 3$ and outside the one at $z = -1/2$. Thus, we have a two-sided sequence, namely

$$y(n) = 2\delta(n) + 3\left(-\frac{1}{2}\right)^n u(n) - 4(3)^n u(-n-1). \tag{6.327}$$

c) This ROC is outside of both poles so we have a familiar right-sided sequence, in this case

$$y(n) = 2\delta(n) + 3\left(-\frac{1}{2}\right)^n u(n) + 4(3)^n u(n). \tag{6.328}$$

> *Comment:* Although it may be obvious, we should mention the fact that the partial fraction expansion (PFE) process is not affected by the region of convergence specifications. We proceed as usual with the PFE expansion and then use the ROC to figure out the transform pairs (left- or right-sided) to use.

Region of Convergence—A General Statement. To summarize the situation, consider the general transform (Papoulis, 1977)

$$F(z) = F_1(z) + F_2(z)$$

$$= \sum_{k=1}^{N_1} \frac{C_k z}{z - p_k} + \sum_{r=1}^{N_2} \frac{C_r z}{z - p_r} \qquad \begin{aligned} R_1 &< |z| < R_2 \\ R_1 &< R_2 \end{aligned} \qquad (6.329)$$

where $F_1(z)$ contains all the poles of $F(z)$ outside the radius R_2 and $F_2(z)$ contains all the poles of $F(z)$ inside the radius R_1. Then, the inverse transform of $F(z)$, i.e., $f(n)$ is

$$f(n) = f_1(n) + f_2(n)$$

$$= -\sum_{k=1}^{N_1} C_k (p_k)^n \cdot u(-n-1) + \sum_{r=1}^{N_2} C_r (p_r)^n \cdot u(n). \qquad (6.330)$$

6.11.2 Convergence and Stability

The z-transform of a sequence $f(n)$

$$F(z) = \sum_{n=-\infty}^{+\infty} f(n) z^{-n} \qquad (6.331)$$

is a series that is defined only for those values of z (real and/or complex) for which Eq. 6.331 converges. If we consider the right-sided sequence

$$f(n) = C_1 p_1^n \cdot u(n) + C_2 p_2^n \cdot u(n) + \cdots + C_N p_N^n \cdot u(n) \qquad (6.332)$$

the z-transform of $f(n)$ is

$$F(z) = \frac{C_1 z}{z - p_1} + \frac{C_2 z}{z - p_2} + \cdots + \frac{C_N z}{z - p_N}, \qquad |z| > |p_k| \qquad (6.333)$$

where the region of convergence is outside of the pole p_k having the largest magnitude as shown in Fig. 6.30(a). Now let's consider the transfer function of a causal system

$$H(z) = \frac{C_1 z}{z - p_1} + \frac{C_2 z}{z - p_2} + \cdots + \frac{C_N z}{z - p_N}, \qquad |z| > |p_k| \qquad (6.334)$$

with the unit sample response

$$h(n) = C_1 p_1^n \cdot u(n) + C_2 p_2^n \cdot u(n) + \cdots + C_N p_N^n \cdot u(n). \qquad (6.335)$$

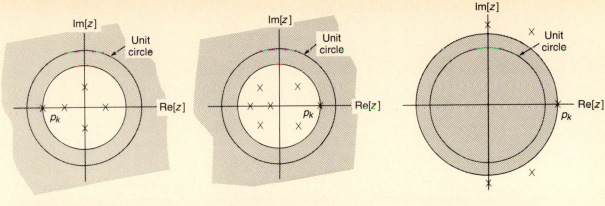

(a) ROC is $|z| > |p_k|$ for $F(z)$ the transform of a right-sided sequence

(b) ROC is $|z| > |p_k|$ for $H(z)$ the transfer function of a stable causal system

(c) ROC is $|z| < |p_k|$ for $H(z)$ the transfer function of a stable anticausal system

FIGURE 6.30 Region of convergence, stability, and causality

If the system is stable, that is if

$$\sum_{n=-\infty}^{\infty} |h(n)| < \infty \qquad (6.336)$$

then we see from Eqs. 6.335 and 6.336 that the magnitudes of all the system poles must be less than 1, that is

$$|p_j| < 1 \qquad j = 1, 2, \ldots, N. \qquad (6.337)$$

For this situation we have Fig. 6.30(b) where we see that the region of convergence is outside of the largest pole p_k of the system transfer function. Notice, however, the important consequence that the ROC includes the unit circle.

> Thus, for a stable, causal system, all poles have magnitudes less than 1 and the ROC of the transfer function $H(z)$ includes the unit circle.

Now let's consider the transfer function of an anticausal system

$$H(z) = \frac{C_1 z}{z - p_1} + \frac{C_2 z}{z - p_2} + \cdots + \frac{C_N z}{z - p_N}, \qquad |z| < |p_k| \qquad (6.338)$$

where the region of convergence lies inside the smallest pole p_k. The corresponding unit sample response is

$$h(n) = -C_1 p_1{}^n \cdot u(-n - 1) - C_2 p_2{}^n \cdot u(-n - 1)$$
$$- \cdots - C_N p_N{}^n \cdot u(-n - 1) \qquad (6.339)$$

and if the system is stable, that is if

$$\sum_{n=-\infty}^{n=\infty} |h(n)| < \infty \qquad (6.340)$$

then we see from Eqs. 6.339 and 6.340 that the magnitudes of all the system poles must be greater than 1 because the p_j's are raised to negative powers. That is

$$|p_j| > 1 \qquad j = 1, 2, \ldots, N. \qquad (6.341)$$

For this situation we have Fig. 6.30(c) where we see that the region of convergence is inside of the pole p_k of the system transfer function that has the smallest magnitude. Notice once more the important consequence that the ROC includes the unit circle.

Thus, for a stable, anticausal system, all poles have magnitudes greater than 1 and the ROC of the transfer function $H(z)$ includes the unit circle.

In general, we see that the definition of stability may be stated as follows:

For a stable system the unit circle is contained in the region of convergence of the system's transfer function $H(z)$. Stable causal systems have all of their poles inside the unit circle whereas stable anticausal systems have all of their poles outside of the unit circle.

6.11.3 The Inversion Formula

A formal way to evaluate inverse transforms is provided by the inversion formula which is done with the *calculus of residues* (Papoulis, 1977). For $z = e^{j\theta}$

$$X(z)\Big|_{z=e^{j\theta}} = \sum_{n=-\infty}^{n=+\infty} x(n)e^{-j\theta n}. \qquad (6.342)$$

Thus, on the unit circle $(z = e^{j\theta})$, $X(z)$ is a periodic function of θ with a period of 2π and the sequence $x(n)$ is given by

$$x(n) = \frac{1}{2\pi} \int_{-\pi}^{\pi} X(e^{j\theta})e^{j\theta n} d\theta. \qquad (6.343)$$

For $z = e^{j\theta}$, $dz = je^{j\theta}d\theta$, or $dz = jzd\theta$, which when substituted into Eq. 6.343 yields

$$x(n) = \frac{1}{2\pi} \int_{-\pi}^{\pi} X(z)z^n(dz/jz)$$

(6.344)

or

$$x(n) = \frac{1}{2\pi j} \oint X(z)z^{n-1}dz$$

(6.345)

which is the inversion integral. The integration in Eq. 6.345 is over a 2π interval in θ and the symbol indicates an integration around a circular closed contour in a counterclockwise sense—contour integration. The radius of the contour chosen can be any value for which $X(z)$ converges. The evaluation of the contour integration can be accomplished by using the residue theorem of complex variable theory (Oppenheim and Schafer, 1975).

6.12 ■■■ REVIEW

This chapter dealt with the algebraic method of z-transforms that is widely used in the analysis and design of discrete-time systems such as digital filters. We used the general definition of the z-transform of a sequence, namely

$$\mathfrak{z}[x(n)] = X(z) = \sum_{n=-\infty}^{n=+\infty} x(n)z^{-n}$$

(6.346)

to develop a short table of transform pairs (Table 6.1) for sequences that are encountered routinely in design and analysis situations. A table of properties (Table 6.2) was also developed. There are problems at the end of the chapter that extend and use these pairs and properties.

Convolution, transfer functions, system stability, and frequency response were encountered once again, this time from the point of view of z-transforms.

Considerable effort was expended on the inverse transform process because getting back to the discrete-time domain is often the final step taken in the analysis of LTI systems. Direct application was made of this inversion process when solving linear difference equations with specified inputs and initial conditions. Noncausal systems were also treated and the region of convergence (ROC) of the power series was shown to control the range of values of n (the sample numbers) for which the unit sample response exists. This ROC concept was then extended and applied to left- and right-sided sequences.

VOCABULARY AND IMPORTANT RELATIONS

a) A sequence is transformed into an algebraic expression in the complex variable z by the defining equation

$$X(z) = \sum_{n=-\infty}^{n=+\infty} x(n)z^{-n}. \qquad (6.1)$$

b) A basic or fundamental pair arises for the right-sided exponential sequence $x(n) = A(a)^n u(n)$ where a may be real or complex. The pair is

$$A(a)^n u(n) \longleftrightarrow A/(1 - az^{-1}), \qquad |a| < |z|. \qquad (6.22)$$

c) A similar pair exists for the left-sided sequence $x(n) = A(a)^n u(-n - 1)$ namely

$$A(a)^n u(-n - 1) \longleftrightarrow -A/(1 - az^{-1}), \qquad |z| < |a|. \qquad (6.320)$$

d) The above pairs can be generalized to give

$$F(z) = \sum_{k=1}^{N_1} \frac{C_k z}{z - p_k} + \sum_{r=1}^{N_2} \frac{C_r z}{z - p_r} \qquad \begin{array}{l} R_1 < |z| < |R_2| \\ R_1 < R_2 \end{array}$$

$$= F_1(z) + F_2(z) \qquad (6.329)$$

where $F_1(z)$ contains all the poles outside a circle of radius R_2 and where $F_2(z)$ contains all the poles inside a circle of radius R_1. Then the inverse transform is

$$f(n) = -\sum_{k=1}^{N_1} C_k(p_k)^n \cdot u(-n-1) + \sum_{r=1}^{N_2} C_r(p_r)^n \cdot u(n). \qquad (6.330)$$

e) Convolution may be described by the pair

$$p(n) = q(n) * r(n) \longleftrightarrow P(z) = Q(z)R(z). \qquad (6.79 \text{ and } 6.80)$$

f) The system transfer function $H(z)$ can be found from at least three points of view.

1. Given the input sequence $x(n)$ and the resulting output sequence $y(n)$, $H(z) = Y(z)/X(z)$.

2. $H(z) = _3[h(n)]$, $\qquad (6.90)$
   where $h(n)$ is the system's unit sample response.

3. $H(z) = \dfrac{Y(z)}{X(z)} = \dfrac{\sum_{k=0}^{L} b_k z^{-k}}{1 - \sum_{k=1}^{N} a_k z^{-k}}$ $\qquad (6.99)$

where the system difference equation is

$$y(n) - \sum_{k=1}^{N} a_k y(n-k) = \sum_{k=0}^{L} b_k x(n-k) \qquad (6.97)$$

and its transform with zero initial conditions is

$$Y(z) - Y(z) \sum_{k=1}^{N} a_k z^{-k} = X(z) \sum_{k=0}^{L} b_k z^{-k}. \qquad (6.98)$$

g) For a stable system the unit circle is contained in the region of convergence of the system's unit sample response. Stable causal systems have all of their poles inside the unit circle whereas stable anticausal systems have all of their poles outside of the unit circle.

h) The frequency response function for a stable LTI system can be determined from the system transfer function by simply substituting $e^{j\theta}$ for z, that is

$$H(e^{j\theta}) = H(z)\Big|_{z=e^{j\theta}}. \qquad (6.113)$$

The poles and zeros of $H(z)$ can be utilized to develop a geometric algorithm for frequency response evaluation.

i) The partial fraction expansion of a rational function of z may be written for simple poles in the form

$$F(z) = C_0 + \sum_{k=1}^{N} \frac{C_k z}{z - p_k}. \qquad (6.189)$$

The PFE constant C_i comes from the evaluation of

$$C_i = \frac{F(z)}{z} (z - p_i)\Big|_{z=p_i}.$$

The corresponding inverse transform $f(n)$ depends on the region of convergence of $F(z)$.

j) Unilateral z-transform

$$F_u(z) = \sum_{n=0}^{n=\infty} f(n) z^{-n}. \qquad (6.192)$$

k) Shifting theorem for unilateral transforms

$$\mathfrak{z}[y(n-m)] = z^{-m} Y(z) + \sum_{\ell=-m}^{-1} y(\ell) z^{-(\ell+m)}. \qquad (6.227)$$

l) Categorization of the parts of the solution of a difference equation. See Fig. 6.15.

m) Initial-value theorem

$$y(0) = \lim_{z \to \infty} Y(z). \tag{6.256}$$

n) Final-value theorem

$$y(\infty) = \lim_{z \to 1} (z - 1) \cdot Y(z) \tag{6.258}$$

provided all poles of $(z - 1) \cdot Y(z)$ lie inside the unit circle.

o) Sinusoidal steady-state—Given a stable system described by the transfer function $H(z) = Y(z)/X(z)$ with an input sequence of $x(n) = X \cos(\theta n)$, the steady-state output sequence is

$$y_{ss}(n) = X|H(e^{j\theta})| \cos(\theta n + \angle H(e^{j\theta}))$$

where

$$H(e^{j\theta}) = H(z)\Big|_{z = e^{j\theta}}. \tag{6.284}$$

TABLES OF TRANSFORMS AND PROPERTIES

TABLE 6.1 RIGHT-SIDED SEQUENCES, $f(n) = 0$ for $n < 0$

Sequence	$F(z)$, z-Transform	Region of Convergence, ROC
1. $A\delta(n)$	A	Everywhere
2. $A \cdot u(n)$	$\dfrac{A}{1 - z^{-1}} = \dfrac{Az}{z - 1}$	$|z| > 1$
3. $Aa^n \cdot u(n)$	$\dfrac{A}{1 - az^{-1}} = \dfrac{Az}{z - a}$	$|z| > |a|$
4. $Aa^n e^{j\theta n} \cdot u(n)$	$\dfrac{A}{1 - ae^{j\theta}z^{-1}} = \dfrac{Az}{z - ae^{j\theta}}$	$|z| > |a|$
5. $Aa^n \cos(\theta n) \cdot u(n)$	$\dfrac{A(1 - az^{-1}\cos\theta)}{1 - (2a\cos\theta)z^{-1} + a^2 z^{-2}} = \dfrac{Az(z - a\cos\theta)}{z^2 - (2a\cos\theta)z + a^2}$	$|z| > |a|$
6. $A\cos(\theta n) \cdot u(n)$	$\dfrac{A(1 - z^{-1}\cos\theta)}{1 - (2\cos\theta)z^{-1} + z^{-2}} = \dfrac{Az(z - \cos\theta)}{z^2 - (2\cos\theta)z + 1}$	$|z| > 1$
7. $A\sin(\theta n) \cdot u(n)$ (See Problem 6.16a)	$\dfrac{Az^{-1}(\sin\theta)}{1 - (2\cos\theta)z^{-1} + z^{-2}} = \dfrac{Az(\sin\theta)}{z^2 - (2\cos\theta)z + 1}$	$|z| > 1$
8. $Aa^n \cos(\theta n + \alpha) \cdot u(n)$ (See Problem 6.16b)	$\dfrac{\dfrac{A}{2}e^{j\alpha}}{1 - ae^{j\theta}z^{-1}} + \dfrac{\dfrac{A}{2}e^{-j\alpha}}{1 - ae^{-j\theta}z^{-1}} = \dfrac{\dfrac{A}{2}e^{j\alpha}z}{z - ae^{j\theta}} + \dfrac{\dfrac{A}{2}e^{-j\alpha}z}{z - ae^{-j\theta}}$ $= \dfrac{Az[z\cos\alpha - a\cos(\alpha - \theta)]}{z^2 - (2a\cos\theta)z + a^2}$	$|z| > |a|$
9. $An \cdot u(n)$	$\dfrac{Az^{-1}}{(1 - z^{-1})^2} = \dfrac{Az}{(z - 1)^2}$	$|z| > 1$

| 10. $An^2 \cdot u(n)$ | $\dfrac{Az^{-1}(1 + z^{-1})}{(1 - z^{-1})^3} = \dfrac{Az(z + 1)}{(z - 1)^3}$ | $|z| > 1$ |
| 11. $Ana^n \cdot u(n)$ | $\dfrac{Aaz^{-1}}{(1 - az^{-1})^2} = \dfrac{Aaz}{(z - a)^2}$ | $|z| > |a|$ |

TABLE 6.2 TRANSFORM PROPERTIES

Property	Sequence	Transform
1. Linearity	$af_1(n) + bf_2(n)$	$aF_1(z) + bF_2(z)$
2. Shifting	$f(n - m)$	$z^{-m}F(z)$
3. Multiplication by n and Derivatives in z	$nf(n)$	$-z\dfrac{dF(z)}{dz}$
4. Convolution	$\displaystyle\sum_{m=-\infty}^{m=\infty} f_1(m)f_2(n - m)$	$F_1(z)F_2(z)$
5. Initial-Value Theorem (See Problem 6.31)	$f(0) = \lim_{z \to \infty} F(z)$	$f(n) = 0, \quad n < 0$
6. Final-Value Theorem (See Problem 6.32)	$f(\infty) = \lim_{z \to 1} (z - 1) \cdot F(z)$ provided all poles of $(z - 1) \cdot F(z)$ lie inside the unit circle.	$f(n) = 0, \quad n < 0$

TABLE 6.4 LEFT-SIDED SEQUENCE, $f(n) = 0$ for $n \geq 0$

Sequence	F(z), z-Transform	Region of Convergence, ROC
$Aa^n \cdot u(-n - 1)$	$\dfrac{-A}{1 - az^{-1}} = \dfrac{-Az}{z - a}$	$|z| < |a|$

PROBLEMS

Reinforcement

6.1 Given the transfer function of a causal system

$$H(z) = \frac{z^3 + z^2 + z + 1}{z^3 - 0.5z^2 - 4z + 2}.$$

a) Find the system poles and zeros and draw the pole-zero diagram. Hint: There is a zero at $z = -1$ and a pole at $z = 0.50$.

b) Is this a stable system? Justify your answer.

c) Find the region of convergence for the transfer function.

6.2 An LTI digital filter is characterized by the transfer function

$$H(z) = \frac{1 - 2z^{-1} + 2z^{-2}}{1 - z^{-1} + 0.5z^{-2}}, \qquad |z| > 0.707.$$

Show that the magnitude of the frequency response is a constant for $0 \le \theta \le \pi$.

6.3 A digital filter has the transfer function

$$H(z) = \frac{z^2 - 0.2z - 0.08}{z^2 - 0.25}, \qquad |z| > 0.5.$$

a) Locate the poles and zeros and show them on a sketch of the z-plane.

b) Is the filter stable? Explain.

c) Find the frequency response (amplitude and phase) at a frequency equal to one-quarter of the sampling frequency.

6.4 A linear phase nonrecursive filter has the poles and zeros shown in Fig. P6.4.

a) Find the filter transfer function $H(z)$.

b) Find the dc gain $(\theta = 0)$ of the frequency response.

c) Write a closed form expression for the amplitude and phase of the frequency response and make approximate sketches of each.

6.5 For a system whose transfer function is

$$H(z) = \frac{z^3 + z}{(z + 0.5)(z^2 + 0.25)}, \qquad |z| > 0.5.$$

a) Find and sketch the poles and zeros of $H(z)$.

b) Is the system stable? Explain.

c) Find the inverse transform of $H(z)$.

d) What is the name used for the response found in part (c)? Explain.

6.6 In this question you are to compare IRA savings with a standard savings account. Both plans are assumed to start with an individual's 25th birthday and are to be compared on the 60th birthday. Do this problem with z-transforms.

IRA	*Savings Account*
Initial deposit $2000, interest of 10% compounded annually, $2000 deposit on each birthday *through* the 60th	Initial deposit $2000, interest of 10% compounded annually, $2000 deposit on each birthday *through* the 60th. Interest is subject to combined federal and state taxes of 30%

6.7 a) Given the transform

$$Y(z) = \frac{z^3 + z}{(z + 0.5)(z^2 + z + 0.5)}, \qquad |z| > 0.707.$$

Find $y(n)$ for $n \ge 0$.

b) The following z-transform converges for $|z| > 1$ and corresponds to a *causal* sequence.

$$Y(z) = \frac{z(2z - 1)}{(z - 1)^2}, \qquad |z| > 1.$$

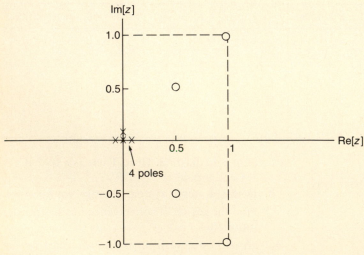

FIGURE P6.4

Determine the corresponding sequence $y(n)$.

6.8 Given an LTI system described by

$$H(z) = \frac{Y(z)}{X(z)} = \frac{z}{z - 0.5}, \qquad |z| > 0.5.$$

a) Find the unit step response.

b) Find the unit ramp response.

c) Find the response to $x(n) = 10 \cos(\pi n/3) \cdot u(n)$.

d) Find the response to $x(n) = 10(0.5)^n \cdot u(n)$.

6.9 Consider a digital filter with the transfer function

$$H(z) = \frac{Y(z)}{X(z)} = \frac{1}{1 + z^{-1}}, \qquad |z| > 1.$$

The input is $x(n) = 1$, $n \geq 0$.

a) Find the analytic expression for the nth sample of $y(n)$.

b) Check your answer to part (a) by using long division.

c) Plot $y(n)$ for $0 \leq n \leq 10$.

6.10 A comb filter has the transfer function

$$H(z) = \frac{1 - z^{-N}}{N}.$$

a) Determine a closed form expression for the frequency response $H(e^{j\theta})$.

b) Sketch the magnitude response for $N = 16$ and label pertinent values.

6.11 In Chapter Three, the rotational motion of a satellite was described by the difference equation $y(n) = y(n-1) - 0.5y(n-2) + 0.5x(n) + 0.5x(n-1)$.

a) Find the transfer function, $H(z) = Y(z)/X(z)$.

b) Determine the unit sample response $h(n) = \mathfrak{z}^{-1}[H(z)]$.

6.12 Given the transform

$$X(z) = \frac{2z^2 + 5z}{z^2 - z - 2}.$$

a) Find $x(n)$ for an ROC of $|z| < 1$.

b) Find $x(n)$ for an ROC of $1 < |z| < 2$.

c) Find $x(n)$ for an ROC of $|z| > 2$.

6.13 An FIR filter is described by the unit sample response $h(n) = \delta(n) - 1.477\delta(n-8)$.

a) Plot the poles and zeros of the transfer function $H(z)$.

b) For $z = e^{j\theta}$, sketch $|H(e^{j\theta})|$ for $0 \leq \theta \leq \pi$. Use the pole-zero plot of part a) to help estimate the shape of this sketch.

c) For an input $x(n) = 10 \cos(3\pi n/8 + \pi/17) \cdot u(n)$, find an analytical expression for the filter output $y(n)$ for $n \geq 0$. Then show that the steady-state output (good for $n \geq 8$) is given by $y_{ss}(n) = 24.77 \cos(3\pi n/8 + \pi/17)$.

6.14 Given the pair for a right-sided sequence

$$\mathfrak{z}[a^n] = \frac{z}{z - a}, \qquad |z| > |a|,$$

start from here and use property number 3 in Table 6.2 to derive

$$\mathfrak{z}[na^n] = \frac{az}{(z - a)^2}, \qquad |z| > |a|.$$

6.15 Given the pair for a right-sided sequence

$$\mathfrak{z}[na^n] = \frac{az}{(z - a)^2}, \qquad |z| > |a|,$$

start from here and use property number 3 in Table 6.2 to derive

$$\mathfrak{z}[n^2 a^n] = \frac{az(z + a)}{(z - a)^3}.$$

6.16 a) Start with the sequence and derive pair number 7 in Table 6.1, i.e., find $\mathfrak{z}[A \sin(\theta n) \cdot u(n)]$.

b) Repeat part a) for the general oscillatory sequence, i.e., find $\mathfrak{z}[Aa^n \cos(\theta n + \alpha) \cdot u(n)]$. This is pair number 8.

6.17 a) From the usual description of a moving average (MA) filter

$$y(n) = \frac{1}{N} \sum_{\ell=0}^{\ell=N-1} x(n - \ell)$$

find the transfer function

$$H(z) = \frac{Y(z)}{X(z)}.$$

b) Write out the polynomial for $H(z)$ with $N = 5$.

6.18 The unit sample response of a system is given in Fig. P6.18(a). The system is subjected to the input shown in Fig. P6.18(b).

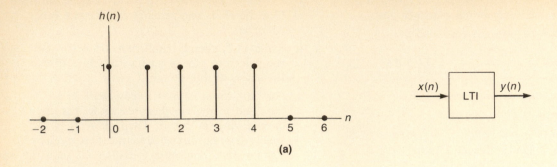

(a)

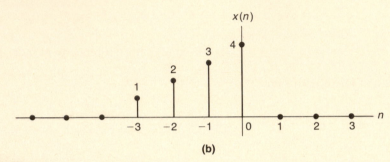

(b)

FIGURE P6.18

a) Is the system stable? Explain.

b) Is the system causal? Explain.

c) Use z-transforms to find and plot the output sequence $y(n)$.

6.19 Given the traditional description of a second-order discrete system $y(n) - [2a \cos \alpha]y(n - 1) + [a^2]y(n - 2) = x(n)$, use z-transforms to find the unit sample response of the system. Put your answer in the form of an oscillatory sinusoidal sequence and compare with the result of Example 3.21.

6.20 Consider the first-order system with input delay, namely $y(n) - a_1 y(n - 1) = b_0 x(n) + b_2 x(n - 2)$. Find the unit sample response and compare your answer with the result of Example 3.22.

6.21 The savings account system of Chapter Three was described at monthly intervals by $y(n) - 1.01y(n - 1) = x(n)$ with $y(n)$ the amount in the account and $x(n)$ the amount deposited, both at the nth sample. Assume that the amount deposited increases in a linear manner as $x(n) = 50 + 5n$, $n \geq 0$. For $y(-1) = 0$, use z-transforms to find the general expression for $y(n)$, $n \geq 0$. Compare your result with that of Example 3.23.

6.22 Consider the same system of Problem 6.21 but with the monthly deposits given by the exponential $x(n) = (1.01)^n \cdot u(n)$. For $y(-1) = 0$ find $y(n)$, $n \geq 0$ by z-transforms. This problem was done by classical methods as Problem 3.34.

6.23 The causal LTI system of Example 3.20 is described by $y(n) + y(n - 2) = x(n) + x(n - 1)$. If the input sequence is $x(n) = 10 \cdot u(n)$ and the given initial conditions are $y(-2) = -10$ and $y(-1) = 0$, find $y(n)$ for $n \geq 0$ by using z-transforms. Compare your answer with the result of Example 3.20.

6.24 In Chapter Three, the satellite system was described by $y(n) + 0.3y(n - 1) - 0.4y(n - 2) = 0.5x(n) + 0.5x(n - 1)$. For no input but with initial conditions of $y(-1) = y(-2) = 1$ find the system response using z-transforms.

6.25 Suppose that the rotational motion of the satellite is described by $y(n) - 2y(n - 1) + y(n - 2) = 0.5x(n) + 0.5x(n - 1)$. For $y(-1) = y(-2) = 1$ and $x(n) = (-1)^n \cdot u(n)$, find $y(n)$ for $n \geq 0$. This problem was solved for $n = 0,1,2,3$ by iterative means in Example 3.3.

6.26 The Fibonacci equation is $y(n + 2) = y(n + 1) + y(n)$, $n \geq 0$, where each number is found by summing the two previous numbers. Find a general expression for $y(n)$ using z-transforms knowing that the first two numbers are $y(0) = y(1) = 1$.

Extension and Generalization

6.27 In Section 6.8.3 a method was presented for evaluating the coefficients in a partial fraction expansion. In this problem, two other approaches will be considered. Assume that we want to evaluate C_1 and C_2 in the expansion

$$X(z) = \frac{4z^2}{(z - 0.5)(z + 0.5)} = \frac{C_1 z}{z - 0.5} + \frac{C_2 z}{z + 0.5}.$$

a) Recombine the right side of the expansion and determine equations that must be satisfied by C_1 and C_2. Solve these equations and compare the results with those of Section 6.8.3.

b) Starting with the above equation, set z equal to two convenient values, which cannot be $z = +0.5$ or $z = -0.5$ (why?), and find two equations that must be satisfied by C_1 and C_2. Solve for the values of C_1 and C_2 and compare with the results of part (a).

c) Based on the results of this problem and Section 6.8.3, describe the advantages and disadvantages of each approach. Be sure to consider how well each method would work on a problem having more than two poles.

6.28 In Section 6.8 the function to be inverse transformed was written in terms of positive powers of z. In this problem we consider an alternative. In Section 6.8 we had the transform

$$X(z) = \frac{4z^2}{(z - 0.5)(z + 0.5)}.$$

a) Write this in terms of z^{-1}.

b) Find a partial fraction expansion in the form

$$X(z) = \frac{C_1}{1 - \alpha z^{-1}} + \frac{C_2}{1 - \beta z^{-1}}$$

and evaluate the coefficients C_1 and C_2.

c) Determine the inverse transform $x(n)$ using Table 6.1.

6.29 In Section 6.8.3 we observed that the presence of complex conjugate poles in a transform leads to terms in the partial fraction expansion that

have complex conjugate coefficients. In this problem you will show that this is a general characteristic when complex poles occur. Assume that the starting point is the transform, already divided by z, in the form

$$\frac{Y(z)}{z} = \frac{N(z)}{D_1(z)(z - ae^{j\theta})(z - ae^{-j\theta})}$$

where $N(z)$ is the numerator polynomial in z and $D_1(z)$ is the part of the denominator polynomial that remains after factoring the terms involving the complex conjugate poles at $z = ae^{j\theta}$ and $z = ae^{-j\theta}$. The partial fraction expansion has the form

$$\frac{Y(z)}{z} = \frac{C_1}{z - ae^{j\theta}} + \frac{C_2}{z - ae^{-j\theta}} + \text{other terms}.$$

Find the expressions for C_1 and C_2 and show that they are complex conjugates of one another.

6.30 When digitizing analog filters as we will do in Chapter Ten, the bilinear transformation

$$s = \frac{2}{T} \frac{1 - z^{-1}}{1 + z^{-1}}$$

provides a useful conformal mapping from the s-plane to the z-plane. It can be derived from the trapezoidal rule of approximating a continuous integral.

a) Approximate the integral shown in Fig. P6.30 by a difference equation by using the trapezoidal rule with $nT \le t < (n + 1)T$.

b) Take the z-transform of the difference equation and solve for the transfer function

$$H(z) = Y(z)/X(z).$$

c) The s-domain transfer function of an integrator is $H(s) = 1/s$. Use the result from part (b) and show that

$$s = \frac{2}{T} \frac{1 - z^{-1}}{1 + z^{-1}}.$$

It is shown in Chapter Ten that the constant $2/T$ is unnecessary and can be ignored.

6.31 Assume that $F(z)$ is a z-transform of a sequence that is zero for $n < 0$. From the definition of the z-transform, $F(z)$ can be written as

$$F(z) = f(0) + f(1)z^{-1} + f(2)z^{-2} + \dots \quad (1)$$

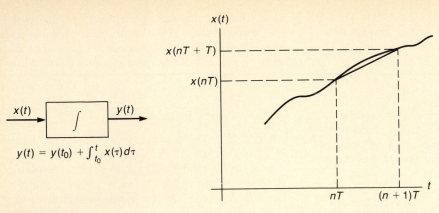

$$y(t) = y(t_0) + \int_{t_0}^{t} x(\tau)\,d\tau$$

FIGURE P6.30

Suppose you were given $F(z)$ in the form of a ratio of two polynomials in z and wanted to find $f(0)$ without either doing long division to obtain $F(z)$ in the form of (1), or by taking the inverse transform of $F(z)$.

a) Show that

$$f(0) = \lim_{z \to \infty} F(z).$$

This result is known as the *initial-value theorem* for z-transforms.

b) Use the result of part (a) to find $f(0)$ for $F(z) = \dfrac{z}{z-1}$. Compare your result with the value of $f(0)$ obtained by long division and also by finding $f(n)$, the inverse transform of $F(z)$.

c) For what is the initial-value theorem useful?

6.32 Assume that $F(z)$ is a z-transform of a sequence that is zero for $n < 0$.

a) Show that $\mathfrak{z}[f(n+1)] = zF(z)$.

b) Use the result of part (a) to show that

$$zF(z) - F(z) = \lim_{N \to \infty} \sum_{n=-N}^{N} [f(n+1) - f(n)]z^{-n}.$$

c) Starting with the equation given in part (b), show that

$$\lim_{z \to 1}[(z-1)F(z)] = \lim_{N \to \infty} f(N)$$

provided that the limit on the right is defined.

d) Under what conditions does the result obtained in part (c), which is known as the *final-value theorem*, hold?

e) For each of the transforms below state whether or not there is a constant final value and, if so, use the final-value theorem to determine $\lim_{n \to \infty} f(n)$. If the final-value theorem does not apply, describe the nature of the response as $n \to \infty$.

i) $\dfrac{z(z+1)}{(z-1)(z-0.5)(z+0.2)}$

ii) $\dfrac{(z+5)}{(z-1)(z-0.5)(z-2)}$

iii) $\dfrac{(z+2)}{(z-0.1)(z+0.5-j0.5)(z+0.5+j0.5)}$

iv) $\dfrac{z(z+0.2)}{(z-1)(z+1)}$

6.33 We want to design a causal LTI system that has the property that if the input is $x(n) = (1/2)^n u(n) - 1/4(1/2)^{n-1}u(n-1)$ then the output is $y(n) = (1/3)^n u(n)$. Find the system transfer function.

6.34 For the following transforms use the initial-value theorem to find the value of $y(n)$ at $n = 0$.

a) $Y(z) = 1 - 2z^{-1} + 3z^{-2} - 4z^{-3}$

b) $Y(z) = 10/(z - 0.5)$, $|z| > 0.5$

c) $Y(z) = 10z/(z - 0.5)$, $|z| > 0.5$

d) $Y(z) = 50\left[\dfrac{101z}{z - 1.01} - \dfrac{100z}{z - 1}\right]$, $|z| > 1.01$.

Integrated Review

6.35 A comb filter is described by $y(n) = x(n) - x(n - 6)$.

a) Find the transfer function, $H(z) = Y(z)/X(z)$.

b) Plot the poles and zeros.

c) Can you show that the frequency response is given by $H(e^{j\theta}) = e^{+j(\pi/2 - 3\theta)}2 \sin 3\theta$?

d) For $H(e^{j\theta}) = Me^{jP}$, sketch M and P vs. θ.

e) For $x(n) = \delta(n) + \delta(n - 6)$, use z-transforms to find $y(n)$.

f) Verify e) by linear convolution.

6.36 Repeat Problem 6.35 for $y(n) = x(n) + x(n - 6)$, only in this case show that in part (c) $H(e^{j\theta}) = e^{-j3\theta}2 \cos 3\theta$.

6.37 An LTI causal system has the unit sample response $h(n) = \delta(n) + 0.735\delta(n - 6)$ where $\delta(n)$ denotes the unit sample.

a) Sketch the pole-zero pattern for $H(z)$.

b) By considering the behavior of the pole and zero vectors as the unit circle is traversed develop an approximate sketch of the magnitude of the frequency response. Label pertinent points.

6.38 Consider the digital signal processing system described by the transfer function

$$\frac{Y(z)}{X(z)} = \frac{z^3 + z}{(z + 0.5)(z^2 + z + 0.5)}.$$

a) For $x(t) = 10 \cos 2\pi ft$ find $y(nT)$ in the steady-state if $f = \dfrac{10^3}{3}$ Hz and the sampling interval T is 1 millisecond.

b) Sketch the magnitude portion of the frequency response labeling pertinent values. Evaluate $H(e^{j\theta})$ by the "graphical" method and you can, of course, check by other methods.

c) Write the algorithm needed to implement this transfer function on a computer. That is, write the filter difference equation.

d) Find an analytical expression for the unit sample response for this filter.

6.39 A system is characterized by the difference equation

$$y(n) = 0.25y(n - 1)$$
$$+ 0.125y(n - 2) + 3x(n - 2). \quad (1)$$

a) Find the transfer function $H(z) = Y(z)/X(z)$.

b) Determine the poles and zeros of the transfer function.

c) If the input is a step function of amplitude 5, i.e., $x(n) = 5u(n)$, find an analytical expression for $y(n)$.

d) Use the expression from part (c) to find the values $y(0)$, $y(1)$, $y(2)$, and $y(3)$.

e) Verify the results of part (d) by iteratively solving equation (1) to obtain $y(0)$, $y(1)$, $y(2)$, and $y(3)$.

f) Verify the results of part (d) by performing long division on $Y(z)$.

6.40 A continuous-time signal $x_s(t)$ that occupies the frequency band $2\pi \times 1000 \leq \omega \leq 2\pi \times 1250$ rad/sec is corrupted by 60-Hz sinusoidal noise. The combined time function can be represented as $x(t) = x_s(t) + x_n(t)$ where $x_s(t)$ is the signal component and $x_n(t)$ is the 60-Hz noise. It is desired to design a simple digital filter to reject the 60-Hz noise while passing the signal component. Assume that $x(t)$ is sampled with a period of $T = 0.25 \times 10^{-3}$s. Sketch the pole-zero pattern of a digital filter that will accomplish the stated objective.

6.41 a) Sketch the magnitude part of the frequency responses of the systems whose pole-zero plots are shown in Fig. P6.41.

b) Write the difference equation for each system.

6.42 A 2-pole digital filter has the transfer function

$$H(z) = \frac{k}{1 - [2a \cos \alpha]z^{-1} + a^2 z^{-2}}.$$

The frequency response of the system is to have a zero frequency (dc) gain of 1.0. The maximum gain value, which is to be 10.0, is to occur at 1/4th of the sampling frequency. With the help of graphical methods find the filter constants a, k, and α.

6.43 Consider the digital signal processing system of Fig. P6.43. The filter is described by

$$H(z) = \frac{Y(z)}{X(z)} = \frac{z^4 - 1}{(z^2 - 0.25)(z^2 - z + 0.5)}.$$

a) Plot the poles and zeros of the filter transfer function $H(z)$.

b) Sketch the magnitude portion of the frequency

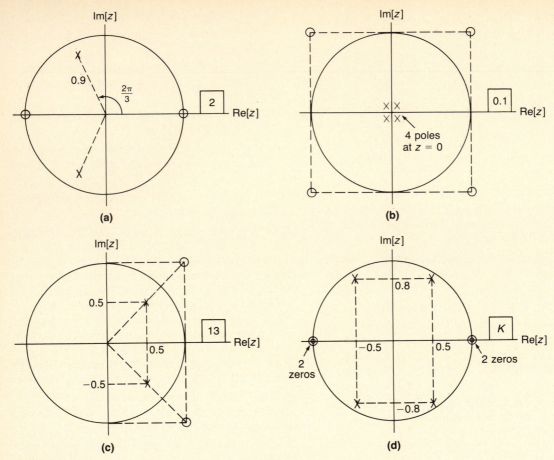

FIGURE P6.41

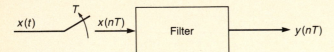

FIGURE P6.43

response labeling pertinent values. Specifically, show the vectors needed for the graphical evaluation of $H(e^{j\omega T})$ for $\omega T = \pi/3$ and estimate M at this frequency.

c) For $x(t) = 10\cos(500\pi t) + 10\cos(250\pi t) + 10\cos(800\pi t)$ find the steady-state output $y(nT)$ if the sampling frequency is 1 kHz.

6.44 A digital filter that is "matched" to its input $x(n)$ has the unit sample response $h(n) = Ax(L - n)$. L is an integer constant and A is a known constant. From the block diagram representation of Fig.

P6.44 find the expression for $Y(z)$ in terms of $X(z)$.

6.45 A digital filter with the pole-zero pattern depicted in Fig. P6.45 is referred to as an all-pass filter. Demonstrate algebraically that $|H(e^{j\theta})|$ is constant.

6.46 An LTI system is described by the difference equation $y(n) + 0.25y(n - 2) = x(n) + 4x(n - 2)$.

Find the following:

a) The system transfer function and a pole-zero plot.

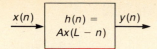

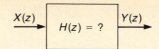

FIGURE P6.44

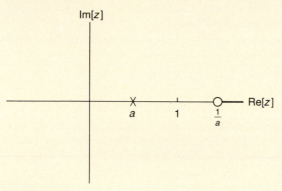

FIGURE P6.45

b) An analytical expression for the unit sample response.

c) The frequency response function and a sketch of the magnitude.

d) A system diagram.

6.47 A moving average (MA) digital filter is described by the difference equation $y(n) = \frac{1}{4}[x(n) + x(n-1) + x(n-2) + x(n-3)]$. That is, the output at any instant n is the average of the current input and the previous three inputs.

a) Find the transfer function of this filter.

b) What are the poles and zeros of this filter? Hint: One zero is at $z = -1$.

c) Evaluate the magnitude of the frequency response at $\omega T = 0$, $\omega T = \pi/4$, $\omega T = \pi/2$, $\omega T = 3\pi/4$, and $\omega T = \pi$. Plot these points and make a rough sketch of $|H(e^{j\omega T})|$ vs. ωT.

6.48 Consider an LTI system with the output $y(n)$, the input $x(n)$, and the unit sample response

$$h(n) = \begin{cases} c^n + d^n, & n \geq 0 \\ 0, & n < 0. \end{cases}$$

The system input is the step sequence $x(n) = A \cdot u(n)$ and all initial conditions are zero.

a) Use convolution to show that $y(n) = k_1 A + k_2 c^{n+1} + k_3 d^{n+1}$, $n \geq 0$.

b) Use z-transforms to show that $y(n) = k_4 + k_5 c^n + k_6 d^n$, $n \geq 0$.

c) Find the values of the constants, $k_1 - k_6$.

6.49 The z-transform of a particular causal sequence $x(n)$ is X(z). If $y(n) = nx(n-2)$, express $Y(z)$ in terms of $X(z)$.

6.50 The system in Fig. P6.50(a) is to be represented by the equivalent system of Fig. P6.50(b).

a) Find $h(n)$ using convolution.

b) Check this result using z-transforms.

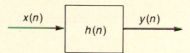

FIGURE P6.50

6.51 A causal second-order system is described by the transfer function

$$H(z) = \frac{N(z)}{z^2 - a_1 z - a_2}.$$

In an $a_1 - a_2$ plane as in Fig. P6.51 show the region for a stable system.

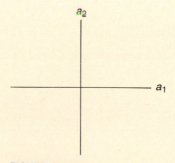

FIGURE P6.51

REFERENCES AND OTHER SOURCES OF INFORMATION

Cadzow, J. A. 1973. *Discrete-Time Systems.* Englewood Cliffs, New Jersey: Prentice-Hall, Inc.

Churchill, R. V. 1960. *Introduction to Complex Variables and Applications.* 2nd Ed., New York: McGraw-Hill Book Company.

Glisson, T. H. 1985. *Introduction to System Analysis.* New York: McGraw-Hill Book Company.

Jong, M. T. 1982. *Methods of Discrete Signal and System Analysis.* New York: McGraw-Hill Book Company.

Kaplan, W. 1962. *Operational Methods for Linear Systems.* Reading, Massachusetts: Addison-Wesley Publishing Company.

Mayhan, R. J. 1984. *Discrete-Time and Continuous-Time Linear Systems.* Reading, Massachusetts: Addison-Wesley Publishing Company.

Oppenheim, A. V., and R. W. Schafer. 1975. *Digital Signal Processing.* Englewood Cliffs, New Jersey: Prentice-Hall, Inc.

Papoulis, A. 1977. *Signal Analysis.* New York: McGraw-Hill Book Company.

Stearns, S. D. 1975. *Digital Signal Analysis.* Rochelle Park, New Jersey: Hayden Book Company.

Terrell, T. J. 1980. *Introduction to Digital Filters.* New York: John Wiley and Sons.

Ziemer, R. E., W. H. Tranter, and D. R. Fannin. 1983. *Signals and Systems, Continuous and Discrete.* New York: Macmillan Publishing Company.

CHAPTER 7

Discrete Fourier Transform

7.0 ▬ PREVIEW

Thus far we have focused on techniques for representing and analyzing discrete linear systems. In this chapter we consider concepts and techniques that apply to digital signal processing.

Our starting point is the simple but important idea that a sequence can be represented by a sum of complex exponentials, or equivalently, a sum of sinusoids. This is an approach based on the work of Jean Baptiste Joseph Fourier (1768–1830). In his paper *Theorie analytique de la chaleur,* published in Paris in 1822 (Van Valkenburg, 1974), Fourier showed how a series of sine and cosine terms could be used in a heat transfer application. He proposed the series, which later became known as the Fourier Series,[†]

$$y(\alpha) = \frac{a_0}{2} + (a_1 \cos \alpha + b_1 \sin \alpha) + (a_2 \cos 2\alpha + b_2 \sin 2\alpha) + \cdots \; [‡] \quad (7.1)$$

to represent periodic waveforms that must satisfy certain other conditions for the series representation to exist (see Appendix B). The trigonometric series of Fourier can also be put into an exponential form, specifically,

$$y(\alpha) = \sum_{n=-\infty}^{n=+\infty} y_n e^{-jn\alpha} \quad (7.2)$$

[†] See Appendix B for a more detailed discussion of the Fourier Series.
[‡] We use α as the continuous independent variable. Often α is proportional to time, but it may be proportional to distance, temperature, or any other continuous variable.

CHAPTER 7 DISCRETE FOURIER TRANSFORM

where using the Euler relationship in Eq. 7.1 it is found that

$$y_n = \frac{1}{2}(a_n \pm jb_n), \qquad n = \pm 1, \pm 2, \ldots \qquad (7.3)$$

and $y_0 = a_0/2$. This representation of periodic waveforms involves an infinite series of complex exponentials. As a practical matter it is necessary to use only a finite number of terms and this introduces the issue of how accurately the finite series approximates the function $y(\alpha)$.

In this chapter we introduce a different type of Fourier Series, one which can be used to represent periodic sequences. Since our concern is with sequences, only a discrete set of values in each period must be represented by the series that is therefore known as the *Discrete Fourier Series*. The periodic complex exponential $e^{j(2\pi/N)nk}$ introduced in Chapter Two plays the central role in the Discrete Fourier Series and we see that a finite sum of these exponentials can exactly match the values of a periodic sequence. As a result, there is no approximation involved and the issue of accuracy does not arise. We also see that it is possible to represent a finite-duration (and therefore nonperiodic) sequence as a finite sum of complex exponentials. This involves thinking of the finite duration sequence as one period of a periodic sequence. The resulting representation as a sum of complex exponentials is known as the *Discrete Fourier Transform*.

At this point it is reasonable to wonder why it should be of interest to represent a sequence by a finite sum of complex exponentials (or sinusoids). There are many good reasons for doing this. One benefit is the additional insight offered by being able to view a signal in the frequency domain. As an example, let us consider the signal shown in Fig. 7.1(a), along with its sample values. Looking at this signal we would probably decide that it is a sinusoid. The time domain representation, however, obscures the fact that the signal is actually not a single sinusoid, but the sum of three sinusoids, that is

$$x(t) = 1.0 \cos(2\pi \cdot 5t) + 100 \cos(2\pi \cdot 10t) + 0.5 \cos(2\pi \cdot 20t). \quad (7.4)$$

That this is the case is readily seen in the frequency domain representation of Fig. 7.1(b). The problem with the time domain representation is that the sinusoid whose amplitude is 100 dominates the picture. We might be tempted to argue that the other two sinusoids are so small as to be inconsequential. Often, however, these small magnitude components may contain important information. Examples include an impending failure of a bearing in a mechanical system, or a physiological dysfunction of a person's heart, or the presence of a particular ship in the vicinity of an acoustic sensor.

Once we have introduced the Discrete Fourier Series (DFS) and Discrete Fourier Transform (DFT), some important properties of these frequency domain representations will be considered. We will also investigate the important relationships among sampling frequency, record

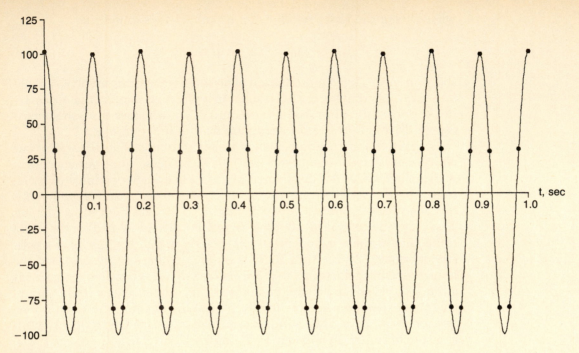

FIGURE 7.1(a) Periodic signal and its sample values

FIGURE 7.1(b) Frequency content of a periodic signal

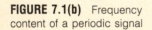

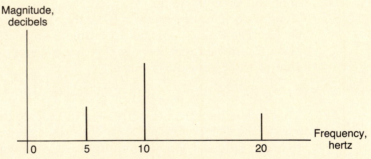

length, and number of samples when a sequence is generated by sampling an analog signal. Another important concept to be considered is the relationship between the Discrete Fourier Transform and an operation known as *circular convolution*. This relationship leads to an indirect way of evaluating the (linear) convolution of two sequences by using DFTs. This provides the basis for computationally efficient methods to be discussed in Chapter Eight for performing convolution. This approach can also be applied to the problem of finding the convolution of a relatively

CHAPTER 7 DISCRETE FOURIER TRANSFORM

short-duration sequence with a very long sequence. The resulting techniques are known as block filtering, or sectioned convolution.

The operation of correlation is next introduced and its properties are compared with those of convolution. As with convolution, it turns out that a correlation sequence can be found directly, or indirectly using DFTs. Finally, we briefly introduce the concept of *spectrum analysis*— the determination of the frequency content of a sequence—and develop methods based on the DFT and correlation for estimating the spectrum from a sequence of data.

Throughout the discussion it should be kept in mind that often the sequences we deal with are samples of analog data. A primary reason for sampling continuous-time signals is the availability of relatively inexpensive and fast digital computers and the existence of efficient algorithms which make it possible to process signals to extract important characteristics.

7.1 ▪▪▪ PERIODIC SEQUENCES

Consider the situation in which we have a periodic sequence of known period denoted by $x_p(n)$. In Fig. 7.2(a), for example, we see that $x_p(n) = x_p(n + 5)$. That is, we can start at any sample value in the sequence and after five samples, the sequence begins to repeat itself. Thus, the period is 5 samples or simply 5. Although the period is 5, we must be careful not to count both the starting and ending samples as part of the period. In the period designated in Fig. 7.2(a), for example, $x(-1)$ and $x(4)$ can't both be counted in a period for this would give an incorrect period of 6 samples. Some other examples of periodic sequences are given in Fig. 7.2(b)–(d) where

$$x_p(n) = x_p(n + N). \tag{7.5}$$

N, which is called the period, is the smallest positive constant for which Eq. 7.5 is satisfied for all n.

7.2 ▪▪▪ COMPLEX EXPONENTIALS

Let us now investigate how we might use complex exponentials to represent a periodic sequence. In Chapter Two, a complex unit exponential was thought of as a rotating unit line, as shown in Fig. 7.3. The rotating line $p(n) = e^{j(2\pi/N)n}$ progresses in the counterclockwise direction an amount of $2\pi/N$ radians per sample n of the periodic sequence. We suspect that we need several complex exponentials to represent a periodic sequence of real numbers. Generally, one such exponential has the same period N as the sequence. This complex exponential is

$$p_1(n) = e^{j(2\pi/N)n} \tag{7.6}$$

FIGURE 7.2 Periodic sequences

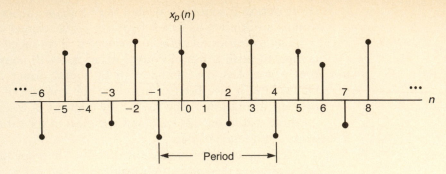

(a) Periodic sequence having a period of 5

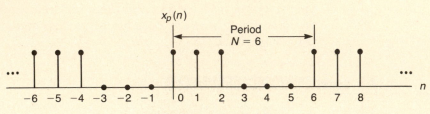

(b) Sequence of period 6

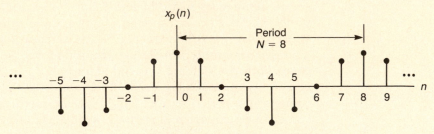

(c) Sequence of period 8

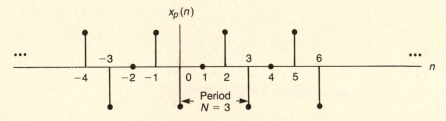

(d) Sequence of period 3

and its values at the samples $n = 0, 1, 2, \ldots$ are

$$e^{j0}, \; e^{j(2\pi/N)(1)}, \; e^{j(2\pi/N)(2)}, \ldots, \; e^{j(2\pi/N)(N)}, \; e^{j(2\pi/N)(N+1)}, \ldots \quad (7.7)$$

As was seen in Chapter Two,

$$e^{j(2\pi/N)N} = e^{j2\pi} = e^{j0}. \quad (7.8)$$

Thus, $p_1(n)$ rotates at $2\pi/N$ radians per sample and completes one revolu-

FIGURE 7.3 Complex exponential as a rotating line

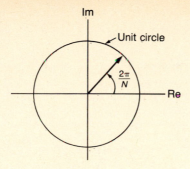

tion (2π radians) in N samples. We also observe that

$$e^{j(2\pi/N)(N+1)} = e^{j(2\pi/N)(N)}e^{j(2\pi/N)} = e^{j(2\pi/N)} \qquad (7.9)$$

so the values generated by this exponential begin to repeat themselves after N samples.

Next, we want an exponential that completes 2 revolutions in N samples, namely

$$p_2(n) = e^{j(2 \cdot 2\pi/N)n} \qquad (7.10)$$

and the values generated by $p_2(n)$ are

$$p_2(0) = e^{j0}, \; p_2(1) = e^{j(2 \cdot 2\pi/N)1}, \; p_2(2) = e^{j(2 \cdot 2\pi/N)2}, \; \ldots \qquad (7.11)$$

These values begin to repeat when

$$e^{j(2 \cdot 2\pi/N)n} = 1 \text{ or } \frac{2 \cdot 2\pi}{N}n = m2\pi \qquad (7.12)$$

where n, N, and m are all integers. For instance, if the period is 8 we have

$$\frac{2 \cdot 2\pi n}{8} = m2\pi \text{ or } n = 4m \qquad (7.13)$$

with the smallest integer that satisfies this being $m = 1$, so the values begin to repeat after one revolution at $n = 4$. To find the number of revolutions when repetition begins for other rotating exponentials of period $N = 8$ we use a similar approach, that is,

$$p_3(n) = e^{j(3 \cdot 2\pi/8)n} \longrightarrow n = \tfrac{8}{3}m \longrightarrow n = 8 \text{ when } m = 3 \text{ or 3 revolutions}$$

$$p_4(n) = e^{j(4 \cdot 2\pi/8)n} \longrightarrow n = \tfrac{8}{4}m \longrightarrow n = 2 \text{ when } m = 1 \text{ or 1 revolution}$$

$$p_5(n) = e^{j(5 \cdot 2\pi/8)n} \longrightarrow n = \tfrac{8}{5}m \longrightarrow n = 8 \text{ when } m = 5 \text{ or 5 revolutions.}$$
$$(7.14)$$

Figure 7.4 shows the rotating lines $p_1(n)$, $p_2(n)$, and $p_3(n)$. In general, the exponential $p_k(n)$ begins repeating when $k(2\pi/N)n = m2\pi$ or $n = mN/k$ and with k and N given we select the smallest value of m to make n equal to an integer ($m \leq k$). The complex exponential begins to repeat at this value of n and this occurs when m revolutions have been made.

FIGURE 7.4 Harmonically related complex exponentials (rotating lines)

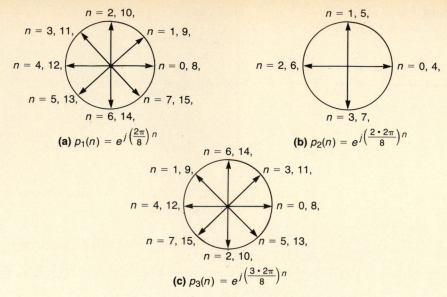

(a) $p_1(n) = e^{j\left(\frac{2\pi}{8}\right)n}$

(b) $p_2(n) = e^{j\left(\frac{2\cdot2\pi}{8}\right)n}$

(c) $p_3(n) = e^{j\left(\frac{3\cdot2\pi}{8}\right)n}$

The pattern can be continued and if the kth such exponential is denoted by

$$p_k(n) = e^{j(k\cdot2\pi/N)n} \tag{7.15}$$

the values generated are

$$p_k(0) = e^{j0},\ p_k(1) = e^{j(k\cdot2\pi/N)1},\ p_k(2) = e^{j(k\cdot2\pi/N)2},\ \ldots \tag{7.16}$$

For the important case where $k = N - 1$, we have

$$p_{N-1}(n) = e^{j([N-1]2\pi/N)n} \tag{7.17}$$

which generates the values

$$p_{N-1}(0) = e^{j0},\ p_{N-1}(1) = e^{j([N-1]2\pi/N)1},$$

$$p_{N-1}(2) = e^{j([N-1]2\pi/N)2},\ \ldots \tag{7.18}$$

and the values begin to repeat when from Eq. 7.17

$$[N-1]\left(\frac{2\pi}{N}\right)(n) = m2\pi. \tag{7.19}$$

For example, if again $N = 8$, selecting $m = 7$ gives $n = 8$ as the sample where the values of the exponential $p_7(n)$ begin to repeat as is seen in Fig. 7.5. Remember that the complex exponential $p_1(n)$ rotates $2\pi/8 = \pi/4$ radians per sample while $p_7(n)$ rotates $7(2\pi/8)$ radians per sample, both counterclockwise. Finally, for $k = N$ we have

$$p_N(n) = e^{j(N\cdot2\pi/N)n} = e^{j2\pi n} \tag{7.20}$$

CHAPTER 7   DISCRETE FOURIER TRANSFORM

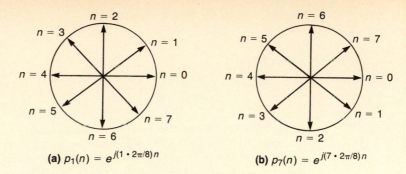

FIGURE 7.5 Periodic exponentials with a period of 8

(a) $p_1(n) = e^{j(1 \cdot 2\pi/8)n}$

(b) $p_7(n) = e^{j(7 \cdot 2\pi/8)n}$

which generates the values

$$p_N(0) = e^{j0} = 1, \; p_N(1) = e^{j2\pi} = 1, \; p_N(2) = e^{j4\pi} = 1, \ldots \quad (7.21)$$

This rotating line appears to be standing still because at each sample it is positioned at an integer multiple of 2π and in fact could be described by

$$p_0(n) = e^{j(0 \cdot 2\pi/N)n} \quad (7.22)$$

which can be written very simply as

$$p_0(n) = e^{j0} = 1. \quad (7.23)$$

Thus, for a family of complex exponentials defined as

$$p_k(n) = e^{j(k \cdot 2\pi/N)n}, \qquad k = 0, 1, 2, \ldots, N-1 \quad (7.24)$$

it can be seen that

$$p_0(n) = p_N(n), \; p_1(n) = p_{N+1}(n), \; \ldots, \; p_{N-1}(n) = p_{2N-1}(n) \quad (7.25)$$

or, in general

$$p_k(n) = p_{N+k}(n) \quad (7.26)$$

and thus only N of these exponentials are distinguishable from one another.

In summary, we have defined a set of N exponentials

$$p_k(n) = e^{j(k \cdot 2\pi/N)n}, \qquad k = 0, 1, 2, \ldots, N-1 \quad (7.27)$$

that will be used to represent a periodic sequence of real numbers. The exponential or rotating line corresponding to $p_0(n)$ does not rotate at all. The complex exponential $p_1(n)$ rotates one revolution with a period equal to that of the sequence, while the remaining exponentials $p_k(n)$ for $k = 2$, $3, \ldots, N-1$ make $2, 3, \ldots, N-1$ revolutions in N samples.

Example 7.1. This example illustrates déjà vu with complex exponentials.

Determine the complex exponentials needed to represent a sequence of period $N = 3$.

Solution: From Eq. 7.27 we have

$$p_k(n) = e^{j(k \cdot 2\pi/N)n}, \qquad k = 0, 1, 2 \qquad (7.28)$$

and specifically

$$p_0(n) = e^{j(0 \cdot 2\pi/N)n} \qquad p_1(n) = e^{j(1 \cdot 2\pi/N)n} \qquad p_2(n) = e^{j(2 \cdot 2\pi/N)n}$$

$$= e^{j0} = 1 \qquad\qquad = e^{j2\pi n/3} \qquad\qquad = e^{j4\pi n/3}. \qquad (7.29)$$

Figure 7.6 shows these three complex exponentials at the sample values and illustrates that after at most three samples, $n = 0, 1, 2$, each rotating line begins to repeat itself. This indicates that the exponentials $p_k(n)$ are periodic in n with period N, as well as being periodic in k with the same period.

At this point we have defined the needed set of complex exponentials. We now see how to represent a periodic sequence $x_p(n)$ in terms of these exponentials. What we shall do is to express $x_p(n)$ as the linear combination of the complex exponentials

$$x_p(n) = \frac{1}{N} \sum_{k=0}^{k=N-1} X_p(k)\, p_k(n), \qquad n = 0, 1, 2, \ldots, N-1 \qquad (7.30)$$

where the coefficients of the exponentials are denoted by $X_p(k)$, $k = 0, 1, 2, \ldots, N-1$.[†] This summation is the *Discrete Fourier Series (DFS)* for the periodic sequence $x_p(n)$. The $1/N$ preceding the summation is simply a convenient scale factor that makes some of the computational arithmetic a bit tidier. Thus, to represent a periodic sequence $x_p(n)$ in the form of Eq. 7.30, we need to solve for the coefficients $X_p(k)$ since the sequence values $x_p(n)$ and the complex exponential values $p_k(n)$ are known. We now illustrate one way to do this, using a three-term sequence as the basis of discussion.

For a given periodic sequence $x_p(n)$ with $N = 3$, writing out the three equations obtained from Eq. 7.30 gives us

FIGURE 7.6 Complex exponentials for Example 7.2

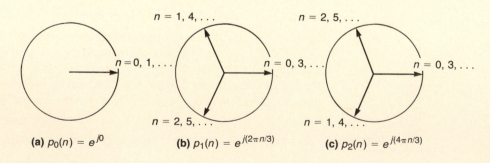

(a) $p_0(n) = e^{j0}$ **(b)** $p_1(n) = e^{j(2\pi n/3)}$ **(c)** $p_2(n) = e^{j(4\pi n/3)}$

[†]We are anticipating by the notation $X_p(k)$ that these coefficients will be periodic in k. We shall soon see this to be the case.

$$x_p(0) = \frac{1}{3}[X_p(0)\,p_0(0) + X_p(1)\,p_1(0) + X_p(2)\,p_2(0)]$$

$$x_p(1) = \frac{1}{3}[X_p(0)\,p_0(1) + X_p(1)\,p_1(1) + X_p(2)\,p_2(1)]$$

$$x_p(2) = \frac{1}{3}[X_p(0)\,p_0(2) + X_p(1)\,p_1(2) + X_p(2)\,p_2(2)] \tag{7.31}$$

which may be written in matrix form as

$$
\begin{bmatrix} x_p(0) \\ x_p(1) \\ x_p(2) \end{bmatrix}
= \frac{1}{3}
\begin{bmatrix}
p_0(0) & p_1(0) & p_2(0) \\
p_0(1) & p_1(1) & p_2(1) \\
p_0(2) & p_1(2) & p_2(2)
\end{bmatrix}
\begin{bmatrix} X_p(0) \\ X_p(1) \\ X_p(2) \end{bmatrix}. \tag{7.32}
$$

Now recalling from Eq. 7.27 that the exponential for $N = 3$ is

$$p_k(n) = e^{j(k2\pi/3)n} = e^{j(2\pi/3)nk} \tag{7.33}$$

and substituting Eq. 7.33 into Eq. 7.32 gives

$$
\begin{bmatrix} x_p(0) \\ x_p(1) \\ x_p(2) \end{bmatrix}
= \frac{1}{3}
\begin{bmatrix}
e^{j(2\pi/3)0(0)} & e^{j(2\pi/3)0(1)} & e^{j(2\pi/3)0(2)} \\
e^{j(2\pi/3)1(0)} & e^{j(2\pi/3)1(1)} & e^{j(2\pi/3)1(2)} \\
e^{j(2\pi/3)2(0)} & e^{j(2\pi/3)2(1)} & e^{j(2\pi/3)2(2)}
\end{bmatrix}
\begin{bmatrix} X_p(0) \\ X_p(1) \\ X_p(2) \end{bmatrix} \tag{7.34}
$$

which may be simplified with $e^{j(2\pi/3)0} = 1$ and $e^{j(8\pi/3)} = e^{j(2\pi/3)}$. Thus, given the input data for $x_p(n)$ we can solve for the coefficients $X_p(k)$ using determinants, matrix inversion, substitution, or preferably, and more practically, a computer program. We illustrate two methods of solution, however, to gain familiarity with the terms in the equations and to prepare ourselves for a general solution for any period N. Equation 7.34 is a matrix equation of the form

$$\mathbf{x}_p(n) = \frac{1}{3}\mathbf{A}\,\mathbf{X}_p(k). \tag{7.35}$$

By using matrix algebra (see Appendix F) the solution obtained is

$$\mathbf{A}^{-1}\,3\mathbf{x}_p(n) = \mathbf{X}_p(k). \tag{7.36}$$

In general, of course, we must ensure that the matrix inverse exists, and for the matrix $\mathbf{A}$ here it can be shown that this is the case. Carrying out the indicated matrix inversion gives

$$
\begin{bmatrix} X_p(0) \\ X_p(1) \\ X_p(2) \end{bmatrix}
=
\begin{bmatrix}
1/3 & 1/3 & 1/3 \\
1/3 & (1/3)e^{-j2\pi/3} & (1/3)e^{j2\pi/3} \\
1/3 & (1/3)e^{j2\pi/3} & (1/3)e^{-j2\pi/3}
\end{bmatrix}
\begin{bmatrix} 3x_p(0) \\ 3x_p(1) \\ 3x_p(2) \end{bmatrix}. \tag{7.37}
$$

Notice that Eq. 7.37 is a general result that is good for any three-point

FIGURE 7.7 A periodic
sequence

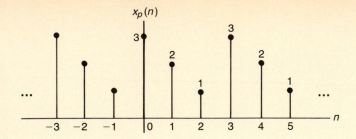

periodic sequence and if $x_p(n)$ as shown in Fig. 7.7 is used, the resulting DFS coefficients are given by

$$\begin{bmatrix} X_p(0) \\ X_p(1) \\ X_p(2) \end{bmatrix} = \begin{bmatrix} 6 \\ \sqrt{3} \, e^{-j\pi/6} \\ \sqrt{3} \, e^{+j\pi/6} \end{bmatrix}. \tag{7.38}$$

Thus, the Discrete Fourier Series which represents $x_p(n)$ from Fig. 7.7 is

$$x_p(n) = \frac{1}{3} \sum_{k=0}^{k=2} X_p(k) \, e^{j(2\pi/3)nk}, \qquad n = 0, 1, 2 \tag{7.39}$$

where the $X_p(k)$'s are given in Eq. 7.38.

There is another way to get to this solution that involves some hindsight. This alternative solution also serves as an introduction to the next section where a general proof of the Discrete Fourier Series pair is presented. Writing out Eq. 7.39 yields equations for $x_p(n)$ for $n = 0, 1, 2$, namely

$$x_p(0) = \frac{1}{3}[X_p(0) + X_p(1) + X_p(2)]$$

$$x_p(1) = \frac{1}{3}[X_p(0) + X_p(1)e^{j(2\pi/3)} + X_p(2)e^{j(2\pi/3)2}]$$

$$x_p(2) = \frac{1}{3}[X_p(0) + X_p(1)e^{j(2\pi/3)2} + X_p(2)e^{j(2\pi/3)4}]. \tag{7.40}$$

We start by multiplying the first equation by $e^{j(2\pi/3)(0)}$, the second by $e^{j(2\pi/3)(-r)}$, and the third by $e^{j(2\pi/3)(-2r)}$. Then, the results are added and the right side is rearranged to give

$$x_p(0)e^{j(2\pi/3)(0)} + x_p(1)e^{j(2\pi/3)(-r)} + x_p(2)e^{j(2\pi/3)(-2r)} =$$

$$\frac{1}{3}X_p(0)[e^{j(2\pi/3)(0)} + e^{j(2\pi/3)(-r)} + e^{j(2\pi/3)(-2r)}]$$

$$+ \frac{1}{3}X_p(1)[e^{j(2\pi/3)(0)} + e^{j(2\pi/3)(1-r)} + e^{j(2\pi/3)(2-2r)}]$$

$$+ \frac{1}{3}X_p(2)[e^{j(2\pi/3)(0)} + e^{j(2\pi/3)(2-r)} + e^{j(2\pi/3)(4-2r)}]. \quad (7.41)$$

If r is made equal to zero we have

$$x_p(0) + x_p(1) + x_p(2) = X_p(0) + \frac{1}{3}X_p(1)[1 + e^{j(2\pi/3)} + e^{j(4\pi/3)}]$$

$$+ \frac{1}{3}X_p(2)[1 + e^{j4\pi/3} + e^{j8\pi/3}]. \quad (7.42)$$

A graphical representation for the vectors that are added together to give the coefficient of $X_p(1)$ is shown in Fig. 7.8(a) where the sum of $(1 + e^{j2\pi/3} + e^{j4\pi/3})$ is clearly zero. A similar situation exists for the coefficient of $X_p(2)$ as is seen in Fig. 7.8(b). So we are left with

$$x_p(0) + x_p(1) + x_p(2) = X_p(0). \quad (7.43)$$

We can find $X_p(1)$ in a similar way by letting $r = 1$ in Eq. 7.41 which gives

$$x_p(0) + x_p(1)e^{j(2\pi/3)(-1)} + x_p(2)e^{j(2\pi/3)(-2)} =$$

$$\frac{1}{3}X_p(0)[1 + e^{j(2\pi/3)(-1)} + e^{j(2\pi/3)(-2)}]$$

$$+ \frac{1}{3}X_p(1)[1 + e^{j(2\pi/3)(0)} + e^{j(2\pi/3)(0)}]$$

$$+ \frac{1}{3}X_p(2)[1 + e^{j(2\pi/3)(1)} + e^{j(2\pi/3)(2)}]. \quad (7.44)$$

But now the coefficients of $X_p(0)$ and $X_p(2)$ are zero as seen in Fig. 7.9 and we are left with

$$x_p(0) + x_p(1)e^{-j2\pi/3} + x_p(2)e^{-j4\pi/3} = X_p(1). \quad (7.45)$$

It is clear that by following a similar procedure we get with $r = 2$ in Eq. 7.41

$$x_p(0) + x_p(1)e^{-j4\pi/3} + x_p(2)e^{-j8\pi/3} = X_p(2). \quad (7.46)$$

FIGURE 7.8 Graphical descriptions for Eq. 7.42

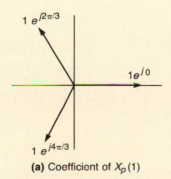

(a) Coefficient of $X_p(1)$

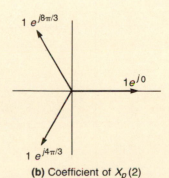

(b) Coefficient of $X_p(2)$

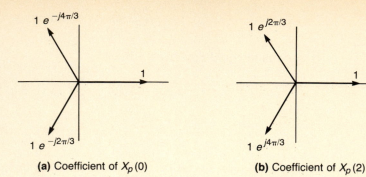

FIGURE 7.9 Graphical data for Eq. 7.44

$1\,e^{-j4\pi/3}$

$1\,e^{-j2\pi/3}$

1

(a) Coefficient of $X_p(0)$

$1\,e^{j2\pi/3}$

$1\,e^{j4\pi/3}$

1

(b) Coefficient of $X_p(2)$

Collecting the results of Eqs. 7.43, 7.45, and 7.46 gives

$$X_p(k) = \sum_{n=0}^{n=2} x_p(n)e^{j(2\pi/3)(-nk)}, \qquad k = 0, 1, 2. \tag{7.47}$$

The reason this all works is that the complex exponential sequences $p_k(n) = e^{j(2\pi/N)nk}$ and $p_\ell(n) = e^{j(2\pi/N)n\ell}$ are mutually orthogonal, i.e.,

$$\sum_{n=0}^{N-1} p_k(n)p_\ell^*(n) = \begin{cases} N, & \ell = k \\ 0, & \ell \neq k. \end{cases} \tag{7.48}$$

Problem 7.47 makes explicit use of this property in generalizing the result of Eq. 7.47.

Example 7.2. This example illustrates the application of Eq. 7.47.

Compute the Fourier coefficients for the periodic sequence shown in Fig. 7.7.

Solution: From Eq. 7.47 we have

$$X_p(0) = \sum_{n=0}^{n=2} x_p(n)e^{j(2\pi/3)(-n)(0)} = x_p(0) + x_p(1) + x_p(2) = 6 \tag{7.49}$$

$$X_p(1) = \sum_{n=0}^{n=2} x_p(n)e^{j(2\pi/3)(-n)(1)} = x_p(0) + x_p(1)e^{-j2\pi/3} + x_p(2)e^{-j4\pi/3}$$

$$= 3 + 2e^{-j2\pi/3} + 1e^{-j4\pi/3}$$

$$= 3 + 2(-0.5 - j0.866) + 1(-0.5 + j0.866)$$

$$= 1.5 - j0.866 = \sqrt{3}\,e^{-j\pi/6} \tag{7.50}$$

$$X_p(2) = \sum_{n=0}^{n=2} x_p(n)e^{j(2\pi/3)(-n)(2)} = 3 + 2e^{-j4\pi/3} + 1e^{-j8\pi/3}$$

$$= \sqrt{3}\,e^{j\pi/6}. \tag{7.51}$$

Comment: These results agree with the matrix solution of Eq. 7.38. In summary, the Discrete Fourier Series that represents the three-sample periodic sequence $x_p(n)$ is

$$x_p(n) = \frac{1}{3} \sum_{k=0}^{k=2} X_p(k)e^{j(2\pi/3)nk}, \quad n = 0, 1, 2 \tag{7.52}$$

and the coefficients are computed from

$$X_p(k) = \sum_{n=0}^{n=2} x_p(n)e^{j(2\pi/3)(-nk)}, \quad k = 0, 1, 2. \tag{7.53}$$

Whenever possible, results should always be checked or verified and $x_p(0)$ can easily be computed from Eq. 7.52 to give

$$x_p(0) = \frac{1}{3} \sum_{k=0}^{k=2} X_p(k)e^{j(2\pi/3)0(k)} = \frac{1}{3}[X_p(0) + X_p(1) + X_p(2)]$$

$$= \frac{1}{3}[6 + 1.5 - j0.866 + 1.5 + j0.866]$$

$$= 3 \tag{7.54}$$

which agrees with Fig. 7.7.

7.3 ■ DISCRETE FOURIER SERIES

Let us now generalize the specific results from the last section. The starting point, as before, is the Discrete Fourier Series representation of the sequence $x_p(n)$ having a period N

$$x_p(n) = \frac{1}{N} \sum_{k=0}^{k=N-1} X_p(k)e^{j(2\pi/N)nk}. \tag{7.55}$$

We want to solve for the Fourier coefficients $X_p(k)$, $k = 0, 1, \ldots, N - 1$. As in the alternative solution of Section 7.2, we start by multiplying the equation for $x_p(0)$ by $e^{j(2\pi/N)(0)}$, then we multiply the equation for $x_p(1)$ by $e^{j(2\pi/N)(-r)}$, the equation for $x_p(2)$ by $e^{j(2\pi/N)(-2r)}$, and so forth, adding the results. In general, the equation for $x_p(n)$ is multiplied by $e^{j(2\pi/N)(-nr)}$ and we use only the equations for $x_p(0), x_p(1), \ldots, x_p(N - 1)$ even though the resulting series represents $x_p(n)$ for all n. Carrying out the indicated multiplications and adding the results gives

$$\sum_{n=0}^{n=N-1} x_p(n)e^{j(2\pi/N)(-nr)}$$

$$= \frac{1}{N} \sum_{n=0}^{n=N-1} \sum_{k=0}^{k=N-1} X_p(k)e^{j(2\pi/N)(nk)}e^{j(2\pi/N)(-nr)}. \tag{7.56}$$

Interchanging the order of summation on the right side yields

$$\sum_{n=0}^{n=N-1} x_p(n)e^{j(2\pi/N)(-nr)} = \frac{1}{N}\sum_{k=0}^{k=N-1} X_p(k)\sum_{n=0}^{n=N-1} e^{j(2\pi/N)(nk-nr)}. \quad (7.57)$$

We can write the last summation in the form

$$\sum_{n=0}^{n=N-1} e^{j(2\pi/N)(n)(k-r)} \quad (7.58)$$

and for $k = r$ we have

$$\sum_{n=0}^{n=N-1} e^{j(2\pi/N)(n)(0)} = \sum_{n=0}^{n=N-1} 1 = N. \quad (7.59)$$

If, however, $k \neq r$ we can again use the formula for a finite geometric sum (see Eq. 3.20) to obtain

$$\sum_{n=0}^{n=N-1} e^{j(2\pi/N)(n)(k-r)} = \frac{1 - e^{j(2\pi/N)(N)(k-r)}}{1 - e^{j(2\pi/N)(k-r)}} = 0 \quad (7.60)$$

since if $(k - r)$ is equal to an integer other than zero, the numerator of Eq. 7.60 is zero and the denominator is nonzero. (Remember that $e^{j(2\pi/N)Nm} = 1$ for $m =$ any integer). Putting Eqs. 7.59 and 7.60 together we get

$$\sum_{n=0}^{n=N-1} e^{j(2\pi/N)(n)(k-r)} = \begin{cases} N \text{ for } k = r \\ 0 \text{ for } k \neq r \end{cases} \quad (7.61)$$

which in terms of a shifted sample function may be written as

$$\sum_{n=0}^{n=N-1} e^{j(2\pi/N)(n)(k-r)} = N\delta(k - r). \quad (7.62)$$

Going back to Eq. 7.57 we now have

$$\sum_{n=0}^{n=N-1} x_p(n)e^{j(2\pi/N)(-nr)} = \frac{1}{N}\sum_{k=0}^{k=N-1} X_p(k)N\delta(k - r)$$

$$= X_p(r). \quad (7.63)$$

So, renaming r as k, the Fourier coefficients are given by

$$\boxed{X_p(k) = \sum_{n=0}^{n=N-1} x_p(n)e^{j(2\pi/N)(-nk)}, \qquad k = \ldots, -2, -1, 0, 1, 2, \ldots}$$

$$(7.64)$$

and with Eq. 7.55 which is the Discrete Fourier Series representation of a periodic sequence, namely

$$x_p(n) = \frac{1}{N} \sum_{k=0}^{k=N-1} X_p(k)e^{j(2\pi/N)(nk)}, \qquad n = \ldots, -2, -1, 0, 1, 2, \ldots$$

(7.65)

the Discrete Fourier Series (DFS) pair is the result. Notice that in Eq. 7.64 we used the values of $x_p(n)$ over one period only ($n = 0$ to $n = N - 1$) to compute the Fourier coefficients and in Eq. 7.65 the corresponding period of the $X_p(k)$ Fourier coefficients ($k = 0$ to $k = N - 1$) is used to describe $x_p(n)$ as a Fourier Series. In addition we have

$$X_p(k + N) = \sum_{n=0}^{N-1} x_p(n)e^{j(2\pi/N)(-n)(k+N)}$$

$$= \sum_{n=0}^{N-1} x_p(n)e^{j(2\pi/N)(-nk)} \underbrace{e^{j(2\pi/N)(-nN)}}_{1}$$

$$= X_p(k)$$

(7.66)

and thus as anticipated $X_p(k)$ is periodic with period N. As a consequence, we can represent $x_p(n)$ as the sum of any N consecutive terms in the Discrete Fourier Series (DFS), i.e.,

$$x_p(n) = \frac{1}{N} \sum_{k=\ell}^{k=\ell+N-1} X_p(k)e^{j(2\pi/N)(nk)}$$

(7.67)

where ℓ is any integer. Of course, the same is true of the expression for $X_p(k)$, that is,

$$X_p(k) = \sum_{n=m}^{n=m+N-1} x_p(n)e^{j(2\pi/N)(-nk)}$$

(7.68)

where m is any integer. The DFS equation pair is often written

$$x_p(n) = \frac{1}{N} \sum_{N} X_p(k)e^{j(2\pi/N)(nk)} \quad \text{and} \quad X_p(k) = \sum_{N} x_p(n)e^{j(2\pi/N)(-nk)}$$
(7.69)

where the N alongside the summation sign indicates a sum over N consecutive terms. It is instructive to show the complex nature of $X_p(k)$ by making a plot of magnitude and phase of these coefficients. In Example 7.2, the Fourier series coefficients $X_p(k)$ were determined for a given periodic sequence $x_p(n)$, and $x_p(n)$ and $X_p(k)$ are shown in Fig. 7.10. Since the Fourier coefficients are complex numbers it is typical to give both a mag-

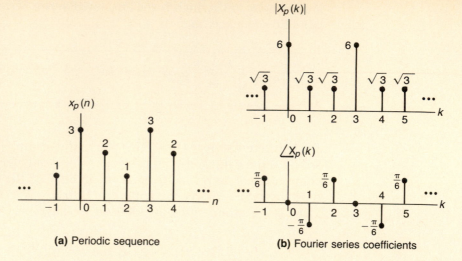

FIGURE 7.10 Periodic time sequence with periodic DFS coefficients

(a) Periodic sequence

(b) Fourier series coefficients

nitude and a phase plot. Notice that $X_p(k)$, like $x_p(n)$, is a periodic sequence of period $N = 3$.

The sequences for $x_p(n)$ and $X_p(k)$ have been expressed in terms of the complex exponentials, $e^{j(2\pi/N)nk}$ and $e^{-j(2\pi/N)nk}$. It is, however, very straightforward and perhaps more familiar to express either of these periodic sequences as cosine functions rather than exponentials. Using Example 7.2 as an illustration and choosing the period to be from $k = -1$ to $k = 1$ in Fig. 7.10(b), we have from Eq. 7.67

$$x_p(n) = \frac{1}{3} \sum_{k=-1}^{k=1} X_p(k)e^{j(2\pi/3)nk}$$

$$= \frac{1}{3}\left[\sqrt{3}\,e^{j\pi/6}\,e^{j(2\pi/3)(n)(-1)} + 6e^{j(2\pi/3)(n)(0)} + \sqrt{3}\,e^{-j\pi/6}\,e^{j(2\pi/3)(n)(1)}\right]$$

$$(7.70)$$

and with the help of the Euler relation we have

$$x_p(n) = 2 + \frac{2}{\sqrt{3}}\cos\left(\frac{2\pi n}{3} - \frac{\pi}{6}\right). \qquad (7.71)$$

We should follow our standard practice of checking results, and doing so we have from Eq. 7.71

$$x_p(-1) = 2 + \frac{2}{\sqrt{3}}\cos\left(\frac{-2\pi}{3} - \frac{\pi}{6}\right) = 1$$

$$x_p(0) = 2 + \frac{2}{\sqrt{3}}\cos\left(0 - \frac{\pi}{6}\right) = 3$$

$$x_p(1) = 2 + \frac{2}{\sqrt{3}}\cos\left(\frac{2\pi}{3} - \frac{\pi}{6}\right) = 2 \qquad (7.72)$$

all three of which agree with the sequence in Fig. 7.10(a). Equation 7.71 is, of course, valid for any value of n and computing $x_p(4)$ we get

$$x_p(4) = 2 + \frac{2}{\sqrt{3}} \cos\left(\frac{8\pi}{3} - \frac{\pi}{6}\right) = 2 \qquad (7.73)$$

which also agrees with the sequence in Fig. 7.10(a). In general, starting with

$$X_p(k) = \sum_{n=0}^{n=N-1} x_p(n)\, e^{-j(2\pi/N)nk} \qquad (7.74)$$

we can use the Euler relation to obtain

$$X_p(k) = \sum_{n=0}^{n=N-1} \left[x_p(n) \cos\left(\frac{2\pi nk}{N}\right) - j\, x_p(n) \sin\left(\frac{2\pi nk}{N}\right) \right]. \qquad (7.75)$$

The same procedure follows for the values of the sequence $x_p(n)$, except that the $X_p(k)$ are generally complex, i.e., $X_p(k) = |X_p(k)|e^{j\angle X_p(k)}$, so

$$x_p(n) = \frac{1}{N} \sum_{k=0}^{N-1} X_p(k)\, e^{j(2\pi/N)nk}$$

$$= \frac{1}{N} \sum_{k=0}^{N-1} |X_p(k)|\, e^{j\angle X_p(k)}\, e^{j(2\pi/N)nk}. \qquad (7.76)$$

Resorting to the Euler relation once again gives us

$$x_p(n) = \frac{1}{N} \sum_{k=0}^{N-1} |X_p(k)|\left\{ \cos\left[\frac{2\pi nk}{N} + \angle X_p(k)\right] + j \sin\left[\frac{2\pi nk}{N} + \angle X_p(k)\right] \right\}. \qquad (7.77)$$

Thus, Eqs. 7.75 and 7.77 are the DFS pair written in terms of a trigonometric series.

Example 7.3. This example illustrates evaluating the DFS coefficients for a cosine sequence.

Given the periodic sequence

$$x_p(n) = A \cos(n\pi/2) \qquad (7.78)$$

as in Fig. 7.11(a), what are the DFS coefficients $X_p(k)$?

Solution: First, by putting the argument in the form $2n\pi/N$ we see that the period is 4 so

$$x_p(n) = A \cos(2\pi n/4) \qquad (7.79)$$

and from the Euler relation

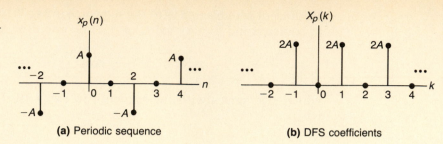

FIGURE 7.11 Sequence and coefficients for Example 7.3

(a) Periodic sequence   **(b)** DFS coefficients

$$x_p(n) = \frac{A}{2} e^{j(2\pi n/4)} + \frac{A}{2} e^{-j(2\pi n/4)}. \tag{7.80}$$

The expression for $x_p(n)$ is from Eq. 7.67

$$x_p(n) = \frac{1}{4} \sum_{k=-1}^{k=2} X_p(k) e^{j(2\pi/4)nk}$$

$$= \frac{1}{4}\left[X_p(-1)e^{-j(2\pi/4)n} + X_p(0) + X_p(1)e^{j(2\pi/4)n} + X_p(2)e^{j(2\pi/4)2n} \right] \tag{7.81}$$

and for our specific sequence we had

$$x_p(n) = \frac{A}{2} e^{-j(2\pi/4)n} + 0 + \frac{A}{2} e^{j(2\pi/4)n} + 0. \tag{7.82}$$

Thus, comparing Eq. 7.81 and Eq. 7.82 we see that

$$X_p(-1) = X_p(1) = 2A \text{ and } X_p(0) = X_p(2) = 0 \tag{7.83}$$

and since these coefficients are all real and positive we plot only the magnitudes as in Fig. 7.11(b).

Comments:

1. Notice that if Eq. 7.64 had been used to find the coefficients, the result would have been $X_p(0) = 0$, $X_p(1) = 2A$, $X_p(2) = 0$, and $X_p(3) = 2A$. This is a consequence of summing from $n = 0$ to $n = 3$ rather than from $n = -1$ to $n = 2$.

2. In this example, $x_p(n)$ was a cosine sequence and the DFS coefficients were determined, in a sense, by inspection. This situation is very special and, in general, we must rely on the definition of Eq. 7.74 or its equivalent Eq. 7.75.

Discussion of many of the important properties of the Discrete Fourier Series (DFS) will be delayed until later in the chapter when we consider the closely related Discrete Fourier Transform (DFT). Properties of the DFS and DFT are the same, or at least very similar, and one exposition is sufficient in most instances.

7.4 ■■■ FINITE DURATION SEQUENCES AND THE DISCRETE FOURIER TRANSFORM

So far in this chapter we've restricted our attention to periodic sequences of period N. We now consider nonperiodic sequences with the goal of using Discrete Fourier Series concepts to represent these sequences. We start with a sequence $x(n)$ which consists of a finite number N of samples and hence is not periodic. This sort of sequence could result from a short "burst," or pulse, or from breaking a very long string of data into finite-length pieces for processing. To follow the pattern of earlier sections of this chapter, we represent the finite sequence as a sum of a finite number of exponentials.

A nonperiodic sequence $x(n)$ can be considered to be one period of a periodic sequence as seen in Fig. 7.12. Thus, for a given periodic sequence $x_p(n)$ of period N, we can define a finite-duration sequence as

$$x(n) = \begin{cases} x_p(n), & 0 \le n \le N - 1 \\ 0, & \text{elsewhere} \end{cases} \tag{7.84}$$

or, we can consider the periodic sequence to be the periodic extension of the finite sequence, namely

$$x_p(n + \ell N) = x(n), \qquad 0 \le n \le N - 1, \; -\infty \le \ell \le \infty. \tag{7.85}$$

Hence, to find the complex exponentials that represent this sequence, we simply find the DFS corresponding to $x_p(n)$ and then use only one period of the resulting periodic sequence. That is, the coefficients for the finite

FIGURE 7.12 A nonperiodic sequence $x(n)$ and a periodic sequence $x_p(n)$

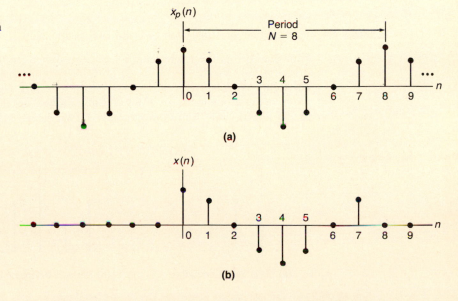

length sequence can be found from

$$X(k) = \sum_{n=0}^{N-1} x_p(n)e^{-j(2\pi/N)nk}, \qquad k = 0, 1, 2, \ldots, N-1. \qquad (7.86)$$

Using the relationship in Eq. 7.84 this becomes

$$X(k) = \sum_{n=0}^{N-1} x(n)e^{-j(2\pi/N)nk}, \qquad k = 0, 1, 2, \ldots, N-1. \qquad (7.87)$$

Now, we define the Discrete Fourier Transform (DFT) pair as

$$X(k) = \sum_{n=0}^{N-1} x(n)e^{-j(2\pi/N)nk}, \qquad k = 0, 1, \ldots, N-1 \qquad (7.88)$$

$$x(n) = \frac{1}{N} \sum_{k=0}^{N-1} X(k)e^{j(2\pi/N)nk}, \qquad n = 0, 1, \ldots, N-1. \qquad (7.89)$$

It is common practice to show this pair with a double-ended arrow to emphasize the "goes either way" nature of the transform. Thus, we have

$$x(n) = \frac{1}{N} \sum_{k=0}^{N-1} X(k)e^{j(2\pi/N)nk} \longleftrightarrow X(k) = \sum_{n=0}^{N-1} x(n)e^{-j(2\pi/N)nk} \qquad (7.90)$$

and it should be emphasized that both sequences $x(n)$ and $X(k)$ are zero outside of the range 0 to $N-1$ in n or k, respectively.

Example 7.4. This example illustrates the DFT and DFS relationship.

Find the DFT of the finite length sequence shown in Fig. 7.13(a).

Solution: We have already determined the Discrete Fourier Series (DFS) for the periodic sequence $x_p(n)$ of Fig. 7.13(b) and we see that $x(n)$ is simply one period of $x_p(n)$ and thus from Example 7.2 we have

FIGURE 7.13 Sequences used in Example 7.4

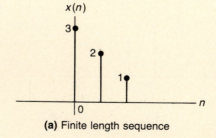

(a) Finite length sequence

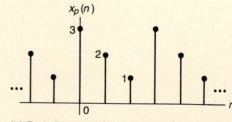

(b) Periodic extension of finite length sequence

CHAPTER 7   DISCRETE FOURIER TRANSFORM

$$X(0) = X_p(0) = 6, \quad X(1) = X_p(1) = \sqrt{3}\, e^{-j\pi/6} \quad \text{and} \quad X(2) = X_p(2) = \sqrt{3}\, e^{j\pi/6} \tag{7.91}$$

with the magnitude and the phase of these coefficients shown in Fig. 7.14.

Let's look at some additional examples of evaluating DFTs.

Example 7.5. This example illustrates the DFT of the unit sample sequence.

Find the DFT of the unit sample sequence

$$x(n) = \delta(n). \tag{7.92}$$

Solution: Substituting into the DFT definition gives

$$X(k) = \sum_{n=0}^{N-1} x(n) e^{-j(2\pi/N)nk}. \tag{7.93}$$

Replacing $x(n)$ with the unit sample function $\delta(n)$ produces

$$X(k) = \sum_{n=0}^{N-1} \delta(n) e^{-j(2\pi/N)nk} \tag{7.94}$$

and since $\delta(n)$ is zero except for $n = 0$ where it is 1 we have

$$X(k) = 1 e^{-j(2\pi/N)(0)(k)} = 1, \qquad k = 0, 1, \ldots, N-1. \tag{7.95}$$

Comment: Notice that this result does not depend upon the value selected for N. The unit sample sequence and its DFT are shown in Fig. 7.15.

Example 7.6. This example illustrates the DFT of a constant sequence.

Find the DFT of the constant sequence

$$x(n) = \begin{cases} A, & n = 0, 1, \ldots, N-1 \\ 0, & \text{otherwise.} \end{cases} \tag{7.96}$$

FIGURE 7.14 Plot of Discrete Fourier Transform, magnitude and phase

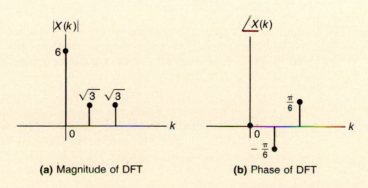

(a) Magnitude of DFT (b) Phase of DFT

FIGURE 7.15 The unit sample sequence and its DFT

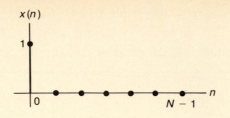

(a) Unit sample sequence

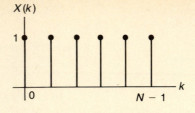

(b) DFT of unit sample sequence

Solution: Using the DFT definition

$$X(k) = \sum_{n=0}^{N-1} Ae^{-j(2\pi/N)nk}, \qquad k = 0, 1, \ldots, N-1, \tag{7.97}$$

for $k = 0$ we have

$$X(0) = \sum_{n=0}^{N-1} Ae^{-j(2\pi/N)(n)(0)}$$

$$= \sum_{n=0}^{N-1} A \cdot 1$$

$$= NA. \tag{7.98}$$

For $k \neq 0$

$$X(k) = \sum_{n=0}^{N-1} Ae^{-j(2\pi/N)nk}$$

$$= A \sum_{n=0}^{N-1} e^{-j(2\pi k/N)n}, \qquad k = 1, 2, \ldots, N-1. \tag{7.99}$$

Using the closed-form expression for the finite geometric series on Eq. 7.99 gives

$$X(k) = A\frac{1 - e^{-j(2\pi k/N)N}}{1 - e^{-j(2\pi k/N)}}$$

$$= A\frac{1 - e^{-j2\pi k}}{1 - e^{-j(2\pi/N)k}} = 0 \qquad \text{for } k = 1, 2, \ldots, N-1 \tag{7.100}$$

which follows since the numerator of the expression for $X(k)$ is zero and the denominator is not. Thus, combining the results of Eqs. 7.98 and 7.100 we see that the DFT of the constant sequence is a sample function of amplitude AN as shown in Fig. 7.16, that is

$$X(k) = NA\delta(k). \tag{7.101}$$

Comment: In comparing Examples 7.5 and 7.6 we notice that, aside from scale factors, if the plots of $X(k)$ and $x(n)$ in Fig. 7.16 were interchanged, they would be identical to the graphs in Fig. 7.15. This is a consequence of the duality property of DFTs, a result derived in Section 7.6.5.

FIGURE 7.16 Constant
sequence and its DFT

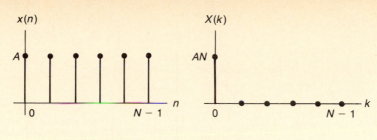

(a) Constant sequence   (b) DFT of constant sequence

7.5 ■ SOME IMPORTANT RELATIONSHIPS

In this section we consider some interrelationships that are of practical importance when DFTs are used. We first consider the relationship between DFTs and Fourier Transforms of sequences. The concept of frequency resolution (spacing) is then introduced and its relationship to the length (record length) of a sequence is discussed. Several examples are included to illustrate these interconnections.

7.5.1 DFTs and the Fourier Transform

In Chapter Four, the frequency response of a causal system having a finite length unit sample response $h(n)$ of length N was defined to be

$$H(e^{j\theta}) = \sum_{n=0}^{n=N-1} h(n)e^{-jn\theta} \tag{7.102}$$

where $H(e^{j\theta})$ is also known as the eigenvalue or characteristic value. $H(e^{j\theta})$ is also sometimes called the Fourier Transform of the sequence $h(n)$. In a similar way,

$$X(e^{j\theta}) = \sum_{n=0}^{N-1} x(n)e^{-jn\theta} \tag{7.103}$$

is referred to as the Fourier Transform[†] of the finite length sequence $x(n)$. Although the mathematical operations of Eqs. 7.102 and 7.103 are the same it is common practice to refer to $X(e^{j\theta})$ as the Fourier Transform of the finite length sequence $x(n)$ and reserve the term frequency response for $H(e^{j\theta})$. Similarly, we refer to $Y(e^{j\theta})$ as the Fourier Transform of the sequence $y(n)$ and so forth. From Eq. 7.88, however, the Discrete Fourier

---

[†] The term Discrete-Time Fourier Transform is also used to distinguish the operation indicated in Eq. 7.103 from the Fourier Transform of a function of a continuous variable, for example time, t. See Appendix E.

FIGURE 7.17 Relationship
between the Fourier Transform and the DFT of a finite
sequence for N = 6

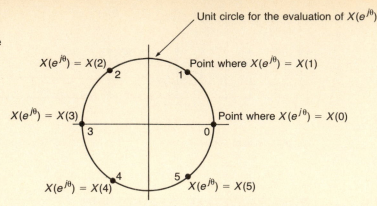

Transform (DFT) of the finite length sequence $x(n)$ is

$$X(k) = \sum_{n=0}^{N-1} x(n)e^{-j(2\pi/N)nk} \qquad (7.104)$$

which is quite similar to the Fourier Transform $X(e^{j\theta})$ in Eq. 7.103. In fact, if θ is set to $(2\pi/N)k$ in Eq. 7.103 we see by comparison with Eq. 7.104 that

$$X(e^{j2\pi k/N}) = \sum_{n=0}^{N-1} x(n)e^{-j2\pi nk/N} = X(k) \qquad (7.105)$$

or

$$X(k) = X(e^{j\theta})\Big|_{\theta=2\pi k/N}. \qquad (7.106)$$

Thus, since $X(e^{j\theta})$ is a continuous function of θ the values of the DFT $X(k)$ are the *samples* of the Fourier Transform $X(e^{j\theta})$ at values of θ starting at $\theta = 0$ and equally spaced from one another by $2\pi k/N$ units as in Fig. 7.17.

Example 7.7. This example illustrates the connection between the DFT and the Fourier Transform.

Find the Fourier Transform for the finite-length sequence of Example 7.4 and then by appropriate sampling determine the DFT of this sequence.

Solution: Using the sequence of Fig. 7.13(a) and the Fourier Transform expression from Eq. 7.103 we have

$$X(e^{j\theta}) = \sum_{n=0}^{n=2} x(n)e^{-jn\theta} \qquad (7.107)$$

and substituting numerical values gives

$$X(e^{j\theta}) = 3 + 2e^{-j\theta} + 1e^{-j2\theta} \qquad (7.108)$$

with the continuous curves for $|X(e^{j\theta})|$ and $\angle X(e^{j\theta})$ shown in Fig. 7.18 in the interval 0 to 2π. If we sample the values of $|X(e^{j\theta})|$ and $\angle X(e^{j\theta})$ for $\theta = \dfrac{2\pi}{3}k$, $k = 0, 1, 2$ we obtain the values

$$X(0) = 6, \; X(1) = \sqrt{3}\, e^{-j\pi/6} \quad \text{and} \quad X(2) = \sqrt{3}\, e^{j\pi/6} \qquad (7.109)$$

as from Example 7.4 and Eq. 7.91.

7.5.2 Relationships Among Record Length, Frequency Resolution, and Sampling Frequency

The sequence $x(n)$ is often produced by sampling a continuous-time signal $x(t)$ resulting in the sequence $x(nT)$. The DFT coefficients for this sampled signal can be written as $X(k\Delta f)$, rather than simply $X(k)$, where Δf represents the frequency spacing of the coefficients. This is the same vein as T in $x(nT)$ representing the time spacing of the sampled signal. Thus, the DFT pair of Eqs. 7.88 and 7.89 can also be written as

$$X(k\Delta f) = \sum_{n=0}^{N-1} x(nT)e^{j(2\pi/N)(-nk)}, \qquad k = 0, 1, \ldots, N-1$$

$$x(nT) = \frac{1}{N}\sum_{k=0}^{N-1} X(k\Delta f)e^{j(2\pi/N)(nk)}, \qquad n = 0, 1, \ldots, N-1 \qquad (7.110)$$

which explicitly indicates the frequencies represented by the DFT coefficients.

Example 7.8. This example illustrates the computation of the DFT coefficients of a sampled signal.

Consider the periodic analog signal

$$x(t) = A\cos(200\pi t) + B\cos(600\pi t) \qquad (7.111)$$

that is sampled at a frequency of 1 kHz.

a) Find the period of the resulting sequence.
b) Determine the DFT coefficients.

Solution:

a) The sampled version of $x(t)$ is

$$x(nT) = A\cos(200\pi nT) + B\cos(600\pi nT) \qquad (7.112)$$

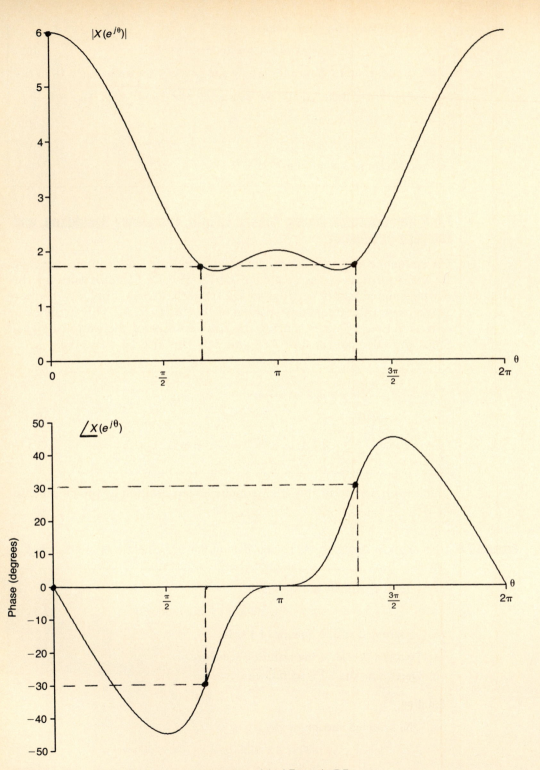

FIGURE 7.18 Fourier Transform of the sequence $x(n)$ of Example 7.7

and for a sampling frequency of $f_s = 1$ kHz $(T = 0.001s)$ this becomes

$$x(0.001n) = A\cos(0.2\pi n) + B\cos(0.6\pi n)$$

$$= A\cos\left(\frac{2\pi n}{10}\right) + B\cos\left(\frac{6\pi n}{10}\right). \qquad (7.113)$$

Thus, the period of the sequence is 10.

b) Following the procedure of Example 7.3 the DFT coefficients for one period $(N = 10)$ are shown in Fig. 7.19(a). An analog frequency scale has also been added which indicates that the fundamental frequency of the analog signal at $f = 100$ Hz corresponds with $k = 1$ in the DFT and $f = 300$ Hz corresponds with $k = 3$ in the DFT.

In Example 7.8, the frequency spacing Δf between DFT coefficients can be computed from

$$\Delta f = f_s/N$$

$$= 10^3/10 = 100 \text{ Hz}. \qquad (7.114)$$

In general, frequency components in the DFT are spaced apart according to

$$\boxed{\Delta f = f_s/N \quad \text{or} \quad \Delta f = 1/NT = 1/T_0} \qquad (7.115)$$

where f_s is the sampling frequency (or T is the sampling interval), N is the period of the resulting sequence, Δf is the frequency spacing, and T_0 is the record length. Δf is also called the frequency resolution. If $x(nT)$ contains frequency components closer together than Δf hertz, the DFT does not represent these as separate and distinct frequencies. To be able to resolve close-together frequencies we need to make Δf appropriately small. This is referred to as increasing the resolution. If we choose to plot the coeffi-

FIGURE 7.19(a) DFT coefficients for Example 7.8

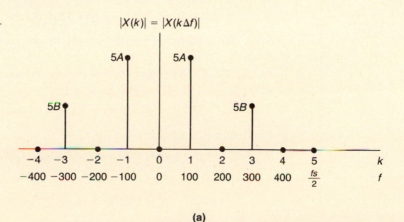

(a)

FIGURE 7.19(b) DFT co-
efficients for Example 7.8
(different period than Fig.
7.19(a))

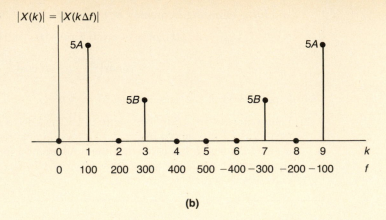

$|X(k)| = |X(k \Delta f)|$

(b)

cients in Example 7.8 for $k = 0, 1, \ldots, 9$ rather than $k = -4, -3, \ldots, 5$
we obtain the plot of Fig. 7.19(b). The analog frequency $f_s/2$, in this case
500 Hz, is called the folding frequency because the DFT components can
be thought of as being folded about that point.

Example 7.9. This example illustrates frequency resolution and record length.

An analog (continuous-time) signal having a two-hundred millisecond record
length is sampled at a frequency of 2.5 kHz.

a) What is the maximum frequency that can be present in this signal if there
   is to be no aliasing?

b) What is the frequency resolution if a DFT is computed for this signal?
   Give your answer in both $\Delta\theta$ and Δf.

c) What analog frequencies are represented in the DFT?

Solution:

a) The Nyquist frequency is

$$f_{max} = f_s/2 = 1250 \text{ Hz} \qquad (7.116)$$

which is the maximum frequency in the analog signal if there is to be no
aliasing.

b) From Eq. 7.115, the frequency spacing is the reciprocal of the record
length, or

$$\Delta f = 1/T_0 = 1/0.2 = 5 \text{ Hz} \qquad (7.117)$$

and knowing that $\theta = 2\pi f T$ we have

$$\Delta\theta = 2\pi \, \Delta f T = (2\pi)(5)(1/2500) = (4\pi)10^{-3} \text{ rad.} \qquad (7.118)$$

c) The record length is $T_0 = 0.2$s and the time between samples is

$$T = 1/2500 = (4 \times 10^{-4}). \qquad (7.119)$$

CHAPTER 7 DISCRETE FOURIER TRANSFORM

Consequently, the number of samples is

$$N = T_0/T$$
$$= (0.2)/(4 \times 10^{-4}) = 500 \text{ samples.}$$
(7.120)

Thus, the frequencies represented are

$$f = 0, 5, 10, \ldots, 1250, -1245, -1240, \ldots, -10, -5 \text{ Hz.}$$
(7.121)

Equation 7.115 is a very important relationship. To gain some insight into the information it contains let's consider the effect of fixing one of the three variables and allowing the others to vary.

Example 7.10. This example illustrates the effect of a fixed number of samples N with two different values of the sampling period T.

Determine the effect on the frequency resolution of holding N constant with the two different sampling periods $T = T^a$ and $T = T^b = 2T^a$.

Solution: Denoting the fixed number of samples as $N = N^a$ we have from Eq. 7.115

$$\Delta f^a = \frac{1}{N^a T^a} \quad \text{and} \quad \Delta f^b = \frac{1}{N^a T^b} = \frac{1}{N^a (2T^a)}$$
(7.122)

and so $\Delta f^b = 0.5 \Delta f^a$. Thus, by doubling the sampling period we also double the record length

$$T_0^b = N^b T^b = 2N^a T^a$$
(7.123)

and the precision of frequency resolution. Figures 7.20(a) and (b) (drawn for $N = 10$) illustrate these observations. We also notice that the highest frequency represented in $|X^b(k)|$ is one-half that of the maximum frequency contained in $|X^a(k)|$.

Example 7.11. This example illustrates the effect of a fixed record length T_0, or a fixed sampling period T.

a) Determine the effect on the frequency resolution of holding T_0 constant with two different numbers of samples $N = N^a$ and $N^c = 2N^a$.

b) Determine the effect on frequency resolution of holding T constant with two different numbers of samples $N = N^a$ and $N^d = 2N^a$.

Solution:

a) The frequency resolution depends only on the record length and since $T_0^c = T_0^a$

$$\Delta f^c = \Delta f^a$$
(7.124)

FIGURE 7.20 The relationship among Δf, N, T_0, and T

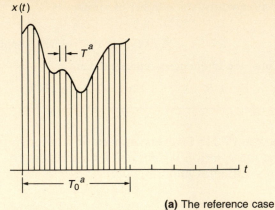

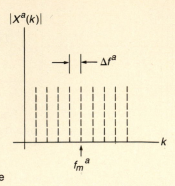

(a) The reference case

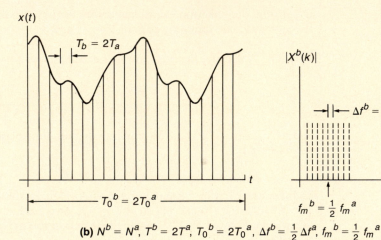

(b) $N^b = N^a$, $T^b = 2T^a$, $T_0^{\,b} = 2T_0^{\,a}$, $\Delta f^b = \frac{1}{2}\,\Delta f^a$, $f_m^{\,b} = \frac{1}{2}\,f_m^{\,a}$

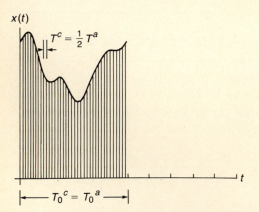

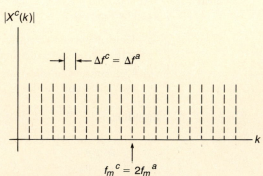

(c) $N^c = 2N^a$, $T^c = \frac{1}{2}\,T^a$, $T_0^{\,c} = T_0^{\,a}$, $\Delta f^c = \Delta f^a$, $f_m^{\,c} = 2f_m^{\,a}$

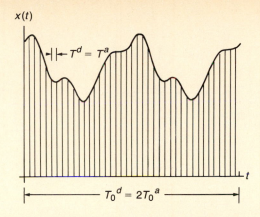

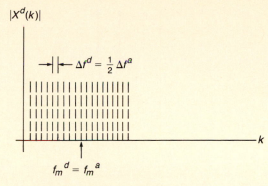

FIGURE 7.20 (cont.)   **(d)** $N^d = 2N^a$, $T^d = T^a$, $T_0^d = 2T_0^a$, $\Delta f^d = \frac{1}{2}\Delta f^a$, $f_m^d = f_m^a$

and comparing Figs. 7.20 (a) and (c) we see that the frequency resolution is unchanged.

b) Figure 7.20 (d) shows the results for $T^d = T^a$ and $N^d = 2N^a$. The record length T_0^d is twice that of T_0^a so $\Delta f^d = 0.5\Delta f^a$ and the highest frequencies represented in $|X^d(k)|$ and $|X^a(k)|$ are the same.

The table below summarizes the relationships found in this example and Example 7.10, and shown in Fig. 7.20.

	N	T	T_0	Δf	f_{max}	
a)	N^a	T^a	T_0^a	Δf^a	f_m^a	← reference case
b)	N^a	$2T^a$	$2T_0^a$	$\frac{1}{2}\Delta f^a$	$\frac{1}{2}f_m^a$	
c)	$2N^a$	$\frac{1}{2}T^a$	T_0^a	Δf^a	$2f_m^a$	
d)	$2N^a$	T^a	$2T_0^a$	$\frac{1}{2}\Delta f^a$	f_m^a	

With the above in mind, it is clear that the DFT can be used to determine the frequency components of a sequence. This sequence could be a periodic pulse train such as the one in Fig. 7.21(a), which produces the spectrum of Fig. 7.21(b), which is plotted for $N = 6$.[†] We have "transformed" the data from the n-domain (time) to the k-domain (frequency). For sampled analog signals, which frequently arise in spectrum analysis applications, the transformation amounts to going from the "time domain" to the "frequency domain."

[†] Those readers having experience with Fourier Transforms of analog signals should recognize the familiar time-domain pulse to frequency domain sin x/x function that is suggested in the plots of Fig. 7.21.

FIGURE 7.21 DFS analysis

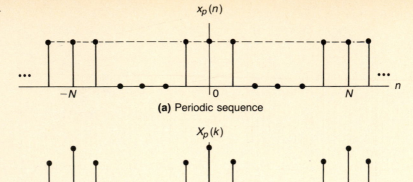

$x_p(n)$

(a) Periodic sequence

$X_p(k)$

(b) Periodic discrete-frequency spectrum

Example 7.12. This example illustrates finding the frequency content of a sequence.

An analog signal $x(t)$ is sampled with $T = 0.01$ and the resulting sequence from Fig. 7.22 is tabulated below.

n	0	1	2	3	4	5
$x(n)$	5.0	-1.5	6.5	-3.0	6.5	-1.5

$$(7.125)$$

Find the frequency content of this sequence.

Solution: To do this we need to determine the DFT coefficients for this sequence. There are six samples and the coefficients are given by

$$X(k) = \sum_{n=0}^{n=5} x(n)e^{j(2\pi/6)(-nk)} \tag{7.126}$$

with the results listed below.

$$X(0) = \sum_{n=0}^{5} x(n) = 12, \qquad X(1) = \sum_{n=0}^{5} x(n)e^{j(2\pi/6)(-n)} = 0$$

$$X(2) = \sum_{n=0}^{5} x(n)e^{j(2\pi/6)(-2n)} = -3, \; X(3) = \sum_{n=0}^{5} x(n)e^{j(2\pi/6)(-3n)} = 24$$

$$X(4) = \sum_{n=0}^{5} x(n)e^{j(2\pi/6)(-4n)} = -3, \; X(5) = \sum_{n=0}^{5} x(n)e^{j(2\pi/6)(-5n)} = 0. \tag{7.127}$$

The amplitudes of the coefficients are plotted in Fig. 7.23 and to interpret these let us describe $x(n)$ in terms of $X(k)$ as

$$x(n) = \frac{1}{6} \sum_{k=0}^{5} X(k)e^{j(2\pi/6)(nk)} \tag{7.128}$$

CHAPTER 7 DISCRETE FOURIER TRANSFORM

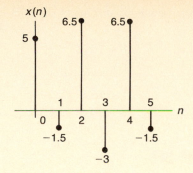

FIGURE 7.22 Sequence resulting from sampling an analog signal

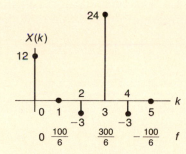

FIGURE 7.23 DFT coefficients of the sequence of Figure 7.22

and using the known values of $X(k)$ we have

$$x(n) = \frac{1}{6}[12 - 3e^{j(2\pi/6)(2n)} + 24e^{j(2\pi/6)(3n)} - 3e^{j(2\pi/6)(4n)}]. \quad (7.129)$$

The result in Eq. 7.129 can be tidied up somewhat by recognizing that

$$e^{j(2\pi/6)4n} = e^{-j(2\pi/6)2n} \quad (7.130)$$

which allows us to write

$$x(n) = 2 - 0.5(e^{j(2\pi/6)(2n)} + e^{-j(2\pi/6)(2n)}) + 4e^{j(2\pi/6)(3n)}$$

$$= 2 - \cos(2\pi n/3) + 4\cos(\pi n) \quad (7.131)$$

because $e^{j(6\pi n/6)} = \cos(\pi n) + j \sin(\pi n)$.

Comments:

1. It is very easy to check this result by substituting for n in Eq. 7.131 giving

$$x(0) = 2 - \cos(0) + 4\cos(0) = 5$$

$$x(1) = 2 - \cos(2\pi/3) + 4\cos(\pi) = -1.5$$

$$x(2) = 2 - \cos(4\pi/3) + 4\cos(2\pi) = 6.5$$

$$x(3) = 2 - \cos(6\pi/3) + 4\cos(3\pi) = -3$$

$$x(5) = 2 - \cos(8\pi/3) + 4\cos(4\pi) = 6.5 \quad (7.132)$$

all of which agree with the data given in Fig. 7.22.

7.5 SOME IMPORTANT RELATIONSHIPS

2. Using Eq. 7.115 the frequency spacing of the DFT coefficients in Fig. 7.23 is

$$\Delta f = 1/NT$$
$$= 1/(6)(0.01)$$
$$= 16.67 \text{ Hz.} \qquad (7.133)$$

7.6 ▄▄ PROPERTIES OF THE DFT

Several properties of the Discrete Fourier Transform are given below. These properties are important in both theoretical developments and applications.

7.6.1 Linearity

If $x_1(n)$ and $x_2(n)$ are finite duration sequences both having length N and whose DFTs are $X_1(k)$ and $X_2(k)$ and if

$$x_3(n) = ax_1(n) + bx_2(n) \qquad (7.134)$$

then from the definition of Eq. 7.88

$$X_3(k) = aX_1(k) + bX_2(k). \qquad (7.135)$$

The proof of this result is left as an exercise for the reader.

Consider the partial implementation of a system as in Fig. 7.24 where $y(n) = as(n) + bg(n)$ with a and b real constants. The sequences $s(n)$ and $g(n)$ have the DFTs $S(k)$ and $G(k)$, respectively, and because of linearity, the output transform $Y(k)$ will contain the components $aS(k)$ and $bG(k)$. That is, the components of $Y(k)$ will appear in the same frequency bands as they did in $S(k)$ and $G(k)$ individually.

FIGURE 7.24 The sequence $y(n)$ is a linear combination of $s(n)$ and $g(n)$.

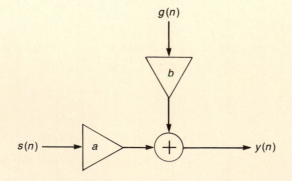

7.6.2 Circular Shift of a Sequence

The next property of interest is the circular shift of a sequence. Starting with a finite length sequence defined for $n = 0, 1, \ldots, N - 1$ as in Fig. 7.25(a) we first form the periodic extension shown in Fig. 7.25(b). Next, consider the sequence $x_p(n + m) = x_{2p}(n)$ shown in Fig. 7.25(c) for $m = 1$, and one period of this sequence $x_2(n)$ as shown in Fig. 7.25(d). We say that $x_2(n)$ is $x_1(n)$ circularly shifted by m units. The reason for this terminology should be clear from Fig. 7.25(e) where $x_2(n)$ is shown on a circle. If this circle is shifted (rotated) clockwise m units we obtain $x_2(n)$ as in Fig. 7.25(f) and in the statement of the circular shift property. If $x_2(n)$ is a circularly shifted version of $x_1(n)$, that is

$$x_2(n) = x_1(n \oplus m) \tag{7.136}$$

FIGURE 7.25 Circular shifting

the DFTs are related by

$$X_2(k) = X_1(k)\, e^{j(2\pi/N)(km)}. \tag{7.137}$$

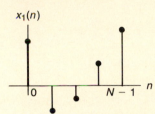

$x_1(n)$

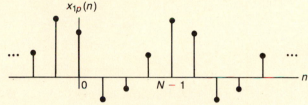

$x_{1p}(n)$

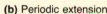

(a) A finite length sequence

(b) Periodic extension

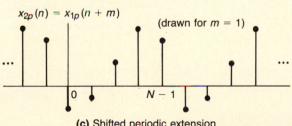

$x_{2p}(n) = x_{1p}(n + m)$

(drawn for $m = 1$)

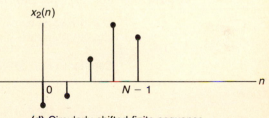

$x_2(n)$

(c) Shifted periodic extension

(d) Circularly shifted finite sequence

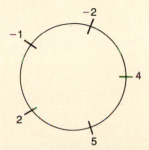

(e) $x_1(n)$ arranged on a circle

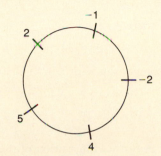

(f) Circularly shifted $x_1(n) = x_1(n \oplus m)$, where $m = 1$ arranged on a circle

Proof: Since we know that $X_1(k)$ represents the DFT coefficients for one period of $X_{1p}(k)$ and that $x_2(n)$ is one period of $x_{1p}(n + m)$, let us first derive the circular shift theorem for periodic sequences

$$X_{2p}(k) = \sum_{n=-m}^{n=-m+N-1} x_{1p}(n + m)\, e^{j(2\pi/N)(-nk)}. \tag{7.138}$$

Now, let $\ell = n + m$ or $n = \ell - m$, then

$$X_{2p}(k) = \sum_{\ell=0}^{\ell=N-1} x_{1p}(\ell)\, e^{j(2\pi/N)(-\ell+m)k}$$

$$= e^{j(2\pi/N)(mk)} \sum_{\ell=0}^{\ell=N-1} x_{1p}(\ell)\, e^{j(2\pi/N)(-\ell k)}$$

$$= e^{j(2\pi/N)(mk)}\, X_{1p}(k). \tag{7.139}$$

Then

$$X_2(k) = \text{DFT}\,[x_2(n)]$$

$$= \text{DFT}\,[x_1(n \oplus m)]$$

$$= e^{j(2\pi/N)mk}\, X_1(k) \tag{7.140}$$

where $X_1(k) = \text{DFT}\,[x_1(n)]$ and $\oplus$ denotes the circular shift operation.

Example 7.13. This example illustrates the circular shift of a finite sequence.

Use the sequences $x_1(n)$ and $x_2(n)$ of Fig. 7.26 and show that their DFTs follow the circular shift property of Eq. 7.140.

Solution: For the sequence $x_1(n)$ in Fig. 7.26(a) the DFT is

$$X_1(k) = 3 + 2e^{-j2\pi k/3} + 1e^{-j4\pi k/3}, \qquad k = 0, 1, 2 \tag{7.141}$$

while the DFT of $x_2(n)$ in Fig. 7.26(b) is

$$X_2(k) = 1 + 3e^{-j2\pi k/3} + 2e^{-j4\pi k/3}, \qquad k = 0, 1, 2 \tag{7.142}$$

and we can write

$$X_2(k) = 3e^{-j2\pi k/3} + 2e^{-j4\pi k/3} + 1e^{-j6\pi k/3} \tag{7.143}$$

which, by comparison with Eq. 7.141, is seen to be

$$X_2(k) = e^{-j2\pi k/3}\, X_1(k) \tag{7.144}$$

where $x_2(n) = x_1(n \oplus [-1])$.

Comment: A further illustration of the consequence of the circular shifting property is given in Fig. 7.27 where it is seen that the magnitudes of the DFTs for $x_1(n)$, $x_2(n)$, and $x_3(n)$ are all the same while the phase values are different.

CHAPTER 7 DISCRETE FOURIER TRANSFORM

FIGURE 7.26 Circularly shifted sequences for Example 7.13

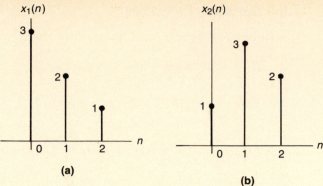

(a)

(b)

FIGURE 7.27 Three related sequences that have the same magnitude DFT but different phase

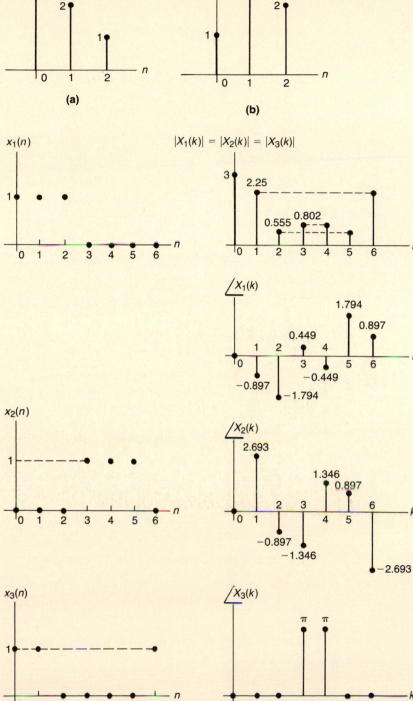

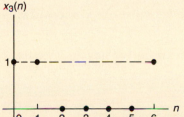

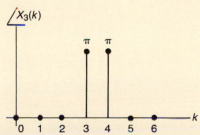

7.6.3 Symmetry Properties

If $x(n)$ is a real sequence of duration N then

$$\text{Re}\,[X(k)] = \text{Re}\,[X(N-k)], \qquad k = 1, 2, \ldots, \frac{N}{2} - 1 \quad \text{for } N \text{ even}$$

$$\text{Im}\,[X(k)] = -\text{Im}\,[X(N-k)], \qquad k = 1, 2, \ldots, \frac{N-1}{2} \quad \text{for } N \text{ odd.}$$

$$(7.145)$$

Therefore, in terms of the magnitude and the phase we can state that

$$|X(k)| = |X(N-k)|, \qquad k = 1, 2, \ldots, \frac{N}{2} - 1 \quad \text{for } N \text{ even}$$

$$\angle X(k) = -\angle X(N-k), \qquad k = 1, 2, \ldots, \frac{N-1}{2} \quad \text{for } N \text{ odd.} \qquad (7.146)$$

Proof: Starting from the basic definition of the DFT we have

$$X(k) = \sum_{n=0}^{N-1} x(n) e^{-j(2\pi/N)nk}, \qquad k = 0, 1, \ldots, N - 1 \qquad (7.147)$$

and using the Euler relation this becomes

$$X(k) = \sum_{n=0}^{N-1} x(n) \left[\cos\left(\frac{2\pi nk}{N}\right) - j \sin\left(\frac{2\pi nk}{N}\right) \right] \qquad (7.148)$$

and thus

$$\text{Re}\,[X(k)] = \sum_{n=0}^{N-1} x(n) \cos\left(\frac{2\pi nk}{N}\right) \qquad (7.149)$$

and

$$\text{Im}\,[X(k)] = -\sum_{n=0}^{N-1} x(n) \sin\left(\frac{2\pi nk}{N}\right). \qquad (7.150)$$

To find $\text{Re}\,[X(N-k)]$ we simply substitute $N-k$ for k to obtain

$$\text{Re}\,[X(N-k)] = \sum_{n=0}^{N-1} x(n) \cos\left[\frac{2\pi n}{N}(N-k)\right]. \qquad (7.151)$$

Expanding the argument of the cosine gives

$$\text{Re}\,[X(N-k)] = \sum_{n=0}^{N-1} x(n) \cos\left[2\pi n - \frac{2\pi nk}{N}\right]. \qquad (7.152)$$

Since $\cos[2\pi n + \alpha] = \cos[\alpha]$ we have

$$\text{Re}\,[X(N - k)] = \sum_{n=0}^{N-1} x(n) \cos\left[\frac{-2\pi nk}{N}\right]$$

$$= \sum_{n=0}^{N-1} x(n) \cos\left[\frac{2\pi nk}{N}\right] = \text{Re}\,[X(k)] \qquad (7.153)$$

as in Eq. 7.149. To find $\text{Im}\,[X(N - k)]$ we have from Eq. 7.150

$$\text{Im}\,[X(N - k)] = -\sum_{n=0}^{N-1} x(n) \sin\left[\frac{2\pi n}{N}(N - k)\right]. \qquad (7.154)$$

Expanding the sine function's argument yields

$$\text{Im}\,[X(N - k)] = -\sum_{n=0}^{N-1} x(n) \sin\left[2\pi n - \frac{2\pi nk}{N}\right]. \qquad (7.155)$$

Finally, using the fact that $\sin[2\pi n + \alpha] = \sin[\alpha]$ gives

$$\text{Im}\,[X(N - k)] = +\sum_{n=0}^{N-1} x(n) \sin\left[\frac{2\pi nk}{N}\right] = -\text{Im}\,[X(k)]. \qquad (7.156)$$

The proof is complete and the magnitude and phase plots have the general characteristics given in Fig. 7.28 for N even.

A consequence of these symmetry conditions is that $|X(k)|$ and $\angle X(k)$ are symmetrical about the point $k = N/2$. The magnitude has an even

FIGURE 7.28 Symmetry characteristics for the DFT of a real sequence $x(n)$, for N even

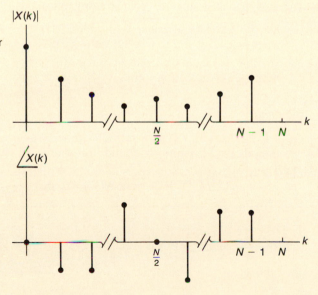

symmetry about the point $N/2$, i.e.,

$$\left| X\left(\frac{N}{2} + \ell\right) \right| = \left| X\left(\frac{N}{2} - \ell\right) \right|.^{\dagger} \tag{7.157}$$

The phase, on the other hand, has odd symmetry about the point $k = N/2$, that is,

$$\angle X\left(\frac{N}{2} + \ell\right) = -\angle X\left(\frac{N}{2} - \ell\right). \tag{7.158}$$

The results expressed in Eqs. 7.157 and 7.158 can be collectively represented by the single expression

$$X\left(\frac{N}{2} + \ell\right) = X^*\left(\frac{N}{2} - \ell\right). \tag{7.159}$$

Thus, in a sense, points for $k > N/2$ contain the same information as the points for which $k < N/2$. This results from the fact that $X(k)$ for $k > N/2$ really represents the DFT values for "folded-over" negative frequencies. By knowing of this symmetry we can use it to check numerical results. If we start with a real sequence and compute its DFT, by hand or computer, we should check the symmetry as a way of detecting errors. If the symmetry conditions are not satisfied, then we know an error has been made. Unfortunately, the converse is not true; even though the symmetry conditions are met the DFT may still be in error.

Example 7.14. This example illustrates the symmetry properties.

a) For the real data sequence $x(n) = \{x(0), x(1), \ldots, x(39)\}$, it is known that $X(19) = 2$. Can you find $X(20)$ from $X(19)$?

b) For the real data sequence $w(n) = \{w(0), w(1), \ldots, w(72)\}$, it is known that $X(36) = 2$. Can you find $X(37)$ from $X(36)$?

Solution:

a) For this 40-point sequence, the symmetry is around $k = 20$ and, consequently, $X(20)$ cannot be found from the given data.

b) For $N = 73$, the symmetry is around $k = 36.5$ and consequently, $X^*(36) = X(37)$ and since $X(36)$ is real, $X(37) = 2$ also.

---

†Note that ℓ is an integer if N is even $\left(\ell = 1, 2, \ldots, \frac{N}{2} - 1\right)$, whereas ℓ is an odd integer multiple of $1/2$ if N is odd $\left(\ell = \frac{1}{2}, \frac{3}{2}, \ldots, \frac{N}{2} - 1\right)$.

CHAPTER 7 DISCRETE FOURIER TRANSFORM

Example 7.15. This example illustrates some ways to check a DFT.

Suppose we are given the six sequences of Fig. 7.29(a) and two points of a DFT for a four-point sequence as in Fig. 7.29(b).

a) List those sequences that have the value of $X(0)$ shown.
b) List those sequences that have the value of $X(2)$ shown.

Solution: The four-point DFT is given by

$$X(k) = \sum_{n=0}^{3} x(n)\, e^{-j(2\pi/4)nk}. \qquad (7.160)$$

a) For $k = 0$, $X(0) = x(0) + x(1) + x(2) + x(3) = 0$ and we see that sequences 1, 3, and 4 give $X(0) = 0$.
b) For $k = 2$, $X(2) = x(0) - x(1) + x(2) - x(3) = 4$ and only sequence 3 gives $X(2) = 4$.

FIGURE 7.29 Data for Example 7.15

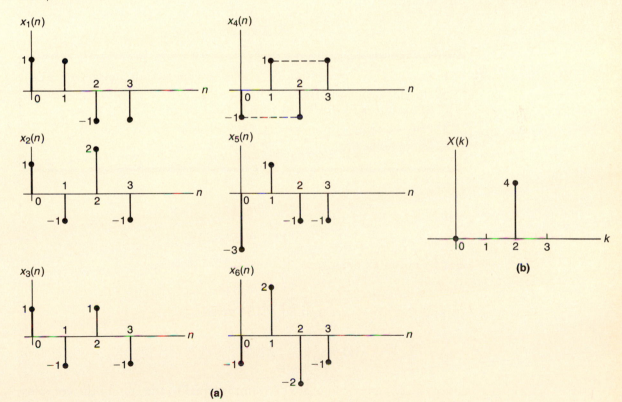

7.6.4 Alternate Inversion Formula

Given the Discrete Fourier Transform pair

$$x(n) = \frac{1}{N} \sum_{k=0}^{N-1} X(k)e^{j(2\pi/N)nk} \longleftrightarrow X(k) = \sum_{n=0}^{N-1} x(n)e^{-j(2\pi/N)nk} \quad (7.161)$$

suppose we have a computer program to evaluate $X(k)$, the DFT of $x(n)$. We assume that the program has been written to accept complex input data for $x(n)$. How can we use this program to evaluate $x(n)$, the Inverse Discrete Fourier Transform *(IDFT)* of $X(k)$? We will show that the inverse transform of $X(k)$ can be written as

$$x(n) = \frac{1}{N} \left[\sum_{k=0}^{N-1} X^*(k)e^{-j(2\pi/N)nk} \right]^* \quad (7.162)$$

where * denotes complex conjugate. Notice that the summation inside the brackets is mathematically equivalent to evaluating the "DFT" of $X^*(k)$ because k is simply a dummy variable of summation. Thus, given $X(k)$ and a program to compute DFTs we can compute $x(n)$ by the following procedure:

PROCEDURE

1. Find the conjugate $X^*(k)$, i.e., change the sign of the imaginary parts.
2. Use the program to take the DFT of $X^*(k)$.
   The result is the bracketed term in Eq. 7.162.
3. Find the complex conjugate of the result from Step 2 for all n.
4. Multiply by $1/N$.

Proof: We start by writing

$$X(k) = |X(k)|e^{j\angle X(k)} \quad (7.163)$$

and its complex conjugate

$$X^*(k) = |X(k)|e^{-j\angle X(k)} \quad (7.164)$$

and putting Eq. 7.164 into Eq. 7.162 gives

$$x(n) = \frac{1}{N} \left[\sum_{k=0}^{N-1} |X(k)|e^{-j\angle X(k)} \, e^{-j(2\pi/N)nk} \right]^*. \quad (7.165)$$

Since the complex conjugate of a sum is equal to the sum of the complex conjugates, taking the complex conjugate of the bracketed term yields

$$x(n) = \frac{1}{N} \sum_{k=0}^{N-1} |X(k)| e^{j\angle X(k)} e^{j(2\pi/N)nk}$$

$$= \frac{1}{N} \sum_{k=0}^{N-1} X(k) e^{j(2\pi/N)nk} \tag{7.166}$$

which is the definition of the Inverse Discrete Fourier Transform. Notice that if the sequence whose IDFT is to be found is known to be a real sequence, then the results of Step 2 in the procedure must be real numbers. This means that Step 3 can be skipped in such cases.

7.6.5 Duality and the DFT

Earlier in the chapter we noticed the similarity of $x(n)$ and $X(k)$ for the unit sample sequence and a constant sequence, respectively. This is more than an accident, in fact, in general

$$x(n) \longleftrightarrow X(k)$$

$$\frac{1}{N} X(n) \longleftrightarrow x(-k). \tag{7.167}$$

Proof: From the definitions of the DFT and the IDFT

$$X(k) = \sum_{n=0}^{N-1} x(n) e^{-j(2\pi/N)nk} \tag{7.168}$$

and

$$x(n) = \frac{1}{N} \sum_{k=0}^{N-1} X(k) e^{j(2\pi/N)nk}. \tag{7.169}$$

We can rewrite Eq. 7.169 using "neutral" symbols (not k or n) as

$$x(\ell) = \frac{1}{N} \sum_{r=0}^{N-1} X(r) e^{j(2\pi/N)\ell r}. \tag{7.170}$$

Then

$$x(-\ell) = \frac{1}{N} \sum_{r=0}^{N-1} X(r) e^{-j(2\pi/N)\ell r} \tag{7.171}$$

and letting $\ell = k$, $r = n$ and moving $1/N$ inside the summation gives us

$$x(-k) = \sum_{n=0}^{N-1} \underbrace{\frac{X(n)}{N}} e^{-j(2\pi/N)nk} \tag{7.172}$$

$$\underbrace{\hspace{4cm}}$$
$$\text{IDFT OF } x(-k)$$

where comparison with Eq. 7.168 shows us that $x(-k)$ is the DFT of $X(n)/N$ or equivalently, that $X(n)/N$ is the IDFT of $x(-k)$. Thus, duality has been proved.

Example 7.16. This example illustrates the duality principle. ⎯⎯⎯⎯⎯

Start with $x(n) = \cos(2\pi n/N)$, $n = 0, 1, \ldots, N - 1$ and $x(n) = 0$, elsewhere as shown in Fig. 7.30(a) for $N = 8$. Complete the relationships below by using the duality principle. That is, find $X(k)$, $\frac{1}{N}X(n)$, and $x(-k)$.

$$x(n) = \cos(2\pi n/N) \longleftrightarrow X(k) = ?$$

$$\frac{1}{N}X(n) = ? \longleftrightarrow x(-k) = ? \tag{7.173}$$

Solution: From the Euler relation

$$x(n) = \cos(2\pi n/N)$$

$$= \frac{1}{2}\left[e^{j2\pi n/N} + e^{-j2\pi n/N}\right] \tag{7.174}$$

and the DFT of Eq. 7.174 is

$$X(k) = \frac{1}{2}\left[\sum_{n=0}^{N-1} e^{j2\pi n/N}\, e^{-j2\pi nk/N} + \sum_{n=0}^{N-1} e^{-j2\pi n/N}\, e^{-j2\pi nk/N}\right]. \tag{7.175}$$

This can be rearranged into the form

$$X(k) = \frac{1}{2}\left[\sum_{n=0}^{N-1} e^{j(2\pi n/N)(1-k)} + \sum_{n=0}^{N-1} e^{j(2\pi n/N)(-1-k)}\right]. \tag{7.176}$$

Using the formula for a finite geometric series we can write

$$\sum_{n=0}^{N-1} e^{j(2\pi(1-k)/N)n} = \sum_{n=0}^{N-1} 1 \qquad \text{for } k = 1$$

$$= N, \tag{7.177}$$

and

$$\sum_{n=0}^{N-1} e^{j(2\pi(1-k)/N)n} = \frac{1 - e^{j2\pi[1-k]}}{1 - e^{j2\pi[1-k]N}} \qquad \text{for } k \ne 1$$

$$= 0. \tag{7.178}$$

Now consider the second sum in Eq. 7.176. Following the approach which led to Eqs. 7.177 and 7.178 gives

$$\sum_{n=0}^{N-1} e^{j(2\pi(-1-k)/N)n} = \begin{cases} N, & k = -1 \quad \text{or} \quad k = N - 1 \\ 0, & k \ne -1 \quad \text{or} \quad k \ne N - 1 \end{cases} \tag{7.179}$$

FIGURE 7.30 The duality principle—Example 7.16

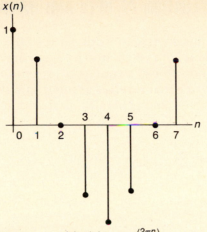

x(n)

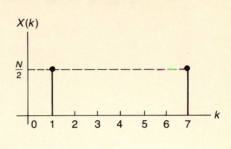

X(k)

(a) $x(n) = \cos\left(\dfrac{2\pi n}{N}\right)$

(b) $X(k) = \dfrac{N}{2}\delta(k-1) + \dfrac{N}{2}\delta(k-N+1)$

$x(-k) = x(k)$

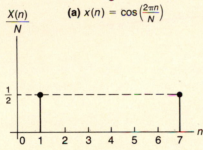

$\dfrac{X(n)}{N}$

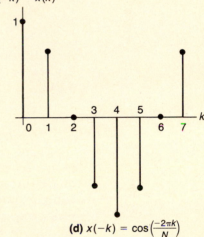

(c) $\dfrac{X(n)}{N} = \dfrac{1}{2}\delta(n-1) + \dfrac{1}{2}\delta(n-N+1)$

(d) $x(-k) = \cos\left(\dfrac{-2\pi k}{N}\right)$

and using the shifted sample function to simplify matters we have

$$X(k) = \frac{N}{2}\delta(k-1) + \frac{N}{2}\delta(k-N+1) \qquad (7.180)$$

as portrayed in Fig. 7.30(b). Next, we form $\dfrac{1}{N}X(n)$ as

$$\frac{1}{N}X(n) = \frac{1}{2}\delta(n-1) + \frac{1}{2}\delta(n-N+1) \qquad (7.181)$$

and using Eq. 7.173 we see that

$$x(-k) = \cos(-2\pi k/N) = \cos(2\pi k/N). \qquad (7.182)$$

Figures 7.30(c) and 7.30(d) complete the pictorial representation of the duality property as applied to this example.

While it may be instructive to work out the DFT (or DFS) coefficients by hand (or with the aid of a calculator) for sequences with only a few points, in general, we want to use a computer program. Let us consider how to develop a subroutine that receives as input data the sequence values $x(n)$, $n = 0, 1, \ldots, N - 1$ and generates as its output the DFT coefficients $X(k)$, $k = 0, 1, \ldots, N - 1$ where

$$X(k) = \sum_{n=0}^{N-1} x(n)e^{-j(2\pi/N)nk}, \qquad k = 0, 1, \ldots, N - 1. \qquad (7.183)$$

For convenience, let us define $\alpha = 2\pi/N$ and $W = e^{-j\alpha}$. We can then express $X(k)$ as

$$X(k) = \sum_{n=0}^{N-1} x(n)W^{nk}, \qquad k = 0, 1, \ldots, N - 1. \qquad (7.184)$$

As in the development of the pseudocode for the frequency response of a discrete system, we can make use here of the "nested form" (see Eq. 4.146)

$$X(k) = (\ldots.((x[N - 1]W^k + x[N - 2])W^k + x[N - 3])W^k + \cdots \\ + x[1])W^k + x(0), \qquad k = 0, 1, \ldots, N - 1 \qquad (7.185)$$

Using Eq. 7.185 as the starting point we are now ready to write the pseudocode for the DFT subroutine. For generality, and for later use in evaluating inverse DFTs, we assume that the input data—the $x(n)$'s—are complex numbers. The input data are assumed to be stored in the complex array $XN(0), XN(1), \ldots, XN(N - 1)$ and the resulting output data are put in the array $XK(0), XK(1), \ldots, XK(N - 1)$. The pseudocode for the DFT subroutine is rather short and is shown in Fig. 7.31. As we did earlier in Chapter Four we assume that the target computer language includes the intrinsic functions COS and SIN for computing the cosine and sine, respectively.

We can also make use of the DFT subroutine to compute inverse DFTs by taking advantage of the alternate inversion formula that is repeated here for convenience

$$x(n) = \frac{1}{N} \left[\sum_{k=0}^{N-1} X^*(k)e^{-j(2\pi/N)nk} \right]^*, \qquad n = 0, 1, \ldots, N - 1. \qquad (7.186)$$

The inverse DFT subroutine assumes that the input data are in the array $XN(0), XN(1), \ldots, XN(N - 1)$. We simply take the complex conjugate of each member of the input array, take the DFT of the resulting array, again conjugate each member of the array and divide each array element by N.

```
SUBROUTINE DFT(N, XN, XK)

(This subroutine computes the DFT of the input data stored in the complex
array XN(0), XN(1),..., XN(N-1) and the output data are stored in the
complex array XK(0), XK(1),...,XK(N-1))

PI ⟵ 3.141593

IF    N=1    THEN

    XK(0) ⟵ XN(0)

ELSE

    ALPHA ⟵ 2·PI/N

    W ⟵ CMPLX(COS(ALPHA), -SIN(ALPHA))

    DO FOR K ⟵ 0   TO   N-1

        WM ⟵ W^k

    (W^k = e^{-j2πk/N})

        XK(k) ⟵ XN(N-1)

        DO FOR   L ⟵ (N-2)   TO   0   BY   STEPS   OF   -1

            XK(K) ⟵ XK(K)·WM + XN(L)

        END DO

    END DO

END IF

RETURN

END DFT
```

FIGURE 7.31   Pseudocode
for DFT subroutine

Figure 7.32 illustrates pseudocode for accomplishing the inverse DFT. We
assume the availability of an intrinsic function CONJG(X) which produces as its output the complex conjugate of the complex number X.

Translation of the pseudocode for the DFT and inverse DFT into a
working program is left as an exercise for the reader (see Problem 7.33).
Notice that a handy way to check the program, after trying some simple
sequences whose DFTs are known, is to define an arbitrary sequence,
evaluate its DFT, and then use this DFT as the input data to the inverse
DFT subroutine. If the result of this DFT/inverse DFT process is the
original input sequence, then we have some confidence that the program
is working correctly. Of course, we need to do more extensive testing to
be sure.

```
SUBROUTINE INVDFT(N, XN, XK)

(This subroutine computes the inverse DFT of the data stored in the
complex array XN(0), XN(1),..., XN(N-1) and stores the result in the
complex array XK(0), XK(1), ..., XK(N-1).  This subroutine calls the
subroutine DFT)

(Conjugate the elements of the input array)

DO FOR    I←——0  TO N-1

    XN(I)←——— CONJG(XN(I))

END DO
(Call the DFT subroutine)
CALL DFT(N, XN, XK)

(Conjugate the output entries from the subroutine DFT and divide each by N)

DO FOR I←——0 TO N-1

    XK(I)←——— CONJG(XK(I))/N

END DO

RETURN

END INVDFT
```

FIGURE 7.32 Pseudocode
for inverse DFT subroutine

7.8 ▬ ANOTHER LOOK AT CONVOLUTION

Convolution was introduced in Chapter Three and its role in the analysis
of LTI systems was explained and illustrated by several examples. We
recall that the convolution operation is defined by

$$x_1(n) * x_2(n) = \sum_{m=-\infty}^{\infty} x_1(m)\, x_2(n-m). \qquad (7.187)$$

We refer to this as *linear convolution* because in this section we develop
another kind of convolution, called *circular convolution*, which also
plays a central role in many signal processing situations.

We would like to determine the time-domain relationship that corresponds to multiplying together two DFTs. That is, if

$$X_3(k) = X_1(k)\, X_2(k) \qquad (7.188)$$

how is $x_3(n)$, the inverse DFT of $X_3(k)$, related to $x_1(n)$ and $x_2(n)$, the
inverse DFTs of $X_1(k)$ and $X_2(k)$? To begin, let's consider the closely related problem of finding the corresponding relationship for periodic sequences and their Discrete Fourier Series coefficients.

7.8.1 Periodic Convolution

Consider the two periodic sequences $x_{1p}(n)$ and $x_{2p}(n)$ that have the same period N with the DFS coefficients

$$X_{1p}(k) = \sum_{\ell=0}^{\ell=N-1} x_{1p}(\ell) e^{j(2\pi/N)(-\ell k)}$$

$$X_{2p}(k) = \sum_{r=0}^{r=N-1} x_{2p}(r) e^{j(2\pi/N)(-rk)}. \tag{7.189}$$

Now, if we have the third set of coefficients $X_{3p}(k)$ defined by

$$X_{3p}(k) = X_{1p}(k) X_{2p}(k) \tag{7.190}$$

we want to relate $x_{3p}(n)$ to $x_{1p}(n)$ and $x_{2p}(n)$. Substituting the expressions of Eq. 7.189 into Eq. 7.190 gives

$$X_{3p}(k) = \sum_{\ell=0}^{N-1} \sum_{r=0}^{N-1} x_{1p}(\ell)\, x_{2p}(r)\, e^{j(2\pi/N)(-\ell k - rk)} \tag{7.191}$$

and the periodic sequence $x_{3p}(n)$ is given by

$$x_{3p}(n) = \frac{1}{N} \sum_{k=0}^{N-1} X_{3p}(k) e^{j(2\pi/N)(nk)}. \tag{7.192}$$

Substituting Eq. 7.191 into Eq. 7.192 gives us the rather complicated expression

$$x_{3p}(n) = \frac{1}{N} \sum_{k=0}^{N-1} \sum_{\ell=0}^{N-1} \sum_{r=0}^{N-1} x_{2p}(r)\, x_{1p}(\ell)\, e^{j(2\pi/N)(-\ell k - rk + nk)}. \tag{7.193}$$

By changing the order of summations this can be written in the form

$$x_{3p}(n) = \frac{1}{N} \sum_{\ell=0}^{N-1} x_{1p}(\ell) \sum_{r=0}^{N-1} x_{2p}(r) \left[\sum_{k=0}^{N-1} e^{j(2\pi/N)(-\ell - r + n)k} \right]. \tag{7.194}$$

Considering only the bracketed term in Eq. 7.194 which is

$$\sum_{k=0}^{N-1} e^{j(2\pi/N)(-\ell - r + n)k} \tag{7.195}$$

we note that with $-\ell - r + n = 0$ the summand is simply 1 and so the corresponding sum is N. We can also use the identity for a finite geometric sum when $-\ell - r + n \neq 0$ to obtain

$$\sum_{k=0}^{N-1} e^{j(2\pi/N)(-\ell - r + n)k} = \frac{1 - e^{j(2\pi/N)(-\ell - r + n)N}}{1 - e^{j(2\pi/N)(-\ell - r + n)}} = 0. \tag{7.196}$$

Putting these results together we have

$$\sum_{k=0}^{N-1} e^{j(2\pi/N)(-\ell-r+n)k} = \begin{cases} N \text{ for } -\ell - r + n = 0 \\ 0 \text{ for } -\ell - r + n \neq 0. \end{cases} \tag{7.197}$$

As in Section 7.3 (see Eq. 7.62), we can describe Eq. 7.197 in terms of a shifted weighted impulse

$$\sum_{k=0}^{N-1} e^{j(2\pi/N)(-\ell-r+n)k} = N\delta(-\ell - r + n). \tag{7.198}$$

Consequently the expression for $x_{3p}(n)$, Eq. 7.194, can be written as

$$x_{3p}(n) = \frac{1}{N} \sum_{\ell=0}^{N-1} x_{1p}(\ell) \sum_{r=0}^{N-1} x_{2p}(r) N\delta(-\ell - r + n)$$

$$= \sum_{\ell=0}^{N-1} x_{1p}(\ell) x_{2p}(n - \ell). \tag{7.199}$$

This is the case because $\delta(-\ell - r + n)$ is 0 except for $r = n - \ell$ where it is 1. Notice the similarity of this result to the familiar operation of linear convolution in Eq. 7.187. There is, however, an important difference—the operation in Eq. 7.199 is carried out only over one period and hence is referred to as *periodic convolution*. This process of periodic convolution of sequences which was derived from the multiplication of their respective Fourier coefficients is often shown as

$$\boxed{x_{3p}(n) = \sum_{\ell=0}^{N-1} x_{1p}(\ell) x_{2p}(n - \ell) \longleftrightarrow X_{3p}(k) = X_{1p}(k) X_{2p}(k)} \tag{7.200}$$

where the double arrow again indicates the "goes either way" nature of these processes.

Example 7.17. This example illustrates the process of performing periodic convolution.

Determine the periodic convolution of the periodic sequences $x_{1p}(n)$ and $x_{2p}(n)$ of length $N = 3$ as shown in Fig. 7.33(a). To keep things simple, $x_{1p}(n)$ and $x_{2p}(n)$ are identical.

Solution: In Fig. 7.33(b) $x_{1p}(\ell)$ and the folded sequence $x_{2p}(-\ell)$ are shown. Next we have the product $x_{1p}(\ell) x_{2p}(-\ell)$ in Fig. 7.33(c). Note carefully that the product is determined only for one period. The value of the periodic convolution for $n = 0$ is then determined from Eq. 7.200 as

$$x_{3p}(0) = \sum_{\ell=0}^{\ell=2} x_{1p}(\ell) x_{2p}(0 - \ell) = 9 + 2 + 2 = 13. \tag{7.201}$$

FIGURE 7.33 Steps in
carrying out periodic convolution

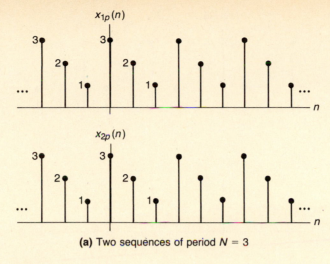

(a) Two sequences of period $N = 3$

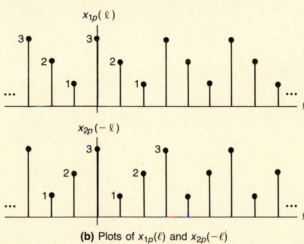

(b) Plots of $x_{1p}(\ell)$ and $x_{2p}(-\ell)$

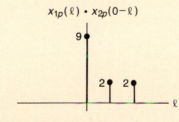

(c) The product $x_{1p}(\ell) \cdot x_{2p}(-\ell)$

FIGURE 7.33 (cont.)

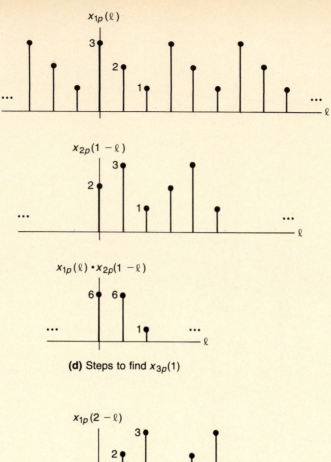

$x_{1p}(\ell)$

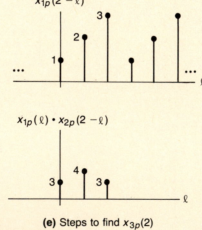

$x_{2p}(1 - \ell)$

$x_{1p}(\ell) \cdot x_{2p}(1 - \ell)$

(d) Steps to find $x_{3p}(1)$

$x_{1p}(2 - \ell)$

$x_{1p}(\ell) \cdot x_{2p}(2 - \ell)$

(e) Steps to find $x_{3p}(2)$

For $n = 1$ we have $x_{1p}(\ell)$, $x_{2p}(1 - \ell)$ and their product $x_{1p}(\ell)\,x_{2p}(1 - \ell)$ as in Fig. 7.33(d) with the value at $n = 1$ determined to be

$$x_{3p}(1) = \sum_{\ell=0}^{\ell=2} x_{1p}(\ell)x_{2p}(1 - \ell) = 6 + 6 + 1 = 13. \qquad (7.202)$$

Finally, $x_{3p}(n)$ for $n = 2$ comes from Fig. 7.33(e) as

$$x_{3p}(2) = 3 + 4 + 3 = 10. \qquad (7.203)$$

It is easily seen that for $n = 3, 4, 5, \ldots$ the same pictures are repeated. Thus, this convolution-like operation of two periodic sequences leads to a periodic result (of the same period) as seen in Fig. 7.34.

An easy way to visualize periodic convolution graphically is as an adaptation of the "sliding-bar" method for linear convolution given in Chapter Three. We begin by writing the samples of one of the sequences, say $x_{1p}(\ell)$, counterclockwise around a circle with the samples equally spaced as in Fig. 7.35(a). Next, on a concentric inner circle we write the values of the other sequence, here $x_{2p}(\ell)$, in a clockwise or "flipped" order as in Fig. 7.35(b). To compute $x_{3p}(n)$ we form the products of the matched up samples on both circles and add the results. From Fig. 7.35(b) the result is

$$x_{3p}(0) = (3 \times 3) + (2 \times 1) + (1 \times 2) = 13. \qquad (7.204)$$

Next, we rotate the inner circle (the outer circle is fixed) in a counter-clockwise direction an amount $2\pi/N$ radians (in this case $2\pi/3$) as in Fig. 7.35(c), the matched up samples are multiplied and the results added giving

$$x_{3p}(1) = (3 \times 2) + (2 \times 3) + (1 \times 1) = 13. \qquad (7.205)$$

Finally, Fig. 7.35(d) shows another rotation of the inner circle counter-clockwise by $2\pi/3$ radians and carrying out the multiplications and additions gives

$$x_{3p}(2) = (3 \times 1) + (2 \times 2) + (1 \times 3) = 10. \qquad (7.206)$$

The interpretation of periodic convolution pictured in Fig. 7.35 as the interaction of concentric circles on which the data for the sequences are

FIGURE 7.34 Result of periodic convolution

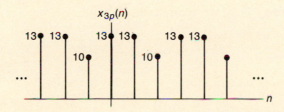

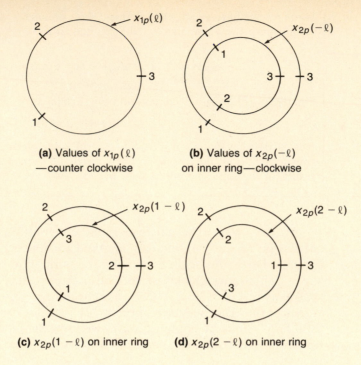

FIGURE 7.35 Set-up for periodic convolution

(a) Values of $x_{1p}(\ell)$
—counter clockwise

(b) Values of $x_{2p}(-\ell)$
on inner ring—clockwise

(c) $x_{2p}(1 - \ell)$ on inner ring

(d) $x_{2p}(2 - \ell)$ on inner ring

written motivates the notation

$$x_{3p}(n) = x_{1p}(n) \circledast x_{2p}(n)$$

$$= \sum_{\ell=0}^{N-1} x_{1p}(\ell)x_{2p}(n - \ell) \qquad (7.207)$$

that is often used to distinguish periodic convolution from linear convolution.

Example 7.18. This example illustrates periodic convolution computed from the Fourier coefficients.

Let's redo the periodic convolution problem of Example 7.17 from the point of view of the Fourier coefficients. That is, compute $X_{3p}(k) = X_{1p}(k)\, X_{2p}(k)$ and then find the corresponding sequence $x_{3p}(n)$.

Solution: First, we compute $X_{1p}(k)$ from

$$X_{1p}(k) = \sum_{n=0}^{n=2} x_{1p}(n)e^{j(2\pi/3)(-nk)}. \qquad (7.208)$$

This was done in Example 7.2 with the results

$$X_{1p}(0) = 6, \ X_{1p}(1) = \sqrt{3}\, e^{-j\pi/6} \quad \text{and} \quad X_{1p}(2) = \sqrt{3}\, e^{j\pi/6}. \qquad (7.209)$$

Since in this simplified problem $x_{1p}(n) = x_{2p}(n)$, we can write

$$X_{2p}(0) = 6, \; X_{2p}(1) = \sqrt{3}\,e^{-j\pi/6} \quad \text{and} \quad X_{2p}(2) = \sqrt{3}\,e^{j\pi/6} \qquad (7.210)$$

and going back to our original definition of Eq. 7.190 we have

$$X_{3p}(k) = X_{1p}(k)X_{2p}(k) \qquad (7.211)$$

which gives

$$X_{3p}(0) = X_{1p}(0)X_{2p}(0) = 36$$

$$X_{3p}(1) = X_{1p}(1)X_{2p}(1) = 3\,e^{-j\pi/3}$$

$$X_{3p}(2) = X_{1p}(2)X_{2p}(2) = 3\,e^{j\pi/3}. \qquad (7.212)$$

The sequence $x_{3p}(n)$ comes from

$$x_{3p}(n) = \frac{1}{3}\sum_{k=0}^{k=2} X_{3p}(k)e^{j(2\pi/3)(nk)} \qquad (7.213)$$

where the value of $x_{3p}(n)$ for $n = 0$ is

$$x_{3p}(0) = \frac{1}{3}[X_{3p}(0) + X_{3p}(1) + X_{3p}(2)]$$

$$= \frac{1}{3}[36 + 3e^{-j\pi/3} + 3e^{j\pi/3}] = 13 \qquad (7.214)$$

and for $n = 1$ we have

$$x_{3p}(1) = \frac{1}{3}[X_{3p}(0) + X_{3p}(1)e^{j2\pi/3} + X_{3p}(2)e^{j4\pi/3}]$$

$$= \frac{1}{3}[36 + 3e^{-j\pi/3}e^{j2\pi/3} + 3e^{j\pi/3}e^{j4\pi/3}] = 13 \qquad (7.215)$$

with the value for $n = 2$ being

$$x_{3p}(2) = \frac{1}{3}[X_{3p}(0) + X_{3p}(1)e^{j4\pi/3} + X_{3p}(2)e^{j8\pi/3}]$$

$$= \frac{1}{3}[36 + 3e^{-j\pi/3}e^{j4\pi/3} + 3e^{j\pi/3}e^{j8\pi/3}] = 10. \qquad (7.216)$$

The two preceding examples illustrate that the periodic convolution of two sequences can be determined in either of two ways: (1) by remaining in the time (n) domain and evaluating the periodic convolution sum in Eq. 7.200 directly; or (2) by utilizing the frequency (k) domain by computing the DFS of the two sequences, multiplying these together, and then using the synthesis (or inverse DFS) relationship of Eq. 7.65. We will see in Chapter Eight why the second approach is often advantageous in applications.

7.8.2 Circular Convolution

Now suppose we have two finite sequences $x_1(n)$ and $x_2(n)$ of duration N whose DFTs are $X_1(k)$ and $X_2(k)$. If $X_3(k)$ is defined as $X_1(k)X_2(k)$, where $x_3(n)$ is the sequence whose DFT is $X_3(k)$, how are $x_1(n)$, $x_2(n)$, and $x_3(n)$ related? From our previous considerations we know that

$x_1(n)$ is one period of a periodic sequence $x_{1p}(n)$

$x_2(n)$ is one period of a periodic sequence $x_{2p}(n)$

$X_1(k)$ is one period of a periodic sequence $X_{1p}(k)$

$X_2(k)$ is one period of a periodic sequence $X_{2p}(k)$

Therefore, $X_3(k)$ is one period of $X_{3p}(k)$, and $x_3(n)$ is one period of $x_{3p}(n)$, and from Section 7.8.1

$$x_{3p}(n) = \sum_{\ell=0}^{N-1} x_{1p}(\ell)\, x_{2p}(n - \ell) \qquad (7.217)$$

which is simply the definition of the periodic convolution

$$x_{3p}(n) = x_{1p}(n) \circledast x_{2p}(n). \qquad (7.218)$$

This allows us to state that

$$x_3(n) = \text{one period of } \left[\sum_{\ell=0}^{N-1} x_{1p}(\ell)\, x_{2p}(n - \ell) \right]$$

$$= \text{one period of } [x_{1p}(n) \circledast x_{2p}(n)]$$

$$= x_1(n) \circledast x_2(n). \qquad (7.219)$$

We define this operation as *circular convolution*.

Symbolically, we can say that if

$$x_1(n) \longleftrightarrow X_1(k)$$

$$x_2(n) \longleftrightarrow X_2(k)$$

$$x_3(n) \longleftrightarrow X_3(k) \qquad (7.220)$$

and, if we define $X_3(k)$ as the product of $X_1(k)$ and $X_2(k)$, or

$$X_3(k) = X_1(k)X_2(k) \qquad (7.221)$$

then $x_3(n)$ is the circular convolution of $x_1(n)$ and $x_2(n)$, or

$$x_3(n) = x_1(n) \circledast x_2(n). \qquad (7.222)$$

It is important to note that the circular convolution $x_1(n) \circledast x_2(n)$ is short-hand notation for "one period of the periodic convolution of $x_{1p}(n)$ and

$x_{2p}(n)$." And using $\mathcal{D}$ to denote the process of taking the Discrete Fourier Transform (DFT) of a sequence we can write

$$\mathcal{D}[x_1(n) \circledast x_2(n)] = X_1(k)X_2(k) \qquad (7.223)$$

which tells us that the circular convolution of two sequences corresponds to a multiplication of their respective DFTs. Again, we can use a double-ended arrow to portray the process, namely

$$x_1(n) \circledast x_2(n) \longleftrightarrow X_1(k)X_2(k). \qquad (7.224)$$

Example 7.19. This example illustrates a comparison of linear and circular convolution.

Consider the two identical sequences of Fig. 7.36(a). In Fig. 7.36(b) the result of one period of the periodic convolution of $x_{1p}(n)$ and $x_{2p}(n)$ is shown as determined in Example 7.18. For comparison, let's compute the linear convolution of the finite duration sequences $x_1(n)$ and $x_2(n)$, i.e.,

$$x_3'(n) = \sum_{\ell=-\infty}^{\ell=+\infty} x_1(\ell) x_2(n - \ell) \qquad (7.225)$$

that, using the notation of Chapter Three, is

$$x_3'(n) = x_1(n) * x_2(n). \qquad (7.226)$$

Solution: The easily verified results are given in Fig. 7.36(c).

FIGURE 7.36 Circular and linear convolution

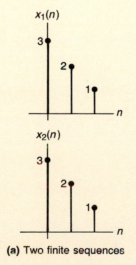

(a) Two finite sequences

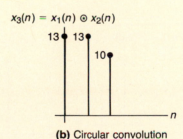

(b) Circular convolution

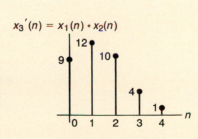

(c) Linear convolution

Comment: Comparing $x_3(n)$ and $x_3'(n)$ we see that not only are the numerical values different, but the lengths of the sequences are not even the same; $x_3(n)$ is of length 3 and $x_3'(n)$ has length 5. Next, we ask if there are any circumstances wherein the results of doing linear and circular convolution of two sequences are the same. The answer is yes, provided that certain conditions are met. The circular convolution of the two sequences of Fig. 7.36(a) resulted in $x_3(n)$, as shown in Fig. 7.36(b). Now suppose $x_1(n)$ and $x_2(n)$ are augmented with zeros and periodically extended to give the sequences $x_{1p}'(n)$ and $x_{2p}'(n)$ as shown in Fig. 7.37(a). What is the periodic convolution of these sequences? Using the concentric ring maneuver of Section 7.8.1 (see Fig. 7.37(b)) and taking one period of the result gives us $x_3'(n)$ shown in Fig. 7.37(c) where we see that the result of this five-point circular convolution is the same as that obtained from linear convolution. The fact that this circular convolution equals the linear convolution is extremely important in many signal processing applications. We expand on this after a few preliminaries.

FIGURE 7.37 Forcing circular convolution to equal linear convolution

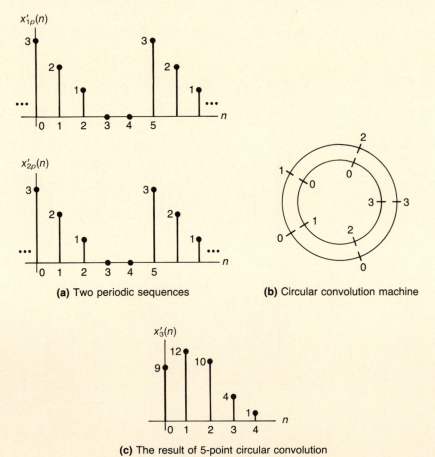

(a) Two periodic sequences

(b) Circular convolution machine

(c) The result of 5-point circular convolution

CHAPTER 7 DISCRETE FOURIER TRANSFORM

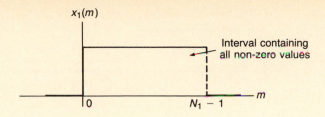

FIGURE 7.38 A graphical display of linear convolution

$x_1(m)$

Interval containing all non-zero values

0 $N_1 - 1$ m

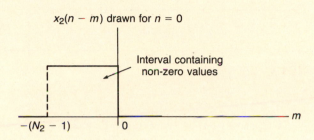

$x_2(n - m)$ drawn for $n = 0$

Interval containing non-zero values

$-(N_2 - 1)$ 0 m

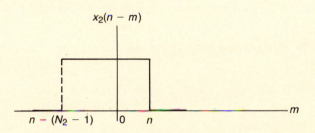

$x_2(n - m)$

$n - (N_2 - 1)$ 0 n m

The linear convolution of a sequence having N_1 samples with a sequence having N_2 samples will result, in general, in a sequence of $N_1 + N_2 - 1$ samples in length. This can easily be seen from the representations shown in Fig. 7.38. As the $x_2(n - m)$ sequence slides to the right for positive and increasing n, it will overlap the $x_1(m)$ sequence from $n = 0$ until the left edge of $x_2(n - m)$ has moved to the right of $m = N_1 - 1$. This occurs when $n - (N_2 - 1) = N_1$ or where $n = N_1 + N_2 - 1$. Thus, the linear convolution will have all of its nonzero values in the interval $0 \le n \le N_1 + N_2 - 2$, a total of $N_1 + N_2 - 1$ points. (The convolution result could just as well begin at $n = n_0$ rather than $n = 0$. The nonzero interval would be $n_0 \le n \le n_0 + N_1 + N_2 - 2$, still a total of $N_1 + N_2 - 1$ points.) We see in Fig. 7.39(a) that if a sequence of duration N_1 is followed by $(N_2 - 1)$ zero values the resulting sequence which has $N_1 + N_2 - 1$ values can be circularly convolved with another sequence of length N_2 augmented by $(N_1 - 1)$ zero values as in Fig. 7.39(b) and the result is the same as if linear convolution had been performed. That is, circular convolution produces the same result as linear convolution with a proper choice for the number of points in the circular convolution. From Fig. 7.39 it can be seen that at least $N_1 + N_2 - 1$ points must be used.

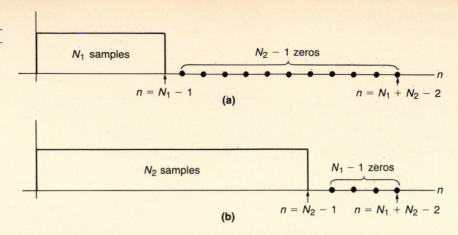

FIGURE 7.39 Zero padding to make circular convolution yield the same result as linear convolution

At this point it is reasonable to ask why the interest in making the linear and circular convolutions identical? By doing this the linear convolution of two sequences $x_1(n)$ and $x_2(n)$ can be obtained in either of two ways:

1. The convolution sum can be evaluated directly from

$$x_3(n) = x_1(n) * x_2(n) = \sum_{\ell=-\infty}^{\ell=+\infty} x_1(\ell)\, x_2(n-\ell). \qquad (7.227)$$

2. The convolution can be found from the inverse DFT of $X_1(k)X_2(k)$ provided that the linear and circular convolutions are the same. That is,

$$x_3'(n) = x_1'(n) \circledast x_2'(n) = \text{IDFT}\,[X_1'(k)X_2'(k)$$
$$= \mathscr{D}^{-1}\,[X_1'(k)X_2'(k)] \qquad (7.228)$$

where $x_1'(n)$ and $x_2'(n)$ are $x_1(n)$ and $x_2(n)$ augmented by an appropriate number of zeros. The diagram of Fig. 7.40 illustrates this procedure.

To illustrate this DFT approach, let's consider again the example done previously by using linear convolution directly. We'll show that DFTs yield the same results.

FIGURE 7.40 Linear convolution implemented by DFT and IDFT

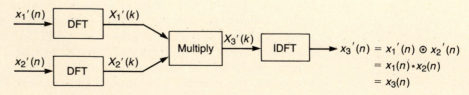

CHAPTER 7 DISCRETE FOURIER TRANSFORM

Example 7.20. This example illustrates that circular convolution of sequences augmented by enough zeros gives the same results as linear convolution.

Determine the linear convolution of the sequences $x_1(n) = x_2(n)$ shown in Fig. 7.41(a) by the DFT approach.

Solution: The sequences are of length 3, but instead of finding the three-point DFTs, we append two additional zero values to each sequence to give sequences of length $N_1 + N_2 - 1 = 3 + 3 - 1 = 5$. This is shown in Fig. 7.41(b). From Eq. 7.88 the DFTs are

$$X_1'(k) = X_2'(k) = \sum_{n=0}^{n=4} x_1'(n)e^{-j(2\pi/5)nk}, \; k = 0, 1, 2, 3, 4 \qquad (7.229)$$

and after inserting the $3 - 2 - 1 - 0 - 0$ sequence for $x_1'(n)$ and writing out the terms we obtain

$$X_1'(k) = X_2'(k) = 3e^{-j0} + 2e^{-j(2\pi/5)1 \cdot k} + 1e^{-j(2\pi/5)2 \cdot k}, \; k = 0, 1, 2, 3, 4. \quad (7.230)$$

Using a computer program based on the DFT pseudocode of Section 7.7 and developed in Problem 7.33 gives

$$X_1'(0) = X_2'(0) = 6$$

$$X_1'(1) = X_2'(1) = 3.754e^{-j0.725} \qquad X_1'(3) = X_2'(3) = 1.706e^{j0.132}$$

$$X_1'(2) = X_2'(2) = 1.706e^{-j0.132} \qquad X_1'(4) = X_2'(4) = 3.754e^{j0.725}. \quad (7.231)$$

FIGURE 7.41 Shows that zero padding can produce linear convolution.

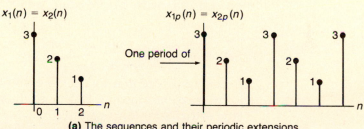

(a) The sequences and their periodic extensions

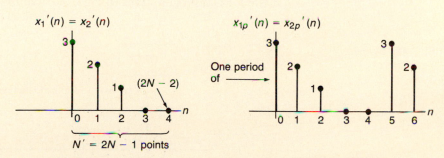

(b) The sequences augmented by zeros and their periodic extensions

Now $X_3'(k) = X_1'(k)X_2'(k)$ so we have

$$X_3'(0) = 36 \qquad\qquad X_3'(3) = 2.910e^{j0.264}$$

$$X_3'(1) = 14.093e^{-j1.450} \qquad X_3'(4) = 14.093e^{j1.450}$$

$$X_3'(2) = 2.910e^{-j0.264} \tag{7.232}$$

The IDFT (Inverse Discrete Fourier Transform) is calculated from Eq. (7.89) as

$$x_3'(n) = \frac{1}{N} \sum_{k=0}^{N-1} X_3'(k)e^{j(2\pi/N)nk}, \; n = 0, 1, 2, 3, 4 \tag{7.233}$$

or

$$x_3'(n) = \frac{1}{5}[36 + 14.093e^{-j1.450}e^{j(2\pi/5)n} + 2.910e^{-j0.264}e^{j(2\pi/5)2n}$$

$$+ \; 2.910e^{j0.264}e^{j(2\pi/5)3n} + 14.093e^{j1.450}e^{j(2\pi/5)4n}], \; n = 0, 1, 2, 3, 4. \tag{7.234}$$

Evaluating $x_3'(n)$ we find, as before, that

$$x_3'(0) = 9, \; x_3'(1) = 12, \; x_3'(2) = 10, \; x_3'(3) = 4, \text{ and } x_3'(4) = 1. \tag{7.235}$$

Now that we know that linear convolution can be performed using DFTs it is appropriate to ask if there is some benefit to doing this. As a basis for comparison, we use the number of multiplies required as a measure of computational complexity and contrast the direct approach for doing convolution with that of the DFT method. For the direct evaluation, we start with two N-point sequences and evaluate

$$y(n) = \sum_{m=-\infty}^{\infty} h(m)x(n-m), \qquad n = n_0, \dots, n_0 + 2N - 2. \tag{7.236}$$

We can easily see that to calculate all of the $(2N - 1)$ nonzero points of $y(n)$ we need to multiply each nonzero value of $h(m)$ with each nonzero value of $x(n - m)$. This requires $N \times N = N^2$ multiplies of the real numbers that are data values for $h(m)$ and $x(n - m)$.

For the DFT approach, refer to Fig. 7.42. We first zero pad each of the

FIGURE 7.42 Machine implementation of linear convolution

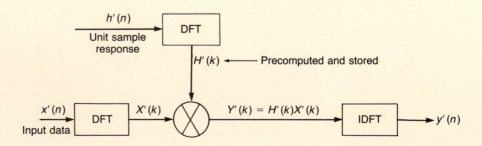

CHAPTER 7 DISCRETE FOURIER TRANSFORM

sequences $h(n)$ and $x(n)$ to $2N$ points—actually $(2N - 1)$ points could be used, but, for simplicity, we use $2N$. To determine the DFTs of $x'(n)$ and $h'(n)$ we evaluate

$$X'(k) = \sum_{n=0}^{2N-1} x'(n)e^{-j(2\pi/(2N))nk}, \qquad k = 0, 1, \ldots, 2N - 1 \quad (7.237)$$

and a similar expression for $H'(k)$. For each value of k we need to multiply the $x'(n)$ values and the complex exponentials. Assuming that the DFT program accepts complex input data, this requires $2N$ complex multiplies and there are $2N$ values of $X'(k)$ to be so obtained. This requires, therefore,

$$2N \times 2N = 4N^2 \qquad complex \text{ multiplies} \quad (7.238)$$

for each $2N$-point DFT. There are three such DFTs needed. (Actually 2 DFTs and an inverse DFT are required, but, by using the alternate inversion formula we see that the multiplies required for an IDFT are essentially the same except for the postmultiplication by the $1/N$ factor which we do not include in our considerations.) Finally, we need to multiply together $X'(k)$ and $H'(k)$ and this requires $2N$ complex multiplies. The total necessary for the DFT approach is then approximately

$$(2N \times 2N) \times 3 + 2N = 12N^2 + 2N \quad (7.239)$$

and these are complex multiplies. To compare with our earlier expression for direct convolution we convert this to real multiplies by including a factor of 4 to give $4 \times (12N^2 + 2N) = 48N^2 + 8N$ real multiplies. For large N this can be approximated by $48N^2$ and we see that this is about 50 times the computational cost of doing convolution directly. If there were nothing we could do about this, we would undoubtedly stick to the direct approach. In the next chapter, however, we see that DFTs can be computed with far fewer multiplies than by using the DFT definition. This capability makes indirect convolution not only feasible, but often much faster than the direct approach.

7.8.3 Frequency Convolution

We've just seen that multiplication of DFTs corresponds to circular convolution of the corresponding sequences, that is

$$x_1(n) \circledast x_2(n) \longleftrightarrow X_1(k)X_2(k) \quad (7.240)$$

where we are assuming, of course, that $x_1(n)$ and $x_2(n)$ are finite duration sequences both having the same length N. We might expect, because of the duality property of DFTs, that multiplication of the sequences corresponds to convolution (circular, of course) of their DFTs, and this is indeed the case. This result, known as the *frequency convolution theorem*, is described by

$$x_1(n)x_2(n) \longleftrightarrow \frac{1}{N} \sum_{\ell=0}^{N-1} X_1(\ell)X_2(k-\ell)$$

$$= \frac{1}{N} X_1(k) \circledast X_2(k). \qquad (7.241)$$

The proof of this result is the topic of Problem 7.48.

Now, let's use the frequency convolution theorem to derive another useful result known as the *modulation* or *frequency translation property*. Suppose we have a sequence $x(n)$ that is the product of the sequences $x_1(n)$ and $x_2(n)$, or

$$x(n) = x_1(n)x_2(n) \qquad (7.242)$$

where $x_1(n)$ is the special complex exponential sequence

$$x_1(n) = e^{j(2\pi/N)Mn}, \; M = \text{a constant}, \; 0 \le M \le N. \qquad (7.243)$$

What is the DFT $X(k)$ in terms of $X_2(k)$? First, we need the DFT of $x_1(n)$, namely

$$X_1(k) = \sum_{n=0}^{N-1} e^{j(2\pi/N)Mn} e^{-j(2\pi/N)nk}, \; k = 0, 1, \ldots, N-1$$

$$= \sum_{n=0}^{N-1} e^{j(2\pi/N)(M-k)n}. \qquad (7.244)$$

Now, from the finite geometric series formula we can see that

$$X_1(k) = \begin{cases} N & \text{for } M - k = N, \\ 0 & \text{for } M - k \ne N. \end{cases} \qquad (7.245)$$

As before, this result can be described in a neater fashion by using a shifted sample function which gives us

$$X_1(k) = N\delta(k + N - M) \qquad (7.246)$$

and, because of the periodic nature of the DFT

$$X_1(k) = N\delta(k - M). \qquad (7.247)$$

Recalling that we are trying to find the DFT of $x(n)$, we can use the frequency convolution theorem of Eq. 7.241 to write

$$X(k) = \frac{1}{N} \sum_{\ell=0}^{N-1} X_1(\ell)X_2(k-\ell)$$

$$= \frac{1}{N} \sum_{\ell=0}^{N-1} N\delta(\ell - M)X_2(k-\ell)$$

$$= X_2(k - M). \qquad (7.248)$$

Thus, the modulation or frequency translation property can be represented as

$$x(n) = e^{j(2\pi/N)Mn}x_2(n) \longleftrightarrow X(k) = X_2(k - M) \qquad (7.249)$$

where $0 \le M \le N$ and $\mathcal{D}[x_2(n)] = X_2(k)$. Or, in words, the effect of multiplying the time sequence $x_2(n)$ by the exponential $e^{j(2\pi/N)Mn}$ is to circularly shift samples (frequencies) in the DFT $X_2(k)$ by M units.

Example 7.21. This example illustrates the frequency translation property.

Suppose that

$$x_1(n) = \begin{cases} \cos(2\pi n/20), & 0 \le n \le 19 \\ 0, & \text{otherwise} \end{cases} \qquad (7.250)$$

and that $x_2(n)$ is the complex exponential sequence

$$x_2(n) = e^{j(2\pi/20)6n}. \qquad (7.251)$$

For $x(n) = x_1(n)x_2(n)$ plot the DFT $X(k)$.

Solution: See Fig. 7.43(a),(b) where the DFT coefficients $X_1(k)$ and $X_2(k)$ are shown and Fig. 7.43(c) which pictures $X(k)$, the convolution (circular) of $X_1(k)$ and $X_2(k)$.

FIGURE 7.43 Convolution in the frequency domain

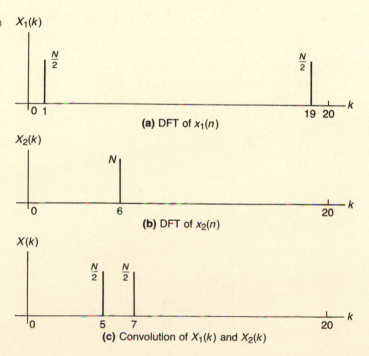

(a) DFT of $x_1(n)$

(b) DFT of $x_2(n)$

(c) Convolution of $X_1(k)$ and $X_2(k)$

Another operation that is often applied in digital signal processing systems is *correlation*. One such application is the detection of a target from a radar signal and another is in estimating the frequency content of a noisy signal. In this section we define the operation of correlation and develop a few of its properties. The correlation of two finite length sequences $x_1(n)$ and $x_2(n)$ is defined as

$$R_{x_1 x_2}(p) = \sum_{m=-\infty}^{m=\infty} x_1(m)x_2(p+m), \qquad -\infty \le p \le \infty. \qquad (7.252)$$

Example 7.22. This example illustrates the graphical evaluation of correlation.

Recall that we used the sliding bar method to perform graphical convolution. Devise an adaptation of this to compute the correlation of the two sequences $x_1(n)$ and $x_2(n)$ of Fig. 7.44(a).

Solution: From Eq. 7.252 it is seen that folding is not needed, thus, we simply write down the sequences $x_1(m)$ and $x_2(m)$ as below:

$$x_1(m) \quad \dots \quad 0 \ \ 0 \ \ 1 \ \ 1 \ \ 1 \ \ 1 \ \ 1 \ \ 1 \ \ 0 \ \ 0 \ \ \dots \ \ 0$$
$$m = 0 \ \updownarrow$$
$$x_2(m) \quad \dots \quad 0 \ \ 0 \ \ 5 \ \ 4 \ \ 3 \ \ 2 \ \ 1 \ \ 0 \ \ 0 \ \ 0 \ \ \dots \ \ 0$$

Multiplying at each value of m and adding results gives the correlation $R_{x_1 x_2}(p)$ for $p = 0$, or $R_{x_1 x_2}(0) = 15$. Then the $x_2(m)$ sequence is simply shifted by an amount p (right for $p < 0$, or left for $p > 0$), multiplies are done at all values of m and the results added. The outcome of this correlation is given in Fig. 7.44(c).

FIGURE 7.44(a) Two sequences

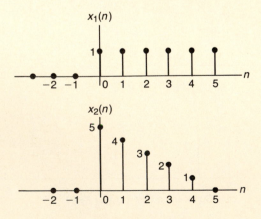

FIGURE 7.44(b) Left shift $(p > 0)$ and right shift $(p < 0)$

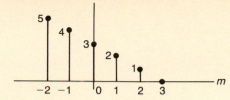

$x_2(p + m), p > 0$ (drawn for $p = 2$)

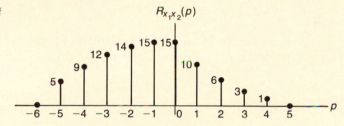

$x_2(p + m), p < 0$ (drawn for $p = -2$)

FIGURE 7.44(c) Result of correlation of $x_1(n)$ and $x_2(n)$

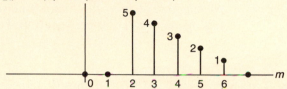

$R_{x_1 x_2}(p)$

The correlation operation defined by Eq. 7.252 is referred to as *cross-correlation* because it generally involves two different sequences. A special case of cross-correlation is *auto-correlation* where both sequences are the same, i.e.

$$R_{x_1 x_1}(p) = \sum_{m=-\infty}^{m=+\infty} x_1(m)x_1(p + m). \tag{7.253}$$

7.9.1 Some Properties of Correlation

Several properties of correlation are given below. The proofs of these properties are developed in Problem 7.49.

1. The auto-correlation is an even sequence, i.e.,

$$R_{x_1 x_1}(p) = R_{x_1 x_1}(-p). \tag{7.254}$$

2. The cross-correlation satisfies

$$R_{x_1 x_2}(p) = R_{x_2 x_1}(-p). \tag{7.255}$$

3. Correlation can be performed by doing convolution in the manner of

$$R_{x_1 x_2}(p) = x_1(-n) * x_2(n) \tag{7.256}$$

or

$$R_{x_2 x_1}(p) = x_1(n) * x_2(-n). \tag{7.257}$$

7.9.2 Circular Correlation

We can also define a circular correlation of finite length sequences that is analogous to circular convolution. For two sequences of equal length we have

$$\tilde{R}_{x_1 x_2}(p) = \sum_{m=0}^{N-1} x_{1p}(m) x_{2p}(p+m), \qquad p = 0, 1, \ldots, N-1$$

$$= \sum_{m=0}^{N-1} x_1(m) x_2(p \oplus m), \qquad p = 0, 1, \ldots, N-1 \tag{7.258}$$

where as before in circular convolution we are really using the periodic extension of the sequences and taking only one period of the result.

Example 7.23. This example illustrates circular correlation.

Consider our familiar three-point sequences $x_1(n) = x_2(n)$ as in Fig. 7.45(a). Use an adaptation of the concentric ring arrangement of Section 7.8 to find the circular correlation of these two sequences.

Solution: In Fig. 7.45(b) the two sequences are arranged on the concentric rings for $p = 0$ where we notice that neither sequence is reversed—they both are marked off in a counterclockwise manner. Multiplying and summing give $\tilde{R}_{x_1 x_2}(0) = 14$. When the inner ring is rotated in the clockwise direction by one step we find the circular correlation $\tilde{R}_{x_1 x_2}(1) = 11$. Shifting one step again and repeating the process gives $\tilde{R}_{x_1 x_2}(2) = 11$. The result is shown in Fig. 7.45(c).

Comment: The linear correlation of these two identical sequences is given in Fig. 7.45(d). Notice that the linear correlation and the circular correlation are quite different, an issue that we now address.

We've already seen that zero padding was required to make circular convolution give the result of linear convolution. The same is true of correlation where we must do zero padding to make circular correlation perform linear correlation. Thus, with $x_1'(n)$ and $x_2'(n)$ the zero-padded versions of $x_1(n)$ and $x_2(n)$ we have $\tilde{R}_{x_1' x_2'}(p) = R_{x_1 x_2}(p)$. If the sequence $x_1(n)$ is of length N_1 and $x_2(n)$ is of length N_2, the resulting linear correlation

FIGURE 7.45 Example
7.23

$x_1(n) = x_2(n)$

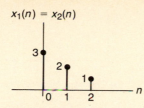

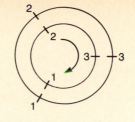

(a) Two identical sequences

(b) Concentric rings for $p = 0$

$\tilde{R}_{x_1 x_2}(p)$

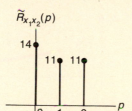

$R_{x_1 x_2}(p)$

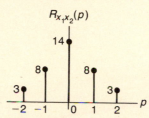

(c) Result of circular correlation

(d) Result of linear correlation

has length $N_1 + N_2 - 1$, and so we need to append $N_2 - 1$ zeros to $x_1(n)$ and $N_1 - 1$ zeros to $x_2(n)$ to yield the padded sequences $x_1'(n)$ and $x_2'(n)$.

Example 7.24. This example illustrates linear correlation by using circular correlation.

Find the linear correlation of the three-point sequences of Fig. 7.46(a) by zero padding and using circular correlation.

Solution: The linear correlation will be $N_1 + N_2 - 1$ or five samples long so we need to pad each sequence with at least two zeros as in Fig. 7.46(b). Then using the concentric rings of Fig. 7.46(c) we find the circular correlation $\tilde{R}_{x_1' x_2'}(p)$ of Fig. 7.46(d). Notice that if we extend $\tilde{R}_{x_1' x_2'}(p)$ to the periodic $\tilde{R}_{px_1' x_2'}(p)$ of Fig. 7.46(e) we see that one period of $\tilde{R}_{px_1' x_2'}(p)$ for $-2 \le p \le 2$ does equal the linear correlation $R_{x_1 x_2}(p)$ of Fig. 7.45(d).

We have seen that circular convolution can be performed by DFTs, namely $\mathscr{D}[x_1(n) \circledast x_2(n)] = X_1(k)X_2(k)$ and we might expect that DFTs can be used to evaluate circular correlations. In fact, this can be done and we have

$$\mathscr{D}[\tilde{R}_{x_1 x_2}(p)] = X_1^*(k)X_2(k) \tag{7.259}$$

and the other half of the pair is

$$\tilde{R}_{x_1 x_2}(p) = \mathscr{D}^{-1}[X_1^*(k)X_2(k)]. \tag{7.260}$$

The details of the proof of Eq. 7.259 are left as an exercise for the reader (see Problem 7.50).

FIGURE 7.46 Example 7.24

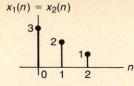

$x_1(n) = x_2(n)$

(a) The original sequences

$x_1'(n) = x_2'(n)$

(b) The padded sequences

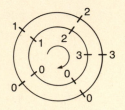

(c) Concentric rings for $p = 0$

$\tilde{R}_{x_1'x_2'}(p)$

(d) Result of circular correlation

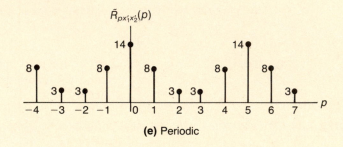

$\tilde{R}_{px_1'x_2'}(p)$

(e) Periodic

Example 7.25. This example illustrates linear correlation by using DFTs.

In Example 7.24 we used circular correlation to perform linear correlation. Now, determine the linear correlation of $x_1(n)$ and $x_2(n)$ by using DFTs.

Solution: In Example 7.24 the sequences were padded out to five samples, and taking a five-point DFT of $x_1'(n) = x_2'(n)$ gives

k	$X_1'(k) = X_2'(k)$
0	6
1	$3.754e^{-j0.725}$
2	$1.706e^{-j0.132}$
3	$1.706e^{j0.132}$
4	$3.754e^{j0.725}$

(7.261)

Next, we form the product $X_1'^*(k)X_2'(k) = |X_1'(k)|^2 = |X_2'(k)|^2$ which is the DFT of the correlation $R_{x_1x_2}(m)$. The result is

---

k	$X_1'^*(k)X_2'(k)$
0	36
1	14.093
2	2.910
3	2.910
4	14.093

$$(7.262)$$

and the correlation comes from the IDFT of $X_1'^*(k) \cdot X_2'(k)$, or

p	$\tilde{R}_{x_1'x_2'}(p) = R_{x_1x_2}(p)$
0	14
1	8
2	3
3	3
4	8

$$(7.263)$$

7.9.3 Computer Evaluation of Correlation

For sequences of any appreciable length that are not described by analytical expressions, correlation is generally performed by using a computer. We should expect a correlation program to be similar to the convolution program developed in Chapter Three. In fact, we can avoid writing a new program by using Property 3 of correlation given in Section 7.9.1, that is,

$$R_{x_2x_1}(p) = x_1(n) * x_2(-n). \qquad (7.264)$$

This property indicates that by replacing $x_2(n)$ by $x_2(-n)$ and then convolving, we obtain the correlation sequence $R_{x_2x_1}(p)$. Thus, we can simply modify the sequence $x_2(n)$ and then call the convolution subroutine developed in Chapter Three (see Problem 3.38).

To see what the necessary steps are, consider the representation of the sequences $x_1(n)$ and $x_2(n)$ shown in Fig. 7.47(a). Keep in mind that we're not actually showing the sequences, but only the intervals within which all nonzero values lie. The right edge of $x_2(n)$ has been shaded as a means of identifying this end of the sequence. We also note that although the sequences have been drawn as though the starting and ending values NS_i and NE_i are positive quantities, they can also be zero or negative but it is required that $NS_i \leq NE_i$. The representation of $x_2(-n)$ is shown in Fig. 7.47(b). The next step is to convolve $x_1(n)$ and $x_2(-n)$ and the program does this by convolving the sequences shown in Fig. 7.47(c) and shifting the resulting output.

The convolution program is set up to accept the sequences as shown

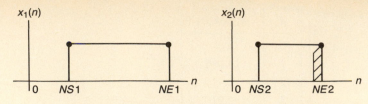

(a) Representation of the sequences to be correlated

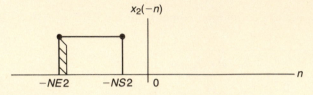

(b) Representation of $x_2(-n)$

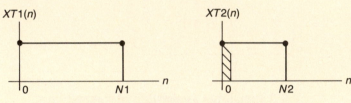

(c) Sequences convolved by the convolution program

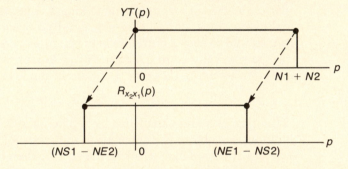

(d) Result of convolution and shifting to obtain $R_{x_2x_1}(p)$

in Fig. 7.47(a), except that the values $x_1(NS1)$, $x_1(NS1 + 1)$, ..., $x_1(NE1)$ are read into the array whose elements are $XT1(0)$, $XT1(1)$, ..., $XT1(N1)$ where $N1 = NE1 - NS1$, and the values $x_2(NS2)$, $x_2(NS2 + 1)$, ..., $x_2(NE2)$ are stored in the array elements $XT2(0)$, $XT2(1)$, ..., $XT2(N2)$, where $N2 = NE2 - NS2$. We then perform the necessary modification of the sequence $XT2(n)$ by time-reversing its entries, do the convolution and shift the resulting output sequence $YT(p)$ to obtain the correlation $R_{x_2x_1}(p)$. Figure 7.47(d) illustrates the appropriate shift of $YT(p)$ to obtain the desired sequence $R_{x_2x_1}(p)$. The required steps are shown in the flow-

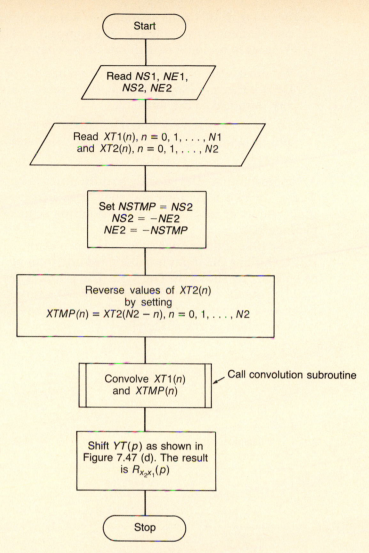

FIGURE 7.48 Flowchart for computer evaluation of correlation

Start

Read $NS1$, $NE1$, $NS2$, $NE2$

Read $XT1(n)$, $n = 0, 1, \ldots, N1$
and $XT2(n)$, $n = 0, 1, \ldots, N2$

Set $NSTMP = NS2$
$NS2 = -NE2$
$NE2 = -NSTMP$

Reverse values of $XT2(n)$
by setting
$XTMP(n) = XT2(N2 - n)$, $n = 0, 1, \ldots, N2$

Convolve $XT1(n)$
and $XTMP(n)$ ⟵ Call convolution subroutine

Shift $YT(p)$ as shown in
Figure 7.47 (d). The result
is $R_{x_2 x_1}(p)$

Stop

chart of Fig. 7.48. Converting this flowchart to a working correlation program is left as an exercise (see Problem 7.52).

7.10 ▬ BLOCK FILTERING OR SECTIONED CONVOLUTION

Often we want to find the result of convolving two sequences; one of length M and the other of length N where $N \gg M$. For example, in a speech processing system the shorter sequence would be the unit sample response $h(n)$ of a discrete linear system, e.g., a filter, and the very long sequence would be the sampled values of the incoming speech waveform

$x(n)$ as in Fig. 7.49. Let us assume that we accomplish the convolution of the two sequences by using the DFT approach of Fig. 7.50. There are two disadvantages to doing this in one step. They are:

1. We must wait until all sequence values are present to compute the DFT of the very long sequence; thus, there is a long time delay before any output data are available.

2. To calculate the very long DFT requires a large amount of memory and computation, adding to the time delay and/or computer resources needed.

An approach that alleviates these difficulties is known as *block filtering*. There are two variations and they both involve partitioning the long input sequence into several equal duration sequences of more manageable length.

The first of these approaches is known as the *overlap-add method*. In this technique the input is subdivided into nonoverlapping sections, each of length L as shown in Fig. 7.51. The samples range from $n = 0$ to $n = L - 1$ in the first section, from $n = L$ to $2L - 1$ in the second, and so forth. Each convolution involves $M + L - 1$ points and the outputs overlap and must be added in the intervals

$$n = L \quad \text{to} \quad L + M - 2$$

$$n = 2L \quad \text{to} \quad 2L + M - 2$$

$$n = kL \quad \text{to} \quad kL + M - 2$$

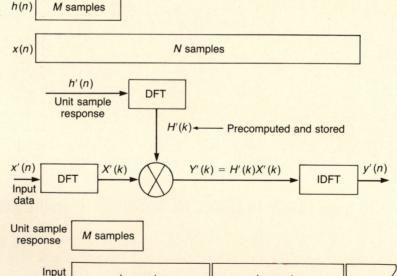

FIGURE 7.49 Two data sequences: the system unit sample response and the input

FIGURE 7.50 Machine implementation of linear convolution

FIGURE 7.51 Preparing the data sequences for the overlap-add method

CHAPTER 7 DISCRETE FOURIER TRANSFORM

as illustrated in Fig. 7.52. We see in the representations of $h(n - m)$ for $0 \leq n \leq L + M - 2$ that computing the linear convolution of $x(n)$ and $h(n)$ requires values from both section 1 and section 2. The overlap-add method obtains these values as shown in Fig. 7.53 where zeros are added (zero-padding) such that each section of $x(n)$, i.e., $x_1'(n)$, $x_2'(n)$, etc., and $h'(n)$ when convolved circularly produce the effect of linear convolution. The results from each section are simply added to obtain $y(n) =$

FIGURE 7.52 Illustration of overlap region in sectioned convolution—overlap-add method

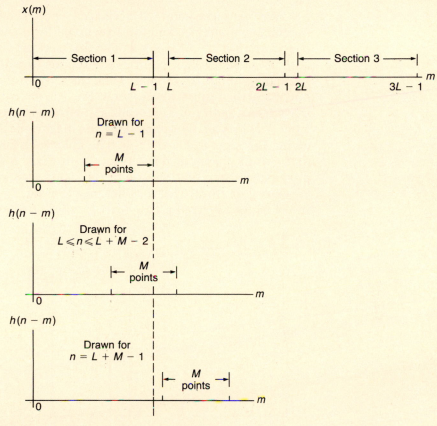

FIGURE 7.53 Zero padding to cause circular convolution to yield the same results as linear convolution

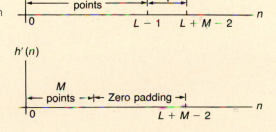

$h(n) * x(n)$ from circular convolution or $y(n) = h'(n) \circledast x'(n) = y'(n)$. And remember that this all is accomplished using $M + L - 1$ point DFTs and a computer.

Let's do a numerical example to illustrate the overlap-add procedure. To keep the situation computationally manageable, we use eight-point DFTs. Consider a very long input $x(n)$ and the finite-length sample response of the system of Fig. 7.54, where we want to obtain the output $y(n)$, the linear convolution of $h(n)$ and $x(n)$ using the mechanism of Fig. 7.50.

With an eight-point DFT decided upon, we section $x(n)$ into segments, $L = 6$ samples long because here $M = 3$ and we can realize linear convolution if $L + M - 1 = 8$. The first section $x_1(n)$ together with $h(n)$, both prepared for eight-point computations by zero-padding, are given as $x_1'(n)$ and $h'(n)$ in Fig. 7.55(a). Then the DFTs of $h'(n)$ and $x_1'(n)$ are computed and the results are shown in Fig. 7.55(b) and Fig. 7.55(c). Note that in each case both the magnitude and phase are given. Next, we compute $Y_1'(k) = H'(k)X_1'(k)$ by multiplying the magnitudes and adding the phases giving the plots in Fig. 7.55(d). The Inverse Discrete Fourier Transform (IDFT) is then computed giving $y_1(n)$ as in Fig. 7.55(e). This completes the processing of the first section of the input sequence.

Next, we turn to $x_2(n)$ as described in Fig. 7.56(a). We are using the index n_2 for processing this section where $n = n_2 + 6$, $x_2(n_2)$ is padded

FIGURE 7.54 An LTI system, its unit sample response, and the input

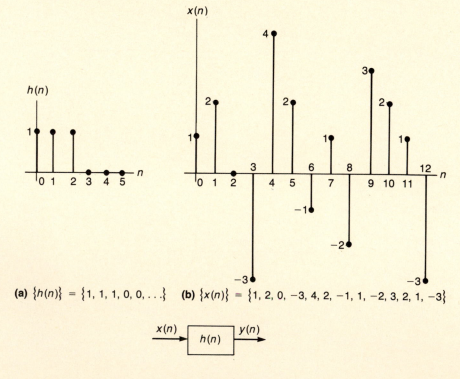

(a) $\{h(n)\} = \{1, 1, 1, 0, 0, \ldots\}$ (b) $\{x(n)\} = \{1, 2, 0, -3, 4, 2, -1, 1, -2, 3, 2, 1, -3\}$

FIGURE 7.55 The first step in machine implementation of the linear convolution of $h(n)$ and $x(n)$

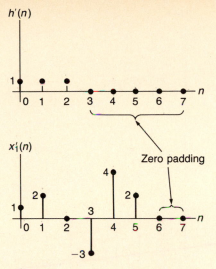

(a) Zero padding for 8-point convolution

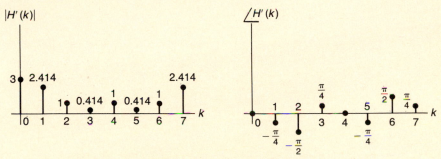

(b) DFT of the zero padded unit sample response $h'(n)$

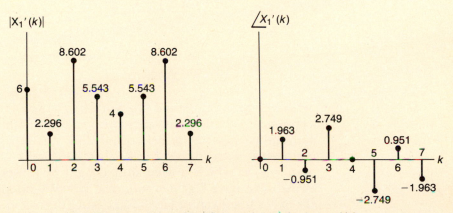

(c) DFT of the zero padded first section of the input $x_1'(n)$

FIGURE 7.55 (cont.)

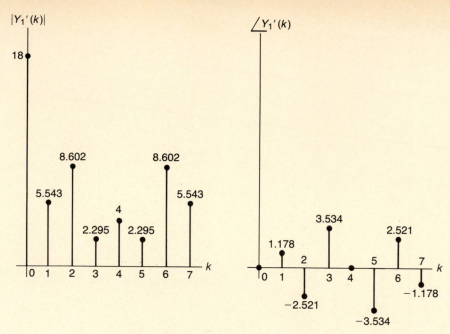

(d) The product of DFTs, i.e. $Y_1'(k) = H'(k)X_1'(k)$

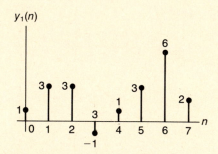

(e) The linear convolution of $h(n)$ and $x_1(n)$

with two zero values and $h(n)$ with five as before. The DFT of $x_2'(n_2)$ is computed and the results are plotted in Fig. 7.56(b). The eight-point DFT for $h'(n)$ is the same as before and $Y_2'(k) = H'(k)X_2'(k)$ is calculated with the result given in Fig. 7.56(c). The IDFT of $Y_2'(k)$ is computed giving $y_2'(n) = y_2(n)$ which is then shifted right by 6 samples as shown in Fig. 7.56(d). We have repeated $y_1(n)$ just below $y_2(n)$ and the output $y(n)$ for $0 \leq n \leq 11$ is given in Fig. 7.56(e). Note that we need to add the outputs $y_1(n)$ and $y_2(n)$ in the ranges $n = 6$ to $6 + 3 - 2$ or 7. If we computed $y_3(n)$ it would be defined in the interval $12 \leq n \leq 17$ and would overlap $y_2(n)$ in the interval $12 \leq n \leq 13$. The pattern is similar for $y_4(n)$, $y_5(n)$, ... Remember that the objective is to obtain the effect of linear convolution by

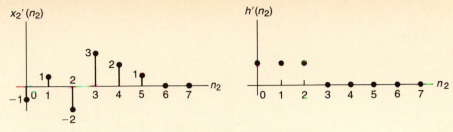

(a) Zero padding for the second iteration

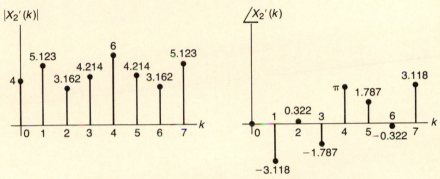

(b) DFT of the zero padded second section of the input $x_2'(n)$

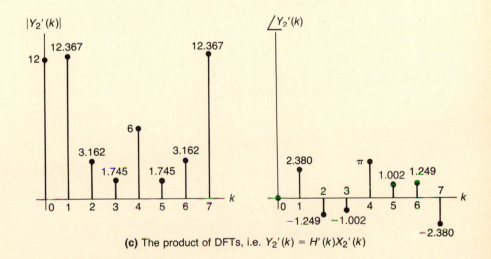

(c) The product of DFTs, i.e. $Y_2'(k) = H'(k)X_2'(k)$

FIGURE 7.56 (cont.)

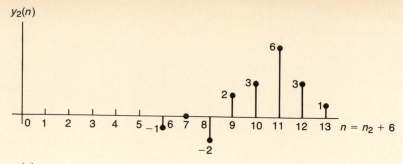

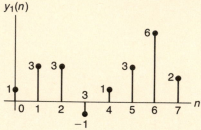

(d) The linear convolution of $h(n)$ and $x_2(n)$; and a repeat of $y_1(n)$

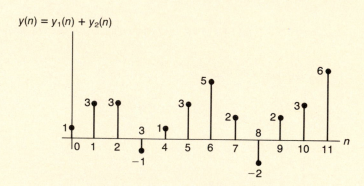

(e) $y(n) = h(n) * x(n)$ for $0 \leqslant n \leqslant 11$

using the DFT. Let's do the linear convolution directly to check the results of Fig. 7.56(e) for $0 \leq n \leq 11$. The sequences are set up for graphical convolution in Figs. 7.57(a) and (b) and the resulting linear convolution is shown in Fig. 7.57(c). We used the convolution sum

$$y(n) = \sum_{m=0}^{m=n} x(m)h(n-m) \tag{7.265}$$

and the result agrees with the overlap-add method for the first two sections of $x(n)$. We won't continue for this is work for a computer but this detailed explanation should put to rest any doubts about the steps required in the method.

FIGURE 7.57 The steps in evaluating the convolution summation

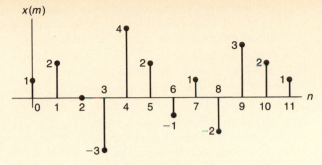

(a) Input sequence $x(m)$

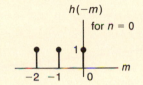

(b) The "flipped" sequence $h(-m)$

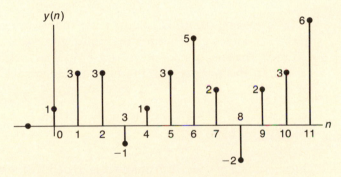

(c) The resultant linear convolution

A recapitulation and a general statement for the overlap-add procedure is now in order.

PROCEDURE

SUMMARY OF OVERLAP-ADD PROCEDURE

1. The number of samples M of the system's sample response (impulse response) $h(n)$ is known so we decide upon P, the number of points for which the DFTs are to be computed. For the moment we will select $P = 2^{\delta}$ (a power of 2) so that a radix-2 Fast Fourier Transform, as described in Chapter Eight, can be used. In addition, the minimum value of δ must be such that $2^{\delta} \geq M + L - 1$. The sequence $h(n)$ is zero-padded so that $2^{\delta} - M$ values are zeros.

2. The input is then sectioned into lengths L such that $M + L - 1 = P$ so that the effect of linear convolution will be achieved. Notice that the last

$(M - 1)$ values of the sequence $x_1'(n)$ are zero values, as are the last $L - 1$ values of $h'(n)$. The DFT $H'(k)$ of the zero-padded sequence $h'(n)$ is computed offline and the values are stored.

3. The complex product $Y_1'(k) = H'(k)X_1'(k)$ is then computed where $X_1'(k)$ is the DFT of the zero-padded sequence $x_1'(n)$.

4. The IDFT of $Y_1'(k)$ is then computed yielding $y_1'(n) = y_1(n)$ for $n = 0$, $1, \ldots, P - 1$.

5. When the input data are available for the next section of L points these data are used to compute the $M + L - 1 = P$-point DFT of $x_2(n)$. In doing this we re-index the points in $x_2'(n)$ from $n = 0$ to $M + L - 2 = P - 1$. Steps 3 and 4 are repeated to obtain $y_2'(n) = y_2(n)$ for $n = 0, 1, \ldots, P - 1$.

6. Next, we time-shift the sequence $y_2(n)$ to obtain $y_2(n - L)$. The sequences $y_1(n)$ and $y_2(n - L)$ overlap in the interval $L \leq n \leq M + L - 2$ and so the sequences are added in this region.

7. We continue as indicated in steps 5 and 6 until the end of the input data is reached.

8. A flowchart showing all of the necessary steps for the overlap-add procedure is shown in Fig. 7.58.

The second method, known as the *overlap-save* or *select-save method* involves partitioning the input into equal, but overlapping, segments S. The specific details of this procedure, which has many features similar to the overlap-add method, are developed in Chapter Problem 7.46.

7.11 ■ SPECTRUM ANALYSIS[†]

The basic idea of spectrum analysis is to determine the frequency content of a signal; that is, if the signal is represented as a sum of sinusoids, what frequencies are present and what are their amplitudes?

As we have seen in Fig. 7.1 it is often possible to see characteristics of a signal in the frequency domain which would not be easily observed in the time domain. In addition, many signal processing and communica-

---

[†]The following paragraph is from a paper by E. A. Robinson, "A Historical Perspective of Spectrum Estimation," *Proc IEEE, Vol. 70, No. 9*, Sept. 1982, pp. 885–905 (Robinson, 1982).

Let us say a few words about the terms "spectrum" and "spectral." Sir Isaac Newton introduced the scientific term "spectrum" using the Latin word for an image. Today, in English, we have the word specter meaning ghost or apparition, and the corresponding adjective spectral. We also have the scientific word spectrum and the dictionary lists the word spectral as the corresponding adjective. Thus "spectral" has two meanings. Many feel that we should be careful to use "spectrum" in place of "spectral" a) whenever the reference is to data or physical phenomena, and b) whenever the word modifies "estimation." They feel that the word "spectral," with its unnecessary ghostly interpretations, should be confined to those usages in a mathematical discipline where the term is deeply embedded.

FIGURE 7.58 Flowchart
summary of the overlap-
add procedure

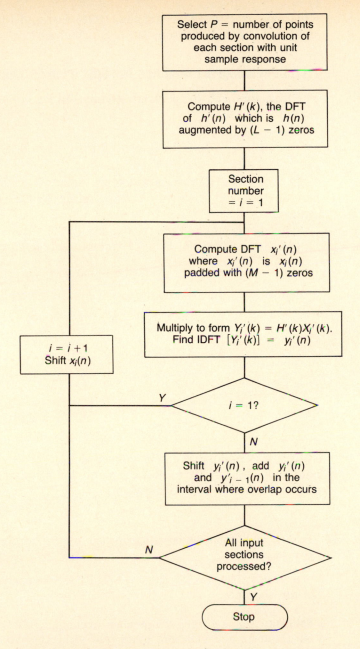

Select $P =$ number of points produced by convolution of each section with unit sample response

Compute $H'(k)$, the DFT of $h'(n)$ which is $h(n)$ augmented by $(L - 1)$ zeros

Section number $= i = 1$

Compute DFT $x_i'(n)$ where $x_i'(n)$ is $x_i(n)$ padded with $(M - 1)$ zeros

Multiply to form $Y_i'(k) = H'(k)X_i'(k)$. Find IDFT $[Y_i'(k)] = y_i'(n)$

$i = i + 1$
Shift $x_i(n)$

$i = 1?$

Shift $y_i'(n)$, add $y_i'(n)$ and $y'_{i-1}(n)$ in the interval where overlap occurs

All input sections processed?

Stop

tions methods are based on frequency domain descriptions of signals. Thus, the topic of spectrum analysis is an important one. It is also rather complex because the methods used to perform spectrum analysis often require knowledge of random processes—background that is not assumed here. Thus, we simply introduce two basic approaches to spectrum analysis. The interested reader will find many references on this topic, a few of which are Harris, 1978; Jackson, 1986; Kay and Marple, 1981; Rabiner and Gold, 1975; Robinson, 1982; and Welch, 1977.

7.11.1 Periodogram Methods for Spectrum Estimation

The first approach to spectrum estimation we consider involves evaluation of

$$S_N(k) = \frac{1}{N}|X(k)|^2 = \frac{1}{N}X^\star(k)\,X(k), \qquad k = 0, 1, \ldots, N - 1. \quad (7.266)$$

$S_N(k)$ is known as the *periodogram spectral estimate,* or simply the periodogram, and it is computed by finding the DFT of the finite duration sequence $x(n)$, $n = 0, 1, \ldots, N - 1$.

We can also relate the periodogram to the z-transform of the sequence $x(n)$ by noting that the DFT of $x(n)$ can be determined as

$$X(k) = X(z)\big|_{z=e^{j(2\pi/N)k}}. \quad (7.267)$$

It also follows that the conjugate of $X(k)$ is given by

$$X^\star(k) = X(z^{-1})\big|_{z=e^{j(2\pi/N)k}}. \quad (7.268)$$

Then, if we define

$$S_N(z) = \frac{1}{N}X(z)\,X(z^{-1}) \quad (7.269)$$

we have the periodogram

$$S_N(k) = S_N(z)\big|_{z=e^{j(2\pi/N)k}}. \quad (7.270)$$

Thus, the periodogram can be viewed as $S_N(z)$ evaluated at equally spaced points on the unit circle of the z-plane. Let's consider an example of the determination of a periodogram.

Example 7.26. This example illustrates the determination of a periodogram of a finite length sequence.

A sequence of length 10 is shown in Fig. 7.59(a). Find and plot the periodogram of this sequence.

Solution: Using a computer program to compute the DFT and then carrying out the operations indicated in Eq. 7.266 yields the plot shown in Fig. 7.59(b). We can easily check the value of $S_{10}(0)$ by observing that

$$X(0) = \sum_{n=0}^{9} x(n) = 13.5 \quad (7.271)$$

so that $S_{10}(0) = (13.5)^2/10 = 18.23$.

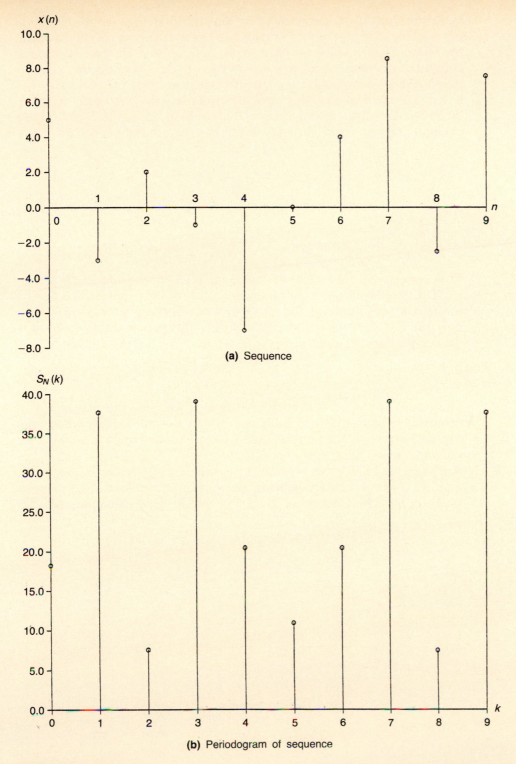

(a) Sequence

(b) Periodogram of sequence

FIGURE 7.59 $x(n)$ and $S_N(k)$ for Example 7.26

Generally, we are dealing with a very long record of data samples and it is not feasible to compute the periodogram of the entire record. In this case, the record is subdivided into reasonably sized pieces, the periodogram is computed for each piece, and the average of the periodograms is computed. We do not discuss the justification for doing this because it is based on statistical considerations. The smaller sized records of length L are generally selected to overlap one another as shown in Fig. 7.60, for example, and this procedure results in the periodogram estimate

$$\overline{S}_N(k) = \frac{1}{M} \sum_{m=1}^{M} S_{Nm}(k) \tag{7.272}$$

where

$$S_{Nm}(k) = \frac{1}{N}|X_m(k)|^2 \quad \begin{cases} k = 0, 1, \ldots, L-1 \\ m = 1, 2, \ldots, M. \end{cases} \tag{7.273}$$

This approach is referred to as the *averaging periodogram method.*

The process of partitioning the long record into subsections can be thought of as multiplying the record by a *window* sequence. This is illustrated in Fig. 7.61 where formation of the subsequence $x_1(n)$ is shown as the product of $x(n)$ and the window sequence $w_{R1}(n)$ defined as

$$w_{R1}(n) = \begin{cases} 1, & 0 \le n \le L-1 \\ 0, & \text{elsewhere.} \end{cases} \tag{7.274}$$

The term window is used because it is as if we view the sequence $x(n)$ through a window of length L and use only those samples that are visible. The window sequence pictured in Fig. 7.61(b) is known as a *rectangular window*, hence the notation $w_{R1}(n)$.

There are other types of windows that have more desirable properties than rectangular windows and we show the use of two of these later in this section. The method of averaging modified periodograms (Welch,

FIGURE 7.60 Overlapping data records of length L

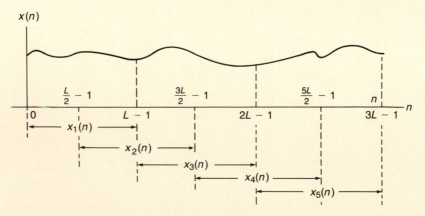

CHAPTER 7 DISCRETE FOURIER TRANSFORM

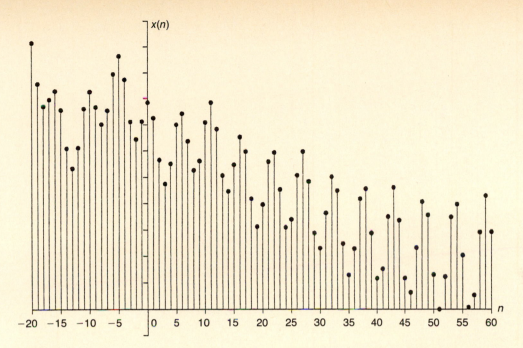

FIGURE 7.61(a) Long sequence of data

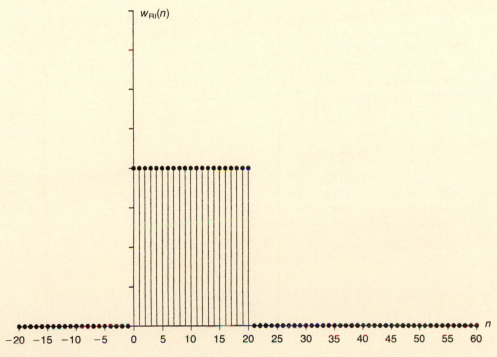

FIGURE 7.61(b) The rectangular window sequence

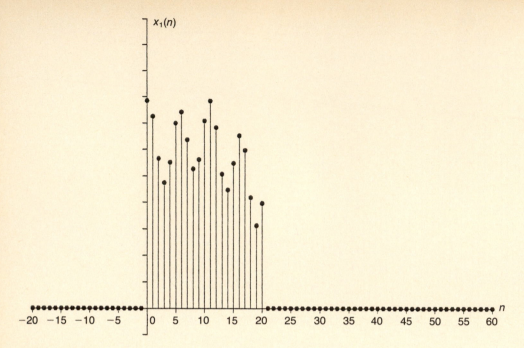

FIGURE 7.61(c) Product of the sequence in part (a) and the window sequence

1977) is similar to the procedure described previously, except that a window sequence other than the rectangular window is used.

Let us now consider another method, based on the autocorrelation function, for estimating the spectrum of a sequence. We begin by defining the *sample estimate of the autocorrelation* of a sequence $x(n)$, $n = 0$, $1, \ldots, N-1$ as

$$r_N(p) = \frac{1}{N} \sum_{m=0}^{N-1-p} x(m)x(p+m), \qquad p = 0, 1, \ldots, N-1. \quad (7.275)$$

This is similar to the autocorrelation function $R_{xx}(p)$ defined in Eq. 7.253 of Section 7.9 except that in Eq. 7.275 there is the multiplier $1/N$, the summation is over the restricted interval $m = 0$ to $N-1-p$ and we consider only non-negative values of p. Let's look at the case where $N = 4$ to see what the elements of the sequence $r_4(p)$ look like. Letting $N = 4$ in Eq. 7.275 we obtain

$$r_4(0) = \frac{1}{4} \sum_{m=0}^{3} x(m)x(m) = \frac{1}{4}[x^2(0) + x^2(1) + x^2(2) + x^2(3)]$$

$$r_4(1) = \frac{1}{4} \sum_{m=0}^{2} x(m)x(1+m) = \frac{1}{4}[x(0)x(1) + x(1)x(2) + x(2)x(3)]$$

$$r_4(2) = \frac{1}{4} \sum_{m=0}^{1} x(m)x(2 + m) = \frac{1}{4}[x(0)x(2) + x(1)x(3)]$$

$$r_4(3) = \frac{1}{4} \sum_{m=0}^{0} x(m)x(3 + m) = \frac{1}{4}x(0)x(3). \tag{7.276}$$

We can also visualize this result from the representation of the sequences $x(m)$, $x(p + m)$, and the product sequence $x(m)x(p + m)$ pictured in Figs. 7.62(a)–(c), or by the sliding bar method shown in Fig. 7.62(d). Notice that the absent sample values for $m < 0$ and $m > N - 1$ are treated as if they were zeros.

FIGURE 7.62 Evaluation of the sample estimate of autocorrelation.

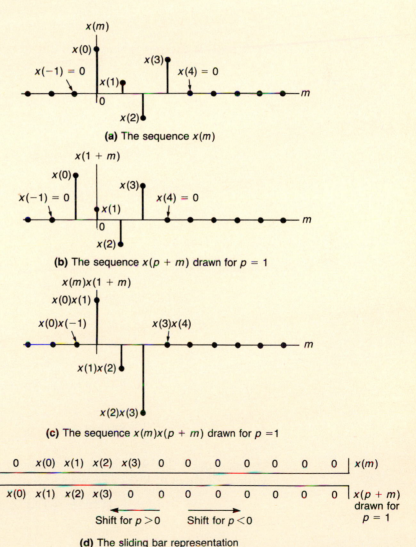

(a) The sequence $x(m)$

(b) The sequence $x(p + m)$ drawn for $p = 1$

(c) The sequence $x(m)x(p + m)$ drawn for $p = 1$

(d) The sliding bar representation

It turns out that the sample estimate of the autocorrelation can be related to the periodogram spectral estimate $S_N(k)$ of Eq. 7.266. To see how this can be done let us consider the z-transform $S_N(z)$ of Eq. 7.269. We have

$$S_N(z) = \frac{1}{N} X(z)X(z^{-1})$$

$$= \frac{1}{N} \left[\sum_{n=0}^{N-1} x(n)z^{-n} \right]\left[\sum_{m=0}^{N-1} x(m)z^{m} \right]$$

$$= \frac{1}{N} \sum_{n=0}^{N-1} \sum_{m=0}^{N-1} x(n)x(m)z^{-n}z^{m}. \qquad (7.277)$$

Let's look at the terms that are included in this expression, by considering the case where $N = 4$. We obtain

$$S_4(z) = \frac{1}{4}[x(0)z^0 + x(1)z^{-1} + x(2)z^{-2} + x(3)z^{-3}][x(0)z^0 + x(1)z^1$$
$$+ x(2)z^2 + x(3)z^3]$$

$$= \frac{1}{4}[x^2(0)z^0 + x(0)x(1)z^1 + x(0)x(2)z^2 + x(0)x(3)z^3 + x(1)x(0)z^{-1}$$

$$+ x^2(1)z^0 + x(1)x(2)z^1 + x(1)x(3)z^2 + x(2)x(0)z^{-2} + x(2)x(1)z^{-1}$$

$$+ x^2(2)z^0 + x(2)x(3)z^1 + x(3)x(0)z^{-3} + x(3)x(1)z^{-2} + x(3)x(2)z^{-1}$$

$$+ x^2(3)z^0]. \qquad (7.278)$$

Rearranging the terms by finding the coefficients of like powers of z gives

$$S_4(z) = \frac{1}{4}[x^2(0) + x^2(1) + x^2(2) + x^2(3)]z^0$$

$$+ \frac{1}{4}[x(0)x(1) + x(1)x(2) + x(2)x(3)][z^1 + z^{-1}]$$

$$+ \frac{1}{4}[x(0)x(2) + x(1)x(3)][z^2 + z^{-2}]$$

$$+ \frac{1}{4}[x(0)x(3)][z^3 + z^{-3}]. \qquad (7.279)$$

Comparing Eq. 7.279 with the expressions for the sample autocorrelation estimate values in Eq. 7.276 we see that

$$S_4(z) = r_4(0)z^0 + r_4(1)[z^1 + z^{-1}]$$
$$+ r_4(2)[z^2 + z^{-2}] + r_4(3)[z^3 + z^{-3}]. \qquad (7.280)$$

In fact, Eq. 7.280 is simply a special case of the general result which may be stated as

$$S_N(z) = \sum_{p=-(N-1)}^{N-1} r_N(p)z^{-p} = \sum_{p=0}^{N-1} r_N(p)[z^{-p} + z^p] - r_N(0) \quad (7.281)$$

where $r_N(p)$ is given by Eq. 7.275 which is repeated here for convenience

$$r_N(p) = \frac{1}{N} \sum_{m=0}^{N-1-p} x(m)x(p+m), \qquad p = 0, 1, \ldots, N-1. \quad (7.275)$$

Evaluating $S_N(z)$ for $z = e^{j(2\pi/N)k}$, $k = 0, 1, \ldots, N-1$, we know from Eq. 7.270 that the result is the periodogram given by Eq. 7.266. Making this substitution for z in Eq. 7.281 gives

$$S_N(z)|_{z=e^{j(2\pi/N)k}} = \sum_{p=0}^{N-1} r_N(p)[e^{-j(2\pi/N)pk} + e^{j(2\pi/N)pk}] - r_N(0). \quad (7.282)$$

This can also be written as

$$S_N(k) = \sum_{p=0}^{N-1} r_N(p)e^{-j(2\pi/N)pk} + \sum_{p=0}^{N-1} r_N(p)e^{+j(2\pi/N)pk} - r_N(0),$$

$$k = 0, 1, \ldots, N-1. \quad (7.283)$$

We recognize the first summation as the DFT of the sequence $r_N(p)$ and denote this as $R_N(k)$, i.e.,

$$R_N(k) = \sum_{p=0}^{N-1} r_N(p)e^{-j(2\pi/N)pk}, \qquad k = 0, 1, \ldots, N-1 \quad (7.284)$$

and the second summation as

$$R_N^*(k) = \sum_{p=0}^{N-1} r_N(p)e^{+j(2\pi/N)pk}, \qquad k = 0, 1, \ldots, N-1. \quad (7.285)$$

Thus we can write Eq. 7.283 as

$$S_N(k) = R_N(k) + R_N^*(k) - r_N(0), \qquad k = 0, 1, \ldots, N-1. \quad (7.286)$$

But we know that

$$R_N(k) = \text{Re}[R_N(k)] + j\text{Im}[R_N(k)] \quad (7.287)$$

and that

$$R_N^*(k) = \text{Re}[R_N(k)] - j\text{Im}[R_N(k)]. \quad (7.288)$$

Thus,

$$R_N(k) + R_N^*(k) = 2\text{Re}[R_N(k)] \quad (7.289)$$

FIGURE 7.63 Two approaches to finding $S_N(k)$

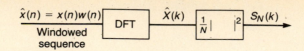

(a) Direct approach to finding $S_N(k)$

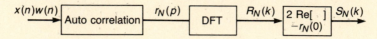

(b) Power spectral density estimate $R_N(k)$ used to find $S_N(k)$

and using Eqs. 7.286 and 7.289 we can write the periodogram spectral estimate as

$$S_N(k) = 2\text{Re}[R_N(k)] - r_N(0), \qquad k = 0, 1, \ldots, N-1 \qquad (7.290)$$

where $R_N(k)$ is sometimes called the *power spectral density estimate*. We now have two ways of estimating the spectrum of a sequence:

1. Form the periodogram by evaluating the DFT of the (truncated) sequence $x(n)$, $n = 0, 1, \ldots, N-1$, and then computing $(1/N)|X(k)|^2$, $k = 0, 1, \ldots, N-1$.

2. Find the sample autocorrelation estimate $r_N(p)$, evaluate its DFT, and then find the periodogram by using Eq. 7.290.

These two methods, which are represented in Fig. 7.63, are illustrated by the following example.

Example 7.27. This example illustrates the computation of the periodogram directly and by using the autocorrelation.

A 10-point sequence is shown in Fig. 7.64(a). Find the periodogram spectral estimate $S_N(k)$ by

a) The direct approach

b) Using the power spectral density estimate $R_N(k)$.

Solution:

a) Using a computer program we compute the 10-point DFT of the sequence $x(n)$ with the result tabulated below.

k	0	1	2	3	4	5
$|X(k)|$	13.500	6.649	1.739	0.209	0.477	0.500
$\frac{1}{10}|X(k)|^2$	18.225	4.421	0.302	0.004	0.023	0.025

where the values for $k = 6, 7, 8,$ and 9 are not shown because, by symme-

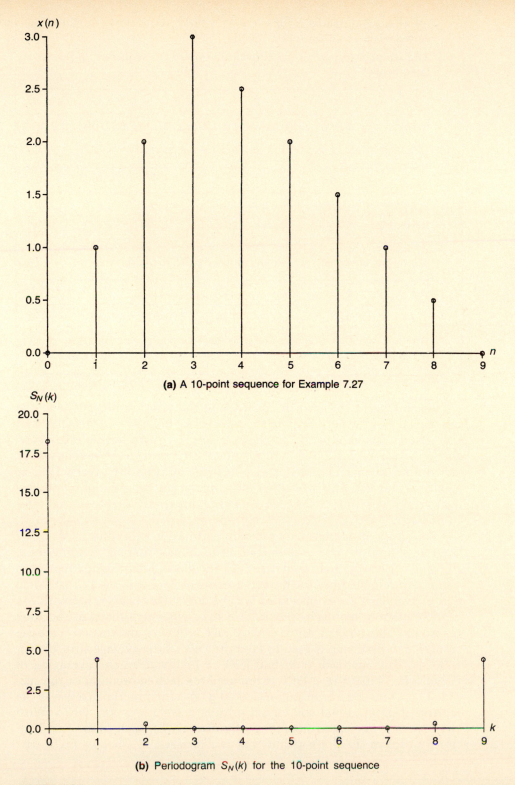

(a) A 10-point sequence for Example 7.27

(b) Periodogram $S_N(k)$ for the 10-point sequence

FIGURE 7.64 Data and results for Example 7.27

try, they are the same as for $k = 4, 3, 2$, and 1, respectively. A plot of the periodogram is shown in Fig. 7.64(b).

b) The sample estimate of the autocorrelation of the sequence $x(n)$ is tabulated below

p	0	1	2	3	4	5	6	7	8	9
$r_{10}(p)$	2.775	2.550	2.050	1.450	0.925	0.500	0.200	0.050	0.0	0.0

The magnitude of the DFT $R_N(k)$ and its real part are

k	0	1	2	3	4	5
$|R_N(k)|$	10.500	6.328	2.618	1.764	1.471	1.400
$\text{Re}[R_N(k)]$	10.500	3.598	1.539	1.390	1.389	1.400

where the values for $k = 6, \ldots, 9$ can be obtained from the tabulated values by using symmetry. Finally, using Eq. 7.290 we have

k	0	1	2	3	4	5
$S_{10}(k)$	18.225	4.421	0.302	0.004	0.023	0.025

which is the same as was obtained by the direct computation of the periodogram.

At this point it is worth considering the relationship between the inverse DFT of the periodogram spectral estimate $S_N(k) = (1/N)|X(k)|^2$ and the sample estimate of the autocorrelation $r_N(p)$. We have already seen that $S_N(k)$ can be expressed in terms of the DFT of $r_N(p)$, so perhaps there is a simple inverse relationship also. It turns out that the inverse DFT of $(1/N)|X(k)|^2$ is equal to $1/N$ times the circular autocorrelation of the sequence $x(n)$, $n = 0, 1, \ldots, N - 1$. Showing this result is left as an exercise in Problem 7.43.

We have considered two spectrum estimation procedures. Which of the two should we use or does each have an advantage depending upon the application? As indicated earlier in the direct periodogram approach, when we are concerned with long streams of data it is likely that some sort of averaging of periodograms will be done. This is also true with the autocorrelation approach; that is, we may elect to subdivide the long record into shorter ones, find $r_N(p)$ for each segment, and then average the results. The final step is then to take the DFT of the average autocorrelations. In this approach only one DFT is involved. In the averaging of periodograms method, a DFT is required for each subsection of the record. Thus, one consideration for deciding on which method to use is the relative computational cost of performing correlations and DFTs. With the advent of fast algorithms for performing DFTs, such as the Fast Fourier Transform (FFT) algorithm that is discussed in Chapter Eight, the computational cost of DFTs has decreased dramatically. In fact, even if the autocorrelation approach is used, FFTs may very well be used to carry out the correlation operations (Rabiner and Gold, 1975). Generally speaking, the direct periodogram methods are probably more computationally efficient at this point, although each situation must be considered for its special characteristics. For example, if we wanted a correlation function to estimate the time delay between sending a radar pulse and receiving its echo, and a power spectral density estimate for further processing, the indirect autocorrelation approach might be the choice.

The spectrum estimation methods that we have discussed both belong to a class known as *nonparametric spectrum estimation techniques.* Some of the disadvantages of these approaches are frequency resolution limited by the length of the data record and introduction of distortion in the spectrum estimate due to leakage caused by windowing effects (Kay and Marple, 1981). To alleviate these limitations, *parametric,* or *model-based,* spectrum estimation techniques have been developed. Model-based procedures typically provide smoother estimates than periodograms and higher resolution for short records (Jackson, 1986). In addition, the modeling approach provides analytical expressions for the spectrum unlike a periodogram which yields tabulated values. The general idea is to represent the data record $x(n)$ as the output of a linear discrete system driven by an input signal having a constant power spectral density. Such an input signal is known as *white noise* because all frequencies (or "colors") are present in equal amounts. The essence of the procedure for obtaining a spectrum estimate for the data record $x(n)$ is to find the parameters that characterize the linear discrete system. There are many ways of doing this and several forms (models) may be assumed for the system. Once the model's parameters have been identified, the power spectrum z-transform is given by

$$S_N(z) = H(z)H^*(z^{-1}) \tag{7.291}$$

and this can be evaluated for $z = e^{j(2\pi/N)k}$ to obtain the spectrum estimate. A survey of a variety of model-based spectrum estimation procedures is given in Kay and Marple, 1981.

7.11.2 Use of Windows in Spectrum Analysis

In this section we introduce the effects of truncating a data record. To keep the situation relatively uncomplicated, let us consider only one long data record, that of a 10-Hz unit amplitude sinusoid sampled at 40 Hz as shown in Fig. 7.65(a). Intuitively, we expect the spectrum of the sequence derived from this analog signal to have only a single frequency. Of course, when we evaluate the DFT, both positive and negative frequencies result and so we actually see two lines. Instead of plotting $|X(k)|^2/N$, we'll simply show $|X(k)|$ which still indicates the relative magnitudes of the frequencies present in the signal. Let's consider the situations illustrated in

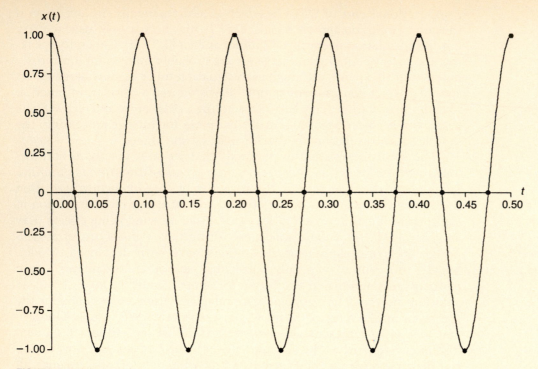

FIGURE 7.65(a) 10-Hz
sinusoid sampled at 40 Hz

Figs. 7.65(b) and (c) where record lengths corresponding to one and three periods of the sinusoid are shown. The resulting DFT magnitudes for these record lengths and for a record length of 20 periods are shown in Figs. 7.65(d), (e), and (f). As expected, in each case, we see only isolated lines at frequencies of ± 10 Hz. We also notice, even though all the other magnitudes are zero, the frequency spacing (or resolution) for a record length $T_0 = 0.1$ s is 10 Hz, for $T_0 = 0.3$ s it is 3.33 Hz, and for $T_0 = 2.0$ s the resolution is 0.5 Hz. Finally, we note that the magnitudes of ± 10 Hz are proportional to the number of periods included in the record lengths. For a one-period record length, the magnitude is 2.0, for a three-period record the magnitude is 6.0, and for the twenty-period record the value is 40.0. In each of these three cases the infinitely long data record for the sinusoidal sequence was truncated so that an integer number of periods was contained in the records. These truncations apparently caused no adverse effects.

What happens, however, if we take the same 10-Hz sinusoid, again sampled with $f_s = 40$ Hz and select a record length that is not an integer multiple of the period of the sinusoid? Figures 7.66(a) and (b) illustrate the result if we select a record length corresponding to 2.5 and 19.5 cycles of the 10-Hz sinusoid. Notice that the spectrum for ten samples ($N = 10$)

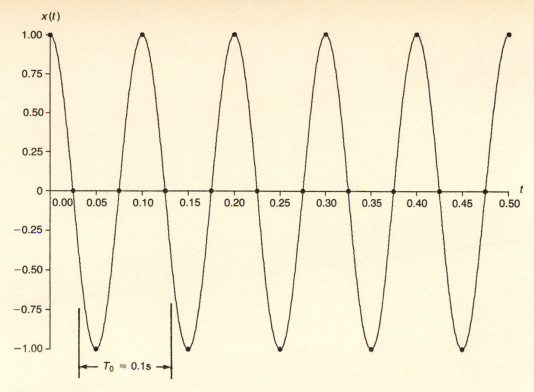

FIGURE 7.65(b) 10-Hz sinusoid sampled at 40 Hz with a record length equal to 1 period

does not include 10 Hz as one of the frequencies—the frequency resolution is 4 Hz because $T_0 = 0.250$. The single frequency line at 10 Hz is "smeared" and two lines of equal magnitude appear at 8 Hz and 12 Hz. This smearing effect is known as *leakage* and we observe that it is not limited to the 8–12 Hz range. There are also significant nonzero DFT values at 0 Hz (dc), 4 Hz, 16 Hz, and 20 Hz, and none of these frequencies are in the original analog signal. A similar effect shows up in Fig. 7.66(b) where the frequency resolution is $1/T_0 = 1/1.950 = 0.513$ Hz and the frequency values nearest to 10 Hz are at frequencies of 9.74 Hz and 10.25 Hz. Notice that 10 Hz is midway between these adjacent frequencies in the DFT and at each of these frequencies the DFT magnitudes are approximately 25. Here also, we see significant nonzero frequency components at all frequencies, again as the result of leakage due to the truncation of the record.

In comparing the spectra in Fig. 7.66 we see that in (a) the magnitudes of the frequency components not adjacent to ±10 Hz are approximately 30 percent to 40 percent of the peak values adjacent to ±10 Hz whereas in (b) this drops to approximately 4 percent to 7 percent. Why the difference? A precise analysis is beyond the scope of our discussion here but an intui-

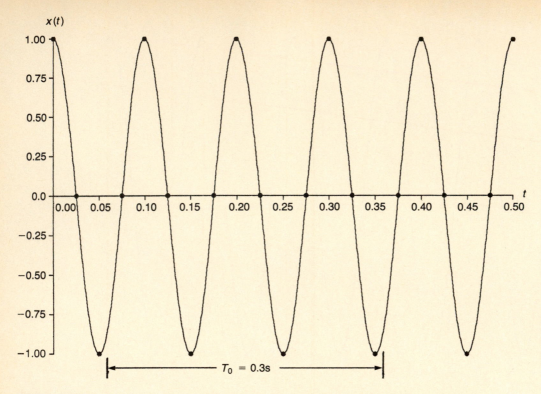

FIGURE 7.65(c) 10-Hz sinusoid sampled at 40 Hz with a record length equal to 3 periods

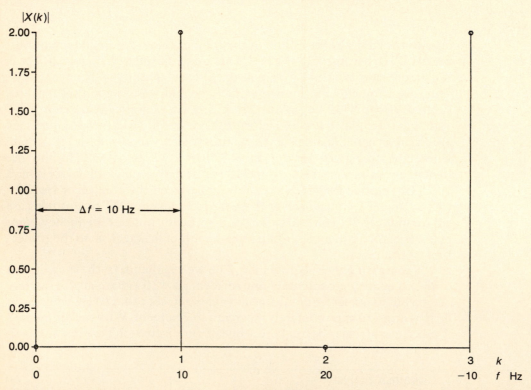

FIGURE 7.65(d) DFT for record length of 1 period ($\Delta f = 10$ Hz)

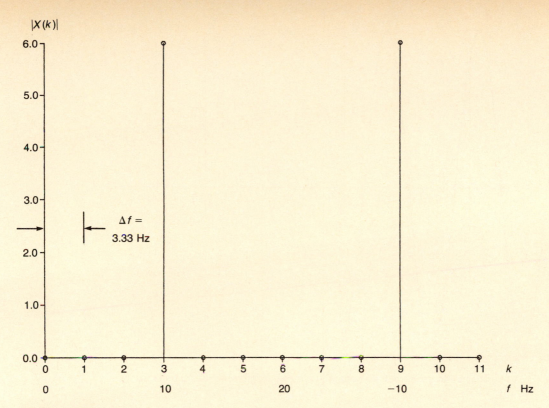

FIGURE 7.65(e) DFT for record length of 3 periods ($\Delta f = 3.33$ Hz)

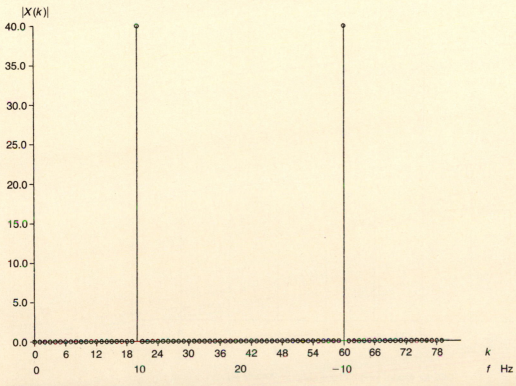

FIGURE 7.65(f) DFT for record length of 20 periods ($\Delta f = 0.5$ Hz)

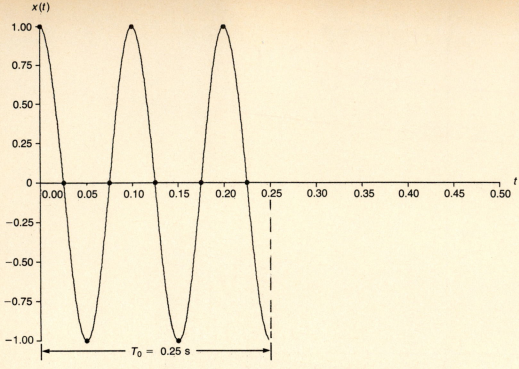

10 hertz sinusoid sampled at 40 hertz with a record length equal to 2.5 periods

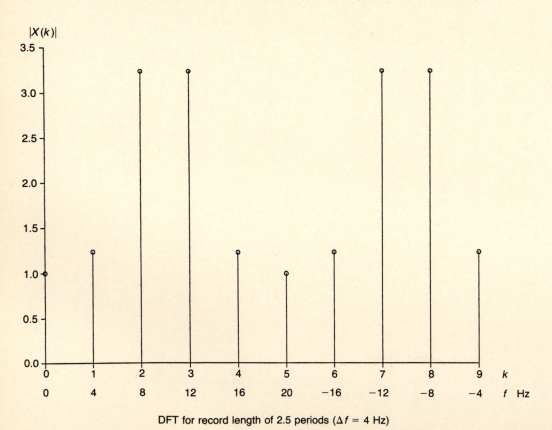

DFT for record length of 2.5 periods ($\Delta f = 4$ Hz)

FIGURE 7.66(a) 2.5 periods of a 10-Hz sinusoid sampled at 40 Hz and its DFT.

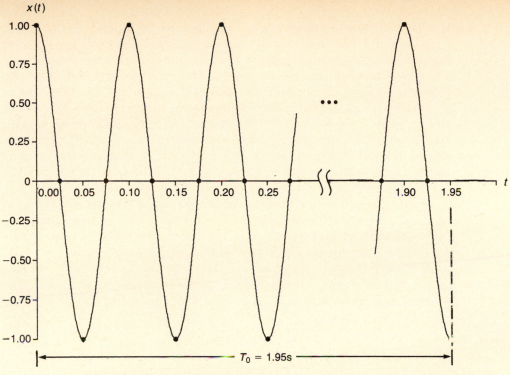

10 hertz sinusoid sampled at 40 hertz with a record length equal to 19.5 periods

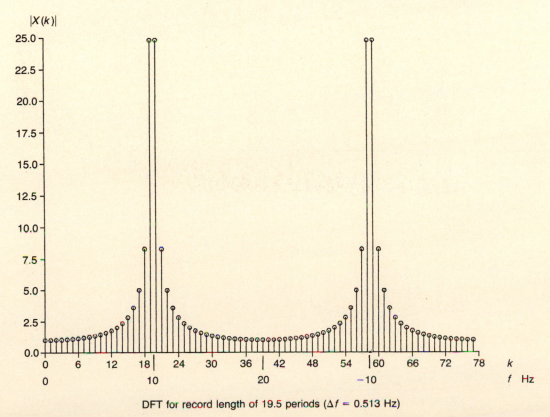

DFT for record length of 19.5 periods ($\Delta f = 0.513$ Hz)

FIGURE 7.66(b) 19.5 periods of a 10-Hz sinusoid sampled at 40 Hz and its DFT.

tive idea of what's going on may be obtained by looking again at the time-domain representations of the two truncated sinusoids in Fig. 7.66. On a heuristic basis we suggest that the "missing" half-cycle in Fig. 7.66(a) represents a larger percentage of the total record length than the "missing" half-cycle does for the 19.5-cycle length of Fig. 7.66(b). Another way of looking at this is to compare the periodic extensions of the two truncated sinusoids with the original 10-Hz signal shown in Fig. 7.65(a). Again, on an intuitive basis, we argue that the periodic extension shown in Fig. 7.67(b) more closely resembles the original sinusoid shown in Fig. 7.65(a) than does the periodic extension shown in Fig. 7.67(a).

A primary source of the leakage seen in the DFTs of Figs. 7.66(a) and (b) is the discontinuity introduced in the periodic extensions of Fig. 7.67 by truncating the sequence. As discussed previously, the truncation can be viewed as the multiplication of the indefinitely long sinusoidal sequence by a rectangular window. When the length of the window is equal to an integer number of periods of the sinusoid, no discontinuity is introduced, and no leakage results. Most sequences of interest are more complicated than the sinusoidal sequence we're considering, however, so it

FIGURE 7.67(a) Periodic extension of 10-Hz sinusoid with record length equal to 2.5 periods

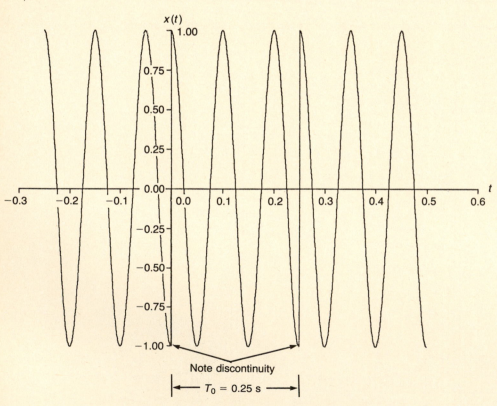

CHAPTER 7 DISCRETE FOURIER TRANSFORM

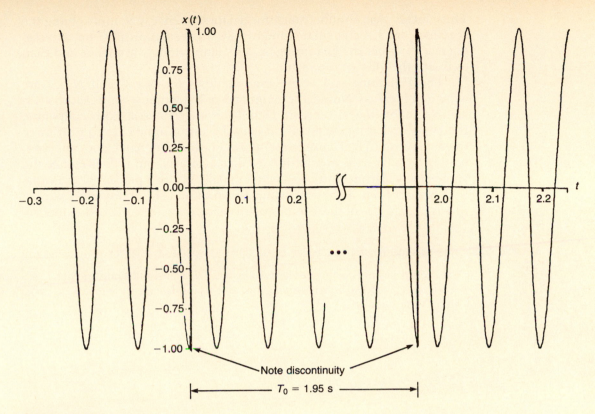

FIGURE 7.67(b) Periodic extension of 10-Hz sinusoid with record length equal to 19.5 periods

may be difficult, or impossible, to avoid introducing a discontinuity caused by the rectangular window. Thus, it is of interest to investigate other window sequences that do not create large discontinuities.

We consider two windows, due to Hamming and von Hann (Harris, 1978), as alternatives to the rectangular window. The fundamental idea upon which these windows are based is to gradually taper the data near the ends of the record, thereby avoiding the abrupt truncation of a rectangular window. We may think of these two new windows as becoming more translucent at both ends of the data record.

For a record consisting of N points indexed from 0 to $N - 1$ the appropriate equations for Hamming and von Hann windows are

$$\text{Hamming:} \quad w(n) = 0.54 - 0.46 \cos\left(\frac{2\pi n}{N-1}\right), \qquad 0 \le n \le N - 1 \quad (7.292)$$

$$\text{von Hann:} \quad w(n) = 0.50 - 0.50 \cos\left(\frac{2\pi n}{N-1}\right), \qquad 0 \le n \le N - 1. \quad (7.293)$$

Thus, rather than simply truncating a data sequence, i.e., multiplying the sequence by a rectangular window, we instead multiply the data sequence by either the Hamming or von Hann window sequence and then evaluate the DFT of the result.

The Hamming and von Hann windows for $N = 8$ and $N = 9$ are shown in Fig. 7.68. Notice the symmetry of the windows and that the von Hann window tapers the data record to zero values at both endpoints, thereby eliminating the possibility of a discontinuity due to truncation of the data record. The Hamming window, on the other hand, does not completely eliminate the possibility of a discontinuity, but it does reduce the value of any discontinuity by a factor of 0.08, i.e., to 8 percent of the value that results from using a rectangular window. The following example illustrates the use of these windows in calculating the DFT of a sequence.

Example 7.28. This example illustrates the use of windows in spectrum analysis.

Two finite duration sequences derived from a 1-Hz sinusoid sampled with $f_s = 40$ Hz by truncating at 10 samples and at 78 samples are shown in Fig. 7.66 along with their DFTs.

FIGURE 7.68(a) Hamming window for $N = 8$

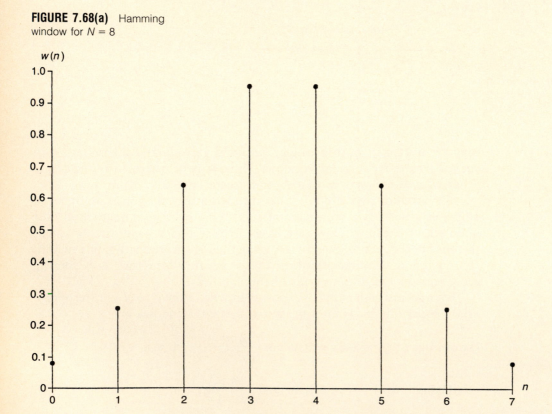

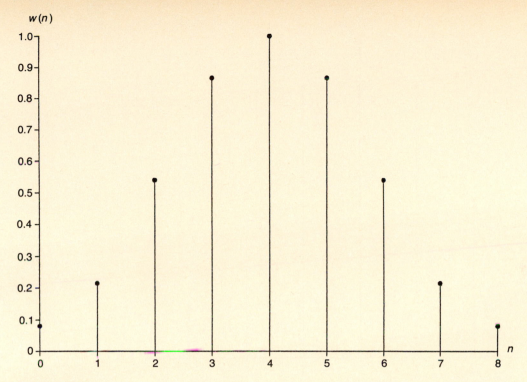

FIGURE 7.68(b) Hamming window for $N = 9$

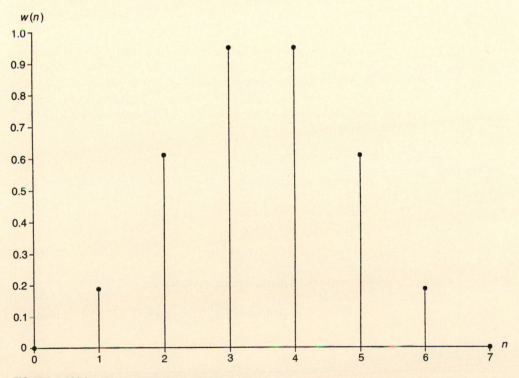

FIGURE 7.68(c) von Hann window for $N = 8$

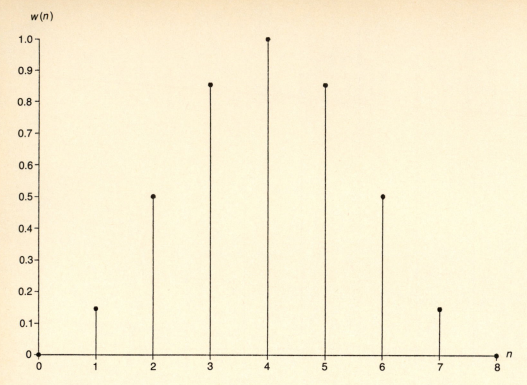

$w(n)$

FIGURE 7.68(d) von Hann window for $N = 9$

a) Modify the two sequences by using the Hamming and von Hann windows on each. Let $x^{(a)}(n)$ and $x^{(b)}(n)$ represent the 10- and 78-point sequences, respectively, which are the sample values of $x_1(t)$ and $x_2(t)$ shown in Fig. 7.66.

b) Determine the DFTs of the four sequences of part (a) and compare with the DFTs of $x^{(a)}(n)$ and $x^{(b)}(n)$ in Fig. 7.66.

Solution:

a) The two new sequences formed from the original 10-point sequence are

$$x_1(n) = x^{(a)}(n)\left[0.54 - 0.46 \cos\left(\frac{2\pi n}{9}\right)\right], \qquad n = 0, 1, \ldots, 9 \quad (7.294)$$

$$x_2(n) = x^{(a)}(n)\left[0.50 - 0.50 \cos\left(\frac{2\pi n}{9}\right)\right], \qquad n = 0, 1, \ldots, 9 \quad (7.295)$$

and from the original 78-point sequence we have

$$x_3(n) = x^{(b)}(n)\left[0.54 - 0.46 \cos\left(\frac{2\pi n}{77}\right)\right], \qquad n = 0, 1, \ldots, 77 \quad (7.296)$$

$$x_4(n) = x^{(b)}(n)\left[0.50 - 0.50 \cos\left(\frac{2\pi n}{77}\right)\right], \qquad n = 0, 1, \ldots, 77 \qquad (7.297)$$

where $x_1(n)$ and $x_3(n)$ are the result of using Hamming windows and $x_2(n)$ and $x_4(n)$ are from von Hann.

b) The windowed sequences $x_1(n)$ and $x_4(n)$ are shown in Figs. 7.69(a) and 7.69(b) and the resulting DFTs are shown in Figs. 7.69(c)–(f). Comparing Figs. 7.69(c)–(f) with the DFTs in Fig. 7.66 we see that the effect of the windows has been to reduce magnitudes of the frequency components that are not adjacent to ±10 Hz. The windows also reduce the main peak values, but not by as large a factor as the reduction of the other frequency components.

Another important issue in spectrum analysis is the ability to detect the presence of two or more frequencies that are close together. This is related to resolution and may be adversely affected by the use of windows which typically suppress sidelobes at the expense of broadening the main lobe. This issue and the use of several other windows are explored in depth in Harris, 1978.

FIGURE 7.69(a) $x_1(n)$— Ten-point sequence multiplied by Hamming window

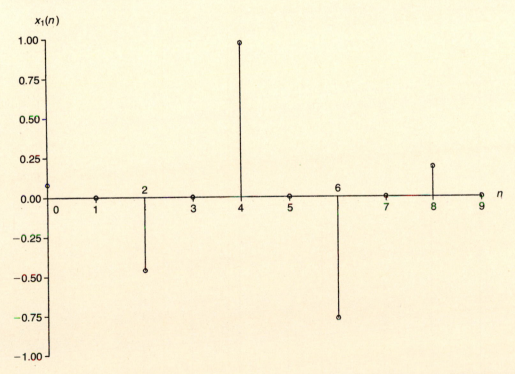

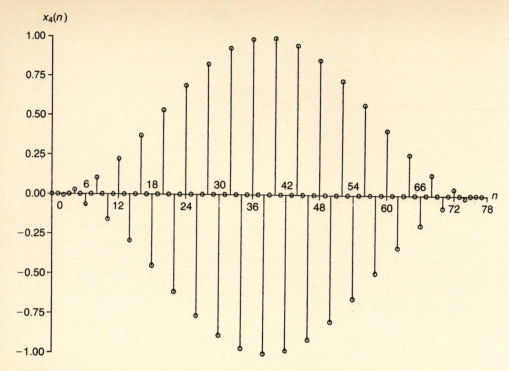

FIGURE 7.69(b) $x_4(n)$—78-point sequence multiplied by von Hann window

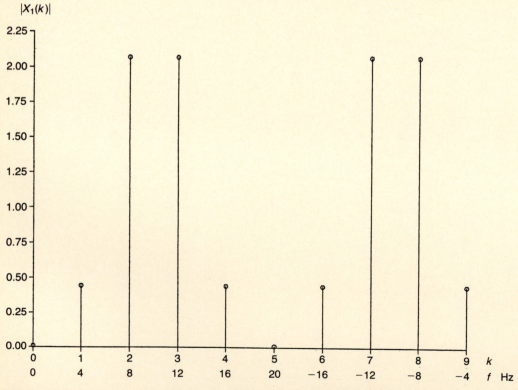

FIGURE 7.69(c) DFT of 10-point sequence with Hamming window ($\Delta f = 4$ Hz)

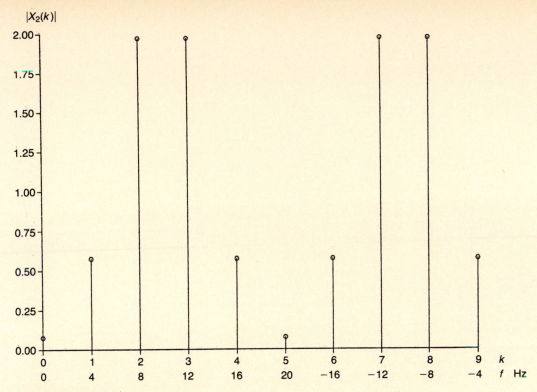

FIGURE 7.69(d) DFT of 10-point sequence with von Hann window ($\Delta f = 4$ Hz)

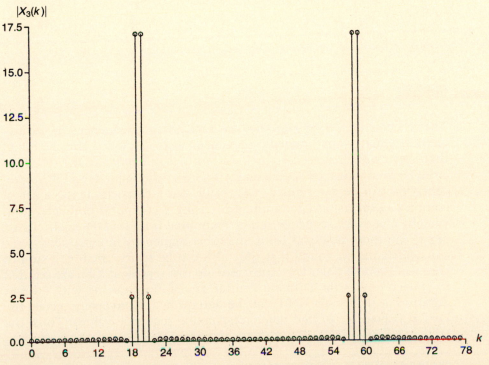

FIGURE 7.69(e) DFT of 78-point sequence with Hamming window ($\Delta f = 0.513$ Hz)

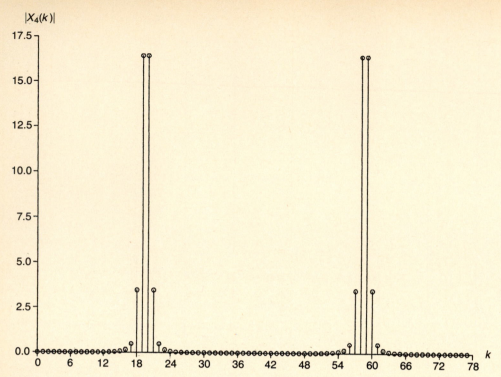

FIGURE 7.69(f) DFT of 78-point sequence with von Hann window ($\Delta f = 0.513$ Hz)

7.12 ■ REVIEW

This chapter presented a method for representing sequences in the frequency domain. First, periodic sequences were discussed and we found that they can be represented by a finite series of exponentials—the Discrete Fourier Series (DFS). Starting with a periodic sequence a DFS representation can be determined. Generally, the DFS coefficients, a set of complex numbers, are determined by using a computer program. Conversely, a periodic sequence can be computed from its DFS coefficients. Next, the more practical finite duration sequences (nonperiodic) were considered and we found that they also can be represented by a sum of complex exponentials. The coefficients in this representation are referred to collectively as the Discrete Fourier Transform. Starting with a finite duration sequence the DFT can be determined. Conversely, given the DFT it is possible to find the corresponding sequence values. Thus, the

DFT and the sequence it represents are referred to as a DFT pair, or a DFT and an inverse DFT. The close relationship between the Discrete Fourier Series and the Discrete Fourier Transform was illustrated by showing that the DFT coefficients can be found from one period of the DFS coefficients if the finite duration sequence $x(n)$ is extended periodically to form the periodic sequence $x_p(n)$. The computer pseudocode for the DFT (or DFS) subroutine is included to provide the basis for a computer program to make the DFT and IDFT computations.

We also found that the DFT can be determined by sampling the Fourier Transform $X(e^{j\theta})$ at $\theta = 2\pi k/N$, N is the number of points in the DFT, and $k = 0, 1, \ldots, N - 1$. This connection between the DFT and the Fourier Transform made it easy to show that the frequency spacing Δf between values of the DFT is governed by the record length T_0 where $\Delta f = 1/T_0$.

After considering some properties of the DFT, including an alternate inversion formula, we introduced the concept of circular convolution. We showed that under certain conditions circular and linear convolution are equivalent and can be performed through the use of DFTs. This led to the development of block filtering, or sectioned convolution, where the problem of finding the convolution of a short-duration sequence with a very long sequence was addressed.

Next, the operation of correlation was introduced and its properties were developed. As with convolution, we found that a correlation sequence can be found directly, or indirectly, using DFTs.

Finally, we introduced an important application of DFTs and correlation known as spectrum analysis. In this brief discussion, we became acquainted with important concepts such as leakage and the use of window sequences in spectrum analysis.

VOCABULARY AND IMPORTANT RELATIONS

a) Periodicity—a periodic sequence having a period N satisfies

$$x_p(n) = x_p(n + N). \tag{7.5}$$

b) Complex exponential

$$p_k(n) = e^{j(k \cdot 2\pi/N)n} \tag{7.15}$$

rotates at a rate of $\dfrac{k \cdot 2\pi}{N}$ radians/sample, has period N and k denotes harmonic number.

c) Discrete Fourier Series (DFS) pair

$$X_p(k) = \sum_{n=0}^{N-1} x_p(n)e^{-j(2\pi/N)nk} \tag{7.64}$$

$$x_p(n) = \frac{1}{N} \sum_{k=0}^{N-1} X_p(k) e^{j(2\pi/N)nk} \tag{7.65}$$

$$x_p(n) \longleftrightarrow X_p(k)$$

d) Nonperiodic sequence in terms of a periodic sequence

$$x(n) = \begin{cases} x_p(n), & 0 \le n \le N-1 \\ 0, & \text{elsewhere} \end{cases} \tag{7.84}$$

e) Discrete Fourier Transform (DFT) pair

$$X(k) = \sum_{n=0}^{N-1} x(n) e^{-j(2\pi/N)nk}, \qquad k = 0, 1, \ldots, N-1 \tag{7.88}$$

$$x(n) = \frac{1}{N} \sum_{k=0}^{N-1} X(k) e^{j(2\pi/N)nk}, \qquad n = 0, 1, \ldots, N-1 \tag{7.89}$$

f) Two important pairs

$$x(n) = \delta(n) \longleftrightarrow X(k) = 1 \tag{7.95}$$
$$x(n) = A \longleftrightarrow X(k) = NA\delta(k)$$
$$n = 0, 1, \ldots, N-1 \qquad k = 0, 1, \ldots, N-1 \tag{7.101}$$

g) The DFT may be thought of as sampled values of the Fourier Transform

$$X(k) = X(e^{j\theta})\Big|_{\theta=2\pi k/N} \tag{7.106}$$

h) The DFT pair for a sampled signal—T is time spacing and Δf is frequency spacing

$$X(k\Delta f) = \sum_{n=0}^{N-1} x(nT) e^{j(2\pi/N)(-nk)}, \qquad k = 0, 1, \ldots, N-1$$

$$x(nT) = \frac{1}{N} \sum_{k=0}^{N-1} X(k\Delta f) e^{j(2\pi/N)(nk)}, \qquad n = 0, 1, \ldots, N-1 \tag{7.110}$$

i) Frequency resolution (spacing)

$$\Delta f = 1/NT = 1/T_0 \qquad \text{where } T_0 \text{ is the record length} \tag{7.115}$$

j) Properties of the DFT

linearity (7.134) and (7.135)

circular shift of a sequence (7.136) and (7.137)

$$\text{symmetry properties} \qquad (7.153) \text{ and } (7.156)$$
$$\text{or}$$
$$(7.157) \text{ and } (7.158) \text{ or } (7.159)$$

$$\text{alternate inversion formula} \qquad (7.162)$$

$$\text{duality} \qquad (7.167)$$

k) Computer evaluation of DFTs—Section 7.7 and Problem 7.33.

l) Periodic convolution

$$x_{3p}(n) \longleftrightarrow X_{3p}(k)$$

$$x_{3p}(n) = \sum_{\ell=0}^{N-1} x_{1p}(\ell)x_{2p}(n-\ell) \longleftrightarrow X_{3p}(k) = X_{1p}(k)X_{2p}(k) \quad (7.200)$$

$$x_{3p}(n) = x_{1p}(n) \circledast x_{2p}(n) \qquad (7.207)$$

m) Circular convolution

$$\mathcal{D}[x_1(n) \circledast x_2(n)] = X_1(k)X_2(k) \text{ or } x_1(n) \circledast x_2(n) \longleftrightarrow X_1(k)X_2(k)$$
$$(7.223) \text{ and } (7.224)$$

n) Linear convolution and circular convolution

$$x_1(n) * x_2(n) = x_3(n) = x_3'(n) = x_1'(n) \circledast x_2'(n) \quad (7.227) \text{ and } (7.228)$$

where $x_1'(n)$ and $x_2'(n)$ are $x_1(n)$ and $x_2(n)$ augmented by the appropriate numbers of zeros.
Linear convolution by DFTs

$$x_3'(n) = \mathcal{D}^{-1}[X_1'(k)X_2'(k)] \qquad (7.228)$$

o) Frequency convolution

$$x_1(n)x_2(n) \longleftrightarrow \frac{1}{N}X_1(k) \circledast X_2(k) \qquad (7.241)$$

p) Modulation or frequency translation

$$x(n) = e^{j(2\pi/N)Mn}x_2(n) \longleftrightarrow X_2(k-M) \qquad (7.249)$$

q) Correlation

$$R_{x_1x_2}(p) = \sum_{m=-\infty}^{m=+\infty} x_1(m)x_2(p+m) \qquad (7.252)$$

Autocorrelation

$$R_{x_1x_1}(p) = \sum_{m=-\infty}^{m=+\infty} x_1(m)x_1(p+m) \qquad (7.253)$$

Circular correlation

$$\tilde{R}_{x_1x_2}(p) = \sum_{m=0}^{N-1} x_1(m)x_2(p \oplus m), \qquad p = 0, 1, \ldots, N-1 \quad (7.258)$$

Correlation by DFTs

$$\mathscr{D}[\bar{R}_{x_1 x_2}(p)] = X_1^*(k)X_2(k) \qquad (7.259)$$

Linear correlation by DFTs.

r) Block filtering or sectioned convolution
overlap-add
overlap-save (see Problem 7.46)

s) Spectrum analysis
Periodogram spectral estimate

$$S_N(k) = \frac{1}{N}|X(k)|^2 = \frac{1}{N}X^*(k)X(k),$$

$$k = 0, 1, \ldots, N-1 \qquad (7.266)$$

z-transform of periodogram spectral estimate

$$S_N(z) = \frac{1}{N}X(z)X(z^{-1}) \qquad (7.269)$$

Sample estimate of autocorrelation

$$r_N(p) = \frac{1}{N}\sum_{m=0}^{N-1-p} x(m)x(p+m),$$

$$p = 0, 1, \ldots, N-1 \qquad (7.275)$$

Periodogram spectral estimate (different form)

$$S_N(k) = 2\mathrm{Re}[R_N(k)] - r_N(0),$$

$$k = 0, 1, \ldots, N-1 \qquad (7.290)$$

where $R_N(k) = \mathscr{D}[r_N(p)]$ is called the power spectral density estimate.
Power spectrum z-transform

$$S_N(z) = H(z)H^*(z^{-1}) \qquad (7.291)$$

Hamming window: $w(n) = 0.54 - 0.46 \cos\left(\dfrac{2\pi n}{N-1}\right), 0 \le n \le N-1$

$$(7.292)$$

von Hann window: $w(n) = 0.50 - 0.50 \cos\left(\dfrac{2\pi n}{N-1}\right),$

$$0 \le n \le N-1 \quad (7.293)$$

Reinforcement

7.1   Determine the periods of each of the periodic sequences shown in Fig. P7.1.

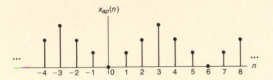

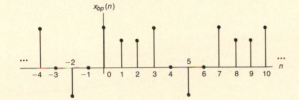

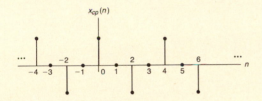

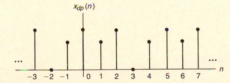

FIGURE P7.1

7.2   a) A periodic sequence has a period of six. Sketch the complex exponentials $p_0(n), p_1(n), \ldots, p_{N-1}(n)$ for the sample values $n = 0, 1, 2, \ldots$.

   b) A periodic sequence has a period of five. Sketch the complex exponentials $p_0(n), p_1(n), \ldots, p_4(n)$ for $n = 0, 1, 2, 3, 4$.

7.3   Find and plot the Discrete Fourier Series coefficients for the periodic sequences

   a) $x_p(n) = 10 \sin(\pi n/3)$

   b) $x_p(n) = 8 \cos(3\pi n/10)$

   c) $x_p(n) = 5 \cos(5\pi n/7)$

7.4   In Example 7.3 we found the DFS coefficients by inspection for $x_p(n) = A \cos(n\pi/2)$. Use the definition of the Discrete Fourier Series coefficients in Eq. 7.64 to find $X_p(k)$ for this periodic sequence and compare your results with Example 7.3.

7.5   Determine the DFS coefficients of the periodic sequences shown in Fig. P7.5.

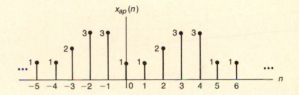

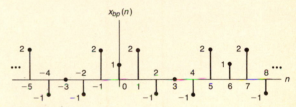

FIGURE P7.5

7.6   a) A plot of the DFS coefficients for a seven-point periodic sequence is shown in Fig. P7.6(a). What harmonics are present and what is the amplitude of each?

   b) Repeat part (a) for the DFS coefficients with $N = 8$ shown in Fig. P7.6(b).

7.7   The eight-point Discrete Fourier Series coefficients for a periodic sequence are shown in Fig. P7.7. Write the sequence as a sum of sinusoidal sequences.

7.8   a) The values of two DFS coefficients for a periodic sequence with a period of $N = 8$ are $X_p(0) = 4$ and $X_p(4) = -2$. To which of the sequences shown in Fig. P7.8 could these values of $X_p(k)$ correspond? Show your reasoning.

---

†The problems marked with the computer designation ⬜ assume that you have available a program to compute the DFT of a sequence of length N, or that you have worked Problem 7.33 in which such a program is developed.

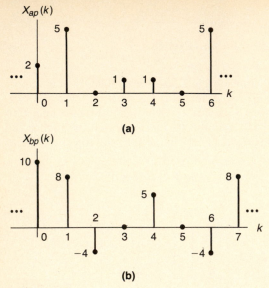

(a)

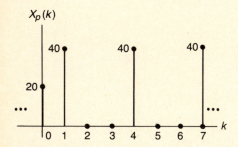

(b)

FIGURE P7.6

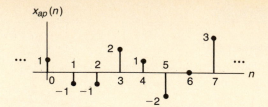

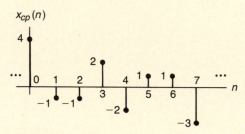

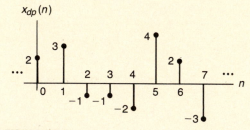

FIGURE P7.8

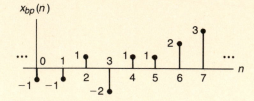

FIGURE P7.7

b) Construct another sequence $x_{pe}(n)$ which could also correspond to the partial DFS given.

c) Can you generalize the results of parts (a) and (b) to other Discrete Fourier Series with N not equal to 8?

d) Can you think of any practical use which could be made of the approach used in this problem?

7.9 A periodic analog signal is given by $x_p(t) = \cos(200\pi t)$. This analog signal is sampled with frequency f_s to yield the periodic sequence $x_p(n) = \cos(200\pi n/f_s)$.

a) Find the period of the sequence and the DFS coefficients for $f_s = 250$ Hz, and $f_s = 450$ Hz.

b) Sketch the DFS coefficients as functions of k

and label the frequency axis with analog frequencies for the sampling frequencies in part (a). Assume that in both cases the record length is such that the samples in the record constitute one period of the sequence.

7.10 A periodic analog signal is sampled at a frequency of 200 Hz. The resulting periodic sequence has a period of 10 and its Discrete Fourier Series coefficients are shown in Fig. P7.10.

a) Show the analog frequency scale on the abscissa of the DFS plot. Assume that the record length is 0.05 s.

b) Write the periodic sequence as a sum of cosine sequences.

c) Determine the amplitudes and analog frequen-

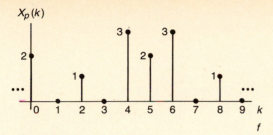

FIGURE P7.10

cies which the DFS indicates are present in the original time signal.

7.11 $x_p(n)$ and $r_p(n)$ are periodic sequences with period $N = 6$ given by

$$x_p(n) = \cos(\pi n/3)$$

$$r_p(n) = \begin{cases} 1, & n = 0, 1 \\ 0, & n = 2, 3, 4 \\ 1, & n = 5 \end{cases}$$

Find the DFS coefficients of the periodic convolution of $x_p(n)$ and $r_p(n)$.

7.12 Find and sketch the periodic convolution of the two sequences of period four specified in the table below.

n	$x_{1p}(n)$	$x_{2p}(n)$
0	1	3
1	2	2
2	−1	0
3	0	1

7.13 A DFT processor is to be used to estimate the frequency spectrum of a real signal. The system must be able to process any signal having frequencies up to 250 Hz. In addition, the interval between frequencies in the DFT spectrum must be less than or equal to 0.5 Hz.

a) Determine the minimum record length, the maximum time between samples, and the minimum number of points in a record.

b) Find the record length, the time between samples, and the number of points in a record if the number of points is to be an integer power of 2.

7.14 A speech signal is sampled at a rate of 20,000 samples/sec. A segment of length 1024 samples is selected and its DFT is computed.

a) What is the time duration of the segment of speech?

b) What is the frequency resolution (spacing in Hz) between the DFT values?

c) Suppose the 1024-point DFT of 512 rather than 1024 samples is computed. (The 512 samples are augmented with 512 zeros before the DFT is computed.) How would this affect the answers to (a) and (b)?

7.15 A finite length analog signal of duration 250 ms is sampled at 512 equally spaced points. Determine the following characteristics of its discrete frequency spectrum:

a) The increment in Hz between successive frequency components.

b) The highest frequency present in the spectrum in Hz.

c) The highest frequency permitted in the spectrum of the analog signal to prevent aliasing.

7.16 a) An analog signal is sampled with a sampling frequency of 40 Hz. There are 256 samples. Find the frequency resolution of the Discrete Fourier Transform.

b) It is desired to determine the Discrete Fourier Transform of the analog signal $y(t) = 10 \cos(12\pi t) \cos(200\pi t)$. Determine the minimum sampling frequency to avoid aliasing.

c) Referring to the analog signal in part (b), if the minimum feasible sampling rate is used, how many samples must be taken to obtain a frequency resolution of 4 Hz?

7.17 Compute the five-point DFT of the sequence shown in Fig. P7.17.

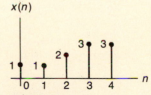

FIGURE P7.17

7.18 a) Find the DFT of the finite duration sequence shown in Fig. P7.18(a).

b) Find an analytical expression for the inverse DFT of the sequence whose five-point DFT is

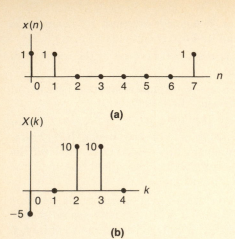

$x(n)$

(a)

$X(k)$

(b)

FIGURE P7.18

shown in Fig. P7.18(b). The expression must not contain any complex numbers.

7.19 Two three-point sequences $x_1(n)$ and $x_2(n)$ are shown in Fig. P7.19. Sketch and label all numerical values for:

a) $x_1(n) * x_2(n)$, the linear convolution of $x_1(n)$ and $x_2(n)$.

b) $x_1(n) \circledast x_2(n)$, the circular convolution of $x_1(n)$ and $x_2(n)$.

c) $R_{x_1 x_2}(p)$, the cross-correlation of $x_1(n)$ and $x_2(n)$.

d) $R_{x_1 x_1}(p)$, the auto-correlation of $x_1(n)$.

e) $\tilde{R}_{x_1 x_1}(p)$, the circular auto-correlation of $x_1(n)$.

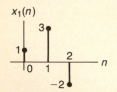

$x_1(n)$

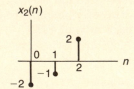

$x_2(n)$

FIGURE P7.19

7.20 Find the DFT of the sequence $x(n) = 0.5 \left[1 - \cos\left(\dfrac{2\pi n}{N}\right) \right]$ for $n = 0, 1, 2, \ldots, N-1$.

7.21 Consider the finite triangularly shaped pulse in Fig. P7.21.

a) Find the Fourier Transform $X(e^{j\theta})$.

b) Sketch this Fourier Transform and indicate the 10-point DFT samples on the plot.

c) Check the results of parts (a) and (b) by using computer methods.

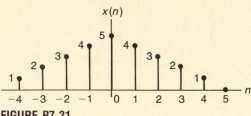

$x(n)$

FIGURE P7.21

7.22 The eight-point DFTs of two sequences $h(n)$ and $x(n)$ are shown in Fig. P7.22. Find the value of $y(2)$ where $y(n) = h(n) \circledast x(n)$.

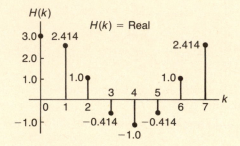

$H(k)$

$H(k) = \text{Real}$

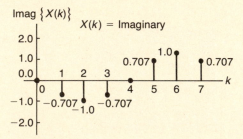

$\text{Imag}\{X(k)\}$

$X(k) = \text{Imaginary}$

FIGURE P7.22

7.23 a) Find and sketch the linear and circular convolutions of the eight-point sequences shown in Fig. P7.23.

b) Find and sketch the linear and circular correlations $R_{x_1 x_2}(p)$ and $\tilde{R}_{x_1 x_2}(p)$ of the sequences in Fig. P7.23.

7.24 Two sequences of length four are shown in Fig. P7.24 along with their DFTs $X_1(k)$ and $X_2(k)$. The values for $X_1(k)$ are expressed in terms of an unknown scale factor A.

a) Determine the value of A.

b) If $Y(k) = X_1(k)X_2(k)$, sketch $Y(k)$ (magnitude

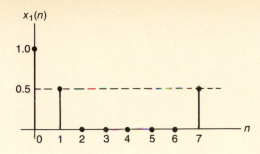

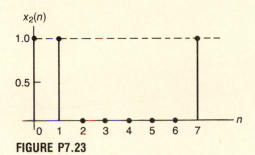

FIGURE P7.23

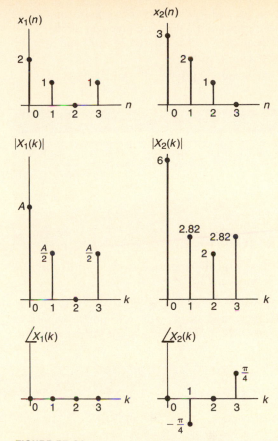

FIGURE P7.24

and phase) as a function of k and label with appropriate numerical values.

c) $y(n)$ is the sequence that corresponds to $Y(k)$. Find $y(n)$, $n = 0, 1, 2, 3$.

d) What is the relationship between $y(n)$, $x_1(n)$, and $x_2(n)$?

7.25 The values of two finite sequences of length four are given in Table P7.25.

TABLE P7.25

n	$x_1(n)$	$x_2(n)$
0	1	3
1	2	2
2	−1	0
3	0	1

a) Find and sketch, labeling all numerical values
   i) The linear convolution $x_1(n) * x_2(n)$.
   ii) The circular convolution $x_1(n) \circledast x_2(n)$.

b) Show graphs of modified sequences $x_1'(n)$ and $x_2'(n)$ for which $x_1'(n) \circledast x_2'(n) = x_1(n) * x_2(n)$.

7.26 Repeat Problem 7.25(a) for the linear and cir-

cular correlations $R_{x_1 x_2}(p)$ and $\tilde{R}_{x_1 x_2}(p)$ of the sequences in Table P7.25.

7.27 Repeat Problem 7.25 for the sequences given in Table P7.27.

TABLE P7.27

n	$x_1(n)$	$x_2(n)$
0	1	−2
1	−1	0
2	0	−1
3	2	3

7.28 Repeat Problem 7.26 for the sequences given in Table P7.27.

7.29 $x_1(n)$ and $x_2(n)$ are two two-point sequences whose four-point DFTs are given in Table P7.29. The sequence $y(n)$ is related to $x_1(n)$ and $x_2(n)$ by $y(n) = x_1(n) * x_2(n)$.

a) Determine $y(n)$.

TABLE P7.29		
k	$X_1'(k)$	$X_2'(k)$
0	$0e^{j0}$	$0e^{j0}$
1	$2.82e^{j\pi/4}$	$1.42e^{-j3\pi/4}$
2	$4.0e^{j0}$	$2.0e^{j\pi}$
3	$2.82e^{-j\pi/4}$	$1.42e^{j3\pi/4}$

b) Use a second approach to check the result obtained in part (a).

7.30 Repeat Problem 7.29 if $y(p) = R_{x_2 x_1}(p)$.

7.31 $x_3(n)$ and $x_4(n)$ are four-point sequences whose DFTs $X_3(k)$ and $X_4(k)$ are tabulated below.

k	$\|X_3(k)\|$ Magnitude (M)	$\angle X_3(k)$ Phase (P)	k	$\|X_4(k)\|$ Magnitude (M)	$\angle X_4(k)$ Phase (P)
0	0.200000E+01	0.000000E+00	0	0.000000E+00	0.000000E+00
1	0.583095E+01	0.590362E+02	1	0.726953E−06	0.154411E+03
2	0.565162E−05	−.899999E+02	2	0.400000E+01	−.180000E+03
3	0.583095E+01	−.590361E+02	3	0.183601E−05	0.899999E+02

When these sequences are zero padded the resulting six-point and eight-point DFTs are as tabulated (labeled as $X_3'(k)$, $X_3''(k)$, $X_4'(k)$, and $X_4''(k)$).

k	$\|X_3'(k)\|$ Magnitude (M)	$\angle X_3'(k)$ Phase (P)	k	$\|X_4'(k)\|$ Magnitude (M)	$\angle X_4'(k)$ Phase (P)
0	0.200000E+01	0.000000E+00	0	0.000000E+00	0.000000E+00
1	0.300000E+01	0.120000E+03	1	0.100000E+01	−.180000E+03
2	0.655743E+01	0.758912E+01	2	0.173205E+01	−.900000E+02
3	0.574187E−05	−.483664E+02	3	0.400000E+01	−.180000E+03
4	0.655743E+01	−.758802E+01	4	0.173205E+01	0.900002E+02
5	0.300000E+01	−.120000E+03	5	0.999999E+00	−.180000E+03

k	$\|X_3''(k)\|$ Magnitude (M)	$\angle X_3''(k)$ Phase (P)	k	$\|X_4''(k)\|$ Magnitude (M)	$\angle X_4''(k)$ Phase (P)
0	0.200000E+01	0.000000E+00	0	0.000000E+00	0.000000E+00
1	0.156322E+01	0.169201E+03	1	0.108239E+01	−.157500E+03
2	0.583095E+01	0.590362E+02	2	0.238419E−06	−.899999E+02
3	0.579278E+01	−.171393E+02	3	0.261312E+01	−.112500E+03
4	0.214577E−05	0.899999E+02	4	0.400000E+01	0.180000E+03
5	0.579278E+01	0.171392E+02	5	0.261312E+01	0.112500E+03
6	0.583095E+01	−.590362E+02	6	0.799680E−06	−.153435E+03
7	0.156321E+01	−.169201E+03	7	0.108239E+01	0.157500E+03

Using the DFTs find the values of

a) $y_1(4)$ where $y_1(n) = x_3(n) * x_4(n)$.

b) $y_2(2)$ where $y_2(n) = x_3(n) \circledast x_4(n)$.

c) $R_{x_4 x_3}(0)$.

d) $R_{x_4 x_4}(0)$.

7.32 It is desired to find the linear convolution of the sequences $h(n)$ and $x(n)$ using the overlap-add method. $h(n) = \{1, 2, 1\}$ and $x(n) = \{1, -1, 2, 1, 2, -1, 1, 3, 1\}$.

a) Section $x(n)$ into three subsequences and compute the linear convolutions of each of these subsequences and $h(n)$. Then show what must be done to get the desired convolution of $h(n)$ and $x(n)$.

b) Describe this in general terms where $h(n)$ is H samples long and $x(n)$ is sectioned into subsequences Q samples long, where $Q > H$.

Extension and Generalization

7.33 Using the pseudocode developed in Section 7.7, write, document, and test a computer subroutine (procedure) to compute the N-point DFT or inverse DFT of a specified sequence. Assume that $0 \le N \le 1024$.

7.34 a) Find the linear convolution of the two 10-point sequences shown in Fig. P7.34.

b) If it is desired to compute the linear convolution of these two sequences by using DFTs, what is the minimum number of points that must be used in the DFT computations?

c) Use DFTs to find $x_1(n) * x_2(n)$ and compare your results with part (a).

7.35 a) Repeat Problem 7.34(a) and (b) for the cir-

cular and linear correlations $\tilde{R}_{x_1 x_2}(p)$ and $R_{x_1 x_2}(p)$ of the sequences in Fig. P7.34.

7.36 Two sequences of duration three and six are shown in Fig. P7.36.

a) Determine and sketch $y_1(n) = x_1(n) \circledast x_2(n)$ by evaluating the convolution summation.

b) Determine and sketch $y_2(n) = x_1(n) * x_2(n)$ by evaluating the convolution summation.

c) Find $y_1(n)$ by using DFTs.

d) Find $y_2(n)$ by using DFTs.

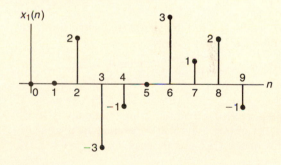

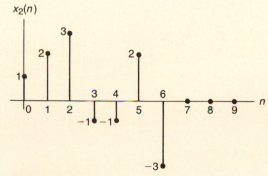

FIGURE P7.34

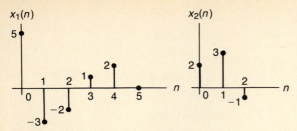

FIGURE P7.36

7.37 For the sequences given in Problem 7.36, find the circular and linear correlations $\tilde{R}_{x_1 x_2}(p)$ and $R_{x_1 x_2}(p)$ directly and by using DFTs.

7.38 Find the Discrete Fourier Transform for each of the following 40-point sequences

a) $x(n) = 1$, $n = 0, 1, 39$
   $x(n) = 0$, otherwise.

b) $x(n) = 1$, $n = 0, 1, 2, 3, 37, 38, 39$
   $x(n) = 0$, otherwise.

c) $x(n) = 1$, $n = 0, 1, 2, 3, 4, 5, 35, 36, 37, 38, 39$
   $x(n) = 0$, otherwise.

d) $x(n) = 0$, $n = 19, 20, 21$
   $x(n) = 1$, otherwise.

For each part plot $|X(k)|$ vs. k and compare your results.

7.39 Evaluate the DFT of the sequence found by sampling the analog signal

$$f(t) = \frac{2f_0 \sin(2\pi f_0 t)}{2\pi f_0 t}$$

and retaining only those values in the interval $-1.0 \le t < 1.0$ s. The sampling frequency is 16 Hz and 32 samples are taken. Find and plot the magnitudes of the DFT coefficients for f_0 equal to

a) 0.5 Hz
b) 1.0 Hz
c) 2.0 Hz
d) 4.0 Hz

Comment on the results obtained.

7.40 a) Use the computer program written in Problem 7.33 to develop a computer program to compute the circular convolution or correlation of two sequences of length N $(N \le 256)$ by using DFTs and inverse DFTs.

b) Test your program on the data of Examples 7.20 and 7.25.

c) Devise some other test problems and do enough testing to convince yourself that your program produces correct answers.

d) Use your program from part (a) to find the circular convolution and correlation of the sequence with $N = 8$ shown in Fig. P7.40(a) with each of the sequences shown in Fig. P7.40(b).

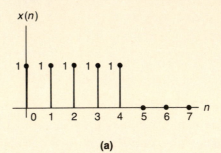

(a)

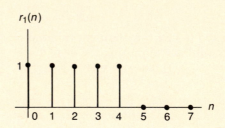

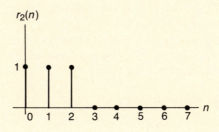

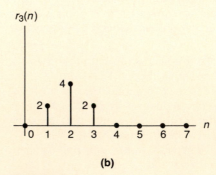

(b)

FIGURE P7.40

7.41 A finite duration sequence $x(n)$ of length eight has the DFT $X(k)$ shown in Fig. P7.41. A new sequence $y(n)$ of length 16 is defined by

$$y(n) = \begin{cases} x\left(\dfrac{n}{2}\right), & \text{for } n \text{ even} \\ 0, & \text{for } n \text{ odd} \end{cases}$$

a) Determine an expression for the DFT $Y(k)$ in terms of $X(k)$.

b) Sketch $Y(k)$ as a function of k.

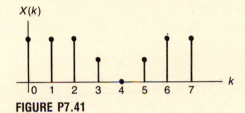

FIGURE P7.41

7.42 a) A finite duration sequence $x_1(n)$ of length N_1 has all of its nonzero values in the interval 0 to $N_1 - 1$ as shown in Fig. P7.42. A second sequence $x_1'(n)$ of duration $2N_1 - 1$ is constructed from $x_1(n)$ by padding N_1 zeros, i.e.,

$$x_1'(n) = \begin{cases} x_1(n), & 0 \le n \le N_1 - 1 \\ 0, & N_1 \le n \le 2N_1 - 1 \end{cases}$$

If $X_1'(\ell)$, $\ell = 0, 1, \ldots, 2N_1 - 1$ and $X_1(k)$, $k = 0, 1, \ldots, N_1 - 1$ are the DFTs of $x_1'(n)$ and $x_1(n)$, respectively, find an expression for the even-indexed components of $X_1'(\ell)$ in terms of $X_1(k)$, i.e., express $X_1'(2\ell)$ in terms of $X_1(k)$.

b) It is desired to generalize the results of part (a) by using the same $x_1(n)$ but with $x_1'(n)$ defined as

$$x_1'(n) = \begin{cases} x_1(n), & n = 0, 1, \ldots, N_1 - 1 \\ 0, & n = N_1, N_1 + 1, \ldots, LN_1 - 1 \end{cases}$$

where L is an integer. Find an expression for $X_1'(L\ell)$ in terms of $X_1(k)$.

7.43 a) Starting with the expression for the periodogram spectral estimate for the sequence $x(n)$, $n = 0, 1, \ldots, N - 1$,

$$S_N(k) = \frac{1}{N}|X(k)|^2, \qquad k = 0, 1, \ldots, N - 1$$

show that

$$\mathcal{D}^{-1}[S_N(k)] = \tilde{R}_{xx}(p), \qquad p = 0, 1, \ldots, N - 1$$

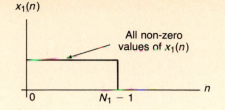

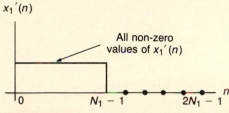

FIGURE P7.42

where $\tilde{R}_{xx}(p)$ denotes the circular auto-correlation of $x(n)$ as defined in Eq. 7.258.

b) For the sequence $x(n)$ shown in Fig. 7.64(a) with periodogram spectral estimate in Fig. 7.64(b) determine

i)   The circular auto-correlation $\tilde{R}_{xx}(p)$.

ii)   The inverse DFT of $S_N(k)$.

iii)   Compare the results found in (i) and (ii).

7.44 a) The input to a stable LTI system is a periodic sequence $x_p(n)$. Show that the steady-state output of the system is

$$y_p(n) = \frac{1}{N}\sum_{k=0}^{N-1} H(e^{j2\pi k/N})\, X_p(k)e^{j(2\pi/N)n}$$

where $X_p(k)$, $k = 0, 1, \ldots, N - 1$ are the DFS coefficients for $x_p(n)$ and $H(e^{j\theta})$ is the system eigenvalue, or frequency response.

b) Use the results of part (a) to find the steady-state output of the system whose unit sample response is $h(n) = (0.6)^n u(n)$ when the input is the periodic sequence $x_p(n) = \{\ldots, 3, 2, 1, 3, 2, 1, \ldots\}$.

7.45 This problem uses the results determined in Problem 7.44(a). Assume that we know the periodic input sequence $x_p(n)$ to a stable LTI discrete system and that the periodic steady-state output sequence $y_p(n)$ is also known.

a) Show the following relationship

$$H(e^{j2\pi k/N}) = \frac{Y_p(k)}{X_p(k)}, \qquad k = 0, 1, \ldots, N - 1$$

where N is the period of the input and output sequence, $X_p(k)$ and $Y_p(k)$ are the DFS coefficients for the input and output sequences, and $H(e^{j\theta})$ is the system's frequency response.

b) Describe how the relationship in part (a) could be used in a situation where the system's frequency response $H(e^{j\theta})$ is unknown.

7.46 In Section 7.10 we considered a method of block filtering known as the overlap-add method. In this method the input sequence $x(n)$ is partitioned into nonoverlapping subsequences and the linear convolution of each subsequence with the filter's unit sample response is computed. The result is a set of sections of the output that overlap one another and must be added together in the overlapping regions. In this problem you are to develop the details of another block filtering technique known as the *overlap-save method*. The development begins with the unit sample response $h(n)$ of length N_1 and the very long input record $x(n)$ shown in Fig. P7.46.

a) We want to partition the input sequence. Let us arbitrarily select $N_2 > N_1$ as the length of these partitions. Consider the partition $x_0(n) = x(n)$, $0 \le n \le N_2 - 1$. Sketch this partition and the interval containing all nonzero points in the convolution $y_0(n) = h(n) * x_0(n)$.

b) Which among the values generated in convolving $h(n)$ and $x_0(n)$ will be the same as those obtained in convolving $h(n)$ and $x(n)$?

c) Now create a second partition of $x(n)$ that overlaps points of $x_0(n)$, that is $x_1(n) = x(n)$, $N_2 - N_1 \le n \le 2N_2 - N_1 - 1$. Sketch $x_1(n)$ and

show the values of n for which $x_1(n) * h(n)$ are the same as $x(n) * h(n)$.

d) How could the results of parts (b) and (c) be combined to give correct values of $x(n) * h(n)$? *Hint:* Which points are correct and what should be done with the other points?

e) Show how circular convolution could be used to generate the subsequences which can be pieced together to form $y(n)$. *Hint:* Use the concentric circles representation of circular convolution for the N_1 points of $h(n)$ and N_2 points of $x(n)$.

f) Describe a general version of the algorithm described in the previous parts and give the general expression for the input segments $x_\ell(n)$, $\ell = 0, 1, \ldots$.

g) Suggest an alternative name for the overlap-save algorithm that is more descriptive of its operations.

7.47 In this problem you are to generalize the result obtained in Eq. 7.47.

a) Consider the family of complex exponentials

$$p_k(n) = e^{j(2\pi/N)nk} \quad \begin{cases} n = 0, 1, \ldots, N - 1 \\ k = 0, 1, \ldots, N - 1 \end{cases}$$

Show that the individual sequences are *mutually orthogonal*, i.e.,

$$\sum_{n=0}^{N-1} p_k(n)p_\ell^*(n) = \begin{cases} A, & \ell = k \\ 0, & \ell \ne k \end{cases}$$

where $p_\ell^*(n)$ is the complex conjugate of $p_\ell(n)$. Find the value of A.

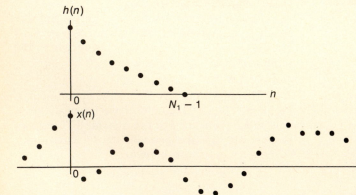

FIGURE P7.46

b) Starting with the expression for the DFS

$$x_p(n) = \frac{1}{N} \sum_{k=0}^{N-1} X_p(k) e^{j(2\pi/N)nk},$$

$$n = 0, 1, 2, \ldots, N-1$$

multiply these equations for $n = 0, 1, 2, \ldots, N-1$ by $p_\ell^*(n) = e^{-j(2\pi/N)n\ell}$ for $\ell =$ an integer in the range $0 \le \ell \le N-1$, and add the resulting equations together.

c) Use the orthogonality property of part (a) to evaluate the sum of the equations found in part (b).

7.48 Assume that $x_1(n)$ and $x_2(n)$ are two sequences of length N and that $x_3(n) = x_1(n)x_2(n)$. Show that $x_3(n) \leftrightarrow \frac{1}{N}X_1(k) \circledast X_2(k)$.

7.49 Prove the properties of correlation sequences stated in Section 7.9.1.

7.50 Show that

$$\mathcal{D}[\tilde{R}_{x_1 x_2}(p)] = X_1^*(k)X_2(k)$$

where $\tilde{R}_{x_1 x_2}(p)$ is the circular correlation of the sequences $x_1(n)$ and $x_2(n)$.

7.51 a) Using the DFT/IDFT subroutines developed in Problem 7.33, write a computer program to determine the periodogram of an N-point sequence ($N \le 1024$).

b) Use your program to verify the results of Examples 7.26 and 7.27.

7.52 a) Using the flowchart of Fig. 7.48 and the convolution subroutine of Problem 3.38 write a program to compute the (linear) correlation of two sequences.

b) Use your program to verify the results of Examples 7.22 and 7.24.

Integrated Review

7.53 Two periodic sequences are described by

$$x_1(n) = \{1, 2, 3, 4, 5, 0, 0\}$$

$$x_2(n) = \{1, 1, 1, 1, 0, 0, 0\}.$$

a) Find the seven-point periodic (circular) convolution of these two sequences. That is, find $y(n) = x_1(n) \circledast x_2(n)$.

b) Now suppose that these sequences are finite rather than periodic. Find the linear convolution of these sequences. That is, find $x_1(n) * x_2(n)$.

c) Are the results of parts (a) and (b) the same or different? If different, explain the difference and show how the two approaches could be made to produce the same results.

7.54 The unit sample response of a system is given by $h(n) = \delta(n) + 0.5\delta(n-5)$.

a) Find the frequency response of the system.

b) Find the expression for the 10-point DFT for $h(n)$.

c) Plot the amplitude spectrum for the DFT found in part (b).

d) Show the relationship between the frequency response in part (a) and the DFT found in part (b).

7.55 The samples in the 15-point sequence shown in Fig. P7.55(a) are spaced 0.5×10^{-3} s apart.

a) What is the maximum frequency that this sequence's DFT would contain?

b) What is the frequency resolution of the DFT?

c) Determine the value of $X(0)$.

d) The partial DFT for a 13-point real-valued sequence (not the sequence in Fig. P7.55(a)) is shown in Fig. P7.55(b). Fill in the rest of the DFT values on the sketch labeling all values with appropriate numbers.

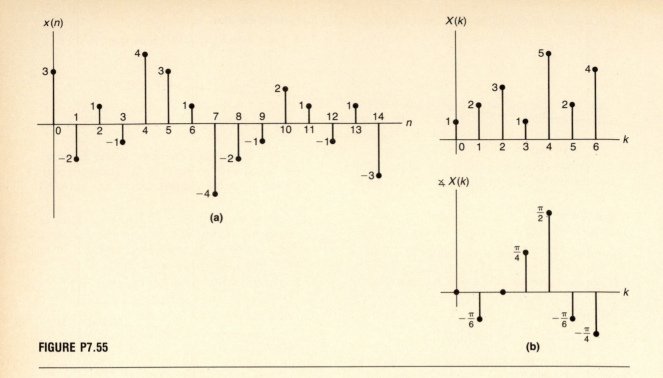

FIGURE P7.55

REFERENCES AND OTHER SOURCES OF INFORMATION

Bozic, S. M. 1975. *Digital and Kalman Filtering.* London: Edward Arnold.

Bellanger, M. 1984. *Digital Processing of Signals.* Chichester, England: John Wiley and Sons. (Originally published under the title *Traitement Numérique Du Signal—Théorie Et Pratique,* Paris, Masson, 1980.)

Hamming, R. W. 1983. *Digital Filters,* 2nd ed., Englewood Cliffs, New Jersey: Prentice-Hall, Inc.

Harris, F. J. 1978. "On the Use of Windows for Harmonic Analysis with the Discrete Fourier Transform." *Proc. of the IEEE.* 66 (January): 51–83.

Jackson, L. B. 1986. *Digital Filters and Signal Processing.* Boston: Kluwer Academic Publishers.

Kay, S. M., and S. L. Marple, Jr. 1981. "Spectrum Analysis—A Modern Perspective." *Proc. of the IEEE.* 69 (November): 1380–1419.

Oppenheim, A. V., and R. W. Schafer. 1975. *Digital Signal Processing.* Englewood Cliffs, New Jersey: Prentice-Hall, Inc.

Oppenheim, A. V., and A. S. Willsky. 1983. *Signals and Systems.* Englewood Cliffs, New Jersey: Prentice-Hall, Inc.

Orfanidis, S. J. 1985. *Optimum Signal Processing: An Introduction.* New York: Macmillan Publishing Company.

Papoulis, A. 1977. *Signal Analysis.* New York: McGraw-Hill Book Co.

Rabiner, L. R., and B. Gold. 1975. *Theory and Application of Digital Signal Processing.* Englewood Cliffs, New Jersey: Prentice-Hall, Inc.

Ramirez, R. W. 1985. *The FFT Fundamentals and Concepts.* Englewood Cliffs, New Jersey: Prentice-Hall, Inc.

Robinson, E. A. 1982. "A Historical Perspective of Spectrum Estimation." *Proc. of the IEEE.* 70 (September): 885–905.

Van Valkenburg, M. E. 1974. *Network Analysis*, 3rd Ed., Englewood Cliffs, New Jersey: Prentice-Hall, Inc.

Welch, P. D. 1977. "On the Variance of Time and Frequency Averages over Modified Periodograms." *Record 1977 IEEE Int. Conf. Acoustics, Speech and Signal Processing*, pp. 58–62.

CHAPTER 8

The Fast Fourier Transform

Science and engineering have changed dramatically during the last three decades because of the concurrent development of high speed computing and efficient algorithms. Our ability to send people to the moon and to explore the solar system has been made possible by the availability of digital computers and computational procedures for determining space-craft trajectories. Another example is the emergence of artificial intelligence as a practical approach to some types of problem solving because of the availability of large computing capacity in small packages, large memory units, efficient algorithms, and programming languages. The field of signal processing has likewise moved ahead rapidly with the digital revolution, in large part because of the development of fast algorithms for computing the Discrete Fourier Transform.

In Chapter Seven we developed the concept of the Discrete Fourier Transform and considered the application of DFTs to spectrum analysis, convolution, and correlation. Although it is possible to compute convolutions and correlations using the indirect approach provided by DFTs, there seems to be little reason for doing so. We showed that convolution of two *N*-point sequences using DFTs requires about 50 times as many multiplies as would be required to do the convolution directly. If we had more efficient procedures for computing DFTs, however, this might be different.

This chapter presents a brief introduction of a class of algorithms that has dramatically changed signal processing by providing a significantly better way to compute DFTs than by using the DFT definition. This approach was initially developed by James Cooley and John W. Tukey who first published their results on the machine computation of Fourier series in 1965 (Cooley and Tukey, 1965; Liu, 1975). In the following year, W. M. Gentleman and G. Sande presented a different procedure that provided a similar increase in computational efficiency (Gentleman and Sande, 1966; Liu, 1975). These papers established two versions of a class of algorithms known as the Fast Fourier Transform (FFT). These techniques have made it possible to compute DFTs in real time in many applications. As a result, when FFTs are used to compute convolution or correlation the procedure is known as *fast convolution*, or *fast correlation*.

Our emphasis in this chapter is the development of two FFT algorithms and the computational benefits they provide. Interestingly, the derivation of these algorithms illustrates the use of a "divide-and-conquer" strategy, an approach to problem solving in which a large problem is subdivided into smaller ones that can be solved more easily. The resulting algorithms that we develop require that the number of points in the DFT is an integer power of 2. Thus, these algorithms are known as radix-2 (or base-2) FFTs. We also show how FFTs can be used to compute linear convolution or correlation and compare the computational efficiency of this method with the direct evaluation of the convolution sum.

8.1 ■ DECOMPOSITION IN TIME

In this section we pursue a divide-and-conquer strategy in which a sequence whose DFT is desired is subdivided into smaller sequences having DFTs that can be more efficiently computed. The result is known as the *Decomposition, or Decimation, In Time* (DIT) version of the Fast Fourier Transform (FFT).

Although it is not the only reasonable measure, we use the number of multiplies required to compute a DFT as the indicator of complexity. Using the definition for the DFT of

$$X(k) = \sum_{n=0}^{N-1} x(n)e^{-j(2\pi/N)nk}, \qquad k = 0, 1, 2, \ldots, N-1 \tag{8.1}$$

and assuming that the input data set $x(n)$ may be complex (for example, we could use the DFT program and the alternate inversion formula of Chapter 7 to compute an inverse DFT) we see that each value of k in Eq. 8.1 requires N complex multiplies. Since there are N such values of k to be considered, this standard DFT requires $N \times N = N^2$ complex multiplies. Thus, our goal here is to develop algorithms that require fewer multiplies than if DFTs are computed using Eq. 8.1. After deriving the basic algorithm in Section 8.1.1 we then develop the pseudocode for computer evaluation of the Decomposition In Time FFT in Section 8.1.2.

8.1.1 Development of the Basic Algorithm

Our approach here is to show how to compute DFTs when $N = 2$, 4, or 8 points and then to generalize to the case where N is an arbitrary power of 2. To simplify the notation we write the DFT definition in the form

$$X(k) = \sum_{n=0}^{N-1} x(n)[W_N]^{nk}, \qquad k = 0, 1, 2, \ldots, N-1 \tag{8.2}$$

where $W_N = e^{-j(2\pi/N)}$, the product nk is the exponent of W_N, and $[W_N]^{nk}$ is known as the *weighting factor*. Although we have written $[W_N]^{nk}$ in Eq. 8.2 to emphasize that the product nk is the exponent of W_N, in the future we'll write the less cumbersome form W_N^{nk}.

Let us begin by considering the computation of a two-point DFT, in which case we have

$$X(k) = \sum_{n=0}^{1} x(n)W_2^{nk} = x(0)W_2^{0k} + x(1)W_2^{1k}, \qquad k = 0, 1 \tag{8.3}$$

where $W_2 = e^{-j(2\pi/2)} = e^{-j\pi} = -1$. Thus, for $n = 0$ and 1 we have $W_2^{0k} = (-1)^{0k} = 1$ and $W_2^{1k} = (-1)^k$, so

$$X(0) = x(0) \cdot 1 + x(1) \cdot 1 = x(0) + x(1)$$

$$X(1) = x(0) \cdot 1 + x(1) \cdot (-1) = x(0) - x(1). \tag{8.4}$$

We notice that in this case no complex multiplication is needed and that the computations involved can be represented by the *signal flow graph* of Fig. 8.1. This graph is simply a pictorial representation of Eq. 8.4 where the inputs are represented at the nodes designated $x(0)$ and $x(1)$ and the outputs are marked at the nodes $X(0)$ and $X(1)$. The branches connect the input and output nodes and are marked with gains (i.e., multipliers) that, in this situation, are either plus or minus one. For obvious reasons, the structure shown in Fig. 8.1 is known as a *butterfly*.

Now let's move up one notch and consider next the DFT of a four-point sequence, that is

$$X(k) = \sum_{n=0}^{n=3} x(n)W_4^{nk}, \qquad k = 0, 1, 2, 3$$

$$= x(0)W_4^{0k} + x(1)W_4^{1k} + x(2)W_4^{2k} + x(3)W_4^{3k}. \tag{8.5}$$

Looking at the first term in Eq. 8.5 we observe that

$$W_4^{0k} = e^{-j(2\pi/4)0k} = e^{-j(2\pi/2)0k} = W_2^0 \tag{8.6}$$

and also from the third term we have

$$W_4^{2k} = e^{-j(2\pi/4)2k} = e^{-j(2\pi/2)k} = W_2^k. \tag{8.7}$$

Thus, grouping together the first and third terms of Eq. 8.5 we have

$$x(0)W_4^{0k} + x(2)W_4^{2k} = x_1(0)W_2^{0k} + x_1(1)W_2^k \tag{8.8}$$

where we have defined a new sequence

$$x_1(n) = x(2n), \qquad n = 0, 1 \tag{8.9}$$

which contains the even-indexed samples of the original sequence. Comparing Eq. 8.8 with Eq. 8.3 we see that

$$X_1(k) = x_1(0)W_2^{0k} + x_1(1)W_2^k \tag{8.10}$$

is the two-point DFT of the sequence $x_1(n)$ defined in Eq. 8.9. Considering

FIGURE 8.1 A signal flow graph known as a butterfly used to determine a two-point DFT

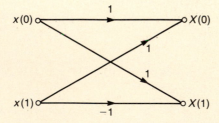

the remaining two terms in the four-point transform of Eq. 8.5 we have

$$x(1)W_4{}^k + x(3)W_4{}^{3k} = W_4{}^k[x(1)W_4{}^{0k} + x(3)W_4{}^{2k}], \quad (8.11)$$

and since $W_4{}^{2k} = W_2{}^k$ from Eq. 8.7

$$x(1)W_4{}^k + x(3)W_4{}^{3k} = W_4{}^k[x_2(0)W_2{}^{0k} + x_2(1)W_2{}^k]$$
$$= W_4{}^k X_2(k). \quad (8.12)$$

As before, we have defined a new sequence

$$x_2(n) = x(2n + 1), \quad n = 0, 1 \quad (8.13)$$

and $X_2(k)$, the term in brackets in Eq. 8.12, is the two-point DFT of $x_2(n)$. Combining Eqs. 8.10 and 8.12 we have the four-point DFT of $x(n) = x_1(n) + x_2(n)$, namely

$$X(k) = x_1(0)W_2{}^{0k} + x_1(1)W_2{}^k + W_4{}^k[x_2(0)W_2{}^{0k} + x_2(1)W_2{}^k] \quad (8.14)$$

or

$$X(k) = X_1(k) + W_4{}^k X_2(k), \quad k = 0, 1, 2, 3. \quad (8.15)$$

Putting Eq. 8.15 into words we can say that

[four-point DFT of $x(n)$] = [two-point DFT of $x_1(n)$]
$$+ W_4{}^k \text{ [two-point DFT of } x_2(n)]. \quad (8.16)$$

Thus, even though we have expressed $X(k)$ in terms of two two-point DFTs, the result is a four-point DFT. We note also that because of the periodicity of the two-point DFTs

$$X_1(k + 2) = X_1(k) \text{ and } X_2(k + 2) = X_2(k), \quad k = 0, 1. \quad (8.17)$$

To express $X(k)$ in terms of the two two-point DFTs we write out Eq. 8.15 to obtain

$$X(0) = X_1(0) + W_4{}^0 X_2(0) = X_1(0) + X_2(0) \quad (8.18)$$

$$X(1) = X_1(1) + W_4{}^1 X_2(1) \quad (8.19)$$

$$X(2) = X_1(2) + W_4{}^2 X_2(2)$$
$$= X_1(0) - X_2(0) \quad (8.20)$$

where we have used the periodicity of $X_1(k)$ and $X_2(k)$ described by Eq. 8.17 and the fact that $W_4{}^2 = -1$. Finally,

$$X(3) = X_1(3) + W_4{}^3 X_2(3) = X_1(3) + W_4{}^1 W_4{}^2 X_2(3)$$
$$= X_1(1) - W_4{}^1 X_2(1). \quad (8.21)$$

In obtaining this last result we have again used the periodicity of $X_1(k)$ and $X_2(k)$ and the knowledge that $W_4{}^2 = -1$. We will refer to Eqs. 8.18–8.21 as the *recomposition equations*. The important results of Eqs. 8.16 and 8.18–8.21 are summarized in the signal flow graph of Fig. 8.2. Al-

FIGURE 8.2 Four-point DFT by decomposition

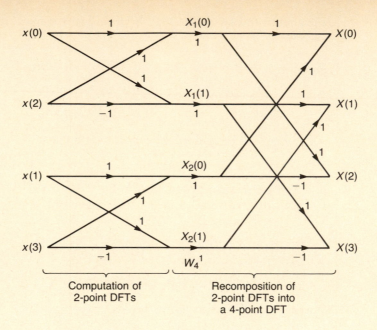

Computation of
2-point DFTs

Recomposition of
2-point DFTs into
a 4-point DFT

though Fig. 8.2 looks a bit complicated, it has a very regular pattern of the butterfly structures, and we notice that only one complex multiplication is required—the one involving W_4^1.

Example 8.1. This example illustrates the four-point DFT decomposition.

Consider an input data string of $x(n) = \{0, 1, 2, 3\}$ and use the graph of Fig. 8.2 to compute the DFT of these data.

Solution: The first stage computed is

$$X_1(0) = x(0) + x(2) = 0 + 2 = 2$$
$$X_1(1) = x(0) - x(2) = 0 - 2 = -2$$
$$X_2(0) = x(1) + x(3) = 1 + 3 = 4$$
$$X_2(1) = x(1) - x(3) = 1 - 3 = -2. \qquad (8.22)$$

These results are the input to the next stage of calculations, and from the graph of Fig. 8.2 the DFTs are

$$X(0) = X_1(0) + X_2(0) = 2 + 4 = 6$$
$$X(1) = X_1(1) + W_4^1 X_2(1) = -2 + e^{-j(2\pi/4)}(-2) = -2 + j2 = 2\sqrt{2}e^{j3\pi/4}$$
$$X(2) = X_1(0) - X_2(0) = 2 - 4 = -2$$
$$X(3) = X_1(1) - W_4^1 X_2(1) = -2 - e^{-j(2\pi/4)}(-2) = -2 - j2 = 2\sqrt{2}e^{j5\pi/4}. \qquad (8.23)$$

Comment: These results seem reasonable because $X(0) = \sum_{n=0}^{3} x(n) = 6$ and because $X(1) = X^*(3)$ due to the symmetry about the point $k = N/2 = 2$. Also, notice that another way of looking at the information of Fig. 8.2 is shown in Fig. 8.3.

Next, let's consider an eight-point DFT before proceeding to the general case. Our starting point is

$$X(k) = \sum_{n=0}^{7} x(n)e^{-j(2\pi/8)nk} = \sum_{n=0}^{7} x(n)W_8^{nk}, \qquad k = 0, 1, \ldots, 7 \quad (8.24)$$

and writing out the terms in the summation gives

$$X(k) = x(0)W_8^{0k} + x(1)W_8^{1k} + x(2)W_8^{2k} + x(3)W_8^{3k}$$
$$+ x(4)W_8^{4k} + x(5)W_8^{5k} + x(6)W_8^{6k} + x(7)W_8^{7k}. \quad (8.25)$$

As before, we group together the $x(n)$ terms having even indices and those having odd indices to obtain

$$X(k) = x(0)W_8^{0} + x(2)W_8^{2k} + x(4)W_8^{4k} + x(6)W_8^{6k}$$
$$+ x(1)W_8^{k} + x(3)W_8^{3k} + x(5)W_8^{5k} + x(7)W_8^{7k}. \quad (8.26)$$

A general property of the weighting factors that is useful here is seen from the identity

$$e^{-j(2\pi/N)2nk} = e^{-j(2\pi/N/2)nk} \quad (8.27)$$

or in terms of the compact notation

$$W_N^{2nk} = W_{N/2}^{nk}. \quad (8.28)$$

Returning to Eq. 8.26 and factoring W_8^k from the second group of four

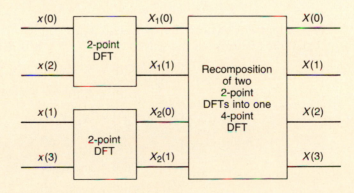

FIGURE 8.3 Block diagram representation of computation of four-point DFT

terms gives

$$X(k) = x(0)W_8^0 + x(2)W_8^{2k} + x(4)W_8^{4k} + x(6)W_8^{6k}$$
$$+ W_8^k[x(1)W_8^0 + x(3)W_8^{2k} + x(5)W_8^{4k} + x(7)W_8^{6k}] \quad (8.29)$$

and using Eq. 8.28 on every term gives

$$X(k) = x(0)W_4^0 + x(2)W_4^k + x(4)W_4^{2k} + x(6)W_4^{3k}$$
$$+ W_8^k[x(1)W_4^0 + x(3)W_4^k + x(5)W_4^{2k} + x(7)W_4^{3k}]. \quad (8.30)$$

To help in recognizing the result, it is convenient to define the sequences

$$x_1(n) = x(2n), \qquad n = 0, 1, 2, 3$$
$$x_2(n) = x(2n + 1), \qquad n = 0, 1, 2, 3. \quad (8.31)$$

Thus, we can write

$$X(k) = x_1(0)W_4^0 + x_1(1)W_4^k + x_1(2)W_4^{2k} + x_1(3)W_4^{3k}$$
$$+ W_8^k[x_2(0)W_4^0 + x_2(1)W_4^k + x_2(2)W_4^{2k} + x_2(3)W_4^{3k}] \quad (8.32)$$

or in more compact form

$$X(k) = \sum_{n=0}^{3} x_1(n)W_4^{nk} + W_8^k \sum_{n=0}^{3} x_2(n)W_4^{nk}, \qquad k = 0, 1, \ldots, 7. \quad (8.33)$$

We recognize the first sum as the four-point DFT of the sequence $x_1(n)$ and the second term as W_8^k times the four-point DFT of the sequence $x_2(n)$, therefore, the eight-point DFT of $x(n)$ can be written as

$$X(k) = \sum_{n=0}^{N/2-1} x_1(n)W_{N/2}^{nk} + W_N^k \sum_{n=0}^{N/2-1} x_2(n)W_{N/2}^{nk}$$

$$= \sum_{n=0}^{3} x(2n)W_4^{nk} + W_8^k \sum_{n=0}^{3} x(2n + 1)W_4^{nk}$$

$$= X_1(k) + W_8^k X_2(k), \qquad k = 0, 1, \ldots, 7. \quad (8.34)$$

It is important to note that although $X_1(k)$ and $X_2(k)$ are four-point DFTs, k still ranges through the values 0, 1, . . . ,7. Thus, from Eq. 8.34 we have

$$X(0) = X_1(0) + W_8^0 X_2(0)$$
$$= X_1(0) + X_2(0)$$
$$X(1) = X_1(1) + W_8^1 X_2(1)$$
$$X(2) = X_1(2) + W_8^2 X_2(2)$$
$$X(3) = X_1(3) + W_8^3 X_2(3)$$
$$X(4) = X_1(4) + W_8^4 X_2(4)$$

$$= X_1(4) - X_2(4)$$

$$X(5) = X_1(5) + W_8{}^4 W_8{}^1 X_2(4)$$

$$= X_1(5) - W_8{}^1 X_2(5)$$

$$X(6) = X_1(6) - W_8{}^2 X_2(6)$$

$$X(7) = X_1(7) - W_8{}^3 X_2(7). \tag{8.35}$$

In writing the expressions for $X(4), \ldots, X(7)$ we have used the properties

$$W_N{}^{(n+\ell)k} = W_N{}^{nk} W_N{}^{\ell k} \quad \text{and} \quad W_N{}^{N/2} = -1. \tag{8.36}$$

To complete the manipulations, we note that

$$X_1(k) = X_1(k + 4) \quad \text{and} \quad X_2(k) = X_2(k + 4), \qquad k = 0, 1, 2, 3. \tag{8.37}$$

Using these to substitute for $X(4)$, $X(5)$, $X(6)$, and $X(7)$ in Eq. 8.35 yields

$$X(0) = X_1(0) + X_2(0) \qquad\qquad X(4) = X_1(0) - X_2(0)$$

$$X(1) = X_1(1) + W_8{}^1 X_2(1) \qquad X(5) = X_1(1) - W_8{}^1 X_2(1)$$

$$X(2) = X_1(2) + W_8{}^2 X_2(2) \qquad X(6) = X_1(2) - W_8{}^2 X_2(2)$$

$$X(3) = X_1(3) + W_8{}^3 X_2(3) \qquad X(7) = X_1(3) - W_8{}^3 X_2(3) \tag{8.38}$$

which are the *recomposition equations*. A combination signal flow graph and block diagram representation of the results contained in Eq. 8.38 is shown in Fig. 8.4.

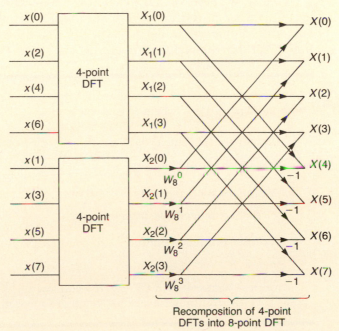

FIGURE 8.4 Calculation of eight-point DFT as recomposition of two four-point DFTs

Recomposition of 4-point DFTs into 8-point DFT

We can now proceed to decompose each of the four-point DFTs shown in Fig. 8.4 as in the development of the DFT of a four-point sequence. We will do this without writing out all of steps in the equations. The key results are

$$X_1(k) = \begin{bmatrix} \text{two-point DFT of} \\ x(0) \text{ and } x(4) \end{bmatrix} + W_4{}^k \begin{bmatrix} \text{two-point DFT of} \\ x(2) \text{ and } x(6) \end{bmatrix}$$

$$= X_{1a}(k) + W_4{}^k X_{1b}(k), \qquad k = 0, 1, 2, 3 \qquad (8.39)$$

$$X_2(k) = \begin{bmatrix} \text{two-point DFT of} \\ x(1) \text{ and } x(5) \end{bmatrix} + W_4{}^k \begin{bmatrix} \text{two-point DFT of} \\ x(3) \text{ and } x(7) \end{bmatrix}$$

$$= X_{2a}(k) + W_4{}^k X_{2b}(k), \qquad k = 0, 1, 2, 3 \qquad (8.40)$$

and the recomposition equations from Eqs. 8.39 and 8.40 are

$$X_1(0) = X_{1a}(0) + X_{1b}(0) \qquad\qquad X_1(2) = X_{1a}(0) - X_{1b}(0)$$

$$X_1(1) = X_{1a}(1) + W_4{}^1 X_{1b}(1) \qquad X_1(3) = X_{1a}(1) - W_4{}^1 X_{1b}(1)$$

$$X_2(0) = X_{2a}(0) + X_{2b}(0) \qquad\qquad X_2(2) = X_{2a}(0) - X_{2b}(0)$$

$$X_2(1) = X_{2a}(1) + W_4{}^1 X_{2b}(1) \qquad X_2(3) = X_{2a}(1) - W_4{}^1 X_{2b}(1). \quad (8.41)$$

A block diagram of the completed process and the more detailed signal flow graph representation are shown in Fig. 8.5. Notice in Fig. 8.5(b) that all weighting factors are expressed in terms of powers of W_8 to simplify the computation. This is easily done by again using the property given in Eq. 8.28, $W_N{}^{2nk} = W_{N/2}{}^{nk}$.

Finally, we observe that signal flow graphs as shown in Fig. 8.5(b) can become rather cluttered, so we adopt the shorthand notation shown for a butterfly calculation in Fig. 8.6(a) which enables us to redraw the signal flow graph for the eight-point case as shown in Fig. 8.6(b).

PROCEDURE

At this point, the general procedure and the result should be clear. Starting with an N-point DFT (where N is a power of 2):

1. Decompose the N-point DFT into two $\frac{N}{2}$-point DFTs and determine the recomposition equations.

2. Decompose each $\frac{N}{2}$-point DFT into two $\frac{N}{4}$-point DFTs and determine the corresponding recomposition equations.

3. Continue this process until $\frac{N}{2}$ two-point DFTs result. This terminates the process.

The result is represented in Fig. 8.7. If we follow this procedure for a sixteen-point DFT the resulting signal flow graph is shown in Fig. 8.8.

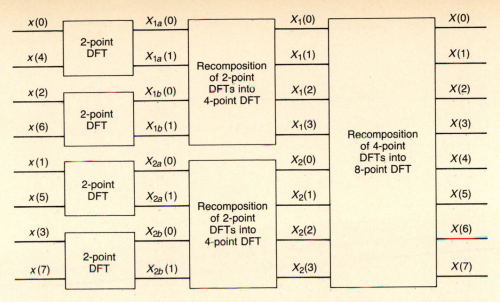

(a) Block diagram of 8-point DFT computed by recomposition of 2-point and 4-point DFTs

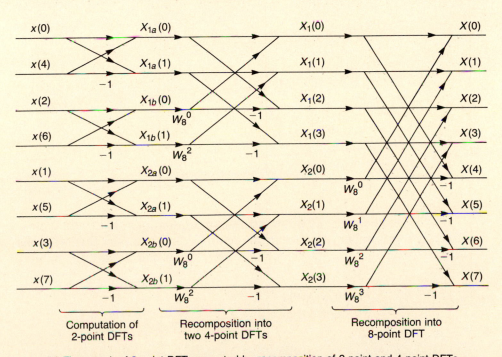

(b) Flow graph of 8-point DFT computed by recomposition of 2-point and 4-point DFTs

FIGURE 8.5

FIGURE 8.6

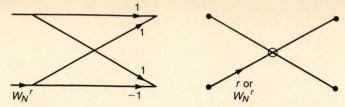

(a) Flow graph and shorthand representation of butterfly calculation

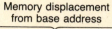

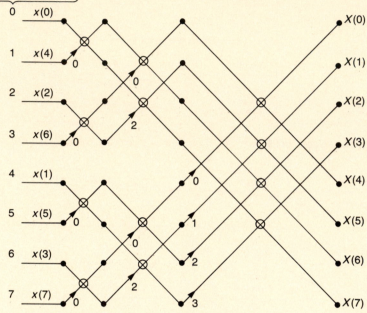

(b) 8-point FFT using shorthand notation

What have we gained by all of these manipulations? Let's take a close look at the number of calculations required and compare this with the calculations required to calculate a DFT from the definition, namely

$$X(k) = \sum_{n=0}^{N-1} x(n)e^{-j(2\pi/N)nk}$$

$$= \sum_{n=0}^{N-1} x(n)W_N^{nk}, \qquad k = 0, 1, \ldots, N-1. \tag{8.42}$$

Looking at Figs. 8.6(b) and 8.8 we see that the computations have been subdivided into several stages. How many stages are there? From the constructive process we see that there will always be one stage required

FIGURE 8.7 Calculation of DFT by successive recomposition of 2-point DFTs

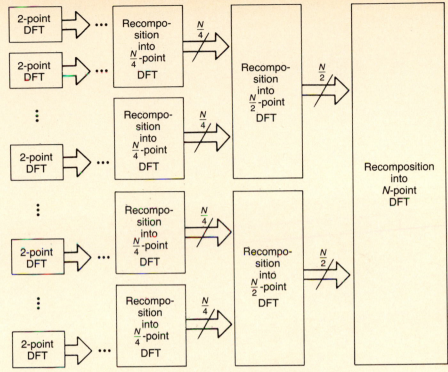

to compute the $\dfrac{N}{2}$ two-point DFTs. In addition, there will be R recomposition stages where R satisfies

$$\frac{N}{2^R} = 2. \qquad (8.43)$$

Taking the logarithm (base 2) of Eq. 8.43 to find R yields

$$\log_2 N - \log_2 2^R = \log_2 2 \qquad (8.44)$$

or

$$\log_2 N - R = 1 \quad \text{and} \quad R = \log_2 N - 1. \qquad (8.45)$$

Consequently, with one stage needed to compute the two-point DFTs, the total number of computational stages required is $R + 1$ or

$$\text{number of stages} = \log_2 N. \qquad (8.46)$$

At each stage there are $N/2$ butterfly calculations required, and with $\log_2 N$ stages, a total of T_B butterflies must be evaluated where

$$\text{number of butterflies} = (\text{number of butterflies/stage})(\text{number of stages}) \qquad (8.47)$$

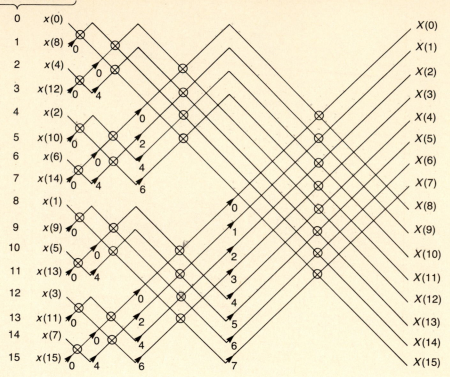

Memory displacement from base address

0	x(0)	X(0)
1	x(8)	X(1)
2	x(4)	X(2)
3	x(12)	X(3)
4	x(2)	X(4)
5	x(10)	X(5)
6	x(6)	X(6)
7	x(14)	X(7)
8	x(1)	X(8)
9	x(9)	X(9)
10	x(5)	X(10)
11	x(13)	X(11)
12	x(3)	X(12)
13	x(11)	X(13)
14	x(7)	X(14)
15	x(15)	X(15)

FIGURE 8.8 Decomposition In Time FFT: 16 points, bit-reversed input, normal-ordered output

or

$$T_B = \frac{N}{2} \log_2 N, \text{ for } N \text{ a power of 2} \qquad (8.48)$$

In general, each butterfly requires one complex multiplication and two additions (actually one addition and one subtraction) so the number of complex multiplies needed to compute a DFT using the DIT FFT algorithm is also given by Eq. 8.48, i.e., $(N/2) \log_2 N$. We have already demonstrated that a DFT computed using the standard definition

$$X(k) = \sum_{n=0}^{N-1} x(n) W_N^{nk} \qquad (8.49)$$

requires N^2 complex multiplies. A comparison of the number of complex multiplies required for the standard DFT computation and for the DIT FFT algorithm is shown in Table 8.1.

TABLE 8.1 NUMBER OF COMPLEX MULTIPLIES FOR DFT AND RADIX-2 FFT

N	Standard DFT	FFT	Ratio DFT/FFT
2	4	1	4.0
4	16	4	4.0
8	64	12	5.3
16	256	32	8.0
32	1024	80	12.8
64	4096	192	21.3
128	16,384	448	36.6
256	65,536	1024	64.0
512	262,144	2304	113.8
1024	1,048,576	5120	204.8
$\vdots$	$\vdots$	$\vdots$	$\vdots$
$2^{20} \approx 10^6$	$\approx 10^{12}$	$\approx 10^7$	$\approx 10^5$

So we see that the FFT provides much faster computation than the standard DFT and, the larger N is, the more significant is the FFTs advantage as portrayed in Fig. 8.9.

To write a computer program to carry out the Decomposition In Time (DIT) FFT algorithm presented in the previous development we need to have formulas that indicate how the weighting factors are generated and where in memory to obtain the points that interact with one another in each butterfly. By inspection of Figs. 8.6(b) and 8.8 we see that the weighting factor exponents are periodic and in every periodic pattern the start-

FIGURE 8.9 Ratio of DFT/FFT complex multiplies vs N

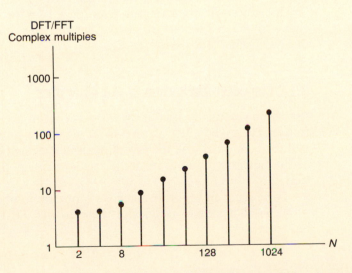

ing exponent is 0. If we number the butterfly stages starting with the leftmost stage as stage 1 and proceeding to 2, . . . , $\log_2 N$, we see that the increment between weighting factor exponents (α in $W_N{}^{\alpha}$) at the Lth stage is $\alpha = N/2^L$. Let us assume that the input sequence values are arranged in memory in the order shown on the signal flow graphs. For example, in Fig. 8.8 $x(0)$ is located at some base address, $x(8)$ at the base address + 1, $x(4)$ at the base address + 2, and so forth. Thus, $x(0)$ and $x(8)$ are separated from one another by one memory location, $x(0)$ and $x(4)$ by two memory locations, etc. It is seen that at the Lth stage the butterfly widths are $2^{(L-1)}$ and this is also the memory address separation of the points which participate in a butterfly calculation.

We must also address the issue of the ordering of the input data. Again referring to Figs. 8.6(b) and 8.8 we see that although the output is in what we think of as normal order, the input is not. We need a way of putting the input data into appropriate memory locations. Thus, as the sequence values $x(0)$, $x(1)$, . . . , $x(N - 1)$ arrive we need to store them in the memory locations shown in Figs. 8.6(b) and 8.8. This can be accomplished by using an algorithm known as *bit-reversing* and to illustrate the idea let's represent the index of a sequence value in binary form. Thus, if we have a sequence with 16 elements the addresses will be

$$0000, 0001, 0010, 0011, \ldots , 1111 \qquad (8.50)$$

corresponding to the sequence values

$$x(0), x(1), x(2), x(3), \ldots , x(15). \qquad (8.51)$$

To determine the desired memory location for a sequence element, we simply reverse the bits of its binary address. For example,

$$x(3) = x(0011) \longrightarrow 1100 \quad \text{or decimal 12.} \qquad (8.52)$$

So, $x(3)$ is stored in memory location 12. Table 8.2 gives the desired memory locations obtained in this way for a 16-point sequence. Comparing this with Fig. 8.8 we see that this algorithm determines the desired memory locations.

8.1.2 Computer Evaluation of the Algorithm

Let us now consider how to develop the computer code for the Decimation In Time (DIT) FFT algorithm. Basically, we need two main sections, one to accomplish the bit reversing, and a second to carry out the stages of the butterfly computations. First, let's develop the bit-reversing section.

If we have an input array of N points (remember, N must be a power of 2) the addresses or indices of these points written as binary numbers have the form

$$A = b_{M-1} \cdot 2^{M-1} + b_{M-2} \cdot 2^{M-2} + \cdots + b_1 \cdot 2^1 + b_0 \cdot 2^0 \qquad (8.53)$$

TABLE 8.2   DETERMINATION OF BIT-REVERSED ORDER ($N = 16$)

Sequence element	Binary address	Bit-reversed address	Desired displacement from base address
$x(0)$	0000	0000	0
$x(1)$	0001	1000	8
$x(2)$	0010	0100	4
$x(3)$	0011	1100	12
$x(4)$	0100	0010	2
$x(5)$	0101	1010	10
$x(6)$	0110	0110	6
$x(7)$	0111	1110	14
$x(8)$	1000	0001	1
$x(9)$	1001	1001	9
$x(10)$	1010	0101	5
$x(11)$	1011	1101	13
$x(12)$	1100	0011	3
$x(13)$	1101	1011	11
$x(14)$	1110	0111	7
$x(15)$	1111	1111	15

where $M = \log_2 N$ and the b_i, $i = 0, 1, \ldots, M$ are either 0 or 1. The bit-reversed version of the address is then

$$A_R = b_0 \cdot 2^{M-1} + b_1 \cdot 2^{M-2} + \cdots + b_{M-2} \cdot 2^1 + b_{M-1} \cdot 2^0. \quad (8.54)$$

Thus, starting from the decimal addresses $0, 1, 2, \ldots, N - 1$ we need to determine the binary coefficients $b_0, b_1, \ldots, b_M$ and then compute the new address (as a decimal number) by carrying out the arithmetic indicated in Eq. 8.54. For example, consider an eight-point input data set as illustrated in Fig. 8.6. We have $M = \log_2 8 = 3$ (notice that this is also the number of butterfly stages) and for the data value $x(6)$ the binary address is 110, which is shorthand notation for $1 \cdot 2^2 + 1 \cdot 2^1 + 0 \cdot 2^0 = 6$ (*decimal*). Thus, the bit-reversed address is $0 \cdot 2^3 + 1 \cdot 2^1 + 1 \cdot 2^0 = 3$ (*decimal*) and, as seen in Fig. 8.6, $x(6)$ resides in the data storage location whose displacement from the base address is 3.

To write a program segment to accomplish this we need to determine the coefficients $b_0, b_1, \ldots, b_{M-1}$. For the least significant bit (b_0) this can be accomplished by dividing the decimal address by 2 and inspecting the resulting remainder which is the value of b_0. Notice that the remainder will always be 0 or 1. Some computer languages (FORTRAN, for example) have an intrinsic function to determine the desired remainder. We assume the existence of such a function and call it the MOD function (for

MODulo). The function has two arguments and is used in the following way

$$x \longleftarrow \text{MOD}(A,2).$$

The result is that the remainder obtained when A is divided by 2 is assigned to x.

Once b_0 has been determined, we next want to find the coefficient b_1. This can be done by dividing the original decimal address by 2, discarding the remainder, and again using the MOD function. To see why this works, consider the result when the expression in Eq. 8.53 is divided by 2

$$b_{M-1} \cdot 2^{M-2} + b_{M-2} \cdot 2^{M-3} + \cdots + b_1 \cdot 2^0 + b_0 \cdot 2^{-1}. \qquad (8.55)$$

The rightmost term in Eq. 8.55 is the remainder. To find b_1 we discard the remainder to obtain $A' = b_{M-1} \cdot 2^{M-2} + b_{M-2} \cdot 2^{M-3} + \cdots + b_1 \cdot 2^0$ and then find b_1 by evaluating MOD $(A',2)$. We then continue this procedure to find $b_2, b_3, \ldots, b_{M-1}$.

To make the computational procedure efficient we can form partial results for the sum of Eq. 8.54 as the b_is are computed. The pseudocode for accomplishing the bit reversal by using the approach just described is shown in Fig. 8.10.

The program section for evaluating the butterflies is characterized by three iterative loops. One of these is the stage loop—for an eight-point FFT, for example, there are three butterfly stages. The other two loops are concerned with selecting the points from memory to participate in a but-

FIGURE 8.10 Pseudocode for bit-reversal section of FFT program

```
(M = log₂N, the input data are stored in the one-dimensional
complex array XTMP (0),...,XTMP(N-1) and the bit-
reversed output data are stored in the one-dimensional
complex array X(0), X(1),...,X(N-1))

DO FOR K←0 TO N-1
    (initialize new address and present address)

    NEWADR ←0

    MADDR ←K

    DO FOR  I← 0  TO M-1

        LRMNDR ← MOD (MADDR, 2)

        NEWADR ← NEWADR + LRMNDR · 2^(M-1-I)

        MADDR ← MADDR/2

        (integer division so remainder is discarded)

    END DO

    X (NEWADR)← XTMP (K)

END DO
```

terfly calculation and setting the appropriate exponent for the weighting factor W_N. Referring to Fig. 8.6 we observe that there are at least two ways of proceeding with the butterfly calculations at a given stage. One approach is to simply work from top to bottom (or bottom to top) accessing pairs of points from memory and computing the weighting factor $W_N^R = e^{-j(2\pi R/N)}$ and the butterfly outputs according to the relationship

$$XNEW(TOP) = XOLD(TOP) + W_N^R \cdot XOLD(BOT)$$

$$XNEW(BOT) = XOLD(TOP) - W_N^R \cdot XOLD(BOT). \qquad (8.56)$$

A disadvantage of proceeding in this way is that the complex-valued weighting factors may have to be computed and recomputed several times at each stage. An alternative that avoids this inefficiency is to calculate a particular value of W_N^R at a given stage and then evaluate all butterflies that use this weighting factor. For example, in Fig. 8.8 at the second stage we could first evaluate the four butterflies that use the weighting factor W_{16}^0 and then evaluate the four butterflies that require W_{16}^4, and so on in the other stages. This is the approach we use.

We use *IWIDTH* to denote the separation in memory of points that participate in a butterfly and *ISPACE* to represent the separation in memory of the top (or bottom) points in consecutive butterflies that use the same weighting factor. Thus, again referring to Fig. 8.8, we see that in the second stage *IWIDTH* = 2 and *ISPACE* = 4. Similarly, at the third stage, *IWIDTH* = 4 and *ISPACE* = 8. In general, at the Lth stage it can be seen that

$$IWIDTH = 2^{L-1} \qquad (8.57)$$

and

$$ISPACE = 2^L. \qquad (8.58)$$

Also, the amount by which the exponent of $W_N = e^{-j2\pi/N}$ changes between adjacent butterflies in a pattern is given at the Lth stage by

$$S = N/2L. \qquad (8.59)$$

It is also observed that Eq. 8.56 can be replaced by an equivalent form which conserves memory use. Once a butterfly is evaluated its input values are no longer needed. Thus, Eq. 8.56 can be modified to the equivalent form

$$TMP = W_N^R \cdot X(BOT)$$

$$X(BOT) = X(TOP) - TMP$$

$$X(TOP) = X(TOP) + TMP. \qquad (8.60)$$

Notice that the order of the last two equations in Eq. 8.60 is important. An equivalent result is not obtained by interchanging these two equations.

FIGURE 8.11 Pseudocode
for butterfly evaluation section of FFT program

(the input data, assumed to be in bit-reversed order, are
stored in the complex array X(0), X(1), . . . , X(N-1))

```
PI ⟵ 3.141593
DO FOR    L ⟵ 1 TO M
    ISPACE ⟵ 2^L
    S ⟵ N/2^L
    IWIDTH ⟵ 2^(L-1)
```

(the above three statements can be much more
computationally efficient by writing them as
ISPACE ⟵ 2^L ; S ⟵ N/ISPACE ; IWIDTH ⟵ ISPACE/2)

```
    DO FOR   J ⟵ 0 TO (IWIDTH -1)
        R ⟵ S·J
        ALPHA ⟵ 2.·PI·R/N
        WTFAC ⟵ CMPLX(COS(ALPHA),-SIN(ALPHA))
        DO FOR ITOP ⟵ J TO (N-2) BY STEPS OF ISPACE
            IBOT ⟵ ITOP  + IWIDTH
            TMP ⟵ X(IBOT) · WTFAC
            X(IBOT) ⟵ X(ITOP) - TMP
            X(ITOP) ⟵ X(ITOP) + TMP
        END DO
    END DO
END DO
```

With this background information we can now determine a pseudocode representation of the butterfly evaluation section of the program.
The result is shown in Fig. 8.11. Notice that we have assumed the availability of the two trigonometric functions cosine (COS) and sine (SIN) and
the function CMPLX (a, b) which accepts the real arguments a and b and
yields the complex value $a + jb$. To produce a working FFT program we
would simply combine the code obtained from Figs. 8.10 and 8.11 with
appropriate code to read input data and write and/or plot both input and
output data. This is left as an exercise for the reader in Problem 8.6.

8.2 ▬ DECOMPOSITION IN FREQUENCY

Another way to decompose the calculation of DFTs is known as *Decomposition*, or *Decimation, In Frequency* (DIF). The idea is similar to the

Decomposition In Time (DIT) algorithm and leads to the same number of multiplies. In this section we briefly outline the development of the DIF algorithm and compare it with the previously discussed DIT approach.

As before, the starting point is with the definition of the DFT

$$X(k) = \sum_{n=0}^{N-1} x(n)W_N^{nk}, \qquad k = 0, 1, \ldots, N-1. \tag{8.61}$$

In the DIT algorithm we partitioned the time sequence into subsequences having even and odd indices. An alternative is to consider the DFTs of subsequences consisting of the first and last halves of the sequence $x(n)$. Doing this allows us to write the DFT as

$$X(k) = \sum_{n=0}^{N/2-1} x(n)W_N^{nk} + \sum_{n=N/2}^{N-1} x(n)W_N^{nk}, \quad k = 0, 1, \ldots, N-1. \tag{8.62}$$

The second summation can be expressed as

$$\sum_{n=N/2}^{N-1} x(n)W_N^{nk} = \sum_{n=0}^{N/2-1} x\left(n + \frac{N}{2}\right)W_N^{(n+N/2)k}$$

$$= \sum_{n=0}^{N/2-1} x\left(n + \frac{N}{2}\right)W_N^{(N/2)k}W_N^{nk}. \tag{8.63}$$

In addition,

$$W_N^{(N/2)k} = e^{-j(2\pi/N)(N/2)k} = e^{-j\pi k} = (-1)^k \tag{8.64}$$

so $X(k)$ from Eq. 8.62 is now given by

$$X(k) = \sum_{n=0}^{N/2-1} \left[x(n) + (-1)^k x\left(n + \frac{N}{2}\right)\right]W_N^{nk},$$

$$k = 0, 1, \ldots, N-1. \tag{8.65}$$

Even though this looks like an $N/2$-point DFT, it really isn't because we have the weighting factor W_N^{nk} rather than $W_{N/2}^{nk}$. A hint as to the next step is provided by the $(-1)^k$ found in the second term in the summation. For even values of k this term will be 1, while for odd values of k it will be -1. Let us then consider the even and odd values of k separately. In other words, we decompose in frequency, hence the term DIF algorithm. Doing this for even k gives

$$X(2k) = \sum_{n=0}^{N/2-1} \left[x(n) + x\left(n + \frac{N}{2}\right)\right]W_N^{2kn}, \quad k = 0, 1, \ldots, \frac{N}{2} - 1 \tag{8.66}$$

and for odd k we have

$$X(2k + 1) = \sum_{n=0}^{N/2-1} \left[x(n) - x\left(n + \frac{N}{2}\right) \right] W_N^{(2k+1)n},$$

$$k = 0, 1, \ldots, \frac{N}{2} - 1. \quad (8.67)$$

Next, we observe that

$$W_N^{2nk} = e^{-j(2\pi/N)2nk} = e^{-j(2\pi/N/2)nk} = W_{N/2}^{nk} \quad (8.68)$$

and

$$W_N^{(2k+1)n} = W_N^n W_N^{2kn} \quad (8.69)$$

but, by using Eq. 8.68 this becomes

$$W_N^{(2k+1)} = W_N^n W_{N/2}^{nk}. \quad (8.70)$$

Thus, we can now write Eq. 8.66 as

$$X(2k) = \sum_{n=0}^{N/2-1} \left[x(n) + x\left(n + \frac{N}{2}\right) \right] W_{N/2}^{nk}, \quad k = 0, 1, \ldots, \frac{N}{2} - 1 \quad (8.71)$$

or, in words,

$$X(2k) = \frac{N}{2}\text{-point DFT of the sequence } [x(n) + x(n + N/2)]. \quad (8.72)$$

In a similar way, using Eq. 8.69 we can now write Eq. 8.67 as

$$X(2k + 1) = \sum_{n=0}^{N/2-1} \left[x(n) - x\left(n + \frac{N}{2}\right) \right] W_N^n W_{N/2}^{nk},$$

$$k = 0, 1, \ldots, \frac{N}{2} - 1 \quad (8.73)$$

or, in words,

$$X(2k + 1) = \frac{N}{2}\text{-point DFT of } \left[x(n) - x\left(n + \frac{N}{2}\right) \right] W_N^n. \quad (8.74)$$

By looking at a signal flow graph representation of these equations we can obtain additional insight into what is required to carry out the computations. Equations 8.71 and 8.73 indicate that we must first form the sequences

$$x(n) + x\left(n + \frac{N}{2}\right) \quad (8.75)$$

and

$$\left[x(n) - x\left(n + \frac{N}{2}\right) \right] W_N^n. \quad (8.76)$$

FIGURE 8.12 Decomposition In Frequency butterfly

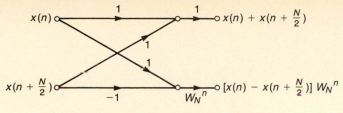

$$x(n) + x(n + \tfrac{N}{2})$$

$$[x(n) - x(n + \tfrac{N}{2})]\, W_N^{\,n}$$

(a) Signal flow graph for DIF butterfly

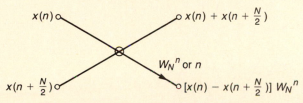

$$x(n) + x(n + \tfrac{N}{2})$$

$$W_N^{\,n} \text{ or } n$$

$$[x(n) - x(n + \tfrac{N}{2})]\, W_N^{\,n}$$

(b) Shorthand notation for DIF butterfly

In signal flow graph notation this is represented as shown in Fig. 8.12(a), or by the shorthand notation of Fig. 8.12(b). Using this notation for a 16-point DFT yields the result shown in Fig. 8.13. This process can then be repeated to decompose each of the eight-point DFTs into two four-point DFTs as shown in Fig. 8.14. Another step in this process yields the shorthand form of the signal flow graph given in Fig. 8.15.

Comparing Fig. 8.15 with its 16-point Decomposition In Time (DIT) counterpart in Fig. 8.8 we observe again the characteristic butterfly structure. In the DIF algorithm it is easily verified that there will also be $\log_2 N$ stages of butterflies and each stage consists of $N/2$ complex butterfly calculations. We note that DIT butterflies require multiplication by the weighting factor prior to addition and subtraction whereas addition and subtraction are followed by multiplication by the weighting factor in the DIF algorithm. Nevertheless, in either algorithm the number of complex multiplies is

$$\boxed{T_B = \frac{N}{2} \log_2 N, \text{ for } N \text{ a power of 2}} \quad . \tag{8.77}$$

As with the DIT algorithm, we see in Fig. 8.15 that the exponents of the weighting factors are periodic and in every periodic pattern the starting exponent is 0. Again numbering the butterfly stages from left to right starting with stage 1 and progressing to stage $\log_2 N$, we see that the increment between weighting factor exponents at the Lth stage is $2^{(L-1)}$. The memory separation of points which participate in a butterfly at the Lth stage is seen to be $N/2^L$. Notice that the exponent increments and the memory separations for the DIF algorithm have exchanged roles when compared with the DIT approach. In fact the two algorithms are charac-

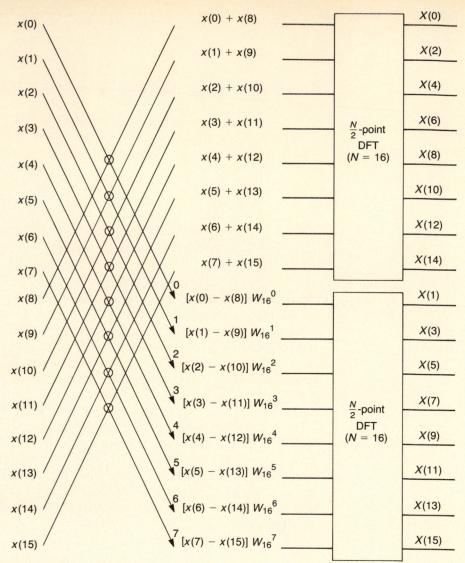

FIGURE 8.13 Decomposition In Frequency—first stage

$x(0)$

$x(1)$

$x(2)$

$x(3)$

$x(4)$

$x(5)$

$x(6)$

$x(7)$

$x(8)$

$x(9)$

$x(10)$

$x(11)$

$x(12)$

$x(13)$

$x(14)$

$x(15)$

$x(0) + x(8)$

$x(1) + x(9)$

$x(2) + x(10)$

$x(3) + x(11)$

$x(4) + x(12)$

$x(5) + x(13)$

$x(6) + x(14)$

$x(7) + x(15)$

$[x(0) - x(8)] W_{16}^0$

$[x(1) - x(9)] W_{16}^1$

$[x(2) - x(10)] W_{16}^2$

$[x(3) - x(11)] W_{16}^3$

$[x(4) - x(12)] W_{16}^4$

$[x(5) - x(13)] W_{16}^5$

$[x(6) - x(14)] W_{16}^6$

$[x(7) - x(15)] W_{16}^7$

$\frac{N}{2}$-point DFT $(N = 16)$

$\frac{N}{2}$-point DFT $(N = 16)$

$X(0)$

$X(2)$

$X(4)$

$X(6)$

$X(8)$

$X(10)$

$X(12)$

$X(14)$

$X(1)$

$X(3)$

$X(5)$

$X(7)$

$X(9)$

$X(11)$

$X(13)$

$X(15)$

terized by a form of duality. This observation is reinforced by noting that normal order is used for the input sequence to the DIF and the resulting output sequence is in bit-reversed order whereas the opposite is true for the DIT algorithm.

8.3 ■ VARIATIONS ON THE BASIC ALGORITHMS

In looking at the signal flow graph representations of the Decomposition In Time (DIT) and Decomposition In Frequency (DIF) FFT algorithms it may be seen that other arrangements of the graphs are possible. As our

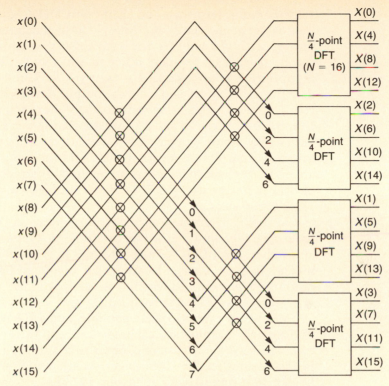

FIGURE 8.14 Decomposition In Frequency after two decomposition stages

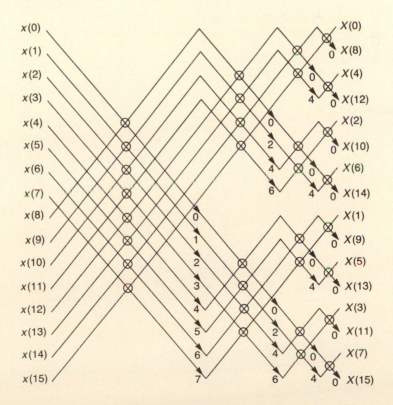

FIGURE 8.15 Sixteen-point DFT calculated by Decomposition In Frequency FFT

starting point, let us use the eight-point DIT SFG shown in Fig. 8.6. As long as the appropriate data values (nodes) continue to participate in butterflies with one another with the correct weighting factors, the graph can be rearranged in many different ways and still produce the correct input-output relationships. For example, we can decide to put the input data in normal order and have the output data in bit-reversed order. The resulting flow graph using the shorthand notation is shown in Fig. 8.16. In comparing Figs. 8.6 and 8.16 we see that whenever two data values are used as the inputs in a butterfly calculation, the output values can be put into the same storage locations that held the input values because these are no longer needed for any subsequent computations. As a consequence of this characteristic, the FFTs shown in Fig. 8.6 and 8.16 are called *in-place algorithms.*

Another arrangement is to have both input and output data in normal order. Fig. 8.17 shows how this can be done. Notice that this is no longer an in-place algorithm because after the first stage we cannot always immediately use a storage location that holds an input value to store the output of a butterfly in which this data participates. Thus, some temporary storage is needed at each stage.

Many other variations are possible, and some of the alternatives may be designed to exploit special hardware capabilities. For example, parallel calculations of more than one butterfly at a time will speed up the overall FFT computation. The interested reader should refer to Oppenheim and Shafer, 1975 and Rabiner and Gold, 1975 for a more complete discussion of this topic.

There are also other approaches to the fast computation of Discrete Fourier Transforms. One of these is known as the Winograd Fourier

FIGURE 8.16 Eight-point Decomposition In Time FFT: input in normal order, output in bit-reversed order

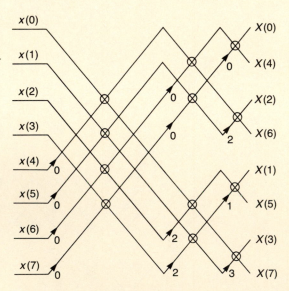

CHAPTER 8 THE FAST FOURIER TRANSFORM

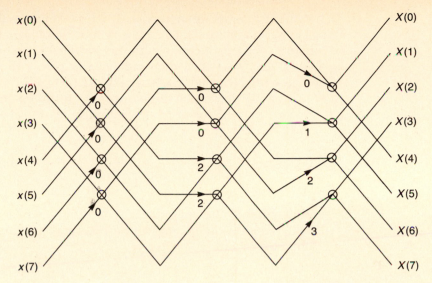

FIGURE 8.17 Eight-point Decomposition In Time FFT: input and output in normal order

Transform (Winograd, 1976, 1978) and another is called the prime factor transform (Good, 1960, 1971; Johnson and Burrus, 1983; Thomas, 1963). For an advanced treatment of these and other fast transforms see Blahut (1985), Elliott and Rao (1983), and McClellan and Rader (1979).

8.4 ■■ FAST CONVOLUTION

In Chapter Seven we showed that circular convolution can be made to yield the same results as linear convolution. This is accomplished by augmenting the sequences to be convolved by a sufficient number of zero-valued samples, a process known as *zero padding*. Thus, if we want to do linear convolution it can be done either by direct evaluation of the convolution sum, or by using the DFT approach. In Chapter Seven we compared the computational requirements for each of these two methods when used to perform the linear convolution of two N-point sequences. The direct approach requires N^2 real multiplies whereas using DFTs $48N^2$ real multiplies must be performed, indicating a great advantage in computation time for the direct approach. Now, however, we have FFTs available as an efficient way to compute DFTs so let's reexamine linear convolution using FFTs. Similar observations hold for performing correlation by FFTs.

Assume that we again wish to carry out the linear convolution of two N-point sequences.[†] Furthermore, let us assume that N is an integer power of 2, and that the number of multiplies is the dominant factor in

_____
[†]The approach used here can also be applied to the situation where the sequences to be convolved have different lengths. See, for example, Problem 8.4.

evaluating computational cost. The first step is to do the necessary zero padding and to use the FFT algorithms discussed previously. It is required that the number of points in the zero padded sequences is a power of 2, so let us add N zeros to each sequence to give a total of $2N$ points. The process to be carried out is illustrated in Fig. 8.18.

Now we determine the number of multiplies required. For each FFT shown, the number of complex multiplies for a sequence $2N$ samples long is

$$\text{number of complex multiplies per FFT} = \frac{2N}{2} \log_2 2N = N \log_2 2N$$

(8.78)

and including the inverse DFT operation, which could be performed using the alternate inversion formula, there are three such FFTs needed. Thus, we require

$$3 \times N \log_2 2N = 3N \log_2 2N \qquad (8.79)$$

complex multiplies for the FFTs. To compute the products $X_3'(k) = X_1'(k)X_2'(k)$ we need to do an additional $2N$ complex multiplies. Thus, the total number of complex multiplies required is

$$\text{number of complex multiplies} = 3N \log_2 2N + 2N. \qquad (8.80)$$

It might seem that the $1/N$ factor in the IDFT requires additional computations, but this can be avoided. Since $N = 2^\delta$, we can ignore the $1/N$ factor in the IDFT calculation and then shift each of the resulting values right by δ bits, thereby accomplishing the division by N. As a result, the total number of complex multiplies is as indicated by Eq. 8.80. Since there are four real multiplies for each complex multiply, the total number of real multiplies required to find $x_3'(n) = x_1(n) * x_2(n) = x_1'(n) \circledast x_2'(n)$ as in Fig. 8.18 is

$$\text{number of real multiplies} = 4[3N \log_2 2N + 2N]$$

$$= 12N \log_2 2N + 8N.$$

FIGURE 8.18 Fast convolution using FFTs

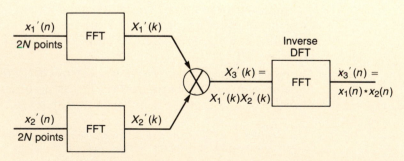

CHAPTER 8   THE FAST FOURIER TRANSFORM

Table 8.3 compares the number of real multiplies required to perform convolution using the radix-2 FFT with the number required for direct convolution. We see that for N of 128 or greater, the FFT approach has a considerable advantage. The table also shows that the number of multiplies required for the FFT approach is dominated by the calculation of the FFTs, not by the multiplication $X_1'(k)X_2'(k)$ because for $N \geq 64$ the FFT multiplies are more than 90 percent of the total.

As a result of the computational advantages of the FFT for large N, convolution using the FFT approach is known as *fast convolution*. It is this computational savings that makes FFTs so valuable, especially in real-time signal processing where convolution and correlation are frequently used operations.

TABLE 8.3 COMPARISON OF REAL MULTIPLIES TO PERFORM LINEAR CONVOLUTION OF TWO N-POINT REAL SEQUENCES USING THE DIRECT APPROACH AND BY FFTs

Number of points	Real multiplies for 3FFTs	Total number of real multiplies for convolution by FFTs	Number of real multiplies for direct convolution
N	$12N \log_2 2N$	$12N \log_2 2N + 8N$	N^2
4	144	176	16
8	384	448	64
16	960	1088	256
32	2304	2560	1024
64	5376	5888	4096
128	12,288	13,312	16,384
256	27,648	29,696	65,536
512	61,440	65,536	262,144
1024	135,168	143,360	1,048,576
2048	294,912	311,296	4,194,304

8.5 ■ REVIEW

Our goal in this chapter was to introduce a computationally efficient algorithm (FFT) for computing the Discrete Fourier Transform (DFT) of a sequence. The algorithms considered, which represent only a few of many possible approaches, require $\dfrac{N}{2} \log_2 N$ complex multiplies for an N-point DFT (remember that N must be an integer power of 2), whereas N^2 complex multiplies are required when the DFT definition is used. Having these FFT algorithms available caused us to reconsider the convolution of two sequences. In Chapter Seven we saw that direct convolution requires approximately 2 percent of the real multiplies needed to do convolution via DFTs. When the FFT is available to compute the DFTs, however, the computational advantage shifts dramatically to convolution using FFTs when N is larger than 128. Thus, in practice, convolution is most often performed by the fast convolution method using FFTs. In Chapter Seven we also saw that correlation can be performed by using DFTs. Thus, all of the foregoing statements about convolution apply to correlation as well. Of course, FFTs are often used in other situations where DFTs are needed, such as in performing spectrum analysis.

VOCABULARY AND IMPORTANT RELATIONS

a) Weighting factor

$$W_N^{nk} = e^{-i(2\pi/N)nk}$$

b) Signal flow graph known as a butterfly. See Fig. 8.1.

c) Decomposition In Time (DIT)

Two-point transform

$$X(k) = x(0) + x(1)W_2^k, \qquad k = 0, 1 \tag{8.3}$$

Four-point transform

$$X(k) = X_1(k) + W_4^k X_2(k), \qquad k = 0, 1, 2, 3 \tag{8.15}$$

where

$$X_1(k) = [\text{two-point transform of } x_1(n) = x(2n)],$$
$$k = 0, 1, 2, 3$$

and

$$X_2(k) = [\text{two-point transform of } x_2(n) = x(2n + 1)],$$

$$k = 0, 1, 2, 3$$

Eight-point transform

$$X(k) = \sum_{n=0}^{3} x_1(n)W_4^{nk} + W_8^k \sum_{n=0}^{3} x_2(n)W_4^{nk}$$

$$= X_1(k) + W_8^k X_2(k), \qquad k = 0, 1, \ldots, 7 \tag{8.34}$$

where

$$X_1(k) = [\text{four-point transform of } x_1(n) = x(2n)],$$

$$k = 0, 1, \ldots, 7$$

and

$$X_2(k) = [\text{four-point transform of } x_2(n) = x(2n + 1)],$$

$$k = 0, 1, \ldots, 7$$

Sixteen-point transform

See Fig. 8.8.

d) Number of butterflies where number of points N is a power of 2

$$T_B = \frac{N}{2} \log_2 N = \text{Number of complex multiplies for an}$$

$$N\text{-point FFT} \tag{8.48}$$

e) Number of complex multiplies as a function of N
See Table 8.1 or Fig. 8.9.

f) Bit-reversing algorithm for $N = 16$
See Table 8.2.

g) Decomposition in Frequency (DIF)
See Figs. 8.12–8.15.

h) In-place algorithms
See Figs. 8.6 and 8.16.

i) Input data and output data in normal order
See Fig. 8.17.

j) Fast convolution
Implementation—See Fig. 8.18.
Compared with direct evaluation of convolution—See Table 8.3.

PROBLEMS

Reinforcement

8.1 The basic butterfly describing in-place computation of the Discrete Fourier Transform of a two-point sequence is given in Fig. P8.1(a). Notice that two complex multiplies are needed.

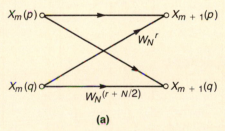

(a)

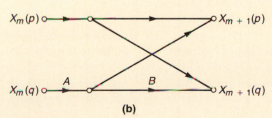

(b)

FIGURE P8.1

a) Write the equations for $X_{m+1}(p)$ and $X_{m+1}(q)$.

b) The butterfly in Fig. P8.1(b) will reduce the complex multiplies to only one per stage. From your results in part (a), find the gains A and B.

8.2 a) Use the signal flow graph in Fig. P8.2 to complete the following matrix equations (no minus signs allowed in the matrices):

$$\mathbf{X}_1 = \begin{bmatrix} X_1(0) \\ X_1(1) \\ X_1(2) \\ X_1(3) \end{bmatrix} = \begin{bmatrix} \\ \\ \\ \end{bmatrix} \begin{bmatrix} x_0(0) \\ x_0(2) \\ x_0(1) \\ x_0(3) \end{bmatrix}$$

$$\mathbf{X}_2 = \begin{bmatrix} X_2(0) \\ X_2(1) \\ X_2(2) \\ X_2(3) \end{bmatrix} = \begin{bmatrix} \\ \\ \\ \end{bmatrix} \mathbf{X}_1$$

b) Suppose that $x_0(n) = \{0, 1, 2, 3\}$. Use either the matrix or the flowgraph to calculate the vectors $\mathbf{X}_1$ and $\mathbf{X}_2$, the outputs of the two stages. How does one find $X(k)$ from the answers?

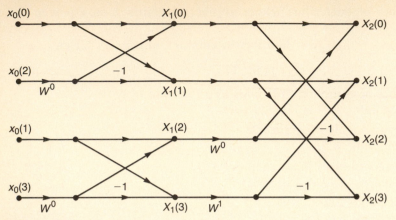

FIGURE P8.2

c) A certain long signal contains about 100,000 points. Assume that an FFT (power of 2) program is available to transform the entire signal as a unit. Determine the approximate ratio of the time required for the FFT to the time required for a direct DFT evaluation.

8.3 Starting with the definition

$$W_N{}^{nk} = e^{-j(2\pi/N)nk}$$

show the following relationships:

a) $W_N{}^0 = W_M{}^0$ for all M and N

b) $W_N{}^{nk\ell} = W_{N/\ell}{}^{nk}$, ℓ = any integer

c) $W_N{}^{(N/2)k} = (-1)^k$

d) $W_N{}^{Nk} = 1$ for all k.

8.4 A real-valued input sequence $x(n)$ has M_1 samples. The data are passed through a digital filter whose unit sample response, $h(n)$, is M_2 samples in duration. It is desired to find $y(n)$, the linear convolution of $x(n)$ and $h(n)$. You are to consider the mathematical complexity of two approaches for doing this:

a) Convolving $x(n)$ with $h(n)$.

b) Calculating the appropriate DFTs (using the radix-2 FFT algorithm) based on $x(n)$ and $h(n)$ and then calculating $y(n)$.

Determine the approximate number of real multiplies that would be required for each of the two alternatives described if $M_1 = 600$ and $M_2 = 100$.

Extension and Generalization

8.5 It is possible to further reduce the number of multiplies required to implement an FFT by not doing any multiplies where the weighting factor $W_N{}^\ell$ is equal to ± 1.

a) Using this method determine the number of real multiplies required for an eight-point DIT FFT.

b) Repeat part (a) for a sixteen-point DIT FFT.

c) Generalize the results of parts (a) and (b) to an arbitrary value of N where N is an integer power of 2.

d) If a computer program for computing FFTs is written to incorporate the results of (a)–(c), how will it differ from a program that does not attempt to reduce the number of multiplies to a minimum?

8.6 a) Using the pseudocode of Figs. 8.10 and 8.11, write and document a digital computer subroutine (procedure) to compute the Decomposition-In-Time radix-2 FFT. Assume that the input data may be complex and that the number of points is $N \le 1024$.

b) Develop and solve several test problems to verify the correctness of the program developed in part (a).

8.7 The result of sampling a 0.5-second interval of an analog signal is a sequence of 1024 equally spaced samples.

a) What is the frequency resolution in Hz of the DFT of the sequence?

b) What is the highest frequency that should be present in the signal from which the samples are taken?

c) Suppose that it is desired to determine the Fourier spectrum only in the range of discrete frequencies between $f_1 = 150$ Hz and $f_2 = 154$ Hz (f_1 and f_2 are included). How many complex multiplies would be needed if

  i) The DIT in-place FFT algorithm with input data in bit-reversed order and output data in normal order is used to compute the DFT for all discrete frequency points.

  ii) The DIF in-place FFT algorithm with input data in normal order and output data in bit-reversed order is used to compute the DFT for all discrete frequency points.

  iii) The definition of the DFT, Eq. 8.1, is used to calculate only those frequency points of interest.

d) For how many frequency points would the DFT coefficients be needed before the FFT algorithm is more computationally efficient than using the DFT definition?

8.8   It is desired to linearly convolve a very long input data stream with a 128-point FIR filter whose unit sample response is $h(n)$. The overlap-add method and a 256-point FFT are to be used.

a) How long should the input records be to use the FFT most efficiently?

b) For what values of the sample index n will the sectional convolutions overlap?

c) How many real multiplies are required for each section of the input record?

d) Compare the result of part (c) with the number of multiplies required for each section if direct convolution is used.

8.9   Consider the multiplication of two complex numbers $(a_1 + jb_1) \cdot (a_2 + jb_2)$.

a) Write out the product as $c_1 + jd_1$ and determine the number of real multiplies and adds required to find the complex number $c_1 + jd_1$.

b) Show that $c_1 = (a_1 - b_1)b_2 + a_1(a_2 - b_2)$ and $d_1 = (a_1 - b_1)b_2 + b_1(a_2 + b_2)$ are equivalent

expressions for the ones you determined in part (a).

c) Determine the number of real multiplies and adds required to determine c_1 and d_1 using the expression in part (b) and compare with the results of part (a).

8.10   If the FFT is used to compute the DFT of an M-point sequence we anticipate a considerable computational savings. Indeed Table 8.1 shows this to be the case. However what if M is not a power of 2? For example, if $M = 20$ a 32-point FFT must be used, so we zero pad the 20-point sequence and compute the FFT of the resulting 32-point sequence. You are to investigate the effect on computational requirements of having to add the zeros. Select some values of M that you believe will be worst in the sense that the FFT will have to be done on a much larger sequence than if the DFT is computed directly from the definition, and compute the computational cost (i.e., number of complex multiplies) for an FFT and a direct DFT approach.

8.11   A signal to be processed is given by $x(t) = \cos(500\pi t)\cos(2000\pi t)$.

a) Determine the minimum sampling frequency to avoid aliasing.

b) $x(t)$ is a periodic signal. Sketch the DFS spectrum you expect if the sampling rate found in part (a) is used.

c) Use an FFT program to compute the DFS of $x(t)$ assuming a record length of 8 ms and 1024 points.

d) Repeat part (c) using a record length of 9 ms and 1024 points.

8.12   Shown in Fig. 8.6(b) is an SFG for an eight-point DIT FFT algorithm where shorthand notation is used for the weighting factors. Draw a similar sort of SFG for a 32-point DIT algorithm.

8.13   a) Use the FFT subroutine written in Problem 8.6 to develop a computer program to compute the circular convolution or correlation of two sequences of length N, where N is an integer power of 2 and $N \le 256$.

  b) Devise some test problems and do enough testing to convince yourself that your program produces correct answers.

c) Use your program from part (a) to find the circular convolution and circular correlation of the sequence with $N = 8$ shown in Fig. P7.40(a) with each of the sequences shown in Fig. P7.40(b).

8.14 FFT programs generally require complex input data. Often, however, the input data are real, so it is natural to consider whether the "extra" capability of the FFT can be used to advantage in such cases. The goal in this problem is to show that when the input data are real it is possible to compute two N-point FFTs simultaneously.

a) Consider two real N-point sequences $f(n)$ and $g(n)$ and the complex N-point sequence $x(n) = f(n) + jg(n)$. Show that the DFT $X(k)$ is given by $\quad X(k) = [F_r(k) - G_i(k)] + j[F_i(k) + G_r(k)]$ where

$$F(k) = \mathcal{D}[f(n)] \quad G(k) = \mathcal{D}[g(n)]$$

$$F_r(k) = \text{Re}[F(k)] \quad F_i(k) = \text{Im}[F(k)]$$

$$G_r(k) = \text{Re}[G(k)] \quad G_i(k) = \text{Im}[G(k)].$$

b) The DFT $X(k)$ can also be written as

$$X(k) = \left[\frac{X_r(k)}{2} + \frac{X_r(N-k)}{2}\right]$$

$$+ \left[\frac{X_r(k)}{2} - \frac{X_r(N-k)}{2}\right]$$

$$+ j\left[\frac{X_i(k)}{2} + \frac{X_i(N-k)}{2}\right]$$

$$+ j\left[\frac{X_i(k)}{2} - \frac{X_i(N-k)}{2}\right] \quad \text{(P8.14)}$$

where $X_r(k) = \text{Re}[X(k)]$ and $X_i(k) = \text{Im}[X(k)]$.

Using the implicit periodicity of a DFT, i.e., $X(N + k) = X(k)$ and $X(-k) = X(N - k)$, show that the terms in Eq. P8.14 can be written as $X(k) = X_{re}(k) + X_{ro}(k) + jX_{ie}(k) + jX_{io}(k)$ where $X_{re}(k)$ and $X_{ie}(k)$ are even functions of k and $X_{ro}(k)$ and $X_{io}(k)$ are odd functions of k.

c) Substitute $f(n) + jg(n)$ for $x(n)$ in the DFT definition, and use the Euler relationship to show that

$$X(k) = \sum_{n=0}^{N-1} f(n) \cos\left(\frac{2\pi nk}{N}\right)$$

$$+ \sum_{n=0}^{N-1} g(n) \sin\left(\frac{2\pi nk}{N}\right)$$

$$+ j \sum_{n=0}^{N-1} g(n) \cos\left(\frac{2\pi nk}{N}\right)$$

$$- j \sum_{n=0}^{N-1} f(n) \sin\left(\frac{2\pi nk}{N}\right).$$

Demonstrate that the first and third terms in this expression are even sequences in k and that the second and fourth terms are odd sequences in k.

d) Use the results from parts (b) and (c) to show that

$$F(k) = \left[\frac{X_r(k) + X_r(N-k)}{2}\right]$$

$$+ j\left[\frac{X_i(k) - X_i(N-k)}{2}\right], \quad k = 0, 1, \ldots, N-1$$

$$G(k) = \left[\frac{X_i(k) + X_i(N-k)}{2}\right]$$

$$- j\left[\frac{X_r(k) - X_r(N-k)}{2}\right], \quad k = 0, 1, \ldots, N-1$$

e) Use the result of part (d) to describe a procedure for computing the two N-point FFTs $F(k)$ and $G(k)$ by instead computing the single N-point FFT $X(k)$ and "unscrambling" the results.

f) Determine the computational savings obtained by following the procedure of part (e). Assume that a complex addition "costs" 0.1 times the cost of a complex multiply.

8.15 A finite impulse response (FIR) filter has been designed to satisfy a given set of specifications. The next step is to consider how to implement the filter. The following four possibilities are to be considered:

i) Computer implementation of the filter's difference equation

$$y(n) = \sum_{k=0}^{L} b_k x(n - k)$$

ii) Direct convolution of the filter's unit sample response $h(n)$ with the input sequence $x(n)$.

iii) Indirect convolution of the filter's unit sample response with the input sequence using Discrete Fourier Transforms.

iv) Same as (iii), but using FFTs.

The following assumptions are to be made:

The value of L is 20.

The input sequence $x(n)$ is real and nonzero only in the interval $0 \leq n \leq 479$.

The DFT and FFT programs available are written to accept complex input data.

a) Find the number of real multiplies required to compute the nonzero values of the output sequence using the filter's difference equation as the implementation.

b) Repeat part (a) for direct convolution of input and unit sample response.

c) Repeat part (a) for DFT implementation of convolution.

d) Repeat part (a) for FFT implementation of convolution.

State clearly any additional assumptions you need to make.

8.16 An infinite impulse response (IIR) filter has been designed to satisfy a given set of specifications. The next step is to consider how to implement the filter. The following four possibilities are to be considered:

i) Computer implementation of the filter's difference equation

$$y(n) = \sum_{k=1}^{N} a_k y(n-k) + \sum_{k=0}^{L} b_k x(n-k).$$

ii) Direct convolution of the filter's unit sample response $h(n)$ with the input sequence $x(n)$.

iii) Indirect convolution of the filter's unit sample response with the input sequence using Discrete Fourier Transforms.

iv) Same as (iii), but using FFTs.

The following assumptions are to be made:

The values of L and N are 20.

When implementing the filter by DFTs or FFTs the Discrete Fourier Transform of the filter's unit sample response can be precomputed and stored.

The input sequence $x(n)$ is nonzero only in the interval $0 \leq n \leq 479$.

The DFT and FFT programs available are written to accept complex input data.

The unit sample response of the filter is essentially zero for $n \geq 50$.

a) Find the number of real multiplies required to compute the nonzero values of the output sequence using the filter's difference equation as the implementation.

b) Repeat part (a) for direct convolution of input and unit sample response.

c) Repeat part (a) for DFT implementation of convolution.

d) Repeat part (a) for FFT implementation of convolution.

e) Comment on your results indicating which approach is best in this case. Also comment on what assumptions might cause one of the other approaches to be better.

8.17 Repeat Problem 8.16 with the number of samples in the input equal to 460 rather than 480.

REFERENCES AND OTHER SOURCES OF INFORMATION

Blahut, R. E. 1985. *Fast Algorithms for Digital Signal Processing.* Reading, Massachusetts: Addison-Wesley.

Cooley, J. W., and J. W. Tukey. 1965. "An Algorithm for the Machine Calculation of Complex Fourier Series." *Math. Comp.* 19:297–301.

Elliott, D. F., and R. Rao. 1983. *Fast Transforms: Algorithms, Analyses and Applications.* New York: Academic Press.

Good, I. J. 1958. "The Interaction Algorithm and Practical Fourier Analysis." *J. Royal Statistical Society.* Ser B 20: 361–375; Addendum, 22 (1960): 372–375.

Good, I. J. 1971. "The Relationship between Two Fast Fourier Transforms." *IEEE Trans. Comp.* C-20: 310–317.

Gentleman, W. M., and G. Sande. 1966. "Fast Fourier Transforms—For Fun and Profit." *AFIPS Proc. 1966 Fall Joint Computer Conf. 29.* Spartan Books, pp. 563–578.

Johnson, H. W., and G. S. Burrus. 1983. "The Design of Optimal DFT Algorithms Using Dynamic Programming." *IEEE Trans. Acoustics, Speech and Signal Processing.* ASSP-31: 378–387.

Liu, B. ed. 1975. *Digital Filters and the Fast Fourier Transform, Benchmark Papers in Electrical Engineering and Computer Science.* Stroudsburg, Pa: Dowden, Hutchinson and Ross.

McClellan, J. H., and C. M. Rader. 1979. *Number Theory in Digital Signal Processing.* Englewood Cliffs, New Jersey: Prentice-Hall, Inc.

Oppenheim, A. V., and R. W. Shafer. 1975. *Digital Signal Processing.* Englewood Cliffs, New Jersey: Prentice-Hall, Inc.

Rabiner, L. R., and B. Gold. 1975. *Theory and Applications of Digital Signal Processing.* Englewood Cliffs, New Jersey: Prentice-Hall, Inc.

Thomas, L. H. 1963. "Using a Computer to Solve Problems in Physics." *Applications of Digital Computers.* Boston, Massachusetts: Ginn and Co.

Winograd, S. 1976. "On Computing the Discrete Fourier Transform." *Proc. Nat. Acad. Sci.,* USA. 73:1005–1006.

Winograd, S. 1978. "On Computing the Discrete Fourier Transform". *Math. Comp.* 32: 175–199.

CHAPTER 9

Nonrecursive Filter Design

9.0 ■ PREVIEW

In Chapters Five and Six, filter design was introduced from an intuitive, elementary, and more or less unstructured point of view. The concepts presented gave us some good ideas about predicting the frequency response of a given filter as well as getting a basic design started from a specified or desired frequency response. No restrictions were placed on the types of filters studied—both recursive (nominally IIR) and nonrecursive (nominally FIR) systems were considered. The definitions of ideal filters were established and we observed the difficulty in approximating these ideal characteristics with simple structures. In this chapter, Nonrecursive Filter Design, and the next, Recursive Filter Design, we develop some systematic procedures for designing filters that approximate desired ideal characteristics.

All the material in this chapter is concerned with nonrecursive filters having difference equations of the form

$$y(n) = \sum_{k=0}^{L} b_k x(n - k) \tag{9.1}$$

that can also be described by a system diagram such as is shown in Fig. 9.1. Much of the discussion is based upon the ubiquitous Fourier Series that was introduced in the preview to Chapter Seven, where we found the exponential series

$$y(\alpha) = \sum_{n=-\infty}^{n=+\infty} y_n e^{-jn\alpha} \tag{9.2}$$

that involves an infinite number of complex exponentials and can represent a periodic waveform. We have been working with the periodic frequency response $H(e^{j\theta})$ of discrete systems described by the summation

$$H(e^{j\theta}) = \sum_{n=-\infty}^{n=+\infty} h(n) e^{-jn\theta} \tag{9.3}$$

that is quite similar to Eq. 9.2, the exponential form of the Fourier Series. The first goal in this chapter, therefore, is to find a way to compute the

FIGURE 9.1 Realization of a nonrecursive filter

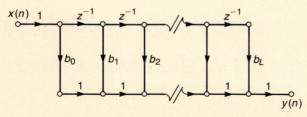

Fourier coefficients y_n of Eq. 9.2 and then relate them to the unit sample response $h(n)$ in Eq. 9.3.

Several different kinds of filters are designed using this Fourier technique. These include filters that approximate piecewise constant characteristics, such as lowpass, highpass, bandpass, and bandstop, as well as special purpose systems that differentiate—an operation needed in many digital processing systems. In the process of investigating several filter designs we observe that although Eq. 9.3 calls for an infinite number of complex exponentials to represent the periodic function $H(e^{j\theta})$, as a practical matter, it is necessary to use only a finite number of terms. This introduces the issue of how accurately a finite series approximates the desired periodic frequency response. We find that the frequency responses of these filters composed from a finite number of terms can be improved by the use of *windowing*, a technique used by R. W. Hamming, J. von Hann, J. F. Kaiser, and others, and comparisons of window functions can be made.

Linear phase as an attribute of an ideal filter was introduced in Chapter Four. Here we examine the properties of linear phase and then use Fourier methods to design filters with this characteristic. Brief mention is also made of computer-aided-design (CAD) techniques that can be used to design linear phase filters. Comb filters are also introduced.

Finally, we use the Discrete Fourier Transform (DFT) and Inverse Discrete Fourier Transform (IDFT) to approximate the Fourier Series coefficients found by analytical methods in the first part of the chapter. We learn that by taking a sufficient number of samples N of the frequency response $H(e^{j\theta})$, the IDFT algorithm can be used to estimate the unit sample response values $h(n)$ that are the Fourier coefficients. If N is a power of 2, an FFT algorithm from Chapter Eight can be used to find the IDFT.

9.1 ▬ DESIGN BY FOURIER SERIES

In Chapter Four, we found that the frequency response of an LTI system was periodic, with a period 2π, i.e., $H(e^{j\theta}) = H(e^{j(\theta+k2\pi)})$, $k = \pm 1$, $\pm 2, \ldots$. Several examples of the magnitude portion of a frequency response are shown in Fig. 9.2. We also discovered that the frequency response $H(e^{j\theta})$ and the unit sample response $h(n)$ are related through the frequency response definition, namely

$$H(e^{j\theta}) = \sum_{n=-\infty}^{n=+\infty} h(n)\, e^{-j\theta n} \qquad (9.4)$$

or for an analog signal sampled at spacing T by

$$H(e^{j\omega T}) = \sum_{n=-\infty}^{n=+\infty} h(nT)\, e^{-j\omega Tn}. \qquad (9.5)$$

FIGURE 9.2 Frequency response magnitude characteristics of four passband filters

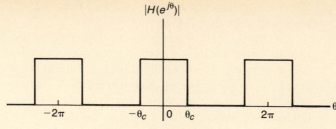

(a) Ideal lowpass filter

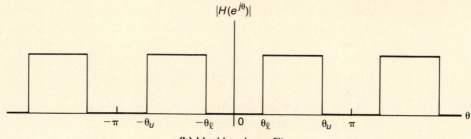

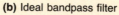

(b) Ideal bandpass filter

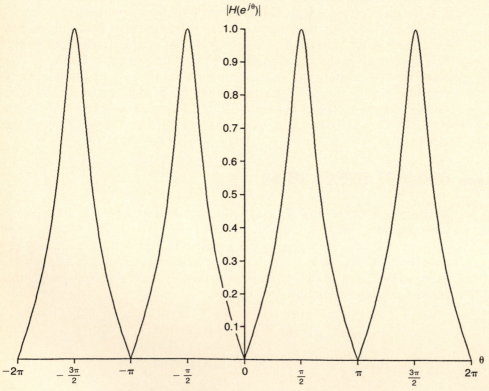

(c) Bandpass digital filter frequency response magnitude

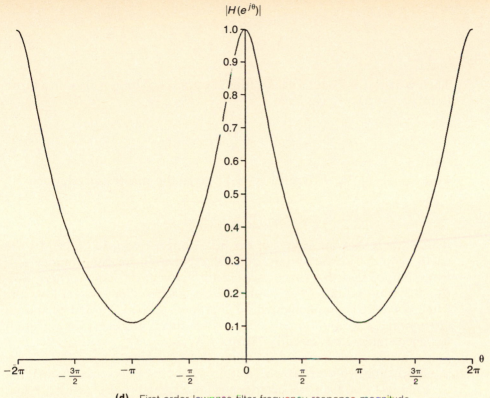

(d) First-order lowpass filter frequency response magnitude

FIGURE 9.2 Frequency response magnitude characteristics of four passband filters

For a causal nonrecursive system described by the difference equation

$$y(n) = \sum_{k=0}^{k=L} b_k\, x(n - k) \tag{9.6}$$

we found in Chapter Four that if the input is $x(n) = e^{jn\theta}$ then the steady-state output is

$$y_{ss}(n) = e^{jn\theta}\, H(e^{j\theta}) \tag{9.7}$$

where $e^{jn\theta}$ is the eigenfunction and $H(e^{j\theta})$ its associated eigenvalue. Substituting Eq. 9.7 into the left side of Eq. 9.6 and $x(n) = e^{jn\theta}$ into the right side we can write out a few terms giving

$$e^{jn\theta}\, H(e^{j\theta}) = b_0 e^{jn\theta} + b_1 e^{jn\theta} e^{-j\theta} + b_2 e^{jn\theta} e^{-j2\theta} + \cdots + b_L e^{jn\theta} e^{-jL\theta}. \tag{9.8}$$

The eigenfunction $e^{jn\theta}$ is present in all terms and can be removed yielding the frequency response

$$H(e^{j\theta}) = b_0 + b_1 e^{-j\theta} + b_2 e^{-j2\theta} + \cdots + b_L e^{-jL\theta} \tag{9.9}$$

or

$$H(e^{j\theta}) = \sum_{n=0}^{n=L} b_n e^{-jn\theta}. \tag{9.10}$$

Then writing Eq. 9.4 for a causal filter, i.e., $h(n) = 0$ for $n < 0$, with a finite number of delays L we have

$$H(e^{j\theta}) = \sum_{n=0}^{n=L} h(n)e^{-jn\theta}. \tag{9.11}$$

Comparison of Eq. 9.10 with Eq. 9.11 gives the important relation

$$\boxed{h(n) = b_n} \tag{9.12}$$

which states that the values of the unit sample response $h(n)$ equal the coefficients b_n in the system difference equation for the nonrecursive filter. Notice that this is the same result derived in Chapter Three (Section 3.3) from a different point of view. As discussed in Chapter Five, the filter is typically implemented by a general purpose computer and an appropriate program, a microcoded digital signal processor, or a custom designed integrated circuit. Figure 9.3 shows the realization of a nonrecursive filter having a finite number of delays.

In filter design we start with a desired frequency response characteristic and must find the filter coefficients (or weights) $b_0, b_1, \ldots, b_L$. Equation 9.4 gives a relation for the frequency response $H(e^{j\theta})$ in terms of the filter weights $h(n)$, but we need an expression for the filter weights in terms of the frequency response. The appropriate relationship, which will be derived in the next section, is

$$h(n) = \frac{1}{2\pi} \int_{\theta_0}^{\theta_0 + 2\pi} H(e^{j\theta})e^{jn\theta}d\theta, \qquad n = 0, \pm1, \pm2, \ldots \tag{9.13}$$

and Eq. (9.13) together with Eq. 9.4 constitute a *Fourier Series pair.* That is, if either $H(e^{j\theta})$ or $h(n)$ is known or given, the other part of the pair can be determined. This is shown diagrammatically in Eq. 9.14 with $\theta_0 = -\pi$. The double-ended arrow indicates the "goes either way" nature of this process.

FIGURE 9.3 A nonrecursive filter with L delays

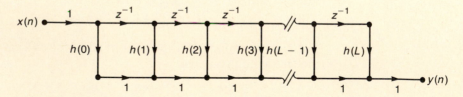

$$H(e^{j\theta}) = \sum_{n=-\infty}^{n=\infty} h(n)\, e^{-jn\theta} \longleftrightarrow h(n) = \frac{1}{2\pi} \int_{-\pi}^{\pi} H(e^{j\theta}) e^{jn\theta} d\theta \qquad (9.14)$$

Synthesis   Analysis

Notice that here, unlike the Discrete Fourier Series of Chapter Seven, we are dealing with an infinite series whose independent variable θ is a continuous variable. As a consequence, the relationship given in the right side of Eq. 9.14 for finding the Fourier coefficients $h(n)$ is an integral rather than a sum as in the discrete case. We also notice a difference in the sign of the exponentials here and in Chapter Seven—this is simply a matter of convenience. The equation for $H(e^{j\theta})$ is known as a *synthesis expression* because the frequency response is synthesized or put together from the weighted sum of an infinite number of complex exponentials $e^{-jn\theta}$, $n = 0, \pm 1, \ldots$ The integral relation for the filter coefficients $h(n)$, on the other hand, is an *analysis expression* in that the area under the $H(e^{j\theta})e^{jn\theta}$ curve determines the corresponding $h(n)$ for all values of n. In the case of the sampled analog situation we write the pair of Eq. 9.14 as

$$H(e^{j\omega T}) = \sum_{n=-\infty}^{n=+\infty} h(nT)e^{-jn\omega T} \longleftrightarrow h(nT) = \frac{1}{\omega_s} \int_{-\omega_s/2}^{\omega_s/2} H(e^{j\omega T}) e^{jn\omega T} d\omega \qquad (9.15)$$

where $\omega_s = 2\pi f_s = 2\pi/T$ is the sampling frequency in rad/s.

A design procedure for a digital filter is now very apparent. The steps are:

PROCEDURE

1. Decide upon a desired frequency response $H(e^{j\theta})$ which will, of course, be determined by the particular application of the filter.

2. Determine the unit sample response $h(n)$ that will produce the desired frequency response. In other words, find the values of $h(n)$ in Eq. 9.13. The details of how to do this are described in the next section.

3. Modify the unit sample response $h(n)$ to produce a practical filter, for from Eq. 9.14, we see that an infinite number of values for $h(n)$ are required to produce the frequency response $H(e^{j\theta})$. This, of course, is impractical and $h(n)$ must be truncated or restricted to a reasonable number of terms.

4. Implement the digital filter by a general purpose computer and an appropriate program, a microcoded digital signal processor, or a custom designed integrated circuit.

We are now ready to begin with item two listed above with the assumption that a desired frequency response has been determined or given.

9.1.1 Fourier Coefficients

We start with the desired frequency response

$$H(e^{j\theta}) = \sum_{m=-\infty}^{m=+\infty} h(m)\, e^{-jm\theta} \tag{9.16}$$

where we want to determine the unit sample response $h(n)$. First, we multiply both sides of Eq. 9.16 by $e^{jn\theta}$ which gives

$$e^{jn\theta}\, H(e^{j\theta}) = \sum_{m=-\infty}^{m=+\infty} h(m)e^{-jm\theta}e^{jn\theta} \tag{9.17}$$

or

$$e^{jn\theta}H(e^{j\theta}) = \sum_{m=-\infty}^{m=+\infty} h(m)e^{j(n-m)\theta}. \tag{9.18}$$

Integrating both sides from $\theta = 0$ to $\theta = 2\pi$ (over one period) we have

$$\int_0^{2\pi} e^{jn\theta}H(e^{j\theta})d\theta = \int_0^{2\pi} \sum_{m=-\infty}^{m=+\infty} h(m)e^{j(n-m)\theta}d\theta. \tag{9.19}$$

Interchanging the order of summation and integration on the right side yields

$$\int_0^{2\pi} H(e^{j\theta})e^{jn\theta}d\theta = \sum_{m=-\infty}^{m=+\infty} h(m)\left[\int_0^{2\pi} e^{j(n-m)\theta}d\theta\right]. \tag{9.20}$$

The key to this development is the bracketed integral on the right which with the help of the Euler relation may be put into a more easily interpreted form, namely

$$\int_0^{2\pi} e^{j(n-m)\theta}d\theta = \int_0^{2\pi} \cos(n-m)\theta d\theta + j\int_0^{2\pi} \sin(n-m)\theta d\theta. \tag{9.21}$$

Now for $n \neq m$, $\cos(n-m)\theta$ and $\sin(n-m)\theta$ are periodic sinusoids that have been drawn for $n - m = 3$ in Fig. 9.4. But, in Eq. 9.21 we are integrating over an interval of 2π radians, and it is clearly seen that the net areas under the $\cos 3\theta$ vs. θ curve and under the $\sin 3\theta$ vs. θ curve are zero in both cases. Thus, the bracketed integral goes to zero except for $m = n$ where we have

$$\int_0^{2\pi} e^{j(n-n)\theta}d\theta = \int_0^{2\pi} 1 d\theta = \theta\Big|_0^{2\pi} = 2\pi, \qquad m = n. \tag{9.22}$$

So the summation on the right side of Eq. 9.20 results in only the single term $h(n) \cdot [2\pi]$, thus

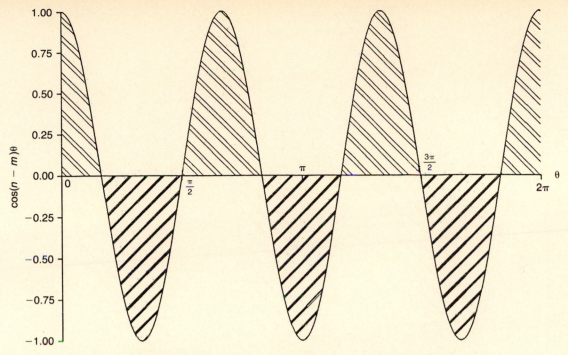

(a) Periodicity of $\cos(n - m)\theta$ resulting in a shaded area of zero

FIGURE 9.4(a)

$$\int_0^{2\pi} H(e^{j\theta})e^{jn\theta}d\theta = h(n) \cdot [2\pi]. \qquad (9.23)$$

The important result is that the Fourier coefficients, which equal the values of the unit sample response, are given by

$$h(n) = \frac{1}{2\pi}\int_0^{2\pi} H(e^{j\theta})e^{jn\theta}d\theta. \qquad (9.24)$$

In a more general way, this may be written

$$h(n) = \frac{1}{2\pi}\int_{\theta_0}^{2\pi+\theta_0} H(e^{j\theta})e^{jn\theta}d\theta \qquad (9.25)$$

because the integrals of Eq. 9.21 (see Fig. 9.4) are zero for any period of 2π radians as long as $m \neq n$. In other words, we can start at any θ_0 and integrate until $\theta = \theta_0 + 2\pi$ and the net area for this period is zero except when $n = m$.

9.1.2 Lowpass Design

We now use the Fourier method to find the coefficients of a filter designed to approximate the ideal lowpass characteristics of Fig. 9.5 where the

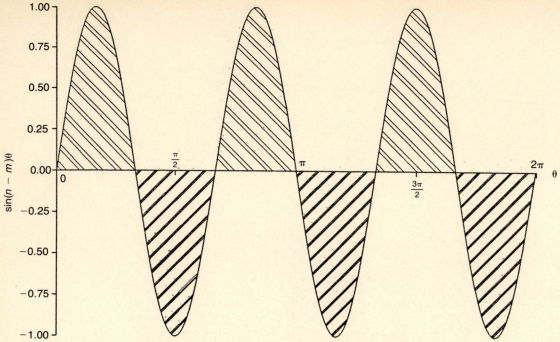

(b) Periodicity of $\sin(n - m)\theta$ resulting in a shaded area of zero

FIGURE 9.4(b)

magnitude is a constant $(M = K)$ over the passband and the phase is linear $(P = -\ell\theta)$ over this same band. As discussed in Chapter Four, this ideal (linear) phase frequency characteristic is caused by a delay of ℓ samples in the filter time response. To simplify the analysis, however, this phase characteristic is neglected temporarily by assuming zero delay $(\ell = 0)$ while computing the filter coefficients. The delay is then included at a

FIGURE 9.5 Characteristics of an ideal lowpass filter

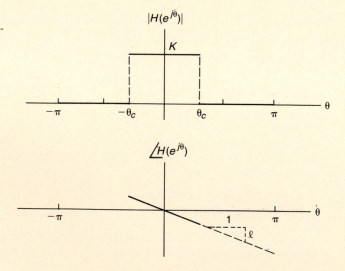

CHAPTER 9 NONRECURSIVE FILTER DESIGN

later stage when considering the practical aspects of realization and implementation. For the moment, therefore, we let $H(e^{j\theta}) = K$ rather than $Ke^{-j\ell\theta}$. Using Eq. 9.25 with $\theta_0 = -\pi$ we have

$$h_{LP}(n) = \frac{1}{2\pi} \int_{-\pi}^{\pi} H(e^{j\theta})e^{jn\theta}d\theta. \tag{9.26}$$

But from Fig. 9.5 $H_{LP}(e^{j\theta}) = K$ in the passband $(-\theta_c \le \theta \le \theta_c)$ and zero otherwise, which gives us

$$h_{LP}(n) = \frac{1}{2\pi} \int_{-\theta_c}^{\theta_c} Ke^{jn\theta}d\theta. \tag{9.27}$$

Evaluating this integral produces

$$h_{LP}(n) = \frac{K}{2\pi} \frac{e^{jn\theta}}{jn}\bigg|_{-\theta_c}^{\theta_c}$$

$$= \frac{K}{\pi n}\left[\frac{e^{jn\theta_c} - e^{-jn\theta_c}}{2j}\right] \tag{9.28}$$

and again applying the Euler relation yields the expression for the low-pass filter coefficients

$$\boxed{h_{LP}(n) = \frac{K}{\pi n} \sin(n\theta_c), \qquad n = 0, \pm 1, \pm 2, \ldots. \tag{9.29}}$$

This result indicates that an infinite number of terms is required to implement this lowpass design which is unrealistic and impractical. So, we simply truncate the expression for $h(n)$ at some reasonable value of n, for example 10. This somewhat arbitrary action yields the tabulated results for $h(n)$ below and their graphical display in Fig. 9.6(a) for a cutoff frequency of $\theta_c = \pi/4$ radians and a gain of $K = 1$. It is important to notice that $h(0)$ can be determined from Eq. 9.29 by using l'Hôpital's rule (Thomas and Finney, 1979) or by finding the average value of the magnitude characteristic in Fig. 9.5. Note also that for a filter gain in the passband of K rather than one, the values of $h(n)$ should be scaled by K.

n	$h_{LP}(n)$	n	$h_{LP}(n)$	n	$h_{LP}(n)$
0	0.25	± 4	0	± 8	0
± 1	0.225	± 5	-0.045	± 9	0.025
± 2	0.159	± 6	-0.053	± 10	0.032
± 3	0.075	± 7	-0.032		

GAINS FOR NONCAUSAL LOWPASS FILTER WITH CUTOFF $\theta_C = \pi/4$

Next, we notice that this sample response $h(n)$ is that of a *noncausal* system because of the terms that exist for $n < 0$. The causality problem is

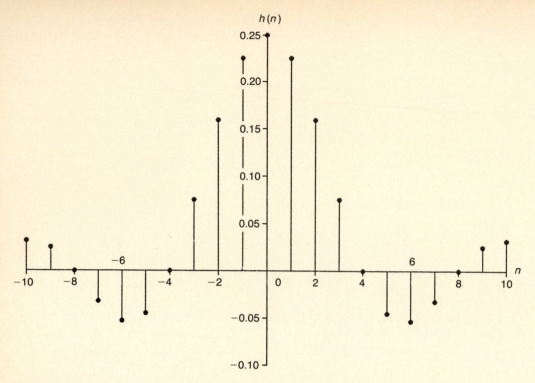

FIGURE 9.6(a) Coefficients for noncausal, nonrecursive filter

easily solved by simply shifting all the coefficients to the right by 10 as in Fig. 9.6(b) which also introduces the necessary delay that was neglected while determining the Fourier coefficients. This shifted sample response, still denoted as $h_{LP}(n)$, comes from Eq. 9.29 by substituting $(n - 10)$ for n on the right side giving

$$h_{LP}(n) = \frac{K}{\pi(n - 10)} \sin([n - 10]\theta_c), \; n = 0, 1, 2, \ldots, 20 \quad (9.30)$$

with the values of the shifted coefficients tabulated below for $\theta_c = \pi/4$ and $K = 1$

n	$h_{LP}(n)$	n	$h_{LP}(n)$	n	$h_{LP}(n)$
10	0.25	6,14	0	2,18	0
9,11	0.225	5,15	−0.045	1,19	0.025
8,12	0.159	4,16	−0.053	0,20	0.032
7,13	0.075	3,17	−0.032		

**GAINS FOR CAUSAL LOWPASS FILTER
WITH CUTOFF $\theta_C = \pi/4$**

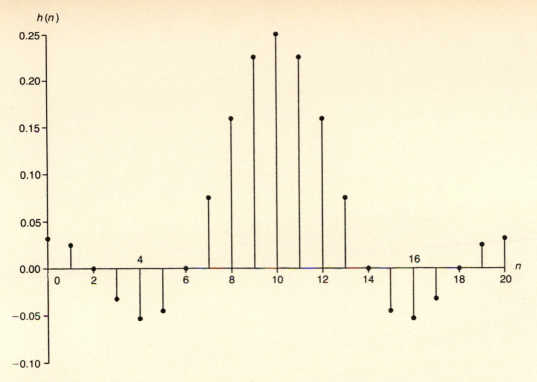

FIGURE 9.6(b) Coeffi-
cients for causal, nonrecursive filter

A realization for the causal filter described by Eq. 9.30 is shown in Fig. 9.7 and the frequency response plots in Fig. 9.8 show (a) the magnitudes for 11, 21, and 31 coefficients, (b) the magnitudes in decibels (dB = 20 $\log_{10} M$) for 11 and 21 coefficients, and (c) the phase for a 21-coefficient filter. As expected, the more terms used to synthesize $H_{LP}(e^{j\theta})$, the better the fit to the ideal frequency response characteristic. More terms also produce a more rapid transition when going from the passband to the stopband, that is, the slope of the magnitude curve is steeper in the transition region, and the attenuation in the stopband is greater. On the other

FIGURE 9.7 A causal,
nonrecursive filter with 20
delays

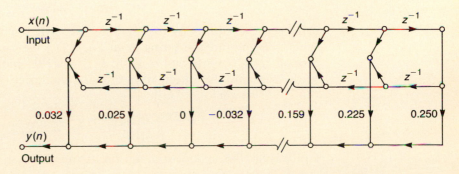

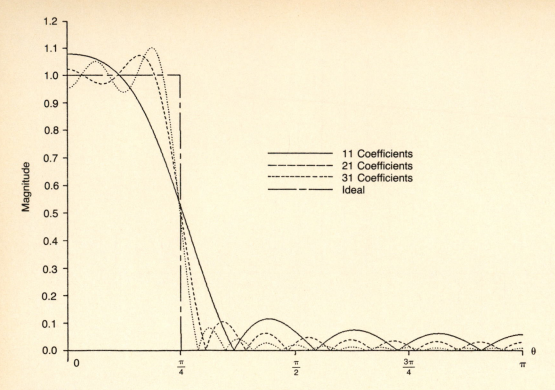

FIGURE 9.8(a) Lowpass filter frequency response magnitudes for 11-, 21-, and 31-coefficient designs

hand, longer delay and more hardware or computer time to implement the filter result from an increased number of terms.

A closed-form expression for the frequency response of this filter may be determined from the general expression

$$H_{LP}(e^{j\theta}) = \sum_{n=0}^{n=20} h_{LP}(n)e^{-jn\theta}$$

$$= h(0) + h(1)e^{-j\theta} + h(2)e^{-j2\theta} + \cdots + h(10)e^{-j10\theta} + \\ \cdots + h(19)e^{-j19\theta} + h(20)e^{-j20\theta}. \quad (9.31)$$

(To keep the equations manageable, we will not use the LP subscript when writing out the terms as in Eq. 9.31.) We know of the symmetry around $n = 10$ with $h(0) = h(20)$, $h(1) = h(19)$, and so forth. With this knowledge and the anticipation of using the Euler relation, we can factor out $e^{-j10\theta}$ to get

$$H_{LP}(e^{j\theta}) = e^{-j10\theta}[h(0)e^{j10\theta} + h(1)e^{j9\theta} + \\ \cdots + h(10) + \cdots + h(19)e^{-j9\theta} + h(20)e^{-j10\theta}]. \quad (9.32)$$

Collecting like exponential terms, using the symmetry relations, and

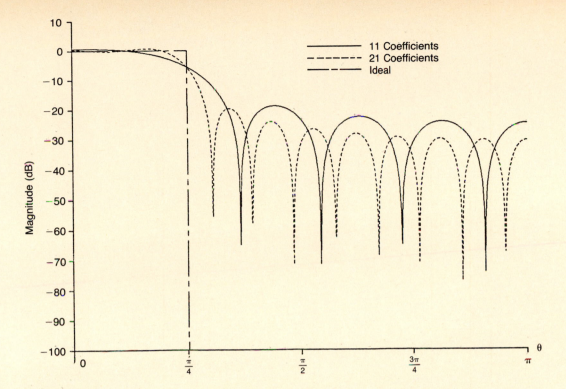

FIGURE 9.8(b) Lowpass filter frequency response magnitudes in dB for 11- and 21-coefficient designs

applying the Euler relation once again produces

$$H_{LP}(e^{j\theta}) = e^{-j10\theta}[2h(0)\cos[10\theta] + 2h(1)\cos[9\theta] + \cdots + 2h(9)\cos[\theta] + h(10)]$$

$$= \left[h_{LP}(10) + 2\sum_{n=0}^{n=9} h_{LP}(n)\cos[(10-n)\theta]\right]e^{-j10\theta} \qquad (9.33)$$

and the more compact expression

$$H_{LP}(e^{j\theta}) = \pm M e^{-j10\theta}. \qquad (9.34)$$

Several comments are necessary concerning Eq. 9.34 as well as the phase plot in Fig. 9.8(c):

1. From Eq. 9.34 it appears that the phase $P = -10\theta$ is linear with frequency and is independent of the filter coefficients. With this said, what accounts for the abrupt changes of phase in Fig. 9.8(c)? First, the 360-degree changes, such as the one at $\theta = \pi/10$, are simply the result of the standard practice of limiting phase plots to the interval $-180° \le P \le +180°$. For instance, the phase at $\theta = \pi/10$ is $P = -180°$ and actually continues to change linearly in a negative sense past this

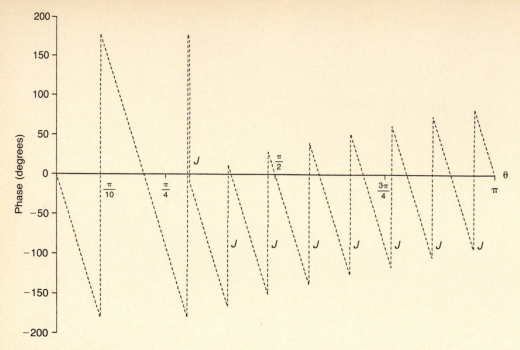

FIGURE 9.8(c) Lowpass filter frequency response phase for 21-coefficient design

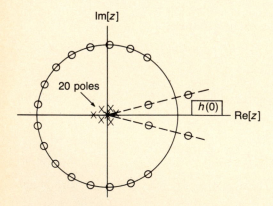

FIGURE 9.8(d) Pole-zero plot for $H(z)$

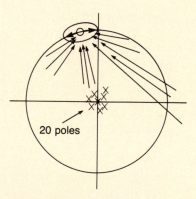

FIGURE 9.8(e) Vectors for frequency response near $\theta = 1.813$

frequency, but to keep phase plots manageable we limit our values to $\pm 180°$. (Consider the phase of a nonrecursive filter with 500 delays, having $P = -500\theta$! We would need a scroll to plot this without our $\pm 180°$ limits.)

2. We have been writing the frequency response as $H(e^{j\theta}) = Me^{jP}$ and now in Eq. 9.34 we have $H(e^{j\theta}) = \pm Me^{jP}$. Why the difference? The bracketed term in Eq. 9.33

$$h_{LP}(10) + 2 \sum_{n=0}^{n=9} h_{LP}(n) \cos[(10 - n)\theta] \qquad (9.35)$$

is a real number, but it can be either positive or negative. Thus, the magnitude M is

$$M = \left| h_{LP}(10) + 2 \sum_{n=0}^{9} h_{LP}(n) \cos\left[(10 - n)\theta\right] \right| = |f(\theta)| \qquad (9.36)$$

and in plotting the phase we absorb any sign changes in $f(\theta)$ as phase jumps of $180°$ as shown in Fig. 9.8(c) at the points labeled J.

3. This can also be interpreted from the pole-zero point of view from Chapters Five and Six. Putting Eq. 9.31 in terms of the complex variable z, we have

$$H(z) = h(0) + h(1)z^{-1} + h(2)z^{-2} + \cdots + h(20)z^{-20} \qquad (9.37)$$

or

$$H(z) = \frac{h(0)z^{20} + h(1)z^{19} + h(2)z^{18} + \cdots + h(20)}{z^{20}}. \qquad (9.38)$$

Equation 9.38 can be written in factored form as

$$H(z) = \frac{h(0)(z - n_1)(z - n_2) \cdots (z - n_{19})(z - n_{20})}{z^{20}} \qquad (9.39)$$

and the pole-zero plot of Fig. 9.8(d) results. A listing of the 20 zeros is given below and we notice that there are 16 zeros on the unit circle and 4 (n_1, n_2, n_{19}, and n_{20}) at angles of ± 0.278 whose magnitudes are reciprocals ($1/1.405 = 0.712$).

$$n_{1,2} = 1.405e^{\pm j0.278} \qquad n_{11,12} = 1.000e^{\pm j2.107}$$

$$n_{3,4} = 1.000e^{\pm j0.958} \qquad n_{13,14} = 1.000e^{\pm j2.402}$$

$$n_{5,6} = 1.000e^{\pm j1.234} \qquad n_{15,16} = 1.000e^{\pm j2.698}$$

$$n_{7,8} = 1.000e^{\pm j1.522} \qquad n_{17,18} = 1.000e^{\pm j2.993}$$

$$n_{9,10} = 1.000e^{\pm j1.813} \qquad n_{19,20} = 0.712e^{\pm j0.278}$$

The reciprocity of roots is characteristic of linear phase systems (see Problem 9.25). The zeros on the unit circle cause the gain to be zero at the frequencies at which they are located, namely $\theta = \pm0.958$, $\theta = \pm1.234$, $\theta = \pm1.522$, $\theta = \pm1.813$, $\theta = \pm2.107$, $\theta = \pm2.402$, $\theta = \pm2.698$, and $\theta = \pm2.993$. These frequencies of zero gain can be seen in Fig. 9.8(a)—see the dashed curve. At these same frequencies the phase jumps of $\pi(180°)$ occur which are shown in Fig. 9.8(c). The abrupt phase changes can be interpreted from a geometric point of view. In Fig. 9.8(e) we have isolated one zero (at $\theta = 1.813$) and it is clear that the vector from that zero to the unit circle goes through a change of π radians (180°) as the frequency changes from "just below" 1.813 to "just above" that frequency while the vectors from the other 19 zeros and the 20 poles change imperceptibly.

PROCEDURE

A summary follows of the steps that need to be taken in the design of an approximation to an ideal lowpass filter:

a) Obtain the desired cutoff frequency θ_c and write the frequency response as

$$H_{LP}(e^{j\theta}) = \begin{cases} K, & -\theta_c \le \theta \le \theta_c \\ 0, & \text{elsewhere in the range } -\pi \le \theta \le \pi. \end{cases} \tag{9.40}$$

That is, ignore the linear phase characteristic for the moment.

b) The filter coefficients are given by

$$h_{LP}(n) = b_n = \frac{K}{\pi n} \sin(n\theta_c), \qquad n = 0, \pm1, \pm2, \ldots. \tag{9.41}$$

Substitute the numerical value of θ_c to obtain the $h_{LP}(n)$ values.

c) Truncate the coefficients with $\pm I$ terms which yields the $(2I + 1)$ filter coefficients

$$h_{LP}(n) = \frac{K}{\pi n} \sin(n\theta_c), \qquad n = 0, \pm1, \pm2, \ldots, \pm I \tag{9.42}$$

where $h(0) = K\theta_c/\pi$. The number of terms to be used is determined by the designer by comparing filter specifications with computer plots of frequency responses for various numbers of terms. This is a decision in which experience plays a major role. That is, we select a number I_1, compute the frequency response $H_1(e^{j\theta})$, decide upon its suitability for the particular design situation, and then repeat the procedure if necessary.

d) Shift $h_{LP}(n)$ to the right by I terms to make the filter causal giving

$$h_{LP}(n) = \frac{K}{\pi(n - I)} \sin([n - I]\theta_c), \qquad n = 0, 1, 2, \ldots, 2I. \tag{9.43}$$

e) Implement the digital filter by a general purpose computer and an appropriate program, a micro-coded digital signal processor, or a custom designed integrated circuit.

9.1.3 Highpass, Bandpass, and Bandstop Design

We first look at the magnitude characteristics of an ideal lowpass and an ideal highpass filter as in Fig. 9.9 where the cutoff frequency of the highpass filter has been defined as $\theta = \pi - \theta_a$. Our goal is to determine filter coefficients or weights to provide this highpass characteristic. Although this could be done by starting with Eq. 9.25 and proceeding as in Section 9.1.2, there is another easier way. We now show that it is possible to derive the unit sample response (filter gains) for the highpass filter from the given or known filter gains of the lowpass filter. If, in Fig. 9.9, we make $\theta_c = \theta_a$ and shift the lowpass filter frequency response by π we obtain the highpass characteristic. That is, we start with a lowpass frequency response designed for $\theta_c = \theta_a$ or

$$H_{LP}(e^{j\theta})|_{\theta_c = \theta_a}$$

and replace θ with $\theta - \pi$ giving

$$H_{HP}(e^{j\theta}) = H_{LP}(e^{j(\theta - \pi)}). \tag{9.44}$$

We know that

$$H_{LP}(e^{j\theta}) = \sum_{n=-\infty}^{n=+\infty} h_{LP}(n)e^{-jn\theta} \tag{9.45}$$

therefore, using Eq. 9.44 we have

$$H_{HP}(e^{j\theta}) = H_{LP}(e^{j(\theta - \pi)}) = \sum_{n=-\infty}^{n=+\infty} h_{LP}(n)e^{-jn(\theta - \pi)}$$

$$= \sum_{n=-\infty}^{n=+\infty} h_{LP}(n)e^{jn\pi}e^{-jn\theta} \tag{9.46}$$

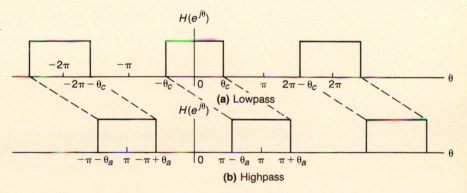

FIGURE 9.9 Magnitude characteristics of ideal lowpass and highpass filters

which can be written as

$$H_{HP}(e^{j\theta}) = \sum_{n=-\infty}^{n=+\infty} h_{LP}(n)(-1)^n e^{-jn\theta}. \tag{9.47}$$

The definition for $H_{HP}(e^{j\theta})$ is given by

$$H_{HP}(e^{j\theta}) = \sum_{n=-\infty}^{n=+\infty} h_{HP}(n)e^{-jn\theta} \tag{9.48}$$

and, consequently, by comparing Eqs. 9.47 and 9.48, we see that the high-pass coefficients can be determined from the known or given lowpass coefficients by the relation

$$h_{HP}(n) = h_{LP}(n)(-1)^n. \tag{9.49}$$

Example 9.1. This example illustrates the design of a highpass filter from the lowpass prototype.

Suppose that we want to design an approximation to an ideal highpass filter that has a passband for frequencies greater than 10 kHz where the system sampling frequency is 50 kHz. A digital filter is to be used and the method of Fourier design is to be employed. Let the passband gain be unity and determine the required coefficients for this highpass filter.

Solution: The first step is to calculate the digital cutoff frequency that corresponds to the analog cutoff frequency of 10 kHz. This analog frequency corresponds to the digital frequency

$$\theta = \omega T$$

$$= 2\pi f \cdot \frac{1}{f_s} = 2\pi(10^4) \cdot \frac{1}{50(10^3)} = 0.4\pi \text{ rad.} \tag{9.50}$$

As indicated in Fig. 9.9(b) we set this digital frequency equal to $(\pi - \theta_a)$ to obtain

$$0.4\pi = \pi - \theta_a \tag{9.51}$$

with the cutoff frequency of the ideal lowpass filter given by

$$\theta_c = \theta_a = \pi - 0.4\pi = 0.6\pi. \tag{9.52}$$

Thus, the filter coefficients for this noncausal lowpass filter are computed from Eq. 9.29 as

$$h_{LP}(n) = \frac{1}{\pi n} \sin(0.6\pi n), \qquad n = 0, \pm 1, \pm 2, \ldots \tag{9.53}$$

and if, once again, we arbitrarily decide upon $I = 10$ terms on either side of $n = 0$, the highpass coefficients that are derived from Eq. 9.49, i.e.,

$$h_{HP}(n) = (-1)^n h_{LP}(n) \tag{9.54}$$

then follow directly.

n	$h_{LP}(n)$	$h_{HP}(n)$	n	$h_{LP}(n)$	$h_{HP}(n)$
0	0.600	0.600	± 6	-0.050	-0.050
± 1	0.303	-0.303	± 7	0.027	-0.027
± 2	-0.094	-0.094	± 8	0.023	0.023
± 3	-0.062	0.062	± 9	-0.034	0.034
± 4	0.076	0.076	± 10	0	0
± 5	0	0			

To make the filter causal we need to shift the coefficients to the right by 10 samples. This results in the following gains (weights) for the causal highpass filter with a cutoff frequency of 0.4π rad.

n	$h_{HP}(n)$	n	$h_{HP}(n)$
0,20	0	6,14	0.076
1,19	0.034	7,13	0.062
2,18	0.023	8,12	-0.094
3,17	-0.027	9,11	-0.303
4,16	-0.050	10	0.600
5,15	0		

Several different frequency response plots for highpass filters designed by the Fourier method are displayed in Fig. 9.10. A general expression for the unit sample response (filter coefficients) for the causal highpass filter of Example 9.1 can be written as

$$h_{HP}(n) = \frac{(-1)^{(n-I)}}{\pi(n-I)} \sin(0.6\pi[n-I]), \qquad n = 0, 1, 2, \ldots, 2I. \quad (9.55)$$

Similar results can be derived for bandpass and bandstop filters with their critical frequencies defined as in Fig. 9.11 with the usual definition of Fig. 9.5 for the lowpass cutoff frequency θ_c. The derivations of the bandpass and bandstop transformations are considered in Problem 9.26, and a summary of all of these transformations is given in Table 9.1.

Example 9.2. This example illustrates the design procedure for a bandpass filter. _____

Suppose we want to design an approximation to an ideal bandpass filter that has a passband gain of one in the interval from 10 kHz to 15 kHz with a system sampling frequency of 50 kHz. Determine the general expression for the filter weights.

Solution: The digital frequency passband is between

$$\theta_\ell = \frac{2\pi(10^4)}{(5)(10^4)} = 0.4\pi \quad \text{and} \quad \theta_u = \frac{2\pi(10^4)(1.5)}{(5)(10^4)} = 0.6\pi \quad (9.56)$$

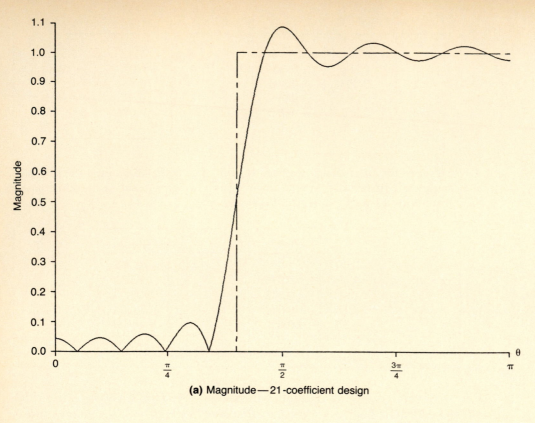

(a) Magnitude—21-coefficient design

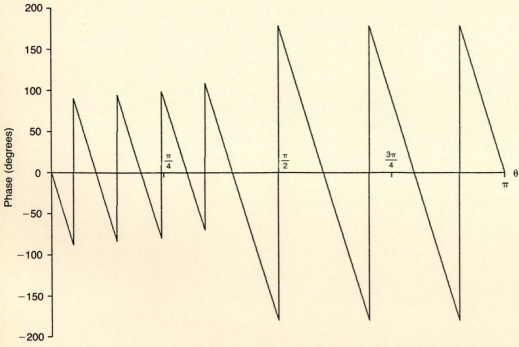

(b) Phase—21-coefficient design

FIGURE 9.10 Highpass filter frequency response

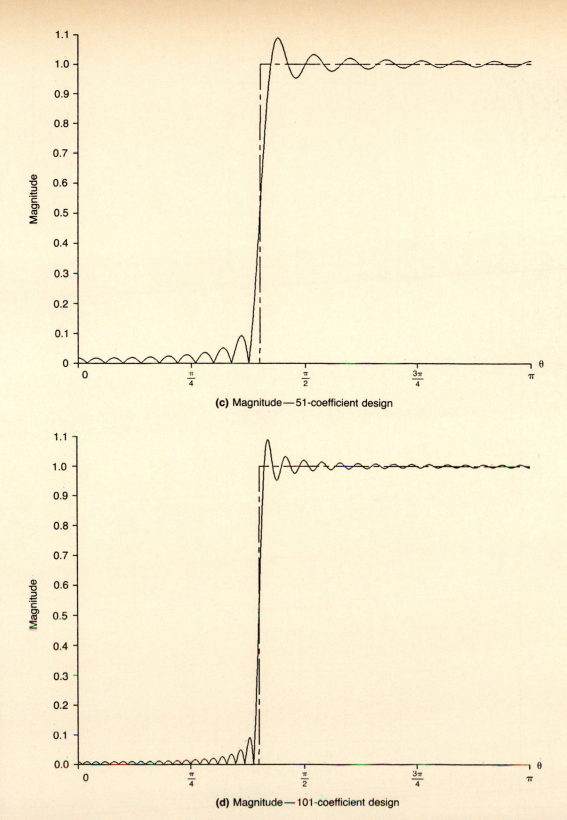

(c) Magnitude—51-coefficient design

(d) Magnitude—101-coefficient design

FIGURE 9.10 Highpass filter frequency response

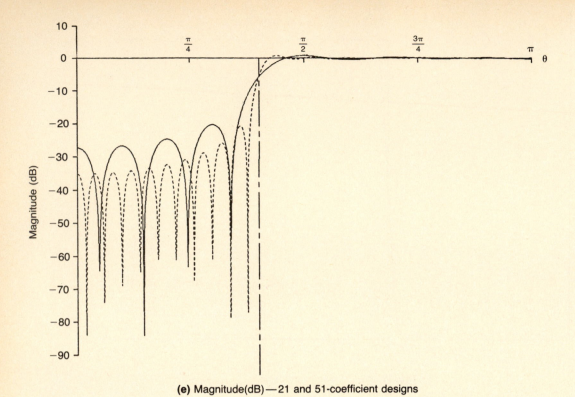

(e) Magnitude(dB)—21 and 51-coefficient designs

FIGURE 9.10 Highpass filter frequency response

FIGURE 9.11 Magnitude characteristics of ideal bandpass and bandstop filters

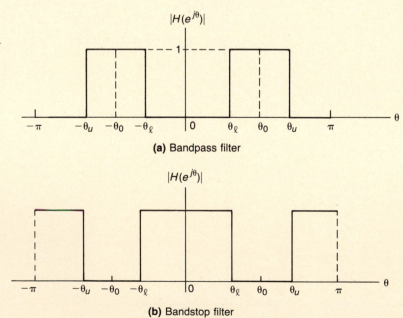

(a) Bandpass filter

(b) Bandstop filter

CHAPTER 9 NONRECURSIVE FILTER DESIGN

and $\theta_0 = 0.5\pi$ is the center of the passband. The corresponding lowpass cutoff frequency from Table 9.1 is

$$\theta_c = \frac{\theta_u - \theta_\ell}{2} = 0.1\pi. \qquad (9.57)$$

Thus, knowing that the coefficients for the ideal noncausal LP filter are

$$h_{LP}(n) = \frac{1}{\pi n} \sin(0.1\pi n), \qquad n = 0, \pm 1, \pm 2, \ldots \qquad (9.58)$$

the corresponding weights for this bandpass filter centered at $\theta_0 = 0.5\pi$ are

$$h_{BP}(n) = [2\cos(0.5\pi n)]h_{LP}(n), \qquad n = 0, \pm 1, \pm 2, \ldots. \qquad (9.59)$$

Frequency response plots in Fig. 9.12 for the causal filter show magnitude (linear and decibel scales) for 21, 61, and 101 coefficients and phase for 21 coefficients.

TABLE 9.1 FREQUENCY TRANSFORMATIONS

Lowpass

$$h_{LP}(n) = \frac{K}{\pi n} \sin(n\theta_c), \qquad n = 0, \pm 1, \pm 2, \ldots, \pm I$$

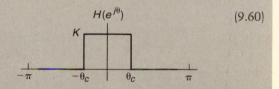

$$(9.60)$$

Highpass

$$h_{HP}(n) = (-1)^n h_{LP}(n), \qquad n = 0, \pm 1, \pm 2, \ldots, \pm I$$

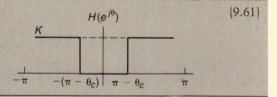

$$(9.61)$$

Bandpass

$$h_{BP}(n) = [2\cos(n\theta_0)]h_{LP}(n), \qquad n = 0, \pm 1, \pm 2, \ldots, \pm I$$

$$\theta_u - \theta_\ell = 2\theta_c, \quad \theta_0 = \frac{\theta_u + \theta_\ell}{2}$$

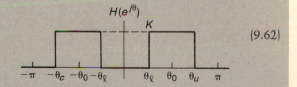

$$(9.62)$$

Bandstop

$$h_{BS}(0) = K - h_{BP}(0)$$

$$h_{BS}(n) = -h_{BP}(n), \qquad n = \pm 1, \pm 2, \ldots, \pm I$$

$$\theta_u - \theta_\ell = 2\theta_c$$

$$\theta_0 = \frac{\theta_u + \theta_\ell}{2}$$

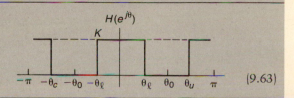

$$(9.63)$$

9.1.4 Gibbs' Phenomenon

Looking back over the filter design examples previously discussed we notice that there is often a significant amount of ripple in the magnitude characteristic. This is due to an effect known as Gibbs' phenomenon, first publicized by Willard Gibbs in 1899 (Hamming, 1983). We now consider how this arises.

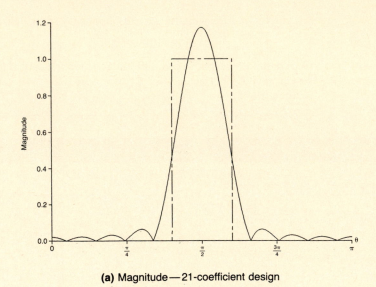

(a) Magnitude—21-coefficient design

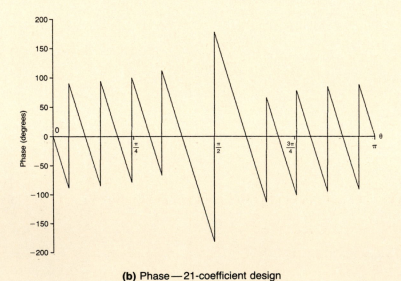

(b) Phase—21-coefficient design

FIGURE 9.12 Bandpass filter frequency response

CHAPTER 9 NONRECURSIVE FILTER DESIGN

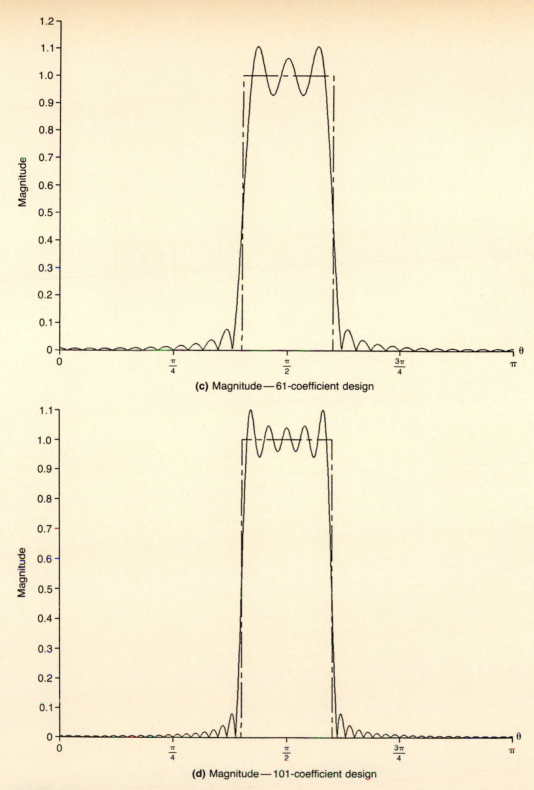

(c) Magnitude—61-coefficient design

(d) Magnitude—101-coefficient design

FIGURE 9.12 Bandpass filter frequency response

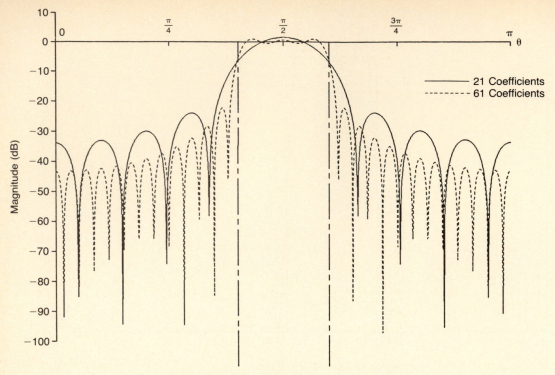

(e) Magnitude (dB)—21- and 61-coefficient designs

FIGURE 9.12 Bandpass filter frequency response

The magnitude portion of the frequency response for an ideal lowpass filter (zero phase) is given in Fig. 9.13 and the appropriate Fourier Series pair is

$$h(n) = \frac{1}{2\pi} \int_{-\theta_c}^{\theta_c} 1 e^{jn\theta} d\theta = \frac{1}{\pi n} \sin(n\theta_c), \qquad n = 0, \pm1, \pm2, \ldots \quad (9.64)$$

with

$$H(e^{j\theta}) = \sum_{n=-\infty}^{n=+\infty} h(n) e^{-jn\theta} \qquad (9.65)$$

FIGURE 9.13 Magnitude characteristic—ideal lowpass filter

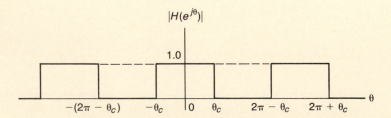

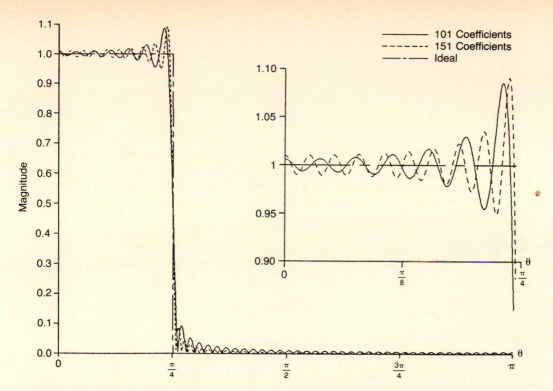

The desired frequency response of Fig. 9.13 cannot be exactly realized by Eq. 9.65 for two reasons. First, we cannot implement a filter with an infinite number of terms as required by the synthesis equation for $H(e^{j\theta})$. Second, when discontinuities exist in the magnitude plot as in Fig. 9.13, even if we could use an almost infinite number of terms, this will not exactly match the desired frequency response at these discontinuities. For filters of high order (I large) there will always be an overshoot of about 8.95 percent near a discontinuity—an effect known as Gibbs' phenomenon. This effect can be clearly seen in Fig. 9.14 where the plot shows the Fourier approximations for a lowpass filter with 101 and 151 coefficients. Note that the peak values of both plots near the discontinuity are approximately 1.09. Thus, both truncating the sample response to a finite number of terms and Gibbs' phenomenon make any Fourier approximation to Fig. 9.13 by means of Eq. 9.65 imperfect. The next section addresses the question of how to make the approximation better.

9.1.5 Windows in Fourier Design

The simple act of truncating an infinite series of terms for the sample response $h(n)$ can be thought of in terms of a window function. (Windows were introduced in Section 7.11.) We think of the filter coefficients of infinite extent (see Fig. 9.15(a)) as being viewed through a window. Only those coefficients that can be "seen" are used in the filter. The filter weights, $h(n)$ for $-25 \leq n \leq 25$, are shown in Fig. 9.15(a) and a rectangular window sequence $w(n)$ is pictured in Fig. 9.15(b) where it can be seen that

$$w(n) = \begin{cases} 1, & |n| \leq I \ (I = 20 \text{ in Fig. } 9.15(b)) \\ 0, & \text{otherwise.} \end{cases} \tag{9.66}$$

A new set of filter weights can be described by $\hat{h}(n) = h(n) \cdot w(n)$ where $\hat{h}(n)$ represents the new or modified values of the sample response $h(n)$ computed from the analysis expression, Eq. 9.64. In the case of the rectangular window, multiplying by $w(n)$ is simply truncating $h(n)$ at $n = \pm I$ as in Fig. 9.15(c). In sequence notation the filter's unit sample response and the window sequence are described as

$$h(n) =$$

$$\{\ldots, h(-193), h(-192), \ldots, h(-20), \ldots, h(-1), h(0), h(1), \ldots,$$
$$h(20), \ldots, h(203), \ldots\}$$

$$w(n) = \{\ldots, 0, 0, 0, 1, 1, \ldots, 1, 1, 1, 0, 0, 0, \ldots\}$$
$$\underset{n = -20}{\uparrow} \qquad \underset{n = 20}{\uparrow} \tag{9.67}$$

for $I = \pm 10$ as in the lowpass filter design example.

FIGURE 9.15 Windowing of filter coefficients

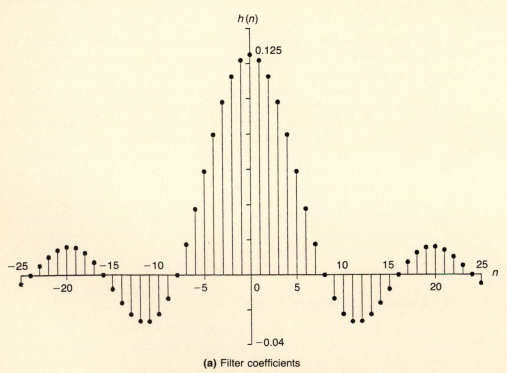

(a) Filter coefficients

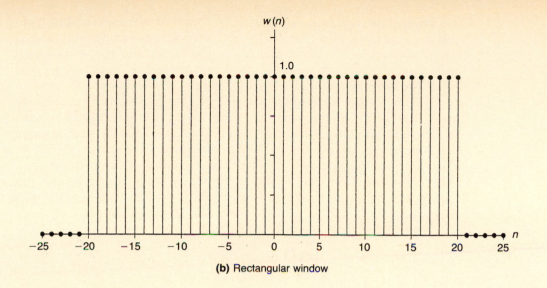

(b) Rectangular window

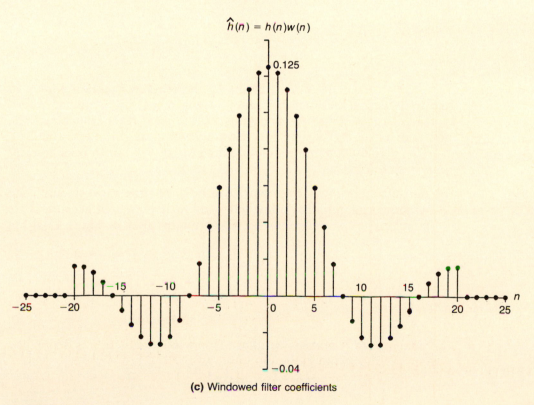

(c) Windowed filter coefficients

FIGURE 9.15 Windowing of filter coefficients

Truncation by a rectangular window function is rather an abrupt operation—the multiplier changes from 1 to zero in one sample. Intuitively, a smoother transition of the weights to the zero value at $n = \pm I$ would seem more desirable so we could guess that a window function $w(n)$ like Fig. 9.16 might be better. The analogy here is of a window which gradually becomes more translucent as one looks further from the center. We know that the higher frequency components of the Fourier Series give the ripples in the frequency response. Therefore, by arbitrarily scaling down the Fourier coefficients for the highest frequency terms, we should be able to reduce the ripple amplitudes. The "windowed" filter weights are then computed from $\hat{h}(n) = h(n) \cdot w(n)$ where $w(n)$ generally falls off monotonically as $|n|$ increases from 0. Alternatively, we can see this effect from the modified value of the frequency response

$$\hat{H}(e^{j\theta}) = \sum_{n=-I}^{n=+I} \hat{h}(n)e^{-jn\theta}$$

$$= \sum_{n=-I}^{n=I} h(n)w(n)e^{-jn\theta} \tag{9.68}$$

where

$$h(n) = \frac{1}{2\pi} \int_{-\pi}^{\pi} H(e^{j\theta})e^{jn\theta}d\theta. \tag{9.69}$$

The effect in Eq. 9.68 of multiplying by the window function $w(n)$ is to implicitly define a desired frequency response that has a gradual rolloff instead of the steep slopes presented by the ideal filter characteristics. The corners on the desired frequency response are, in effect, rounded.

Two window functions are illustrated in Fig. 9.17 and a brief description of each follows.

a) *Bartlett or triangular window.* Although not the most widely used window function, this triangular window is presented because of its simplicity. The equations for the straight lines of Fig. 9.17(a) are

$$w(n) = \begin{cases} 1 - \dfrac{1}{I}n, & 0 \leq n \leq I \\ 1 + \dfrac{1}{I}n, & -I \leq n \leq 0 \\ 0, & \text{otherwise.} \end{cases} \tag{9.70}$$

b) *Generalized Hamming window.* This window function is defined by

$$w(n) = \begin{cases} \alpha + (1 - \alpha)\cos\left(\dfrac{n\pi}{I}\right), & -I \leq n \leq I \\ 0, & \text{otherwise} \end{cases} \tag{9.71}$$

where $0 \leq \alpha \leq 1$. If $\alpha = 0.54$ this window is called a *Hamming win-*

FIGURE 9.16 A smoothing window function

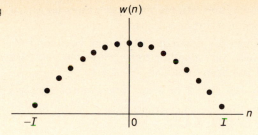

FIGURE 9.17 Two window functions

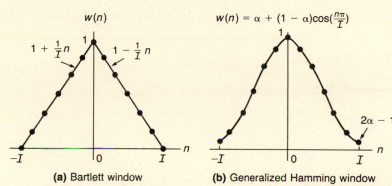

(a) Bartlett window

(b) Generalized Hamming window

dow (after Richard W. Hamming). For $\alpha = 0.5$ we have a *von Hann* (after Julius von Hann) or *raised cosine window*. Thus, for the non-zero portions of the windows we have

$$w(n) = 0.54 + 0.46 \cos\left(\frac{n\pi}{I}\right) \qquad \text{Hamming} \qquad (9.72)$$

$$w(n) = 0.50 + 0.50 \cos\left(\frac{n\pi}{I}\right) \qquad \text{von Hann} \qquad (9.73)$$

and as shown in Fig. 9.17(b) window values at the end points $(n = \pm I)$ are 0.08 for Hamming and 0 for von Hann. There are several other commonly used window functions treated in a thorough fashion in Harris (1976, 1978).

Outlined below are the steps required to design a nonrecursive filter using window functions.

DESIGN PROCEDURE

1. Translate the filter specifications to those of a lowpass filter (with zero phase) as was done in Examples 9.1 and 9.2.

2. Design a nonrecursive lowpass filter by determining the Fourier Series coefficients, i.e. find $h_{LP}(n)$.

3. Select an appropriate number of terms $(2I + 1)$.

4. Select a (favorite) window function $w(n)$.

5. Form the unit sample response values for the windowed lowpass filter, that is, $\hat{h}_{LP}(n) = h_{LP}(n) \cdot w(n)$.

6. Although it's not required, it may be a good idea to find the frequency response corresponding to $\hat{h}_{LP}(n)$ of step 5 to ensure that the correct passband has been obtained.

7. Return to step 3 or 4 and repeat until the specifications are satisfied.

8. Determine the appropriate $\hat{h}_{HP}(n)$, $\hat{h}_{BP}(n)$, or $\hat{h}_{BS}(n)$ using the transformations of Table 9.1.

9. Shift the sample response to the right by I terms to make the filter causal.

10. Implement the digital filter as appropriate.

Example 9.3. This example illustrates nonrecursive filter design using windows. _____

To illustrate the use of windows in design, repeat Example 9.1 following the steps outlined above.

Solution:

1. The highpass cutoff frequency of 0.4π (10 kHz with $T = 20\mu s$) was translated to the lowpass cutoff frequency of 0.6π.

2. Then the lowpass coefficients were determined from

$$h_{LP}(n) = \frac{1}{\pi n} \sin(0.6\pi n), \qquad n = 0, \pm 1, \pm 2, \ldots. \qquad (9.74)$$

3. Next truncate with $I = 10$ terms (refer to Example 9.1) on either side of $n = 0$ giving

$$h_{LP}(n) = \frac{1}{\pi n} \sin(0.6\pi n), \qquad n = 0, \pm 1, \pm 2, \ldots, \pm 10. \qquad (9.75)$$

4. We arbitrarily select a Hamming window which for this filter is described by

$$w(n) = 0.54 + 0.46 \cos\left(\frac{n\pi}{10}\right), \qquad -10 \le n \le 10. \qquad (9.76)$$

5. Now, we compute the filter weights for the windowed lowpass filter as $\hat{h}_{LP}(n) = h_{LP}(n) \cdot w(n)$.

6. We have been quite arbitrary about the number of terms used ($I = 10$) and the kind of window chosen (Hamming), and computer simulation is necessary to compare the frequency response with the specifications to be satisfied. The magnitude plot is shown in Fig. 9.18(a) where the unwindowed response has been included to emphasize the desirable effect of using a window. Let's assume that the response shown is satisfactory and, consequently, we can move directly to step 8 of the design procedure.

7. Not required.

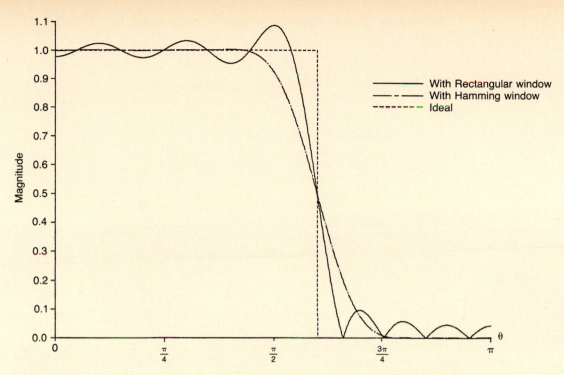

FIGURE 9.18(a) 21-coefficient lowpass filter magnitude response with and without Hamming window

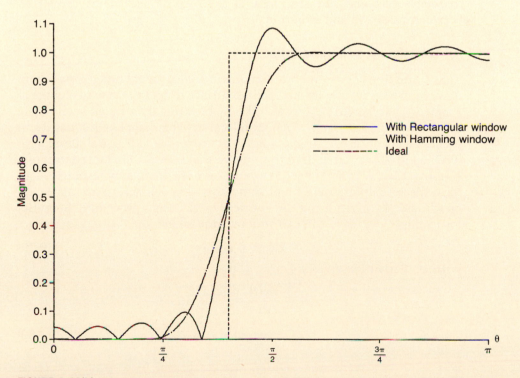

FIGURE 9.18(b) 21-coefficient highpass filter magnitude response with and without Hamming window

8. Since we are designing a highpass filter, the weights from Table 9.1 are given by

$$\hat{h}_{HP}(n) = (-1)^n \hat{h}_{LP}(n)$$

$$= (-1)^n \left[\frac{1}{\pi n} \sin(0.6\pi n) \right] \left[0.54 + 0.46 \cos\left(\frac{\pi n}{10}\right) \right], \qquad -10 \leq n \leq 10.$$

$$(9.77)$$

9. The filter weights for the causal filter are given by

$$\hat{h}_{HP}(n) = (-1)^{(n-10)} \left[\frac{1}{\pi(n-10)} \sin(0.6\pi[n-10]) \right] \times$$

$$\left[0.54 + 0.46 \cos\left(\frac{\pi[n-10]}{10}\right) \right], \qquad n = 0, 1, 2, \ldots, 20 \quad (9.78)$$

with the corresponding frequency response plots of Fig. 9.18(b).

10. The design is now complete and the remaining step is to implement the filter as appropriate.

In Fig. 9.19(a), the magnitude characteristic for an ideal lowpass filter is plotted together with the plots for a 101-coefficient filter with a Hamming window (dotted curve) and without (solid curve). Figure 9.19(b) shows the same plots for a bandpass filter. The conclusion is obvious. Windows, other than rectangular, are very necessary if a smooth frequency response is desired. We do pay a price, however, for the smooth frequency response; the steepness of the filter is less in the transition between passband and stopband.

9.1.6 Design of a Differentiator

Many situations occur in both digital and analog signal processing where it is required or advantageous to differentiate to find the rate of change of a signal. That is, we often want to know how rapidly a signal is changing as well as keeping track of its actual value. This happens frequently in process-control applications where a Proportional-Integral-Derivative (PID) controller is often used to improve the dynamic characteristics of a given system. We now proceed to determine the frequency response of an ideal discrete differentiator and show how this characteristic can be approximated by again using the Fourier Series design procedure. Suppose, for example, we have the continuous-time signal

$$x(t) = A \cos \omega t \tag{9.79}$$

with its derivative given by

$$y(t) = \frac{dx(t)}{dt} = -A\omega \sin \omega t$$

$$= A\omega \cos(\omega t + \pi/2). \tag{9.80}$$

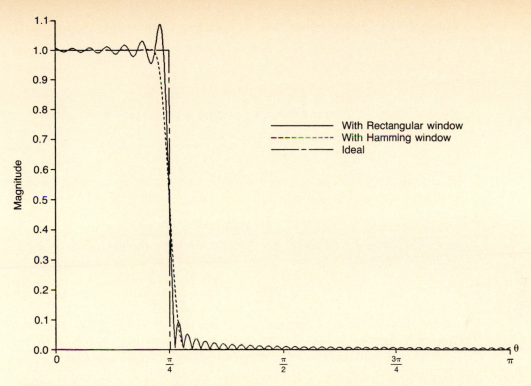

FIGURE 9.19(a)   Lowpass filter frequency response with and without Hamming window for 101-coefficient design

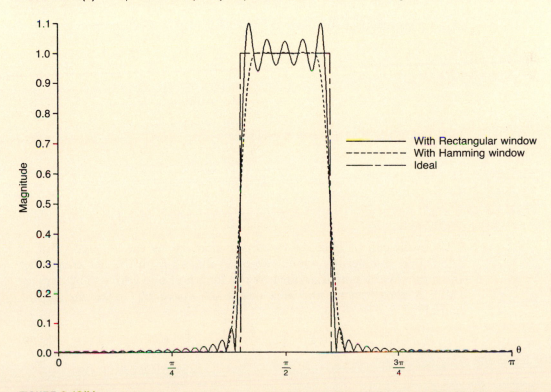

FIGURE 9.19(b)   Bandpass filter frequency response with and without Hamming window for 101-coefficient design

Using the complex exponential concept from Chapter Two we can write

$$x(t) = \text{Re}[Ae^{j\omega t}] \tag{9.81}$$

and

$$y(t) = \text{Re}[A\omega e^{j(\omega t + \pi/2)}]. \tag{9.82}$$

Considering the ratio of these two complex exponentials we obtain

$$\frac{A\omega e^{j\omega t}e^{j\pi/2}}{Ae^{j\omega t}} = \omega e^{j\pi/2} = j\omega. \tag{9.83}$$

The quantity $j\omega$ can be considered to be the frequency response of this continuous-time operation of differentiation and is denoted by

$$H(j\omega) = j\omega. \tag{9.84}$$

In terms of the digital frequency $\theta = \omega T$, we have the desired digital frequency response of

$$H(e^{j\theta}) = j\frac{\theta}{T} \tag{9.85}$$

where the ideal magnitude and phase are shown in Fig. 9.20. The next step is to determine the Fourier Series that approximates this function. The Fourier coefficients (or filter weights) are determined from

$$h(n) = \frac{1}{2\pi}\int_{-\pi}^{\pi} H(e^{j\theta})e^{jn\theta}d\theta \tag{9.86}$$

and substitution of the desired frequency response of Eq. 9.85 gives

$$h(n) = \frac{1}{2\pi}\int_{-\pi}^{\pi} \frac{j\theta}{T}e^{jn\theta}d\theta$$

$$= \frac{j}{2\pi T}\int_{-\pi}^{\pi} \theta e^{jn\theta}d\theta. \tag{9.87}$$

Evaluating Eq. 9.87 for $n = 0$ gives us

$$h(0) = \frac{j}{2\pi T}\int_{-\pi}^{\pi} \theta d\theta$$

$$= \frac{j}{2\pi T}\frac{\theta^2}{2}\bigg|_{-\pi}^{\pi} = 0. \tag{9.88}$$

This result can be checked by noting that $h(0)$ is the average value of $H(e^{j\theta})$ over one period, which can be evaluated from the net area under the curve over a period divided by the length of one period. The average value is zero because the area under the curve $j\theta/T$ over one period, namely

$$\text{area} = \int_{-\pi}^{\pi} j\frac{\theta}{T}d\theta = \frac{j}{T}\int_{-\pi}^{\pi} \theta d\theta \tag{9.89}$$

FIGURE 9.20 Ideal frequency response of a differentiator

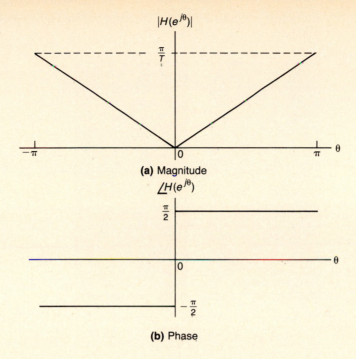

(a) Magnitude

(b) Phase

is clearly zero. For all other values of n the integral in Eq. 9.87 is of the form

$$\int xe^{ax}dx = \frac{e^{ax}}{a^2}(ax - 1) \qquad (9.90)$$

and so using this expression with $x = \theta$ and $a = jn$ we have an exercise in algebra that produces

$$h(n) = \frac{j}{2\pi T}\left[\frac{e^{jn\theta}}{(jn)^2}(jn\theta - 1)\right]_{-\pi}^{\pi}. \qquad (9.91)$$

Evaluating Eq. 9.91 at the limits of $\pm\pi$ gives us

$$h(n) = \frac{j}{(2\pi T)(-n^2)}[e^{jn\pi}(jn\pi - 1) - e^{-jn\pi}(-jn\pi - 1)] \qquad (9.92)$$

or

$$h(n) = \frac{j}{(2\pi T)(-n^2)}[jn\pi(e^{jn\pi} + e^{-jn\pi})]. \qquad (9.93)$$

Equation 9.93 can be simplified to

$$h(n) = \frac{(-1)^n}{nT}, \quad |n| = 1, 2, \ldots \qquad (9.94)$$

and we've already found that $h(n) = 0$ for $n = 0$.

Limiting $|n|$ to 10 and then shifting to the right to make the filter causal yields

n	$T \cdot h(n)$
0	$-1/10$
1	$1/9$
2	$-1/8$
3	$1/7$
4	$-1/6$
5	$1/5$
6	$-1/4$
7	$1/3$
8	$-1/2$
9	1
10	0

n	$T \cdot h(n)$
11	-1
12	$1/2$
13	$-1/3$
14	$1/4$
15	$-1/5$
16	$1/6$
17	$-1/7$
18	$1/8$
19	$-1/9$
20	$1/10$

This differentiator can be represented by the difference equation

$$y(n) = \frac{1}{T}\left[-\frac{1}{10}x(n) + \frac{1}{9}x(n-1) - \frac{1}{8}x(n-2) + \cdots + x(n-9) + \right.$$

$$0x(n-10) - x(n-11) + \cdots + \frac{1}{8}x(n-18)$$

$$\left. -\frac{1}{9}x(n-19) + \frac{1}{10}x(n-20) \right]. \quad (9.95)$$

This difference equation can be implemented as a program for a general purpose digital computer or as special purpose digital hardware. The frequency response is plotted for $0 \le \theta \le \pi$ in Fig. 9.21(a) where the ideal magnitude characteristic is included and the linear phase characteristic is apparent. Included is a magnitude characteristic for an 80th-order filter, Fig. 9.21(b), as well as the results after applying a window as in Fig. 9.21(c).

Example 9.4. This example illustrates the design of a lowpass differentiator.

In some signal processing applications the input to a filter consists of signal components at low frequencies and noise components at higher frequencies. As can be seen from the frequency response of a differentiator, the higher frequencies are amplified. Thus, it is often necessary to restrict the range of frequencies over which the differentiation occurs, so as not to amplify the noise more than the signal components.

Find the filter weights for an ideal lowpass differentiator that has the frequency response

$$H(e^{j\theta}) = \begin{cases} j\theta/T, & -\theta_c \le \theta \le \theta_c \\ 0, & \text{elsewhere.} \end{cases} \quad (9.96)$$

Solution: Using Eq. 9.91 we can replace $\pm\pi$ with $\pm\theta_c$ which gives

$$h(n) = \frac{j}{2\pi T}\left[\frac{e^{jn\theta}}{(jn)^2}(jn\theta - 1)\right]_{-\theta_c}^{\theta_c}$$

$$= \frac{j}{2\pi T(-n^2)}[e^{jn\theta_c}(jn\theta_c - 1) - e^{-jn\theta_c}(-jn\theta_c - 1)]$$

$$= \frac{j}{2\pi T(-n^2)}[jn\theta_c\{e^{jn\theta_c} + e^{-jn\theta_c}\} - e^{jn\theta_c} + e^{-jn\theta_c}]. \qquad (9.97)$$

Equation 9.97 can be put into the form

$$h(n) = \frac{\theta_c}{n\pi T}\cos(n\theta_c) + \frac{j(-j)}{-n^2\pi T}\left[\frac{-e^{jn\theta_c} + e^{-jn\theta_c}}{-2j}\right]$$

$$= \frac{\theta_c}{n\pi T}\cos(n\theta_c) - \frac{1}{n^2\pi T}\sin(n\theta_c). \qquad (9.98)$$

For $\theta_c = \pi$ we get

$$h(n) = \frac{\pi}{n\pi T}\cos(n\pi) - \frac{1}{n^2\pi T}\sin(n\pi)$$

$$= \frac{(-1)^n}{nT}, \qquad |n| = 1, 2, \ldots$$

(9.99)

as before in Eq. 9.94.

FIGURE 9.21 Frequency response results for a 20th-order differentiator with and without a Hamming window, and results for an 80th-order differentiator with a rectangular window

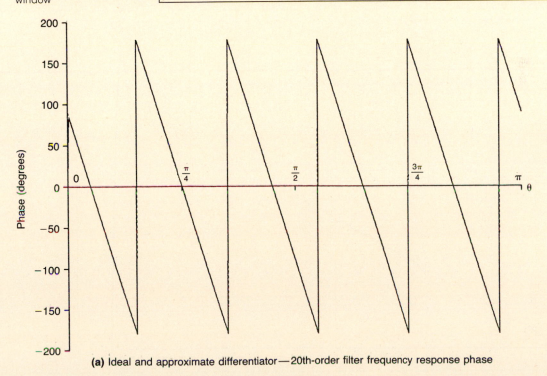

(a) Ideal and approximate differentiator—20th-order filter frequency response phase

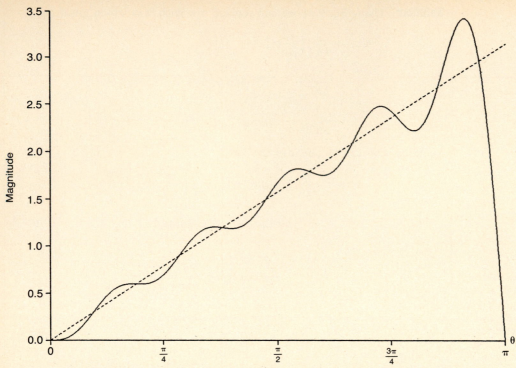

(a) Ideal and approximate differentiator—20th order filter frequency response magnitude

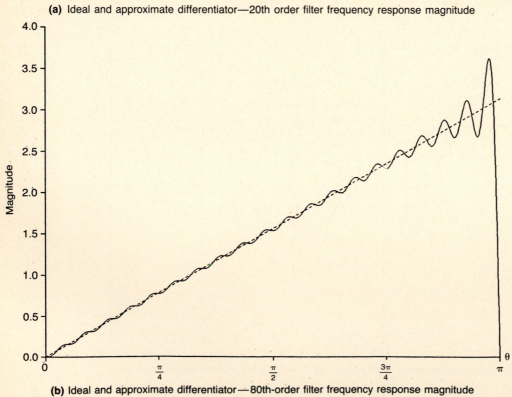

(b) Ideal and approximate differentiator—80th-order filter frequency response magnitude

FIGURE 9.21(b)

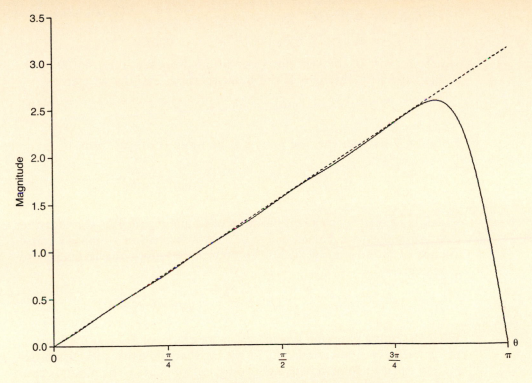

(c) 20th-order filter with a Hamming window

FIGURE 9.21(c)

9.2 ▬ LINEAR PHASE CHARACTERISTICS

In Chapter Four, the idea of linear phase was introduced where we defined ideal filters to have this desirable characteristic in their passbands. In Sections 9.1.2–9.1.5, filters were designed by Fourier Series methods and an important resulting characteristic was that of linear phase. The unit sample response of the noncausal version (before shifting the coefficients to the right) of these filters possessed the property of even symmetry[†] about $n = 0$ and contained an odd number (e.g., 21, 51, . . .) of weights. That is, centered about $h(0)$ at $n = 0$ were

$$h_{nc}(1) = h_{nc}(-1), \; h_{nc}(2) = h_{nc}(-2), \ldots, h_{nc}(I) = h_{nc}(-I) \quad (9.100)$$

where we are using the subscript nc to denote noncausal and the number of terms is $N = 2I + 1$ (an odd number) with I terms on either side of $h(0)$. The frequency response for this finite number of terms is

---

[†] The unit sample response $h(n)$ of the differentiators that were discussed in Section 9.1.6 possessed odd (anti) symmetry. This kind of symmetry is treated later in this section.

$$H_{nc}(e^{j\theta}) = h_{nc}(-I)e^{jI\theta} + \cdots + h_{nc}(-2)e^{j2\theta} + h_{nc}(-1)e^{j\theta} + h_{nc}(0)$$
$$+ h_{nc}(1)e^{-j\theta} + h_{nc}(2)e^{-j2\theta} + \cdots + h_{nc}(I)e^{-jI\theta} \qquad (9.101)$$

which, because of the symmetry conditions imposed in Eq. 9.100 or Fig. 9.22(a), and with the help of the Euler relation, may be written as

$$H_{nc}(e^{j\theta}) = h_{nc}(0) + 2h_{nc}(1)\cos[\theta] + 2h_{nc}(2)\cos[2\theta] + \cdots + 2h_{nc}(I)\cos[I\theta]. \qquad (9.102)$$

Equation 9.102 can then be put into the more compact form of

$$H_{nc}(e^{j\theta}) = h_{nc}(0) + 2\sum_{n=1}^{n=I} h_{nc}(n)\cos[n\theta] \qquad (9.103)$$

which is recognized as a real function of frequency (θ) that can be either positive or negative. This is said to be a zero-phase filter which is a consequence of its noncausal sample response. Rewriting the frequency response gives

$$H_{nc}(e^{j\theta}) = \pm M, \quad M = \left| h_{nc}(0) + 2\sum_{n=1}^{n=I} h_{nc}(n)\cos[n\theta] \right| = |f(\theta)|. \qquad (9.104)$$

When designing passband type filters as we did using Fourier methods, M in Eq. 9.104 is almost constant in the passband because $f(\theta)$ is approximately equal to some positive constant and, of course, the phase is zero. In the stopband of these filters, $f(\theta)$ is very small and typically changes from a small positive number to a small negative one, and vice-versa, as θ varies. When such a change from positive to negative or negative to positive occurs, the sign attached to M will reverse. Associating this sign with the phase causes phase jumps of 180° as we saw in Fig. 9.8(c). This is due

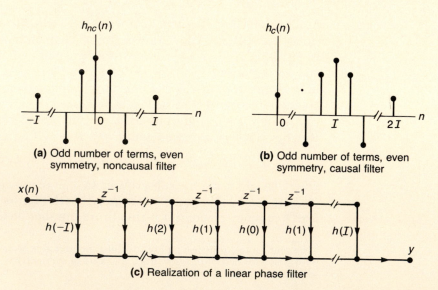

FIGURE 9.22 Linear phase filter—odd number of terms, even symmetry

(a) Odd number of terms, even symmetry, noncausal filter

(b) Odd number of terms, even symmetry, causal filter

(c) Realization of a linear phase filter

to a zero of the generalized frequency response or transfer function $H(z)$ being on the unit circle.

This noncausal filter can be made causal by shifting all the filter weights to the right by I samples giving the causal sample response $h_c(n)$ of Fig. 9.22(b). Recalling that this shift of the sample weights in the time domain results in a phase shift in the frequency domain we have the causal filter

$$H_c(e^{j\theta}) = \pm M e^{-jI\theta} \tag{9.105}$$

where the magnitude M is defined in terms of the noncausal weights as in Eq. 9.104. For the causal filter we also note that the magnitude M is an even function of θ and the phase P is an odd function of θ. Thus, the magnitude of the frequency response is symmetrical, $M(\theta) = M(-\theta)$, and the phase is antisymmetric, $P(\theta) = -P(-\theta)$. Most importantly, the linear phase characteristic doesn't depend upon the specific values of the unit sample response but only upon the symmetry property. This said, we see that the magnitude of the frequency response can be designed to achieve various results such as lowpass, bandpass, and so forth while giving linear phase if the symmetry conditions are met. The phase, $P = -I\theta$, is determined from the number of delays in the realization and it is customary to limit the graphical displays to $-180° \le P \le 180°$ as we discussed in Section 9.1.2 on lowpass design. There may be 180° jumps in the phase plots due to zeros on the unit circle when filters with stopbands are considered.

To review the situation we see that many different magnitude characteristics can be achieved that have this linear phase characteristic in the passband. We simply design a noncausal filter as in Fig. 9.22(a) giving the filter weights $h_{nc}(n)$ of Eq. 9.100 which are then shifted as in Fig. 9.22(b) to produce the realization of Fig. 9.22(c) where the symmetrical weights

$$h_{nc}(1) = h_{nc}(-1), \; h_{nc}(2) = h_{nc}(-2), \; \ldots , \; h_{nc}(I) = h_{nc}(-I) \tag{9.106}$$

are selected to produce a desired frequency response (magnitude) that is guaranteed to have linear phase in the passband.

Filter coefficients can also have another type of symmetry. For example, shown in Fig. 9.23(a) are noncausal filter weights satisfying the conditions

$$h_{nc}(1) = -h_{nc}(-1), \; h_{nc}(2) = -h_{nc}(-2), \; \ldots , \; h_{nc}(I) = -h_{nc}(-I). \tag{9.107}$$

These filter weights, as illustrated by the differentiators of Section 9.1.6, are said to possess odd symmetry, or to be antisymmetric. The frequency response for this filter is

$$H_{nc}(e^{j\theta}) = h_{nc}(-I)e^{jI\theta} + \cdots + h_{nc}(-1)e^{j\theta} + h_{nc}(1)e^{-j\theta} + \cdots + h_{nc}(I)e^{-jI\theta} \tag{9.108}$$

which because of the symmetry conditions imposed in Eq. 9.107 and shown in Fig. 9.23(a), and with the help of the Euler relation, may be written as

FIGURE 9.23 Linear phase filter—odd number of terms, odd symmetry

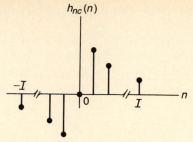

$h_{nc}(n)$

(a) Odd number of terms, odd symmetry, noncausal filter

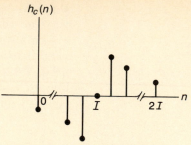

$h_c(n)$

(b) Odd number of terms, odd symmetry, causal filter

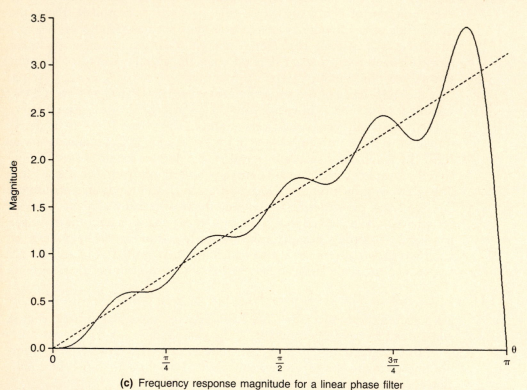

(c) Frequency response magnitude for a linear phase filter

$$H_{nc}(e^{j\theta}) = -2jh_{nc}(1)\sin[\theta] - 2jh_{nc}(2)\sin[2\theta] - \cdots - 2jh_{nc}(I)\sin[I\theta].$$
(9.109)

Equation 9.109 can be put into the more compact form of

$$H_{nc}(e^{j\theta}) = -2j\sum_{n=1}^{I} h_{nc}(n)\sin[n\theta] \qquad (9.110)$$

which is recognized as an imaginary function of frequency that can be

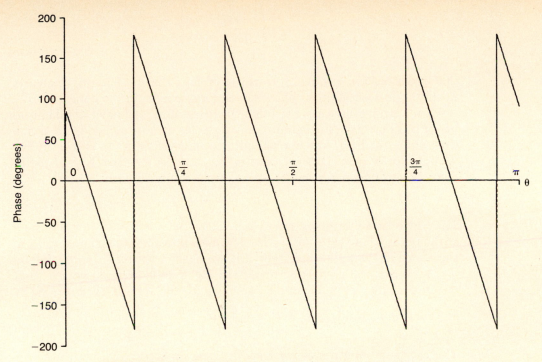

FIGURE 9.23(c) Frequency response phase for a linear phase filter

either positive or negative. Thus,

$$H_{nc}(e^{j\theta}) = \pm M e^{-j\pi/2}, \quad M = \left| 2 \sum_{n=1}^{I} h_{nc}(n) \sin[n\theta] \right|. \qquad (9.111)$$

This noncausal filter can be made causal by the standard shift of I to the right giving the causal sample response $h_c(n)$ as in Fig. 9.23(b) and the frequency response of

$$H_c(e^{j\theta}) = \pm M e^{j(-\pi/2 - I\theta)} \qquad (9.112)$$

where the magnitude M is defined in terms of the noncausal weights as in Eq. 9.111. Again, the magnitude M is an even function of frequency (θ) and the phase is an odd function of θ offset by a constant $\pi/2$ radians. As before, the phase doesn't depend upon the specific values of the unit sample response, but only upon the antisymmetry property of Eq. 9.107. Thus, the frequency response can be designed to achieve various odd-function characteristics such as a differentiator, which was considered in the previous section. There, we found that for a sampling interval of T, the filter weights are given by

$$h_{nc}(n) = \begin{cases} \dfrac{(-1)^n}{nT}, & |n| \neq 0 \\ 0, & n = 0 \end{cases} \qquad (9.113)$$

that produces the frequency response of Fig. 9.23(c). The phase clearly exhibits the desired linear phase characteristic (within the constant $\pi/2$).

Thus far, we have assumed that the filters designed have an odd number of coefficients. This is not required, so let us now consider the situation where the filter has an even number of coefficients as shown in Fig. 9.24(a). Notice that Fig. 9.24(a) portrays a causal filter, with $N = 2I$ coefficients, even symmetry, and a unit sample response with

$$h_c(n) = h_c(2I - 1 - n), \qquad n = 0, 1, \ldots, I - 1. \qquad (9.114)$$

The line of symmetry appears in Fig. 9.24(a) between $n = I - 1$ and $n = I$ at the point where $(2I - 1)/2 = I - 1/2$, a noninteger value. Thus, to form the noncausal sample response $h_{nc}(n)$, we need to shift $h_c(n)$ to the left by $(I - 1/2)$ samples, giving the results in Fig. 9.24(b). There, we see filter weights located at "half-sample" values with the symmetry described by

$$h_{nc}(-1/2) = h_{nc}(1/2), \ h_{nc}(-3/2) = h_{nc}(3/2), \ \ldots ,$$
$$h_{nc}(-I + 1/2) = h_{nc}(I - 1/2). \qquad (9.115)$$

The corresponding frequency response (see Problem 9.28) becomes

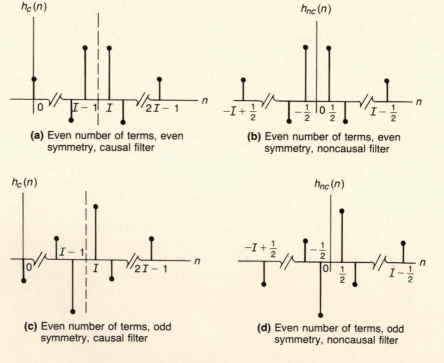

FIGURE 9.24 Unit sample responses for filters with an even number of terms

(a) Even number of terms, even symmetry, causal filter

(b) Even number of terms, even symmetry, noncausal filter

(c) Even number of terms, odd symmetry, causal filter

(d) Even number of terms, odd symmetry, noncausal filter

$$H_c(e^{j\theta}) = \pm M e^{-j(I-1/2)\theta}, \quad M = \left| 2 \sum_{n=0}^{n=I-1} h_c(n) \cos[(I - n - 1/2)\theta] \right|.$$

(9.116)

An alternative is the odd symmetry situation shown for a causal filter in Fig. 9.24(c) where, in general,

$$h_c(n) = -h_c(2I - 1 - n), \qquad n = 0, 1, \ldots, I - 1 \qquad (9.117)$$

which leads to the noncausal filter weights described by

$$h_{nc}(-1/2) = -h_{nc}(1/2), \ldots, h_{nc}(-I + 1/2) = -h_{nc}(I - 1/2). \quad (9.118)$$

The corresponding frequency response is

$$H_c(e^{j\theta}) = \pm M e^{j(\pi/2 - (I-1/2)\theta)}, \quad M = \left| 2 \sum_{n=0}^{n=I-1} h_c(n) \sin[(I - n - 1/2)\theta] \right|.$$

(9.119)

9.3 ■ COMB FILTERS

We now consider the design of *comb filters*. Having the linear phase property, these filters are used when it is desired to remove a particular frequency component and its harmonics from a signal. The unit sample response is of the form

$$h(n) = K[\delta(n) - \delta(n - L)] \qquad (9.120)$$

and is shown in Fig. 9.25(a). The frequency response is

$$H(e^{j\theta}) = K[1 - e^{-jL\theta}] \qquad (9.121)$$

which can be maneuvered into a more useful form, namely

$$H(e^{j\theta}) = K e^{-j(L/2)\theta} [e^{j(L/2)\theta} - e^{-j(L/2)\theta}]$$

$$= 2K \sin\left(\frac{L}{2}\theta\right) e^{j(\pi/2 - (L/2)\theta)} \qquad (9.122)$$

or

$$H(e^{j\theta}) = \pm M e^{jP} \qquad (9.123)$$

with the magnitude and phase plots displayed in Fig. 9.25(b). This filter

FIGURE 9.25 Comb filter characteristics

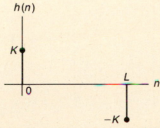

(a) Unit sample response of a comb filter

FIGURE 9.25 (cont.)

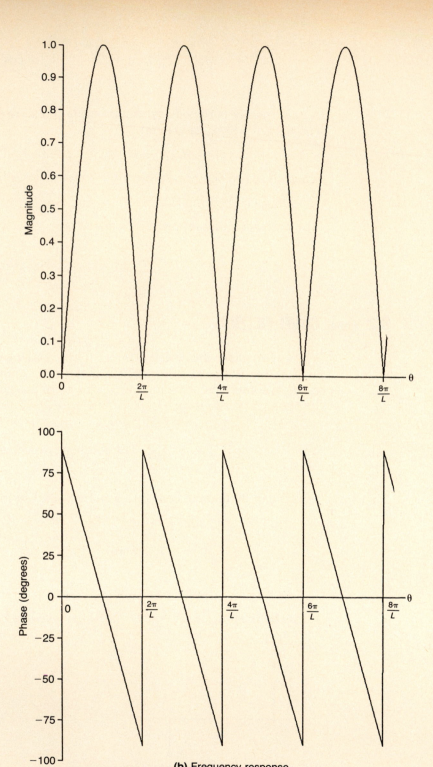

(b) Frequency response

FIGURE 9.25 (cont.)

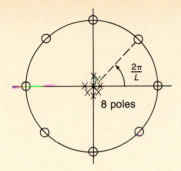

(c) Pole-zero diagram

"notches out" (with zero gain) the harmonically related frequencies

$$\theta = 0, \frac{2\pi}{L}, \frac{4\pi}{L}, \ldots, \pi \qquad (9.124)$$

and has the desired linear phase characteristic. We can also use the graphical approach in Chapter Five to illustrate the notching property of the comb filter by writing Eq. 9.121 in terms of z as

$$H(z) = K[1 - z^{-L}] \qquad (9.125)$$

or

$$H(z) = K\frac{z^L - 1}{z^L}. \qquad (9.126)$$

There are clearly L poles at the origin $(z = 0)$ and the zeros are determined from

$$z^L - 1 = 0 \qquad (9.127)$$

or

$$z^L = 1$$
$$= 1e^{jm2\pi}, \qquad m = 0, 1, 2, \ldots, L - 1. \qquad (9.128)$$

The L roots that satisfy Eq. 9.128 are

$$z_m = (1)^{1/L}e^{j(m2\pi/L)}, \qquad m = 0, 1, 2, \ldots, L - 1$$
$$= 1e^{j(m2\pi/L)}. \qquad (9.129)$$

Thus, we see that the zeros of the transfer function of Eq. 9.126 lie on the unit circle separated by $2\pi/L$ radians as in Fig. 9.25(c) which has been drawn for $L = 8$. It is clear that the zeros totally control the magnitude characteristic because each pole contributes a gain of one at any frequency θ.

Example 9.5. This example illustrates the characteristics of a comb filter. ⎯⎯⎯⎯

Obtain the pole-zero plot and the frequency response plots for a comb filter that has the realization of Fig. 9.26(a).

Solution: From Fig. 9.26(a) the difference equation is

$$y(n) = x(n) - x(n - 12) \tag{9.130}$$

which leads to the transfer function

$$H(z) = 1 - z^{-12}. \tag{9.131}$$

To find the poles and zeros we rewrite $H(z)$ as

$$H(z) = \frac{z^{12} - 1}{z^{12}}. \tag{9.132}$$

Using Eq. 9.129 the 12 zeros are

$$z_m = 1e^{j(m2\pi/12)}, \; m = 0, 1, 2, \ldots, 11. \tag{9.133}$$

The filter transfer function in factored form is

$$H(z) = \frac{(z - 1)(z - 1e^{j\pi/6})(z - 1e^{j\pi/3}) \ldots (z - 1e^{j11\pi/6})}{z^{12}} \tag{9.134}$$

and the pole-zero plot is in Fig. 9.26(b) where from the graphical point of view we can see that the gain (magnitude) goes to zero every $\pi/6$ radians for $0 \le \theta \le$

FIGURE 9.26 Data and results for Example 9.5

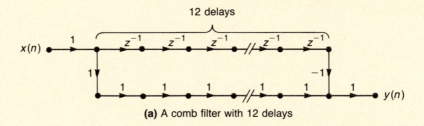

(a) A comb filter with 12 delays

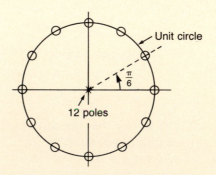

(b) Poles and zeros of a 12th-order comb filter

2π. We can write the frequency response from Eq. 9.122 with $K = 1$ and $L = 12$ as

$$H(e^{j\theta}) = 2\sin[6\theta]\, e^{j(\pi/2 - 6\theta)} = \pm M e^{j(\pi/2 - 6\theta)}. \qquad (9.135)$$

A computer plot of this function is given in Fig. 9.27. Notice that the 180° phase jumps occur when the digital frequency θ passes through a range of values where a zero lies. Or, put in a different way, when the term $2\sin[6\theta]$ changes sign with Eq. 9.135 written as

$$H(e^{j\theta}) = \pm M e^{j(\pi/2 - 6\theta)} \qquad (9.136)$$

the sign change shows up as a 180° phase jump.

9.4 ▬ DESIGN BY FREQUENCY SAMPLING

In Section 9.1 of this chapter, nonrecursive filters were designed using a Fourier Series and window functions. In this approach, the desired frequency response is described by an analytical expression, and the filter

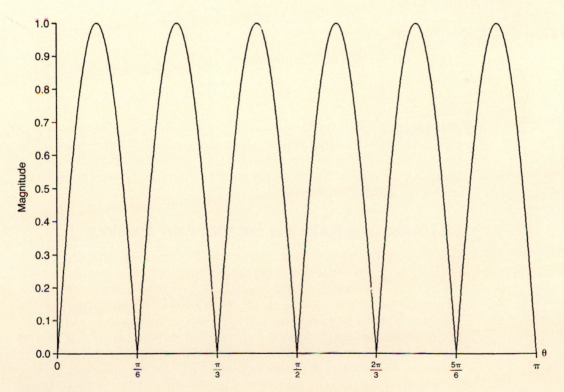

FIGURE 9.27(a) Frequency response magnitude—12th-order comb filter

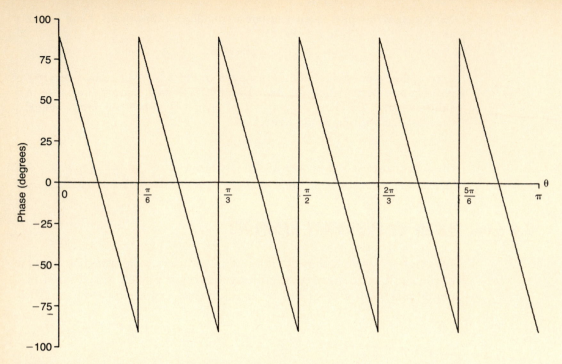

FIGURE 9.27(b) Frequency response phase—12th-order comb filter

coefficients are determined from

$$h(n) = \frac{1}{2\pi} \int_{-\pi}^{\pi} H(e^{j\theta})e^{jn\theta}d\theta, \qquad n = 0, \pm 1, \ldots \qquad (9.137)$$

This procedure is suitable for passband filters (lowpass, highpass, bandpass, and bandstop) and for other special filters such as differentiators. In this section, we present two methods for filter design that are based upon sampling the desired frequency response without necessarily knowing an analytical expression for $H(e^{j\theta})$.

9.4.1 Design Using the Inverse Discrete Fourier Transform

Here, we exploit the Discrete Fourier Transform (DFT) and the Inverse Discrete Fourier Transform (IDFT) to approximate the Fourier Series coefficients that are usually found by analytical methods. By taking a sufficient number of samples to obtain a reasonable approximation of the continuous frequency response, the IDFT algorithm can be used to determine satisfactory estimates of the unit sample response $h(n)$—the Fourier coefficients. A window function may then be applied as in our earlier procedure. This method is now outlined.

Consider the periodic frequency response of Fig. 9.28(a) with its linear phase characteristic. First, we select one period of this response and take

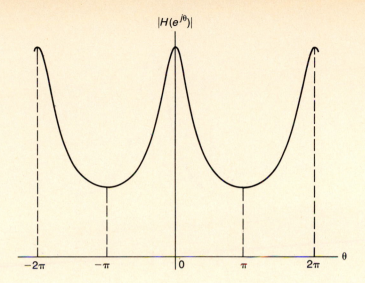

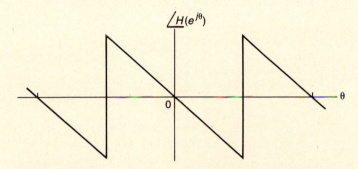

FIGURE 9.28(a) The periodic nature of a discrete system's frequency response

N samples. As in Section 9.1 it is convenient to assume zero phase thereby designing a noncausal filter that can be made causal by an appropriate shift of the filter weights. We choose the period of $H(e^{j\theta})$ as in Fig. 9.28(b) where a period $(-\pi$ to $\pi)$ is shown.

1. The frequency response is

$$H(e^{j\theta}) = \sum_N h(n)e^{-j\theta n} \qquad (9.138)$$

where we are using the notation Σ_N to indicate the number of terms in the summation. With $H(e^{j\theta})$ sampled at intervals of $\theta = 2\pi k/N$ the result is

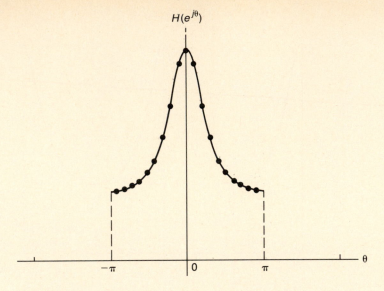

$H(e^{j\theta})$

$-\pi$ 0 π θ

FIGURE 9.28(b)   One period of the frequency response

$$H(k) = H(e^{j\theta})\Big|_{\theta = 2\pi k/N}$$

$$= \sum_N h(n)e^{-j(2\pi/N)nk} \qquad (9.139)$$

and this Discrete Fourier Transform (DFT) of the unit sample response $h(n)$ has N values over one period of 2π radians.

2. Next, we evaluate the Inverse Discrete Fourier Transform (IDFT) to find the N unit sample response values

$$h(n) = \frac{1}{N} \sum_N H(k)e^{j(2\pi/N)nk}. \qquad (9.140)$$

3. As in Section 9.1.5 an appropriate window function $w(n)$ of length M can be selected to obtain the windowed weights

$$\hat{h}(n) = h(n)w(n). \qquad (9.141)$$

Notice that there are M windowed weights $\hat{h}(n)$ that are derived from the N unwindowed weights $h(n)$. L. R. Rabiner (1971) states that the number of frequency samples N should be much greater than the number of Fourier coefficients M under the window $w(n)$. That is, if a filter with M weights (Fourier coefficients) is desired, N samples of the desired frequency response should be used with $N \gg M$.

4. Finally, the filter is implemented by any of the methods previously discussed.

Example 9.6. This example illustrates nonrecursive filter design using the IDFT.

In Example 9.1 we found the Fourier coefficients by analytical means to approximate the frequency response of the highpass filter of Fig. 9.29. Let's use the IDFT approach on this same problem.

a) Find the approximate Fourier coefficients using 101 frequency samples.

b) Use a 21-sample rectangular window to reduce the number of coefficients to 21 and plot the frequency response.

c) Use a 21-sample Hamming window and plot the frequency response.

Solution:

a) The sample values of $H(e^{j\theta})$ are shown in Fig. 9.30 with the input sequence to the IDFT program described by

$$H(k) = \begin{cases} 1, & -50 \leq k \leq -21 \\ 0, & -20 \leq k \leq 20 \\ 1, & 21 \leq k \leq 50. \end{cases} \tag{9.142}$$

With $N = 101$, the spacing between samples is $\Delta\theta = 2\pi/101 = 0.062$ rad yielding 20 values for $H(k)$ of 0 on either side of $k = 0$.

Remember that we are using zero phase in our input data. A linear phase filter characteristic is obtained by shifting the resulting noncausal filter coefficients. Next, we enter the data of Eq. 9.142 into an IDFT program to find the 101-term (N) unit sample response.

b) A 21-sample rectangular window, i.e.,

$$w(n) = \begin{cases} 1, & -10 \leq n \leq 10 \\ 0, & \text{otherwise} \end{cases} \tag{9.143}$$

is applied to the 101-coefficient unit sample response giving the results below. Alongside are the values of $h(n)$ determined by the Fourier Series approach in Example 9.1. The frequency response for the filter designed

n	$h(n)$, IDFT	$h(n)$, analytical
0	0.594	0.600
± 1	−0.305	−0.303
± 2	−0.088	−0.094
± 3	0.067	0.062
± 4	0.074	0.076
± 5	−0.006	0
± 6	−0.052	−0.050
± 7	−0.022	−0.027
± 8	0.028	0.023
± 9	0.032	0.034
± 10	−0.006	0

using the IDFT weights is given in Fig. 9.31 and should be compared with the frequency response for the weights using the Fourier design method of Section 9.1 in Fig. 9.18(b).

c) The 21-coefficient Hamming window is described by

$$w(n) = \begin{cases} 0.54 + 0.46 \cos\left(\dfrac{n\pi}{10}\right), & -10 \le n \le 10 \\ 0, & \text{otherwise} \end{cases} \qquad (9.144)$$

and the windowed weights $\hat{h}(n)$ are given below. The frequency response is shown in Fig. 9.32 and should also be compared with Fig. 9.18(b).

n	$\hat{h}(n)$
0	0.594
±1	−0.298
±2	−0.081
±3	0.054
±4	0.050
±5	−0.003
±6	−0.021
±7	−0.006
±8	0.005
±9	0.003
±10	−0.000 ⟵ (0.08)(−0.006)

FIGURE 9.29 Ideal high-pass filter (zero phase)

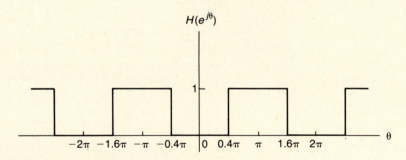

FIGURE 9.30 One period of the ideal highpass filter of Fig. 9.29 sampled an odd number of times

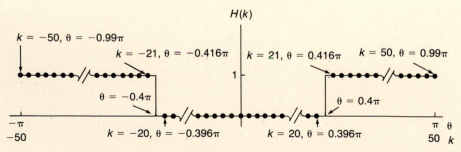

CHAPTER 9 NONRECURSIVE FILTER DESIGN

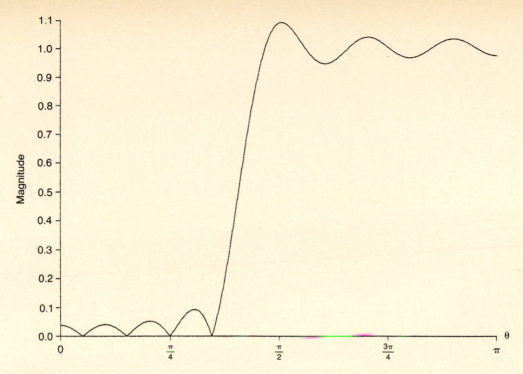

FIGURE 9.31 Frequency response for highpass digital filter: IDFT design and rectangular window

In Example 9.6 we selected the number of sampling points of the frequency response to be an odd number, in this case $N = 101$. Now, we need to address the question "What is the consequence of choosing N to be an even number, say 2^δ, as in an FFT program?" It is shown in Rabiner, Gold, and McGonegal (1970) that if a set of frequency samples $H(k)$ is chosen so that $H(k) = H(N - k)$, the unit sample response $h(n)$ will not be symmetric, and the resulting frequency response $H(e^{j\theta})$ will not have linear phase. But if the substitution

$$H'(k) = \begin{cases} H(0), & k = 0 \\ H(k)e^{j\pi k/N}, & k = 1, \ldots, N/2 - 1 \\ 0, & k = N/2 \\ -H(k)e^{j\pi k/N}, & k = N/2 + 1, \ldots, N - 1 \end{cases} \quad (9.145)$$

is made, then $h(n)$ is a real sequence with the symmetry property

$$h'(n) = h'(N - 1 - n), n = 0, 1, 2, \ldots, \frac{N}{2} - 1. \quad (9.146)$$

This procedure is shown in the following simple example.

9.4 DESIGN BY FREQUENCY SAMPLING

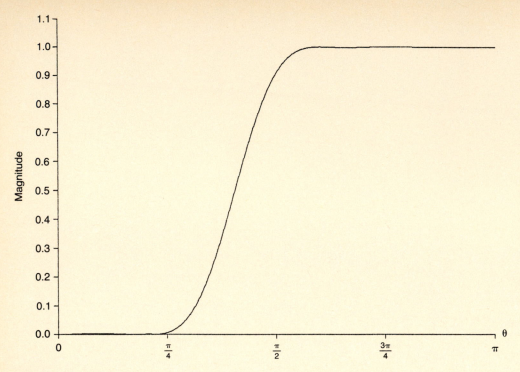

FIGURE 9.32 Frequency response for highpass digital filter: IDFT design and Hamming window

Example 9.7. This example illustrates frequency sampling for N an even number.

Given the ideal lowpass characteristic of Fig. 9.33(a), use $N = 8$ and find:

a) The frequency samples $H'(k)$.

b) The resulting unit sample response $h'(n)$.

Solution:

a) The values of $H'(k)$, chosen according to Eq. 9.145, are

$$H'(0) = 1$$
$$H'(1) = 0.5e^{j\pi/8}$$
$$H'(2) = H'(3) = H'(4) = H'(5) = H'(6) = 0$$
$$H'(7) = -0.5e^{j7\pi/8} = 0.5e^{-j\pi/8}. \tag{9.147}$$

The value of 0.5 was used at $k = 1$ as an average of 1 in the passband and 0 in the stopband.

FIGURE 9.33 IDFT design using an even number of samples—Example 9.7

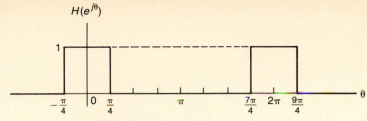

(a) Ideal lowpass filter characteristic

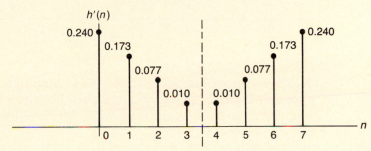

(b) Symmetrical unit sample response $h'(n)$

b) Using an IDFT program we find the eight values of $h'(n)$ to be

$$h'(0) = h'(7) = 0.240$$

$$h'(1) = h'(6) = 0.173$$

$$h'(2) = h'(5) = 0.077$$

$$h'(3) = h'(4) = 0.010. \qquad (9.148)$$

This gives the causal sequence shown in Fig. 9.33(b) that is symmetric about a line drawn between $n = 3$ and $n = 4$.

Comment: In a realistic problem with $N \gg 8$, the windowing procedures of Example 9.6 need to be followed and the $h'(n)$ samples realigned as discussed in Rabiner, Gold, and McGonegal (1970).

Filters designed by taking samples of the frequency response and then using an IDFT algorithm to find $h(n)$ always have the desired frequency response at the frequencies of the sampled values, i.e. at the θ_ks. The response, however, may be significantly different between the sample points. L. R. Rabiner, B. Gold, and C. A. McGonegal (1970) describe the following procedure for smoothing the frequency response. Consider the lowpass filter of Fig. 9.34 with $N = 15$ frequency samples and a 2-sample passband. Two transition samples (T_1 and T_2) have been added between the passband ($H(k) = 1$) and the stopband ($H(k) = 0$). A minimization algorithm is then used to find the values of these transition samples T_1 and

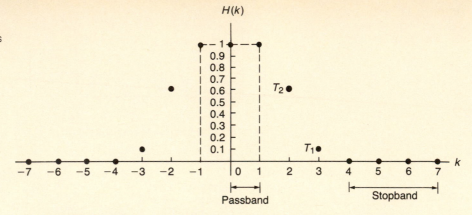

FIGURE 9.34 Ideal low-pass filter characteristic with two transition samples

T_2. Different criteria can be used for the minimization procedure but the approach described in the reference uses the concept of varying the transition point values until the maximum sidelobe of the frequency response is a minimum.

The results of the minimization process can be tabulated for various bandwidths (cutoff frequencies) and numbers of transition points. For instance, tables are provided in Rabiner, Gold, and McGonegal (1970) for lowpass filter design with 1, 2, or 3 transition points, several bandwidths, and odd and even values of the number of frequency samples N. Included is the minimum value in dB of the maximum sidelobe (minimax) with the data from these tables for $N = 15$ given in Table 9.2. Type-1 data refers to the first frequency sample taken to be at $\theta = 0$.

TABLE 9.2 TRANSITION POINT COEFFICIENTS (PARTIAL TABLE)

Lowpass Filter Design, One Transition Coefficient (Type-1 Data, N Odd)

BW	Minimax (dB)	T_1
	$N = 15$	
1	−42.30932283	0.43378296
2	−41.26299286	0.41793823
3	−41.25333786	0.41047363
4	−41.94907713	0.40405884
5	−44.37124538	0.39268189
6	−56.01416588	0.35766525

Lowpass Filter Design, Two Transition Coefficients (Type-1 Data, N Odd)

BW	Minimax (dB)	T_1	T_2
	$N = 15$		
1	−70.60540585	0.09500122	0.58995418

2	−69.26168156	0.10319824	0.59357118
3	−69.91973495	0.10083618	0.58594327
4	−75.51172256	0.08407593	0.55715312
5	−103.46078300	0.05180206	0.49917424

Lowpass Filter Design, Three Transition Coefficients (Type-1 Data, N Odd)

BW	Minimax (dB)	T_1	T_2	T_3
		$N = 15$		
1	−94.61166191	0.01455078	0.18457882	0.66897613
2	−104.99813080	0.01000977	0.17360713	0.65951526
3	−114.90719318	0.00873413	0.16397310	0.64711264
4	−157.29257584	0.00378799	0.12393963	0.60181154

Source: Table adapted from L. R. Rabiner, B. Gold, and C. A. McGonegal, "An Approach to the Approximation Problem for Nonrecursive Digital Filters," *IEEE Trans. Audio Electroacoust.* AU–18 (June 1970): 83–106.

Example 9.8. This example illustrates the effect of transition points in design by frequency sampling.

Use the data from Table 9.2 and plot the magnitude of the frequency response for filters with 0, 1, 2, and 3 transition points. Use a three-sample bandwidth (BW) with $N = 15$.

Solution: From Table 9.2 we find that

a) For a 3-sample bandwidth (BW) the value of the one transition point is $T_1 = 0.41047363$.

b) For a 3-sample bandwidth the values of the two transition points are $T_1 = 0.10083618$ and $T_2 = 0.58594327$.

c) For a 3-sample bandwidth the values of the three transition points are $T_1 = 0.00873413$, $T_2 = 0.16397310$, and $T_3 = 0.64711264$.

Figure 9.35 shows the frequency response magnitude (M vs. θ) plots for 0, 1, 2, and 3 transition points. As with the use of windows, it is observed that the price for less ripple in the passband and lower sidelobes in the stopband is the more gradual transition from passband to stopband.

Comment: If you want to verify these curves the following input data to an IDFT program were used:

Transition points	$k \rightarrow$	0	±1	±2	±3	±4	±5	±6	±7
0	$H(k)$	1	1	1	0	0	0	0	0
1	$H(k)$	1	1	1	0.410	0	0	0	0
2	$H(k)$	1	1	1	0.586	0.101	0	0	0
3	$H(k)$	1	1	1	0.647	0.164	0.009	0	0

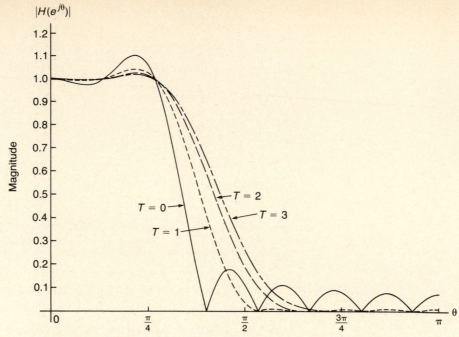

FIGURE 9.35 Lowpass filter frequency response magnitudes: IDFT designs for different transition points

The following unit sample responses $h(n)$—the outputs of the IDFT program— were used to determine the frequency response plots of Fig. 9.35.

Transition points	$n \rightarrow$	0	± 1	± 2	± 3	± 4	± 5	± 6	± 7
0	$h(n)$	0.333	0.278	0.142	0	−0.077	−0.067	0	0.058
1	$h(n)$	0.388	0.295	0.098	−0.044	−0.061	−0.012	0.017	0.014
2	$h(n)$	0.425	0.300	0.066	−0.059	−0.041	0.005	0.013	0.004
3	$h(n)$	0.443	0.301	0.050	−0.062	−0.032	0.008	0.010	0.002

9.4.2 Frequency Sampling Filters

It is also possible to use the same idea of sampling the desired frequency response to find the filter transfer function and subsequent difference equation implementation without actually determining the unit sample response $h(n)$. We now consider how this can be done. Starting with Eq. 9.139 the sampled values of the desired frequency response $H(e^{j\theta})$ are given by

$$H(k) = \sum_{n=0}^{N-1} h(n)e^{-j(2\pi/N)nk} \qquad (9.149)$$

and from Eq. 9.140 the unit sample response is given by

$$h(n) = \frac{1}{N} \sum_{k=0}^{N-1} H(k) e^{j(2\pi/N)nk}, \qquad n = 0, 1, \ldots, N-1. \quad (9.150)$$

The filter transfer function $H(z)$ results from taking the z-transform of Eq. 9.150, i.e.,

$$H(z) = \mathfrak{z}[h(n)]$$

$$= \sum_{n=0}^{N-1} \left[\frac{1}{N} \sum_{k=0}^{N-1} H(k) e^{j(2\pi/N)nk} \right] z^{-n}. \quad (9.151)$$

By interchanging the order of the summations in Eq. 9.151 we can write

$$H(z) = \frac{1}{N} \sum_{k=0}^{N-1} H(k) \sum_{n=0}^{N-1} e^{j(2\pi/N)nk} z^{-n} \quad (9.152)$$

or

$$H(z) = \frac{1}{N} \sum_{k=0}^{N-1} H(k) \sum_{n=0}^{N-1} \{ e^{j(2\pi/N)k} z^{-1} \}^n. \quad (9.153)$$

Using the expression for the closed form of a finite geometric series the right-hand summation of Eq. 9.153 can be written as

$$\sum_{n=0}^{N-1} \{ e^{j(2\pi/N)k} z^{-1} \}^n = \frac{1 - e^{j(2\pi/N)kN} z^{-N}}{1 - e^{j(2\pi/N)k} z^{-1}}$$

$$= \frac{1 - z^{-N}}{1 - e^{j2\pi k/N} z^{-1}}. \quad (9.154)$$

Substituting Eq. 9.154 into Eq. 9.153 produces the filter transfer function

$$H(z) = \frac{1 - z^{-N}}{N} \sum_{k=0}^{N-1} \frac{H(k)}{1 - e^{j2\pi k/N} z^{-1}}. \quad (9.155)$$

The transfer function $H(z)$ of Eq. 9.155 can be thought of as the product of the transfer functions

$$H_1(z) = \frac{1 - z^{-N}}{N} \quad (9.156)$$

and

$$H_2(z) = \sum_{k=0}^{N-1} \frac{H(k)}{1 - e^{j2\pi k/N} z^{-1}}. \quad (9.157)$$

Notice that $H_1(z)$ in Eq. 9.156 is the transfer function of a comb filter, a nonrecursive filter that has N poles at the origin $(z = 0)$ and N zeros located on the unit circle as given by Eq. 9.129. From Eq. 9.157

$$H_2(z) = \frac{H(0)}{1 - z^{-1}} + \frac{H(1)}{1 - e^{j2\pi/N}z^{-1}}$$
$$+ \frac{H(2)}{1 - e^{j4\pi/N}z^{-1}} + \cdots + \frac{H(N-1)}{1 - e^{j(2\pi/N)(N-1)}z^{-1}} \quad (9.158)$$

and we observe that $H_2(z)$ is actually the sum of N transfer functions, each having a single pole. In general, the $H(k)$ values are complex but there is a symmetry, i.e.,

$$H(k) = H^*(N - k)^\dagger \quad (9.159)$$

that allows us to combine two first-order terms into a second-order term with real coefficients. That is,

$$P(z) = \frac{H(k)}{1 - z^{-1}e^{j2\pi k/N}} + \frac{H^*(k)}{1 - z^{-1}e^{j(2\pi k/N)(N-k)}}$$
$$= \frac{z|H(k)|e^{j\angle H(k)}}{z - e^{j2\pi k/N}} + \frac{z|H^*(k)|e^{j\angle H^*(k)}}{z - e^{-j2\pi k/N}}$$
$$= \frac{z^2\{2\mathrm{Re}|H(k)|\} - 2z|H(k)|\{\cos(2\pi k/N - \angle H(k)\}}{z^2 - 2z\cos(2\pi k/N) + 1}. \quad (9.160)$$

We can write Eq. 9.160 in the general second-order form

$$P(z) = \frac{b_0 z^2 + b_1 z}{z^2 - a_1 z + 1}$$
$$= \frac{b_0 + b_1 z^{-1}}{1 - a_1 z^{-1} + z^{-2}}. \quad (9.161)$$

We now show that the zeros of $H_1(z)$ cancel the poles of $H_2(z)$, assuming the use of infinite precision arithmetic. From Eq. 9.129 the zeros of $H_1(z)$ are deduced from

$$z^N - 1 = 0 \quad (9.162)$$

or

$$z = 1e^{j2\pi k/N}, \qquad k = 0, 1, \ldots, N - 1. \quad (9.163)$$

Putting the sum of Eq. 9.157 over a common denomination gives

$$H_2(z) =$$
$$\frac{Q(z)}{(z - e^{j(2\pi \cdot 0/N)})(z - e^{j(2\pi \cdot 1/N)})(z - e^{j(2\pi \cdot 2/N)}) \cdots (z - e^{j(2\pi/N)(N-1)})} \quad (9.164)$$

---

†This can be readily seen by substituting $(N - k)$ for k in Eq. 9.149 and simplifying.

where $Q(z)$ is a polynomial in z. Thus, we have

$$H(z) = H_1(z)H_2(z)$$

$$= \frac{1}{N} \frac{(z - e^{j(2\pi \cdot 0/N)})(z - e^{j(2\pi \cdot 1/N)}) \cdots (z - e^{j(2\pi/N)(N-1)})}{} \times$$

$$\frac{Q(z)}{(z - e^{j(2\pi \cdot 0/N)})(z - e^{j(2\pi \cdot 1/N)}) \cdots (z - e^{j(2\pi/N)(N-1)})} \quad (9.165)$$

and the zeros of $H_1(z)$ cancel the poles of $H_2(z)$ giving

$$H(z) = \frac{1}{N} Q(z). \quad (9.166)$$

The transfer function $H(z)$ of Eq. 9.166 describes a nonrecursive filter having a unit sample response $h(n)$ of finite duration.

In reality, however, $H_2(z)$ is represented by the sum of terms like Eq. 9.158 that when represented with finite precision arithmetic have poles that are not exactly on the unit circle and, consequently, do not cancel the zeros of $H_1(z)$. The result is a filter that has both poles and zeros and, consequently, is recursive with a unit sample response that is not of finite duration. The system diagram for this filter, given in Fig. 9.36, ap-

FIGURE 9.36 Signal flow graph for a frequency sampling filter

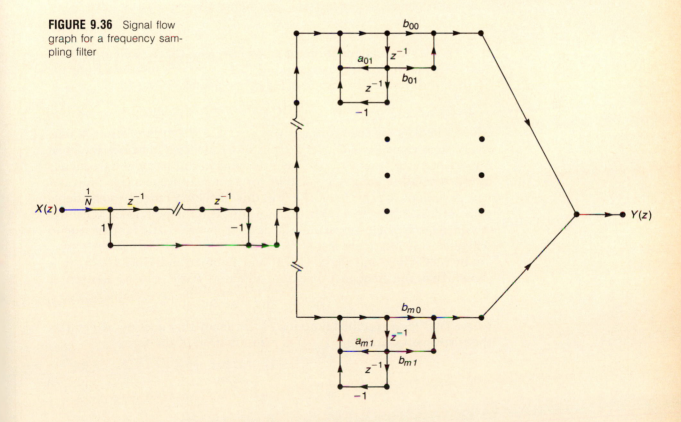

pears to be complicated but is actually fairly simple. This is due to the fact that many of the $H(k)$ terms in Eq. 9.158 are zero yielding a filter that has a small number of nonzero coefficients.

9.5 ▬ COMPUTER-AIDED DESIGN (CAD) OF LINEAR PHASE FILTERS

The basic concept of computer-aided design, or optimization, is relatively straightforward. First, a desired frequency response characteristic is defined, and a recursive or nonrecursive filter type and order are selected. A measure of the deviation between the desired frequency response and the frequency response of the selected filter is then defined. Finally, the filter coefficients are iteratively adjusted to provide a filter frequency response that minimizes the deviation from the desired frequency response. To aid in the iterative optimization, it is important to take advantage of any filter characteristics that simplify or speed up the process.

The approach described in McClellan and Parks (1973) and Rabiner and Gold (1975) uses the linear phase characteristics of nonrecursive filters that we have observed throughout this chapter. It can be shown that for the four cases discussed in Section 9.2—even or odd symmetry with an even or odd number of terms—the frequency response of a nonrecursive linear phase (i.e., possessing symmetry) filter can be written as

$$H(e^{j\theta}) = e^{-j\theta(N-1)/2}e^{j(\pi/2)L}\tilde{H}(e^{j\theta}). \tag{9.167}$$

$\tilde{H}(e^{j\theta})$ is a real-valued function that may have negative as well as positive values. A measure of the deviation of this frequency response from the desired (real) frequency response $H_d(e^{j\theta})$ is given by

$$E(\theta) = W(\theta)[H_d(e^{j\theta}) - \tilde{H}(e^{j\theta})] \tag{9.168}$$

where $E(\theta)$ denotes the error and $W(\theta) \geq 0$ is a weighting factor. A relatively large value of $W(\theta)$ over a range of frequencies indicates the great importance attached by the designer to errors in this particular frequency range. A small or zero value of $W(\theta)$ for a range of frequencies indicates that deviations of $H_d(e^{j\theta})$ and $\tilde{H}(e^{j\theta})$ in this frequency range are considered to be of less importance. When an optimization is performed the filter designed tends to closely match the desired characteristic for frequencies where $W(\theta)$ is relatively large.

In McClellan and Parks (1973) and Rabiner and Gold (1975) it is shown that the frequency response function $\tilde{H}(e^{j\theta})$ can be written as

$$\tilde{H}(e^{j\theta}) = P(e^{j\theta})Q(e^{j\theta}) \tag{9.169}$$

where $Q(e^{j\theta})$ is a specified function of frequency that does not depend on the filter coefficients and $P(e^{j\theta})$ is a summation of the form

$$P(e^{j\theta}) = \sum_{n=0}^{L} \alpha(n)g(\theta\ell) \tag{9.170}$$

where L, ℓ, and the function g depend on whichever of the four cases (even or odd symmetry, even or odd number of terms) is being considered. Depending on the particular case ℓ is either equal to n or $(n - 1/2)$ and g is either a sine or a cosine function.

The $\alpha(n)$ depend on the filter's coefficients. Thus, all of the dependency of $H(e^{j\theta})$ on the filter coefficients is associated with the function $P(e^{j\theta})$. This allows us to rewrite Eq. 9.168 as

$$E(\theta) = W(\theta)[H_d(e^{j\theta}) - P(e^{j\theta})Q(e^{j\theta})]$$

$$= W(\theta)Q(e^{j\theta})\left[\frac{H_d(e^{j\theta})}{Q(e^{j\theta})} - P(e^{j\theta})\right]. \tag{9.171}$$

Or, defining $W(\theta)Q(e^{j\theta})$ as $\hat{W}(\theta)$ and $H_d(e^{j\theta})/Q(e^{j\theta})$ as $\hat{H}_d(e^{j\theta})$

$$E(\theta) = \hat{W}(\theta)[\hat{H}_d(e^{j\theta}) - P(e^{j\theta})]. \tag{9.172}$$

This is now in the form of a Chebyshev approximation problem in which the goal is to find the $\alpha(n)$ values (from which the filter coefficients can be determined) to minimize the maximum absolute value of $E(\theta)$ over the frequency range of interest, i.e.,

$$E_{\text{optimum}} = \min_{\alpha(n)}\left[\max_{\theta}|E(e^{j\theta})|\right]. \tag{9.173}$$

McClellan and Parks (1973) and Rabiner and Gold (1975) show that the actual optimization can be performed by the Remez exchange algorithm, or by linear programming, although the latter is less efficient for this particular optimization problem. Computer programs are readily available to perform the optimization and so we leave it to the interested reader to consult the references for additional information.

9.6 REVIEW

Use of a Fourier Series is a fundamental approach in many scientific and engineering disciplines. In Chapter Seven we used the Discrete Fourier Series to represent a periodic sequence $x_p(n)$ by a finite sum of exponentials, while in this chapter we used an infinite number of exponentials to describe the frequency response $H(e^{j\theta})$, a periodic function of the continuous frequency variable θ. And, in developing a design procedure for nonrecursive filters, we were able to establish that the Fourier coefficients are equal to the filter's unit sample response values $h(n)$.

We then considered the role of the number of filter coefficients and also how to obtain causal filter realizations. The filter design procedure that was developed for lowpass filters can also be applied to highpass, bandpass, and bandstop filters by use of frequency transformations. Thus, we find it convenient to design all passband-type filters as if they were lowpass filters and then transform the filter coefficients to yield a highpass, bandpass, or bandstop filter as appropriate. We also considered the design of other types of filters, specifically a differentiator and a comb filter.

One problem that arises in the Fourier design procedure is the presence of the Gibbs' effect. This is caused by discontinuities in the ideal filter frequency response characteristics when approximated by a Fourier Series. The use of window sequences was shown to be an effective way of reducing this undesirable Gibbs' effect and, although the steps in the design procedure are straightforward, some trial and error may be needed to determine the appropriate number of filter coefficients and an acceptable window sequence.

We also exploited the use of the IDFT (perhaps using an FFT algorithm) to find the filter coefficients after sampling a desired frequency response function $H(e^{j\theta})$. This machine computation allows us to find the unit sample response that corresponds to a graphical description of the frequency response. That is, we don't need an analytical expression for $H(e^{j\theta})$.

Of special importance is the linear phase characteristic of a nonrecursive filter which is obtained as long as the filter coefficients possess appropriate symmetry characteristics. We discussed the four symmetry conditions (N odd and even, even and odd symmetry) that produce the desired linear phase condition needed in certain speech processing and data transmission applications.

Finally, we note that nonrecursive filters are always stable, even if the zeros are not placed exactly where they are specified to be by the design procedure. Such inaccuracies may result from finite wordlength effects of digital hardware, for example. On the other hand, one undesirable characteristic of nonrecursive filters is that the number of coefficients required to obtain an acceptable frequency response magnitude may be considerably larger than for a recursive filter. On an intuitive level we can attribute this to the fact that the nonrecursive filter's frequency response magnitude is determined solely by the location of its zeros (the poles are all located at the origin and so contribute only phase). Recursive filters, on the other hand, have both poles and zeros that can be placed at appropriate locations. Thus, for a given filter order, a recursive design offers essentially twice as many degrees of freedom as for a nonrecursive filter.

VOCABULARY AND IMPORTANT RELATIONS

a) Nonrecursive filter

$$y(n) = b_0 x(n) + b_1 x(n-1) + \cdots + b_L x(n-L) = \sum_{k=0}^{L} b_k x(n-k)$$

b) Relationship among frequency response, unit sample response, and filter coefficients for a nonrecursive causal filter

$$H(e^{j\theta}) = \sum_{n=0}^{n=L} h(n)e^{-jn\theta} = \sum_{n=0}^{n=L} b_n e^{-jn\theta}, \quad \text{so} \quad b_n = h(n) \quad (9.10\text{--}9.12)$$

c) Fourier Series pair

$$H(e^{j\theta}) = \sum_{n=-\infty}^{n=\infty} h(n)e^{-jn\theta} \quad \text{where} \quad h(n) = \frac{1}{2\pi} \int_{-\pi}^{\pi} H(e^{j\theta})e^{jn\theta}d\theta \quad (9.14)$$

d) Filter coefficients (noncausal) for lowpass prototype filter with cutoff frequency θ_c

$$h_{\mathrm{LP}}(n) = \frac{K}{\pi n} \sin(n\theta_c), \qquad n = 0, \pm1, \pm2, \ldots \quad (9.29)$$

e) Transformations of LP filter coefficients into HP, BP, and BS from Table 9.1

$$h_{\mathrm{HP}}(n) = h_{\mathrm{LP}}(n)(-1)^n \quad (9.61)$$

$$h_{\mathrm{BP}}(n) = [2\cos n\theta_0]h_{\mathrm{LP}}(n), \qquad \begin{aligned} \theta_c &= (\theta_u - \theta_\ell)/2 \\ \theta_0 &= (\theta_u + \theta_\ell)/2 \end{aligned} \quad (9.62)$$

$$h_{\mathrm{BS}}(0) = K - h_{\mathrm{BP}}(0)$$

$$h_{\mathrm{BS}}(n) = -h_{\mathrm{BP}}(n), \qquad n = \pm1, \pm2, \ldots \quad (9.63)$$

f) Gibbs' effect

g) Windows:
Generalized Hamming window

$$w(n) = \begin{cases} \alpha + (1-\alpha)\cos\left(\dfrac{n\pi}{I}\right), & -I \le n \le I \\ 0, & \text{otherwise} \end{cases} \quad (9.71)$$

other windows are rectangular, Bartlett, Kaiser, etc.

h) Differentiator

$$H(e^{j\theta}) = j\frac{\theta}{T}, \quad h(n) = \begin{cases} 0, & n = 0 \\ \dfrac{(-1)^n}{nT}, & |n| = 1, 2, \ldots \end{cases} \quad (9.94)$$

i) Linear phase characteristics:
Symmetry of coefficients

even symmetry, odd number of terms in $h(n)$	(9.100)
odd (anti) symmetry, odd number of terms in $h(n)$	(9.107)
even symmetry, even number of terms in $h(n)$	(9.115)
odd (anti) symmetry, odd number of terms in $h(n)$	(9.118)

j) Comb filter

$$h(n) = K[\delta(n) - \delta(n - L)] \qquad (9.120)$$

$$H(e^{j\theta}) = 2K \sin\left(\frac{L\theta}{2}\right) e^{j(\pi/2 - [L/2]\theta)} \qquad (9.122)$$

k) Design by frequency sampling
   Inverse Discrete Fourier Transform (IDFT)

$$H(k) = H(e^{j\theta})|_{\theta = 2\pi k/N}$$

$$= \sum_N h(n) e^{-j(2\pi/N)nk} \qquad (9.139)$$

l) Transition points (see Table 9.2)
m) Frequency sampling filters

$$H(z) = \frac{1 - z^{-N}}{N} \sum_{k=0}^{N-1} \frac{H(k)}{1 - e^{j(2\pi k/N)} z^{-1}} \qquad (9.155)$$

n) CAD
   Filter coefficients minimize maximum absolute value of

$$E(\theta) = \hat{W}(\theta)[\hat{H}_d(e^{j\theta}) - P(e^{j\theta})] \qquad (9.172)$$

PROBLEMS

Reinforcement

9.1 A desired ideal lowpass frequency response has a cutoff frequency of 100 kHz, with zero phase shift at all frequencies. The system sampling rate is $T = 1$ microsecond ($f_s = 10^6$ Hz). Using the Fourier design procedure and a rectangular window

a) Sketch ideal frequency response characteristics for the analog and digital filters that meet the given specifications.

b) Find a general expression for the noncausal digital filter coefficients.

9.2 This problem is a continuation of Problem 9.1 and involves computer generated frequency response plots.

a) Plot the frequency response for filters having 5, 9, and 41 coefficients.

b) If the input consists of samples of the sequence $x(t) = 5 \cos(\pi \cdot 10^5 t) + 4 \cos(3\pi \cdot 10^5 t)$ at $t = \ldots, -2T, -T, 0, T, 2T, \ldots$, find the

expression for the steady-state filter output for the 41-coefficient filter. Use the frequency response plot of part (a) to determine the required values of $H(e^{j\theta})$.

c) Repeat parts (a) and (b) for the 41-coefficient filter with a von Hann window.

9.3 A 7-coefficient causal nonrecursive filter is to be designed using the Fourier Series approach to approximate the frequency response characteristic shown in Fig. P9.3.

a) Find the transfer function of the filter.

b) Find the transfer function of the filter if a Hamming window is used.

9.4 It is desired to design a nonrecursive digital bandpass filter to replace an analog filter which has its passband in the frequency range 40 kHz $\leq f \leq$ 80 kHz. It is known that the highest frequency present in the analog filter input signal is 100 kHz.

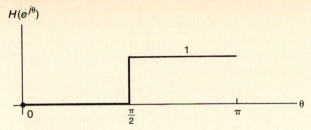

FIGURE P9.3

a) What is the minimum sampling frequency that could be used for the digital filter?

b) For the sampling frequency found in part (a), what is the digital frequency passband?

c) Find an expression for the bandpass noncausal digital filter coefficients using a rectangular window.

9.5 In an effort to relax the requirements imposed by an ideal lowpass filter as a desired frequency response, Roger Vaughan defines the desired frequency response shown in Fig. P9.5. Derive an expression for the unit sample response values for a noncausal, nonrecursive filter that approximates the desired frequency response.

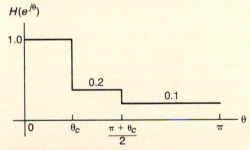

FIGURE P9.5

9.6 It is desired to design a digital bandstop filter to replace an analog filter that has its stopband in the frequency range $40 \text{ kHz} \leq f \leq 80 \text{ kHz}$. It is known that the highest frequency present in the analog filter input signal is 100 kHz.

a) What is the minimum sampling frequency that could be used for the digital filter?

b) For the minimum sampling frequency found in part (a), what is the digital frequency stopband?

c) Find an expression for the bandstop noncausal

digital filter coefficients using a rectangular window.

9.7 It is desired to design a bandpass nonrecursive digital filter that approximates the specifications

$$H(f) = \begin{cases} 1, & 160 \leq f \leq 200 \text{ Hz} \\ 0, & \text{elsewhere in the range } 0 \leq f \leq \dfrac{f_s}{2} \end{cases}$$

where f is analog frequency. Use the Fourier Series approach with a sampling frequency of 800 samples/second and limit the duration of the impulse response to 50 msec.

a) Sketch the desired analog filter frequency response characteristic.

b) Sketch the desired digital frequency response characteristic.

c) How many coefficients are needed?

d) Determine the expression for the filter weights (coefficients) of the noncausal bandpass filter that approximates the desired frequency response. Compute numerical values for $h(0)$, $h(\pm 1)$, $h(\pm 2)$.

e) Compute the numerical values for the windowed weights $h(0)$, $h(\pm 1)$, $h(\pm 2)$ using a Hamming window.

9.8 A nonrecursive noncausal filter with symmetric coefficients and five terms is described by the frequency response $H(e^{j\theta}) = h(-2)e^{j2\theta} + h(-1)e^{j\theta} + h(0) + h(1)e^{-j\theta} + h(2)e^{-j2\theta}$ where $h(-2) = h(2)$ and $h(-1) = h(1)$.

a) Simplify the expression for the frequency response of the filter in terms of the coefficients $h(0)$, $h(1)$, and $h(2)$. Hint: think Euler.

b) Sketch what you expect the phase of the frequency response to be in the interval $0 \leq \theta \leq \pi$, labeling important values wherever possible.

c) Comment on the generality of the results from parts (a) and (b), that is, what can you say about the expression for the frequency response (especially the phase) for a nonrecursive, noncausal filter whose coefficients have the symmetry described above?

9.9 For the desired lowpass characteristic shown in Fig. P9.9, design a nonrecursive filter and

a) Plot the frequency response with 21 terms for

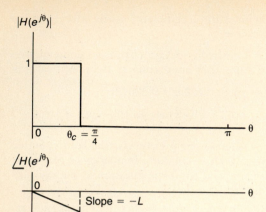

FIGURE P9.9

only) for the filter having 51 coefficients with and without a Hamming window.

9.11 A nonrecursive, noncausal highpass filter is to be designed to meet the following ideal filter specifications

$$H(f) = \begin{cases} 0, & f < 100 \text{ Hz} \\ 1, & 100 \leq f \leq 200 \text{ Hz.} \end{cases}$$

There are no frequencies above 200 Hz in the input signal and the sampling frequency is 800 Hz.

a) Find the general expression for the filter coefficients if the Fourier Series design method is used.

b) For $I = 10$ (10 terms on either side of $h(0)$), *plot* the magnitude of the frequency response using a rectangular window, a Hamming window, and a von Hann window.

9.12 A bandpass analog filter has the desired frequency response

$$\text{Filter gain} = \begin{cases} 1, & 250 \leq f \leq 750 \text{ Hz} \\ 0, & \text{otherwise.} \end{cases}$$

The sampling frequency is $f_s = 2000$ Hz and the digital filter is to have 30 delays.

a) Find a general expression for the coefficients of a nonrecursive, noncausal digital filter that approximates the desired characteristics.

b) Plot the frequency response—magnitude only.

9.13 A nonrecursive bandpass filter is to be designed using the Fourier Series approach along with known frequency transformations. The ideal characteristic is given in Fig. P9.13.

a) Find the expression for the filter coefficients.

b) Using numerical values, write the equation for the frequency response of the noncausal filter having five coefficients in the form $H(e^{j\theta}) = \pm Me^{jP}$ and find M and P.

a noncausal filter and a causal filter. What are the similarities and differences between the plots?

b) Plot the frequency responses with the number of terms equal to 5, 11, 15, and 31. Comment on your results.

9.10 It is desired to design a highpass filter that has a cutoff frequency of 750 Hz. It is known that there are no frequencies in the filter input signal above 1000 Hz and so the sampling frequency for the signal is selected as $f = 4000$ Hz.

a) Sketch an ideal highpass characteristic that could be used to design a digital filter to meet these specifications.

b) Using the ideal characteristic from part (a), determine an expression for the filter coefficients.

c) Plot the frequency response curve (magnitude

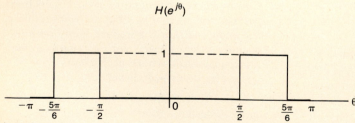

FIGURE P9.13

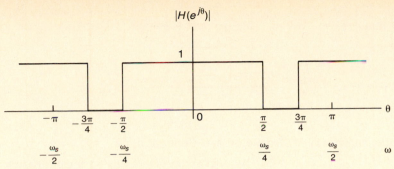

FIGURE P9.14

c) Plot the frequency response for a filter with 51 coefficients.

9.14 A bandstop nonrecursive filter is to be designed using the Fourier Series approach. The ideal magnitude characteristic of this filter is shown in Fig. P9.14.

a) Find the unit sample response values $h(n)$ for $n = 0, \pm1, \pm2, \pm3$.

b) Plot the frequency response for the bandstop filter that approximates the characteristic in Fig. P9.14 and has 51 coefficients.

9.15 A highpass filter is to have an analog cutoff frequency of 8 kHz. The filter is to be implemented by a digital filter having a sampling frequency of 40 kHz.

a) Over what range of analog frequencies can the digital filter be used?

b) Find the coefficients for a four-delay causal highpass digital filter using a Hamming window.

c) What are the gain and phase of the filter found in part (b) at the cutoff frequency?

d) Plot the frequency response of the filter with and without a Hamming window if 51 coefficients are used.

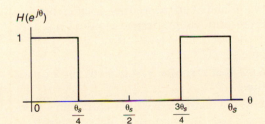

FIGURE P9.16

9.16 A desired frequency response characteristic is shown in Fig. P9.16.

a) Determine the filter weights using the Fourier design method.

b) Plot the gain in dB and the phase in degrees of the frequency response of the causal filter for the unwindowed design with seven coefficients, an unwindowed design for which you select the number of coefficients, and a design having the same number of coefficients just selected but with a Hamming window.

9.17 The simplified block diagram of part of an aircraft control system is shown in Fig. P9.17. The purpose of the bandstop filter is to remove the effects of vibrations in the frequency range 6 Hz to 15 Hz from the control loop. The sampling frequency is $f_s = 100$ Hz.

a) Sketch an ideal digital filter characteristic that could be used to design an appropriate bandstop filter.

b) Using the Fourier Series design procedure, determine the expression for the bandstop filter coefficients with a rectangular window.

c) Plot the magnitude portion of the frequency response for a filter having 31 coefficients.

d) Repeat part (c) using a von Hann window.

9.18 An analog signal has an unwanted 60-Hz component along with its harmonics of 120 Hz, 180 Hz, 240 Hz, 300 Hz, 360 Hz. The sampling frequency for the analog signal is 1200 Hz.

a) Design a digital filter that essentially removes the 60-Hz component along with its undesirable harmonics.

b) Draw a realization of the filter of part (a).

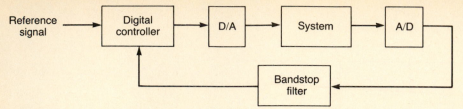

FIGURE P9.17

9.19 The expression for the filter coefficients of an approximation to an ideal differentiator is

$$h(n) = \begin{cases} \dfrac{(-1)^n}{nT}, & n = \pm 1, \pm 2, \ldots \\ 0, & n = 0. \end{cases}$$

a) Find the filter coefficients for the causal differentiator with 11 coefficients using a rectangular window, a Bartlett window, a Hamming window, and a von Hann window.

b) Plot and compare the frequency responses of the filters determined in part (a). Assume that $T = 0.1$ ms.

9.20 In Section 9.4.1 we discussed the use of the Inverse Discrete Fourier Transform (IDFT) to determine the Fourier coefficients.

a) For the ideal filter characteristic of Fig. P9.9, find the unit sample response $h(n)$ by the IDFT method. Use 15 samples of the frequency response.

b) For the filter coefficients generated in part (a) make a frequency response plot using all 15 coefficients.

c) For 201 samples of the frequency response, find the unit sample response $h(n)$. Use rectangular and Hamming windows of 15 samples and plot the resulting frequency responses.

9.21 Repeat parts (a),(b) of Problem 9.20 using (a) 1 and (b) 2 transition points, respectively.

9.22 A nonrecursive bandpass filter is to be designed using the IDFT approach. The ideal characteristic is given in Fig. P9.13. Use 255 frequency samples and find 51 filter coefficients using

a) A rectangular window

b) A Hamming window

c) Plot the frequency response for the filters of parts (a) and (b) and compare with the result of Problem 9.13(c).

Extension and Generalization

9.23 Often when implementing an approximation to an ideal differentiator it is desirable to restrict the bandwidth. A desired frequency response characteristic for such a band-limited differentiator is given by

$$H(e^{j\theta}) = \begin{cases} j\dfrac{\theta}{T}, & \theta_1 \leq \theta \leq \theta_2 \\ 0, & \text{elsewhere in the range } 0 \leq \theta \leq \pi \end{cases}$$

where T is the sampling period.

a) Sketch the magnitude and phase of $H(e^{j\theta})$.

b) Use the Fourier Series design procedure to determine an expression for the coefficients of a noncausal, nonrecursive filter to approximate the desired frequency response.

c) Check your results by letting $\theta_1 = 0$ and $\theta_2 = \pi$ and show that you obtain the same expression as was derived in the text when the differentiator was not band limited.

d) Find the numerical values of the coefficients for a five-term noncausal filter. Assume that the sampling frequency is 1 kHz, and that $\theta_1 = \pi/4$ and $\theta_2 = 3\pi/4$.

e) Find the coefficients for a five-term causal band-limited differentiator using a von Hann window. Assume $f_s = 1$ kHz, $\theta_1 = \pi/4$, and $\theta_2 = 3\pi/4$.

9.24 For the ideal differentiating filter in Section 9.1.6 we found that the Fourier coefficients and hence the unit sample response values are antisymmetric for a noncausal filter, i.e., $h_{nc}(-m) = -h_{nc}(m)$.

a) Show that a similar result holds for a causal filter.

b) With the nonrecursive filter coefficients truncated and the number of delays chosen to yield a causal filter, the output is given by

$y(n) = h_c(0)x(n) + h_c(1)x(n-1) + \cdots + h_c(N-1)x(n-(N-1))$. Use the result of part (a) to show that $y(n)$ is a linear combination of symmetrically located differences of sample values of the input sequence.

9.25 Consider the transfer function for a five-coefficient nonrecursive filter with symmetric coefficients $H(z) = h(0) + h(1)z^{-1} + h(2)z^{-2} + h(3)z^{-3} + h(4)z^{-4}$ where $h(0) = h(4)$ and $h(1) = h(3)$.

a) If z^{-1} is substituted for z, the polynomial $H(z^{-1})$ results. Make this substitution and show that, except for poles or zeros at $z = 0$, $H(z)$ and $H(z^{-1})$ have the same zeros.

b) $H(z)$ can also be written as $H(z) = (z - r_1 e^{j\theta_1})(z - r_2 e^{j\theta_2}) \cdots (z - r_4 e^{j\theta_4})$ where the zeros of $H(z)$ are $z = r_1 e^{j\theta_1}, r_2 e^{j\theta_2}, \ldots, r_4 e^{j\theta_4}$. Show that $H(z^{-1})$ has zeros $z = \dfrac{1}{r_1}e^{-j\theta_1}, \dfrac{1}{r_2}e^{-j\theta_2}, \ldots,$ $\dfrac{1}{r_4}e^{-j\theta_4}$, that is, that the roots of $H(z^{-1})$ are the reciprocals of the roots of $H(z)$.

c) From the results of parts (a) and (b), what can be said about possible locations of the roots of $H(z)$?

d) Are the results of parts (a)–(c) general, i.e., would they apply to an N-coefficient symmetric filter? Explain.

9.26 a) Show that the relationships given in Table 9.1 for the transformation of a lowpass filter into a bandpass filter can be derived by shifting and adding two replicas of an ideal lowpass filter characteristic having an appropriate bandwidth.

b) Starting with Eq. 9.14 derive the Fourier coefficients for a bandpass filter whose characteristic is shown in Table 9.1. Then, by inspection of the expression for the coefficients of an ideal lowpass filter having $\theta_c = (\theta_u - \theta_\ell)/2$, determine the relationship between the lowpass and bandpass characteristics.

c) Using the technique of part (a), derive the relationship given in Table 9.1 for the transformation of a bandpass filter into a bandstop filter. Also express the bandstop filter coefficients in terms of the corresponding lowpass filter coefficients.

9.27 The Fourier design method applied to a differentiator results in a filter having an odd number of coefficients that are antisymmetric. Thus, the frequency response is given by

$$H_c(e^{j\theta}) = \sum_{n=0}^{2I} h_c(n)e^{-jn\theta}$$

where $h_c(n) = -h_c(2I - n)$, $n = 0, 1, \ldots, I - 1$.

a) Show that the frequency response can be written as $H_c(e^{j\theta}) = \pm M e^{-jI\theta}e^{-j\pi/2}$ and find and simplify the expression for M.

b) Determine the value of the frequency response at $\theta = \pi$ radians.

c) If the differentiator is to have its passband from $0 \le \theta \le \pi$, what can you say about the error at $\theta = \pi$ between the ideal differentiator and the approximate differentiator designed using the Fourier Series approach?

9.28 Using the Fourier Series design method presented in this chapter leads to nonrecursive filters having an odd number of coefficients. We have seen, however, that it is possible to use other methods to design nonrecursive filters having an even number of coefficients. The frequency response characteristic of a causal nonrecursive filter having an even number of symmetrical coefficients is given by

$$H_c(e^{j\theta}) = \sum_{n=0}^{2I-1} h_c(n)e^{-jn\theta}$$

where $h_c(n) = h_c(2I - 1 - n)$, $n = 0, 1, \ldots, I - 1$.

a) The frequency response can be written as $H_c(e^{j\theta}) = \pm M e^{-j((2I-1)/2)\theta}$ where M is a real quantity. Find and simplify the expression for M.

b) What is the value of $H(e^{j\pi})$?

c) Comment on the suitability of this type of filter for lowpass, highpass, bandpass, and bandstop filters.

9.29 A Hilbert transform is a mathematical operation used in processing single sideband modulated signals. An ideal Hilbert "transformer" has the desired frequency response characteristic

$$H_d(e^{j\theta}) = \begin{cases} -j, & \theta_\ell \le \theta \le \theta_u \\ +j, & -\theta_u \le \theta \le -\theta_\ell \end{cases}$$

where $\theta_u \le \pi$.

a) Sketch the magnitude and phase of $H_d(e^{j\theta})$ for $-\pi \le \theta \le \pi$. Let $\theta_\ell = \pi/8$ and $\theta_u = \pi/4$.

b) Use the Fourier Series design procedure to determine an expression for the coefficients of a noncausal, nonrecursive filter to approximate the desired frequency response.

c) Find the numerical values for the coefficients for a five-term noncausal Hilbert transformer. Assume that $\theta_\ell = \pi/8$ and $\theta_u = \pi/4$.

d) Find the numerical values of coefficients for a five-term causal Hilbert transformer using a von Hann window.

9.30 a) By following a development along similar lines to that given in Section 9.2, show that a causal nonrecursive filter with an even number of terms $(2I)$ has linear phase provided that $h(n) = h(2I - 1 - n)$, $n = 0, 1, \ldots, (I - 1)$.

b) Find the expression for the magnitude and phase of $H(e^{j\theta})$.

9.31 Given the filter frequency response

$$H(e^{j\theta}) = \sum_{m=0}^{m=2I} h(m)e^{-jm\theta}$$

where the filter weights $h(m)$, $0 \leq m \leq 2I$ are real, I is an integer, and $h(m) = h(2I - m)$, $0 \leq m \leq I - 1$.

a) Deduce a general expression for the magnitude of the frequency response, namely $|H(e^{j\theta})|$.

b) For $I = 2$ we want to satisfy the conditions $|H(e^{j0})| = 1$ and $|H(e^{j\pi})| = 0$. Show that the filter weights are $h(1) = 1/4$ and $h(2) = [1/2 - 2h(0)]$ when $h(0)$ is arbitrary.

c) For $h(0) = 1/4$, can you show that $|H(e^{j\pi/3})| = 0$?

9.32 Repeat Problem 9.22 for 256 frequency samples and 52 coefficients. Compare the frequency response found with that of Problem 9.22.

9.33 In this chapter digital differentiators were designed using the Fourier Series approach. This analytical method becomes somewhat complicated when applied to a digital integrator and the approximate method of computing the Fourier coefficients by using the IDFT comes to mind. The process of integration is described by the continuous-time frequency response $H(j\omega) = 1/j\omega$ that in terms of the digital frequency $\theta = \omega T$ gives the desired digital frequency response $H(e^{j\theta}) = T/j\theta$. There is a problem with $\theta = 0$ (why?). To avoid this difficulty let's design a bandpass integrator by frequency sampling and the IDFT with the desired frequency response characteristic defined as

$$H_d(e^{j\theta}) = \begin{cases} T/j\theta, & \theta_\ell \leq \theta \leq \theta_u \\ 0, & \text{otherwise.} \end{cases}$$

a) For $T = 1.0$ obtain 101 samples of one period of $H_d(e^{j\theta})$ with $\theta_\ell = 0.1\pi$ and $\theta_u = 0.95\pi$. Use these samples in the IDFT algorithm to find the approximate Fourier coefficients.

b) Use a rectangular window to obtain a unit sample response $h(n)$, $n = 0, 1, \ldots, N - 1$, of length 21 and plot the resulting frequency response.

c) Repeat part (b) using a Hamming window.

NOTE: The following three problems are intended to be more representative of realistic design problems in that specifications are given for passband and stopband gain, as well as bandwidth. The designer then attempts to determine the minimum number of filter coefficients and an appropriate window to meet these specifications. All three problems require trial-and-error solutions using a computer.

9.34 The requirements to be met by an analog highpass filter are shown in the specification diagram of Fig. P9.34 where the unshaded regions represent the desired response characteristic. These specifications are to be met by a nonrecursive digital filter designed by the Fourier Series approach. The sampling frequency is $f_s = 10$ kHz.

a) Find the minimum filter order and an appropriate window sequence to meet the given specifications.

b) Plot the resulting digital filter's frequency response and verify that it meets the given specifications.

9.35 Repeat Problem 9.34 for the specifications given in Fig. P9.35. Use $f_s = 20$ kHz.

9.36 Repeat Problem 9.34 for the lowpass specifications given in Fig. P9.36. The sampling frequency is 20 kHz and the zero-frequency gain of the filter is to be 0 dB.

Integrated Review

9.37 A causal lowpass analog filter has the following desired characteristics

FIGURE P9.34 Specification diagram for highpass filter

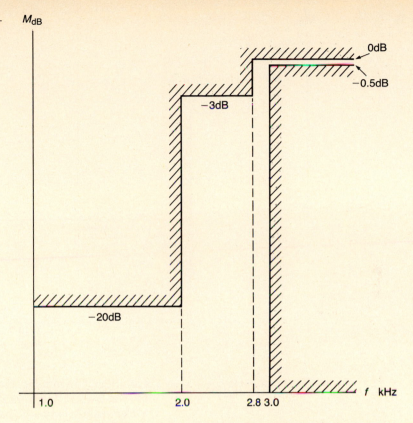

FIGURE P9.35 Specification diagram for bandstop filter

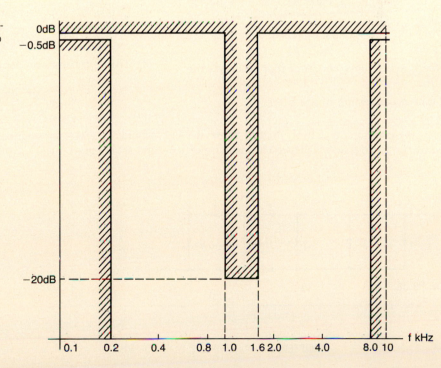

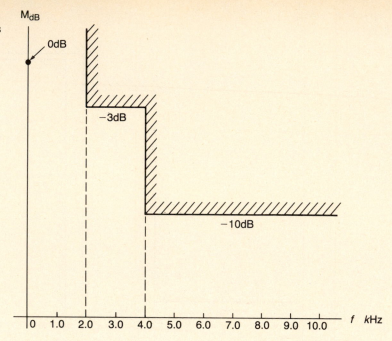

Filter gain $= \begin{cases} 1, & 0 \le f \le 500 \text{ Hz} \\ 0, & \text{otherwise} \end{cases}$

The sampling frequency is 2000 Hz and the digital filter's unit sample response is to have a duration of 30 ms.

a) Find the unit sample response values for the filter.

b) Write a difference equation that describes the filter.

c) Draw a realization of the filter.

9.38 A five-coefficient causal digital filter designed by the Fourier Series method has the implementation shown in Fig. P9.38. A rectangular window was used to design this lowpass filter that has an ideal gain of π in the passband.

a) What is the cutoff frequency?

b) Determine the unit sample response $h(n)$.

c) Determine the transfer function $H(z)$. What can you say about its poles and zeros?

d) This filter is to process the analog signal

$$x(t) = \sum_{k=1}^{5} \frac{10}{k} \sin(2000 \pi kt)$$

where the sampling frequency is $f_s = 12$ kHz. Find the steady-state filter output $y_{ss}(n)$.

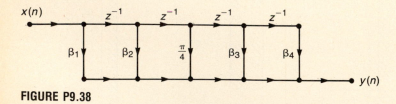

FIGURE P9.38

CHAPTER 9 NONRECURSIVE FILTER DESIGN

REFERENCES AND OTHER SOURCES OF INFORMATION

Antoniou, A. 1979. *Digital Filters: Analysis and Design.* New York: McGraw-Hill Book Co.

Bozic, S. M. 1979. *Digital and Kalman Filtering.* London: Edward Arnold Ltd.

Blackman, R. D., and J. W. Tukey. 1958. *The Measurement of Power Spectra.* New York: Dover Publications, Inc.

Hamming, R. W. 1983. *Digital Filters,* 2nd Ed., Englewood Cliffs, New Jersey: Prentice-Hall, Inc.

Harris, F. J. 1976. *Trigonometric Transforms.* San Diego, California: Spectral Dynamics Corporation.

Harris, F. J. 1978. "On the Use of Windows for Harmonic Analysis with the Discrete Fourier Transform." *Proc. of the IEEE.* 66 (January): 51–83.

McClellan, J. H., and T. W. Parks. 1973. "A Unified Approach to the Design of Optimum FIR Linear Phase Filters." *IEEE Trans. on Circuit Theory.* 20, No. 6 (November): 697–701.

McClellan, J. H., T. W. Parks, and L. R. Rabiner. 1979. "FIR Linear Phase Filter Design Program." *Programs for Digital Signal Processing.* New York: IEEE Press.

Oppenheim, A. V., and A. S. Willsky. 1983. *Signals and Systems.* Englewood Cliffs, New Jersey: Prentice-Hall, Inc.

Parks, T. W., and J. H. McClellan. 1972. "Chebyshev Approximation for Nonrecursive Digital Filters with Linear Phase." *IEEE Trans. on Circuit Theory.* 19 (March): 189–194.

Rabiner, L. R. 1971. "Techniques for Designing Finite-Duration Impulse-Response Digital Filters." *IEEE Trans. on Communications Technology.* Vol. Com-19 (April): 188–195.

Rabiner, L. R. 1972. "The Design of Finite Impulse Response Digital Filters Using Linear Programming Techniques." *Bell Syst. Tech. J* (July–Aug.): 1177–1198.

Rabiner, L. R., and B. Gold. 1975. *Theory and Application of Digital Signal Processing.* Englewood Cliffs, New Jersey: Prentice-Hall, Inc.

Rabiner, L. R., B. Gold, and C. A. McGonegal, 1970. "An Approach to the Approximation Problem." *IEEE Trans. on Audio Electroacoust.* Vol. AU-18 (June): 83–106.

Rabiner, L. R., J. H. McClellan, and T. W. Parks, 1975. "FIR Digital Filter Design Techniques Using Weighted Chebyshev Approximation." *Proc. of the IEEE* (April): 595–610.

Remes, E. Y. 1957. "General Computational Methods of Tchebyshev Approximation." Kiev (Atomic Energy Commission Translation 4491, pp. 1–85).

Stanley, W. D., G. R. Dougherty, and R. Dougherty. 1984. *Digital Signal Processing,* 2nd Ed., Reston, Virginia: Reston Publishing Co.

Thomas, G. B., Jr., and R. L. Finney. 1979. *Calculus and Analytic Geometry,* 5th Ed., Reading, Massachusetts: Addison-Wesley Publishing Co.

Van Valkenburg, M. E. 1974. *Network Analysis,* 3rd Ed., Englewood Cliffs, New Jersey: Prentice-Hall, Inc.

CHAPTER 10

Recursive Filter Design

VOCABULARY AND IMPORTANT RELATIONS
PROBLEMS
REFERENCES AND OTHER SOURCES OF INFORMATION

10.0 ▬ PREVIEW

Recursive and nonrecursive filters were designed in Chapter Five by making use of poles and zeros and a graphical approach. The approach used was essentially a trial and error procedure, and, although it produces reasonable results, it is not a structured or organized way to design filters. In Chapter Nine we employed methods based on the Fourier Series and IDFT to design nonrecursive filters. Satisfactory results were achieved but often at the expense of a large number of terms (delays).

Now we consider a systematic approach for the design of recursive (IIR) filters. One possibility is to make use of the extensive and exhaustive literature available for designing analog (continuous-time) filters and then convert these analog filters into a form suitable for digital implementation. The step of going from analog to digital is quite mechanical so the heart of the matter lies in the design of an analog filter to meet some given requirements such as those shown in the specification diagram of Fig. 10.1 (Ghausi and Laker, 1981).

Analog filter transfer functions are described in terms of the complex variable s (Laplace variable s) with a typical transfer function being

$$H(s) = \frac{Y(s)}{X(s)} = \frac{k(s + 1)}{s^2 + 5s + 6} \tag{10.1}$$

where $X(s)$ represents the Laplace transform of $x(t)$, the filter input, and $Y(s)$ is the Laplace transform of $y(t)$, the filter output. The standard notation is

$$X(s) = \mathcal{L}[x(t)] \text{ and } Y(s) = \mathcal{L}[y(t)] \tag{10.2}$$

where $\mathcal{L}$ denotes the operation of "taking the transform." No previous experience with Laplace transform theory is required to be able to proceed with this chapter. Appendix C provides a brief explanation of the "s-domain" techniques needed for the design of analog filters at this introductory level.

Initially, several important continuous-time concepts such as a system's unit impulse response, its sinusoidal steady-state response, and its frequency response are developed from the point of view of the Laplace transform and are applied to study certain properties and characteristics of analog filters. Three classes of filters, Butterworth, Chebyshev, and elliptic are considered with the primary focus being on determining the order of the filter required to meet given design specifications. Certain

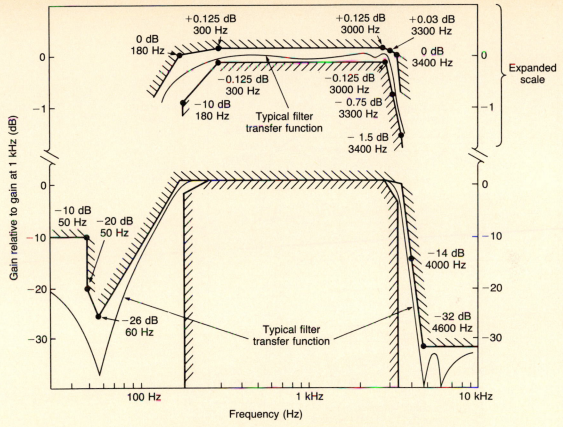

(a) Specification diagram for transmitting filter

FIGURE 10.1

Source: M. S. Chausi and K. R. Laker, *Modern Filter Design*, Englewood Cliffs, New Jersey, Prentice-Hall, Inc., © 1981.

other filter characteristics must also be studied but the final act of determining the transfer function is often a straightforward table look-up procedure. As in Chapter Nine, we concentrate on the design of lowpass filters (prototype) and then we derive the lowpass (LP), highpass (HP), bandpass (BP), and bandstop (BS) transfer functions through well-known frequency transformations.

The digitization of analog filters is then discussed. This process of obtaining a discrete transfer function (z-domain) from an analog transfer function (s-domain) can be done in several different ways. The methods we consider are the matched z-transform, impulse- and step-invariant transformations, and the bilinear transformation.

Finally, a set of formulae are given that permit digital lowpass filters to be made into other types of digital passband filters. This gives us an alternative design procedure in that an existing prototype lowpass digital filter with a characteristic frequency response can easily be turned into an LP, HP, BP, or BS digital filter.

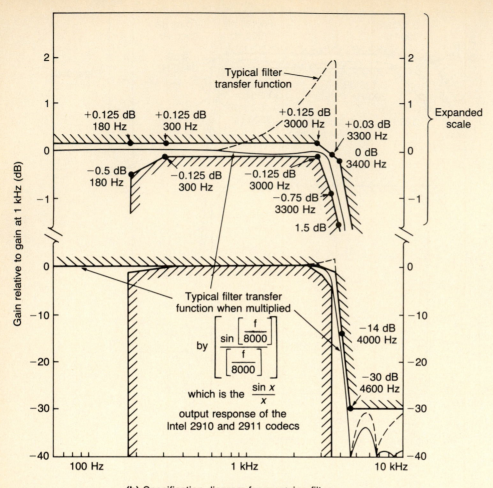

(b) Specification diagram for receiving filter

FIGURE 10.1 cont.

In a sense, this chapter deals with transformations—Laplace transformations, analog filter frequency transformations, and digital filter frequency transformations. All of these transformations contribute to the collection of tools needed for recursive (IIR) filter design. With our previous work in Chapters Four, Five, and Nine we will, at the conclusion of this chapter, have several ways of designing digital filters.

10.1 ■ ANALOG FILTER CHARACTERISTICS

An analog filter is described by the transfer function

$$H(s) = \frac{Y(s)}{X(s)} = \frac{k(s^L + b_{L-1}s^{L-1} + \cdots + b_1 s + b_0)}{s^N + a_{N-1}s^{N-1} + \cdots + a_1 s + a_0} \tag{10.3}$$

where N denotes the order of the filter, k is a real constant, and the numerator order L is less than or equal to the denominator order N. The filter block diagram is given in Fig. 10.2(a) and a realization using operational amplifiers (op amps), resistors, and capacitors of a second-order bandpass filter is shown in Fig. 10.2(b). We shall not be concerned with being able to derive this realization (Van Valkenburg, 1982) but it is presented for general background.

As was the case in discrete systems, the question of stability is important in the use of an analog filter. If we consider the impulse response of the filter of Figure 10.2(b) we have

$$Y(s) = H(s) \cdot X(s)$$

$$\doteq \frac{ks}{s^2 + a_1 s + a_0} \cdot 1 \tag{10.4}$$

because $\mathcal{L}[x(t)] = \mathcal{L}[\delta(t)] = 1$ from Table C1 in Appendix C. Then, using a partial fraction expansion, we have

$$Y(s) = \frac{ks}{s^2 + a_1 s + a_0}$$

$$= \frac{ks}{(s - d_1)(s - d_2)} \equiv \frac{C_1}{s - d_1} + \frac{C_2}{s - d_2} \; ^\dagger \tag{10.5}$$

where d_1 and d_2 are the poles of $H(s)$, and also the poles of $Y(s)$ when the

FIGURE 10.2 An analog filter

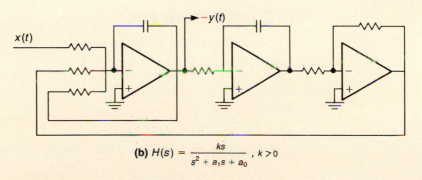

(a) System block diagram

(b) $H(s) = \dfrac{ks}{s^2 + a_1 s + a_0}$, $k > 0$

---

†From Appendix C the "canonical pair" in the s-domain that we are using is $ke^{\alpha t}u(t) \leftrightarrow \dfrac{k}{s - \alpha}$ compared with the z-domain equivalent of $k\alpha^n u(n) \leftrightarrow \dfrac{kz}{z - \alpha}$. Thus, in the s-domain the logical expansion is $Y(s)$ rather than the z-domain expansion of $Y(z)/z$.

FIGURE 10.3 The s-plane and the stable region

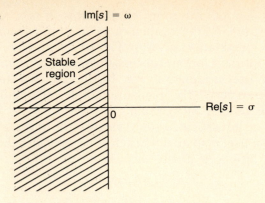

input is a unit impulse. Taking the inverse transform yields the unit impulse response

$$y(t) = h(t) = C_1 e^{d_1 t} + C_2 e^{d_2 t}, \; t \geq 0. \tag{10.6}$$

To ensure a stable system, the unit impulse response must eventually decay to zero, that is,

$$\lim_{t \to \infty} h(t) = 0. \tag{10.7}$$

Inspection of Eq. 10.6 reveals that d_1 and d_2 must be real and negative or complex with negative real parts for the stability condition of Eq. 10.7 to be satisfied. This stability result may be extended to higher-order systems and the result will be the same: All poles of the system transfer function $H(s)$ must lie to the left of the imaginary axis of the s-plane, as in Fig. 10.3. Thus, when "digitizing" an analog filter to create a digital filter, we normally start with a stable analog filter—one that satisfies Eq. 10.7 or whose poles lie in the stable region as portrayed in Fig. 10.3.

10.1.1 Sinusoidal Steady-State

If a system's input is $x(t) = X_1 \cos(\omega t)$ and if the system's input and output are related by the system transfer function $H(s) = Y(s)/X(s)$ whose poles are all in the left-half plane, then the system's steady-state output is given by

$$y_{ss}(t) = X_1 |H(j\omega)| \cos(\omega t + \underline{/H(j\omega)}) \tag{10.8}$$

where $H(j\omega) = H(s)\big|_{s=j\omega}$. This is the sinusoidal steady-state formula that is used to find the response of a *stable analog system* (Strum and Ward, 1985) and should be compared with Eq. 4.85 for discrete systems. Let's see how this is derived. First, the Laplace transform of the output is

$$Y(s) = H(s)X(s) \tag{10.9}$$

and replacing $X(s)$ with the transform of $x_1(t) = X_1 \cos(\omega t)$ we have

$$Y(s) = H(s) \cdot \frac{X_1 s}{s^2 + \omega^2}. \tag{10.10}$$

The usual partial fraction expansion is performed giving both system terms and terms due to the input, namely

$$Y(s) = \underbrace{\frac{C_1}{s - d_1} + \frac{C_2}{s - d_2} + \cdots + \frac{C_N}{s - d_N}}_{\text{system terms}} + \underbrace{\frac{\frac{A}{2} e^{j\alpha}}{s - j\omega} + \frac{\frac{A}{2} e^{-j\alpha}}{s + j\omega}}_{\text{input terms}} \tag{10.11}$$

where the last two terms have been put in the form of pair number 8 in Table C.1. Provided all poles d_i, $i = 1, \ldots, N$ of $H(s)$ are in the left half of the s-plane, the inverse transform of all terms except the last two will decay to zero as $t \to \infty$. Since we are interested in the steady-state output, we need consider only the last pair of terms. Evaluating the partial fraction constant $(A/2)e^{j\alpha}$ in the usual way,

$$\frac{A}{2} e^{j\alpha} = H(s) \frac{X_1 s}{(s + j\omega)} \Big|_{s = j\omega}$$

$$= H(j\omega) \frac{X_1 j\omega}{2j\omega}$$

$$= \frac{X_1}{2} H(j\omega). \tag{10.12}$$

Writing the complex number $H(j\omega)$ in terms of its magnitude and phase allows us to express the partial fraction constant as

$$\frac{A}{2} e^{j\alpha} = \frac{X_1}{2} |H(j\omega)| e^{j\angle H(j\omega)}. \tag{10.13}$$

The inverse transform of the last pair of terms in the PFE of Eq. 10.11 is

$$y_{ss}(t) = \frac{X_1}{2} |H(j\omega)| e^{j\angle H(j\omega)} e^{j\omega t} + \frac{X_1}{2} |H(j\omega)| e^{-j\angle H(j\omega)} e^{-j\omega t} \tag{10.14}$$

which, with the help of the Euler relation, can be written as the sinusoid

$$y_{ss}(t) = X_1 |H(j\omega)| \cos(\omega t + \angle H(j\omega)) \tag{10.15}$$

the result we set out to derive.

Example 10.1. This example illustrates the sinusoidal steady-state response of a lowpass filter.

Consider a stable lowpass filter described by

$$\frac{Y(s)}{X(s)} = H(s) = \frac{1}{s^2 + \sqrt{2}s + 1} \qquad (10.16)$$

subjected to a sinusoidal input, $x(t) = 10 \cos(t)$. Find the steady-state output, $y_{ss}(t)$.

Solution: Before using the sinusoidal steady-state formula of Eq. 10.15, we must always check the system for stability. The system poles are the roots of the characteristic equation

$$s^2 + \sqrt{2}s + 1 = 0 \qquad (10.17)$$

or

$$s_{1,2} = -0.707 \pm j0.707. \qquad (10.18)$$

The poles are clearly in the left half of the s-plane so the system is stable. (The characteristic equation $as^2 + bs + c = 0$ with a, b, and c of the same sign always describes a stable system. See Problem 10.13.) Having the stability check out of the way we need to evaluate the filter transfer function at the frequency of the input $\omega = 1$, i.e., let $s = j1$,

$$H(j1) = H(s)\Big|_{s=j1}$$

$$= \frac{1}{s^2 + \sqrt{2}s + 1}\Big|_{s=j1}$$

$$= \frac{1}{(j1)^2 + \sqrt{2}(j1) + 1}$$

$$= \frac{1}{\sqrt{2}(j1)} = \frac{1}{\sqrt{2}} e^{-j\pi/2}. \qquad (10.19)$$

Thus, from Eq. 10.15 with $\omega = 1$ and $X_1 = 10$

$$y_{ss}(t) = 10\left(\frac{1}{\sqrt{2}}\right) \cos(t - \pi/2) = 7.07 \sin(t). \qquad (10.20)$$

Comment: Since the input signal has been attenuated by $1/\sqrt{2}$, this frequency ($\omega = 1$) is the -3 dB frequency for this filter because the decibel gain is given by

$$dB = 20 \log_{10}\left(\frac{1}{\sqrt{2}}\right) = -3. \qquad (10.21)$$

10.1.2. Frequency Response, Graphical Method

The transfer function of Eq. 10.3 may be factored as

$$H(s) = k \frac{(s - n_1)(s - n_2) \cdots (s - n_L)}{(s - d_1)(s - d_2) \cdots (s - d_N)} \qquad (10.22)$$

and when evaluated at $s = j\omega$ for sinusoidal inputs, we obtain the frequency response function

$$H(j\omega) = k\frac{(j\omega - n_1)(j\omega - n_2)\cdots(j\omega - n_L)}{(j\omega - d_1)(j\omega - d_2)\cdots(j\omega - d_N)}.$$ (10.23)

Equation 10.23 may be written in terms of vectors just as was done for the frequency response of discrete systems in Chapter Five. This gives the standard form

$$H(j\omega) = k\frac{(N_1 e^{j\alpha_1})(N_2 e^{j\alpha_2})\cdots(N_L e^{j\alpha_L})}{(D_1 e^{j\beta_1})(D_2 e^{j\beta_2})\cdots(D_N e^{j\beta_N})}$$

$$= \frac{kN_1 N_2 \cdots N_L}{D_1 D_2 \cdots D_N}e^{j(\alpha_1 + \alpha_2 + \cdots + \alpha_L - \beta_1 - \beta_2 - \cdots - \beta_N)}$$ (10.24)

and the familiar expression for the frequency response of

$$H(j\omega) = Me^{jP}.$$ (10.25)

The N's, D's, α's, and β's can be identified in the pole-zero plot of $H(s)$, as indicated in Fig. 10.4.

A graphical procedure to estimate the frequency response may now be defined. To find $H(j\omega)$ for a selected value of ω, draw vectors from all the poles and zeros to the point $j\omega$. Measure, calculate, or estimate the N's, D's, α's and β's. Compute $H(j\omega) = Me^{jP}$ where

$$M = \frac{kN_1 N_2 \cdots N_L}{D_1 D_2 \cdots D_N} \quad \text{and}$$

$$P = \alpha_1 + \alpha_2 + \cdots + \alpha_L - (\beta_1 + \beta_2 + \cdots + \beta_N).$$ (10.26)

Example 10.2. This example illustrates the graphical evaluation of frequency response.

The poles and zeros of an all-pass analog filter are plotted in Fig. 10.5(a). Use

FIGURE 10.4 Graphical evaluation of frequency response

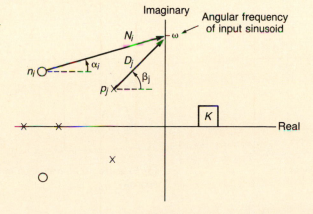

the graphical method to show that the magnitude M of the frequency response is constant for $0 \leq \omega \leq \infty$.

Solution: Referring to Fig. 10.5(b), we have

$$H(j\omega) = \frac{0.5(N_1 e^{j\alpha_1})(N_2 e^{j\alpha_2})}{(D_1 e^{j\beta_1})(D_2 e^{j\beta_2})} \tag{10.27}$$

but $N_1 = D_1$ and $N_2 = D_2$. Therefore $|H(j\omega)| = 0.5$ for all ω.

IMPORTANT COMMENT

As with discrete systems, this graphical method for evaluating frequency response yields approximate answers or a good estimate (Example 10.2 is an exception), and that is all that is intended. For all but the simplest filters, plots of phase P vs. frequency ω are difficult to estimate using this approach. Consequently, only magnitude plots are estimated using this method.

10.1.3 Computer Evaluation of Frequency Response

We now consider how to write a program to compute the frequency response of an analog system. The starting point is a transfer function that is assumed to be of the form

$$H(s) = \frac{\beta_0 s^L + \beta_1 s^{L-1} + \beta_2 s^{L-2} + \cdots + \beta_{L-1} s + \beta_L}{\alpha_0 s^N + \alpha_1 s^{N-1} + \alpha_2 s^{N-2} + \cdots + \alpha_{N-1} s + \alpha_N}. \tag{10.28}$$

To find the frequency response we substitute $j\omega$ for s with the result

FIGURE 10.5

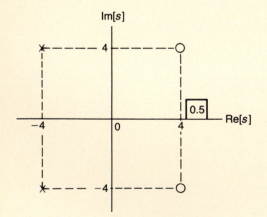

(a) Poles & zeros of $H(s)$, Example 10.2

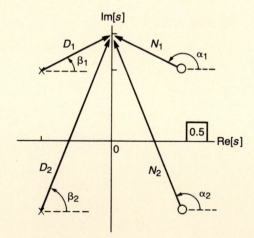

(b) Example 10.2, evaluation of frequency response

$$H(j\omega) = \frac{\beta_0(j\omega)^L + \beta_1(j\omega)^{L-1} + \beta_2(j\omega)^{L-2} + \cdots + \beta_{L-1}(j\omega) + \beta_L}{\alpha_0(j\omega)^N + \alpha_1(j\omega)^{N-1} + \alpha_2(j\omega)^{N-2} + \cdots + \alpha_{N-1}(j\omega) + \alpha_N}$$

$$= \frac{\displaystyle\sum_{k=0}^{L} \beta_k(j\omega)^{L-k}}{\displaystyle\sum_{k=0}^{N} \alpha_k(j\omega)^{N-k}}. \qquad (10.29)$$

Comparing Eq. 10.29 with Eq. 4.141, which was used to find the frequency response of a discrete system, we see that the two equations have exactly the same form. Thus, we can use the same computer code as for the discrete case, but with $j\omega$ replacing z in Eq. 4.141.

We will not repeat the discrete frequency response pseudocode here. In developing the analog frequency response program, which is left as an exercise (see Problem 10.44), use can be made of the pseudocode in Fig. 4.20 and the solution of Problem 4.22.

10.1.4 Determination of Filter Transfer Function from Frequency Response

Suppose we are given the frequency response function $H(j\omega)$, or, as is more usual, the magnitude-squared function $|H(j\omega)|^2$, how can we find the transfer function $H(s)$? The frequency response function $H(j\omega)$ or the magnitude-squared function $|H(j\omega)|^2$ could originally be in experimental or graphical form, but we are assuming that an analytical expression has been determined for either of these quantities (Van Valkenburg, 1982). Given the frequency response function

$$H(j\omega) = u + jv = re^{j\phi} \qquad (10.30)$$

then its complex conjugate is

$$H^*(j\omega) = u - jv = re^{-j\phi} \qquad (10.31)$$

and the magnitude-squared function is

$$|H(j\omega)|^2 = r^2 = u^2 + v^2$$

$$= H(j\omega) \cdot H^*(j\omega). \qquad (10.32)$$

But we know that $H^*(j\omega) = H(-j\omega)$ and consequently from Eq. 10.32

$$|H(j\omega)|^2 = H(j\omega) \cdot H(-j\omega). \qquad (10.33)$$

We also know that

$$H(j\omega) = H(s)\Big|_{s=j\omega} \quad \text{and thus} \quad H(-j\omega) = H(s)\Big|_{s=-j\omega} \qquad (10.34)$$

and the second term can be written as

$$H(-j\omega) = H(-s)\Big|_{s=j\omega}. \tag{10.35}$$

Then, using Eqs. 10.33, 10.34, and 10.35, we have the result

$$H(j\omega) \cdot H(-j\omega) = |H(j\omega)|^2 = H(s) \cdot H(-s)\Big|_{s=j\omega}. \tag{10.36}$$

Recalling that the goal is to determine $H(s)$ from $H(j\omega)$, we begin by using Eq. 10.36 the other way with $\omega = -js$ giving

$$|H(j\omega)|^2\Big|_{\omega=-js} = H(s) \cdot H(-s). \tag{10.37}$$

We investigate the right side of Eq. 10.37 by considering the general transfer function

$$H(s) = \frac{k(s - n_1)(s - n_2) \cdots (s - n_L)}{(s - d_1)(s - d_2) \cdots (s - d_N)} \tag{10.38}$$

with poles at $d_1, d_2, \ldots, d_N$ and zeros at $n_1, n_2, \ldots n_L$. Then replacing s with $-s$ in Eq. 10.38 gives

$$H(-s) = \frac{k(-s - n_1)(-s - n_2) \cdots (-s - n_L)}{(-s - d_1)(-s - d_2) \cdots (-s - d_N)} \tag{10.39}$$

with poles at $-d_1, -d_2, \ldots, -d_N$ and zeros at $-n_1, -n_2, \ldots, -n_L$. So if $H(s)$ has all of its poles in the left-half plane (LHP), $H(-s)$ has all of its poles in the right-half plane (RHP) and similarly for the zeros of $H(s)$ and $H(-s)$. Consequently, to find $H(s)$ from $|H(j\omega)|^2$ we proceed as follows:

PROCEDURE

1. Substitute $-js$ for ω in $|H(j\omega)|^2$ to find $H(s) \cdot H(-s)$.
2. Factor the expression $H(s) \cdot H(-s)$ to obtain the poles ($2N$ in number) and the $2L$ zeros.
3. Assign the LHP poles and zeros to $H(s)$.[†]

10.2 ▪▪▪ ANALOG FILTER DESIGN

The most common approach to the design of recursive digital filters is to make use of the extensive literature available for designing analog filters and then convert these analog filters into a form suitable for digital im-

---

[†]Strictly speaking, $H(s)$ can have right-half plane zeros but by putting the zeros of $H(s)$ in the left-half plane a minimum phase transfer function results (Van Valkenburg, 1960).

plementation. Entire books (see Ghausi and Laker, 1981; Lindquist, 1977; Lam, 1979; Van Valkenburg, 1982; and Zverev, 1967, to list a few) are devoted to analog filter design so in this section we present only the most fundamental aspects of the process. Butterworth, Chebyshev, and elliptic filters are introduced with much of our attention devoted to the Butterworth approximation. This has been done because of the simplicity that makes it easier to understand the steps required in the Butterworth design process. Chebyshev and elliptic filters are somewhat more complicated, but have wider use in the practice of analog filter design.

10.2.1 Butterworth Lowpass Prototype Design

One approximation to an ideal lowpass filter, credited to the British engineer S. Butterworth (Butterworth, 1930; Van Valkenburg, 1960) is called *maximally flat.*[†] Its magnitude-squared function is defined by

$$|H_{\text{LP}}(j\omega)|^2 = \frac{1}{1 + (\omega/\omega_c)^{2N}} \quad \text{or} \quad |H_{\text{LP}}(j\omega)| = \frac{1}{(1 + [\omega/\omega_c]^{2N})^{1/2}} \quad (10.40)$$

where N is the order of the filter and ω_c is defined as the *cutoff frequency* where the filter magnitude response is $1/\sqrt{2}$ times the *dc* gain ($\omega = 0$). For a cutoff, or critical, frequency of 1 the result is called a *prototype lowpass filter* which gives

$$|H_{\text{LP}_p}(j\omega)|^2 = \frac{1}{1 + \omega^{2N}} \quad \text{or} \quad |H_{\text{LP}_p}(j\omega)| = \frac{1}{(1 + \omega^{2N})^{1/2}} \quad (10.41)$$

as the general form of the Butterworth response of Fig. 10.6 where curves for three different values of N are shown. Several observations are in order:

1. For $\omega = 1$ the magnitude $M = |H_{\text{LP}_p}(j\omega)| = 1/\sqrt{2}$ or $M^2 = |H_{\text{LP}_p}(j\omega)|^2 = 1/2$ for all values of N. This corresponds to $M_{\text{dB}} = -3$ dB.

2. $|H_{\text{LP}_p}(j\omega)| \to 0$ as $\omega \to \infty$.

3. $|H_{\text{LP}_p}(j\omega)|^2 = |H_{\text{LP}_p}(j\omega)| = 1$ for $\omega = 0$ regardless of N.

4. The magnitude characteristic is said to be maximally flat because $d^n M/d\omega^n|_{\omega=0} = 0$ for $n = 1, 2, \ldots, 2N - 1$ (see Problem 10.42).

5. The steepness of $|H_{\text{LP}_p}(j\omega)|$ vs ω is a direct function of N and at $\omega = 1$ $d|H_{\text{LP}_p}(j\omega)|/d\omega = -0.354N$ (see Problem 10.41).

6. $M = |H_{\text{LP}_p}(j\omega)|$ is a monotonically decreasing function of frequency, i.e., $|H_{\text{LP}_p}(j\omega_2)| < |H_{\text{LP}_p}(j\omega_1)|$ for any values of ω_1 and ω_2 such that $0 \leq \omega_1 < \omega_2$.

[†]The term "maximally flat" is credited to V. D. Landon, "Cascade Amplifiers with Maximal Flatness," *RCA Rev.* 5, pp. 347–362, 1941.

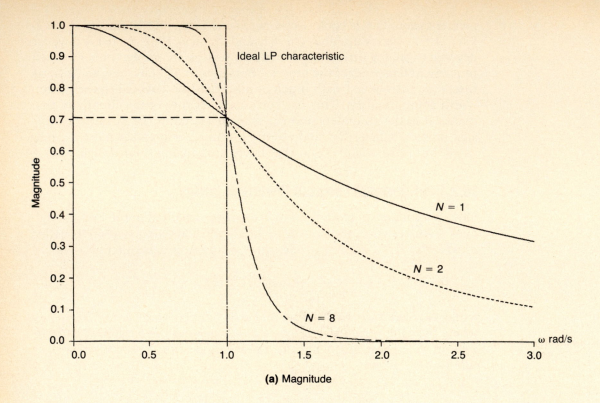

(a) Magnitude

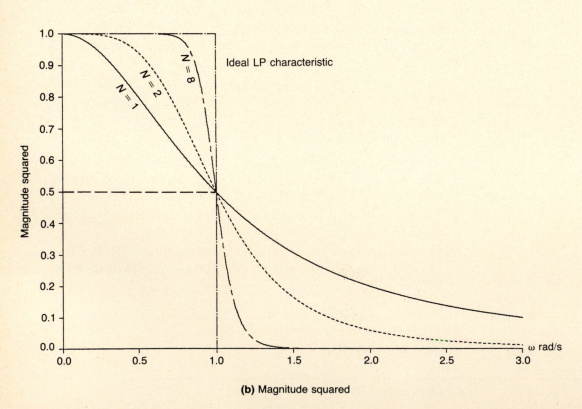

(b) Magnitude squared

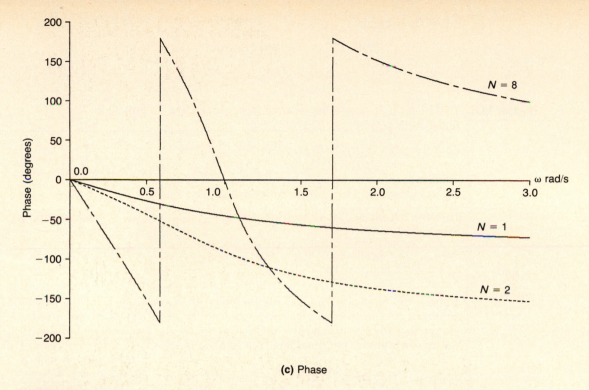

(c) Phase

FIGURE 10.6 Prototype lowpass Butterworth filter frequency responses for $N = 1, 2,$ and 8

To determine the poles[†] of the lowpass prototype Butterworth filter we start with

$$|H_{\text{LP}_p}(j\omega)|^2 = \frac{1}{1 + \omega^{2N}} \tag{10.42}$$

and then we need to find $H_{\text{LP}_p}(s)H_{\text{LP}_p}(-s)$ as

$$H_{\text{LP}_p}(s)H_{\text{LP}_p}(-s) = \frac{1}{1 + \omega^{2N}}\bigg|_{\omega = -js}. \tag{10.43}$$

Thus, for the poles of $H_{\text{LP}_p}(s)H_{\text{LP}_p}(-s)$ we have

$$1 + (-js)^{2N} = 0 \tag{10.44}$$

which may be written as

$$1 + (-s^2)^N = 0. \tag{10.45}$$

For N odd we have

$$1 - s^{2N} = 0, \ s^{2N} = 1 \text{ and the roots are } s_k = 1e^{j(k2\pi/2N)} = 1e^{jk\pi/N},$$
$$k = 0, 1, 2, \ldots, 2N - 1 \tag{10.46}$$

[†]If the poles of the Butterworth filter are known it is an easy matter to determine the denominator coefficients for $H(s)$ that are required in a design situation.

and with N even

$$1 + s^{2N} = 0, \; s^{2N} = -1 \text{ and the roots are } s_k = 1e^{j(\pi+k2\pi)/2N},$$

$$k = 0, 1, 2, \ldots, 2N - 1. \tag{10.47}$$

Example 10.3. This example illustrates the determination of the lowpass prototype Butterworth poles.

Find the poles of $H_{LP_p}(s)H_{LP_p}(-s)$ for $N = 1, 2,$ and 3.

Solution:
For $N = 1$ we use Eq. 10.46 to get $s_0 = 1$ and $s_1 = 1e^{j\pi}$.

For $N = 2$ from Eq. 10.47 we find $s_0 = 1e^{j\pi/4}$, $s_1 = 1e^{j3\pi/4}$, $s_2 = 1e^{j5\pi/4}$, and $s_3 = 1e^{j7\pi/4}$.

For $N = 3$, from Eq. 10.46 $s_0 = 1$, $s_1 = 1e^{j\pi/3}$, $s_2 = 1e^{j2\pi/3}$, $s_3 = 1e^{j\pi}$, $s_4 = 1e^{j4\pi/3}$, and $s_5 = 1e^{j5\pi/3}$.

Comment: Shown in Fig. 10.7 are the poles of $H_{LP_p}(s)H_{LP_p}(-s)$ for the three values of N, and in each plot the poles to be used in $H_{LP_p}(s)$ are encircled. Notice that all poles are on the unit circle of the s-plane and that the first three Butterworth prototype filters have the transfer functions

$$H_1(s) = \frac{1}{s+1}, \; H_2(s) = \frac{1}{s^2 + \sqrt{2}s + 1}, \; \text{and} \; H_3(s) = \frac{1}{s^3 + 2s^2 + 2s + 1}.$$

$$\tag{10.48}$$

The coefficients for the first eight lowpass prototype Butterworth filters are given in Table 10.1.

The only design variable for Butterworth lowpass filters is the order of the filter N. Thus, design is simply a matter of determining the smallest value of N (for minimum complexity) for which given specifications are met. Suppose that a specified frequency response (magnitude) for a lowpass filter has the shape of Fig. 10.8(a) or 10.8(c) where the $M = 0.707$

FIGURE 10.7 Poles of $H(s) \cdot H(-s)$, $N = 1, 2,$ and 3

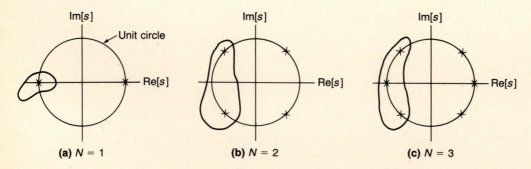

(a) $N = 1$ (b) $N = 2$ (c) $N = 3$

N	a_1	a_2	a_3	a_4	a_5	a_6	a_7	a_8
1	1.0000							
2	1.4141	1.0000						
3	2.0000	2.0000	1.0000					
4	2.6131	3.4142	2.6131	1.0000				
5	3.2361	5.2361	5.2361	3.2361	1.0000			
6	3.8637	7.4641	9.1416	7.4641	3.8637	1.0000		
7	4.4940	10.0978	14.5918	14.5918	10.0978	4.4940	1.0000	
8	5.1258	13.1371	21.8462	25.6884	21.8462	13.1371	5.1258	1.0000

TABLE 10.1 BUTTERWORTH PROTOTYPE COEFFICIENTS

$$H_{LP_p}(s) = \frac{1}{1 + a_1 s + a_2 s^2 + \cdots + a_N s^N}$$

Source: M. E. Van Valkenburg, *Introduction to Modern Network Synthesis*, New York, John Wiley and Sons, 1960.

FIGURE 10.8 Frequency response for a lowpass prototype filter

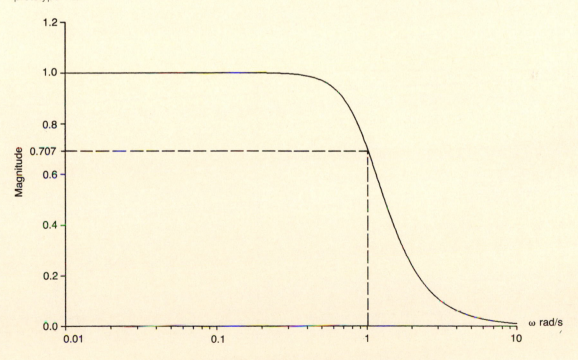

(a) Frequency response magnitude for a lowpass prototype filter

FIGURE 10.8 cont.

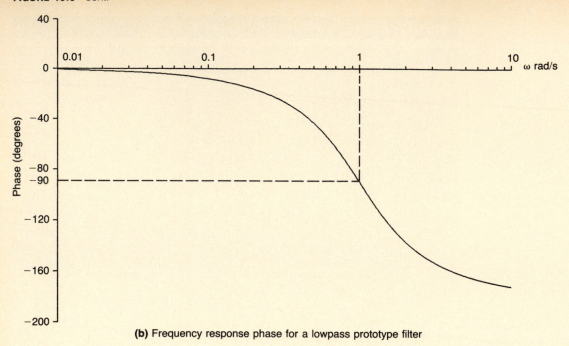

(b) Frequency response phase for a lowpass prototype filter

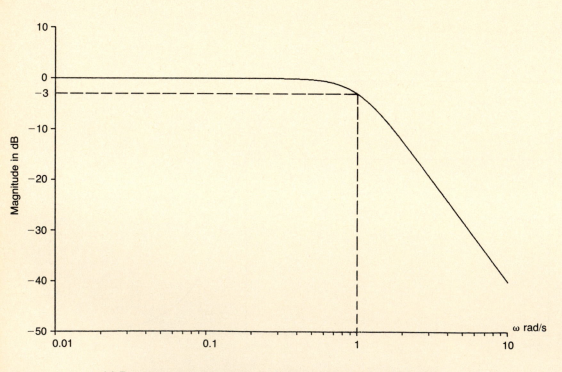

(c) Frequency response magnitude in dB for a lowpass prototype filter

or $M_{dB} = -3$ dB cutoff frequency is $\omega_c = 1$ rad/s and that there is a frequency ω_a for which the gain is specified to be less than, or greater than, some value M. This suggests a Butterworth filter because of the monotonically decreasing gain curve and the flat characteristic in the passband. Thus, to design a Butterworth filter that will produce the desired frequency response, we need to find the filter order N and then use a table such as Table 10.1 to determine the prototype (normalized to $\omega_c = 1$) transfer function $H_{LP_p}(s)$. Then, a suitable frequency transformation is needed to find the unnormalized (actual) transfer function. This is discussed later.

To find N we start with the *normalized* $(\omega_c = 1)$ *magnitude function*

$$M = |H_{LP_p}(j\omega)| = \frac{1}{(1 + \omega^{2N})^{1/2}} \tag{10.49}$$

that may be expressed in decibels (dB) as

$$M_{dB} = 20 \log_{10} M$$
$$= 10 \log_{10} M^2. \tag{10.50}$$

Thus, at a specified frequency ω_a we have

$$M_{dB} = 10 \log_{10} |H_{LP_p}(j\omega_a)|^2$$
$$= 10 \log_{10} \frac{1}{1 + \omega_a^{2N}}$$
$$= 10 \log_{10} 1 - 10 \log_{10}[1 + \omega_a^{2N}]. \tag{10.51}$$

Hence, at $\omega = \omega_a$

$$M_{dB} = -10 \log_{10}[1 + \omega_a^{2N}]. \tag{10.52}$$

Solving for the filter order N we have

$$-M_{dB}/10 = \log_{10}[1 + \omega_a^{2N}] \tag{10.53}$$

which becomes

$$10^{-[M_{dB}/10]} = 1 + \omega_a^{2N} \tag{10.54}$$

or

$$10^{-[M_{dB}/10]} - 1 = \omega_a^{2N}. \tag{10.55}$$

Taking the logarithm of Eq. 10.55 gives us

$$\log_{10}(10^{-[M_{dB}/10]} - 1) = 2N \log_{10} \omega_a \tag{10.56}$$

and the filter order needed due to the gain (M) specification at $\omega = \omega_a$ is

$$\boxed{N = \frac{\log_{10}(10^{-[M_{dB}/10]} - 1)}{2 \log_{10} \omega_a}} \; . \tag{10.57}$$

In general, the value of N which results from solving Eq. 10.57 will not be an integer. If specifications are given at several frequencies, all of these must be used with Eq. 10.57 and the largest value of N obtained is then increased to the next higher integer and used for the filter. Finally, it must be emphasized that Eq. 10.57 was derived for a prototype (normalized), lowpass Butterworth filter.

Example 10.4. This example illustrates the design of a prototype Butterworth analog filter.

Design a prototype lowpass Butterworth filter with a -3 dB frequency of 1 rad/s and a gain of less than 0.1 (-20 dB) for frequencies greater than 2 rad/s. Find the filter transfer function $H_{LP_p}(s)$.

Solution: From Eq. 10.57 with $M_{dB} \leq -20$ for $\omega \geq 2$ rad/s the filter order must be at least

$$N = \frac{\log_{10}(10^{-[-20/10]} - 1)}{2 \log_{10} 2}$$

$$= 3.31 \tag{10.58}$$

which gives us $N = 4$. Then from Table 10.1

$$H_{LP_p}(s) = \frac{1}{s^4 + 2.613s^3 + 3.414s^2 + 2.613s + 1}. \tag{10.59}$$

Comment: To check this result we substitute $s = j2$ into Eq. 10.59 giving

$$H_{LP_p}(j2) = \frac{1}{(j2)^4 + 2.613(j2)^3 + 3.414(j2)^2 + 2.613(j2) + 1}. \tag{10.60}$$

After some complex arithmetic we have

$$H_{LP_p}(j2) = \frac{1}{3.35 - j15.68} = 0.0624e^{jP} \tag{10.61}$$

which has a magnitude in dB of -24 that is less than the required -20.

10.2.2 Chebyshev Lowpass Prototype Design

Another type of filter is based on the use of Chebyshev polynomials as a means of approximating an ideal lowpass filter frequency response characteristic. This mathematical approximation, referred to as an equal-ripple approximation, is due to Pafnuti L. Chebyshev[†], who published his work in 1899 in connection with studying steam engines. Equal-ripple filters can be placed into the following three categories: a Chebyshev with equal-ripple in the passband, an inverse Chebyshev with equal-ripple in the stopband, and an elliptic with equal-ripple in both the pass-

[†]Pafnuti L. Chebyshev (1821–1894), a Russian mathematician. An alternative transliteration is the German Tschebysheff.

band and stopband.[†] The filters we consider here are of the first type, Chebyshev with equal-ripple in the passband, and we offer a brief treatment of elliptic filters in Section 10.2.3. The magnitude-squared characteristic of an LP prototype Chebyshev filter is given by

$$|H_{LP_p}(j\omega)|^2 = \frac{1}{1 + \epsilon^2 C_N^2(\omega)} \tag{10.62}$$

where the Nth-order Chebyshev polynomial is

$$C_N(\omega) = \cos(N \cos^{-1} \omega), \qquad 0 \le \omega \le 1 \tag{10.63}$$

and

$$C_N(\omega) = \cosh(N \cosh^{-1} \omega), \qquad \omega > 1. \tag{10.64}$$

Notice that if we allow $\omega > 1$ in Eq. 10.63 $\cos^{-1} \omega$ must be imaginary, hence, it is more convenient to restrict the range of ω and introduce Eq. 10.64 for $\omega > 1$. The equations are equivalent in the sense that Eq. 10.64 can be derived from Eq. 10.63 and so the result is a single Chebyshev polynomial that applies for $0 \le \omega \le \infty$ (see Problem 10.51). The parameter ϵ $(0 < \epsilon < 1)$ sets the ripple amplitude in the *ripple passband* which is defined as $0 \le \omega \le 1$ as in Fig. 10.9. The half-power frequency (cutoff) comes from Eq. 10.62 with $|H(j\omega)|^2 = 0.5$ or

$$\epsilon^2 C_N^2(\omega) = 1 \tag{10.65}$$

and consequently depends upon both the ripple parameter ϵ and the filter order N. Consider, for example, $N = 1$ in both Eq. 10.63 and Eq. 10.64. The first-order Chebyshev polynomial is

$$C_1(\omega) = \cos(1 \cos^{-1} \omega) = \omega \text{ and } C_1(\omega) = \cosh(1 \cosh^{-1} \omega) = \omega \tag{10.66}$$

from both equations and the magnitude-squared function is

$$|H_{LP_p}(j\omega)|^2 = \frac{1}{1 + \epsilon^2 \omega^2} \tag{10.67}$$

with the cutoff (half-power) frequency being greater than one, namely

$$\omega_c = \frac{1}{\epsilon}. \tag{10.68}$$

As illustrated in Eq. 10.66 one polynomial can be written that is valid for all ω and a recursive relation can be determined that allows the computation of $C_{N+1}(\omega)$ from the two previous polynomials $C_N(\omega)$ and $C_{N-1}(\omega)$ as

$$C_{N+1}(\omega) = 2\omega C_N(\omega) - C_{N-1}(\omega) \tag{10.69}$$

[†] Chebyshev filters and inverse Chebyshev filters can be thought of as special cases of elliptic filters. Although they do not bear his name, Sidney Darlington of the Bell Telephone Laboratories did much of the original work on elliptic filters (Daniels, 1974; Darlington, 1939 and 1952).

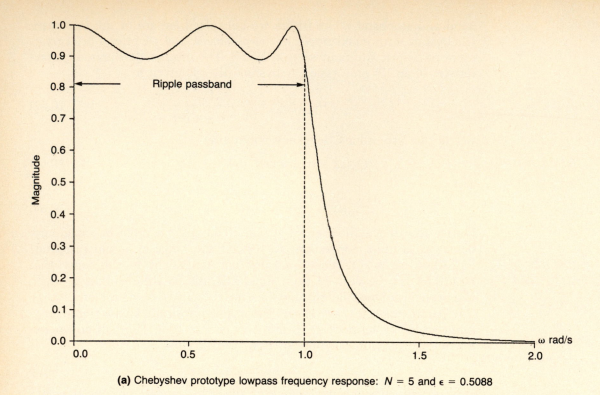

(a) Chebyshev prototype lowpass frequency response: $N = 5$ and $\epsilon = 0.5088$

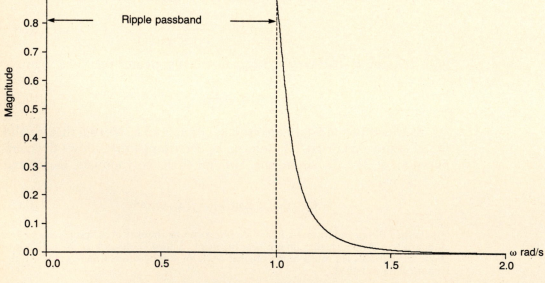

(b) Chebyshev prototype lowpass frequency response: $N = 6$ and $\epsilon = 0.5088$

FIGURE 10.9 Chebyshev prototype frequency responses

which we derive from Eq. 10.63. Beginning with

$$C_{N+1}(\omega) = \cos[(N + 1) \cos^{-1} \omega] \qquad (10.70)$$

we define $\alpha = \cos^{-1} \omega$ which allows us to write Eq. 10.70 as

$$C_{N+1}(\omega) = \cos[(N + 1)\alpha]. \qquad (10.71)$$

Then applying the identity $\cos(\alpha + \beta) = \cos\alpha \cos\beta - \sin\alpha \sin\beta$ we get

$$C_{N+1}(\omega) = \cos(N\alpha) \cos(\alpha) - \sin(N\alpha) \sin(\alpha). \qquad (10.72)$$

In a similar way

$$C_{N-1}(\omega) = \cos[(N - 1)\alpha]$$

$$= \cos(N\alpha) \cos(\alpha) + \sin(N\alpha) \sin(\alpha). \qquad (10.73)$$

Adding Eq. 10.72 and Eq. 10.73 produces

$$C_{N+1}(\omega) + C_{N-1}(\omega) = 2 \cos(\alpha) \cos(N\alpha) \qquad (10.74)$$

and substituting $\alpha = \cos^{-1} \omega$ gives

$$C_{N+1}(\omega) + C_{N-1}(\omega) = 2 \cos(\cos^{-1} \omega) \cos(N \cos^{-1} \omega) = 2\omega \cos(N \cos^{-1} \omega). \qquad (10.75)$$

Going back to Eq. 10.63 where the Nth-order Chebyshev polynomial was given as

$$C_N(\omega) = \cos(N \cos^{-1} \omega) \qquad (10.76)$$

we can substitute Eq. 10.76 into Eq. 10.75 to obtain

$$C_{N+1}(\omega) + C_{N-1}(\omega) = 2\omega C_N(\omega) \qquad (10.77)$$

or

$$\boxed{C_{N+1}(\omega) = 2\omega C_N(\omega) - C_{N-1}(\omega)} \qquad (10.78)$$

which is Eq. 10.69, the result we set out to derive. The same relationship can also be determined by starting with Eq. 10.64. See Problem 10.14.

We notice that Eq. 10.78 is actually a constant coefficient linear difference equation in $C_N(\omega)$. We can make this more obvious by defining $y(N + 1) = C_{N+1}(\omega)$, $y(N) = C_N(\omega)$, $y(N - 1) = C_{N-1}(\omega)$, and $2\omega = a$ and writing

$$y(N + 1) = ay(N) - y(N - 1). \qquad (10.79)$$

To solve this second-order difference equation we need two initial conditions. Letting $N = 0$ and 1 we find from Eq. 10.63 that $C_0(\omega) = \cos(0 \cos^{-1} \omega) = 1$ and $C_1(\omega) = \cos(1 \cos^{-1} \omega) = \omega$. Alternatively, from Eq. 10.64 with $N = 0$ and 1 we obtain $C_0(\omega) = \cosh(0 \cosh^{-1} \omega) = 1$ and $C_1(\omega) = \cosh(1 \cosh^{-1} \omega) = \omega$. So, the Chebyshev polynomials for all $\omega \geq$

0 can be found by solving the difference equation

$$C_{N+1}(\omega) = 2\omega C_N(\omega) - C_{N-1}(\omega) \tag{10.80}$$

with the "initial conditions" $C_0(\omega) = 1$ and $C_1(\omega) = \omega$.

Let's use this result to generate a few more Chebyshev polynomials. For the second-order Chebyshev polynomial we use Eq. 10.80 to obtain

$$
\begin{aligned}
C_2(\omega) &= 2\omega C_1(\omega) - C_0(\omega) \\
&= 2\omega \cdot \omega - 1 = 2\omega^2 - 1
\end{aligned}
\tag{10.81}
$$

and for the third-order polynomial we have

$$
\begin{aligned}
C_3(\omega) &= 2\omega C_2(\omega) - C_1(\omega) \\
&= 4\omega^3 - 2\omega - \omega = 4\omega^3 - 3\omega.
\end{aligned}
\tag{10.82}
$$

The results of solving this recursive relationship for $1 \le N \le 8$ are given in Table 10.2.

TABLE 10.2 CHEBYSHEV POLYNOMIALS

N	$C_N(\omega)$
1	ω
2	$2\omega^2 - 1$
3	$4\omega^3 - 3\omega$
4	$8\omega^4 - 8\omega^2 + 1$
5	$16\omega^5 - 20\omega^3 + 5\omega$
6	$32\omega^6 - 48\omega^4 + 18\omega^2 - 1$
7	$64\omega^7 - 112\omega^5 + 56\omega^3 - 7\omega$
8	$128\omega^8 - 256\omega^6 + 160\omega^4 - 32\omega^2 + 1$

Important Characteristics of Lowpass Prototype Chebyshev Filters. Let us now look at some important properties of Chebyshev filters. The magnitude function is

$$|H_{\mathrm{LP}_p}(j\omega)| = \frac{1}{[1 + \epsilon^2 C_N^2(\omega)]^{1/2}} \tag{10.83}$$

and, with the help of Fig. 10.10 where the solid line corresponds to $N = 5$ and the dotted line is for $N = 6$, we observe the following important characteristics:

1. At $\omega = 0$

$$C_N^2(\omega)\Big|_{\omega=0} = [\cos(N \cos^{-1} \omega)]^2 \Big|_{\omega=0}$$

$$= [\cos(N \cos^{-1} 0)]^2 \tag{10.84}$$

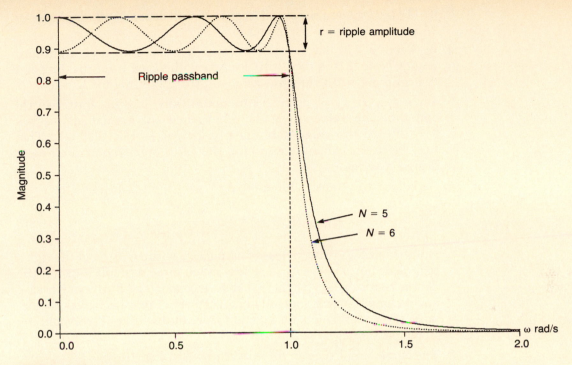

FIGURE 10.10 Two Chebyshev prototype lowpass frequency responses with $\epsilon = 0.5088$

which takes on the two values

$$C_N^2(0) = \begin{cases} 0, & N \text{ odd} \\ 1, & N \text{ even.} \end{cases} \qquad (10.85)$$

This makes the magnitude function of Eq. 10.83 become

$$|H(j0)| = 1, \; N \text{ odd} \qquad (10.86)$$

or

$$|H(j0)| = \frac{1}{(1 + \epsilon^2)^{1/2}}, \; N \text{ even.} \qquad (10.87)$$

2. At $\omega = 1$

$$C_N^2(\omega)\Big|_{\omega=1} = [\cos(N\cos^{-1} 1)]^2 = 1, \text{ for all } N \qquad (10.88)$$

which results in

$$|H(j1)| = \frac{1}{(1 + \epsilon^2)^{1/2}}, \text{ for all } N. \qquad (10.89)$$

3. The *prototype ripple bandwidth* is from $\omega = 0$ to $\omega = 1$; the -3 dB cutoff frequency is greater than 1 since $\epsilon < 1$. Thus, from Eq. 10.89,

$|H(j1)| > 1/\sqrt{2}$ and the cutoff frequency will depend both on the order N and on the ripple parameter ϵ.

4. Between $\omega = 0$ and $\omega = 1$, there are N maximum and minimum points. Note that in Fig. 10.10, for $N = 5$, there are three maxima and two minima, with three maxima and three minima for $N = 6$.

5. For $\omega > 1$, $|H_{\mathrm{LP}_p}(j\omega)|$ decreases monotonically (like the Butterworth) and for large values of ω the Chebyshev polynomial approaches $2^{N-1}\omega^N$ and the magnitude function $|H(j\omega)| \to 1/(\epsilon \cdot 2^{N-1}\omega^N)$. This may be useful when determining the filter order required to meet design requirements.

6. As before, the transfer function is

$$H_{\mathrm{LP}_p}(s)H_{\mathrm{LP}_p}(-s) = \left. \frac{1}{1 + \epsilon^2 C_N^2(\omega)} \right|_{\omega = -js} \qquad (10.90)$$

and the left-half plane poles are associated with $H_{\mathrm{LP}_p}(s)$ and the right-half plane poles with $H_{\mathrm{LP}_p}(-s)$. It is much more difficult to factor the denominator of $H_{\mathrm{LP}_p}(s)H_{\mathrm{LP}_p}(-s)$ than it was in the Butterworth case and a computer will generally be necessary. Table 10.3 gives the denominator coefficients for several values of the filter order N and the ripple parameter ϵ.

7. The ripple amplitude in dB is given by (see Fig. 10.10)

$$r_{\mathrm{dB}} = -10 \log_{10} \frac{1}{1 + \epsilon^2} = 10 \log_{10} (1 + \epsilon^2). \qquad (10.91)$$

The transfer function of a lowpass prototype Chebyshev filter is based upon the desired ripple which is set by ϵ and the order N which is found by knowing a desired half-power or -3 dB frequency and/or the required stopband characteristics. Once we have $|H_{\mathrm{LP}_p}(j\omega)|$ or $|H_{\mathrm{LP}_p}(j\omega)|^2$, $H_{\mathrm{LP}_p}(s)$ follows from Eq. 10.90 or preferably from a table such as Table 10.3.

TABLE 10.3 A SELECTION OF CHEBYSHEV PROTOTYPE DENOMINATOR POLYNOMIALS

N	1/2-dB ripple ($\epsilon = 0.3493$, $\epsilon^2 = 0.1220$)
1	$s + 2.863$
2	$s^2 + 1.425s + 1.516$
3	$s^3 + 1.253s^2 + 1.535s + 0.716$
4	$s^4 + 1.197s^3 + 1.717s^2 + 1.025s + 0.379$
5	$s^5 + 1.173s^4 + 1.937s^3 + 1.310s^2 + 0.753s + 0.179$

1-dB ripple ($\epsilon = 0.5088$, $\epsilon^2 = 0.2589$)	
N	
1	$s + 1.965$
2	$s^2 + 1.098s + 1.103$
3	$s^3 + 0.988s^2 + 1.238s + 0.491$
4	$s^4 + 0.953s^3 + 1.454s^2 + 0.743s + 0.276$
5	$s^5 + 0.937s^4 + 1.689s^3 + 0.974s^2 + 0.581s + 0.123$
2-dB ripple ($\epsilon = 0.7648$, $\epsilon^2 = 0.5849$)	
N	
1	$s + 1.308$
2	$s^2 + 0.804s + 0.823$
3	$s^3 + 0.738s^2 + 1.022s + 0.327$
4	$s^4 + 0.716s^3 + 1.256s^2 + 0.517s + 0.206$
5	$s^5 + 0.707s^4 + 1.500s^3 + 0.694s^2 + 0.459s + 0.082$

Source: M. S. Ghausi and K. R. Laker, *Modern Filter Design*, Englewood Cliffs, New Jersey, Prentice-Hall, Inc., 1981.

FIGURE 10.11 Lowpass filter specifications

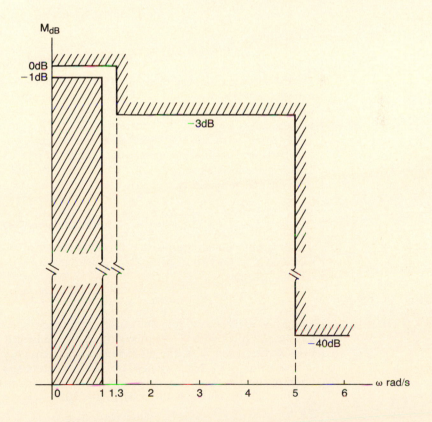

Example 10.5. This example illustrates the Chebyshev design of a lowpass prototype filter.

We want to design a prototype Chebyshev lowpass filter to meet the following specifications:

a) Maximum passband ripple = 1 dB

b) Cutoff frequency, $\omega \leq 1.30$ rad/s

c) Attenuation in the stopband of at least 40 dB for $\omega \geq 5$ rad/s

Determine the filter transfer function, $H_{\mathrm{LP}_p}(s)$.

Solution: Fig. 10.11 on page 637 provides a graphical display of these specifications. First, we need to find the ripple parameter ϵ which in this case is given in Table 10.3. However, let's go through the procedure to illustrate the general approach. From item 7 of the previous discussion, the ripple in dB is

$$r_{\mathrm{dB}} = 10 \log_{10}(1 + \epsilon^2) \tag{10.92}$$

and for a 1-dB ripple

$$1 = 10 \log_{10}(1 + \epsilon^2) \tag{10.93}$$

or

$$0.1 = \log_{10}(1 + \epsilon^2). \tag{10.94}$$

Taking the antilog of Eq. 10.94 gives us

$$1.2589 = 1 + \epsilon^2 \tag{10.95}$$

from which

$$\epsilon^2 = 0.2589 \text{ and } \epsilon = 0.5088. \tag{10.96}$$

For the specification, therefore, $\epsilon = 0.5088$ as in Table 10.3. At this point an experienced designer would use design curves or nomograms (Lindquist, 1977) to find the filter order N, but here let's use a trial-and-error procedure in order to gain familiarity with the equations.

Starting with the first-order filter where the Chebyshev polynomial is $C_1(\omega) = \omega$ we first find the gain at the desired cutoff (-3 dB) frequency of $\omega = 1.30$. We are looking for $|H(j1.30)| \leq 0.707$ or $|H(j1.30)|^2 \leq 0.500$. The magnitude-squared function is

$$\left. \frac{1}{1 + \epsilon^2 C_1^{\,2}(\omega)} \right|_{\omega=1.30} = \left. \frac{1}{1 + 0.2589\omega^2} \right|_{\omega=1.30} = 0.69 \tag{10.97}$$

which is not enough attenuation (0.500 is required) at the cutoff frequency. Going to $N = 2$ where $C_2(\omega) = 2\omega^2 - 1$ we have

$$\left. \frac{1}{1 + \epsilon^2 C_2^{\,2}(\omega)} \right|_{\omega=1.30} = \left. \frac{1}{1 + 0.2589(2\omega^2 - 1)^2} \right|_{\omega=1.30} = 0.41 \tag{10.98}$$

which is satisfactory for the cutoff frequency specification. Thus, any Chebyshev filter with $N \geq 2$ meets the 3-dB bandwidth (cutoff) requirement, because the larger N is, the more rapidly the frequency response magnitude decreases for $\omega > 1$. Next we need to check the stopband characteristic at $\omega = 5$ where the attenuation must be at least 40 dB which translates to a "gain" less than or equal to -40 dB or $|H(j\omega)|^2 \leq 10^{-4}$.

Thus, for $N = 2$ the magnitude-squared function is

$$\frac{1}{1 + \epsilon^2 C_2^2(\omega)}\bigg|_{\omega=5} = \frac{1}{1 + 0.2589(2\omega^2 - 1)^2}\bigg|_{\omega=5} = 1.6 \times 10^{-3} \quad (10.99)$$

which is too large for we are looking for $|H(j\omega)|^2 \leq 10^{-4}$. Going to $N = 3$ we need to check the stopband only because the cutoff frequency requirement was satisfied with $N = 2$. So for the third-order filter

$$\frac{1}{1 + \epsilon^2 C_N^2(\omega)}\bigg|_{\omega=5} = \frac{1}{1 + 0.2589(4\omega^3 - 3\omega)^2}\bigg|_{\omega=5} = 1.6 \times 10^{-5} \quad (10.100)$$

which satisfies the requirement. Thus, a third-order filter is required and using the 1-dB ripple entry from Table 10.3, the transfer function is

$$H_{\text{LP}_p}(s) = \frac{k}{s^3 + 0.988s^2 + 1.238s + 0.491} \quad (10.101)$$

and the gain k may be chosen in any way by the designer. In this case, with N an odd number, let's set $k = 0.491$ to make the $\omega = 0(dc)$ gain equal to one to match the zero frequency characteristic of Fig. 10.9(a).

10.2.3 Elliptic Lowpass Prototype Design

An elliptic filter has an equal-ripple response in both its passband and its stopband and the magnitude-squared response of a lowpass prototype of order N is given by

$$|H_{\text{LP}_p}(j\omega)|^2 = \frac{1}{1 + \epsilon^2 E_N^2(\omega)} \quad (10.102)$$

where $E_N^2(\omega)$ is a Chebyshev rational function of ω determined from the specified ripple characteristics. A typical magnitude-squared characteristic is given in Fig. 10.12 with a *passband ripple-edge frequency* of ω_{1P} and a *stopband ripple-edge frequency* of ω_{2P}. A Chebyshev prototype lowpass filter has a passband ripple-edge frequency of $\omega = 1$ whereas in an elliptic filter $\omega = 1$ is the geometric mean of ω_{1P} and ω_{2P}, i.e.,

$$1 = (\omega_{1P}\omega_{2P})^{1/2}. \quad (10.103)$$

A constant R, called the *selectivity factor*, representing the sharpness of the transition region is defined as

$$R = \omega_{2P}/\omega_{1P} \quad (10.104)$$

and consequently a large value of R indicates a wide transition band while a small value means a narrow transition band. Contrasted with Butterworth and Chebyshev filters, that have only finite poles, elliptic filters have finite zeros as well. The transfer function of a lowpass proto-

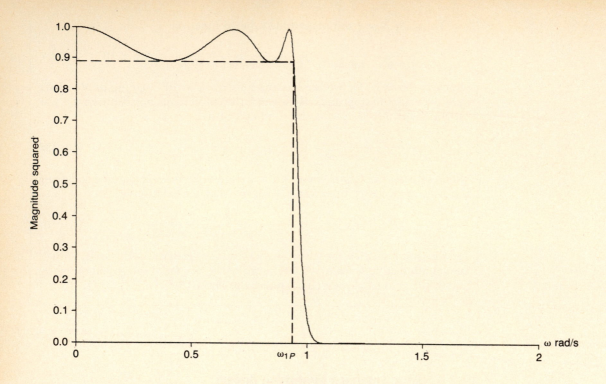

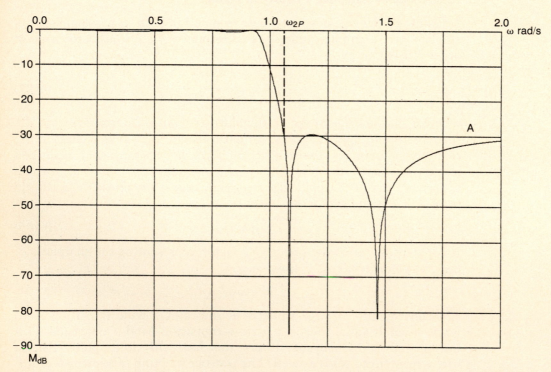

FIGURE 10.12 Elliptic prototype magnitude-squared characteristic

type elliptic filter of order N is given by

$$H_{\text{LP}_p}(s) = \frac{H_0}{D(s)} \prod_{i=1}^{r} \frac{s^2 + A_{0i}}{s^2 + B_{1i}s + B_{0i}} \qquad (10.105)$$

where

$$r = \begin{cases} \dfrac{N-1}{2}, & N \text{ odd} \\[2mm] \dfrac{N}{2}, & N \text{ even} \end{cases} \qquad (10.106)$$

and

$$D(s) = \begin{cases} s + s_0, & N \text{ odd} \\ 1, & N \text{ even.} \end{cases} \qquad (10.107)$$

From Eq. 10.105 we notice that the transfer function is specified by the following:

1. N, the order of the filter (by way of r in the product notation Π)
2. $D(s)$, the single pole factor with a pole at $s = -s_0$ for N odd, and $D(s) = 1$ for N even
3. A_{0i}, the numerator coefficients that determine the zeros
4. B_{0i} and B_{1i}, the denominator coefficients that determine the poles.

The shape of the frequency response magnitude-squared plot shown in Fig. 10.12 depends on three parameters, i.e., ϵ, A, and $R = \omega_{2P}/\omega_{1P}$. Alternatively, we can express ϵ in terms of an acceptable passband ripple as the gain

$$M_{\text{dB}} = -10 \log_{10}(1 + \epsilon^2) = 20 \log_{10}|H(j\omega_{1P})| \qquad (10.108)$$

and A in terms of an acceptable stopband gain as

$$M_{\text{dB}} = A = 20 \log_{10}|H(j\omega_{2P})| \qquad (10.109)$$

and we still have $R = \omega_{2P}/\omega_{1P}$. With three free parameters rather than two in the Chebyshev case and one for Butterworth filters, a simple table of elliptic filter transfer functions is not possible as it is with Butterworth and Chebyshev filters. One way out of this dilemma is to restrict the passband ripples and the stopband grains to be among a certain set (Ludeman, 1986). Tables have been generated that list the filter coefficients for filter orders from two to nine. The selectivity parameter R will not be an integer value, but a value can be selected that satisfies the design requirements. A partial listing of elliptic filter coefficients is given in Table 10.4.

TABLE 10.4 ELLIPTIC FILTER COEFFICIENTS (PARTIAL TABLE)

$$H_{\text{LP}_p}(s) = \frac{H_0}{D(s)} \prod_{i=1}^{r} \frac{s^2 + A_{0i}}{s^2 + B_{1i}s + B_{0i}} \qquad D(s) = \begin{cases} s + s_0, & N \text{ odd} \\ 1, & N \text{ even} \end{cases}$$

(a) Passband ripple = 0.5 dB; stopband gain = −20 dB

N	i	A_{0i}	B_{0i}	B_{1i}	H_0/s_0	R
2	1	5.33789	0.566660	0.809390	0.100220E + 000	2.76261
3	1	1.75640	0.808321	0.359160	0.306214E + 000	1.42189
					0.667292	
4	1	4.38105	0.611195	0.931959	0.100219E + 000	1.13188
	2	1.21841	0.927132	0.136543		
5	1	1.65076	0.827787	0.412816	0.303895E + 000	1.04465
	2	1.07211	0.973640	0.049395	0.667292	
6	1	4.36790	0.611899	0.933855	0.100218E + 000	1.01553
	2	1.19243	0.934830	0.156221		
	3	1.02486	0.990620	0.017576		
7	1	1.64918	0.828092	0.413652	0.303861E + 000	1.00545
	2	1.06401	0.976479	0.056384	0.667292	
	3	1.00870	0.996681	0.006219		
8	1	4.36811	0.611846	0.933864	0.100192E + 000	1.00192
	2	1.19207	0.934928	0.156548		
	3	1.02213	0.991634	0.020051		
	4	1.00306	0.998827	0.002197		
9	1	1.64927	0.828047	0.413695	0.303786E + 000	1.00068
	2	1.06390	0.976512	0.056505	0.667292	
	3	1.00775	0.997041	0.007093		
	4	1.00108	0.999586	0.000775		

(b) Passband ripple = 0.5 dB; stopband gain = −30 dB

N	i	A_{0i}	B_{0i}	B_{1i}	H_0/s_0	R
2	1	9.51248	0.318702	0.639007	0.316294E − 001	4.80880
3	1	2.46997	0.597384	0.382044	0.121878E + 000	1.92322
					0.503922	
4	1	6.46603	0.398996	0.822201	0.316297E − 001	1.32446
	2	1.47114	0.798764	0.191032		
5	1	2.14490	0.648724	0.480774	0.118807E + 000	1.12912
	2	1.18132	0.907216	0.088080	0.511761	
6	1	6.38228	0.402050	0.828822	0.316296E − 001	1.05394
	2	1.38680	0.826821	0.237025		
	3	1.07474	0.958727	0.039181		

	1	2.13439	0.650591	0.484325	0.118701E + 000	1.02299
7	2	1.15171	0.920785	0.108419	0.511761	
	3	1.03168	0.981925	0.017159		
	1	6.37941	0.402154	0.829052	0.316289E − 001	1.00989
8	2	1.38394	0.827819	0.238663		
	3	1.06301	0.964898	0.048043		
	4	1.01359	0.992137	0.007464		
	1	2.13409	0.650636	0.484454	0.118683E + 000	1.00427
9	2	1.15070	0.921256	0.109144	0.511761	
	3	1.02680	0.984652	0.021005		
	4	1.00586	0.996589	0.003238		

Source: From page 149 in *Fundamentals of Digital Signal Processing* by Lonnie C. Ludeman. Copyright © 1986 by Harper and Row, Publishers, Inc. Reprinted by permission of Harper & Row, Publishers, Inc.

We now look at the first entry to obtain a better understanding of the selectivity factor R. For $N = 2$, passband ripple of 0.5 dB and stopband gain of -20 dB the filter transfer function is

$$H_{\mathrm{LP}_p}(s) = 0.10022 \frac{s^2 + 5.33789}{s^2 + 0.809390s + 0.566660} \tag{10.110}$$

with the selectivity factor $R = 2.76261$. From Eqs. 10.103 and 10.104 we know that

$$\omega_{1P} = 1/\omega_{2P} \text{ and } R = \omega_{2P}/\omega_{1P}. \tag{10.111}$$

Solution of these two equations gives the passband ripple-edge frequency of

$$\omega_{1P} = 1/\sqrt{R}$$

$$= 1/\sqrt{2.76261} = 0.6016 \text{ rad/s} \tag{10.112}$$

and the stopband ripple-edge frequency of

$$\omega_{2P} = \sqrt{R} = 1.6621 \text{ rad/s}. \tag{10.113}$$

From Eq. 10.110 the magnitude of the frequency response at the passband ripple-edge frequency of $\omega_{1P} = 0.6016$ rad/s is

$$|H_{\mathrm{LP}_p}(j0.6016)| = \left| 0.10022 \frac{-0.36192 + 5.33789}{-0.36192 + j0.48692 + 0.56666} \right|$$

$$= 0.94415 \tag{10.114}$$

and, thus

$$|H(j0.6016)|_{\mathrm{dB}} = -0.50 \tag{10.115}$$

as advertised. At the stopband ripple-edge frequency of $\omega_{2P} = 1.6621$ we have

$$|H(j1.6621)| = \left| 0.10022 \frac{-2.76257 + 5.33789}{-2.76257 + j1.34529 + 0.56666} \right|$$

$$= 0.10022 \tag{10.116}$$

and, therefore

$$|H(j1.6621)|_{dB} = -20 \tag{10.117}$$

as expected.

Example 10.6. This example illustrates the design of an elliptic lowpass prototype filter.

A lowpass prototype elliptic filter is to be designed to meet the following specifications:

Passband ripple of   0.5 dB

Stopband gain ≤ -20 dB

$$\frac{\text{stopband ripple-edge frequency}}{\text{passband ripple-edge frequency}} = 1.5625$$

Solution: From the partial design table we see that $\omega_{2P}/\omega_{1P} = 1.42189$ for $N = 3$ is the lowest order filter that meets the selectivity requirement of 1.5625. Using $N = 3$ and the table entries for a stopband gain of -20 dB, the transfer function is

$$H_{LP_p}(s) = \frac{0.306}{s + 0.667} \frac{s^2 + 1.756}{s^2 + 0.359s + 0.808} \tag{10.118}$$

A plot for $H_{LP_p}(j\omega)$ for this filter is given in Fig. 10.13 where we see that the stopband gain $\to -20$ dB for large ω. (The 0.5 dB passband ripple can't be noticed with the scale used.)

Comment: The actual selectivity requirement of $R = 1.422$ gives a passband ripple-edge frequency of

$$\omega_{1P} = 1/\sqrt{R} = 0.839 \text{ rad/s} \tag{10.119}$$

and a stopband ripple-edge frequency of

$$\omega_{2P} = \sqrt{R} = 1.192 \text{ rad/s.} \tag{10.120}$$

Some alternative methods for designing elliptic filters are:

1. The approach of Antoniou (1979) that follows that of Grossman (1957) consists of an ordered set of computations that yields the order of the filter required and then, by use of a computer program, the filter transfer function.

2. A computer program is given in Daniels (1974) that can be used to find the minimum degree of an elliptic lowpass filter that meets the requirements of M_{pass}, M_{stop}, and $R = \omega_{2P}/\omega_{1P}$. The poles and zeros of

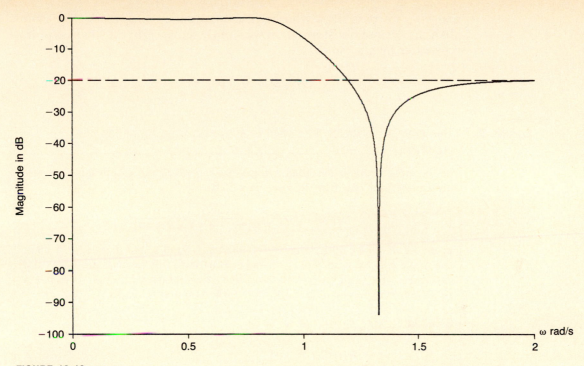

FIGURE 10.13 Frequency response magnitude in dB for Example 10.6

$E_N^2(\omega)$ are then found and, finally, the filter transfer function is determined.

3. Nomograms to determine the required order for an elliptic filter are given in Lindquist (1977) and Zverev (1967).

10.2.4 Analog Frequency Transformations

Design procedures have been established for lowpass prototype filters using Butterworth, Chebyshev, or elliptic approximations to an ideal lowpass characteristic. Let us now extend these procedures to the design of nonprototype (unnormalized) lowpass, highpass, bandpass, and bandstop filters.

Lowpass Prototype to Lowpass Filter. Consider a lowpass prototype analog filter with a critical frequency (cutoff, ripple-edge, etc.) of unity ($\omega = 1$) that has the transfer function

$$H_{\text{LP}_p}(s) = \frac{Q(s)}{D(s)}. \tag{10.121}$$

Suppose we want to design a lowpass analog filter for which

$$H_{\text{LP}}(j\omega_c) = H_{\text{LP}_p}(j1) \tag{10.122}$$

that is, a lowpass filter whose critical frequency is ω_c rad/s. To accomplish the desired transformation we simply replace s in the lowpass prototype filter by s/ω_c so that

$$H_{\text{LP}}(s) = H_{\text{LP}_p}(s)\Big|_{s=s/\omega_c}. \tag{10.123}$$

Example 10.7. This example illustrates the design of a lowpass filter from a lowpass prototype.

In Example 10.5 we designed a third-order, 1-dB ripple Chebyshev lowpass prototype filter that had the transfer function

$$H_{\text{LP}_p}(s) = \frac{0.491}{s^3 + 0.988s^2 + 1.238s + 0.491}. \tag{10.124}$$

From Fig. 10.14 we notice that $M = 0$ dB at $\omega = 0$ rad/s, and that $M = -1$ dB at the ripple-edge frequency of $\omega = 1$ rad/s. Start with this lowpass prototype and determine the third-order lowpass Chebyshev transfer function that has a ripple-edge frequency of $\omega = 10^2$ rad/s rather than $\omega = 1$ rad/s.

Solution: Using Eq. 10.123 we have

$$H_{\text{LP}}(s) = H_{\text{LP}_p}(s)\Big|_{s=s/10^2}$$

$$= \frac{491,000}{s^3 + 98.8s^2 + 12,380s + 491,000}. \tag{10.125}$$

Notice that $|H_{\text{LP}}(j0)| = 1$ and that

$$|H_{\text{LP}}(j10^2)| = \frac{491,000}{-j10^6 - 988,000 + j1,238,000 + 491,000}$$

$$= 0.891$$

$$= -1 \text{ dB} \tag{10.126}$$

as it should be at the ripple-edge.

Lowpass Prototype to Highpass Filter. Here, one requires the magnitude characteristic to be inverted with respect to the frequency scale, that is, the prototype behavior at low frequencies becomes the highpass behavior at high frequencies and vice-versa. The transformation from lowpass prototype to highpass is accomplished by the substitution

$$H_{\text{HP}}(s) = H_{\text{LP}_p}(s)\Big|_{s=\omega_c/s} \tag{10.127}$$

where ω_c is the critical highpass frequency. This is illustrated in the frequency response magnitude characteristics of Figs. 10.15(a) and (b) where we notice the following:

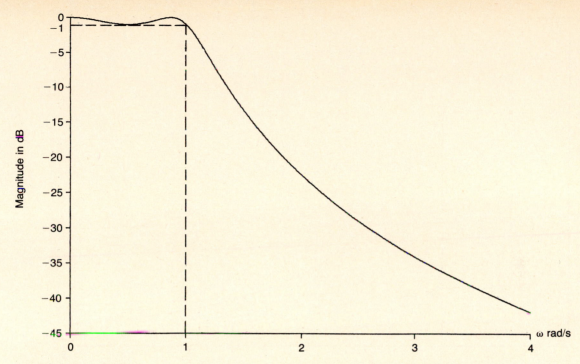

FIGURE 10.14 Chebyshev lowpass filter for Example 10.7

a) $M = 1$ at $\omega = 0$ in the prototype while $M \to 1$ as $\omega \to \infty$ in the high-pass.

b) $M \to 0$ as $\omega \to \infty$ in the prototype while $M = 0$ at $\omega = 0$ in the high-pass.

c) $M = 0.707$ at $\omega = 1$ in the prototype while $M = 0.707$ at $\omega = \omega_c$ in the highpass. (This happens to be a Butterworth characteristic. If it were Chebyshev or elliptic we could set the ripple passband in the range $0 \le \omega \le 1$ for the prototype and in the frequency interval $\omega_c \le \omega$ for the highpass.)

Example 10.8. This example illustrates the transformation of a lowpass prototype to a highpass filter.

From Table 10.1, we know that the second-order Butterworth prototype transfer function is given by

$$H_{\mathrm{LP}_p}(s) = \frac{1}{s^2 + \sqrt{2}s + 1}. \tag{10.128}$$

Start with this prototype filter and determine the transfer function of a high-pass Butterworth filter that has a cutoff frequency (-3 dB point) of 10^4 rad/s.

Solution: To do this we simply substitute $10^4/s$ for s in the transfer function of

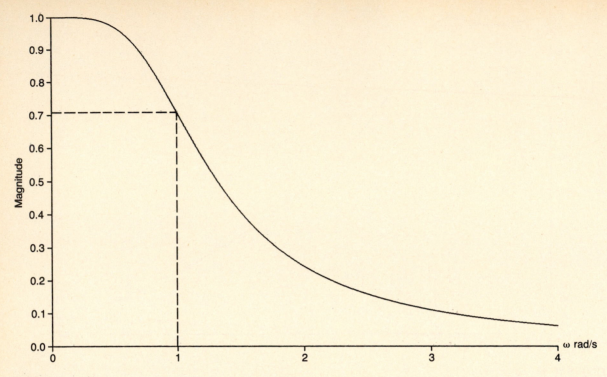

FIGURE 10.15(a) Prototype lowpass frequency response

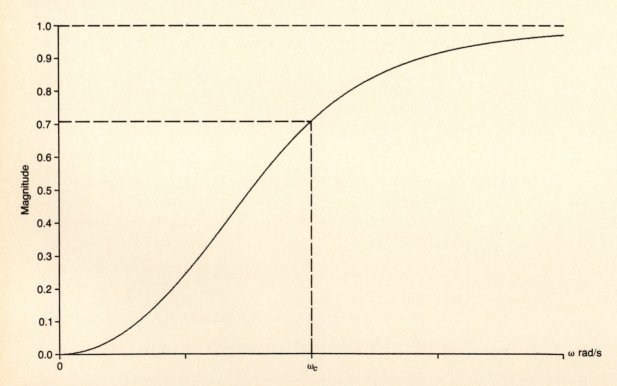

FIGURE 10.15(b) Highpass frequency response

the lowpass prototype, namely Eq. 10.128 giving

$$H_{HP}(s) = \frac{1}{s^2 + \sqrt{2}s + 1}\bigg|_{s=10^4/s}$$

$$= \frac{1}{(10^4/s)^2 + \sqrt{2}(10^4/s) + 1} = \frac{s^2}{s^2 + \sqrt{2}(10^4)s + (10^4)^2}. \quad (10.129)$$

Comment: As we've said before, all answers should be checked for being reasonable before proceeding. Looking at $H_{HP}(j\omega)$ we have

$$H_{HP}(j\omega) = \frac{(j\omega)^2}{(j\omega)^2 + \sqrt{2}(10^4)j\omega + (10^4)^2} \quad (10.130)$$

which when written in terms of magnitude and phase is

$$H_{HP}(j\omega) = Me^{jP}. \quad (10.131)$$

We see that $M = 0$ at $\omega = 0$, $M \to 1$ (0 dB) as $\omega \to \infty$ and $M = 1/\sqrt{2}$ (-3 dB) at $\omega = 10^4$ giving the magnitude plot in dB of Fig. 10.16 which is that of a high-pass filter.

Lowpass Prototype to Bandpass and Bandstop Filters. We now discuss the more interesting and complex characteristics of bandpass and bandstop filters. Consider the magnitude plots in Fig. 10.17 with the negative frequency axes included to help show the geometrical properties of the transformation required to obtain a bandpass filter from a lowpass proto-type.

A Butterworth characteristic was used to generate the plots in Fig. 10.17 but Chebyshev or elliptic, or any other characteristics could just as well have been used. The *passband width* of a bandpass characteristic is defined by $B = \omega_u - \omega_\ell$ where the filter gain is M_B at $\omega = \pm 1$ in the prototype and at $\omega = \omega_u$ and ω_ℓ in the bandpass as noted in Fig. 10.17. The passband width is typically based on the -3 dB cutoff frequencies, the width of a ripple band or some other desired characteristic. It is also common practice to define a center frequency ω_0 as the *geometric mean* of ω_u and ω_ℓ or $\omega_0 = (\omega_u\omega_\ell)^{1/2}$.

Further comparison of the two curves in Fig. 10.17 produces the following observations:

a) $M = 1$ at $\omega = 0$ in the prototype while $M = 1$ at $\omega = \pm\omega_0$ in the bandpass.

b) We have already noted that $M = M_B$ at $\omega = \pm 1$ in the prototype while $M = M_B$ at $\omega = +\omega_u$ and $\omega = +\omega_\ell$ in the bandpass (positive frequency plot).

c) $M \to 0$ as $\omega \to \pm\infty$ in the prototype while $M = 0$ at both $\omega = 0$ and as $\omega \to \infty$ in the bandpass.

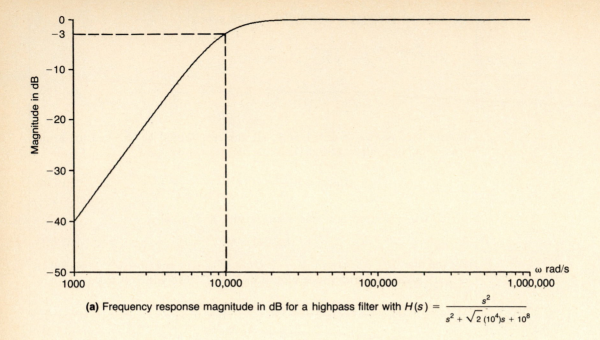

(a) Frequency response magnitude in dB for a highpass filter with $H(s) = \dfrac{s^2}{s^2 + \sqrt{2}\,(10^4)s + 10^8}$

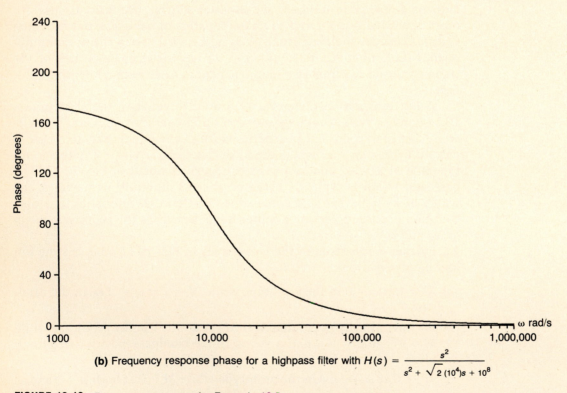

(b) Frequency response phase for a highpass filter with $H(s) = \dfrac{s^2}{s^2 + \sqrt{2}\,(10^4)s + 10^8}$

FIGURE 10.16 Frequency response for Example 10.8

CHAPTER 10 RECURSIVE FILTER DESIGN

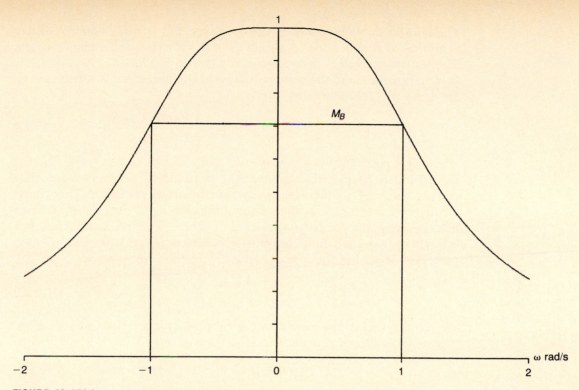

FIGURE 10.17(a) Lowpass prototype characteristic

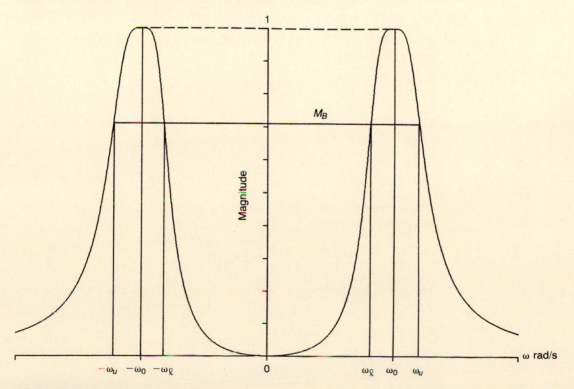

FIGURE 10.17(b) Bandpass characteristic

The relationship between ω in the prototype and ω in the bandpass filter is neither as simple nor as apparent as in the lowpass and highpass cases. The transformation is derived in many books (Lindquist, 1977) on filter design, however, and the result is that ω in the prototype is related to the bandpass (BP) frequency by

$$\omega_{LP_p} = \frac{1}{B}\left[\frac{\omega_{BP}^2 - \omega_u\omega_\ell}{\omega_{BP}}\right] = \frac{1}{B}\left[\frac{\omega_{BP}^2 - \omega_0^2}{\omega_{BP}}\right] \tag{10.132}$$

where B = passband width = $\omega_u - \omega_\ell$ and $\omega_0^2 = \omega_u\omega_\ell$. As we shall see, Eq. 10.132 is useful when finding the normalized LP frequencies that correspond to BP frequencies where specifications are given. This transformation is referred to as the ω-form (omega form) of the LP prototype to BP frequency transformation. The other form of the transformation that is used to find the bandpass transfer function $H_{BP}(s)$ from the lowpass prototype $H_{LP_p}(s)$ is the replacement of s in the prototype by

$$\frac{1}{B}\left[\frac{s^2 + \omega_0^2}{s}\right]. \tag{10.133}$$

We refer to this as the s-form of the LP prototype to BP transformation. Thus, the bandpass transfer function is given by

$$H_{BP}(s) = H_{LP_p}(s)\Big|_{s = \frac{s^2 + \omega_0^2}{Bs}} . \tag{10.134}$$

Let's look at a few key frequencies from Eq. 10.132 to verify the correctness of the ω-form of this transformation.

a) Using Eq. 10.132 the bandpass frequency of $\omega = \omega_0$ corresponds to the prototype frequency of

$$\frac{1}{B}\left[\frac{\omega_0^2 - \omega_0^2}{\omega_0}\right] = 0. \tag{10.135}$$

b) The bandpass upper edge frequency of $\omega = \omega_u$ corresponds to the prototype frequency of

$$\frac{1}{B}\left[\frac{\omega_u^2 - \omega_u\omega_\ell}{\omega_u}\right] = \frac{1}{B}\left[\frac{\omega_u(B)}{\omega_u}\right] = 1. \tag{10.136}$$

c) The bandpass lower edge frequency of $\omega = \omega_\ell$ corresponds to the prototype frequency of

$$\frac{1}{B}\left[\frac{\omega_\ell^2 - \omega_u\omega_\ell}{\omega_\ell}\right] = \frac{1}{B}\left[\frac{\omega_\ell(-B)}{\omega_\ell}\right] = -1. \tag{10.137}$$

d) The bandpass frequency of $\omega = 0$ corresponds to the prototype frequency of

$$\frac{1}{B}\left[\frac{0^2 - \omega_0^2}{0}\right] \longrightarrow -\infty. \tag{10.138}$$

e) The bandpass frequency of $\omega \to \infty$ corresponds to the prototype frequency of

$$\frac{1}{B}\left[\frac{(\infty)^2 - \omega_0{}^2}{\infty}\right] \longrightarrow \infty. \tag{10.139}$$

We can represent these relationships as

ω_{BP}	ω_{LP_p}
ω_0	0
ω_u	1
ω_ℓ	-1
0	$-\infty$
$+\infty$	$+\infty$

and this mapping is illustrated in Fig. 10.18.

Example 10.9. This example illustrates the transformation from a lowpass Chebyshev prototype to a bandpass Chebyshev filter.

Starting with the transfer function of a second-order, 1-dB ripple ($\epsilon = 0.5088$) Chebyshev lowpass prototype, determine the corresponding transfer function for a bandpass filter with a center frequency of $\omega_0 = 10^4$ rad/s and a ripple band of $B = 10^3$ rad/s.

Solution: From Table 10.3 the lowpass prototype transfer function is

$$H_{LP_p}(s) = \frac{k}{s^2 + 1.098s + 1.103} \tag{10.140}$$

and for $N = 2$ we will make $H(j0) = 1/(1 + \epsilon^2)^{1/2} = 0.891$. Thus, for $s = j0$

$$H_{LP_p}(j0) = 0.891 = k/1.103 \tag{10.141}$$

giving $k = 0.983$. The bandpass transfer function comes from Eq. 10.134 as

$$H_{BP}(s) = H_{LP_p}(s)\Big|_{s = \frac{s^2 + \omega_0{}^2}{Bs}}$$

$$= \frac{0.983}{s^2 + 1.098s + 1.103}\Big|_{s = \frac{s^2 + (10^4)^2}{10^3 s}}$$

$$= \frac{0.983}{\left(\dfrac{s^2 + 10^8}{10^3 s}\right)^2 + 1.098\left(\dfrac{s^2 + 10^8}{10^3 s}\right) + 1.103}$$

$$= \frac{0.983(10^6)s^2}{s^4 + 1.098(10^3)s^3 + 2.011(10^8)s^2 + 1.098(10^{11})s + 10^{16}}. \tag{10.142}$$

Comment: The result appears to be reasonable for $H_{BP}(j\omega) = 0$ at $\omega = 0(s = j0)$ and $H_{BP}(j\omega) \to 0$ as $\omega \to \infty$ (s^2 in the numerator and s^4 in the denominator). To

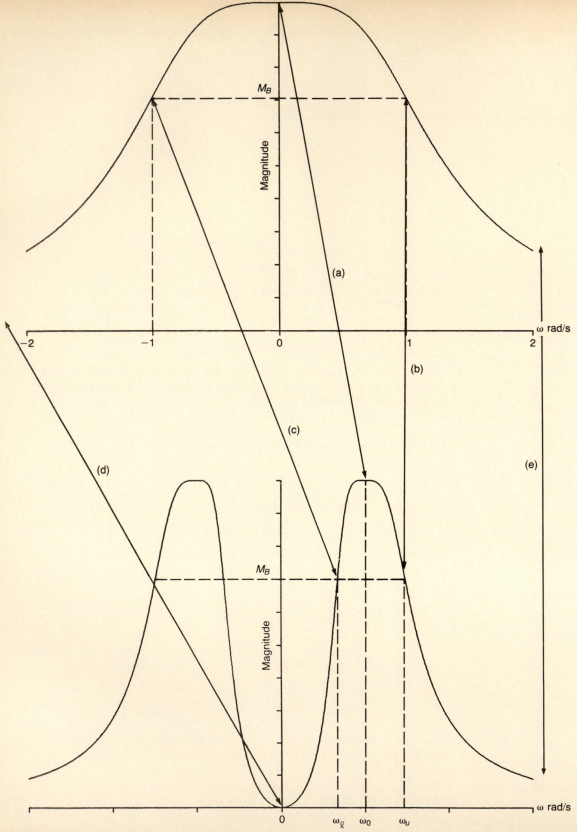

FIGURE 10.18 Prototype to bandpass mapping

locate the upper ripple-edge frequency ω_u that corresponds to $\omega_{LP_p} = 1$ we write

$$s = \frac{s^2 + \omega_0{}^2}{Bs} \qquad (10.143)$$

and substitute $s = j1$ on the left side and $s = j\omega_u$ on the right, i.e.,

$$j1 = \frac{(j\omega_u)^2 + 10^8}{10^3 j\omega_u}. \qquad (10.144)$$

This gives the quadratic equation

$$\omega_u{}^2 - 10^3\omega_u - 10^8 = 0 \qquad (10.145)$$

that has the positive frequency solution of

$$\omega_u = 10{,}512.5 \text{ rad/s}. \qquad (10.146)$$

Similarly, using $s = -j1$ and $s = j\omega_\ell$ in Eq. 10.143 gives

$$\omega_\ell{}^2 + 10^3\omega_\ell - 10^8 = 0 \text{ or } \omega_\ell = 9512.5 \text{ rad/s}. \qquad (10.147)$$

The ripple passband is $B = \omega_u - \omega_\ell = 10{,}512.5 - 9512.5 = 10^3$ rad/s as desired and notice that the geometric mean of ω_u and ω_ℓ is $\omega_0 = (\omega_u\omega_\ell)^{1/2} = 10^4$ rad/s as required in the design specifications.

The four substitutions that generate lowpass, highpass, bandpass, and bandstop filters from a lowpass prototype transfer function are given in Table 10.5. As might be expected, the transformation from the lowpass prototype to a bandstop filter is simply the reciprocal of that for prototype to bandpass. Verification of this substitution is the subject of Problem 10.7. Following Table 10.5 we have listed several important filter frequencies and their equivalents for the lowpass prototype (normalized) filter. This listing is simply an extended version of the ω column in Table 10.5.

Some useful ω-form relationships from Table 10.5.

a) Lowpass (ω_{LP}) $\longrightarrow$ Normalized lowpass prototype (ω_{LP_p})

ω_{LP}	$\omega_{LP_p} = \omega_{LP}/\omega_c$
ω_c	1
ω_a	ω_a/ω_c
0	0
$\rightarrow \infty$	$\rightarrow \infty$

b) Highpass (ω_{HP}) $\longrightarrow$ Normalized lowpass prototype (ω_{LP_p})

ω_{HP}	$\omega_{LP_p} = \omega_c/\omega_{HP}$
ω_c	1
ω_a	ω_c/ω_a
0	$\rightarrow \infty$
$\rightarrow \infty$	0

TABLE 10.5 ANALOG FILTER FREQUENCY TRANSFORMATIONS

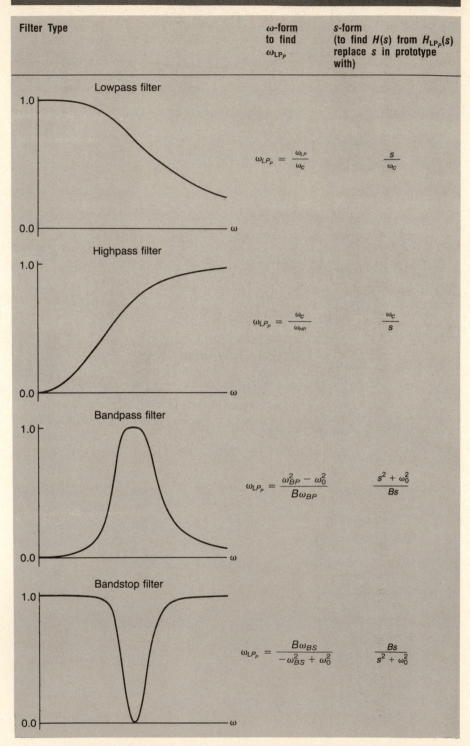

Filter Type	ω-form to find ω_{LP_p}	s-form (to find $H(s)$ from $H_{LP_p}(s)$ replace s in prototype with)
Lowpass filter	$\omega_{LP_p} = \dfrac{\omega_{LP}}{\omega_C}$	$\dfrac{s}{\omega_C}$
Highpass filter	$\omega_{LP_p} = \dfrac{\omega_C}{\omega_{HP}}$	$\dfrac{\omega_C}{s}$
Bandpass filter	$\omega_{LP_p} = \dfrac{\omega_{BP}^2 - \omega_0^2}{B\omega_{BP}}$	$\dfrac{s^2 + \omega_0^2}{Bs}$
Bandstop filter	$\omega_{LP_p} = \dfrac{B\omega_{BS}}{-\omega_{BS}^2 + \omega_0^2}$	$\dfrac{Bs}{s^2 + \omega_0^2}$

c) Bandpass (ω_{BP}) $\longrightarrow$ Normalized lowpass prototype (ω_{LP_p})

$$\omega_{BP} \qquad \omega_{LP_p} = \frac{\omega_{BP}^2 - \omega_0^2}{B\omega_{BP}}$$

$\pm\omega_0$	0
$\pm\omega_u$	± 1
$\pm\omega_\ell$	∓ 1
ω_a	$\dfrac{\omega_a^2 - \omega_0^2}{B\omega_a}$

d) Bandstop (ω_{BS}) $\longrightarrow$ Normalized lowpass prototype (ω_{LP_p})

$$\omega_{BS} \qquad \omega_{LP_p} = \frac{B\omega_{BS}}{-\omega_{BS}^2 + \omega_0^2}$$

$\pm\omega_0$	$\rightarrow \pm\infty$
$\pm\omega_u$	∓ 1
$\pm\omega_\ell$	± 1
ω_a	$\dfrac{B\omega_a}{-\omega_a^2 + \omega_0^2}$

Comment: For LP and HP designs, we normally use ω_c as the cutoff frequency for a Butterworth filter and as the ripple passband edge frequency for a Chebyshev filter. For elliptic LP and HP designs ω_c can be the geometric mean frequency $(\omega_{1P}\omega_{2P})^{1/2}$, or ω_{1P} or ω_{2P}, as desired. For BP and BS designs ω_u and ω_ℓ are selected as the cutoff frequencies for a Butterworth filter, whereas the ripple passband edge frequencies are typically used for Chebyshev and elliptic designs.

10.2.5 Design of Lowpass, Highpass, Bandpass, and Bandstop Filters

Here are the steps to be followed in the design procedure for analog filters. We assume that specifications (requirements) to be met in both the passband and the stopband are known.

ANALOG FILTER DESIGN PROCEDURE

Step 1

Translate specifications to those for a prototype (normalized) lowpass filter where $\omega_{LP_p} = 1$ (cutoff, ripple-edge, or geometric mean) by using the ω-form of the transformations in Table 10.5. These new specifications are called the prototype or normalized specifications.

Step 2

Design a prototype lowpass filter to satisfy all the prototype specifications. The choice of either Butterworth, Chebyshev, or elliptic, or many other approximations, may be determined by the specifications, or be based on the personal experience of the designer. The filter order N is generally determined from either a nomogram, tables, or design curves (see Problems 10.46–10.48), but in the case of Butterworth filters we can use

$$N = \frac{\log_{10}(10^{-[M_{dB}/10]} - 1)}{2 \log_{10} \omega_a} \tag{10.148}$$

where ω_a is a frequency at which a prototype specification is given. With N known we can use Table 10.1, Table 10.3, or an extended version of Table 10.4 to find the lowpass prototype transfer function $H_{LP_p}(s)$.

Step 3

Check on the design by finding a computer-generated frequency response plot for the prototype lowpass filter $H_{LP_p}(s)$. Compare with the normalized specifications.

Step 4

Determine $H_{LP}(s)$, $H_{HP}(s)$, $H_{BP}(s)$, or $H_{BS}(s)$ from $H_{LP_p}(s)$ by using the s-form of the appropriate frequency transformation in Table 10.5.

Step 5

Check on the correctness of the frequency transformation by finding a computer-generated frequency response plot for the filter. Compare with the original specifications.

Example 10.10. This example illustrates the design of a Butterworth highpass filter.

Suppose that the desired magnitude characteristics for a Butterworth highpass filter are as pictured in Fig. 10.19(a). From the given specifications, we note that the −3 dB cutoff frequency is 3×10^4 rad/s, and the gain is, at most, −26 dB for $\omega \le 1 \times 10^4$ rad/s. Determine the transfer function $H_{HP}(s)$ of lowest order N that will meet these specifications.

Solution: We follow the procedure just outlined.

Step 1—We use the relationship $\omega_{LP_p} = \omega_c/\omega_{HP}$ to determine the lowpass pro-

totype specifications corresponding to the given highpass requirements. The highpass cutoff frequency of $\omega_c = 3 \times 10^4$ is normalized to
$\omega = 1$ in the prototype. The stopband frequency of $\omega = 10^4$ is translated to its corresponding value of $\omega = 3$ in the prototype. The gains at
these prototype frequencies are shown in Fig. 10.19(b).

Step 2—For $\omega_{LP_p} = 3$ and $M_{dB} = -26$ the necessary filter order is

$$N = \frac{\log_{10}(10^{2.6} - 1)}{2 \log_{10} 3}$$

$$= 2.72 \tag{10.149}$$

which tells us to use $N = 3$. From Table 10.1, therefore, the lowpass
prototype transfer function is

$$H_{LP_p}(s) = \frac{1}{s^3 + 2s^2 + 2s + 1}. \tag{10.150}$$

Step 3—The magnitude portion of the frequency response is given in Fig.
10.19(c) and it satisfies the normalized specification of $M_{dB} \leq -26$ at
$\omega_{LP_p} = 3$.

Step 4—We then use the s-form of the lowpass to highpass transformation in
Table 10.5 to determine $H_{HP}(s)$. The result is

$$H_{HP}(s) = H_{LP_p}(s)\Big|_{s = \frac{3 \times 10^4}{s}}$$

$$= \frac{1}{\left(\dfrac{3 \times 10^4}{s}\right)^3 + 2\left(\dfrac{3 \times 10^4}{s}\right)^2 + 2\left(\dfrac{3 \times 10^4}{s}\right) + 1}$$

$$= \frac{s^3}{s^3 + 6(10^4)s^2 + 18(10^8)s + 27(10^{12})}. \tag{10.151}$$

Step 5—The frequency response for the highpass filter is given in Fig. 10.19(d)
and it satisfies all the desired characteristics of Fig. 10.19(a) so the
design is complete. All that remains is the digitization which is discussed in Section 10.3.

The design of analog filters is straightforward because it relies heavily
on the repeated use of analysis procedures. However, the first step in the
previously discussed analog filter design procedure—translating the
given specifications to those for a lowpass prototype—can be a bit tricky.
We now organize this step in order to make the whole design process
almost automatic.

The ω-forms of the frequency relationships in Table 10.5 are used to
generate a specification table where the suggested format is

ω LP HP BP BS	LP, HP, BP, or BS specification	ω_{LP_p}	Prototype LP specification

FIGURE 10.19 Design of a highpass filter

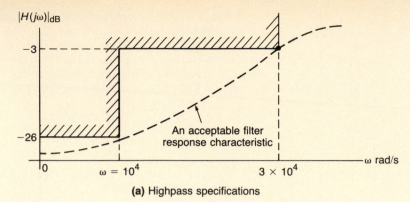

(a) Highpass specifications

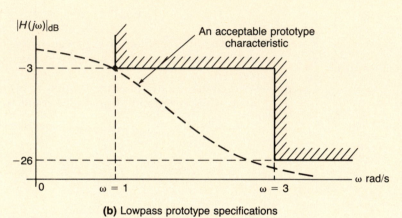

(b) Lowpass prototype specifications

For each frequency, or range of frequencies, where a specification is given, an entry is included in the table. The last two columns then provide the specifications from which the lowpass prototype is designed. The following example shows how this approach is used.

Example 10.11. This example illustrates the design of a bandpass analog filter.

It is desired to design a Butterworth analog filter that meets the following specifications:

Lower cutoff frequency 600 Hz

Upper cutoff frequency 900 Hz

Maximum attenuation of 0.2 dB in the frequency range $f_0 \leq f \leq 800$ Hz

Minimum attenuation of 50 dB for $0 \leq f \leq 200$ Hz.

Find the transfer function for this bandpass filter.

Solution:

1. The first step is to translate the bandpass specifications to those of a low-

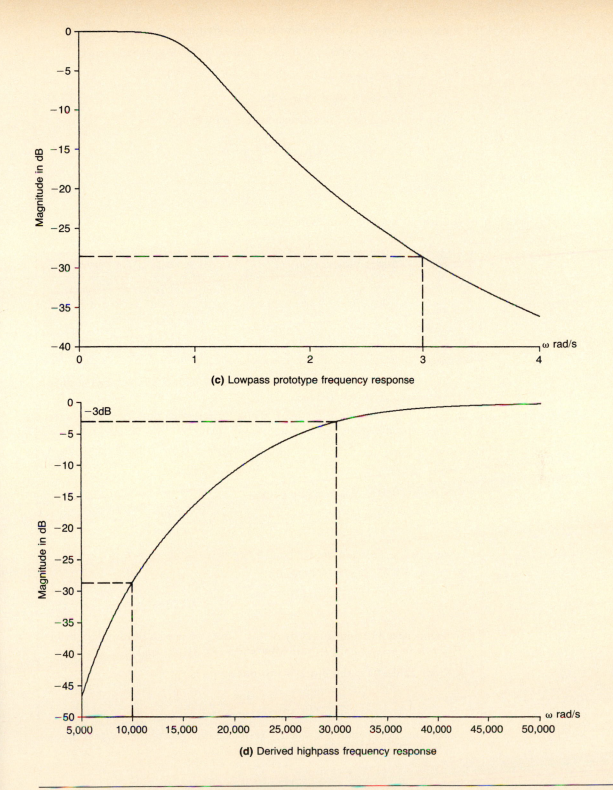

(c) Lowpass prototype frequency response

(d) Derived highpass frequency response

pass prototype. The important bandpass frequencies are:

$$\omega_\ell = 2\pi \cdot 600 = 3770 \text{ rad/s and } \omega_u = 2\pi \cdot 900 = 5655 \text{ rad/s}$$

$$\omega_0^2 = \omega_\ell \omega_u = 21.32 \times 10^6 \text{ rad/s or } f_0 = 735 \text{ Hz}$$

$$B = \omega_u - \omega_\ell = 1885 \text{ rad/s.} \tag{10.152}$$

The prototype equivalent frequencies come from

$$\omega_{LP_p} = \frac{\omega_{BP}^2 - \omega_0^2}{B\omega_{BP}}$$

$$= \frac{\omega_{BP}^2 - 21.32 \times 10^6}{1885\, \omega_{BP}} \tag{10.153}$$

with the specification table given below.

ω_{BP}	Bandpass specification	ω_{LP_p}	Prototype LP specification
$2\pi \times 800$	maximum attenuation of 0.2 dB for $f_0 \le f \le 800$ Hz	0.418	maximum attenuation of 0.2 dB for $0 \le \omega \le 0.418$ rad/s
$2\pi \times 200$	minimum attenuation of 50 dB for $0 \le f \le 200$ Hz	8.35	minimum attenuation of 50 dB for $\omega \ge 8.35$ rad/s

The translated specifications are portrayed in Fig. 10.20(a) where the unacceptable regions are shaded.

2. Next we need to find the order N of a Butterworth prototype that meets these specifications. We use Eq. 10.148, namely

$$N = \frac{\log_{10}(10^{-(M_{dB}/10)} - 1)}{2 \log_{10} \omega_a}. \tag{10.154}$$

a) For $\omega_a = 0.418$, $M_{dB} = -0.20$ giving

$$\frac{\log_{10}(10^{0.02} - 1)}{2 \log_{10} 0.418} = \frac{\log_{10}(0.047)}{-0.758} = \frac{-1.327}{-0.758} = 1.75 \tag{10.155}$$

so this specification is met by $N = 2$.

b) For $\omega_a = 8.35$, $M_{dB} = -50$ giving

$$\frac{\log_{10}(10^5 - 1)}{2 \log_{10} 8.35} = \frac{5}{1.843} = 2.71 \tag{10.156}$$

so this specification is met by $N = 3$. Thus, we need a third-order Butterworth to satisfy both specifications.

3. From Table 10.1, the Butterworth prototype is

$$\frac{1}{s^3 + 2s^2 + 2s + 1} \tag{10.157}$$

and the corresponding frequency response that meets the lowpass prototype specifications is shown in Fig. 10.20(b) where the unacceptable regions (except the 0.2 dB region) are shown.

4. To obtain the bandpass filter transfer function we use Table 10.5 and replace s by $(s^2 + \omega_0^2)/Bs$. Thus,

$$H_{BP}(s) = H_{LP_p}(s)\Big|_{s=(s^2+\omega_0^2)/Bs}$$

$$= \frac{1}{s^3 + 2s^2 + 2s + 1}\Bigg|_{s = \frac{s^2 + 21.32 \times 10^6}{(1885)s}}$$

$$= \frac{1}{\left(\dfrac{s^2 + 21.32(10^6)}{(1885)s}\right)^3 + 2\left(\dfrac{s^2 + 21.32(10^6)}{(1885)s}\right)^2 + 2\left(\dfrac{s^2 + 21.32(10^6)}{(1885)s}\right) + 1}$$

$$= \frac{ks^3}{s^6 + a_5 s^5 + a_4 s^4 + a_3 s^3 + a_2 s^2 + a_1 s + a_0} \qquad (10.158)$$

where

$$k = 6.70 \times 10^9$$

$$a_0 = 9.691 \times 10^{21} \qquad a_3 = 1.675 \times 10^{11}$$

$$a_1 = 1.713 \times 10^{18} \qquad a_4 = 7.106 \times 10^7$$

$$a_2 = 1.515 \times 10^{15} \qquad a_5 = 3.77 \times 10^3. \qquad (10.159)$$

5. The magnitude of the frequency response is plotted in Fig. 10.20(c) where we see that the design specifications have been satisfied.

FIGURE 10.20(a) Translated filter specifications for Example 10.11

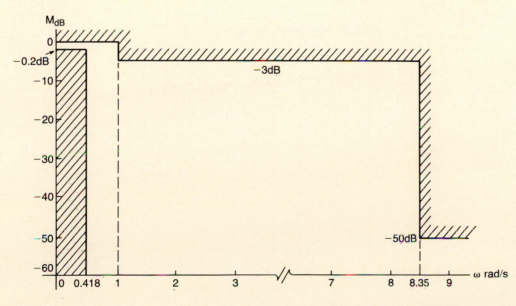

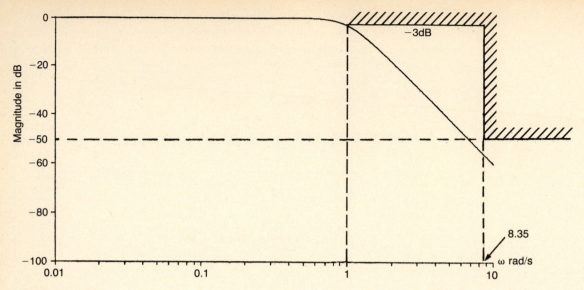

FIGURE 10.20(b) Frequency response magnitude in dB for normalized lowpass prototype of Example 10.11

FIGURE 10.20(c) Frequency response magnitude in dB for the bandpass filter of Example 10.11

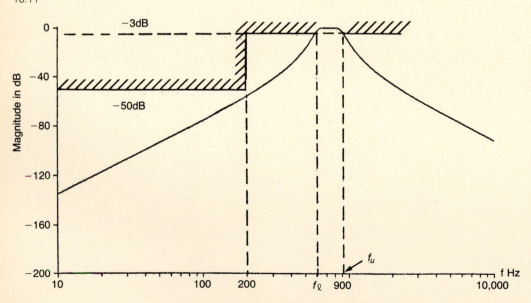

Thus far, we've designed several Butterworth filters. The same approach applies also to Chebyshev and elliptic filters, as illustrated in the next example.

Example 10.12. This example illustrates the design of a lowpass elliptic filter.

Determine the transfer function of a lowpass elliptic filter designed to meet the following specifications:

Passband ripple	0.5 dB	passband ripple-edge frequency ≥ 2 kHz
Stopband gain	-30 dB	stopband ripple-edge frequency ≤ 2.5 kHz

Solution: To use Table 10.4 we need to express the above requirements in terms of the prototype frequencies. In this case we elect to choose the critical frequency as

$$\omega_c = (\omega_1 \omega_2)^{1/2}$$
$$= [4\pi^2 (2)(2.5)(10^6)]^{1/2}$$
$$= (2\pi)(2.236)(10^3)$$
$$= 14,049 \qquad (10.160)$$

as the critical frequency for "normalizing" the lowpass characteristics. From Table 10.5

$$\omega_{\mathrm{LP}_P} = \frac{\omega_a}{14,049} \qquad (10.161)$$

and the desired passband ripple-edge frequency is

$$\omega_{1P} = \frac{2\pi(2)(10^3)}{14,049}$$
$$= 0.895 \qquad (10.162)$$

with a desired stopband ripple-edge frequency of

$$\omega_{2P} = \frac{2\pi(2.5)(10^3)}{14,049}$$
$$= 1.118. \qquad (10.163)$$

The desired design constant $R = \omega_{2P}/\omega_{1P}$ is

$$R = \frac{1.180}{0.895} = 1.249 \qquad (10.164)$$

and from Table 10.4 we see that $N = 5$ meets the transition requirement. Thus, using this table and rounding coefficients to three places the prototype transfer function is

$$H_{\mathrm{LP}_P}(s) = \frac{0.119}{(s + 0.512)} \frac{s^2 + 2.145}{(s^2 + 0.481s + 0.649)} \frac{s^2 + 1.181}{(s^2 + 0.088s + 0.907)}$$

$$= \frac{0.119(s^4 + 3.326s^2 + 2.533)}{s^5 + 1.081s^4 + 1.889s^3 + 1.311s^2 + 0.841s + 0.301}. \qquad (10.165)$$

This transfer function has a selectivity ratio of $R = 1.129$ which gives actual values of $\omega_{1P} = 0.941$ and $\omega_{2P} = 1.063$. Since it is desired to translate the prototype frequency $\omega = 1$ to the critical frequency $\omega_c = 14,049$, we use $s/14,049$ as the substitution in $H_{LP_p}(s)$ to obtain the desired lowpass filter transfer function. This frequency transformation scales the prototype passband ripple-edge frequency to

$$\omega_1 = 0.941 \times 14,049 = 13,220 \text{ rad/s or } f_1 = 2.104 \text{ kHz} \qquad (10.166)$$

and the prototype stopband ripple edge frequency to

$$\omega_2 = 1.063 \times 14,049 = 14,934 \text{ rad/s or } f_2 = 2.377 \text{ kHz} \qquad (10.167)$$

which is well below 2.5 kHz, and so the stopband requirement is satisfied.

The transfer function that results is

$$H_{LP}(s) = H_{LP_p}(s)\Big|_{s=\dot{s}/14,049}$$

$$= \frac{1.672(10^3)[s^4 + 6.565(10^8)s^2 + 9.868(10^{16})]}{s^5 + 1.519(10^4)s^4 + 3.728(10^8)s^3 + 3.635(10^{12})s^2 + 3.276(10^{16})s + 1.647(10^{20})}$$

$$(10.168)$$

If all of the significant figures of Table 10.4 are used and retained throughout the calculations, the results are slightly different.

10.3 ■ DIGITAL FILTER DESIGN

We now have a procedure for designing analog filters that is straightforward and almost mechanical. But the goal of this chapter is to design recursive digital filters. In this section we consider several ways to digitize analog filters to yield digital filters, that is, to find an $H(z)$ from an $H(s)$ by means of a suitable mapping or transformation. Later, in Section 10.3.5, we design digital filters directly by starting from a set of previously determined lowpass prototype digital transfer functions.

10.3.1 Matched z-Transform Design

This design procedure is conceptually straightforward. Poles and zeros of the transfer function $H(s)$ are mapped directly to poles and zeros of the transfer function $H(z)$ by making a simple substitution. Consider a term representing a simple real pole such as $1/(s + a)$. The development leading to the appropriate substitution goes this way.

$$\mathscr{L}^{-1}\left[\frac{1}{s+a}\right] = e^{-at} \xrightarrow[\text{yields}]{\text{sampled}} e^{-anT} \xrightarrow[\text{yields}]{z\text{-transformed}} \frac{1}{1 - e^{-aT}z^{-1}}$$

$$(10.169)$$

and we say that a pole or zero factor such as

$$(s + a) \xrightarrow{\text{goes to}} (1 - e^{-aT} z^{-1}) \tag{10.170}$$

or the analog pole/zero at $s = -a$ maps to a digital pole/zero at $z = e^{-aT}$.

Example 10.13. This example illustrates the matched z-transform method of digitizing an analog transfer function.

Use the matched z-transform method to find the discrete transfer function $H(z)$ that corresponds to

$$H(s) = \frac{s + 1}{(s + 2)(s + 3)} \tag{10.171}$$

with a sampling frequency of 10 Hz $(T = 0.1)$.

Solution: Using Eq. 10.170 we find that

$$(s + 1) \longrightarrow (1 - e^{-T} z^{-1}) = (1 - 0.905z^{-1})$$

$$(s + 2) \longrightarrow (1 - e^{-2T} z^{-1}) = (1 - 0.819z^{-1})$$

$$(s + 3) \longrightarrow (1 - e^{-3T} z^{-1}) = (1 - 0.741z^{-1}) \tag{10.172}$$

and the discrete transfer function becomes

$$H(z) = \frac{1 - 0.905z^{-1}}{(1 - 0.819z^{-1})(1 - 0.741z^{-1})}$$

$$= \frac{z(z - 0.905)}{(z - 0.819)(z - 0.741)}. \tag{10.173}$$

Notice that the stable poles of $H(s)$ at $s = -2$ and $s = -3$ become stable poles of $H(z)$ at $z = e^{-2T} = 0.819$ and $z = e^{-3T} = 0.741$. From Eq. 10.170 we see that a real left-half plane pole $(a > 0)$ corresponds to a pole inside the unit circle at $z = e^{-aT}$. A plot of the magnitude of the frequency response for both $H(s)$ and $H(z)$ is given in Fig. 10.21.

Comment: When comparing analog and digital lowpass filters it is common practice to adjust their respective gains to make the magnitudes of the frequency response plots equal at $\omega = \theta = 0$. In this case

$$H(s)\Big|_{s=j0} = 0.167 \quad \text{and} \quad H(z)\Big|_{z=e^{j0}} = 2.026 \tag{10.174}$$

and so the analog plot was scaled by $1/0.167 = 6$ and the digital plot by $1/2.026 = 0.494$ to make them equal at zero frequency.

For complex terms, following the same line of reasoning gives

$$(s + a - jb) \xrightarrow{\text{goes to}} (1 - e^{-(a-jb)T} z^{-1}) \tag{10.175}$$

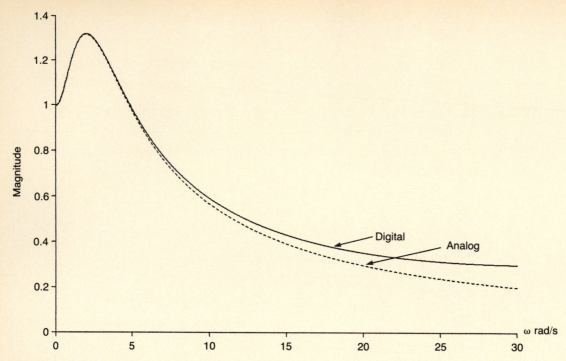

FIGURE 10.21 Digital and analog filter frequency responses for matched z-transform design

and from Problem 10.10

$$(s + a - jb)(s + a + jb) \xrightarrow{\text{goes to}} (1 - e^{-aT} e^{jbT} z^{-1})(1 - e^{-aT} e^{-jbT} z^{-1})$$
$$= (1 - 2z^{-1} e^{-aT} \cos bT + e^{-2aT} z^{-2}). \quad (10.176)$$

The matched z-transform procedure is very easy to apply but it suffers from the fact that, unlike other methods, an all pole analog filter becomes an all pole digital filter. Consequently, in this case there are no zeros to help shape the frequency response. Even if $H(s)$ does have zeros, if their imaginary parts are greater than $\omega_s/2$, the corresponding zeros in $H(z)$ will produce serious aliasing errors.

10.3.2 Impulse- and Step-Invariant Design

This design procedure is based upon the impulse response or the step response of a continuous-time (analog) filter as represented in Fig. 10.22. We are considering only two different inputs, an impulse and a step, but, in general, other inputs such as exponential and ramps could be used as the basis for deriving similar design methods (see Problem 10.43).

Impulse-Invariant Design. As the name impulse invariant suggests, the design procedure is based on the impulse response $h(t)$ of a continuous-

FIGURE 10.22 Contin-
uous-time (analog filter)

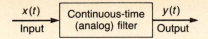

$x(t)$
Input
Continuous-time
(analog) filter
$y(t)$
Output

time (analog) filter. For a unit impulse input of $x(t) = \delta(t)$, the Laplace transform of the output is

$$Y(s) = H(s) \cdot X(s)$$
$$= H(s) \qquad (10.177)$$

because $X(s) = 1$. Defining the output $y(t)$ caused by a unit impulse input as $h(t)$ we have

$$y(t) = h(t) = \mathcal{L}^{-1}[H(s)]. \qquad (10.178)$$

The impulse-invariant design method consists simply of making the unit sample response values $h(nT)$ of the digital filter equal to the sampled values of the unit impulse response $h(t)$ of the analog filter. That is,

$$h(nT) = h(t)\Big|_{t=nT} \qquad (10.179)$$

and the discrete (digital) transfer function is

$$\mathfrak{z}[h(nT)] = H(z). \qquad (10.180)$$

Notice that the digital transfer function $H(z)$ is the z-transform of the sampled unit impulse response $h(nT)$ while the analog transfer function $H(s)$ is the Laplace transform of the unit sample response $h(t)$. Don't be tempted to write $H(z) = H(s)|_{s=z}$, because this is incorrect.

Example 10.14. This example illustrates the digital implementation of an analog transfer function using the impulse-invariant design method.

Given a lowpass analog filter described by the transfer function

$$H(s) = \frac{1}{(s + 1)(s + 2)} \qquad (10.181)$$

determine the digital transfer function $H(z)$ with the design based on the impulse-invariant method.

Solution: First, the unit impulse response of the analog filter is computed from

$$h(t) = \mathcal{L}^{-1}[H(s)]$$

$$= \mathcal{L}^{-1}\left[\frac{1}{(s + 1)(s + 2)}\right] = \mathcal{L}^{-1}\left[\frac{1}{s + 1} - \frac{1}{s + 2}\right] \qquad (10.182)$$

and by taking the inverse Laplace transform of $H(s)$ we have

$$h(t) = e^{-t} - e^{-2t}, \qquad t \geq 0. \qquad (10.183)$$

The sampled version is found by substituting nT for t in Eq. 10.183 giving

$$h(nT) = e^{-nT} - e^{-2nT}, \qquad n = 0, 1, \ldots \qquad (10.184)$$

and both $h(t)$ and $h(nT)$ are shown in Fig. 10.23(a) for $T = 0.1$ s.

The discrete transfer function is then the z-transform of $h(nT)$ or

$$H(z) = \mathfrak{z}[h(nT)]$$

$$= \frac{1}{1 - e^{-T}z^{-1}} - \frac{1}{1 - e^{-2T}z^{-1}}$$

$$= \frac{z^{-1}(e^{-T} - e^{-2T})}{(1 - e^{-T}z^{-1})(1 - e^{-2T}z^{-1})}, \qquad |z| > e^{-T}. \qquad (10.185)$$

Comment: The magnitude portion of the frequency response of the analog filter and that of the digital filter for two different sampling intervals ($T = 0.1$ and $T = 0.50$) are given in Fig. 10.23(b).

Let us now generalize this procedure and at the same time show that $H(z)$ can be obtained directly from $H(s)$ without the intervening steps of finding $h(t)$ and then $h(nT)$. Consider an analog filter with N different poles that has the s-domain transfer function written in partial fraction expansion form as

$$H(s) = \sum_{k=1}^{k=N} \frac{C_k}{s - d_k} \qquad (10.186)$$

with the corresponding unit impulse response

$$h(t) = \sum_{k=1}^{k=N} C_k e^{d_k t}. \qquad (10.187)$$

If this response is sampled every T seconds ($t = nT$) we have the sampled response

$$h(nT) = \sum_{k=1}^{k=N} C_k e^{d_k nT}. \qquad (10.188)$$

Finally, we take the z-transform of Eq. 10.188 to obtain the discrete transfer function of

$$H(z) = \mathfrak{z}[h(nT)]$$

$$= \sum_{k=1}^{N} \frac{C_k}{1 - e^{d_k T} z^{-1}}. \qquad (10.189)$$

The steps outlined above are shown in Fig. 10.24 and from Eq. 10.186 and

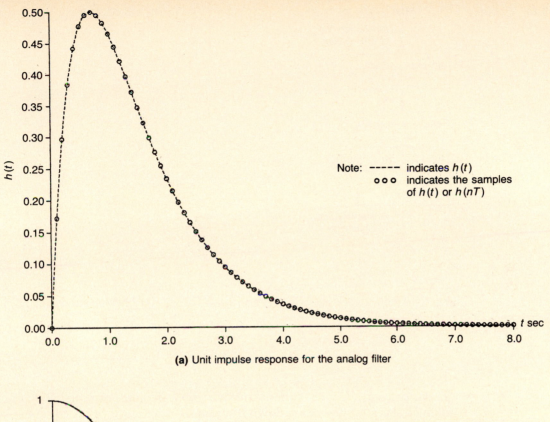

Note: ----- indicates $h(t)$
o o o indicates the samples
of $h(t)$ or $h(nT)$

(a) Unit impulse response for the analog filter

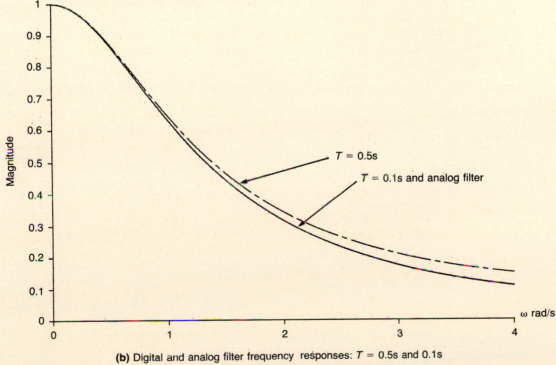

$T = 0.5$s

$T = 0.1$s and analog filter

(b) Digital and analog filter frequency responses: $T = 0.5$s and 0.1s

FIGURE 10.23 Impulse and frequency responses for Example 10.14

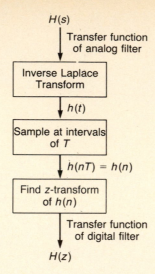

FIGURE 10.24 Impulse-invariant design

$H(s)$

Transfer function of analog filter

Inverse Laplace Transform

$h(t)$

Sample at intervals of T

$h(nT) = h(n)$

Find z-transform of $h(n)$

Transfer function of digital filter

$H(z)$

Eq. 10.189 we see that the $\dot{h}(t)$ and $h(nT)$ steps may be omitted and $H(z)$ can be found directly from $H(s)$ as

$$H(s) = \sum_{k=1}^{k=N} \frac{C_k}{s - d_k} \longrightarrow H(z) = \sum_{k=1}^{k=N} \frac{C_k}{1 - e^{d_k T} z^{-1}}. \qquad (10.190)$$

Thus, the partial fraction constants C_k must be computed for $H(s)$ and then $H(z)$ is simply written down from Eq. 10.190. Notice that the substitution made for the poles in the partial fraction expansion is the same as found earlier by the matched z-transform approach.

Example 10.15. This example illustrates the direct application of the impulse-invariant design method.

A third-order Butterworth lowpass filter has the transfer function

$$H(s) = \frac{1}{(s + 1)(s^2 + s + 1)}. \qquad (10.191)$$

Start with Eq. 10.191 and determine the discrete transfer function $H(z)$ by using Eq. 10.190.

Solution: The partial fraction expansion is

$$\frac{1}{(s + 1)(s + 0.5 - j0.866)(s + 0.5 + j0.866)} \equiv \frac{C_1}{s + 1} + \frac{C_2}{s + 0.5 - j0.866} +$$

$$\frac{C_2{}^*}{s + 0.5 + j0.866} \qquad (10.192)$$

where the usual algebra, which is considerable and error prone, gives

$$H(s) = \frac{1}{s + 1} + \frac{0.577 e^{-j2.62}}{s + 0.5 - j0.866} + \frac{0.577 e^{j2.62}}{s + 0.5 + j0.866}. \qquad (10.193)$$

The three poles are

$$d_1 = -1, \quad d_2 = -0.5 + j0.866, \quad \text{and} \quad d_3 = -0.5 - j0.866 \qquad (10.194)$$

and from Eq. 10.190

$$H(z) = \frac{1}{1 - e^{-T}z^{-1}} + \frac{0.577 e^{-j2.62}}{1 - e^{(-0.5+j0.866)T}z^{-1}} + \frac{0.577 e^{j2.62}}{1 - e^{(-0.5-j0.866)T}z^{-1}}$$

$$= \frac{1}{1 - e^{-T}z^{-1}} + \frac{0.577 e^{-j2.62}}{1 - e^{-0.5T}e^{j0.866T}z^{-1}} + \frac{0.577 e^{j2.62}}{1 - e^{-0.5T}e^{-j0.866T}z^{-1}}. \qquad (10.195)$$

The last two terms can be combined to give

$$H(z) = \frac{1}{1 - e^{-T}z^{-1}} +$$

$$\frac{2(0.577)\cos(-2.62) - 2(0.577)e^{-0.5T}z^{-1}\cos(-2.62 - 0.866T)}{1 - 2e^{-0.5T}\cos(0.866T)z^{-1} + e^{-T}z^{-2}}$$

$$= \frac{z}{z - e^{-T}} + \frac{-z^2 - 1.154z\, e^{-0.5T}\cos(5\pi/6 + 0.866T)}{z^2 - 2e^{-0.5T}\cos(0.866T)z + e^{-T}}. \qquad (10.196)$$

In terms of the sampling interval T the filter transfer function is

$$H(z) = \frac{b_0 z^2 + b_1 z}{z^3 - a_1 z^2 - a_2 z - a_3} \qquad (10.197)$$

where

$$b_0 = -2e^{-0.5T}\cos(0.866T) + e^{-T} + 1.154 e^{-0.5T}\cos(5\pi/6 + 0.866T)$$

$$b_1 = e^{-T} + 1.154 e^{-1.5T}\cos(5\pi/6 + 0.866T)$$

$$a_1 = e^{-T} + 2e^{-0.5T}\cos(0.866T)$$

$$a_2 = -e^{-T} - 2e^{-1.5T}\cos(0.866T)$$

$$a_3 = e^{-2T}. \qquad (10.198)$$

Comment: The magnitude frequency response plots for the third-order analog Butterworth filter and for the impulse-invariant designed digital filter for two different values of T are shown in Fig. 10.25.

Step-Invariant Design. As the name step invariant suggests, the design procedure is based on the step response of a continuous-time (analog) filter. For a unit step input of $x(t) = u(t)$, the transform of the output $y_s(t)$ is

$$Y_s(s) = H(s) \cdot X(s)$$

$$= \frac{H(s)}{s} \qquad (10.199)$$

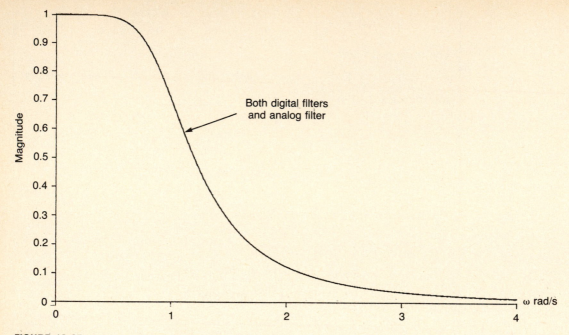

FIGURE 10.25 Digital and analog filter frequency responses: $T = 0.5s$ and $T = 0.1s$

because $X(s) = 1/s$. The step-invariant design method consists simply of defining the unit step sequence response values $y_s(nT)$ of the digital filter as being equal to the sampled values of the unit step response $y_s(t)$ of the analog filter. That is,

$$y_s(nT) = y_s(t)\Big|_{t=nT} \tag{10.200}$$

and the z-transform of the output sequence $y_s(nT)$ is

$$\mathfrak{z}[y_s(nT)] = Y_s(z). \tag{10.201}$$

The digital transfer function $H(z)$ is then computed from

$$H(z) = \frac{Y_s(z)}{X(z)} \tag{10.202}$$

where $X(z) = \mathfrak{z}[u(n)] = 1/(1 - z^{-1})$, $|z| > 1$.

Example 10.16. This example illustrates the step-invariant method of design.

Given the system transfer function of Example 10.14, namely

$$H(s) = \frac{1}{(s + 1)(s + 2)} \tag{10.203}$$

determine the digital transfer function $H(z)$ with the design based on the step-invariant method.

Solution: The Laplace transform of the output for a unit step input is given by

$$Y_s(s) = H(s) \cdot \frac{1}{s}$$

$$= \frac{1}{s(s+1)(s+2)}. \tag{10.204}$$

This can be written in terms of partial fractions as

$$Y_s(s) = \frac{0.5}{s} - \frac{1}{s+1} + \frac{0.5}{s+2} \tag{10.205}$$

with the output given by

$$y_s(t) = 0.5 - e^{-t} + 0.5e^{-2t}, \qquad t \geq 0. \tag{10.206}$$

The sampled output is

$$y_s(nT) = 0.5 - e^{-nT} + 0.5e^{-2nT}, \qquad t \geq 0 \tag{10.207}$$

and the z-transform of the output is

$$Y_s(z) = \frac{0.5}{1 - z^{-1}} - \frac{1}{1 - e^{-T}z^{-1}} + \frac{0.5}{1 - e^{-2T}z^{-1}}, \qquad |z| > 1. \tag{10.208}$$

Putting Eq. 10.208 over a common denominator gives

$$Y_s(z) = \frac{z^{-1}(0.5 - e^{-T} + 0.5e^{-2T}) + z^{-2}(0.5e^{-T} - e^{-2T} + 0.5e^{-3T})}{(1 - z^{-1})(1 - e^{-T}z^{-1})(1 - e^{-2T}z^{-1})} \tag{10.209}$$

the z-transform of the sampled output $y_s(nT)$. The filter transfer function $H(z)$ is found from

$$H(z) = \frac{Y_s(z)}{X(z)} \tag{10.210}$$

where $X(z)$ is the z-transform of the step input, i.e.,

$$X(z) = \frac{1}{1 - z^{-1}}. \tag{10.211}$$

Thus, dividing Eq. 10.209 by Eq. 10.211 gives the transfer function

$$H(z) = \frac{z^{-1}(0.5 - e^{-T} + 0.5e^{-2T}) + z^{-2}(0.5e^{-T} - e^{-2T} + 0.5e^{-3T})}{(1 - e^{-T}z^{-1})(1 - e^{-2T}z^{-1})}$$

$$= \frac{z(0.5 - e^{-T} + 0.5e^{-2T}) + 0.5e^{-T} - e^{-2T} + 0.5e^{-3T}}{(z - e^{-T})(z - e^{-2T})}$$

$$= \frac{b_0 z + b_1}{z^2 - a_1 z - a_2} \tag{10.212}$$

where

$$b_0 = 0.5 - e^{-T} + 0.5e^{-2T}$$

$$b_1 = 0.5e^{-T} - e^{-2T} + 0.5e^{-3T}$$

$$a_1 = e^{-T} + e^{-2T}$$

$$a_2 = -e^{-3T}. \tag{10.213}$$

Comment: The frequency response magnitudes of the analog filter and the digital filter for two different sampling intervals ($T = 0.1$ and $T = 0.5$) are given in Fig. 10.26.

10.3.3 Bilinear Transformation Design

This widely used method for designing digital filters from an already designed analog filter may be interpreted as a mathematical transformation from the s-domain to the z-domain, or, from a numerical analysis point of view as in Problem 6.30. An appropriate transformation is to replace s in $H(s)$ with $(z - 1)/(z + 1)$ to form $H(z)$. That is,

$$H(z) = H(s)\Big|_{s = \frac{z-1}{z+1}} \cdot \tag{10.214}$$

This transformation

$$s = \frac{z - 1}{z + 1} \tag{10.215}$$

may be written as

$$sz + s - z + 1 = 0 \tag{10.216}$$

where it is seen to be linear in s and linear in z, or bilinear in s and z. Hence, it is known as a *bilinear transformation* (Churchill, 1960). Let's see how certain regions of the s-plane are transformed (mapped) onto the

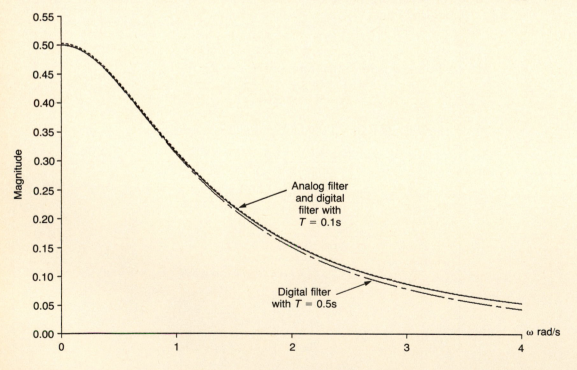

FIGURE 10.26 Digital and analog filter frequency responses: $T = 0.5s$ and $0.1s$

z-plane through this transformation. To do this we need an expression for z in terms of s, so starting with

$$s = \frac{z - 1}{z + 1} \qquad (10.217)$$

we obtain

$$z = \frac{1 + s}{1 - s}. \qquad (10.218)$$

Using the general value of $s = \sigma + j\omega$ gives

$$z = \frac{1 + \sigma + j\omega}{1 - \sigma - j\omega}. \qquad (10.219)$$

Writing z in exponential form, i.e.,

$$z = re^{j\psi} \qquad (10.220)$$

we see by comparing Eq. 10.219 and Eq. 10.220 that

$$r = |z| = \frac{\sqrt{(1 + \sigma)^2 + \omega^2}}{\sqrt{(1 - \sigma)^2 + \omega^2}} \quad \text{and} \quad \psi = \arg(z)$$

$$= \tan^{-1}\left(\frac{\omega}{1 + \sigma}\right) - \tan^{-1}\left(\frac{-\omega}{1 - \sigma}\right)$$

$$= \tan^{-1}\left(\frac{\omega}{1 + \sigma}\right) + \tan^{-1}\left(\frac{\omega}{1 - \sigma}\right). \qquad (10.221)$$

From Eq. 10.221 we can deduce the following:

a) For $\sigma > 0$, $r > 1$—the right-half of the s-plane maps to the exterior of the unit circle of the z-plane.

b) For $\sigma < 0$, $r < 1$—the left-half of the s-plane maps to the interior of the unit circle of the z-plane.

c) For $\sigma = 0$, $r = 1$—the entire imaginary axis of the s-plane maps to the unit circle of the z-plane.

These three regions are indicated in Fig. 10.27 and it is clear that this transformation produces a stable digital filter from a stable analog filter and that a nonlinear relationship exists between the analog frequencies ω and the digital frequencies θ. For $s = j\omega$ (the imaginary axis) and $z = e^{j\theta}$ (the unit circle), the bilinear transformation becomes

$$j\omega = \frac{e^{j\theta} - 1}{e^{j\theta} + 1}$$

$$= \frac{e^{j\theta/2}(e^{j\theta/2} - e^{-j\theta/2})}{e^{j\theta/2}(e^{j\theta/2} + e^{-j\theta/2})}$$

$$= \frac{j \sin(\theta/2)}{\cos(\theta/2)} = j \tan(\theta/2) \qquad (10.222)$$

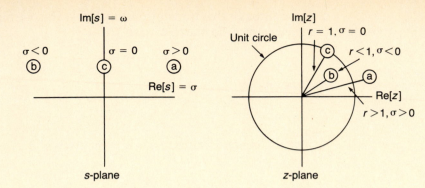

FIGURE 10.27 Effect of bilinear transformation $s = \dfrac{z-1}{z+1} = \dfrac{1-z^{-1}}{1+z^{-1}}$

and thus the imaginary axis in the s-plane is related to the unit circle in the z-plane through the relation

$$\omega = \tan(\theta/2). \tag{10.223}$$

In Fig. 10.27 the analog frequency range $0 \le \omega \le \infty$ of the s-plane corresponds to the digital frequency range $0 \le \theta \le \pi$ of the z-plane. Figure 10.28 portrays the nonlinear relationship of Eq. 10.223.

The bilinear transformation

$$s = \frac{z-1}{z+1} \tag{10.224}$$

and the nonlinear relationship between the analog and digital frequencies

$$\omega = \tan(\theta/2) \tag{10.225}$$

provide the important elements of the bilinear transformation design procedure that follows.

PROCEDURE

1. Given a set of analog specification frequencies ω_i, $i = 1, 2, \ldots, r$ the corresponding digital frequencies $\theta_i = \omega_i T$, $i = 1, 2, \ldots, r$ are determined.

2. Using Eq. 10.225, a new set of analog frequencies is determined as

$$\omega_i' = \tan(\theta_i/2), \qquad i = 1, 2, \ldots, r. \tag{10.226}$$

This step is known as *prewarping*. The purpose is to predistort the analog frequency scale to compensate for the nonlinear relationship between analog and digital frequencies.

3. An analog filter is designed with the transfer function $H(s)$ based upon the specifications at the prewarped frequencies ω_i', $i = 1, 2, \ldots, r$.

4. The digital filter transfer function is determined from

$$H(z) = H(s)\Big|_{s = \frac{z-1}{z+1}}. \tag{10.227}$$

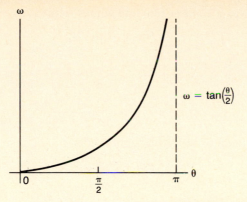

FIGURE 10.28 Nonlinear relationship between ω and θ from the bilinear transformation

$$\omega = \tan\!\left(\tfrac{\theta}{2}\right)$$

Example 10.17. This example illustrates the design of a lowpass digital filter using the bilinear transformation procedure.

Design a digital filter for a 20-kHz sampling rate that is maximally flat in the passband of 0 to the -3 dB cutoff frequency of 2,000 Hz and has attenuation of at least 10 dB for frequencies greater than 4,000 Hz.

Solution:

1. Because of the flatness in the passband a Butterworth design is called for and the specification frequencies of the digital filter are

$$\theta_1 = \omega_1 T = 2\pi(2000)/20{,}000 = 0.2\pi \tag{10.228}$$

and

$$\theta_2 = \omega_2 T = 2\pi(4000)/20{,}000 = 0.4\pi. \tag{10.229}$$

2. The prewarped analog frequencies become

$$\omega_1' = \tan(\theta_1/2) = \tan(0.1\pi) = 0.325 \tag{10.230}$$

$$\omega_2' = \tan(\theta_2/2) = \tan(0.2\pi) = 0.726. \tag{10.231}$$

3. To find the lowpass prototype filter the prewarped analog frequencies need to be translated to those for the prototype

$$\omega_1' = 0.325 \longrightarrow \omega = 1 \tag{10.232}$$

$$\omega_2' = 0.726 \longrightarrow \omega_a = \frac{0.726}{0.325} = 2.234. \tag{10.233}$$

Using Eq. 10.148 to find the filter order gives

$$N = \frac{\log_{10}(10^{-M_{\mathrm{dB}}/10} - 1)}{2 \log_{10} \omega_a}$$

$$= \frac{\log_{10}(10^1 - 1)}{2 \log_{10} 2.234}$$

$$= 1.37 \quad \text{or} \quad N = 2. \tag{10.234}$$

The lowpass transfer function comes from

$$H_{LP}(s) = H_{LP_p}(s)\Big|_{s = \frac{s}{0.325}}$$

$$= \frac{1}{s^2 + \sqrt{2}s + 1}\Big|_{s = \frac{s}{0.325}}$$

$$= \frac{0.106}{s^2 + 0.460s + 0.106}.$$

$$(10.235)$$

4. The digital filter transfer function is

$$H_{LP}(z) = H_{LP}(s)\Big|_{s = \frac{z-1}{z+1}}$$

$$= \frac{0.068(z + 1)^2}{z^2 - 1.142z + 0.413}$$

$$(10.236)$$

and the difference equation that describes this filter is

$$y(n) = 1.142y(n - 1) - 0.413y(n - 2) + 0.068x(n)$$

$$(10.237)$$

$$+ 0.136x(n - 1) + 0.068x(n - 2).$$

Example 10.18. This example illustrates the design of a bandpass digital filter using the bilinear transformation method.

A Chebyshev digital bandpass filter is to be designed to meet the following specifications:

a) 1-dB ripple in the range of 600 to 900 Hz
b) Sampling frequency f_s of 3000 Hz
c) Maximum gain of -40 dB for $0 \le f \le 200$ Hz

Use the bilinear transformation method to find the transfer function $H(z)$ for the digital filter.

Solution:

1. Using $\theta = 2\pi f / f_s$ the specification frequencies of the desired digital filter are

$$\text{lower ripple band frequency } \theta_\ell = \frac{2\pi(600)}{3000} = 0.4\pi = 1.26 \text{ rad.}$$

$$\text{upper ripple band frequency } \theta_u = \frac{2\pi(900)}{3000} = 0.6\pi = 1.88 \text{ rad.}$$

$$\text{ripple band center frequency } \theta_0 = \sqrt{\theta_\ell \theta_u} = 0.49\pi = 1.54 \text{ rad.}$$

$$\text{stopband frequency } \theta_{st} = \frac{2\pi(200)}{3000} = 0.133\pi = 0.418 \text{ rad.}$$

$$(10.238)$$

2. Using $\omega_i' = \tan(\theta_i/2)$ the prewarped analog frequencies in rad/s are

$$\text{lower ripple band frequency } \omega_\ell' = \tan(1.26/2) = 0.729 \text{ rad/s}$$

$$\text{upper ripple band frequency } \omega_u' = \tan(1.88/2) = 1.369 \text{ rad/s}$$

$$\text{ripple band center frequency } \omega_0' = \sqrt{\omega_\ell' \omega_u'} = 1.00 \text{ rad/s}$$

$$\text{stopband frequency } \omega_{st}' = \tan(0.418/2) = 0.212 \text{ rad/s}$$

and the prewarped passband is

$$B = \omega_u' - \omega_\ell' = 1.369 - 0.729 = 0.640 \text{ rad/s.} \tag{10.239}$$

3. Next we need to convert these prewarped analog frequencies to those of an equivalent lowpass prototype. From Table 10.5 we have

$$\omega_{\text{LP}_p} = \frac{\omega_{\text{BP}}^2 - \omega_0^2}{B\omega_{\text{BP}}}$$

$$= \frac{\omega_{\text{BP}}^2 - 1}{0.64\omega_{\text{BP}}} \tag{10.240}$$

and from the prewarped bandpass frequencies we obtain the following lowpass prototype frequencies.

ω_{BP}'	ω_{LP_p}
0.729	−1
1.369	1
1.000	0
0.212	−7.04

$$\tag{10.241}$$

Looking back at the prototype to bandpass mapping of Fig. 10.18 we recall that the bandpass frequencies less than ω_0 are mapped from negative frequencies in the prototype. But the prototype frequency response is symmetrical about $\omega = 0$, so we use $\omega = +7.04$ rather than $\omega = -7.04$ in our design computations.

The desired gain of -40 dB translates to $M = 10^{-2}$ for $|H(j\omega)|$ or 10^{-4} for $|H(j\omega)|^2$ and consequently the magnitude squared function to be satisfied is

$$|H(j\omega)|^2 = \frac{1}{1 + \epsilon^2 C_N^2(\omega)}\bigg|_{\omega=7.04} < 10^{-4} \tag{10.242}$$

where $\epsilon^2 = 0.2589$ for a 1-dB ripple.

Guessing that a first-order filter $(N = 1)$ is insufficient to satisfy this requirement we start with $N = 2$ and find that

$$|H_2(j\omega)|^2 = \frac{1}{1 + 0.2589(2\omega^2 - 1)^2}\bigg|_{\omega=7.04}$$

$$= \frac{1}{1 + 0.2589(99.12 - 1)^2} = 4.01 \times 10^{-4} \tag{10.243}$$

which is slightly greater than 10^{-4} so it seems apparent that $N = 3$ will be adequate. For $N = 3$

$$|H_3(j\omega)|^2 = \frac{1}{1 + 0.2589(4\omega^3 - 3\omega)^2}\Bigg|_{\omega = 7.04}$$

$$= \frac{1}{1 + 0.2589(1395.65 - 21.12)^2} = 2.044 \times 10^{-6} \ (10.244)$$

which meets the requirement. From Table 10.3 (1-dB ripple and $N = 3$) the lowpass prototype transfer function is

$$H_{\mathrm{LP}_p}(s) = \frac{0.491}{s^3 + 0.988s^2 + 1.238s + 0.491} \tag{10.245}$$

where the numerator has been chosen as 0.491 to make $|H(j0)| = 1$.

Using Table 10.5 once again to determine the bandpass analog filter to be digitized gives us

$$H_{\mathrm{BP}}(s) = H_{\mathrm{LP}_p}(s)\Bigg|_{s = \frac{s^2 + \omega_0^2}{Bs}}$$

$$= \frac{0.491}{\left(\dfrac{s^2 + 1}{0.64s}\right)^3 + 0.988\left(\dfrac{s^2 + 1}{0.64s}\right)^2 + 1.238\left(\dfrac{s^2 + 1}{0.64s}\right) + 0.491}$$

$$= \frac{0.129s^3}{s^6 + 0.632s^5 + 3.507s^4 + 1.394s^3 + 3.507s^2 + 0.632s + 1}. \tag{10.246}$$

The magnitude of the frequency response of this bandpass filter $|H_{\mathrm{BP}}(j\omega)|$ is given in Fig. 10.29 where we see the 1-dB ripple ($M = 0.891$) between $0.729 \le \omega \le 1.369$ and that $|H(j0.212)| < 10^{-2}$.

4. Finally, the transfer function of the digital filter is

$$H_{\mathrm{BP}}(z) = H_{\mathrm{BP}}(s)\Big|_{s = \frac{z-1}{z+1}}$$

$$= \frac{0.129\left(\dfrac{z-1}{z+1}\right)^3}{\left(\dfrac{z-1}{z+1}\right)^6 + 0.632\left(\dfrac{z-1}{z+1}\right)^5 + 3.507\left(\dfrac{z-1}{z+1}\right)^4 + 1.394\left(\dfrac{z-1}{z+1}\right)^3 + 3.507\left(\dfrac{z-1}{z+1}\right)^2 + 0.632\left(\dfrac{z-1}{z+1}\right) + 1}$$

$$= \frac{0.129(z + 1)^3(z - 1)^3}{11.672z^6 + 25.124z^4 + 20.848z^2 + 6.356}$$

$$= \frac{0.011(z^6 - 3z^4 + 3z^2 - 1)}{z^6 + 2.153z^4 + 1.786z^2 + 0.545}. \tag{10.247}$$

The magnitude portion of the frequency response $H(e^{j\theta})$ is given in Fig. 10.30 where we notice the 1-dB ripple ($M = 0.891$) between $\theta_\ell = 1.26$ rad and $\theta_u = 1.88$ rad and that the gain is less than -40 dB ($M = 0.01$) for $\theta \le 0.418$ rad.

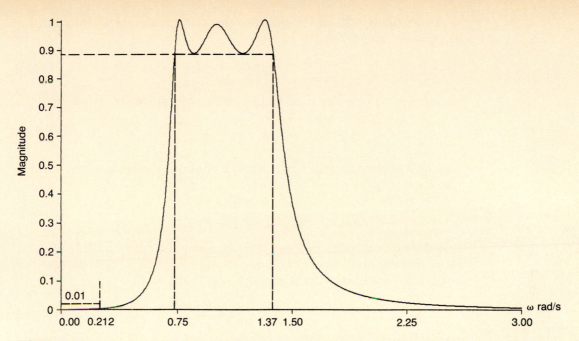

FIGURE 10.29 Frequency response for bandpass analog filter of Example 10.18

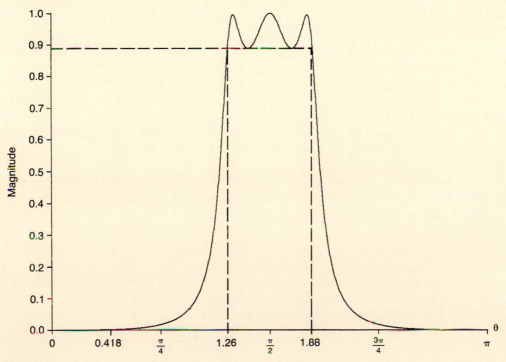

FIGURE 10.30 Frequency response for bandpass digital filter of Example 10.18

In Problem 6.30 of Chapter Six the s-domain transfer function for integration, namely

$$H(s) = \frac{1}{s} \qquad (10.248)$$

was shown to be equivalent to the z-domain transfer function of

$$H(z) = \frac{T}{2} \frac{z+1}{z-1}. \qquad (10.249)$$

The equivalence of these two transfer functions produces the bilinear transformation of

$$s = \frac{2}{T} \frac{z-1}{z+1} \qquad (10.250)$$

that differs from what we have been using by the constant $2/T$. We now show that the constant $2/T$ is unnecessary. Using Eq. 10.250 with $s = j\omega$ and $z = e^{j\theta}$ we obtain the imaginary axis mapping of

$$\omega = \frac{2}{T} \tan\left(\frac{\theta}{2}\right) \qquad (10.251)$$

rather than

$$\omega = \tan\left(\frac{\theta}{2}\right). \qquad (10.252)$$

Now suppose that we have an arbitrary digital frequency of θ_a that requires prewarping of the corresponding analog frequency

$$\omega_a' = \frac{2}{T} \tan\left(\frac{\theta_a}{2}\right). \qquad (10.253)$$

The analog filter is designed from these prewarped analog frequencies to obtain the lowpass prototype transfer function $H_{LP_p}(s)$.

Prototype to lowpass: $H_{LP_p}(s)$ to $H_{LP}(z)$. For this case we replace s in the lowpass prototype design by s/ω_c' where ω_c' is the prewarped critical frequency given by (see Eq. 10.253)

$$\omega_c' = \frac{2}{T} \tan(\theta_c/2). \qquad (10.254)$$

The analog-to-digital conversion accomplished by the bilinear transformation of Eq. 10.250 involves replacing s by $(2/T)(z-1)/(z+1)$. Putting these substitutions together gives

$$s \longrightarrow \frac{s}{\omega_c'} \longrightarrow \frac{\dfrac{\cancel{2}}{\cancel{T}} \dfrac{z-1}{z+1}}{\dfrac{\cancel{2}}{\cancel{T}} \tan(\theta_c/2)} \qquad (10.255)$$

and we see that the sampling interval T is lost in the transformation. Using the substitution of Eq. 10.255 in the analog lowpass prototype $H_{LP_p}(s)$ allows us to go directly to the lowpass digital filter $H_{LP}(z)$. Thus, we avoid the extra step of finding the lowpass analog transfer function $H_{LP}(s)$.

Example 10.19. This example illustrates an alternative bilinear transformation design procedure.

In Example 10.17 we digitized a lowpass analog filter $H_{LP}(s)$ by means of the bilinear transformation $s = (z - 1)/(z + 1)$. We now use the substitution derived above on the lowpass prototype $H_{LP_p}(s)$ to find $H_{LP}(z)$.

Solution: Looking back at Example 10.17 we find that a second-order filter was required. Thus, the digital filter is described by

$$H_{LP}(z) = H_{LP_p}(s)\Big|_{s = \frac{1}{\tan\left(\frac{\theta_c}{2}\right)}\frac{z-1}{z+1}}$$

$$= \frac{1}{s^2 + \sqrt{2}s + 1}\Big|_{s = \frac{1}{0.325}\frac{z-1}{z+1}}$$

$$= \frac{0.067(z + 1)^2}{z^2 - 1.143z + 0.413} \tag{10.256}$$

as before (to calculator accuracy).

This gives us an alternative procedure for finding the digital lowpass transfer function $H_{LP}(z)$ directly from the analog lowpass prototype $H_{LP_p}(s)$. We would expect that highpass, bandpass, and bandstep digital filters could be determined in a similar way. Problem 10.49 addresses the derivations of the required substitutions and Table 10.6 summarizes the results for all four cases.

10.3.4 Digital Frequency Transformations

In Table 10.5 we presented frequency transformations that allowed a lowpass prototype analog filter to be transformed into a "denormalized" lowpass, highpass, bandpass, or bandstop analog filter. These transformations formed the basis for the design procedure of turning all specifications into those for an analog lowpass prototype, designing the lowpass filter, and then using the frequency transformations of Table 10.5 to determine the transfer function of the analog filter being designed. The digital filter transfer function can then be obtained by using one of the analog-to-digital transformations discussed previously. An alternative approach to be explored here is to use one of the analog-to-digital transformations to convert the lowpass analog prototype into a lowpass digital prototype and

TABLE 10.6 ALTERNATIVE BILINEAR TRANSFORMATION DESIGN PROCEDURE

Given the lowpass prototype $H_{\mathrm{LP}_p}(s)$, find the appropriate $H(z)$ by making the substitution indicated.

Lowpass: $H_{\mathrm{LP}}(z) = H_{\mathrm{LP}_p}(s)\Big|_{s = \frac{1}{\tan(\theta_c/2)}\frac{z-1}{z+1}}$

Highpass: $H_{\mathrm{HP}}(z) = H_{\mathrm{LP}_p}(s)\Big|_{s = \tan(\theta_c/2)\frac{z+1}{z-1}}$

Bandpass: $H_{\mathrm{BP}}(z) = H_{\mathrm{LP}_p}(s)\Big|_{s = \dfrac{\left(\frac{z-1}{z+1}\right)^2 + \tan^2(\theta_0/2)}{\left(\frac{z-1}{z+1}\right)[\tan(\theta_v/2) - \tan(\theta_\ell/2)]}}$

Bandstop: $H_{\mathrm{BS}}(z) = H_{\mathrm{LP}_p}(s)\Big|_{s = \dfrac{\left(\frac{z-1}{z+1}\right)[\tan(\theta_v/2) - \tan(\theta_\ell/2)]}{\left(\frac{z-1}{z+1}\right)^2 + \tan^2(\theta_0/2)}}$

then use an appropriate digital frequency transformation to obtain a digital lowpass, highpass, bandpass, or bandstop filter as desired. These digital frequency transformations are the subject of this section (Constantinides, 1970).

Assume that we have the transfer function $H_{\mathrm{LP}_p}(z)$ of a lowpass digital filter, which will be called the LP digital prototype, that has been designed according to some previously determined procedure. The transformation or mapping that makes $H_{\mathrm{LP}_p}(z)$ into an LP, HP, BP, or BS filter must preserve stability, that is, with the poles of $H_{\mathrm{LP}_p}(z)$ located inside the unit circle, the poles of the denormalized filter must also lie inside the unit circle.

As a consequence, it is desired that the value of $H_{\mathrm{LP}_p}(e^{j\theta})$ for $\theta = \theta_a$ (a particular value of θ) be the same as $H_T(e^{j\theta})$ for $\theta = \theta_a'$, where the subscript T is used to denote filter type. In a particular situation T will be LP, HP, BP, or BS as appropriate.

Lowpass prototype-lowpass transformation. With this transformation the magnitude characteristic must be unaltered except for compressing or expanding the frequency scale as is shown in Fig. 10.31. These plots show that the magnitude characteristics at $\theta = 0$ and $\theta = \pi$ are the same and a defined frequency of interest θ_a (for instance the cutoff frequency) has been compressed to θ_a'. The appropriate transformation is to replace z in $H_{\mathrm{LP}_p}(z)$ with

$$z = \frac{z - \alpha}{1 - \alpha z} \tag{10.257}$$

where α is a real constant. Making this substitution in $H_{\mathrm{LP}_p}(z)$ yields the

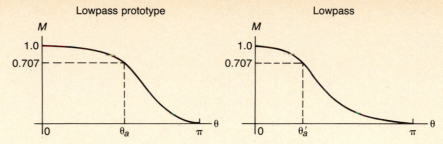

FIGURE 10.31 Lowpass prototype-lowpass transformation

Lowpass prototype

Lowpass

"nonprototype" transfer function $H_{\mathrm{LP}}(z)$. Notice that

$$\frac{z-\alpha}{1-\alpha z}\bigg|_{z=1+j0} = \frac{1-\alpha}{1-\alpha} = 1 + j0 \tag{10.258}$$

and

$$\frac{z-\alpha}{1-\alpha z}\bigg|_{z=-1+j0} = \frac{-1-\alpha}{1+\alpha} = -1 + j0. \tag{10.259}$$

Thus, the values of $H_{\mathrm{LP}_p}(z)$ and $H_{\mathrm{LP}}(z)$ are equal to one another at $z = 1 + j0$ and at $z = -1 + j0$. For $H_{\mathrm{LP}_p}(z)$, the critical frequency is $z = e^{j\theta_c}$ and for $H_{\mathrm{LP}}(z)$ it is $z = e^{j\theta_c'}$. For θ_c to map to θ_c' we have from Eq. 10.257

$$e^{j\theta_c} = \frac{e^{j\theta_c'} - \alpha}{1 - \alpha e^{j\theta_c'}} \tag{10.260}$$

which when solved for α gives the design constant

$$\alpha = \frac{\sin(\theta_c/2 - \theta_c'/2)}{\sin(\theta_c/2 + \theta_c'/2)}. \tag{10.261}$$

Example 10.20. This example illustrates the LP prototype to LP transformation.

A lowpass prototype digital filter is described by the transfer function

$$H_{\mathrm{LP}_p}(z) = \frac{0.5(z + 1)}{z} \tag{10.262}$$

and has the corresponding frequency response

$$H_{\mathrm{LP}_p}(e^{j\theta}) = 0.5\frac{e^{j\theta} + 1}{e^{j\theta}}. \tag{10.263}$$

The frequency response magnitude is plotted in Fig. 10.32 (a) for $0 \le \theta \le \pi$. The cutoff frequency is $\theta_c = \pi/2$ where the gain is $M = 0.707$. Design a lowpass digital filter from this prototype so that the cutoff frequency is $\theta_c' = 2\pi/3$ where the gain is also $M = 0.707$.

Solution: Using Eq. 10.261 we have

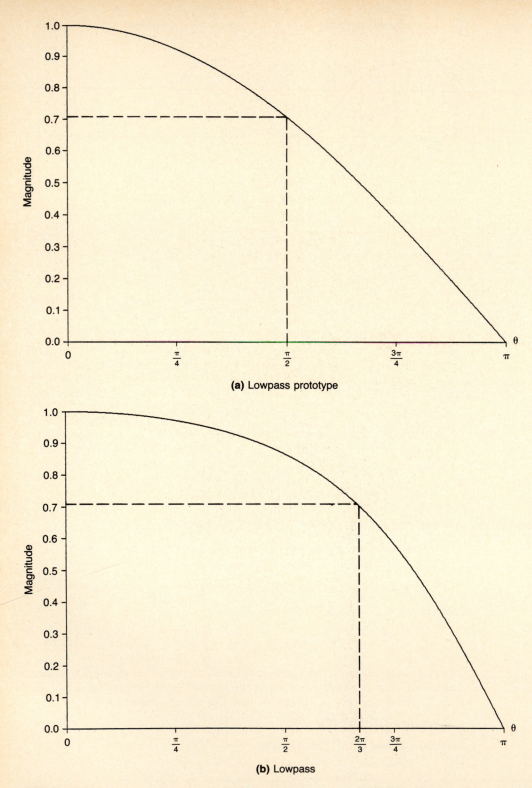

(a) Lowpass prototype

(b) Lowpass

FIGURE 10.32 Frequency response for Example 10.20

$$\alpha = \frac{\sin(\pi/4 - \pi/3)}{\sin(\pi/4 + \pi/3)} = -0.268 \qquad (10.264)$$

and from Eq. 10.257 the transfer function of the new LP filter is

$$H_{\text{LP}}(z) = H_{\text{LP}_p}\Big|_{z = \frac{z-\alpha}{1-\alpha z}}$$

$$= 0.5 \frac{z+1}{z}\Big|_{z = \frac{z+0.268}{1+0.268z}}$$

$$= 0.634 \frac{z+1}{z+0.268}. \qquad (10.265)$$

Comment: The magnitude portion of the frequency response for this LP filter is plotted in Fig. 10.32(b) where we see that the gain $M = 0.707$ at $\theta_c' = 2\pi/3$ is the same as the gain at $\theta_c = \pi/2$ in the prototype. Notice that there is a zero at $z = -1$ for both filters which is a desirable characteristic for a lowpass filter.

The transformations for all four possible situations are summarized in Table 10.7. As was the case for analog filters, the transformations to bandpass and bandstop are biquadratic rather than bilinear because of the two passbands or stopbands (lower and upper) that need to be generated for these filters. See Constantinides (1970) if you are interested in the derivations of the transformations other than digital lowpass prototype to digital lowpass.

10.3.5 Direct Design of Digital Lowpass, Highpass, Bandpass, and Bandstop Filters

Lowpass prototype analog Butterworth filters were discussed in Section 10.2.1 where an Nth-order filter is characterized by the transfer function

$$H_{\text{LP}_p}(s) = \frac{1}{1 + a_1 s + a_2 s^2 + \cdots + s^N} \qquad (10.266)$$

and the a's in Eq. 10.266 are found in Table 10.1. If the bilinear transformation is applied to Eq. 10.266 for different values of the filter order N we obtain a set of lowpass prototype transfer functions for digital Butterworth filters. That is,

$$H_{\text{LP}_p}(z) = H_{\text{LP}_p}(s)\Big|_{s = \frac{z-1}{z+1}} \qquad (10.267)$$

and the design of lowpass, highpass, bandpass, and bandstop Butterworth digital filters can be achieved by a procedure similar to that which was used for analog filters—a lowpass digital prototype is designed to meet the translated specifications, and the transfer function for the LP, HP, BP, or BS is found by using the appropriate transformation in Table 10.7 of

TABLE 10.7 DIGITAL FILTER FREQUENCY TRANSFORMATIONS

Type	Transformation Replace z in LP digital prototype with the expression listed below	Design Constants
1. Lowpass	$\dfrac{z - \alpha}{1 - \alpha z}$	$\alpha = \dfrac{\sin(\theta_c/2 - \theta_c'/2)}{\sin(\theta_c/2 + \theta_c'/2)}$
2. Highpass	$-\dfrac{z - \alpha}{1 - \alpha z}$	$\alpha = \dfrac{\cos(\theta_c/2 - \theta_c'/2)}{\cos(\theta_c/2 + \theta_c'/2)}$
3. Bandpass	$-\dfrac{z^2 - \dfrac{2\alpha k}{k + 1}z + \dfrac{k - 1}{k + 1}}{1 - \dfrac{2\alpha k}{k + 1}z + \dfrac{k - 1}{k + 1}z^2}$	$\alpha = \dfrac{\cos(\theta_u'/2 + \theta_\ell'/2)}{\cos(\theta_u'/2 - \theta_\ell'/2)}$ $k = \tan\dfrac{\theta_c}{2}\cot(\theta_u'/2 - \theta_\ell'/2)$
4. Bandstop	$\dfrac{z^2 - \dfrac{2\alpha}{1 + k}z + \dfrac{1 - k}{1 + k}}{1 - \dfrac{2\alpha}{1 + k}z + \dfrac{1 - k}{1 + k}z^2}$	$\alpha = \dfrac{\cos(\theta_u'/2 + \theta_\ell'/2)}{\cos(\theta_u'/2 - \theta_\ell'/2)}$ $k = \tan\dfrac{\theta_c}{2}\tan(\theta_u'/2 - \theta_\ell'/2)$

Source: A. G. Constantinides, "Spectral Transformations for Digital Filters," Proc. *IEEE* 117, pp. 1585–1590, August 1970.

Section 10.3.4. Given in Table 10.8 on page 691 are the digital lowpass prototype Butterworth transfer functions for $1 \leq N \leq 5$. A plot of the magnitude of the frequency response for each of these filters is given in Fig. 10.33(a) with a dB plot shown in Fig. 10.33(b) for $0 \leq \theta \leq \pi/2$ and for $\pi/2 \leq \theta \leq \pi$ in Fig. 10.33(c). From Fig. 10.33 and Table 10.8 we notice the following.

a) $|H(e^{j0})| = 1$. This is because $z = 1 + j0$ corresponds to $s = 0$ (see Eq. 10.267) and from Eq. 10.266

$$H_{\mathrm{LP}_p}(s)\Big|_{s=0} = 1. \tag{10.268}$$

b) $|H(e^{j\pi/2})| = 0.707$ and $|H(e^{j\pi/2})|_{\mathrm{dB}} = -3$. The fact that the cutoff frequency is now $\theta_c = \pi/2$ for the digital lowpass prototype is seen from the nonlinear analog-to-digital relationship

$$\omega = \tan(\theta/2) \tag{10.269}$$

TABLE 10.8 BUTTERWORTH DIGITAL LOWPASS PROTOTYPE FILTERS

N	$H_{LP_P}(z)$	zeros	poles
1	$\dfrac{0.5(z+1)}{z}$	$z = -1$	$z = 0$
2	$\dfrac{0.293(z+1)^2}{z^2 + 0.173}$	$z_{1,2} = -1$	$z_{1,2} = 0.414e^{\pm j\pi/2}$
3	$\dfrac{0.167(z+1)^3}{z(z^2 + 0.333)}$	$z_{1-3} = -1$	$z_1 = 0$ $z_{2,3} = 0.577e^{\pm j\pi/2}$
4	$\dfrac{0.094(z+1)^4}{z^4 + 0.486z^2 + 0.018}$	$z_{1-4} = -1$	$z_{1,2} = 0.201e^{\pm j\pi/2}$ $z_{3,4} = 0.667e^{\pm j\pi/2}$
5	$\dfrac{0.0528(z+1)^5}{z(z^4 + 0.633z^2 + 0.056)}$	$z_{1-5} = -1$	$z_1 = 0$ $z_{2,3} = 0.314e^{\pm j\pi/2}$ $z_{4,5} = 0.731e^{\pm j\pi/2}$

FIGURE 10.33 Butterworth digital prototype frequency responses

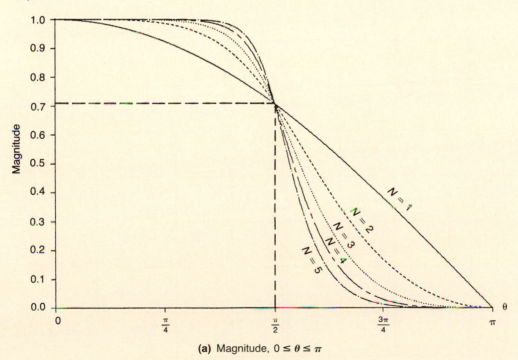

(a) Magnitude, $0 \le \theta \le \pi$

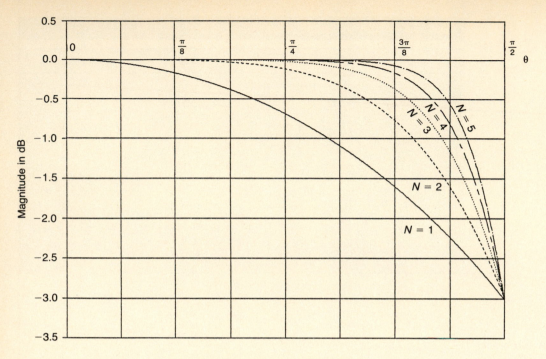

(b) Magnitude in dB, $0 \leq \theta \leq \pi/2$

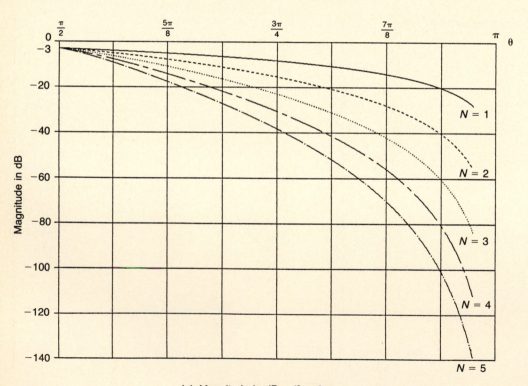

(c) Magnitude in dB, $\pi/2 \leq \theta \leq \pi$

FIGURE 10.33   cont.

which is satisfied for the analog cutoff frequency $\omega = 1$ and the corresponding digital cutoff frequency of $\theta_c = \pi/2$.

c) We know that all of the analog poles are on the unit circle and they are transformed to digital poles on the imaginary axis. This is verified from

$$z = \frac{1 + s}{1 - s} \qquad (10.270)$$

which for $s = 1e^{j\psi}$ (the unit circle in the s-plane) becomes

$$z = \frac{1 + 1e^{j\psi}}{1 - 1e^{j\psi}}$$

$$= \frac{e^{j\psi/2}(e^{-j\psi/2} + e^{+j\psi/2})}{e^{j\psi/2}(e^{-j\psi/2} - e^{j\psi/2})}$$

$$= \frac{2\cos(\psi/2)}{-2j\sin(\psi/2)}$$

$$= j\cot(\psi/2) = \frac{j}{\tan(\psi/2)}. \qquad (10.271)$$

For example, the second-order Butterworth analog poles $s_{1,2} = 1e^{\pm j3\pi/4}$ become the digital poles

$$z_{1,2} = j\cot(\pm 3\pi/8)$$

$$= \pm j0.414 \qquad (10.272)$$

which agrees with the second entry of Table 10.8. We observe that the left-half plane part of the unit circle in the s-plane where $\pi/2 < \psi < 3\pi/2$ maps into the portion of the imaginary axis in the z-plane where $-1 < \text{Im}[z] < 1$. Thus, the resulting digital Butterworth filter is guaranteed to be stable.

d) There are N zeros at $z = -1$ which aids the high frequency attenuation of the lowpass prototype filter.

Turning our attention to lowpass prototype analog Chebyshev filters we recall that the denominator polynomials for three values of the ripple parameter (ϵ) and for filters of five different orders (N) are given in Table 10.3. The analog transfer functions are of the form

$$H_{\text{LP}_p}(s) = \frac{k}{a_0 + a_1 s + \cdots + s^N} \qquad (10.273)$$

where the numerator constant k is often set to satisfy a $|H_{\text{LP}_p}(j0)|$ criterion. Applying the bilinear transformation to these transfer functions yields the lowpass prototype Chebyshev filters described in Table 10.9. The constant k in Eq. 10.273 has been set to give $|H_{\text{LP}_p}(j0)| = 1$ for N odd and $|H_{\text{LP}_p}(j0)| = 1/\sqrt{1 + \epsilon^2}$ for N even. The magnitudes of the frequency

TABLE 10.9 CHEBYSHEV DIGITAL LOWPASS PROTOTYPE FILTERS

$$H_{\text{LP}_p}(z)\Big|_{z=1} = 1 \text{ for } N \text{ odd and } H_{\text{LP}_p}(z)\Big|_{z=1} = \frac{1}{\sqrt{1 + \epsilon^2}} \text{ for } N \text{ even}$$

0.5-dB ripple ($\epsilon = 0.3493$)

N	$H_{\text{LP}_p}(z)$
1	$\dfrac{2.863(z + 1)}{3.863z + 1.863}$
2	$\dfrac{1.430(z + 1)^2}{3.941z^2 + 1.032z + 1.091}$
3	$\dfrac{0.716(z + 1)^3}{4.504z^3 - 0.570z^2 + 2.360z - 0.566}$
4	$\dfrac{0.358(z + 1)^4}{5.318z^4 - 2.828z^3 + 4.840z^2 - 2.140z + 0.874}$
5	$\dfrac{0.179(z + 1)^5}{6.351z^5 - 5.993z^4 + 9.145z^3 - 6.115z^2 + 3.367z - 1.029}$

1-dB ripple ($\epsilon = 0.5088$)

N	$H_{\text{LP}_p}(z)$
1	$\dfrac{1.965(z + 1)}{2.965z + 0.965}$
2	$\dfrac{0.983(z + 1)^2}{3.201z^2 + 0.206z + 1.005}$
3	$\dfrac{0.491(z + 1)^3}{3.717z^3 - 1.277z^2 + 2.247z - 0.759}$
4	$\dfrac{0.246(z + 1)^4}{4.426z^4 - 3.316z^3 + 4.748z^2 - 2.476z + 1.034}$
5	$\dfrac{0.123(z + 1)^5}{5.303z^5 - 6.169z^4 + 8.936z^3 - 6.631z^2 + 3.725z - 1.235}$

2-dB ripple ($\epsilon = 0.7648$)

1	$\dfrac{1.308(z + 1)}{2.308z + 0.308}$
2	$\dfrac{0.654(z + 1)^2}{2.627z^2 - 0.354z + 1.019}$
3	$\dfrac{0.327(z + 1)^3}{3.087z^3 - 1.735z^2 + 2.221z - 0.957}$
4	$\dfrac{0.164(z + 1)^4}{3.695z^4 - 3.574z^3 + 4.724z^2 - 2.778z + 1.229}$
5	$\dfrac{0.082(z + 1)^5}{4.441z^5 - 6.139z^4 + 8.763z^3 - 7.077z^2 + 4.104z - 1.477}$

responses for these 15 filters (3 values of ϵ and $1 \leq N \leq 5$) are shown in Fig. 10.34(a) and decibel versions are given in Fig. 10.34(b). Notice that all parts of Fig. 10.34 have been plotted only for frequencies greater than the critical frequency—the ripple passband edge of $\theta_c = \pi/2$ rad.

It is possible, of course, to also construct tables of transfer functions for elliptic lowpass prototype digital filters, however, we will not pursue this here.

Given the frequency response plots of Figs. 10.33 and 10.34 together with the listing of the corresponding transfer functions in Tables 10.8 and 10.9, digital filters can be designed directly in the z-domain by the following procedure:

DIRECT DIGITAL FILTER DESIGN PROCEDURE

1. From the filter specifications, either a Butterworth or a Chebyshev design is decided upon.

2. The digital specification frequencies are determined from $\theta_i' = \omega_i T$. These must include the critical frequencies—the cutoff frequency for Butterworth design and ripple-edge for Chebyshev design.

3. The design constants α and k are determined using the appropriate relations from Table 10.7. We use θ_i' (primed) to denote a frequency of the filter being designed and θ_i (unprimed) for the corresponding frequency in the lowpass prototype. Use $\theta_c = \pi/2$ in Table 10.7 because it is the Butterworth prototype cutoff frequency as well as the ripple-edge frequency in the Chebyshev prototype.

4. Translate the specification frequencies θ_i' to those in the prototype θ_i. This is accomplished by replacing z by $e^{j\theta_i}$ in the prototype and z by $e^{j\theta_i'}$ for the filter being designed and solving for θ_i. To do this we use the appropriate transformation relationship in Table 10.7. For a highpass design, for instance, we have

$$e^{j\theta_i} = -\frac{e^{j\theta_i'} - \alpha}{1 - \alpha e^{j\theta_i'}}. \tag{10.274}$$

Armed with the values of θ_i for the prototype, the filter order is determined from the curves of Fig. 10.33 or Fig. 10.34 and the lowpass prototype transfer function $H_{\text{LP}_p}(z)$ is found from Table 10.8 or Table 10.9. The filter transfer function then is derived by using the proper transformation of Table 10.7. For a highpass design, for instance,

$$H_{\text{HP}}(z) = H_{\text{LP}_p}(z)\Big|_{z = -\frac{z-\alpha}{1-\alpha z}}. \tag{10.275}$$

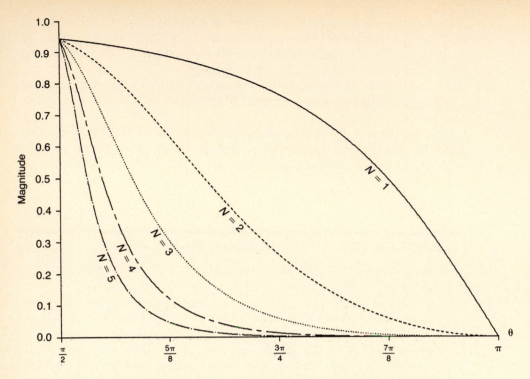

(a) Chebyshev digital prototype frequency responses (0.5-dB ripple)

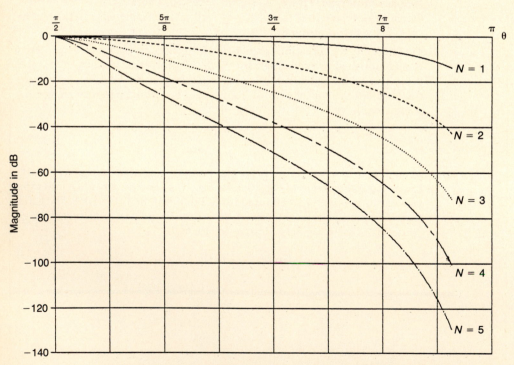

(b) Chebyshev digital prototype frequency responses (0.5-dB ripple)

FIGURE 10.34

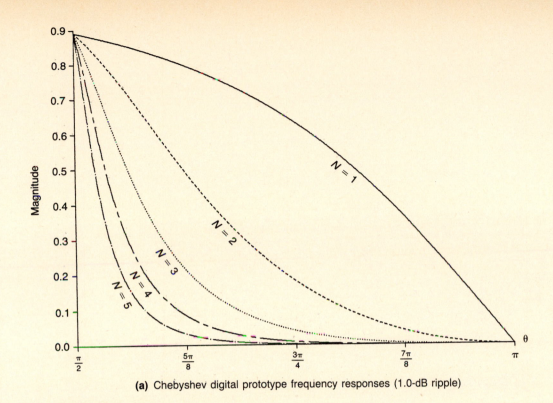

(a) Chebyshev digital prototype frequency responses (1.0-dB ripple)

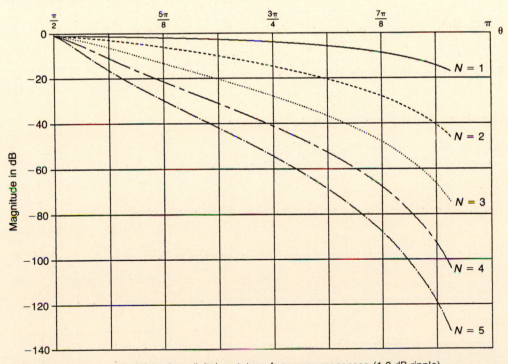

(b) Chebyshev digital prototype frequency responses (1.0-dB ripple)

FIGURE 10.34

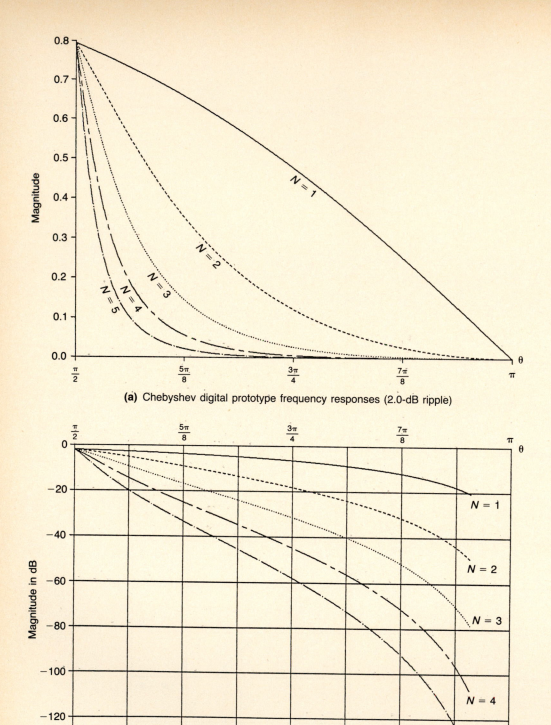

(a) Chebyshev digital prototype frequency responses (2.0-dB ripple)

(b) Chebyshev digital prototype frequency responses (2.0-dB ripple)

FIGURE 10.34

Example 10.21 This example illustrates the direct design of a digital lowpass filter.

Design a lowpass digital filter for a 20-kHz sampling rate that is maximally flat in the passband of 0 to the −3 dB cutoff frequency of 2 kHz and must have a gain of at most −10 dB for frequencies greater than 4 kHz.

Solution:

1. Butterworth design is called for because of the maximally flat passband.
2. The specification frequencies are the cutoff frequency (the critical frequency)

$$\theta_c' = \omega_c T = \frac{\omega_c}{f_s} = \frac{2\pi(2000)}{20,000} = 0.2\pi \qquad (10.276)$$

and the stopband frequency

$$\theta_{st}' = \omega_{st} T = \frac{\omega_{st}}{f_s} = \frac{2\pi(4000)}{20,000} = 0.4\pi. \qquad (10.277)$$

3. For a lowpass filter the only design constant needed is α, computed from

$$\alpha = \frac{\sin(\theta_c/2 - \theta_c'/2)}{\sin(\theta_c/2 + \theta_c'/2)} \qquad (10.278)$$

where θ_c represents the prototype critical frequency and θ_c' the corresponding critical frequency in the lowpass filter. For the Butterworth lowpass digital prototype the critical frequency is the −3 dB cutoff frequency, so we use $\theta_c = \pi/2$. This corresponds to the frequency $\theta_c' = 0.2\pi$ for the lowpass filter being designed. Thus, from Eq. 10.278

$$\alpha = \frac{\sin(0.5\pi/2 - 0.2\pi/2)}{\sin(0.5\pi/2 + 0.2\pi/2)}$$

$$= \frac{\sin(0.25\pi - 0.1\pi)}{\sin(0.25\pi + 0.1\pi)} = \frac{\sin(0.15\pi)}{\sin(0.35\pi)} = \frac{0.454}{0.891} = 0.510. \qquad (10.279)$$

4. To find the filter order N we translate the lowpass stopband frequency of $\theta_{st}' = 0.4\pi$ to the equivalent frequency in the prototype. From Table 10.7 the lowpass prototype to lowpass transformation is

$$z = \frac{z - \alpha}{1 - \alpha z} \qquad (10.280)$$

which for $z = e^{j\theta_{st}}$ in the prototype and $z = e^{j\theta_{st}'} = e^{j0.4\pi}$ in the highpass becomes

$$e^{j\theta_{st}} = \frac{e^{j0.4\pi} - 0.510}{1 - 0.510e^{j0.4\pi}}$$

$$= \frac{0.309 + j0.951 - 0.510}{1 - (0.158 + j0.485)}$$

$$= 1e^{j2.30} \qquad (10.281)$$

and $\theta_{st} = 2.30$ in the prototype. Thus, in Fig. 10.33(c) we need to find the minimum value of filter order N where the gain is at most -10 dB for frequencies above 2.30. This is satisfied with $N = 2$ with the corresponding prototype transfer function from Table 10.8 of

$$H_{LP_p}(z) = \frac{0.293(z + 1)^2}{z^2 + 0.173}. \tag{10.282}$$

The desired lowpass filter is found from the lowpass prototype by

$$H_{LP}(z) = H_{LP_p}(z)\bigg|_{z = \frac{z - 0.510}{1 - 0.510z}}$$

$$= \frac{0.293(z + 1)^2}{z^2 + 0.173}\bigg|_{z = \frac{z - 0.510}{1 - 0.510z}}$$

$$= \frac{0.067(z + 1)^2}{z^2 - 1.145z + 0.414}. \tag{10.283}$$

The frequency response is given in Fig. 10.35 where we notice that the gain is 0.707 at the cutoff frequency of $\theta'_c = 0.2\pi = 0.628$ and that the gain is less than $0.316(-10$ dB) at the stopband frequency of $\theta'_{st} = 0.4\pi = 1.257$. The design specifications have been met and the filter transfer function is the same (within calculator roundoff) as we found in Examples 10.17 and 10.19 by other methods.

FIGURE 10.35 Frequency response for lowpass digital filter of Example 10.21

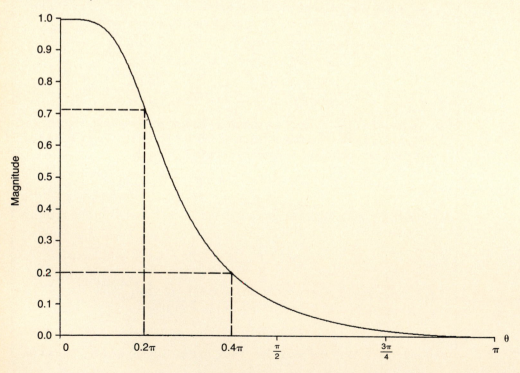

CHAPTER 10 RECURSIVE FILTER DESIGN

Example 10.22 This example illustrates the direct design of a digital bandpass filter. _____

A Chebyshev digital bandpass filter is to be designed to meet the following specifications:

a) A 1-dB ripple in the frequency range of 600 to 900 Hz.

b) A sampling frequency of 3000 Hz.

c) A maximum gain of -40 dB for $0 \leq f \leq 200$ Hz.

Solution:

1. A Chebyshev design has been specified

2. Converting the analog specification frequencies to digital frequencies gives

$$\theta'_\ell = 2\pi f_\ell/f_s = \frac{2\pi(600)}{3000} = 0.4\pi = 1.25 \text{ rad}$$

$$\theta'_u = 2\pi f_u/f_s = \frac{2\pi(900)}{3000} = 0.6\pi = 1.88 \text{ rad}$$

$$\theta'_{st} = 2\pi f_{st}/f_s = \frac{2\pi(200)}{3000} = 0.133\pi = 0.418 \text{ rad}$$

$$\theta'_0 = \sqrt{\theta_e \cdot \theta_u} = \sqrt{(1.25)(1.88)} = 1.53 \text{ rad.} \tag{10.284}$$

3. From entry number 3 in Table 10.7 the design constant α is

$$\alpha = \frac{\cos(\theta'_u/2 + \theta'_\ell/2)}{\cos(\theta'_u/2 - \theta'_\ell/2)} \tag{10.285}$$

where $\theta'_u = 0.6\pi$ and $\theta'_\ell = 0.4\pi$. This gives

$$\alpha = \frac{\cos(0.3\pi + 0.2\pi)}{\cos(0.3\pi - 0.2\pi)} = 0. \tag{10.286}$$

The design constant k is

$$k = \tan\frac{\theta_c}{2}\cot(\theta'_u/2 - \theta'_\ell/2) \tag{10.287}$$

where for a Chebyshev lowpass digital prototype we use the ripple passband edge as the critical frequency $\theta_c = \pi/2$. Thus,

$$k = \tan\left(\frac{0.5\pi}{2}\right)\cot\left(\frac{0.6\pi}{2} - \frac{0.4\pi}{2}\right)$$

$$= 3.07. \tag{10.288}$$

4. We need to convert the stopband frequency $\theta'_{st} = 0.133\pi$ to its prototype equivalent and from Table 10.7 the lowpass prototype to bandpass transformation is

$$z = -\frac{z^2 - \dfrac{2\alpha k}{k+1}z + \dfrac{k-1}{k+1}}{1 - \dfrac{2\alpha k}{k+1}z + \dfrac{k-1}{k+1}z^2}. \tag{10.289}$$

Replacing z on the left with $e^{j\theta_{st}}$ and on the right by $e^{j\theta'_{st}}$ gives us

$$e^{j\theta_{st}} = -\frac{e^{j2\theta'_{st}} - \dfrac{2\alpha k}{k+1}e^{j\theta'_{st}} + \dfrac{k-1}{k+1}}{1 - \dfrac{2\alpha k}{k+1}e^{j\theta'_{st}} + \dfrac{k-1}{k+1}e^{j2\theta'_{st}}} \tag{10.290}$$

and with the known values of α, k, and θ'_{st} we have

$$e^{j\theta_{st}} = -\frac{e^{j0.836} + 0.509}{1 + 0.509e^{j0.836}}$$

$$= 1e^{-j2.84} \tag{10.291}$$

giving the prototype stopband frequency of $\theta_{st} = 2.84$ rad.

In the prototype we need a gain of at most -40 dB at $\theta_{st} = 2.84$ rad and from Fig. 10.34(b) $N = 3$ is the minimum order that satisfies this specification. From Table 10.9 the prototype transfer function is

$$H_{LP_p}(z) = \frac{0.491(z + 1)^3}{3.717z^3 - 1.277z^2 + 2.247z - 0.759}. \tag{10.292}$$

Finally, we need to use Table 10.7 to convert the prototype to the bandpass filter and with $\alpha = 0$ and $k = 3.07$ we have

$$H_{BP}(z) = H_{LP_p}(z)\Big|_{z = -\frac{z^2 + 0.509}{1 + 0.509z^2}}$$

$$= \frac{0.011(z^6 - 3z^4 + 3z^2 - 1)}{z^6 + 2.135z^4 + 1.768z^2 + 0.540} \tag{10.293}$$

which agrees approximately with the result of Example 10.18. The differences in the denominator coefficients of Eqs. 10.247 and 10.293 may be due both to calculation roundoff and inherent differences in the two methods. In any case, the frequency response curves are virtually identical for the two systems.

10.3.6 Optimization

The design of recursive digital filters can be accomplished by methods other than the digitization of an existing or specifically designed analog filter. The use of optimization procedures to design IIR filters is an approach that has several attractive features. The basic idea of this method is as follows:

Define a measure of deviation of the actual frequency response from a desired frequency response and use a search algorithm to determine the filter coefficients that minimize this performance measure.

A typical measure of performance is defined as

$$J_{2p}(\mathbf{v}) = \sum_{i=1}^{M} W(\theta_i) \, [||H_d(e^{j\theta_i})|| - |H(e^{j\theta_i})||]^{2p} \qquad (10.294)$$

where

θ_i = the ith sample frequency

$W(\theta_i)$ = the value of a real non-negative weighting factor at the ith frequency sample

$|H_d(e^{j\theta_i})|$ = magnitude of the desired frequency response at the ith frequency sample

$|H(e^{j\theta_i})|$ = magnitude of the frequency response of the filter being designed at the ith frequency sample

M = number of frequency points to be considered

p = a positive integer

and $\mathbf{v}$ is the vector of filter coefficients.

The weighting factor $W(\theta_i)$ is used to place more, by increasing W, or less, by decreasing W, weight on a particular frequency, thereby reflecting the relative importance attached to deviations of the desired and actual frequency response.

A commonly used performance measure based on Eq. 10.294 is the sum of error squared criterion found by letting $p = 1$ and $W(\theta_i) = 1$ for all i, that is

$$J_2(\mathbf{v}) = \sum_{i=1}^{M} [||H_d(e^{j\theta_i})|| - |H(e^{j\theta_i})||]^2. \qquad (10.295)$$

The goal is to find the value of the vector $\mathbf{v}$, denoted by $\bar{\mathbf{v}}$, which minimizes $J_2(\mathbf{v})$, that is, find $\bar{\mathbf{v}}$ for which

$$J_2(\bar{\mathbf{v}}) \leq J_2(\mathbf{v}) \text{ for all } \mathbf{v}. \qquad (10.296)$$

To achieve the result implicit in Eq. 10.296 requires the use of an optimization algorithm such as the Fletcher-Powell algorithm, or other search techniques. This is an iterative search procedure and the length of the search (the number of iterations) is controlled by the designer. A design procedure such as the following could be used.

1. Select a desired frequency response magnitude characteristic, the number of frequency samples M, the weighting factor values $W(\theta_i)$, $i = 1,2, \ldots M$, and the starting values of the filter coefficients.

2. Use a computer algorithm to adjust filter parameters to minimize a selected or given performance measure.

3. Determine the frequency response and compare with the desired response.

For a more complete discussion of this general approach, see Lam (1979) and Rabiner and Gold (1975). A similar approach that takes advantage of the characteristic of linear phase was discussed for nonrecursive filters in Section 9.5.

10.3.7 Some Comments on Recursive and Nonrecursive Filters

We now discuss some of the important properties of the methods that have been presented for the design of recursive filters.

Bilinear transformation. This procedure is probably the most popular method used to digitize analog filters. The magnitude of the desired frequency response must be piecewise constant but, fortunately, this includes the large class of LP, HP, BP, and BS filters. We also used the bilinear transformation to develop tables of lowpass digital prototype transfer functions. With design curves available to determine the order of the filter, it is possible to design other passband filters directly in the z-domain. This was done for Butterworth and Chebyshev filters.

Impulse and Step Invariant. The analog filter must be band-limited over the analog frequency range of $-\pi/T \leq \omega \leq \pi/T$, but the discussion of this is beyond the scope of the text.

Matched z-transform. This procedure is very easy to apply but no zeros appear in $H(z)$ if none are present in $H(s)$ which somewhat limits the frequency response characteristics of the digital filter. Also, the zeros of the analog filter can be aliased for low sampling frequencies.

In Chapter Nine we saw that it was relatively easy to design nonrecursive filters that have linear phase that are used in speech processing and data transmission systems. Fourier methods (analytical and IDFT) were used to design these filters. We found that nonrecursive filters are always stable, but a large order filter might be required to meet design specifications.

With recursive filters, on the other hand, we can generally achieve a desired frequency response characteristic with a filter of lower order than for a nonrecursive filter. On an intuitive basis this is because a nonrecursive filter has all of its poles at the origin and thus only the zero locations can be selected to achieve the desired frequency response. A recursive filter, however, has both poles and zeros that can be selected, hence, there are more free parameters than for a nonrecursive filter of the same order. The presence of poles at locations other than $z = 0$ for recursive filters means, however, that stability is not assured when there are poles close to the unit circle and the effects of finite computer word length are considered. Finally, the phase of a recursive filter is generally not linear in the passband. Thus, if linear phase is desired, phase equalization is often needed with recursive filters.

10.4 ▄▄ REVIEW

The first part of this chapter was devoted to the study of the design of analog filters using the Butterworth (maximally flat), Chebyshev (equal ripple in the passband), and elliptic (equal ripple in both the passband and the stopband) approximations. The first step in the design procedure was to translate the given specifications to those for a prototype lowpass filter with a cutoff frequency of $\omega = 1$ in the case of Butterworth, a ripple-band edge frequency of $\omega = 1$ for Chebyshev filters, and $\omega = (\omega_{1P}\omega_{2P})^{1/2} = 1$ for elliptic filters.

Next, a prototype lowpass analog filter was designed that satisfied all the prototype specifications. For Butterworth filters this amounted to finding only the order N of the filter. In the Chebyshev case both the filter order N and the ripple factor ϵ must be determined, whereas for elliptic filters the shape of the frequency response plot is a function of three parameters, i.e., the passband ripple ϵ, the stopband gain A, and the transition band selectivity, $R = \omega_{2P}/\omega_{1P}$. For all three filter types knowing the order of the required prototype enables us to use filter tables to find the prototype transfer function $H_{LP_p}(s)$. Nomograms or computer programs could also be used.

At this point there are two possible routes to follow. One approach is to use analog frequency transformations to convert the lowpass analog prototype to an analog LP, HP, BP, or BS filter, as appropriate, and then apply an analog-to-digital conversion to obtain the transfer function of the digital filter. An alternative is to apply an analog-to-digital conversion to the lowpass analog prototype to obtain a lowpass digital prototype, and then use digital frequency transformations to obtain an LP, HP, BP, or BS digital filter transfer function, as desired. These two approaches are illustrated in Fig. 10.36. Whichever path is taken, extensive use is made of computer-generated frequency response plots to verify that specifications are satisfied at intermediate stages of the design process.

There are several possible analog-to-digital conversions that can be used in either of the design approaches of Fig. 10.36. We discussed the matched z-transform technique, the impulse- and step-invariant design methods, as well as the very popular bilinear transformation procedure that was explored from two different points of view. Because of an aliasing effect whose explanation is beyond the scope of this book (see Lam, 1979), the impulse- and step-invariant methods are applicable only to lowpass and bandpass filters. The bilinear transformation provides a simple mapping between analog and digital filters which maps the entire $j\omega$-axis of the s-plane onto the unit circle of the z-plane. This highly

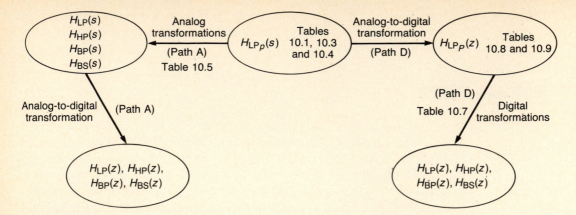

FIGURE 10.36 The digitization of a prototype lowpass analog filter

nonlinear relationship makes the process of prewarping necessary so that the application of the bilinear transformation yields a digital filter with the desired specification frequencies. This method is limited to analog filters whose desired frequency response is piecewise constant (Rabiner and Gold, 1975).

We also found that the procedure represented as path D in Fig. 10.36 can be shortened by developing tables of lowpass digital prototype transfer functions. This was done, for example, for Butterworth and Chebyshev filters using the bilinear transformation. The availability of these lowpass digital prototype transfer functions allows us to design other passband filters directly in the z-domain.

VOCABULARY AND IMPORTANT RELATIONS

a) Analog transfer function

$$H(s) = \frac{Y(s)}{X(s)} = \frac{k(s^L + b_{L-1}s^{L-1} + \cdots + b_1 s + b_0)}{s^N + a_{N-1}s^{N-1} + \cdots + a_1 s + a_0} \qquad (10.3)$$

b) Sinusoidal steady-state (continuous-time) response

$$y_{ss}(t) = X_1|H(j\omega)| \cos(\omega t + \underline{/H(j\omega)})$$

The input is $x(t) = X_1\cos(\omega t)$ and $H(j\omega) = H(s)\big|_{s=j\omega}$ \qquad (10.8)

c) Magnitude-squared function

$$|H(j\omega)|^2\big|_{\omega=-js} = H(s) \cdot H(-s) \qquad (10.37)$$

d) Butterworth lowpass design (maximally flat)

$$|H_{LP}(j\omega)|^2 = \frac{1}{1 + (\omega/\omega_c)^{2N}} \qquad (10.40)$$

where ω_c is the cutoff frequency and N is the order of the filter. Butterworth lowpass prototype poles

$$N \text{ odd—} s_k = 1e^{jk\pi/N}, \qquad k = 0, 1, 2, \ldots, 2N-1 \qquad (10.46)$$

$$N \text{ even—} s_k = 1e^{j(\pi+k2\pi)/2N}, \qquad k = 0, 1, 2, \ldots, 2N-1 \qquad (10.47)$$

Butterworth filter coefficients (see Table 10.1, page 627.)
Butterworth filter order

$$N = \frac{\log_{10}(10^{-[M_{dB}/10]} - 1)}{2 \log_{10} \omega_a} \qquad (10.57)$$

where M_{dB} is the dB gain at the frequency ω_a.

e) Chebyshev lowpass prototype design (equal passband ripple)

$$|H_{LP_p}(j\omega)|^2 = \frac{1}{1 + \epsilon^2 C_N^2(\omega)} \qquad (10.62)$$

where the ripple amplitude in dB is

$$r_{dB} = 10 \log_{10}(1 + \epsilon^2) \qquad (10.92)$$

and the Chebyshev polynomial $C_N(\omega)$ is found from

$$C_{N+1}(\omega) = 2\omega C_N(\omega) - C_{N-1}(\omega) \text{ with } C_0(\omega) = 1 \text{ and } C_1(\omega) = \omega. \qquad (10.78)$$

See Table 10.2 (page 634) for the first eight Chebyshev polynomials and Table 10.3 (page 636) for some typical filter coefficients.

f) Elliptic lowpass prototype design (equal ripple in passband and stopband)

$$\left|H_{LP_p}(j\omega)\right|^2 = \frac{1}{1 + \epsilon^2 E_N(\omega)} \qquad (10.102)$$

Passband ripple-edge frequency $= \omega_{1P}$

Stopband ripple-edge frequency $= \omega_{2P}$

Geometric mean of ω_{1P} and $\omega_{2P} = (\omega_{1P}\omega_{2P})^{1/2} = 1 \qquad (10.103)$

Sharpness of transition region, $R = \omega_{2P}/\omega_{1P} \qquad (10.104)$

See Table 10.4 (page 642) for a sample of some typical filter coefficients

g) Analog frequency transformations (See Table 10.5, page 656.)

h) Impulse-invariant design

$$h(nT) = h(t)\Big|_{t=nT} \qquad (10.179)$$

$$\mathfrak{z}[h(nT)] = H(z) \qquad (10.180)$$

$$H(s) = \sum_{k=1}^{N} \frac{C_k}{s - d_k} \longrightarrow H(z) = \sum_{k=1}^{N} \frac{C_k}{1 - e^{d_k T} z^{-1}} \qquad (10.190)$$

i) Step-invariant design
Output Laplace transform

$$Y_s(s) = H(s) \cdot X(s) = H(s) \cdot \frac{1}{s} \qquad (10.199)$$

Output sequence

$$y_s(nT) = y_s(t)\Big|_{t=nT} \qquad (10.200)$$

Output z-transform

$$\mathfrak{z}[y_s(nT)] = Y_s(z) \qquad (10.201)$$

Filter transfer function

$$\frac{Y_s(z)}{X(z)} = H(z) \text{ where } X(z) = 1/(1 - z^{-1}) \qquad (10.202)$$

j) Bilinear transformation

$$H(z) = H(s)\Big|_{s = \frac{1 - z^{-1}}{1 + z^{-1}} = \frac{z - 1}{z + 1}} \qquad (10.214)$$

Frequency warping effect

$$\omega = \tan\left(\frac{\theta}{2}\right) \qquad (10.225)$$

where ω is the analog frequency and θ the corresponding digital frequency.

Alternative bilinear design procedure (see Table 10.6, page 686.)

k) Digital frequency transformations (see Table 10.7, page 690.)

l) Direct design of digital filters
Prototypes derived from the bilinear transformation:

Butterworth (see Table 10.8, page 691 and Fig. 10.33, page 691)

$$1 \le N \le 5$$

Chebyshev (see Table 10.9, page 694 and Fig. 10.34, page 696)

$$1 \le N \le 5 \text{ for 0.5-dB, 1-dB, and 2-dB ripple}$$

CHAPTER 10   RECURSIVE FILTER DESIGN

PROBLEMS

For your convenience, the following listing of tables and important figures is provided.

Reinforcement

10.1 A stable analog system is described by the transfer function

$$H(s) = \frac{Y(s)}{X(s)} = \frac{13s + 7}{s^3 + 10s^2 + 8s + 5}.$$

Find the steady-state output $y_{ss}(t)$ for the input signal $x(t) = 2\cos t$.

10.2 A filter has the transfer function

$$H(s) = \frac{10^3 s}{s^2 + 50s + 10^4}.$$

a) Find the poles and zeros that describe the filter. Is it LP, HP, BP, or BS?

b) Plot the poles and zeros and estimate the shape of the frequency response magnitude plot, $|H(j\omega)|$ vs. ω. What is the gain at $\omega = 100$ rad/s?

c) Revise the sketch of part (b) to show $|H(j\omega)|_{dB}$ vs. ω. Three easily computed points are $\omega = 0$, $\omega \to \infty$, and $\omega = 100$ rad/s.

10.3 Repeat Problem 10.2 for the filter transfer function $H(s) = \dfrac{20(s^2 + 10^4)}{s^2 + 50s + 10^4}$.

10.4 The magnitude-squared function of an analog filter is known to be

$$|H(j\omega)|^2 = \frac{10^6 \omega^2}{\omega^4 + 17{,}500\omega^2 + 10^8}.$$

Determine the filter transfer function $H(s)$.

10.5 a) For the second-order bandpass filter described by

$$H(s) = \frac{s}{s^2 + \alpha_1 s + \alpha_2}$$

where α_1 and α_2 are positive real constants, determine the equations for the two -3 dB frequencies, ω_ℓ and ω_u.

b) At what frequency is the phase zero?

10.6 Given the definitions for a bandpass filter $\omega_0^2 = \omega_\ell \omega_u$ and $B = \omega_u - \omega_\ell$, where ω_u and ω_ℓ are the -3 dB cutoff frequencies, find expressions for ω_ℓ and ω_u in terms of the center frequency ω_0 and bandwith B. Under what conditions is

$$\omega_0 \approx \frac{\omega_\ell + \omega_u}{2}?$$

10.7 The lowpass-to-bandstop filter substitution is given in Table 10.5 as

$$H_{BS}(s) = H_{LP_p}(s)\Big|_{s = \frac{Bs}{s^2 + \omega_0^2}}.$$

Verify the correctness of this substitution by finding the prototype frequencies that correspond to the bandstop frequencies of $\omega = \omega_0$, $\omega = \omega_u$, $\omega = \omega_\ell$, $\omega = 0$, and $\omega = +\infty$.

10.8 a) Starting with the transfer function $H_{\text{LP}_p}(s)$ of a third-order analog Butterworth lowpass prototype determine $H_{\text{LP}}(s)$ of the third-order lowpass filter that is derived from the prototype if the −3 dB cutoff frequency is 3 $krad/s$.

b) Find $H_{\text{HP}}(s)$ for a 1-dB ripple second-order Chebyshev highpass filter that is derived from a second-order Chebyshev lowpass prototype. The passband ripple-edge is to be at $f = 10$ kHz.

c) Find $H_{\text{LP}}(s)$ for a third-order elliptic lowpass filter having 0.5 dB passband ripple and −30 dB stopband gain that is derived from a third-order elliptic prototype. The passband ripple-edge frequency is to be at $f = 2$ kHz.

d) Find $H_{\text{BS}}(s)$ for a second-order Butterworth bandstop filter that is to remove 60 Hz and have a 3-dB passband of 10 Hz.

10.9 a) The transfer function of a first-order digital Butterworth lowpass prototype is $H_{\text{LP}_p}(z) = \dfrac{0.5(z + 1)}{z}$. A second-order Butterworth digital bandpass filter having upper and lower cutoff frequencies of $\theta_u = 0.833\pi$ rad and $\theta_\ell = 0.667\pi$ rad, respectively, is to be derived from the lowpass prototype. Find the transfer function $H_{\text{BP}}(z)$.

b) The transfer function $H_{\text{HP}}(z)$ of a second-order digital Chebyshev highpass filter with 0.5-dB ripple in the ripple passband is to be found from the second-order Chebyshev digital lowpass prototype. The passband ripple-edge frequency is 0.4π rad.

c) Find $H_{\text{BS}}(z)$ for a second-order digital Butterworth bandstop filter that has a 3-dB passband between 0.46π and 0.54π rad. This filter is to be derived from a lowpass prototype from Table 10.8.

10.10 a) In Section 10.3.1 we showed that the matched z-transform results in $(s + a - jb)$, $\xrightarrow[\text{to}]{\text{goes}} 1 - e^{-(a-jb)T}z^{-1}$. Show that $(s + a - jb)$ $(s + a + jb) \xrightarrow[\text{to}]{\text{goes}} (1 - 2z^{-1}e^{-aT}\cos bT + e^{-2aT}z^{-2})$.

b) In the impulse- and step-invariant methods of digitizing analog filters partial fraction expansions are used and we often encounter a second-order expression such as

$$F_k(s) = \frac{C_k}{s + a - jb} + \frac{C_k^*}{s + a + jb}$$

that becomes in the z-domain

$$F_k(z) = \frac{A + Bz^{-1}}{1 + Cz^{-1} + Dz^{-2}}.$$

Find the z-domain constants A, B, C, and D in terms of a, b, C_k, and the sampling interval T.

10.11 For each of the filter specifications given in parts (a) and (b) below, draw the specification diagram for the lowpass analog prototype, and find the transfer function of a lowpass analog prototype that could be used to design the filters. Assume that the prototype is to be a Butterworth filter.

a) Lowpass filter with

$$-0.5 \text{ dB} \leq M_{\text{dB}} \leq 0 \text{ dB} \quad \text{for} \quad 0 \leq f \leq 6 \text{ kHz}$$

$$M_{\text{dB}} \leq -3 \text{ dB} \quad \text{for} \quad f \geq 10 \text{ kHz}$$

$$M_{\text{dB}} \leq -10 \text{ dB} \quad \text{for} \quad f \geq 30 \text{ kHz}$$

$$M_{\text{dB}} \leq -50 \text{ dB} \quad \text{for} \quad f \geq 100 \text{ kHz}.$$

b) Bandpass filter with

$$-0.5 \text{ dB} \leq M_{\text{dB}} \leq 0 \text{ dB} \quad \text{for} \quad 53.5 \text{ kHz} \leq f \leq 56 \text{ kHz}$$

$$M_{\text{dB}} \leq -3 \text{ dB} \quad \text{for} \quad f \leq 50 \text{ kHz} \quad \text{and} \quad f \geq 60 \text{ kHz}$$

$$M_{\text{dB}} \leq -20 \text{ dB} \quad \text{for} \quad f \leq 5 \text{ kHz} \quad \text{and} \quad f \geq 600 \text{ kHz}.$$

10.12 Repeat Problem 10.11 for the filter specifications given below. Assume that a Chebyshev filter is to be used as the lowpass prototype.

a) Highpass filter with

$$-1 \text{ dB} \leq M_{\text{dB}} \leq 0 \text{ dB} \quad \text{for} \quad f \geq 40 \text{ kHz}$$

$$M_{\text{dB}} \leq -3 \text{ dB} \quad \text{for} \quad f \leq 30 \text{ kHz}$$

$$M_{\text{dB}} \leq -40 \text{ dB} \quad \text{for} \quad f \leq 10 \text{ kHz}.$$

b) Bandstop filter with

$$-1 \text{ dB} \leq M_{\text{dB}} \leq 0 \text{ dB} \quad \text{for} \quad f \leq 2.5 \text{ kHz} \quad \text{and}$$
$$f \geq 300 \text{ kHz}$$

$$M_{\text{dB}} \leq -3 \text{ dB} \quad \text{for} \quad 25 \text{ kHz} \leq f \leq 26.5 \text{ kHz}$$
$$\text{and} \quad 28 \text{ kHz} \leq f \leq 30 \text{ kHz}$$

$$M_{\text{dB}} \leq -30 \text{ dB} \quad 26.5 \text{ kHz} \leq f \leq 28 \text{ kHz}.$$

10.13 The characteristic equation of a second-order analog filter is $as^2 + bs + c = 0$ where a, b,

CHAPTER 10 RECURSIVE FILTER DESIGN

and c are real constants. Find the required conditions on the constants a, b, and c so that the characteristic roots are always in the left half of the s-plane.

10.14 Starting with Eq. 10.64 show that $C_{N+1}(\omega) = 2\omega C_N(\omega) - C_{N-1}(\omega)$.

10.15 The elliptic filter coefficients given in Table 10.4 yield lowpass prototype analog filters with $\dfrac{\omega_{2P}}{\omega_{1P}} = R$ and $\omega_{1P}\omega_{2P} = 1$ which means that $\omega_{1P} = 1/\sqrt{R}$ and $\omega_{2P} = \sqrt{R}$. Suppose that it is desired to convert Table 10.4 so that the coefficients give filters with the passband ripple edge of $\omega'_{1P} = 1$.

a) Show how this can be done by using a simple lowpass-lowpass analog transformation.

b) If this transformation is used, what is the resulting value of ω'_{2P}, the stopband edge frequency?

c) Use the transformation of part (a) on the third-order elliptic filter with a stopband gain of -30dB and a passband ripple of 0.5 dB and demonstrate that the filter has the appropriate gains for $\omega'_{1P} = 1$ and ω'_{2P}.

10.16 It is desired to design a lowpass analog filter to meet the following specifications:

i) Maximum attenuation of 0.1 dB in the frequency range $0 \le \omega \le 5{,}000$ rad/s, i.e., $-0.1 \le 10 \log_{10}|H(j\omega)|^2 \le 0.0$ for $0 \le \omega \le 5{,}000$ rad/s.

ii) Cutoff frequency of not more than 10,000 rad/s.

iii) Attenuation of at least 25 dB for $\omega \ge 30{,}000$ rad/s.

a) Use the Butterworth approximation to find the transfer function $H(s)$ of the filter.

b) Plot the frequency response of the analog filter found in part (a).

10.17 A sketch (not to scale) of the specification diagram for a bandstop analog filter is given in Fig. P10.17 where the unshaded regions define the desired characteristics. This problem is concerned with some preliminary steps that might be used in finding a digital filter design to meet the specifications.

a) Assume that the digital filter is designed by using a Butterworth prototype and a digital transformation that does not require prewarping. Determine appropriate specifications for a lowpass analog prototype and draw the corresponding specification diagram.

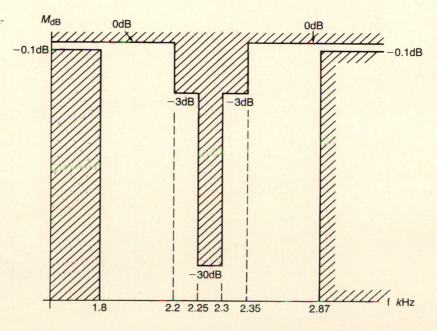

FIGURE P10.17 Specification diagram for bandstop filter

b) Find the transfer function $H_{LP_p}(s)$ for a lowpass Butterworth prototype that meets the specifications of part (a).

c) Assume that the digital filter is to be designed by using the bilinear transformation with prewarping to determine the lowpass analog specifications. If the sampling period is $T = 1.6 \times 10^{-4}$s, find the revised lowpass analog filter specifications and represent them on a specification diagram. Compare your results with part (a).

d) Assume that a Chebyshev prototype is to be used to design the digital filter using an analog-digital transformation that requires no prewarping. Find an appropriate set of lowpass prototype specifications and draw the specification diagram.

10.18 A digital recursive bandpass filter is to be designed to satisfy the following analog specifications which are shown in a sketch (not to scale) of the specification diagram of Fig. P10.18.

i) Lower cutoff frequency $\geq 50 \times 10^3$ Hz.

ii) Upper cutoff frequency $\leq 54 \times 10^3$ Hz.

iii) -1 dB $\leq |H|_{dB} \leq 0$ dB for 51×10^3 Hz $\leq f \leq 53 \times 10^3$ Hz.

iv) $|H|_{dB} \leq -32$ dB for $f \geq 64 \times 10^3$ Hz.

v) $|H|_{dB} \leq -32$ dB for $f \leq 40 \times 10^3$ Hz.

A lowpass Butterworth filter is to be used as the analog prototype.

a) If the digital filter is to be designed by using some method other than the bilinear transformation, determine the lowpass prototype specifications that must be satisfied and show them on a specification diagram.

b) Determine the transfer function of the lowest order Butterworth filter that meets the lowpass prototype specifications found in part (a).

c) Plot the frequency response of the lowpass prototype found in part (b) and compare with the lowpass prototype specifications found in part (a).

d) Determine the transfer function for the bandpass analog filter based on the lowpass prototype found in part (b).

e) Plot the frequency response of the bandpass filter found in part (d) and compare with the original specifications.

10.19 Repeat Problem 10.18 for a Chebyshev filter.

10.20 An analog bandpass filter is to be designed to

FIGURE P10.18 Specification diagram for bandpass filter

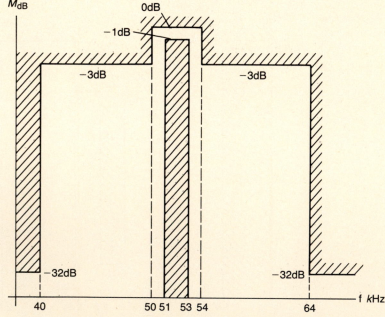

meet the following specifications

$-0.5\text{dB} \le M_{\text{dB}} \le 0 \text{ dB}$ for
$$2.5 \text{ kHz} \le f \le 3.6 \text{ kHz}$$
$M_{\text{dB}} \le -30 \text{ dB}$ for $f \le 2.0 \text{ kHz}$ and
$$f \ge 4.5 \text{ kHz}.$$

Both Chebyshev and elliptic designs are to be considered.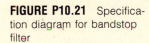

a) Draw a specification diagram.

b) Determine a set of appropriate lowpass proto-type specifications and represent these in a specification diagram.

c) Find the transfer function for a lowpass Chebyshev prototype that meets the specifications in part (b).

d) Repeat part (c) for an elliptic lowpass filter.

e) Find the bandpass filter transfer functions, $H_{\text{BP}}(s)$, corresponding to the lowpass prototype designs of parts (c) and (d).

f) Plot the frequency responses of the bandpass filters of part (e) and compare with the given specifications.

10.21 The specification diagram for a bandstop fil-ter is shown in Fig. P10.21 with the unshaded re-gions representing the desired response character-istics.

a) Find a Chebyshev bandstop analog filter trans-fer function that meets the specifications.

b) Plot the frequency response for the filter ob-tained in part (a).

c) Repeat parts (a) and (b) for an elliptic bandstop filter.

10.22 An analog bandpass filter is to be designed to have a maximally flat response in the passband. The specifications to be satisfied are pictured in Fig. P10.22 where the unacceptable regions are shaded.

a) What type of filter would you use to meet these specifications?

b) Find the specifications to be used in designing a lowpass prototype.

c) Determine the transfer function for the low-pass prototype.

d) Find the transfer function $H_{\text{BP}}(s)$ for the band-pass analog filter.

FIGURE P10.21 Specifica-tion diagram for bandstop filter

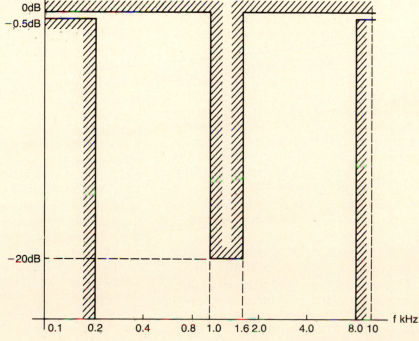

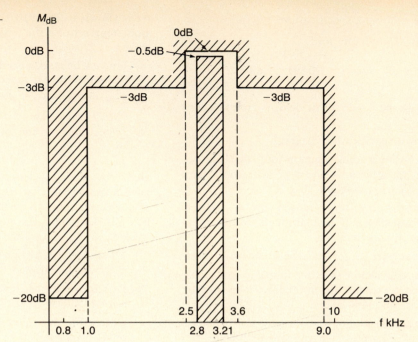

FIGURE P10.22 Specification diagram for bandpass filter

e) Plot the frequency response for $H_{BP}(s)$ and compare it with the original specifications.

10.23 Repeat Problem 10.22 for an equal-ripple response in the frequency band 2.8 kHz $\leq f \leq$ 3.21 kHz with the remaining specifications the same.

10.24 In Problem 10.22 a Butterworth analog bandpass filter was designed to meet the specifications of Fig. P10.22. Now, we want to satisfy these specifications with a digital filter in a system where the sampling frequency is 50 kHz. Use the bilinear transformation procedure with prewarping as described in Section 10.3.3 to determine the transfer function $H(z)$ of the appropriate digital filter. Make a frequency response plot.

10.25 Repeat Problem 10.24 by using the alternative bilinear transformation design procedure of Table 10.6.

10.26 Repeat Problem 10.24 by using the direct design procedure as discussed in Section 10.3.5.

10.27 In Problem 10.23 a Chebyshev analog bandpass filter was designed to meet the amended specifications of Fig. P10.22. Now, we want to satisfy these specifications with a digital filter in a system

where the sampling frequency is 50 kHz. Use the bilinear transformation procedure of Section 10.3.3 to determine the transfer function $H(z)$ of the appropriate digital filter.

10.28 Repeat Problem 10.27 by using the alternative bilinear design procedure of Table 10.6.

10.29 Repeat Problem 10.27 by using the direct design procedure as discussed in Section 10.3.5.

10.30 Design a highpass digital filter for a 20-kHz sampling rate that is maximally flat in the passband defined by the -3 dB cutoff frequency of 8 kHz and the maximum frequency of 10 kHz. The gain is at most -10 dB for frequencies less than 6 kHz. Use the direct design procedure of Section 10.3.5 to find the filter transfer function $H(z)$.

10.31 a) For the analog highpass filter designed in Example 10.10, find a corresponding digital filter using the matched z-transform method. The sampling frequency is 20 kHz.

b) Plot the frequency response of the digital highpass filter considered in part (a) and compare the results with the original specifications. Adjust the gains so that $M = 1$ at $\theta = \pi$ in the digital filter.

10.32 A digital bandpass filter is to be designed to

meet the specifications given in Problem 10.22. The design is to be accomplished by using the impulse-invariant transformation. The sample period is $T = 5.0 \times 10^{-5}s$.

a) Find an appropriate analog bandpass transfer function and convert it to a digital bandpass filter by using the impulse-invariant transformation.

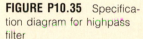 b) Plot the frequency response for $H_{BP}(z)$ found in part (a) and compare it with the original specifications.

10.33 Repeat Problem 10.32 using the matched z-transform method.

10.34 Repeat Problem 10.32 using the step-invariant transformation.

10.35 The specification diagram for a highpass filter is shown in Fig. P10.35 with the unshaded regions representing the desired response characteristics. We want to design a digital filter to meet

these specifications by using the bilinear transformation and a sampling frequency of 10 kHz. A Butterworth filter is to be used as the prototype.

a) Find the lowpass specifications for an appropriate analog prototype and draw the specification diagram.

b) Find the transfer function of a lowpass analog prototype that meets the specifications of part (a).

c) Plot the frequency response of the lowpass analog prototype filter found in part (b) and compare with the specifications of part (a).

d) What is the order of the digital filter that would be obtained by applying the bilinear transformation to the lowpass analog prototype filter of part (c)?

10.36 Repeat Problem 10.35 for a Chebyshev filter.

10.37 Repeat Problem 10.35 for an elliptic filter.

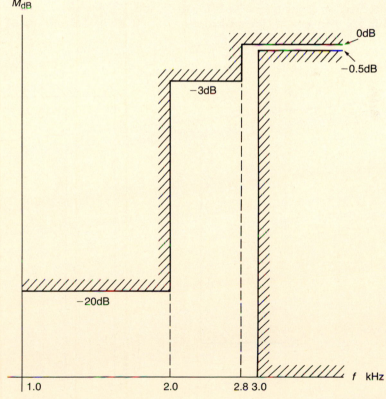

FIGURE P10.35 Specification diagram for highpass filter

10.38 It is desired to design a maximally flat lowpass digital filter to meet the following specifications:

i) Maximum attenuation of 0.1 dB in the frequency range $0 \le \omega \le 5{,}000$ rad/s.

ii) 3-dB cutoff frequency of not more than 10,000 rad/s.

iii) Attenuation of at least 25 dB for $\omega \ge$ 30,000 rad/s.

Use the direct design procedure of Section 10.3.5 to find the filter transfer function $H(z)$. The system sampling frequency is 25 kHz.

10.39 The specification diagram for a highpass filter is shown in Fig. P10.39 with the unshaded regions representing the desired frequency response characteristics. We want to design a Butterworth digital filter using the method of Section 10.3.5.

a) Find the transfer function $H_{HP}(z)$ for a sampling frequency of 10 kHz.

b) Plot the frequency response of the digital filter.

10.40 The specification diagram for a bandstop filter is shown in Fig. P10.40 with the unshaded re-

gions representing the desired response characteristics. We want to design a Chebyshev digital filter using the method of Section 10.3.5.

a) Find the transfer function $H_{BS}(z)$ for a sampling frequency of 0.2π MHz.

b) Plot the frequency response of the digital filter.

Extension and Generalization

10.41 For the Butterworth magnitude function $M = |H(j\omega)| = \dfrac{1}{(1 + \omega^{2N})^{1/2}}$ we have stated that the steepness of decay (slope) of $|H(j\omega)|$ vs. ω is described by $d|H(j\omega)|/d\omega = -0.354N$ at $\omega = 1$ where N is the order of the filter and $\omega = 1$ is the normalized cutoff frequency. Derive this result and give the corresponding expression if $|H(j\omega)|$ is measured in dB.

10.42 The Butterworth approximation is called maximally flat because $d^n|H(j\omega)|/d\omega^n\Big|_{\omega=0} = 0$ for $n = 1, 2, \ldots, 2N - 1$. Show that this is the case.

10.43 In Section 10.3.2 the impulse- and step-

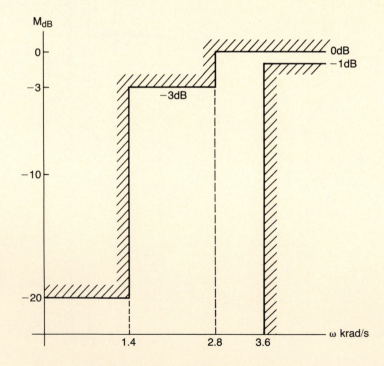

FIGURE P10.39

FIGURE P10.40

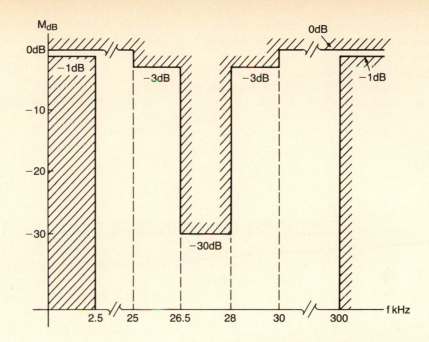

invariant transformations were discussed. The goal in this problem is to extend this approach to obtain a ramp-invariant transformation. That is, if $r_a(t)$ is the response of the analog filter with $x(t) = tu(t)$, then we want the ramp response values $r_d(nT)$ of the digital filter to equal the sampled values of the unit ramp response of the analog filter, or

$$r_d(nT) = r_a(t)\Big|_{t=nT}.$$

a) Describe the general ramp-invariant design procedure.

b) For an analog system with the transfer function $H(s) = s/(s + 1)(s + 2)$ find the digital transfer function $H(z)$ that results when the ramp-invariant transformation is applied. Assume $T = 1s$.

10.44 Using the pseudocode of Fig. 4.20 write a computer subroutine to evaluate the frequency response of an analog system. Assume that the frequency response function is in the form of Eq. 10.29 with $L \leq 10$ and $N \leq 10$. The program should be capable of evaluating the frequency response for as many as 1000 frequency points.

10.45 a) Show that the −3 dB frequency, ω_{3dB} for

an LP Chebyshev filter is given by $\omega_{3dB} = \cosh[(1/N)\cosh^{-1}(1/\epsilon)]$.

b) Find the −3 dB frequency for a Chebyshev filter of order 3 that has a 1-dB ripple.

10.46 Figure 10.33 provides design curves for digital lowpass prototype Butterworth filters of orders $N = 1, 2, \ldots, 5$ derived from the bilinear transformation. In this problem you are to determine similar design curves for analog lowpass prototype Butterworth filters of orders $N = 1, 2, \ldots, 5$.

a) Obtain plots of M_{dB} vs. ω for $0 \leq \omega \leq 1.0$ rad/s for Butterworth filters of orders 1 through 5.

b) Repeat part (a) for the frequency range $1 \leq \omega \leq 10$ rad/s.

10.47 a) Repeat Problem 10.46(b) for Chebyshev filters with $N = 1, 2, \ldots, 5$ and with a ripple of 0.5 dB.

b) Suppose that it was desired to compare Butterworth and Chebyshev lowpass filters by modifying the Chebyshev filters to have −3 dB cutoff frequencies of 1 rad/s. Explain how this could be done.

10.48 Repeat Problem 10.47(a) for elliptic filters with $N = 2, 3, 4, 5$ for a passband ripple of 0.5 dB and a stopband gain of −30 dB.

10.49 Verify the substitutions indicated in the alternative bilinear transformation design procedure of Table 10.6.

10.50 Unless tables of coefficient values are available the amount of algebra may be considerable in using some of the transformations we have considered. For example, in using the bilinear transformation with prewarping, the substitution $s = \dfrac{z-1}{z+1}$ is made and then the algebra begins. It is possible, however, to modify a program that computes the frequency response of a discrete system so that the frequency response can be checked before doing the algebra. Describe how this can be done.

10.51 Show that Eq. 10.63, $C_N(\omega) = \cos(N \cos^{-1} \omega)$ can be expressed as Eq. 10.64, $C_N(\omega) = \cosh(N \cosh^{-1} \omega)$.

REFERENCES AND OTHER SOURCES OF INFORMATION

Antoniou, A. 1979. *Digital Filters: Analysis and Design.* New York: McGraw-Hill Book Company.

Butterworth, S. 1930. "On the Theory of Filter Amplifiers." *Wireless Engineer* 7 (May): 536–541.

Christian, E., and E. Eisenmann, 1966. *Filter Design Tables and Graphs.* New York: John Wiley & Sons, Inc.

Churchill, R. V. 1960. *Complex Variables and Applications.* New York: McGraw-Hill Book Company.

Constantinides, A. G. 1970. "Spectral Transformations for Digital Filters," *Proc. of the IEEE.* 117, (August): 1585–1590.

Daniels, R. W. 1974. *Approximation Methods for Electronic Filter Design.* New York: McGraw-Hill Book Company.

Darlington, S. 1939. "Synthesis of Reactance 4-poles." *Journal Math. and Phys.* Vol. 18(4): 257–353.

Darlington, S. 1952. "Network Synthesis using Tschebycheff Polynomial Series." *Bell System Technical Journal* 31 (July): 613–665.

Ghausi, M. S., and K. R. Laker, 1981. *Modern Filter Design.* Englewood Cliffs, New Jersey: Prentice-Hall, Inc.

Gold, B., and C. M. Rader. 1969. *Digital Processing of Signals.* New York: McGraw-Hill Book Company.

Grossman, A. J. 1957. "Synthesis of Tchebysheff Parameter Symmetrical Filters." *Proc. IRE* 45 (April): 454–473.

Lam, H. Y-F. 1979. *Analog and Digital Filters: Design and Realization.* Englewood Cliffs, New Jersey: Prentice-Hall, Inc.

Lindquist, C. S. 1977. *Active Network Design with Signal Filtering Applications.* Long Beach, California: Steward & Sons.

Ludeman, L. 1986. *Fundamentals of Digital Signal Processing.* New York: Harper and Row Publishers.

Rabiner, L. R., and B. Gold, 1975. *Theory and Application of Digital Signal Processing.* Englewood Cliffs, New Jersey: Prentice-Hall, Inc.

Strum, R. D., and J. R. Ward, 1985. *Electric Circuits and Networks*. 2nd Ed. Engle-wood Cliffs, New Jersey: Prentice-Hall, Inc.

Terrell, T. J. 1980. *Introduction to Digital Filters*. New York: John Wiley and Sons, Inc.

Van Valkenburg, M. E. 1960. *Introduction to Modern Network Synthesis*. New York: John Wiley and Sons, Inc.

Van Valkenburg, M. E. 1974. *Circuit Theory: Foundations and Classical Contri-butions*. Stroudsburg, PA.: Dowden, Hutchinson and Ross.

Van Valkenburg, M. E. 1982. *Analog Filter Design*. New York: Holt, Rinehart and Winston.

Weinberg, L. 1962. *Network Analysis and Synthesis*. New York: McGraw-Hill Book Company.

Zverev, A. L. 1967. *Handbook of Filter Synthesis*. New York: John Wiley and Sons, Inc.

CHAPTER 11

Structures, State Equations, and Applications

11.0 ■■■ PREVIEW

In this final chapter we discuss several topics that are useful in discrete system analysis and in digital signal processing applications. We begin by returning to the notion of representing an LTI system by a block diagram or signal flow graph. The direct, cascade, parallel, and lattice forms are treated with special emphasis placed on second-order substructures that are then used to synthesize the transfer function. An algorithm known as Mason's Gain Rule is introduced. This rule makes possible a very straightforward calculation of the transfer function between the input and any output of the system diagram (signal flow graph).

As an alternative to the Nth-order form of the difference equation

$$y(n) = \sum_{k=1}^{N} a_k y(n - k) + \sum_{k=0}^{L} b_k x(n - k) \tag{11.1}$$

the state-space description is introduced wherein N first-order difference equations are used to describe an LTI system. These equations can be written as the matrix equation

$$\mathbf{v}(n + 1) = \mathbf{A}\,\mathbf{v}(n) + \mathbf{B}\,x(n) \tag{11.2}$$

where $\mathbf{v}(n)$ is an $N \times 1$ vector of the newly defined states, $x(n)$ is the usual system input, and $\mathbf{A}$ and $\mathbf{B}$ are matrices. The state-space description requires an output equation of the form

$$y(n) = \mathbf{C}\,\mathbf{v}(n) + \mathbf{D}\,x(n) \tag{11.3}$$

where $y(n)$ is the output and $\mathbf{C}$ and $\mathbf{D}$ are matrices. Upon solving the state equation in an iterative fashion we find that the result is separated nicely into the initial condition response and forced response (a vector version of the convolution sum). This discrete-time domain solution is compared with the result obtained by taking the z-transform of the original state equation and stability concepts are revisited from the state-space point of view.

The chapter closes with some other examples of the use of z-transforms in the analysis and design of LTI discrete systems including the digital signal processing application of deconvolution or inverse filtering.

11.1 ■■■ SYSTEM IMPLEMENTATIONS

We previously considered several models for LTI discrete systems, including representations by a difference equation, the unit sample response, and a transfer function. In this section, we take a more detailed look at transfer functions and how they can be implemented. Surprisingly, perhaps, we find that several different structures can represent the same transfer function. When we get to the point of actually implementing a digital filter, some of these structures have superior properties insofar as finite word length effects are concerned.

11.1.1 Direct Structure

We can write the transfer function for recursive digital filters as the ratio of two polynomials

$$H(z) = \frac{Y(z)}{X(z)} = \frac{b_0 + b_1 z^{-1} + b_2 z^{-2} + \cdots + b_L z^{-L}}{1 - a_1 z^{-1} - a_2 z^{-2} - \cdots - a_N z^{-N}} \tag{11.4}$$

where the a_i and b_j are real coefficients. Putting Eq. 11.4 into a more compact form gives us

$$H(z) = \frac{Y(z)}{X(z)} = \frac{\sum\limits_{k=0}^{k=L} b_k z^{-k}}{1 - \sum\limits_{k=1}^{k=N} a_k z^{-k}} \tag{11.5}$$

which can be written as the product of two transfer functions, namely

$$H(z) = \frac{Y(z)}{X(z)} = \frac{\sum\limits_{k=0}^{k=L} b_k z^{-k}}{1} \cdot \frac{1}{1 - \sum\limits_{k=1}^{N} a_k z^{-k}}. \tag{11.6}$$

It is convenient to define a new variable $W(z)$[†] such that

$$\frac{Y(z)}{W(z)} \cdot \frac{W(z)}{X(z)} = \frac{\sum\limits_{k=0}^{k=L} b_k z^{-k}}{1} \cdot \frac{1}{1 - \sum\limits_{k=1}^{k=N} a_k z^{-k}} \tag{11.7}$$

where

$$\frac{Y(z)}{W(z)} = \sum\limits_{k=0}^{k=L} b_k z^{-k} \tag{11.8}$$

and

$$\frac{W(z)}{X(z)} = \frac{1}{1 - \sum\limits_{k=1}^{k=N} a_k z^{-k}}. \tag{11.9}$$

[†]The symbol W was chosen for Professor R. C. H. Wheeler of the Naval Postgraduate School who developed a similar method for synthesizing transfer functions on analog computers in the 1950s.

Then, solving Eq. 11.9 for $W(z)$ gives

$$W(z) = X(z) + \sum_{k=1}^{N} a_k z^{-k} W(z) \qquad (11.10)$$

which corresponds to the difference equation

$$w(n) = x(n) + \sum_{k=1}^{N} a_k w(n - k). \qquad (11.11)$$

From Eq. 11.8 we can write $Y(z)$ as

$$Y(z) = \sum_{k=0}^{L} b_k z^{-k} W(z) \qquad (11.12)$$

which gives the difference equation

$$y(n) = \sum_{k=0}^{L} b_k w(n - k). \qquad (11.13)$$

Equations 11.11 and 11.13 define the *direct structure* of Fig. 11.1(a) which

FIGURE 11.1 Signal flow graph representation of direct structures

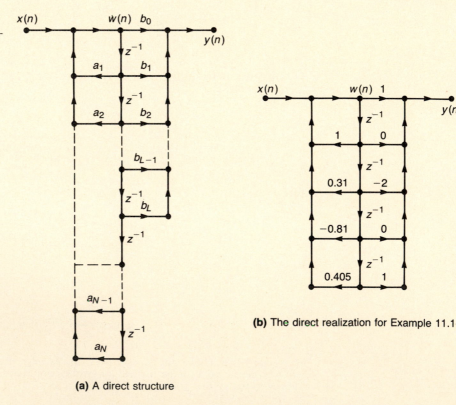

(a) A direct structure

(b) The direct realization for Example 11.1

can be called a canonical realization because it possesses the minimum number of delay elements for the transfer function of Eq. 11.4.

Example 11.1. This example illustrates the direct realization of a fourth-order filter.

Given the transfer function of a fourth-order filter

$$H(z) = \frac{Y(z)}{X(z)} = \frac{z^4 - 2z^2 + 1}{z^4 - z^3 - 0.31z^2 + 0.81z - 0.405} \tag{11.14}$$

draw its direct structure realization.

Solution: First, we write the transfer function in negative powers of z as

$$H(z) = \frac{Y(z)}{X(z)} = \frac{1 - 2z^{-2} + z^{-4}}{1 - z^{-1} - 0.31z^{-2} + 0.81z^{-3} - 0.405z^{-4}} \tag{11.15}$$

and define $W(z)$ from Eq. 11.10 as

$$W(z) = X(z) + \sum_{k=1}^{4} a_k z^{-k} W(z) \tag{11.16}$$

where substitution of $a_1 z^{-1}$, $a_2 z^{-2}$, $a_3 z^{-3}$, and $a_4 z^{-4}$ from Eq. (11.15) gives us

$$W(z) = X(z) + [z^{-1} + 0.31z^{-2} - 0.81z^{-3} + 0.405z^{-4}]W(z). \tag{11.17}$$

Then, from Eq. 11.12

$$Y(z) = \sum_{k=0}^{4} b_k z^{-k} W(z) \tag{11.18}$$

which for this example is

$$Y(z) = [1 - 2z^{-2} + z^{-4}]W(z) \tag{11.19}$$

and the direct realization is given in Fig. 11.1(b).

11.1.2 Second-Order Substructures

In order to minimize coefficient sensitivity problems, we can realize a transfer function $H(z)$ as a cascade or parallel combination of second-order structures of the form

$$H_1(z) = \frac{b_0 + b_1 z^{-1} + b_2 z^{-2}}{1 - a_1 z^{-1} - a_2 z^{-2}} \tag{11.20}$$

with the second-order realization given in Fig. 11.2. The appropriate difference equations for each second-order structure are

$$w(n) = x(n) + a_1 w(n-1) + a_2 w(n-2)$$

$$y(n) = b_0 w(n) + b_1 w(n-1) + b_2 w(n-2) \tag{11.21}$$

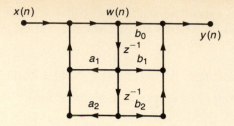

FIGURE 11.2 A second-order substructure

$x(n)$ $w(n)$ b_0 $y(n)$

z^{-1}

a_1 b_1

z^{-1} b_2

a_2

and we note from Fig. 11.2 that there are only two time delays and two summing junctions. Also, these equations should be calculated in the order given. That is, with zero initial conditions, we would calculate in order

$$w(0) = x(0), \quad y(0) = b_0 w(0), \quad w(1) = x(1) + a_1 w(0), \quad y(1) = b_0 w(1) + b_1 w(0),$$

$$w(2) = x(2) + a_1 w(1) + a_2 w(0), \quad y(2) = b_0 w(2) + b_1 w(1) + b_2 w(0),$$

and so forth.

11.1.3 Cascade Realization

A structure built from second-order substructures connected in cascade (series) is illustrated in Fig. 11.3(a). Utilizing the second-order structure of Eq. 11.20, we have for a cascade of three the product of the three transfer functions, namely

$$H(z) = H_1(z) \cdot H_2(z) \cdot H_3(z) \tag{11.22}$$

or

$$H(z) = \frac{b_{10} + b_{11}z^{-1} + b_{12}z^{-2}}{1 - a_{11}z^{-1} - a_{12}z^{-2}} \cdot \frac{b_{20} + b_{21}z^{-1} + b_{22}z^{-2}}{1 - a_{21}z^{-1} - a_{22}z^{-2}} \cdot$$

$$\frac{b_{30} + b_{31}z^{-1} + b_{32}z^{-2}}{1 - a_{31}z^{-1} - a_{32}z^{-2}} \cdot \tag{11.23}$$

Thus, for M of these structures we can write the general expression for a cascade connection as

$$H(z) = \frac{\displaystyle\prod_{k=1}^{k=M} (b_{k0} + b_{k1}z^{-1} + b_{k2}z^{-2})}{\displaystyle\prod_{k=1}^{k=M} (1 - a_{k1}z^{-1} - a_{k2}z^{-2})} \tag{11.24}$$

FIGURE 11.3(a) A cascade connection of three subsections

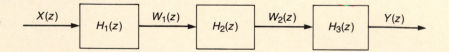

$X(z)$ $H_1(z)$ $W_1(z)$ $H_2(z)$ $W_2(z)$ $H_3(z)$ $Y(z)$

CHAPTER 11 STRUCTURES, STATE EQUATIONS, AND APPLICATIONS

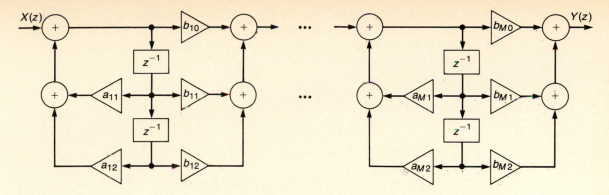

FIGURE 11.3(b) A cascade connection of M subsections

where Π in Eq. 11.24 denotes products of the terms that follow and the system diagram is given in Fig. 11.3(b).

Note that if the filter is of an odd order, say five, we can realize this with three second-order structures and simply set certain gains to zero (a_{k2}, b_{k2}, and possibly b_{k1}) in one of them.

Example 11.2. This example illustrates a cascade realization of a fourth-order filter.

Determine a cascade realization of the filter of Example 11.1.

Solution: The first step is to factor the transfer function into second-order terms. With the help of a computer we can find the zeros and poles and then recombine them into the form required by Eq. 11.24. Proceeding, we have

$$H(z) = \frac{Y(z)}{X(z)} = \frac{z^4 - 2z^2 + 1}{z^4 - z^3 - 0.31z^2 + 0.81z - 0.405} \tag{11.25}$$

where the numerator factors into

$$
\begin{aligned}
(z^4 - 2z^2 + 1) &= (z^2 - 1)^2 \\
&= (z + 1)^2 (z - 1)^2.
\end{aligned}
\tag{11.26}
$$

The poles are

$$z_{1,2} = 0.5 \pm j0.5 \quad \text{and} \quad z_{3,4} = \pm 0.9 \tag{11.27}$$

consequently the denominator may be written as

$$(z^2 - z + 0.5)(z^2 - 0.81) \tag{11.28}$$

and the transfer function is

$$H(z) = \frac{(z + 1)^2 (z - 1)^2}{(z^2 - z + 0.5)(z^2 - 0.81)} \tag{11.29}$$

or in terms of negative powers of z needed to represent delays we have

$$H(z) = \frac{(1 + z^{-1})^2 (1 - z^{-1})^2}{(1 - z^{-1} + 0.5z^{-2})(1 - 0.81z^{-2})}. \tag{11.30}$$

We must group complex poles together as well as complex zeros in order that the filter gains (constants) on the implementation diagram (SFG) are real numbers. Otherwise, the decomposition of $H(z)$ into the product $H_1(z) \cdot H_2(z)$ is quite arbitrary and we can define

$$H_1(z) = \frac{(1 + z^{-1})^2}{1 - z^{-1} + 0.5z^{-2}} \quad \text{and} \quad H_2(z) = \frac{(1 - z^{-1})^2}{1 - 0.81z^{-2}} \quad (11.31)$$

that is,

$$H_1(z) = \frac{1 + 2z^{-1} + z^{-2}}{1 - z^{-1} + 0.5z^{-2}} \quad \text{and} \quad H_2(z) = \frac{1 - 2z^{-1} + z^{-2}}{1 - 0.81z^{-2}}. \quad (11.32)$$

This realization is given in Fig. 11.4. There are, of course, other ways to break the original transfer function up into second-order sections to connect in cascade.

11.1.4 Parallel Realization (Partial Fraction Expansion)

A parallel structure is built from M second-order substructures connected in parallel as in Fig. 11.5 where the system transfer function is

FIGURE 11.4 Cascade realization of a fourth-order system (Example 11.2)

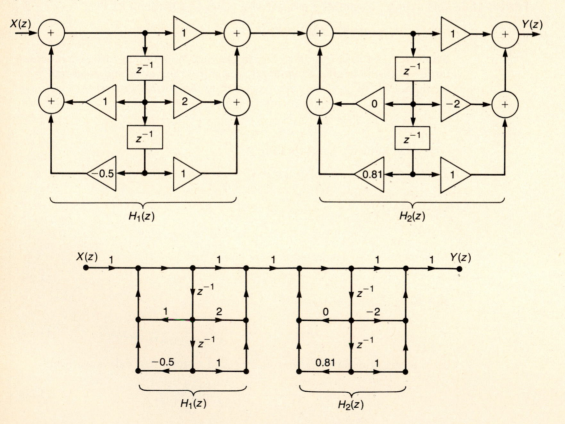

CHAPTER 11 STRUCTURES, STATE EQUATIONS, AND APPLICATIONS

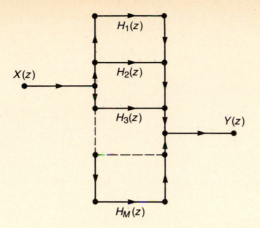

FIGURE 11.5 Parallel (PFE) connection

$$\frac{Y(z)}{X(z)} = H(z) = H_1(z) + H_2(z) + \cdots + H_M(z). \tag{11.33}$$

For nonrepeated poles, the Partial Fraction Expansion (PFE) of $H(z)$ into first-order terms is

$$H(z) = C_0 + \sum_{k=1}^{N} \frac{C_k z}{z - p_k} \tag{11.34}$$

where the first parallel structure is $H_0(z) = C_0 = H(z)|_{z=0}$. To obtain terms in the second-order form for use in this parallel realization, we combine two first-order terms such as

$$\frac{C_1 z}{z - p_1} + \frac{C_2 z}{z - p_2} = \frac{(C_1 + C_2)z^2 - (C_1 p_2 + C_2 p_1)z}{z^2 - z(p_1 + p_2) + p_1 p_2} \tag{11.35}$$

where, of course, p_1 and p_2 may be complex conjugates that must be grouped together. In this situation, C_1 and C_2 will also be complex conjugates. Thus, each second-order term has the form

$$Q(z) = \frac{b_0 z^2 + b_1 z}{z^2 - a_1 z - a_2}$$

$$= \frac{b_0 + b_1 z^{-1}}{1 - a_1 z^{-1} - a_2 z^{-2}} \tag{11.36}$$

where for real p_1 and p_2

$$b_0 = C_1 + C_2, \; b_1 = -[C_1 p_2 + C_2 p_1], \; a_1 = (p_1 + p_2), \; a_2 = -p_1 p_2 \tag{11.37}$$

and for $p_1{}^* = p_2$ and $C_1{}^* = C_2$

$$b_0 = 2 \, \text{Re}[C_1], \; b_1 = -2|C_1| \, |p_1| \cos(\angle C_1 - \angle p_1)$$

$$a_1 = 2 \, \text{Re}[p_1], \; a_2 = -|p_1|^2. \tag{11.38}$$

Thus, we can now write the transfer function in the form

$$H(z) = C_0 + \sum_{k=1}^{M} Q_k(z) \tag{11.39}$$

where

$$Q_k(z) = \frac{b_{k0} + b_{k1}z^{-1}}{1 - a_{k1}z^{-1} - a_{k2}z^{-2}} \tag{11.40}$$

in the style of Eq. 11.36. Note that there are M second-order systems in parallel as in Fig. 11.5 and that the C_0 term of Eq. 11.39 has not been included.

Example 11.3. This example illustrates a parallel realization of a fourth-order filter.

For the transfer function of Examples 11.1 and 11.2

$$H(z) = \frac{z^4 - 2z^2 + 1}{z^4 - z^3 - 0.31z^2 + 0.81z - 0.405} \tag{11.41}$$

determine a parallel realization using second-order sections.

Solution: The first requirement is to factor the denominator of $H(z)$ into second-order terms to match up with the form of the denominator of $Q(z)$ in Eq. 11.36. We can use the result from Example 11.2, namely Eq. 11.29, to write the transfer function as

$$H(z) = \frac{z^4 - 2z^2 + 1}{(z^2 - z + 0.5)(z^2 - 0.81)}$$

$$= \frac{1 - 2z^{-1} + z^{-4}}{(1 - z^{-1} + 0.5z^{-2})(1 - 0.81z^{-2})}. \tag{11.42}$$

We want to expand $H(z)$ in the manner of Eq. 11.39 with a constant and two second-order sections in parallel as

$$H(z) = C_0 + \frac{b_{10} + b_{11}z^{-1}}{1 - z^{-1} + 0.5z^{-2}} + \frac{b_{20} + b_{21}z^{-1}}{1 - 0.81z^{-2}} \tag{11.43}$$

or

$$H(z) = C_0 + \frac{b_{10}z^2 + b_{11}z}{z^2 - z + 0.5} + \frac{b_{20}z^2 + b_{21}z}{z^2 - 0.81}. \tag{11.44}$$

The easiest way to find the values of b_{10}, b_{11}, b_{20}, and b_{21} for the second-order sections is to use Eq. 11.35 which means expanding $H(z)$ as first-order terms and then recombining as indicated in Eq. 11.35 through Eq. 11.38. So we go back and write the denominator of $H(z)/z$ as a product of first-order terms, namely

$$\frac{H(z)}{z} = \frac{z^4 - 2z^2 + 1}{z(z - 0.707e^{j\pi/4})(z - 0.707e^{-j\pi/4})(z + 0.9)(z - 0.9)} \tag{11.45}$$

which becomes in terms of a partial fraction expansion

$$\frac{H(z)}{z} \equiv \frac{C_0}{z} + \frac{C_1}{z - 0.707e^{j\pi/4}} + \frac{C_1{}^*}{z - 0.707e^{-j\pi/4}} + \frac{C_3}{z + 0.9} + \frac{C_4}{z - 0.9}$$

(11.46)

where the complex poles have been written in polar form to match pair number 8 in Table 6.1. In the usual way

$$C_0 = \left.\frac{H(z)}{z} \cdot z\right|_{z=0} = \frac{1}{-0.405} = -2.47.$$

(11.47)

Evaluation of the partial fraction constant for the complex conjugate pole at $z = 0.707e^{j\pi/4}$ is far more complicated but the procedure is the same, so in the usual way

$$C_1 = \left.\frac{H(z)}{z} \cdot (z - 0.707e^{j\pi/4})\right|_{z=0.707e^{j\pi/4}}$$

(11.48)

or

$$C_1 = \left.\frac{(z^4 - 2z^2 + 1)(z - 0.707e^{j\pi/4})}{z(z - 0.707e^{j\pi/4})(z - 0.707e^{-j\pi/4})(z^2 - 0.81)}\right|_{z=0.707e^{j\pi/4}}$$

$$= \frac{(0.707e^{j\pi/4})^4 - 2(0.707e^{j\pi/4})^2 + 1}{(0.707e^{j\pi/4})(0.707e^{j\pi/4} - 0.707e^{-j\pi/4})([0.707e^{j\pi/4}]^2 - 0.81)}$$

(11.49)

and finally,

$$C_1 = 1.857e^{j0.41} = 1.702 + j0.743$$

(11.50)

and its complex conjugate is

$$C_1{}^* = 1.702 - j0.743.$$

(11.51)

The second-order equation derived from the poles, $p_{1,2} = 0.707e^{\pm j\pi/4} = 0.5 \pm j0.5$, is

$$H_1(z) = \frac{(C_1 + C_1{}^*)z^2 - (C_1p_1{}^* + C_1{}^*p_1)z}{z^2 - (p_1 + p_2)z + p_1p_2}$$

$$= \frac{3.40z^2 - 2.44z}{z^2 - z + 0.5} = \frac{3.40 - 2.44z^{-1}}{1 - z^{-1} + 0.5z^{-2}}.$$

(11.52)

For the other two constants

$$C_3 = \left.\frac{H(z)}{z} \cdot (z + 0.9)\right|_{z=-0.9}$$

$$= 0.010$$

(11.53)

and

$$C_4 = \left.\frac{H(z)}{z} \cdot (z - 0.9)\right|_{z=0.9}$$

$$= 0.054.$$

(11.54)

The second-order section derived from the poles, $p_{3,4} = \pm 0.9$, is

$$H_2(z) = \frac{(C_3 + C_4)z^2 - (0.9C_3 - 0.9C_4)z}{z^2 - 0.81}$$

$$= \frac{0.064z^2 + 0.040z}{z^2 - 0.81} = \frac{0.064 + 0.040z^{-1}}{1 - 0.81z^{-2}}. \qquad (11.55)$$

Now we have all the unknown constants from Eq. 11.43 and the filter implementation can be drawn as in Fig. 11.6.

11.1.5 Lattice Filters

We have just discussed the realization of system transfer functions or algorithms as direct, cascade, or parallel structures. Now, we give a brief introduction to the nonrecursive lattice structure, that occurs, for example, in the analysis and synthesis of speech for simulating the vocal tract. These structures are also prominent in systems designed for the purpose of linear prediction. The basic idea of the lattice structure is given in Fig. 11.7(a) with the input $x(n)$ and the outputs $y_1(n)$ and $w_1(n)$ related by

$$y_1(n) = x(n) + k_1x(n - 1)$$

$$w_1(n) = k_1x(n) + x(n - 1) \qquad (11.56)$$

If another section is cascaded with the first one as shown in Fig. 11.7(b) the describing equations are

$$y_2(n) = y_1(n) + k_2w_1(n - 1)$$

$$= x(n) + k_1x(n - 1) + k_2[k_1x(n - 1) + x(n - 2)]$$

$$= x(n) + [k_1 + k_1k_2]x(n - 1) + k_2x(n - 2) \qquad (11.57)$$

FIGURE 11.6 Parallel realization for Example 11.3

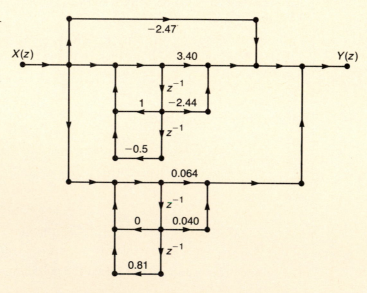

FIGURE 11.7 Cascade connection of lattice sections

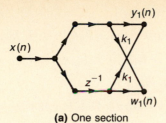

(a) One section

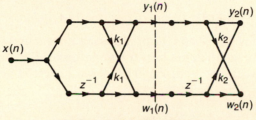

(b) Two sections in cascade

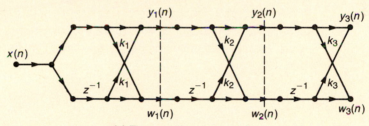

(c) Three sections in cascade

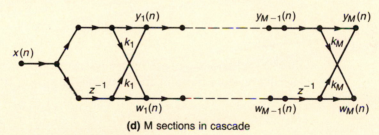

(d) M sections in cascade

$$w_2(n) = k_2 y_1(n) + w_1(n-1)$$

$$= k_2 x(n) + k_1 k_2 x(n-1) + [k_1 x(n-1) + x(n-2)]$$

$$= k_2 x(n) + [k_1 + k_1 k_2]x(n-1) + x(n-2). \qquad (11.58)$$

Finally, adding a third section in a cascade connection as in Fig. 11.7(c) gives

$$y_3(n) = x(n) + [k_1 + k_1 k_2 + k_2 k_3]x(n-1) +$$

$$[k_2 + k_1 k_3 + k_1 k_2 k_3]x(n-2) + k_3 x(n-3) \qquad (11.59)$$

and

$$w_3(n) = k_3x(n) + [k_2 + k_1k_3 + k_1k_2k_3]x(n-1) +$$
$$[k_1 + k_1k_2 + k_2k_3]x(n-2) + x(n-3). \qquad (11.60)$$

We can write Eq. 11.59 as

$$y_3(n) = x(n) + b_1x(n-1) + b_2x(n-2) + b_3x(n-3) \qquad (11.61)$$

and using the same coefficients (values of b_i) Eq. 11.60 becomes

$$w_3(n) = b_3x(n) + b_2x(n-1) + b_1x(n-2) + x(n-3). \qquad (11.62)$$

Equations 11.61 and 11.62 describe nonrecursive (FIR) filters that have the same coefficients but in reverse order. For a cascade connection of M lattice sections as in Fig. 11.7(d) we have the general expressions

$$y_M(n) = \sum_{i=0}^{M} b_ix(n-i) \quad \text{and} \quad w_M(n) = \sum_{i=0}^{M} b_{M-i}x(n-i) \qquad (11.63)$$

where we set (define) $b_0 = 1$. If we let $x(n) = \delta(n)$, the z-transforms of the unit sample responses of Eq. 11.63 are given by the polynomials

$$Y_M(z) = \sum_{i=0}^{M} b_iz^{-i} \qquad (11.64)$$

and

$$W_M(z) = \sum_{i=0}^{M} b_{M-i}z^{-i} \qquad (11.65)$$

where $Y_M(z)$ and $W_M(z)$ are *image polynomials*, which means that we can describe one polynomial in terms of the other, that is

$$W_M(z) = z^{-M} Y_M(1/z) \qquad (11.66)$$

Example 11.4. This example illustrates the relationship of $Y_M(z)$ to $W_M(z)$.

Given the polynomial

$$Y_2(z) = 1 - 0.9z^{-1} + 0.8z^{-2} \qquad (11.67)$$

and the two-stage lattice realization of Fig. 11.7(b), use Eq. 11.66 to derive the polynomial $W_M(z)$.

Solution: Using $M = 2$ in Eq. 11.66 gives

$$W_2(z) = z^{-2}Y_2(1/z)$$
$$= z^{-2}\{Y_2(z)\}|_{z=1/z} \qquad (11.68)$$

and substituting Eq. 11.67 into Eq. 11.68 with z replaced by $1/z$ we have

$$W_2(z) = z^{-2}\,[1 - 0.9z + 0.8z^2]$$

$$= 0.8 - 0.9z^{-1} + z^{-2} \qquad (11.69)$$

which is the image polynomial of $Y_2(z)$.

The next question to answer is how are the filter gains (the k_m) calculated from a given unit sample response $Y_M(z)$ or $W_M(z)$? By inspection of Fig. 11.7(d) we see that the gains of the last lattice section (the Mth section) are equal to the coefficient b_M in Eqs. 11.64 and 11.65, that is

$$k_M = b_M \qquad (11.70)$$

We now show an example of computing all of the filter coefficients by brute force before giving the general computational procedure.

Example 11.5. This example illustrates the calculation of the filter gains for a two-stage lattice filter.

For the same FIR unit sample response (polynomial) of Example 11.4

$$Y_2(z) = 1 - 0.9z^{-1} + 0.8z^{-2} \qquad (11.71)$$

and the lattice realization of Fig. 11.8, find the filter coefficients k_1 and k_2.

Solution: From Eq. 11.57, Eq. 11.70, or Fig. 11.8 we have

$$k_2 = b_2$$

$$= 0.8. \qquad (11.72)$$

And from Fig. 11.8 or Eq. 11.57 we have

$$k_1 + k_1 k_2 = b_1 \qquad (11.73)$$

or

$$k_1 + 0.8k_1 = -0.9 \qquad (11.74)$$

giving

$$k_1 = -0.5. \qquad (11.75)$$

FIGURE 11.8   Lattice
structure for Example 11.5

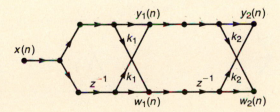

The orderly procedure for calculating the filter coefficients is based upon Eq. 11.70 which states that the gains of the last section (k_M) equal the last coefficient (b_M) in the M-section polynomial

$$Y_M(z) = \sum_{i=0}^{M} b_i z^{-i}. \tag{11.76}$$

Now consider the mth section $(1 \le m \le M)$ in the cascade connection of M lattice sections as in Fig. 11.9 where we see that

$$Y_m(z) = Y_{m-1}(z) + k_m z^{-1} W_{m-1}(z) \tag{11.77}$$

and

$$W_m(z) = k_m Y_{m-1}(z) + z^{-1} W_{m-1}(z). \tag{11.78}$$

We would like to obtain a relationship for $Y_{m-1}(z)$ in terms of $Y_m(z)$ and k_m. To do this we first solve Eq. 11.78 for $W_{m-1}(z)$ and substitute it into Eq. 11.77 giving

$$Y_m(z) = Y_{m-1}(z) + k_m z^{-1} \left[\frac{W_m(z) - k_m Y_{m-1}(z)}{z^{-1}} \right] \tag{11.79}$$

which when solved for $Y_{m-1}(z)$ yields

$$Y_{m-1}(z) = \frac{Y_m(z) - k_m W_m(z)}{1 - k_m^2} \tag{11.80}$$

for $k_m \ne 1$. Recalling Eq. 11.66 which states that the two image polynomials are related by

$$W_M(z) = z^{-M} Y_M(1/z) \tag{11.81}$$

and when Eq. 11.81 with $M = m$ is substituted into Eq. 11.80 we find that

$$\boxed{Y_{m-1}(z) = \frac{Y_m(z) - k_m z^{-m} Y_m(1/z)}{1 - k_m^2}}. \tag{11.82}$$

Thus, from Eq. 11.82 we see that the next lower order polynomial $Y_{m-1}(z)$ is calculated from $Y_m(z)$ and, consequently, the next set of filter coefficients. This step-down procedure (Markel and Gray, 1976) makes it possi-

FIGURE 11.9 The mth section in a cascade connection of M lattice sections

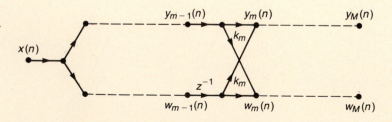

CHAPTER 11 STRUCTURES, STATE EQUATIONS, AND APPLICATIONS

ble to determine the filter coefficients k_m for $m = 1, 2, \ldots, M$ by beginning at $m = M$ and working backwards to $m = 1$.

Example 11.6 This example illustrates a step in developing the general procedure for finding lattice filter coefficients.

For our familiar unit sample response (polynomial)

$$Y_2(z) = 1 - 0.9z^{-1} + 0.8z^{-2} \tag{11.83}$$

use Eq. 11.82 and the knowledge that $k_2 = 0.8$ for Example 11.5 to calculate the filter gain k_1 of the first section.

Solution: We want to find the polynomial $Y_1(z)$ which from Eq. 11.82 is

$$Y_1(z) = \frac{Y_2(z) - k_2 z^{-2} Y_2(1/z)}{1 - k_2^{\,2}}$$

$$= \frac{[1 - 0.9z^{-1} + 0.8z^{-2}] - 0.8z^{-2}[1 - 0.9z + 0.8z^2]}{1 - (0.8)^2}$$

$$= \frac{1}{0.36}[0.36 - 0.18z^{-1}]$$

$$= 1 - 0.5z^{-1} \tag{11.84}$$

and the filter coefficient is $k_1 = -0.5$ as in Example 11.5.

Comment: If we had started with $Y_M(z)$ we could iteratively compute $Y_{M-1}(z)$, $Y_{M-2}(z), \ldots, Y_1(z)$.

To illustrate the general computational algorithm used to find the filter gains we first write the $Y_M(z)$ polynomial of Eq. 11.64 in the form

$$Y_M(z) = \sum_{i=0}^{M} b_{Mi} z^{-i} \tag{11.85}$$

where M is the number of lattice sections.

Replacing M with m we have the polynomial for m sections, namely

$$Y_m(z) = \sum_{i=0}^{m} b_{mi} z^{-i}. \tag{11.86}$$

Then, replacing z with $1/z$ gives

$$Y_m(1/z) = \sum_{i=0}^{m} b_{mi} z^{i} \tag{11.87}$$

and to make it easier to keep track of the coefficients as we step through the procedure from $m = M$ to $m = 1$, Eq. 11.87 can be expressed as

$$Y_m(1/z) = \sum_{i=0}^{m} b_{m,m-i} z^{m-i}.$$

(11.88)

To illustrate this change of indexing, consider the polynomial $Y_m(z)$ for $m = 3$

$$Y_3(z) = \sum_{i=0}^{3} b_{3i} z^{-i}$$

$$= b_{30} + b_{31} z^{-1} + b_{32} z^{-2} + b_{33} z^{-3}$$

(11.89)

and

$$Y_3(1/z) = b_{30} + b_{31} z + b_{32} z^2 + b_{33} z^3.$$

(11.90)

Notice that Eq. 11.90 follows the forms of both Eqs. 11.87 and 11.88. With these definitions in hand we return to Eq. 11.82, namely

$$Y_{m-1}(z) = \frac{Y_m(z) - k_m z^{-m} Y_m(1/z)}{1 - k_m^2}$$

(11.91)

that using Eqs. 11.86 and 11.88 can be put into the form

$$\sum_{i=0}^{m-1} b_{m-1,i} z^{-i} = \frac{\sum_{i=0}^{m} b_{mi} z^{-i} - k_m z^{-m} \sum_{i=0}^{m} b_{m,m-i} z^{m-i}}{1 - k_m^2}$$

$$= \frac{\sum_{i=0}^{m} b_{mi} z^{-i} - k_m \sum_{i=0}^{m} b_{m,m-i} z^{-i}}{1 - k_m^2}.$$

(11.92)

Thus, by equating the coefficients of like powers of z on both sides the computational expression for the coefficients is (Markel and Gray, 1976)

$$\boxed{b_{m-1,i} = \frac{b_{mi} - k_m b_{m,m-i}}{1 - k_m^2}}$$

with $k_m = b_{mm}$ for $m = M, M - 1, \ldots, 1$

and $i = 0, 1, \ldots, m - 1$, $|k_m| \neq 1$[†]

(11.93)

[†] In applications of lattice filters it is often desirable to synthesize $1/Y_m(z)$ rather than $Y_m(z)$. To ensure the stability of the resulting filter in such cases it is required that $|k_m| < 1$.

CHAPTER 11 STRUCTURES, STATE EQUATIONS, AND APPLICATIONS

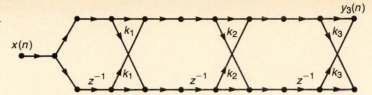

FIGURE 11.10 The three-stage lattice filter for Example 11.7

$y_3(n)$

$x(n)$

z^{-1} k_1 k_1 z^{-1} k_2 k_2 z^{-1} k_3 k_3

Example 11.7. This example illustrates the use of the computational algorithm for finding lattice filter coefficients.

An FIR filter is described by the transform of its unit sample response

$$Y_3(z) = 1 + 0.5z^{-1} + 0.2z^{-2} - 0.5z^{-3}. \tag{11.94}$$

For the lattice filter of Fig. 11.10 use the computational algorithm of Eq. 11.93 to determine the filter gains k_1, k_2, and k_3.

Solution: The transform to be realized is described by the polynomial

$$Y_3(z) = 1 + 0.5z^{-1} + 0.2z^{-2} - 0.5z^{-3} \tag{11.95}$$

which when put into the form of Eq. 11.86 is

$$Y_3(z) = 1 + b_{31}z^{-1} + b_{32}z^{-2} + b_{33}z^{-3}. \tag{11.96}$$

Starting with $m = 3$ we have from Eq. 11.93

$$\begin{aligned} k_3 &= b_{33} \\ &= -0.5. \end{aligned} \tag{11.97}$$

Now, we need to generate the coefficients for $Y_2(z)$ and from Eq. 11.93

$$b_{m-1,i} = \frac{b_{mi} - k_m b_{m,m-i}}{1 - k_m{}^2} \tag{11.98}$$

and for $m = 3$, $k_m = k_3 = -0.5$, and $i = 0$ we have

$$\begin{aligned} b_{20} &= \frac{b_{30} - k_3 b_{33}}{1 - k_3{}^2} \\ &= \frac{1 - (-0.5)(-0.5)}{1 - (-0.5)^2} = 1. \end{aligned} \tag{11.99}$$

Next, for $m = 3$, $k_3 = -0.5$, and $i = 1$ we get b_{21}

$$\begin{aligned} b_{21} &= \frac{b_{31} - k_3 b_{32}}{1 - (-0.5)^2} \\ &= \frac{0.5 - (-0.5)(0.2)}{1 - (-0.5)^2} = 0.8 \end{aligned} \tag{11.100}$$

and finally

$$\begin{aligned} b_{22} &= \frac{b_{32} - k_3 b_{31}}{1 - (k_3)^2} \\ &= \frac{0.2 - (-0.5)(0.5)}{1 - (-0.5)^2} = 0.6. \end{aligned} \tag{11.101}$$

From Eq. 11.93 this is also k_2. The new polynomial is

$$Y_2(z) = 1 + b_{21}z^{-1} + b_{22}z^{-2}$$
$$= 1 + 0.8z^{-1} + 0.6z^{-2}. \tag{11.102}$$

Stepping down to the first stage we calculate b_{11} which is

$$b_{11} = \frac{b_{21} - k_2 b_{21}}{1 - (k_2)^2}$$

$$= \frac{0.8 - (0.6)(0.8)}{1 - (0.6)^2} = 0.5 \tag{11.103}$$

which is, of course, k_1. The iterative process is complete and the filter gains for Fig. 11.10 are

$$k_1 = 0.5, \; k_2 = 0.6, \quad \text{and} \quad k_3 = -0.5 \tag{11.104}$$

which will yield the given FIR unit sample response of

$$Y_3(z) = 1 + 0.5z^{-1} + 0.2z^{-2} - 0.5z^{-3}. \tag{11.105}$$

11.2 ■■■ MASON'S GAIN RULE

According to C. S. Lorens (1964) the concept of a signal flow graph was originally worked out by C. E. Shannon (1942) in a classified report dealing with analog computers. This work was essentially unknown until 1956 when it was mentioned by Shannon at M.I.T. where Professor S. J. Mason (1952, 1953, 1956) was formulating and organizing precise rules for manipulating graphs that dealt with the flow of electronic signals. A very significant development of Mason's was the rule (or algorithm) that can be used for calculating transfer functions between input and output nodes of a signal flow graph. (With a slight modification this rule also applies to a block diagram representation of an LTI system.) A proof of this rule is based on Cramer's method for solving a set of simultaneous algebraic equations and, consequently, we can apply the Mason Gain Rule (MGR) in the algebraic z-domain. We explain the rule by using an SFG which is the cascade connection of a second-order section and a first-order section.

Now let's consider the following general definitions and their applicability to the particular graph of Fig. 11.11(a).

Branch—A directed line segment, having an associated gain, that connects two nodes. If the gain of a branch is unmarked it is customary to assume that the gain is unity. We follow that custom. Three easily identified branches are the delays with gains of z^{-1}.

Nodes—Points on the graph where the signals appear. All the heavy dots are nodes. The most important of these are $X(z)$, $Q(z)$, and $Y(z)$. At any node, the quantities associated with the incoming branches

FIGURE 11.11 A signal
flow graph with its paths
and loops

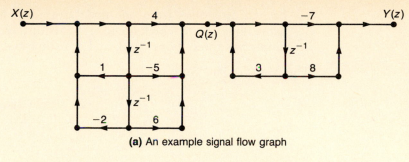

(a) An example signal flow graph

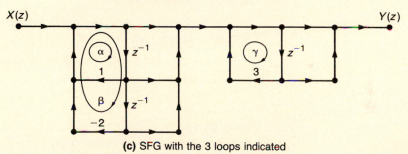

(b) SFG with the 6 paths indicated

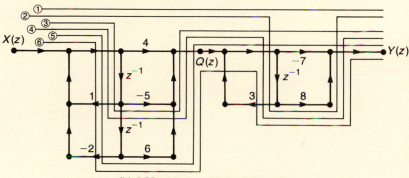

(c) SFG with the 3 loops indicated

are summed, while the outgoing branches have no effect on the signal at the node.

Input node—Can have no incoming branches. Obviously $X(z)$ is the only input node.

Output node—Must have at least one incoming branch. All the rest of the nodes of the graph are output nodes. We use the node $Y(z)$ to represent the system output.

Path—A continuous sequence of branches, traversed in the indicated branch direction, along which no node is encountered more than once. From $X(z)$ to $Y(z)$ there are six paths (P_1, P_2, P_3, P_4, P_5, and P_6) as marked in Fig. 11.11(b).

Loop—A continuous sequence of branches, traversed in the indicated branch directions from one node around a closed path back to the same node, along which no node is encountered more than once. This graph has three loops: α, β, and γ, as marked in Fig. 11.11(c).

The Mason Gain Rule is:

$$H(z) = \frac{Y(z)}{X(z)} = \frac{\displaystyle\sum_{k=1}^{M} P_k(z) \cdot \Delta_k(z)}{\Delta(z)} \qquad (11.106)$$

where

$H(z)$ = the transfer function relating an output node to an input node

$\Delta(z)$ = the graph determinant

$P_k(z)$ = the gain of the kth path from input to output

$\Delta_k(z)$ = cofactor of the kth path

These terms are defined as we find the transfer function $H(z) = Y(z)/X(z)$ for the SFG of Fig. 11.11 where there is a particular order required for the calculation of the three quantities $\Delta(z)$, $P_k(z)$, and $\Delta_k(z)$ of Eq. 11.106.

The first quantity to calculate is the graph determinant $\Delta(z)$ where

$\Delta(z) = 1 - \Sigma$ loop gains

      $+ \Sigma$ products of the gains of nontouching loops taken two at a time

      $- \Sigma$ products of the gains of nontouching loops taken three at a time

      $+$ and so on   (11.107)

where a loop gain L_j is simply the products of the gains around the jth loop. The three loop gains, consequently, from Fig. 11.11(c) are $L_1 = z^{-1}$ around the α loop, $L_2 = -2z^{-2}$ around the β loop, and $L_3 = 3z^{-1}$ around the γ loop. Loops α and γ do not touch[†] nor do loops β and γ, but α and β do touch, sharing several branches. Thus, $\Delta(z)$ of Eq. 11.107 is

$$\Delta(z) = 1 - \underbrace{(z^{-1} - 2z^{-2} + 3z^{-1})}_{\text{loop gains}} + \underbrace{[(z^{-1})(3z^{-1}) + (-2z^{-2})(3z^{-1})]}_{\substack{\text{nontouching loops} \\ \text{2 at a time}}} + 0$$

$$= 1 - 4z^{-1} + 5z^{-2} - 6z^{-3} \qquad (11.108)$$

The 0 has been written in $\Delta(z)$ to emphasize the termination in the calculation of $\Delta(z)$ where the maximum number of nontouching loops is two.

Next, we turn to the path gains $P_k(z)$ and their cofactors $\Delta_k(z)$ where

$$P_k(z) = \text{gain of the } k\text{th path from input to output}$$

[†] Two loops touch if they have at least one node in common.

and

$$\Delta_k(z) = \text{cofactor of the } k\text{th path, formed by striking out from } \Delta(z) \text{ all terms associated with loops that are touched by the } k\text{th path.}$$

So for the graph of Fig. 11.11(b) where the paths are marked we have

$$P_1(z) = -28 \quad \text{and } \Delta_1(z) = 1: P_1 \text{ touches all loops}$$

$$P_2(z) = 32z^{-1} \quad \text{and } \Delta_2(z) = 1: P_2 \text{ touches all loops}$$

$$P_3(z) = 35z^{-1} \quad \text{and } \Delta_3(z) = 1: P_3 \text{ touches all loops}$$

$$P_4(z) = -40z^{-2} \text{ and } \Delta_4(z) = 1: P_4 \text{ touches all loops}$$

$$P_5(z) = -42z^{-2} \text{ and } \Delta_5(z) = 1: P_5 \text{ touches all loops}$$

$$P_6(z) = 48z^{-3} \quad \text{and } \Delta_6(z) = 1: P_6 \text{ touches all loops.}$$

Returning to Eq. 11.106, the transfer function $H(z) = Y(z)/X(z)$ is

$$H(z) =$$
$$\frac{P_1(z)\Delta_1(z) + P_2(z)\Delta_2(z) + P_3(z)\Delta_3(z) + P_4(z)\Delta_4(z) + P_5(z)\Delta_5(z) + P_6(z)\Delta_6(z)}{\Delta(z)}$$

$$= \frac{-28(1) + 32z^{-1}(1) + 35z^{-1}(1) - 40z^{-2}(1) - 42z^{-2}(1) + 48z^{-3}(1)}{1 - 4z^{-1} + 5z^{-2} - 6z^{-3}}$$

$$(11.109)$$

or

$$H(z) = \frac{-28z^3 + 67z^2 - 82z + 48}{z^3 - 4z^2 + 5z - 6}. \tag{11.110}$$

The procedure for calculating a transfer function $H(z) = Y(z)/X(z)$ by using Mason's Gain Rule (MGR) is summarized below.

PROCEDURE

1. Identify all the loops in the graph and compute all the loop gains, L_j. Then calculate the graph determinant $\Delta(z)$ according to Eq. 11.107, namely

$$\Delta(z) = 1 - \Sigma \text{ loop gains}$$

$$+ \Sigma \text{ products of the gains of nontouching loops taken two at a time}$$

$$- \Sigma \text{ products of the gains of nontouching loops taken three at a time}$$

$$+ \text{ and so on.} \tag{11.111}$$

2. Locate the specified input node $X(z)$ and the specified output node $Y(z)$. Find all of the paths, P_k, $k = 1, 2, \ldots, M$ from $X(z)$ to $Y(z)$ and calculate the $P_k(z)\Delta_k(z)$ products according to the rules

$$P_k(z) = \text{gain of the } k\text{th path from } X(z) \text{ to } Y(z) \tag{11.112}$$

$$\Delta_k(z) = \text{cofactor of the } k\text{th path, formed by striking out from the graph determinant } \Delta(z) \text{ all of the terms associated with loops that are touched by the } k\text{th path.} \qquad (11.113)$$

3. The transfer function is then given by

$$H(z) = \frac{\displaystyle\sum_{k=1}^{M} P_k(z) \cdot \Delta_k(z)}{\Delta(z)}. \qquad (11.114)$$

Comment: Notice that when other transfer functions are determined from the same graph, we do not have to repeat Step #1. The graph determinant $\Delta(z)$ is a system characteristic and does not change with the selection of what particular transfer function is being determined.

Example 11.8. This example illustrates the transfer function calculation for the fourth-order filter of Example 11.1.

Given the direct realization of a fourth-order filter in Fig. 11.12(a), use MGR to find

a) $H_1(z) = Y(z)/X(z)$
b) $H_2(z) = W(z)/X(z)$.

Solution: We follow the steps in the procedure just outlined.

1. In Fig. 11.12(b) we identify four loops. Their gains are

$$L_1 = z^{-1}, \; L_2 = 0.31z^{-2}, \; L_3 = -0.81z^{-3}, \quad \text{and} \quad L_4 = 0.405z^{-4}. \quad (11.115)$$

The loops all touch so the graph determinant is simply

$$\Delta(z) = 1 - (z^{-1} + 0.31z^{-2} - 0.81z^{-3} + 0.405z^{-4})$$
$$= 1 - z^{-1} - 0.31z^{-2} + 0.81z^{-3} - 0.405z^{-4}. \qquad (11.116)$$

2a. For $H_1(z) = Y(z)/X(z)$ there are three paths marked as P_1, P_2, and P_3 in Fig. 11.12(c). Since all three paths touch all four loops the path gain-path cofactor products are

$$P_1(z) \cdot \Delta_1(z) = 1 \cdot 1 = 1$$
$$P_2(z) \cdot \Delta_2(z) = -2z^{-2} \cdot 1 = -2z^{-2}$$
$$P_3(z) \cdot \Delta_3(z) = z^{-4} \cdot 1 = z^{-4}. \qquad (11.117)$$

2b. For $H_2(z) = W(z)/X(z)$ there is one path and it is part of all of the loops, so we have from Fig. 11.12(d)

$$P_1(z) \cdot \Delta_1(z) = 1 \cdot 1 = 1. \qquad (11.118)$$

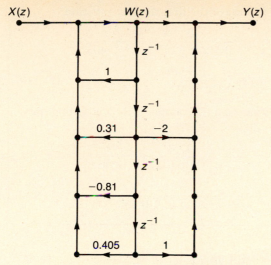

(a) Direct realization of a 4th-order filter.

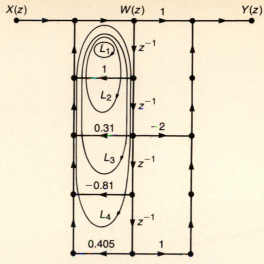

(b) 4 loops are identified

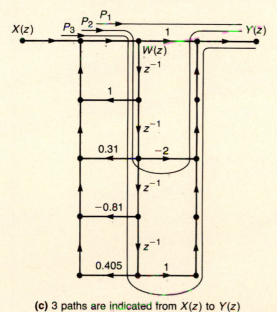

(c) 3 paths are indicated from $X(z)$ to $Y(z)$

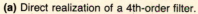

(d) 1 path from $X(z)$ to $W(z)$.

FIGURE 11.12   Data and results for Example 11.8

3. Using MGR from Eq. 11.114 we have the first transfer function

$$H_1(z) = \frac{Y(z)}{X(z)} = \frac{1 - 2z^{-2} + z^{-4}}{1 - z^{-1} - 0.31z^{-2} + 0.81z^{-3} - 0.405z^{-4}}$$

$$= \frac{z^4 - 2z^2 + 1}{z^4 - z^3 - 0.31z^2 + 0.81z - 0.405} \tag{11.119}$$

which was the given transfer function in Example 11.1. The second transfer function relating $W(z)$ to $X(z)$ is

$$H_2(z) = \frac{W(z)}{X(z)} = \frac{1}{1 - z^{-1} - 0.31z^{-2} + 0.81z^{-3} - 0.405z^{-4}}$$

$$= \frac{z^4}{z^4 - z^3 - 0.31z^2 + 0.81z - 0.405} \tag{11.120}$$

Example 11.9. This example illustrates the use of MGR on a different realization of the same transfer function.

From the cascade realization of a fourth-order filter given in Fig. 11.13(a), use MGR to compute the transfer function $H(z) = Y(z)/X(z)$.

Solution: From the prescribed procedure we have the following:

1. Marked on Fig. 11.13(b) are three loops whose gains are

$$L_1 = z^{-1}, \; L_2 = -0.5z^{-2}, \quad \text{and} \quad L_3 = 0.81z^{-2}. \tag{11.121}$$

With both L_1 and L_2 not touching L_3, the graph determinant is

$$\Delta(z) = 1 - (L_1 + L_2 + L_3) + (L_1L_3 + L_2L_3)$$

$$= 1 - (z^{-1} - 0.5z^{-2} + 0.81z^{-2}) + (0.81z^{-3} - 0.405z^{-4})$$

$$= 1 - z^{-1} - 0.31z^{-2} + 0.81z^{-3} - 0.405z^{-4}. \tag{11.122}$$

2. In Fig. 11.13(a) we have nine paths where all of the paths touch all of the loops, so we have

$$
\begin{array}{ll}
P_1(z)\Delta_1(z) = 1 & P_6(z)\Delta_6(z) = 2z^{-3} \\
P_2(z)\Delta_2(z) = -2z^{-1} & P_7(z)\Delta_7(z) = z^{-2} \\
P_3(z)\Delta_3(z) = z^{-2} & P_8(z)\Delta_8(z) = -2z^{-3} \\
P_4(z)\Delta_4(z) = 2z^{-1} & P_9(z)\Delta_9(z) = z^{-4} \\
P_5(z)\Delta_5(z) = -4z^{-2} &
\end{array}
\tag{11.123}
$$

3. Putting steps 1. and 2. together gives the transfer function

$$H(z) = \frac{Y(z)}{X(z)}$$

$$= \frac{1 - 2z^{-2} + z^{-4}}{1 - z^{-1} - 0.31z^{-2} + 0.81z^{-3} - 0.405z^{-4}} \tag{11.124}$$

FIGURE 11.13 Use of MGR on a cascade realization

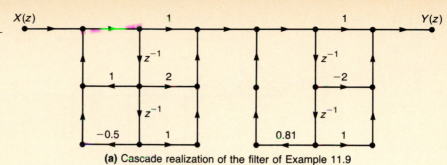

(a) Cascade realization of the filter of Example 11.9

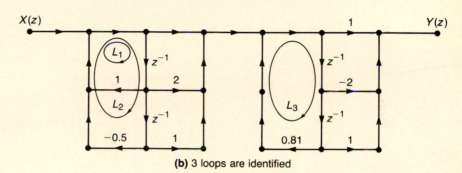

(b) 3 loops are identified

or in positive powers of z

$$H(z) = \frac{z^4 - 2z^2 + 1}{z^4 - z^3 - 0.31z^2 + 0.81z - 0.405} \qquad (11.125)$$

as in Eq. 11.119 from Example 11.8.

Example 11.10. This example illustrates the use of MGR on a parallel realization of the same transfer function.

From the parallel realization of Fig. 11.14 use MGR to determine $H(z) = Y(z)/X(z)$.

Solution:

1. There are still three loops and their gains are

$$L_1 = z^{-1}, \quad L_2 = -0.5z^{-2}, \quad \text{and} \quad L_3 = 0.81z^{-2} \qquad (11.126)$$

and the graph determinant is

$$\Delta = 1 - (L_1 + L_2 + L_3) + (L_1L_3 + L_2L_3)$$

$$= 1 - z^{-1} - 0.31z^{-2} + 0.81z^{-3} - 0.405z^{-4}. \qquad (11.127)$$

2. There are five paths and the path gain-path cofactor products are

$$P_1\Delta_1 = P_1(1 - L_1 - L_2 - L_3 + L_1L_3 + L_2L_3) = P_1\Delta$$

$$= -2.47(1 - z^{-1} - 0.31z^{-2} + 0.81z^{-3} - 0.405z^{-4}) \qquad (11.128)$$

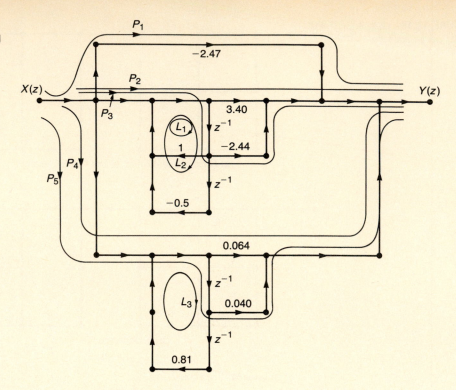

FIGURE 11.14 Parallel realization with loops and paths indicated.

$$P_2\Delta_2 = P_2(1 - L_3)$$

$$= 3.40(1 - 0.81z^{-2}) \tag{11.129}$$

$$P_3\Delta_3 = P_3(1 - L_3)$$

$$= -2.44z^{-1}(1 - 0.81z^{-2}) \tag{11.130}$$

$$P_4\Delta_4 = P_4(1 - L_1 - L_2)$$

$$= 0.064(1 - z^{-1} + 0.5z^{-2}) \tag{11.131}$$

$$P_5\Delta_5 = P_5(1 - L_1 - L_2)$$

$$= 0.040z^{-1}(1 - z^{-1} + 0.5z^{-2}). \tag{11.132}$$

3. For this parallel realization the transfer function is computed from the MGR as

$$H(z) = \frac{P_1\Delta_1 + P_2\Delta_2 + P_3\Delta_3 + P_4\Delta_4 + P_5\Delta_5}{\Delta}. \tag{11.133}$$

By substituting the results of parts 1. and 2. and with a fair amount of algebraic effort we get

$$H(z) = \frac{z^4 - 2z^2 + 1}{z^4 - z^3 - 0.31z^2 + 0.81z - 0.405} \tag{11.134}$$

as we did in Examples 11.8 and 11.9.

11.3 ▬ STATE DIFFERENCE EQUATIONS

We are used to working with a difference equation of the form

$$y(n) = a_1 y(n-1) + \cdots + a_N y(n-N) + b_0 x(n) + b_1 x(n-1) + \cdots + b_L x(n-L)$$

$$(11.135)$$

or in the notation

$$y(n) = \sum_{k=1}^{N} a_k y(n-k) + \sum_{k=0}^{L} b_k x(n-k) \qquad (11.136)$$

that is called the *Nth-order* form. An alternative is to describe an LTI system with N first-order difference equations and an output equation. This alternative form for describing a linear time-invariant system is known as the *state-space* description and can be written as a matrix equation

$$\mathbf{v}(n+1) = \mathbf{A}\,\mathbf{v}(n) + \mathbf{B}\,x(n) \qquad \text{state equation} \qquad (11.137)$$

with the system output given by

$$y(n) = \mathbf{C}\,\mathbf{v}(n) + \mathbf{D}\,x(n) \qquad \text{output equation.} \qquad (11.138)$$

In Eqs. 11.137 and 11.138, $\mathbf{v}(n)$ is a vector with N rows and 1 column (an $N \times 1$ vector or column matrix) of newly defined variables called the states, $x(n)$ is the system input, and $y(n)$ its output. (We will generalize this later to take care of multi-input, multi-output problems.) In the matrix state equation of Eq. 11.137 the matrix $\mathbf{A}$ must be an $N \times N$ matrix and the $\mathbf{B}$ matrix an $N \times 1$ vector. The scalar output $y(n)$ is defined by Eq. 11.138 where $\mathbf{C}$ is a $1 \times N$ row matrix and $\mathbf{D}$ is simply a real number that multiplies (or scales) the input $x(n)$. The elements in $\mathbf{A}$, $\mathbf{B}$, $\mathbf{C}$, and $\mathbf{D}$ are constants that depend only upon the system parameters.

11.3.1 Writing State Equations

To illustrate this approach to the modeling of LTI systems we return to a version of the Nth-order difference equation described as a simplified auto-regressive moving average (ARMA) model, namely

$$y(n) = a_1 y(n-1) + a_2 y(n-2) + \cdots + a_N y(n-N) + b_0 x(n). \quad (11.139)$$

We define the state variables (states) as the quantities

$$v_1(n),\ v_2(n),\ \ldots,\ v_N(n) \qquad (11.140)$$

and we see that the number of delays in the y terms is N and from Eq. 11.137 the number of state variables required is also N, the order of the system. So one possible set of definitions is

$$v_1(n) \triangleq y(n - N)$$
$$v_2(n) \triangleq y(n - N + 1)$$
$$v_3(n) \triangleq y(n - N + 2)$$
$$\vdots$$
$$v_{N-1}(n) \triangleq y(n - N + [N - 2]) = y(n - 2)$$
$$v_N(n) \triangleq y(n - 1). \tag{11.141}$$

Then, we can easily establish the following relationships

$$v_1(n + 1) = y(n - N + 1] = v_2(n)$$
$$v_2(n + 1) = y(n - N + 1 + 1) = v_3(n)$$
$$\vdots$$

$$v_{N-1}(n + 1) = v_N(n)$$
$$v_N(n + 1) = y(n) = a_1 y(n - 1) + a_2 y(n - 2) + \cdots + a_N y(n - N) + b_0 x(n)$$
$$= a_1 v_N(n) + a_2 v_{N-1}(n) + \cdots + a_N v_1(n) + b_0 x(n). \tag{11.142}$$

We can always use matrices and vectors to tidy things up and organize our results into a form more suitable for computation. In this case we define the state vector as

$$\mathbf{v}(n) \triangleq [v_1(n)\, v_2(n) \cdots v_N(n)]^T = \begin{bmatrix} v_1(n) \\ v_2(n) \\ \vdots \\ v_N(n) \end{bmatrix} \tag{11.143}$$

where the superscript T denotes the operation of matrix transposition and the state equations of Eq. 11.142 become the matrix state equation

$$\mathbf{v}(n + 1) = \underbrace{\begin{bmatrix} 0 & 1 & 0 & & \cdots & 0 \\ 0 & 0 & 1 & 0 & \cdots & 0 \\ \vdots & & & & & \\ 0 & 0 & 0 & & \cdots & 1 \\ a_N & a_{N-1} & & & \cdots & a_1 \end{bmatrix}}_{\mathbf{A}} \underbrace{\begin{bmatrix} v_1(n) \\ v_2(n) \\ \vdots \\ v_{N-1}(n) \\ v_N(n) \end{bmatrix}}_{\mathbf{v}(n)} + \underbrace{\begin{bmatrix} 0 \\ 0 \\ \vdots \\ b_0 \end{bmatrix}}_{\mathbf{B}} x(n) \tag{11.144}$$

It is very easy to establish the state equations by starting with the system diagram (flow graph). An SFG that describes Eq. 11.139 is given in Fig. 11.15(a). In Fig. 11.15(b) a typical unit delay is shown to illustrate that if $v_j(n)$ is the delay's output, its input is $v_j(n + 1)$. The states correspond to

FIGURE 11.15 Matrix state equation SFG

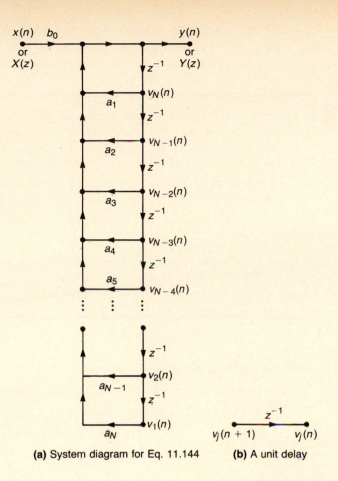

(a) System diagram for Eq. 11.144   (b) A unit delay

the outputs of unit delays, thus, we have by inspection

$$v_1(n + 1) = v_2(n)$$
$$v_2(n + 1) = v_3(n)$$
$$\vdots$$
$$v_{N-2}(n + 1) = v_{N-1}(n)$$
$$v_{N-1}(n + 1) = v_N(n)$$
$$v_N(n + 1) = a_N v_1(n) + \cdots + a_1 v_N(n) + b_0 x(n). \tag{11.145}$$

From Eqs. 11.139 and 11.141 the output equation is

$$y(n) = [a_N \quad a_{N-1} \cdots a_2 \quad a_1] \, v(n) + b_0 x(n) \tag{11.146}$$

and we have illustrated an easy way to determine a set of state equations as well as the output equation from an SFG. Assuming that we are starting with a given system difference equation or transfer function, a procedure for finding the state and output equations follows:

PROCEDURE

1. Draw an SFG that represents the system. This can be the direct, cascade, parallel, or lattice form, for example.

2. Label the outputs of all delays (the z^{-1} branches) as states. These can be done in any order but there must be N states.

3. At the input to the unit delay whose output is defined as $v_j(n)$, write a state equation of the form

$$v_j(n + 1) = \text{a weighted sum of } v_1(n),\ v_2(n),\ \ldots,\ v_N(n),\ \text{and } x(n). \quad (11.147)$$

Repeat this for each of the unit delays.

4. Obtain an equation for the output $y(n)$. This should be reduced so that $y(n)$ is a linear combination of the N states $v_1(n),\ \ldots,\ v_N(n)$ and the input $x(n)$.

5. Put all of this in matrix form if desired.

Example 11.11. This example illustrates writing state equations from a transfer function.

Given the transfer function for an LTI system, namely

$$H(z) = \frac{Y(z)}{X(z)} = \frac{3 + 5z^{-1} - 2z^{-2}}{1 + 6z^{-1} + 5z^{-2} + 2z^{-3} + z^{-4}} \quad (11.148)$$

write a matrix state equation and the corresponding output equation that describe this system.

Solution: We follow the steps outlined above.

1. The direct form representation of Eq. 11.148 is given in Fig. 11.16.

2. Four states are defined as shown in Fig. 11.16. Notice that we are mixing discrete-time notation (i.e., $v_1(n)$, etc.) with z-domain notation (z^{-1}). The numbering of the states is quite arbitrary.

3. At the input to each unit delay, whose output is defined as $v_j(n)$, we write a state equation of the form

$$v_j(n + 1) = \text{a weighted sum of } v_1(n),\ v_2(n),\ \ldots,\ v_N(n) \text{ and } x(n).$$

This is done for each of the unit delays and from Fig. 11.16 we have the state equations

$$v_1(n + 1) = v_2(n)$$
$$v_2(n + 1) = v_3(n)$$
$$v_3(n + 1) = v_4(n)$$
$$v_4(n + 1) = -v_1(n) - 2v_2(n) - 5v_3(n) - 6v_4(n) + x(n). \quad (11.149)$$

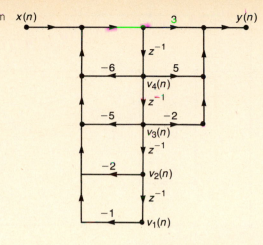

FIGURE 11.16 Direct form for Eq. 11.148 and four assigned states

4. From Fig. 11.16 we see that

$$y(n) = 3v_4(n + 1) + 5v_4(n) - 2v_3(n) \qquad (11.150)$$

and we can eliminate $v_4(n + 1)$ by substituting the last equation from Eq. 11.149 giving

$$y(n) = 3[-v_1(n) - 2v_2(n) - 5v_3(n) - 6v_4(n) + x(n)] + 5v_4(n) - 2v_3(n)$$
$$= -3v_1(n) - 6v_2(n) - 17v_3(n) - 13v_4(n) + 3x(n). \qquad (11.151)$$

5. The state equations and the output equation in matrix form are

$$\mathbf{v}(n + 1) = \begin{bmatrix} 0 & 1 & 0 & 0 \\ 0 & 0 & 1 & 0 \\ 0 & 0 & 0 & 1 \\ -1 & -2 & -5 & -6 \end{bmatrix} \mathbf{v}(n) + \begin{bmatrix} 0 \\ 0 \\ 0 \\ 1 \end{bmatrix} x(n)$$

$$y(n) = \begin{bmatrix} -3 & -6 & -17 & -13 \end{bmatrix} \mathbf{v}(n) + 3x(n). \qquad (11.152)$$

Example 11.12. This example illustrates finding the state equations for a parallel realization.

A parallel realization of the transfer function

$$H(z) = \frac{z^4 - 2z^2 + 1}{z^4 - z^3 - 0.31z^2 + 0.81z - 0.405} \qquad (11.153)$$

was determined in Example 11.3 and is repeated as an SFG in Fig. 11.17 where four states have already been designated. Write a set of state equations and the output equation for this system.

Solution: We again follow the step-by-step procedure outlined previously in Example 11.11.

Steps **1.** and **2.** are not required for we started with an SFG with the states already chosen.

11.3 STATE DIFFERENCE EQUATIONS

753

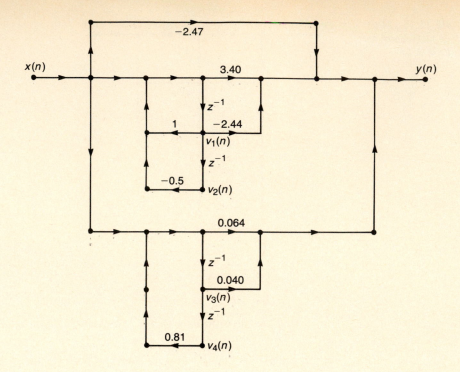

FIGURE 11.17 Parallel form and four assigned states

3. From the diagram the four state equations are

$$v_1(n + 1) = v_1(n) - 0.5v_2(n) + x(n)$$

$$v_2(n + 1) = v_1(n)$$

$$v_3(n + 1) = 0.81v_4(n) + x(n)$$

$$v_4(n + 1) = v_3(n).$$ (11.154)

4. The output $y(n)$ is

$$y(n) = -2.47x(n) + 3.40v_1(n + 1) - 2.44v_1(n) + 0.064v_3(n + 1) + 0.040v_3(n)$$

$$= -2.47x(n) + 3.40[v_1(n) - 0.50v_2(n) + x(n)] - 2.44v_1(n)$$

$$+ 0.064[0.81v_4(n) + x(n)] + 0.040v_3(n)$$

$$= 0.96v_1(n) - 1.70v_2(n) + 0.040v_3(n) + 0.0518v_4(n) + 0.994x(n).$$ (11.155)

5. The matrix state equation is

$$\mathbf{v}(n + 1) = \begin{bmatrix} 1 & -0.5 & 0 & 0 \\ 1 & 0 & 0 & 0 \\ 0 & 0 & 0 & 0.81 \\ 0 & 0 & 1 & 0 \end{bmatrix} \mathbf{v}(n) + \begin{bmatrix} 1 \\ 0 \\ 1 \\ 0 \end{bmatrix} x(n)$$ (11.156)

and the output equation in matrix form is

$$y(n) = [0.96 \quad -1.70 \quad 0.040 \quad 0.0518] \, \mathbf{v}(n) + 0.994x(n). \qquad (11.157)$$

We've only considered recursive systems up to this point but we follow the same procedure for writing state equations for nonrecursive systems. Starting from the general transfer function for a nonrecursive system, namely

$$H(z) = \sum_{k=0}^{L} b_k x(n - k) \qquad (11.158)$$

we draw the corresponding signal flow graph of Fig. 11.18 where the output of each delay has been defined as a state. Remember that the numbering of the states in Fig. 11.18 is arbitrary but there must be a total of L states assigned. Then from the diagram we have the state equations

$$v_1(n + 1) = v_2(n)$$
$$v_2(n + 1) = v_3(n)$$
$$\vdots$$
$$v_{L-1}(n + 1) = v_L(n)$$
$$v_L(n + 1) = x(n) \qquad (11.159)$$

and the output equation

$$y(n) = b_L v_1(n) + b_{L-1} v_2(n) + \cdots + b_1 v_L(n) + b_0 x(n). \qquad (11.160)$$

In matrix form we have

$$\mathbf{v}(n + 1) = \begin{bmatrix} 0 & 1 & 0 & \cdots & 0 \\ 0 & 0 & 1 & \cdots & 0 \\ & & \vdots & & \\ 0 & 0 & 0 & \cdots & 1 \\ 0 & 0 & 0 & \cdots & 0 \end{bmatrix} \mathbf{v}(n) + \begin{bmatrix} 0 \\ 0 \\ \vdots \\ 0 \\ 1 \end{bmatrix} x(n) \qquad (11.161)$$

and

$$y(n) = [b_L \quad b_{L-1} \cdots b_2 \quad b_1] \, \mathbf{v}(n) + b_0 x(n). \qquad (11.162)$$

Notice that the states are simply delayed versions of the input.

FIGURE 11.18 SFG used to write the state equations for a nonrecursive system

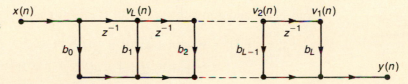

11.3.2 Solution of State Equations

Now that we have the state equations, what can we do with them? For one thing we can easily deduce the general form of the solution to the system's equations, namely

$$\mathbf{v}(n + 1) = \mathbf{A}\,\mathbf{v}(n) + \mathbf{B}\,x(n). \tag{11.163}$$

We assume that the $\mathbf{A}$ and $\mathbf{B}$ matrices are known as is the initial condition vector $\mathbf{v}(0)$. First, for $n = 0$ we get

$$\mathbf{v}(1) = \mathbf{A}\,\mathbf{v}(0) + \mathbf{B}\,x(0). \tag{11.164}$$

Next, substituting Eq. 11.164 into Eq. 11.163 gives

$$\mathbf{v}(2) = \mathbf{A}\,\mathbf{v}(1) + \mathbf{B}\,x(1) = \mathbf{A}[\mathbf{A}\,\mathbf{v}(0) + \mathbf{B}\,x(0)] + \mathbf{B}\,x(1)$$

$$= \mathbf{A}^2\,\mathbf{v}(0) + \mathbf{A}\,\mathbf{B}x(0) + \mathbf{B}\,x(1). \tag{11.165}$$

Continuing the process we have

$$\mathbf{v}(3) = \mathbf{A}^3\,\mathbf{v}(0) + \mathbf{A}^2\,\mathbf{B}\,x(0) + \mathbf{A}\,\mathbf{B}\,x(1) + \mathbf{B}\,x(2) \tag{11.166}$$

$$\vdots$$

$$\mathbf{v}(n) = \underbrace{\mathbf{A}^n\,\mathbf{v}(0)}_{\substack{\text{Initial} \\ \text{condition} \\ \text{(IC)} \\ \text{response}}} + \underbrace{\sum_{m=0}^{n-1} \mathbf{A}^{n-m-1}\mathbf{B}\,x(m)}_{\substack{\text{Convolution sum} \\ \text{or} \\ \text{forced response}}} = \mathbf{v}_{\text{IC}}(n) + \mathbf{v}_{\text{F}}(n) \tag{11.167}$$

which is the general result for any value of n. Notice that the solution is nicely separated into the initial condition (IC) response and the forced response.

We can also approach the solution from the z-transform point of view by taking the transform of the matrix state equation, namely

$$\mathfrak{z}[\mathbf{v}(n + 1)] = \mathfrak{z}[\mathbf{A}\,\mathbf{v}(n) + \mathbf{B}\,x(n)]. \tag{11.168}$$

Before proceeding we need the transform of the left side of the above equation. Using a unilateral transform for a scalar term gives

$$\mathfrak{z}[v(n + 1)] = \sum_{n=0}^{\infty} v(n + 1)z^{-n}$$

$$= v(1) + v(2)z^{-1} + v(3)z^{-2} + \cdots \tag{11.169}$$

and if we add and subtract $zv(0)$ the result is

$$\mathfrak{z}[v(n + 1)] = -zv(0) + zv(0) + v(1) + v(2)z^{-1} + v(3)z^{-2} + \cdots$$

$$= -zv(0) + z[v(0) + v(1)z^{-1} + v(2)z^{-2} + v(3)z^{-3} + \cdots]$$

$$= -zv(0) + zV(z) \tag{11.170}$$

where $V(z) = \mathfrak{z}[v(n)]$. This is easily generalized to the matrix case and the transform of the state equation Eq. 11.168 becomes, after rearranging terms,

$$zV(z) - AV(z) = zv(0) + BX(z). \tag{11.171}$$

In order to proceed to the solution for $V(z)$ we need to multiply the first term by the identity matrix I which gives

$$zIV(z) - AV(z) = zv(0) + BX(z). \tag{11.172}$$

Now we can factor out $V(z)$ to get

$$(zI - A)\,V(z) = zv(0) + BX(z). \tag{11.173}$$

To solve for $V(z)$ we need to premultiply Eq. 11.173 by the inverse of the square matrix $(zI - A)$, which gives

$$V(z) = (zI - A)^{-1}\,zv(0) + (zI - A)^{-1}\,BX(z). \tag{11.174}$$

Now taking the inverse z-transform produces the solution

$$v(n) = \mathfrak{z}^{-1}[V(z)] = \mathfrak{z}^{-1}[(zI - A)^{-1}\,zv(0)] + \mathfrak{z}^{-1}[(zI - A)^{-1}\,BX(z)] \tag{11.175}$$

which can be separated into the IC response

$$v_{IC}(n) = \mathfrak{z}^{-1}[(zI - A)^{-1}zv(0)] \tag{11.176}$$

and the forced response

$$v_F(n) = \mathfrak{z}^{-1}[(zI - A)^{-1}\,BX(z)]. \tag{11.177}$$

Comparing these two solutions with those we found by staying in the discrete-time domain, namely Eq. 11.167 we have

$$v_{IC}(n) = A^n\,v(0) = \mathfrak{z}^{-1}[(zI - A)^{-1}\,zv(0)] \quad \text{initial condition} \atop \text{response} \tag{11.178}$$

and

$$v_F(n) = \sum_{m=0}^{n-1} A^{n-m-1}\,B\,x(m) = \mathfrak{z}^{-1}[(zI - A)^{-1}\,BX(z)] \quad \text{forced response} \tag{11.179}$$

Example 11.13. This example illustrates the z-transform solution of a state equation.

The system equation for Example 3.20 and Example 6.11 was

$$y(n) + y(n - 2) = x(n) + x(n - 1) \tag{11.180}$$

and the state and output equations are

$$\begin{bmatrix} v_1(n+1) \\ v_2(n+1) \end{bmatrix} = \underbrace{\begin{bmatrix} 0 & -1 \\ 1 & 0 \end{bmatrix}}_{\mathbf{A}} \begin{bmatrix} v_1(n) \\ v_2(n) \end{bmatrix} + \underbrace{\begin{bmatrix} 1 \\ 0 \end{bmatrix}}_{\mathbf{B}} x(n)$$

$$y(n) = [1 \quad -1]\, \mathbf{v}(n) + x(n). \tag{11.181}$$

Use the z-transform approach for solution of the state equation to find $y(n)$ for $x(n) = 10 \cdot u(n)$, $y(-2) = -10$, and $y(-1) = 0$.

Solution: The transform of the initial condition solution is

$$\mathbf{V}_{IC}(z) = (z\mathbf{I} - \mathbf{A})^{-1}\, z\mathbf{v}(0) \tag{11.182}$$

where we first find $(z\mathbf{I} - \mathbf{A})^{-1}$. Forming $(z\mathbf{I} - \mathbf{A})$ we have

$$\begin{bmatrix} z & 0 \\ 0 & z \end{bmatrix} - \begin{bmatrix} 0 & -1 \\ 1 & 0 \end{bmatrix} = \begin{bmatrix} z & 1 \\ -1 & z \end{bmatrix} \tag{11.183}$$

and the inverse is

$$(z\mathbf{I} - \mathbf{A})^{-1} = \begin{bmatrix} \dfrac{z}{z^2+1} & \dfrac{-1}{z^2+1} \\ \dfrac{1}{z^2+1} & \dfrac{z}{z^2+1} \end{bmatrix}. \tag{11.184}$$

The initial condition response from Eq. 11.176 is

$$\mathbf{v}_{IC}(n) = \mathfrak{z}^{-1}[(z\mathbf{I} - \mathbf{A})^{-1}\, z\mathbf{v}(0)] \tag{11.185}$$

so we need to determine the initial condition vector $\mathbf{v}(0)$ from the given initial conditions $y(-2)$ and $y(-1)$. The first move is to find the derived initial conditions of $y(0)$ and $y(1)$ which from Eq. 11.180 or Example 3.20 are $y(0) = y(1) = 20$ for $y(-2) = -10$ and $y(-1) = 0$. Now, we need to find the corresponding values for $v_1(0)$ and $v_2(0)$ that are the derived initial conditions for the state vector $\mathbf{v}(0)$ needed to initialize the unit delays whose outputs are the states $\mathbf{v}(n)$. So, on our way to the vector $\mathbf{v}(0)$ we write the output equation from Eq. 11.181 for $n = 0, 1$ to obtain

$$y(0) = v_1(0) - v_2(0) + x(0)$$

$$y(1) = v_1(1) - v_2(1) + x(1). \tag{11.186}$$

We are trying to find $v_1(0)$ and $v_2(0)$, so to express $v_1(1)$ and $v_2(1)$ in terms of $v_1(0)$ and $v_2(0)$ we use the state equation from Eq. 11.181 for $n = 0$ getting

$$v_1(1) = -v_2(0) + x(0)$$

$$v_2(1) = v_1(0). \tag{11.187}$$

Substituting $v_1(1)$ and $v_2(1)$ from Eq. 11.187 into Eq. 11.186 and with $y(0) = y(1) = 20$ and $x(0) = x(1) = 10$ we obtain

$$v_1(0) - v_2(0) = 10$$

$$-v_1(0) - v_2(0) = 0 \tag{11.188}$$

with the solution of these two equations being the initial condition vector

$$\mathbf{v}(0) = [5 \quad -5]^T. \tag{11.189}$$

Returning to Eq. 11.185 the initial condition response is

$$\mathbf{v}_{IC}(n) = \mathfrak{z}^{-1}[(z\mathbf{I} - \mathbf{A})^{-1} z\mathbf{v}(0)]$$

$$= \mathfrak{z}^{-1} \begin{bmatrix} \dfrac{z}{z^2 + 1} & \dfrac{-1}{z^2 + 1} \\[2ex] \dfrac{1}{z^2 + 1} & \dfrac{z}{z^2 + 1} \end{bmatrix} \begin{bmatrix} 5z \\[2ex] -5z \end{bmatrix}$$

$$= \mathfrak{z}^{-1} \begin{bmatrix} \dfrac{5z^2 + 5z}{z^2 + 1} \\[2ex] \dfrac{5z - 5z^2}{z^2 + 1} \end{bmatrix} \tag{11.190}$$

and after a fairly simple partial fraction expansion we have the initial condition response vector

$$\mathbf{v}_{IC}(n) = \begin{bmatrix} 5\sqrt{2}\,\cos(\pi n/2 - \pi/4) \\ 5\sqrt{2}\,\cos(\pi n/2 - 3\pi/4) \end{bmatrix}. \tag{11.191}$$

Turning to the forced solution we have

$$\mathbf{v}_F(n) = \mathfrak{z}^{-1}[(z\mathbf{I} - \mathbf{A})^{-1} \mathbf{B}X(z)]$$

$$= \mathfrak{z}^{-1} \begin{bmatrix} \dfrac{z}{z^2 + 1} & \dfrac{-1}{z^2 + 1} \\[2ex] \dfrac{1}{z^2 + 1} & \dfrac{z}{z^2 + 1} \end{bmatrix} \begin{bmatrix} 1 \\[2ex] 0 \end{bmatrix} \dfrac{10z}{z - 1}$$

$$= \mathfrak{z}^{-1} \begin{bmatrix} \dfrac{10z^2}{(z^2 + 1)(z - 1)} \\[2ex] \dfrac{10z}{(z^2 + 1)(z - 1)} \end{bmatrix} \tag{11.192}$$

and after a PFE we have the forced response of

$$\mathbf{v}_F(n) = \begin{bmatrix} 5\sqrt{2}\,\cos(\pi n/2 - 3\pi/4) + 5 \\ 5\sqrt{2}\,\cos(\pi n/2 - 5\pi/4) + 5 \end{bmatrix}. \tag{11.193}$$

Adding the initial condition solution and the forced solution gives us the total solution for the state equations of

$$\mathbf{v}(n) = \mathbf{v}_{IC}(n) + \mathbf{v}_F(n)$$

$$= \begin{bmatrix} 10 \cos(\pi n/2 - \pi/2) + 5 \\ 10 \cos(\pi n/2 - \pi) + 5 \end{bmatrix}. \tag{11.194}$$

The system output comes from Eq. 11.181, namely

$$y(n) = v_1(n) - v_2(n) + x(n)$$

$$= 10 \cos(\pi n/2 - \pi/2) + 5 - 10 \cos(\pi n/2 - \pi) - 5 + 10$$

$$= 10\sqrt{2}\,\cos(\pi n/2 - \pi/4) + 10, \qquad n \geq 0. \tag{11.195}$$

Comment: The result in Eq. 11.195 agrees with what we found in Examples 3.20 and 6.11. This method involves considerable algebraic manipulation as does any z-transform approach and is to be avoided when analyzing higher-order systems where a computer solution is more easily obtained. We do, however, gain insight into the parts that constitute the solution of this fairly simple problem and this information can often be extended to more complex systems.

Stability—Revisited. One definition of stability for a causal system is the following:

The initial condition response of a stable causal system approaches zero as $n \to \infty$.

We investigate this from the point of view of state-space equations. First, the initial condition response is given by

$$\mathbf{v}_{\text{IC}}(n) = \mathbf{A}^n \, \mathbf{v}(0) \tag{11.196}$$

and in order that $\mathbf{v}_{\text{IC}}(n) \to \mathbf{0}$ as $n \to \infty$ we see that $\mathbf{A}^n$ must approach the matrix $\mathbf{0}$ as $n \to \infty$. That is, all the elements of the $\mathbf{A}^n$ matrix must approach zero as n approaches infinity.

From z-transforms we have seen that

$$\mathbf{V}_{\text{IC}}(z) = (z\mathbf{I} - \mathbf{A})^{-1} \, z\mathbf{v}(0) \tag{11.197}$$

where the matrix inverse can be found from

$$(z\mathbf{I} - \mathbf{A})^{-1} = \frac{\textbf{adjoint}(z\mathbf{I} - \mathbf{A})}{\det(z\mathbf{I} - \mathbf{A})}. \tag{11.198}$$

In Eq. 11.198 the numerator term, **adjoint** $(z\mathbf{I} - \mathbf{A})$, is a matrix and the denominator term, $\det(z\mathbf{I} - \mathbf{A})$ or $|z\mathbf{I} - \mathbf{A}|$, is the characteristic polynomial that when set to zero becomes the characteristic equation

$$\det(z\mathbf{I} - \mathbf{A}) = |z\mathbf{I} - \mathbf{A}| = 0. \tag{11.199}$$

From linear algebra we know that the eigenvalues of $\mathbf{A}$ are the roots of the characteristic equation and we can write the denominator of Eq. 11.198 as

$$(z - \lambda_1)(z - \lambda_2) \cdots (z - \lambda_N) = (z - p_1)(z - p_2) \cdots (z - p_N) \tag{11.200}$$

where $\lambda_i = p_i$ are the eigenvalues of $\mathbf{A}$ and the poles of the system. If we were to take the inverse transform of $\mathbf{V}_{\text{IC}}(z)$, keeping in mind that $\mathbf{v}(0)$ is a constant vector, we obtain the PFE for the jth row of $\mathbf{V}_{\text{IC}}(z)$

$$V_{\text{IC}j}(z) = \frac{C_{1j}z}{z - p_1} + \frac{C_{2j}z}{z - p_2} + \cdots + \frac{C_{Nj}}{z - p_N} \tag{11.201}$$

where the partial fraction constants C_{ij} depend upon the values of $\mathbf{v}(0)$ and the poles and zeros of the system. We have assumed that the system has no repeated eigenvalues. Thus, the time domain terms that result are of the form

$$v_{ICj}(n) = C_{1j}(p_1)^n + C_{2j}(p_2)^n + \cdots + C_{Nj}(p_N)^n, \qquad n \geq 0$$

(11.202)

and we see that for $v_{ICj}(n)$ to approach zero for arbitrary C_{ij}, it is necessary and sufficient that

$$|p_i| < 1, \; i = 1, 2, \ldots, N.$$

(11.203)

That is, for stability in a causal system all the eigenvalues (system poles) must lie within the unit circle.

Example 11.14. This example illustrates stability determination from the state-space equations.

The causal filter of Problem 6.1 can be described by the matrix state equation

$$\mathbf{v}(n + 1) = \begin{bmatrix} 0 & 1 & 0 \\ 0 & 0 & 1 \\ -2 & 4 & 0.5 \end{bmatrix} \mathbf{v}(n) + \begin{bmatrix} 0 \\ 0 \\ 1 \end{bmatrix} x(n)$$

(11.204)

and the output equation

$$y(n) = \begin{bmatrix} -1 & 5 & 1.5 \end{bmatrix} \mathbf{v}(n) + x(n).$$

(11.205)

Is this system stable?

Solution: First, we need to form the matrix $(z\mathbf{I} - \mathbf{A})$ which is

$$z\mathbf{I} - \mathbf{A} = \begin{bmatrix} z & 0 & 0 \\ 0 & z & 0 \\ 0 & 0 & z \end{bmatrix} - \begin{bmatrix} 0 & 1 & 0 \\ 0 & 0 & 1 \\ -2 & 4 & 0.5 \end{bmatrix}$$

$$= \begin{bmatrix} z & -1 & 0 \\ 0 & z & -1 \\ 2 & -4 & z - 0.5 \end{bmatrix}$$

(11.206)

The determinant $|z\mathbf{I} - \mathbf{A}|$ can be found by expanding Eq. 11.206 on the first row giving

$$|z\mathbf{I} - \mathbf{A}| = z(z^2 - 0.5z - 4) + 2$$

(11.207)

and the characteristic equation is

$$z^3 - 0.5z^2 - 4z + 2 = 0.$$

(11.208)

Here we have a cubic equation and can resort to a computer to find the roots. In Problem 6.1, the hint states that there is a real root at $z_1 = +0.5$. Knowing this means we can use long division to reduce Eq. 11.208 to a quadratic as

$$
\begin{array}{r}
z^2 - 4.0 \\
z - 0.5\overline{\smash{)}z^3 - 0.5z^2 - 4.0z + 2.0} \\
\underline{z^3 - 0.5z^2} \\
-4.0z + 2.0 \\
\underline{-4.0z + 2.0}
\end{array}
$$

and solving the quadratic, $z^2 - 4 = 0$, gives $z_2 = +2$ and $z_3 = -2$. There are two roots outside of the unit circle so the filter of Eq. 11.204 and Problem 6.1 is unstable.

Multiple-Input, Multiple-Output Systems. As a final observation we note that there are situations where a system has more than one input and there may be several outputs. In this situation the inputs are represented by the vector

$$
\mathbf{x}(n) = [x_1(n)\, x_2(n) \cdots x_m(n)]^T \text{ an } m \times 1 \text{ vector} \qquad (11.209)
$$

and the outputs by the vector

$$
\mathbf{y}(n) = [y_1(n)\, y_2(n) \cdots y_q(n)]^T \text{ a } q \times 1 \text{ vector.} \qquad (11.210)
$$

The state-space matrix equation becomes

$$
\mathbf{v}(n + 1) = \mathbf{A}\, \mathbf{v}(n) + \mathbf{B}\, \mathbf{x}(n) \qquad (11.211)
$$

and the outputs are now given by the matrix equation

$$
\mathbf{y}(n) = \mathbf{C}\, \mathbf{v}(n) + \mathbf{D}\, \mathbf{x}(n). \qquad (11.212)
$$

11.3.3 Computer Solution of State Equations

The solution of state difference equations by using a computer proceeds in a similar way to the computer solution of a single difference equation as in Section 3.1.3. Again, N initial conditions are needed to begin the solution for an Nth-order system. The equations to be solved are Eqs. 11.211 and 11.212 which are repeated here for convenience

$$
\mathbf{v}(n + 1) = \mathbf{A}\, \mathbf{v}(n) + \mathbf{B}\, \mathbf{x}(n) \qquad (11.211)
$$

$$
\mathbf{y}(n) = \mathbf{C}\, \mathbf{v}(n) + \mathbf{D}\, \mathbf{x}(n)^\dagger. \qquad (11.212)
$$

The initial time is arbitrarily assumed to be $n = 0$ and the N initial conditions required are the N components of the vector $\mathbf{v}(0)$.

To accomplish the computer solution we see that two matrix operations are required—multiplication of a matrix times a vector, as in the products $\mathbf{Av}(n)$, $\mathbf{Bx}(n)$, $\mathbf{Cv}(n)$ and $\mathbf{Dx}(n)$; and vector addition, as in the sums $\mathbf{Av}(n) + \mathbf{Bx}(n)$ and $\mathbf{Cv}(n) + \mathbf{Dx}(n)$. The pseudocode for matrix subroutines that carry out these operations is given in Fig. 11.19(a).

---

†We assume here, for generality, that there may be m inputs, represented by the vector $\mathbf{x}(n)$ and q outputs, represented by the vector $\mathbf{y}(n)$.

```
SUBROUTINE MVMPY (AMAT, VIN, VOUT, NROW, NCOL)
(this subroutine calculates the product of the NROW × NCOL matrix
AMAT times the vector VIN having NCOL components)

DO FOR I◄───────1 TO NROW

    VOUT (I)◄────0.0

    DO FOR J◄───────1 TO NCOL

        VOUT (I)◄───────VOUT (I) + AMAT (I,J)·VIN (J)

    END DO

END DO

RETURN

END MVMPY

SUBROUTINE VADD (VIN1, VIN2, VOUT, N1)
(this subroutine calculates the sum of two vectors, VIN1 and VIN2,
each having N1 components.  The result is stored in the N1 - vector
VOUT)

DO FOR I◄───────1 TO N1

    VOUT (I)◄───────VIN1 (I) + VIN2 (I)

END DO

RETURN

END VADD
```

FIGURE 11.19(a) Pseudocode for subroutines for matrix-vector multiplication (MVMPY) and vector addition (VADD)

The solution proceeds as follows:

1. Set $n = 0$
2. Solve

$$\mathbf{v}(n + 1) = \mathbf{A}\,\mathbf{v}(n) + \mathbf{B}\,\mathbf{x}(n) \qquad (11.211)$$

for $\mathbf{v}(n + 1)$ and

$$\mathbf{y}(n) = \mathbf{C}\,\mathbf{v}(n) + \mathbf{D}\,\mathbf{x}(n) \qquad (11.212)$$

for $\mathbf{y}(n)$. Store the results for $\mathbf{v}(n + 1)$ in the array $VS(I, J)$, where the argument (or subscript) I represents the component of the vector $\mathbf{v}(n + 1)$ and the argument J represents the time sample number $(n + 1$, in this case). Store the value of $\mathbf{y}(n)$ calculated in the array $YS(I, J)$, where I represents the component of the vector $\mathbf{y}(n)$ and J represents the time sample number n.

3. If $n = NSTOP - 1$ proceed to Step 4; otherwise, increase n by 1 and return to Step 2.

4. The final step is to compute the value of $\mathbf{y}(NSTOP)$, since for $n = NSTOP - 1$ the final values of the state $\mathbf{v}$ and output $\mathbf{y}$ calculated within the preceding loop are $\mathbf{v}(NSTOP)$ and $\mathbf{y}(NSTOP - 1)$. Thus, we evaluate

$$\mathbf{y}(NSTOP) = \mathbf{C}\,\mathbf{v}(NSTOP) + \mathbf{D}\,\mathbf{x}(NSTOP). \qquad (11.213)$$

This concludes the process except for printing and/or plotting the results.

The pseudocode for the essence of the procedure is given in Fig. 11.19(b). Perhaps the most challenging part of the procedure is keeping straight the time index. Notice that the computation proceeds by the following stages

STAGE NUMBER	QUANTITIES COMPUTED
0	$\mathbf{v}(1)$, $\mathbf{y}(0)$
1	$\mathbf{v}(2)$, $\mathbf{y}(1)$
$\vdots$	
$NSTOP - 1$	$\mathbf{v}(NSTOP)$, $\mathbf{y}(NSTOP - 1)$

and then $\mathbf{y}(NSTOP)$ is computed following the end of the main iterative loop.

```
(read the values of the number of states N, the number of inputs M,
the number of outputs Q, and the stopping value for the time index
NSTOP;

read the N × N matrix A, the N × M matrix B, the Q × N matrix C, and
the Q × M matrix D and store in two-dimensional arrays; read the
initial condition vector v(0) and store its N components in the

array V(I) with I = 1,2,...,N ; read, or generate by a user-supplied
subroutine, the input values x(I), I = 0,1,...,NSTOP and store them in
the array XS(I,J), I = 1,2,..., M, J = 0,1,..., NSTOP)

(store the value of v(0) in the two-dimensional array VS(I,J) with
I = 1,2,..., N and J = 0)

DO FOR I←——1 TO N

    VS(I,0)←———V(I)

END DO

(begin main iteration loop)
```

FIGURE 11.19(b) Pseudocode for iterative solution of state equations

```
DO FOR NS ←——— 0 TO NSTOP-1

    DO FOR I ←——— 1 TO M

        X(I) ←——— XS(I,NS)

    END DO

    CALL MVMPY(A,V,V0,N,N)

    CALL MVMPY(B,X,V1,N,M)

    CALL VADD(V0,V1,V2,N)

    CALL MVMPY(C,V,V0,Q,N)

    CALL MVMPY(D,X,V1,Q,M)

    CALL VADD(V0,V1,Y,Q)

(store the results in the arrays VS(I,J) and YS(I,J))

    DO FOR I ←——— 1 TO N

        VS(I,NS+1) ←——— V2(I)

(update the vector V(I))

        V(I) ←——— V2(I)

    END DO

    DO FOR I ←——— 1 TO Q

        YS(I,NS) ←——— Y(I)

    END DO

END DO
(end main iteration loop)
(compute the output vector at time NSTOP and store it in the array YS(I,J)
    at locations I = 1,2,..., Q and J = NSTOP)

DO FOR I ←——— 1 TO M

    X(I) ←——— XS(I,NSTOP)

END DO

CALL MVMPY(C,V2,V0,Q,N)

CALL MVMPY(D,X,V1,Q,M)

CALL VADD(V0,V1,Y,Q)

DO FOR I ←——— 1 TO Q

    YS(I,NSTOP) ←——— Y(I)

END DO

STOP

END
```

FIGURE 11.19(b) (cont.)

11.4 ▬▬ TWO DIFFERENT SYSTEMS

In this section we take a brief look at two applications of z-transforms and introduce some topics that may be of interest for further study. Each topic itself is worthy of a textbook chapter or even an entire textbook, so our discussions here are brief, but hopefully stimulating.

11.4.1 Digital Control of a Continuous-Time System

A typical arrangement for a digitally controlled system is shown in Fig. 11.20. Some observations about this configuration follow.

1. State equations are useful to describe a control system such as is depicted where the "pipe-like" lines indicate that more than a single variable may be represented. For the continuous-time plant the matrix state differential equation is

$$\dot{\mathbf{v}}(t) = \mathbf{F}\,\mathbf{v}(t) + \mathbf{G}\,x(t) \text{ with the initial conditions } \mathbf{v}(0) \quad (11.214)$$

and the output equation is

$$y(t) = \mathbf{M}_1\,\mathbf{v}(t) + \mathbf{M}_2\,x(t). \quad (11.215)$$

We assume a single-input single-output plant (SISO), but this is not necessary because multivariable systems are easy to describe with state equations. $\dot{\mathbf{v}}(t)$ represents the vector whose elements are the derivatives with respect to time of the state vector $\mathbf{v}(t)$ and $\mathbf{F}$, $\mathbf{G}$, $\mathbf{M}_1$, and $\mathbf{M}_2$ are constant matrices of appropriate dimensions.

2. If we assume that the analog-to-digital converter (A/D) samples its input signals every T seconds, i.e., at $t = 0, T, \ldots, nT, nT + T, \ldots$, and that the output of the digital-to-analog converter is piecewise constant over a period of time T as shown in Fig. 11.21, then we can describe the input to the plant as

$$x(t) = x(nT), \qquad nT \le t < nT + T. \quad (11.216)$$

3. With the analog plant inputs restricted to the special but often used situation of Eq. 11.216 it can be shown (see Appendix G) that the continuous system can be described at the sampling instants only by

$$\mathbf{v}(nT + T) = \boldsymbol{\phi}(T)\,\mathbf{v}(nT) + \boldsymbol{\Delta}(T)\,x(nT) \quad (11.217)$$

FIGURE 11.20 A typical digital control system

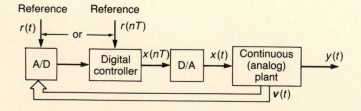

CHAPTER 11 STRUCTURES, STATE EQUATIONS, AND APPLICATIONS

FIGURE 11.21 A piecewise constant input signal $x(t) = x(nT)$, $nT \leq t < nT + T$

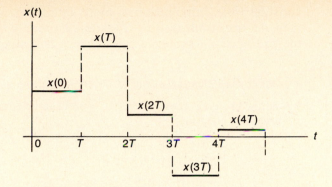

where the $\phi(T)$ and $\Delta(T)$ matrices can be found from a computer program or for low-order systems from Eqs. G.9, G.11, and G.14 in Appendix G. The output equation, Eq. 11.215 can be written at the sampling instants as

$$y(nT) = \mathbf{M}_1\, \mathbf{v}(nT) + \mathbf{M}_2\, x(nT) \qquad (11.218)$$

and, consequently, the output is easily calculated from the states $\mathbf{v}(nT)$ which can be found from the iterative solution of Eq. 11.217 with the input $x(nT)$, the sampled value of $x(t)$. It is important to remember that the plant being controlled is a continuous-time system, not a discrete-time system, and that we are observing the output (response) at the sampling instants only as in Fig. 11.22.

4. We notice that Eq. 11.217 above and Eq. 11.137 are of the same form with $\phi(T)$ and $\Delta(T)$ in the roles of $\mathbf{A}$ and $\mathbf{B}$ respectively. Henceforth, to simplify matters, we write all state equations in the form $\mathbf{v}(n + 1) = \mathbf{A}\, \mathbf{v}(n) + \mathbf{B}\, x(n)$. In a similar way, the system output is described by Eq. 11.218 above and by Eq. 11.138 with $\mathbf{M}_1$ and $\mathbf{M}_2$ in the roles of $\mathbf{C}$ and $\mathbf{D}$, respectively. We write all output equations in the form $y(n) = \mathbf{C}\, \mathbf{v}(n) + \mathbf{D}\, x(n)$.

5. In Fig. 11.20 the simplifying assumption is made that all of the states are sampled and made available to the digital controller. Let us now

FIGURE 11.22 System output observed at the sampling instants only

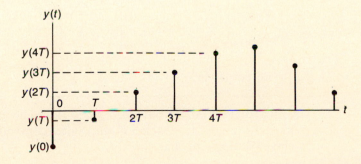

consider this configuration in more detail through a series of examples. An important result is illustrated, namely that it is often possible to improve a system's performance by using feedback.

Example 11.15. This example illustrates the z-domain description of the state equation.

An undamped second-order system $\ddot{y}(t) = x(t)$ can be described by the continuous-time state equation

$$\begin{bmatrix} \dot{v}_1(t) \\ \dot{v}_2(t) \end{bmatrix} = \begin{bmatrix} 0 & 1 \\ 0 & 0 \end{bmatrix} \begin{bmatrix} v_1(t) \\ v_2(t) \end{bmatrix} + \begin{bmatrix} 0 \\ 1 \end{bmatrix} x(t), \qquad t \geq 0 \tag{11.219}$$

where $y(t) = v_1(t)$ and $\dot{y}(t) = v_2(t)$. If the system input is piecewise constant as

$$x(t) = x(nT), \qquad nT \leq t < nT + T \tag{11.220}$$

then using the results from Appendix G we have

$$\begin{bmatrix} v_1(nT + T) \\ v_2(nT + T) \end{bmatrix} = \begin{bmatrix} 1 & T \\ 0 & 1 \end{bmatrix} \begin{bmatrix} v_1(nT) \\ v_2(nT) \end{bmatrix} + \begin{bmatrix} T^2/2 \\ T \end{bmatrix} x(nT), \qquad n \geq 0 \tag{11.221}$$

which describes the continuous-time system at the sampling instants, $t = nT$, $n = 0, 1, 2, \ldots$. Use the results of Section 11.3 to find the z-domain description of Eq. 11.221.

Solution: From Eq. 11.174 the z-transform of the state equation of Eq. 11.221 is

$$\mathbf{V}(z) = (z\mathbf{I} - \mathbf{A})^{-1} z\,\mathbf{v}(0) + (z\mathbf{I} - \mathbf{A})^{-1} \mathbf{B}\, X(z) \tag{11.222}$$

and we find $(z\mathbf{I} - \mathbf{A})^{-1}$ to be

$$(z\mathbf{I} - \mathbf{A})^{-1} = \begin{bmatrix} z - 1 & -T \\ 0 & z - 1 \end{bmatrix}^{-1}$$

$$= \begin{bmatrix} \dfrac{1}{z - 1} & \dfrac{T}{(z - 1)^2} \\ 0 & \dfrac{1}{z - 1} \end{bmatrix}. \tag{11.223}$$

Thus, the z-domain description of this system is

$$\mathbf{V}(z) = \begin{bmatrix} \dfrac{1}{z - 1} & \dfrac{T}{(z - 1)^2} \\ 0 & \dfrac{1}{z - 1} \end{bmatrix} \begin{bmatrix} zv_1(0) \\ zv_2(0) \end{bmatrix} + \begin{bmatrix} \dfrac{T^2/2}{z - 1} + \dfrac{T^2}{(z - 1)^2} \\ \dfrac{T}{z - 1} \end{bmatrix} X(z) \tag{11.224}$$

and the output is $y(nT) = v_1(nT)$ or $Y(z) = V_1(z)$.

Notice that so far we have described the plant only and the overall system that includes feedback and the digital controller has not yet come into play. We'll get to that shortly.

Example 11.16. This example illustrates the unit step response of an undamped system.

Suppose we consider the same system as in Example 11.15 with the sampling interval T set to unity. Find the response of this system at the sampling instants if the input $x(t)$ is piecewise constant in the form of Fig. 11.23(a). Use the z-transform results from Example 11.15.

Solution: The initial conditions are assumed to be zero so that we can find the system response due to the input alone. Thus, from Eq. 11.224 with $T = 1$ we have

$$\mathbf{V}_F(z) = \left[\frac{\dfrac{1/2}{z-1} + \dfrac{1}{(z-1)^2}}{\dfrac{1}{z-1}} \right] X(z) \qquad (11.225)$$

and from Fig. 11.23(a) the input is a unit step function, consequently $X(z) = \dfrac{z}{z-1}$ which gives

$$\mathbf{V}_F(z) = \left[\frac{\dfrac{0.5(z+1)}{(z-1)^2}}{\dfrac{1}{z-1}} \right] \frac{z}{z-1}$$

$$= \left[\frac{\dfrac{0.5z(z+1)}{(z-1)^3}}{\dfrac{z}{(z-1)^2}} \right]. \qquad (11.226)$$

The output $y(nT) = v_1(nT)$ or $y(n) = v_1(n)$ so we need only find

$$y(n) = \mathfrak{z}^{-1}[V_1(z)]$$

$$= \mathfrak{z}^{-1}\left[\frac{0.5z(z+1)}{(z-1)^3} \right] \qquad (11.227)$$

FIGURE 11.23 Input and output for Example 11.16

$x(t)$

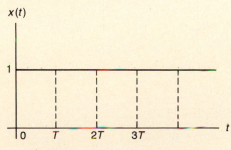

(a) System input for Example 11.16

$y(n) = y(t)|_{t=nT}$

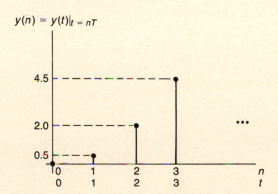

(b) System output at the sampling instants for Example 11.16

and from pair number 10 in Table 6.1 we have

$$y(n) = (0.5)n^2 \cdot u(n) \tag{11.228}$$

which is portrayed in Fig. 11.23(b).

Comment: This is an unsatisfactory response in that $y(n) \to \infty$ as $n \to \infty$, so now let's use feedback and a digital controller to improve the situation.

In Example 11.16 the system eigenvalues (characteristic roots) can be found from Eq. 11.221 as

$$|z\mathbf{I} - \mathbf{A}| = 0 \tag{11.229}$$

and with $T = 1$ we have the characteristic equation

$$|(z - 1)(z - 1)| = 0 \tag{11.230}$$

with two equal roots $z_{1,2} = 1$, an unstable system. One way to improve performance as well as ensure stability is to employ state feedback to produce a modified $\mathbf{A}$ matrix that has eigenvalues at some predetermined values of z. These values of z will be determined by the experience and goals of the designer of the control system.

A common and important task occurs when a system (plant) is required to follow or track a reference input. Referring to Fig. 11.20 this happens when the output $y(t)$ is required to follow a reference input $r(t)$. We can achieve this by using the control algorithm

$$x(n) = -\mathbf{F}\,\mathbf{v}(n) + r(n) \tag{11.231}$$

where $r(n)$ is the reference to be tracked and $\mathbf{F}$ is a matrix of feedback gains, the values of which are to be determined by the designer.

Example 11.17. This example illustrates the modification of system characteristics by feedback.

Consider the system state equation from Example 11.15 ($T = 1$)

$$\mathbf{v}(n + 1) = \begin{bmatrix} 1 & 1 \\ 0 & 1 \end{bmatrix} \mathbf{v}(n) + \begin{bmatrix} 0.5 \\ 1 \end{bmatrix} x(n) \tag{11.232}$$

and the output equation

$$y(n) = v_1(n) \tag{11.233}$$

subjected to the control law (algorithm)

$$x(n) = -\mathbf{F}\,\mathbf{v}(n) + r(n) \tag{11.234}$$

where $r(n)$ is a reference input as in Fig. 11.20.

a) Find the modified state equation described by

$$\mathbf{v}(n + 1) = \mathbf{A}'\,\mathbf{v}(n) + \mathbf{B}'\,r(n) \tag{11.235}$$

where $\mathbf{A}'$ and $\mathbf{B}'$ include the effect of the feedback gain matrix, $\mathbf{F} = [f_1 \quad f_2]$.

b) For the feedback gain matrix $\mathbf{F} = [1 \quad 1.5]$, find the matrices $\mathbf{A}'$ and $\mathbf{B}'$ from part (a).

c) Use the results of part (b) to determine the transfer function $H(z) = Y(z)/R(z)$. You may want to refer to Eq. 11.222.

d) Find the unit step response of the system.

Solution:

a) With $\mathbf{F} = [f_1 \quad f_2]$ and $x(n) = -[f_1 \quad f_2] \mathbf{v}(n) + r(n)$, Eq. 11.232 becomes

$$\mathbf{v}(n + 1) = \begin{bmatrix} 1 & 1 \\ 0 & 1 \end{bmatrix} \mathbf{v}(n) + \begin{bmatrix} 0.5 \\ 1 \end{bmatrix} \cdot \{-f_1 v_1(n) - f_2 v_2(n) + r(n)\} \quad (11.236)$$

or

$$\mathbf{v}(n + 1) = \underbrace{\begin{bmatrix} 1 - 0.5f_1 & 1 - 0.5f_2 \\ -f_1 & 1 - f_2 \end{bmatrix}}_{\mathbf{A}'} \begin{bmatrix} v_1(n) \\ v_2(n) \end{bmatrix} + \underbrace{\begin{bmatrix} 0.5 \\ 1 \end{bmatrix}}_{\mathbf{B}'} r(n). \quad (11.237)$$

b) With $\mathbf{F} = [1 \quad 1.5]$ we have

$$\mathbf{v}(n + 1) = \begin{bmatrix} 0.5 & 0.25 \\ -1 & -0.5 \end{bmatrix} \begin{bmatrix} v_1(n) \\ v_2(n) \end{bmatrix} + \begin{bmatrix} 0.5 \\ 1 \end{bmatrix} r(n). \quad (11.238)$$

c) The z-transform solution of the modified state equation is

$$\mathbf{V}(z) = (z\mathbf{I} - \mathbf{A}')^{-1} z\mathbf{v}(0) + (z\mathbf{I} - \mathbf{A}')^{-1} \mathbf{B} \, R(z) \quad (11.239)$$

where we find $(z\mathbf{I} - \mathbf{A}')^{-1}$ to be

$$(z\mathbf{I} - \mathbf{A}')^{-1} = \begin{bmatrix} z - 0.5 & -0.25 \\ 1 & z + 0.5 \end{bmatrix}^{-1}$$

$$= \begin{bmatrix} \dfrac{z + 0.5}{z^2} & \dfrac{0.25}{z^2} \\ \dfrac{-1}{z^2} & \dfrac{z - 0.5}{z^2} \end{bmatrix}. \quad (11.240)$$

For the forced response we have

$$\mathbf{V}_F(z) = (z\mathbf{I} - \mathbf{A}')^{-1} \mathbf{B} \, R(z)$$

$$= \begin{bmatrix} \dfrac{z + 0.5}{z^2} & \dfrac{0.25}{z^2} \\ \dfrac{-1}{z^2} & \dfrac{z - 0.5}{z^2} \end{bmatrix} \begin{bmatrix} 0.5 \\ 1 \end{bmatrix} R(z) \quad (11.241)$$

and with $Y(z) = V_1(z)$ the desired transfer function is

$$\frac{Y(z)}{R(z)} = \frac{0.5(z + 0.5) + 0.25}{z^2} = \frac{0.5(z + 1)}{z^2}. \quad (11.242)$$

d) For $r(n) = u(n)$ we have

$$Y(z) = \frac{0.5(z + 1)}{z^2} \cdot R(z)$$

$$= \frac{0.5(z + 1)}{z^2} \cdot \frac{z}{z - 1}$$

$$= \frac{0.5(z + 1)}{z(z - 1)} \qquad (11.243)$$

and

$$\frac{Y(z)}{z} = \frac{0.5(z + 1)}{z^2(z - 1)}$$

$$= \frac{-0.5}{z^2} - \frac{1}{z} + \frac{1}{z - 1} \qquad (11.244)$$

or

$$Y(z) = \frac{-0.5}{z} - 1 + \frac{z}{z - 1} \qquad (11.245)$$

giving the output sequence of

$$y(n) = -0.5\delta(n - 1) - \delta(n) + u(n) \qquad (11.246)$$

which is plotted in Fig. 11.24. The response reaches its steady-state value of $y(2) = 1$ in two samples without any overshoot. As a result, this output behavior is referred to as deadbeat response.

The approach illustrated in the preceding example can, of course, be generalized. The development begins with the state and output equations that describe the analog plant at sampling instants, i.e.,

$$\mathbf{v}(n + 1) = \mathbf{A}\,\mathbf{v}(n) + \mathbf{B}\,\mathbf{x}(n)$$

$$\mathbf{y}(n) = \mathbf{C}\,\mathbf{v}(n) + \mathbf{D}\,\mathbf{x}(n) \qquad (11.247)$$

where we have assumed the possibility of multiple inputs and outputs. If the plant input signal is generated as

$$\mathbf{x}(n) = -\mathbf{F}\mathbf{v}(n) + \mathbf{r}(n) \qquad (11.248)$$

FIGURE 11.24 System output with state feedback—deadbeat response

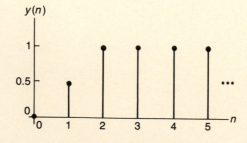

then the system can be described as

$$\mathbf{v}(n+1) = [\mathbf{A} - \mathbf{BF}]\mathbf{v}(n) + \mathbf{Br}(n)$$

$$= \mathbf{A}'\mathbf{v}(n) + \mathbf{Br}(n). \qquad (11.249)$$

11.4.2 Deconvolution

The process of *deconvolution* (or inverse filtering) has applications in seismic, radar, and sonar configurations where it is required to remove undesirable components from a received sequence. A typical problem is pictured in Fig. 11.25 where $x(n)$ is the desired sequence that is to be observed but $w(n)$ is the actual sequence that results from $x(n)$ passing through the contaminating medium. The objective is to find a filter whose output $y(n)$ is equal to the desired signal $x(n)$. From convolution we know that

$$w(n) = h_c(n) * x(n) \qquad (11.250)$$

and that

$$y(n) = h_f(n) * w(n) \qquad (11.251)$$

where $h_c(n)$ and $h_f(n)$ represent the unit sample responses of the contaminating medium and the inverse filter, respectively. Putting Eqs. 11.250 and 11.251 together we have

$$y(n) = h_f(n) * h_c(n) * x(n) \qquad (11.252)$$

or in terms of z-transforms we have

$$Y(z) = H_f(z) \cdot H_c(z) \cdot X(z). \qquad (11.253)$$

Remember that we want $y(n)$ to equal $x(n)$, which means that

$$H_c(z) \cdot H_f(z) = 1 \qquad (11.254)$$

or the filter transfer function must be the reciprocal of that for the contaminating medium, i.e.,

$$H_f(z) = 1/H_c(z). \qquad (11.255)$$

In terms of the discrete-time domain Eq. 11.254 becomes

$$h_c(n) * h_f(n) = \delta(n) \qquad (11.256)$$

and both Eqs. 11.255 and 11.256 indicate the inverse nature of the problem and, hence, the name inverse filtering.

FIGURE 11.25 A typical inverse filtering configuration

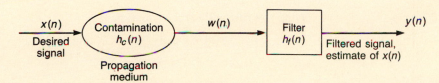

$x(n)$
Desired signal

Contamination $h_c(n)$

Propagation medium

$w(n)$

Filter $h_f(n)$

$y(n)$
Filtered signal, estimate of $x(n)$

Example 11.18. This example illustrates inverse filtering. ────────

Suppose that the propagation medium has a finite length unit sample response given by the sequence

$$h_c(n) = \{h_c(0), h_c(1), h_c(2), \ldots, h_c(L)\}. \tag{11.257}$$

Determine the transfer function of the inverse filter so that the sequence $y(n)$ in Fig. 11.25 equals the desired sequence $x(n)$.

Solution: From Eq. 11.255

$$H_f(z) = \frac{1}{H_c(z)} \tag{11.258}$$

and putting the given sequence in the form of the transfer function $H_c(z)$ gives

$$H_c(z) = h_c(0) + h_c(1)z^{-1} + \cdots + h_c(L)z^{-L} \tag{11.259}$$

so

$$H_f(z) = \frac{1}{h_c(0) + h_c(1)z^{-1} + h_c(2)z^{-2} + \cdots + h_c(L)z^{-L}}. \tag{11.260}$$

Example 11.19. This example illustrates the determination of the algorithm for an inverse filter.

The medium between a radar target and the receiver on the ground is represented by the transfer function $H_c(z)$ in Fig. 11.26. This transfer function can be approximated by

$$\frac{W(z)}{X(z)} = H_c(z) = \frac{z^2}{z^2 - [2a \cos \alpha]z + a^2}. \tag{11.261}$$

Find the algorithm that relates the filter output $y(n)$ and its input $w(n)$ so that $y(n) = x(n)$. Then draw an implementation of this algorithm.

Solution: We want

$$\frac{Y(z)}{W(z)} = H_f(z) = \frac{1}{H_c(z)}$$

$$= \frac{z^2 - [2a \cos \alpha]z + a^2}{z^2}$$

$$= 1 - [2a \cos \alpha]z^{-1} + a^2 z^{-2} \tag{11.262}$$

or

$$Y(z) = (1 - [2a \cos \alpha]z^{-1} + a^2 z^{-2}) \, W(z) \tag{11.263}$$

giving the filter difference equation

$$y(n) = w(n) - [2a \cos \alpha] \, w(n-1) + a^2 \, w(n-2) \tag{11.264}$$

and the realization of Fig. 11.27.

FIGURE 11.26 Block dia-
gram representation of Example 11.19

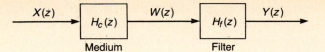

FIGURE 11.27 Filter real-
ization for Example 11.19

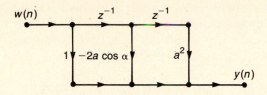

In looking at the results of the two preceding examples we notice that a contaminating medium modeled as an FIR system leads to an IIR deconvolution filter and vice-versa.

11.5 ■ REVIEW

In this chapter we first considered four structures for representing transfer functions—the direct, cascade, parallel, and lattice forms. As motivation for studying these structures we note that they have different sensitivities to finite wordlength effects, such as rounding of products and a limited number of bits to represent filter coefficients. Thus, one structure may be better than another when implementing a given transfer function.

Extensive use was made of signal flow graphs, and this prompted a discussion of Mason's Gain Rule, an efficient way to find transfer functions directly from the graph. We also found signal flow graphs useful in introducing state equations, another model for representing discrete systems. State equations were written starting from a signal flow graph, but at this point we should be able to start from any box in Fig. 11.28 and obtain any of the other system descriptions indicated. It was noted that

FIGURE 11.28 Six models
of an LTI system

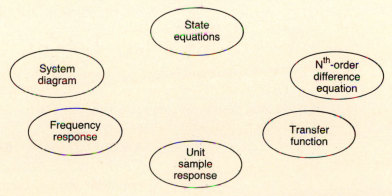

state equations provide a unified framework for representing systems with several inputs and outputs, as well as the more familiar single-input, single-output systems. We also found that the numerical solution of state equations is easily accomplished by a computer program that makes use of some simple matrix manipulation routines. Analytical solutions of state equations were obtained by using z-transforms.

The chapter concluded with consideration of how state space methods can be used to analyze digital control systems. A brief introduction of deconvolution, or inverse filtering, was also given.

VOCABULARY AND IMPORTANT RELATIONS

a) System implementations

Direct structure—see Fig. 11.1(a)
Cascade connection—see Fig. 11.3
Parallel (PFE) connection—see Fig. 11.5
Lattice structure—see Fig. 11.7

b) Mason's Gain Rule (MGR)

$$H(z) = \frac{\displaystyle\sum_{k=1}^{M} P_k(z) \cdot \Delta_k(z)}{\Delta(z)} \tag{11.114}$$

where

$H(z)$ = the transfer function relating an output node to an input node

$\Delta(z)$ = the graph determinant

$P_k(z)$ = the gain of the kth path from input to output

$\Delta_k(z)$ = cofactor of the kth path

For calculation of these quantities, see Eqs. 11.111 through 11.113.

c) State matrix difference equation

$$\mathbf{v}(n + 1) = \mathbf{A}\,\mathbf{v}(n) + \mathbf{B}\,x(n) \tag{11.137}$$

d) State output equation

$$y(n) = \mathbf{C}\,\mathbf{v}(n) + \mathbf{D}\,x(n) \tag{11.138}$$

e) Writing state and output equations. See the procedure described after Eq. 11.146.

f) System response from state equations (time-domain)

$$\mathbf{v}(n) = \underbrace{\mathbf{A}^n\mathbf{v}(0)}_{\text{IC response}} + \underbrace{\sum_{m=0}^{n-1} \mathbf{A}^{n-m-1}\mathbf{B}\,x(m)}_{\text{forced response}} \tag{11.167}$$

g) System response from state equations (z-domain)

$$\mathbf{v}_{IC}(n) = \mathfrak{z}^{-1}[(z\mathbf{I} - \mathbf{A})^{-1} z \, \mathbf{v}(0)] \tag{11.176}$$

$$\mathbf{v}_F(n) = \mathfrak{z}^{-1}[(z\mathbf{I} - \mathbf{A})^{-1} \mathbf{B} \, X(z)] \tag{11.177}$$

h) State and output equations for multi-input, multi-output systems

$$\mathbf{v}(n + 1) = \mathbf{A} \, \mathbf{v}(n) + \mathbf{B} \, \mathbf{x}(n) \qquad \text{state equation} \tag{11.211}$$

$$\mathbf{y}(n) = \mathbf{C} \, \mathbf{v}(n) + \mathbf{D} \, \mathbf{x}(n) \qquad \text{output equation} \tag{11.212}$$

i) Computer solution of state equations—see Fig. 11.19.

j) State feedback algorithm

$$\mathbf{x}(n) = -\mathbf{F} \, \mathbf{v}(n) + \mathbf{r}(n) \tag{11.231}$$

k) Deconvolution or inverse filtering

$h_c(n) =$ unit sample response of the contaminating medium

$h_f(n) =$ unit sample response of the inverse filter

$$h_c(n) * h_f(n) = \delta(n) \tag{11.256}$$

$$H_c(z) \cdot H_f(z) = 1 \tag{11.254}$$

PROBLEMS

Reinforcement

11.1 Given the filter transfer function

$$\frac{Y(z)}{X(z)} = H(z) = \underbrace{\frac{4z^2}{z^2 - 0.25}}_{H_1(z)} \cdot \underbrace{\frac{z}{z^2 + 0.25}}_{H_2(z)}$$

a) Mark the gains on the cascade realization shown in Fig. P11.1.

b) Repeat part (a) for the parallel realization of Fig. P11.1.

c) Use Mason's Gain Rule to calculate the transfer function $H(z)$ for each of these realizations. You should, of course, find the same $H(z)$ that was given,

$$H(z) = \frac{4z^2}{z^2 - 0.25} \cdot \frac{z}{z^2 + 0.25} = \frac{4z^3}{z^4 - 0.0625}$$

11.2 A linear time-invariant causal discrete system is described by

$$\mathbf{v}(n + 1) = \begin{bmatrix} 0 & 1 & 0 \\ 0 & 0 & 1 \\ 0 & -1 & 2.5 \end{bmatrix} \mathbf{v}(n) + \begin{bmatrix} 0 \\ 0 \\ 2 \end{bmatrix} x(n)$$

$$y(n) = \begin{bmatrix} 1 & 1 & 0 \end{bmatrix} \mathbf{v}(n).$$

a) Determine whether or not the system is stable.

b) Find $y(1)$, $y(2)$, and $y(3)$ if

$$\mathbf{v}(0) = \begin{bmatrix} 1 & -2 & 0 \end{bmatrix}^T \quad \text{and} \quad x(n) = nu(n).$$

11.3 The discrete transfer function

$$\frac{Y(z)}{X(z)} = H(z) = \frac{10(z - 1)(z^2 + \sqrt{2}z)}{(z + 0.5)(z^2 - 0.9z + 0.81)}$$

is to be realized as in Fig. P11.3 where some designated states are marked on the diagram.

a) Label the proper gains on the diagram.

b) Write the state and output equations for this sytem and put them into matrix form.

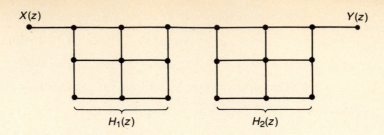

$X(z)$ $Y(z)$

$H_1(z)$ $H_2(z)$

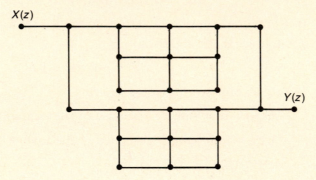

$X(z)$

$Y(z)$

FIGURE P11.3 $x(n)$ $y(n)$

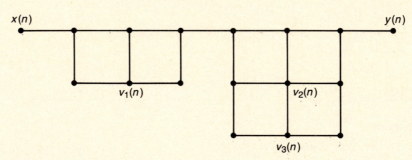

$v_1(n)$ $v_2(n)$

$v_3(n)$

11.4 An LTI system is described by the signal flow graph of Figure P11.4.

a) Find the system transfer function $H(z) = Y(z)/X(z)$.

b) Find the range of values of k for a stable system.

c) Find the unit step response of the system for $k = 1$. That is, find $y(n)$ with $x(n) = u(n)$.

11.5 The transfer function of an LTI discrete system is

$$H(z) = \frac{(z - 0.5)(z^2 - z + 0.5)}{z(z^2 + z + 0.5)} = \frac{-0.5}{z} + 3 +$$

$$\frac{3.16e^{j1.89}z}{z + 0.5 - j0.5} + \frac{3.16e^{-j1.89}z}{z + 0.5 + j0.5}.$$

a) Draw an SFG realization of $H(z)$ using a cascade connection of a second-order and a first-order section.

b) Write a set of state and output equations for the realization found in part (a), putting them in the matrix form

$$\mathbf{v}(n + 1) = \mathbf{A}\,\mathbf{v}(n) + \mathbf{B}\,x(n)$$

$$y(n) = \mathbf{C}\,\mathbf{v}(n) + \mathbf{D}\,x(n).$$

c) Draw an SFG realization of $H(z)$ using a parallel connection of a second-order and a first-order section.

d) Write a set of state and output equations for the realization of part (c) and put them in the matrix form

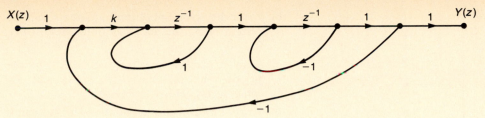

FIGURE P11.4

$$\mathbf{v}(n + 1) = \mathbf{A}\,\mathbf{v}(n) + \mathbf{B}\,x(n)$$

$$y(n) = \mathbf{C}\,\mathbf{v}(n) + \mathbf{D}\,x(n).$$

e) Is the system stable?

11.6 A two-input single-output system is described by the signal flow graph of Fig. P11.6.

a) Find the system transfer functions $H_1(z) = Y(z)/X_1(z)$, with $x_2(n) = 0$ and $H_2(z) = Y(z)/X_2(z)$, with $x_1(n) = 0$.

b) Write the state and output equations for this system.

c) Find $y(n)$ for $x_1(n) = \left(\dfrac{1}{2}\right)^n \cdot u(n)$ and $x_2(n) = \left(-\dfrac{1}{2}\right)^n \cdot u(n)$.

11.7 Consider the macroeconomic model $Y(n) = C(n) + I(n)$ where $Y(n) =$ income in year n, $I(n) =$ investment in year n, and $C(n) =$ consumption in year n. The assumptions are that total consumption is proportional to the total income in the previous year, or $C(n) = aY(n - 1)$ and that the investment is proportional to the increase in income in the previous year over the year before, or $I(n) = b[Y(n - 1) - Y(n - 2)]$. Describe this system in state-space form with $C(n)$ and $I(n)$ as the states. Notice that there is no input to this system.

11.8 A fourth-order lowpass digital Butterworth filter is described by the transfer function

$$H(z) = \frac{Y(z)}{X(z)} = \frac{0.094(z + 1)^4}{z^4 + 0.486z^2 + 0.0818}$$

a) Find a state-space description for this filter.

b) Using part (a), determine the filter's characteristic equation and compare your answer with the original transfer function. What do you notice?

c) Use the result of part (b) to calculate the characteristic roots and verify your results with Table 10.8.

d) The filter's unit sample response will be of the form

$$h(n) = C_0 + C_1(a_1)^n \cos(\theta_1 n + \psi_1) + C_2(a_2)^n \cos(\theta_2 n + \psi_2)$$

Find C_0, a_1, θ_1, a_2, and θ_2.

11.9 Given the difference equation for a digital filter

$$y(n) - 1.8y(n - 1) + 0.81y(n - 2) = x(n) + 1.8x(n - 1) + 0.81x(n - 2)$$

a) Mark the gains on the system diagram of Fig. P11.9 and then write state and output equations for the system.

FIGURE P11.6

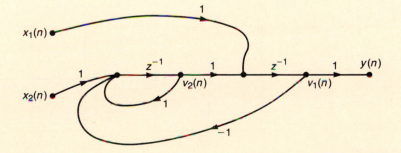

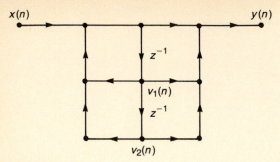

FIGURE P11.9

b) Use Mason's Gain Rule to find the transfer function, $H(z) = Y(z)/X(z)$.

c) Determine the poles and zeros of $H(z)$ and estimate the type of filter that this might be (lowpass, highpass, bandpass, bandstop, etc.).

d) Calculate an analytical expression for the unit sample response $h(n)$.

11.10 A fourth-order digital filter is described by the transfer function

$$H(z) = \frac{Y(z)}{X(z)} = \frac{z^4 + 1}{z^4 + 0.5z^2 + 0.707}.$$

This filter is to be realized (implemented) as a cascade connection of two second-order filters as $H(z) = H_1(z) \cdot H_2(z)$. Factor $H(z) = H_1(z) \cdot H_2(z)$ as

$$H_1(z) = \frac{z^2 - b_1z + 1}{z^2 - a_1z + a_0} \quad \text{and}$$

$$H_2(z) = \frac{z^2 + b_1z + 1}{z^2 + a_1z + a_0}$$

where b_1, a_1, and a_0 that appear in both transfer functions are positive numbers.

a) Mark the gains on the cascade system diagram of Fig. P11.10.

b) Write the state and output equations for this system using the states as numbered in Fig. P11.10.

c) Draw a parallel structure consisting of the second-order sections $H_a(z)$, $H_b(z)$, and the constant C_0. (Hint: $C_0 = 1.41$)

d) Write state and output equations for the parallel implementation of part (d).

11.11 A discrete system is described by the signal flow graph shown in Fig. P11.11(a).

a) What is the order of the system?

b) Write a set of state and output equations for the system.

c) Find the characteristic equation for the system.

d) A signal flow graph drawn in direct form is given in Fig. P11.11(b). Label the gains, c_1, c_2, c_3, and c_4.

11.12 A single-input, single-output system is characterized by the state and output equations

$$v_j(n + 1) = a_jv_j(n) + b_jx(n), \quad j = 1, 2, 3.$$

$$y(n) = \sum_{j=1}^{3} c_jv_j(n)$$

a) Write these equations in matrix form.

b) Draw a signal flow graph for the system.

c) Find the expression for

$$H(z) = \frac{Y(z)}{X(z)}$$

but do not simplify.

d) For what ranges of values of a_j, b_j, and c_j is the system stable? Explain your answer.

e) For the input $x(n) = u(n)$, the derived initial

FIGURE P11.10

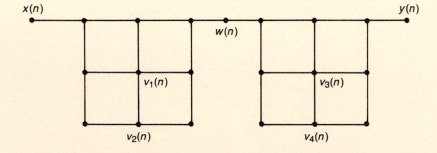

FIGURE P11.11(a)

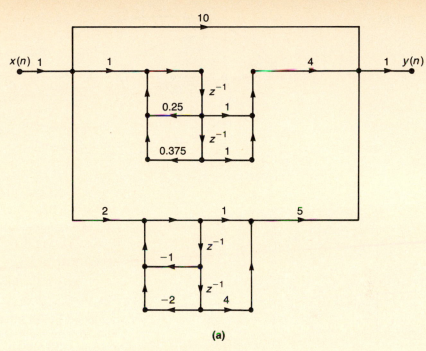

(a)

FIGURE P11.11(b)

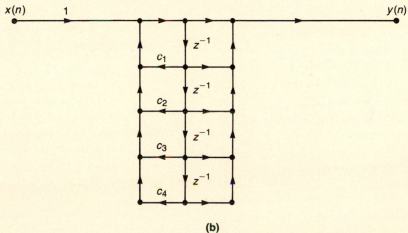

(b)

conditions are given by $\mathbf{v}(0) = [12 \quad 3 \quad 0]^T$ and the system constants are

$$a_1 = 1/2 \quad a_2 = -1/4 \quad a_3 = 1/3$$

$$b_1 = 1 \quad b_2 = 2 \quad b_3 = -1$$

$$c_1 = 2 \quad c_2 = 0 \quad c_3 = -3.$$

Find the system output $y(n)$, $n = 0, 1, 2, 3$.

f) For the system constants, input signal, and

initial conditions of part (e) what is $y(n)$ as $n \to \infty$? Is the system stable?

11.13 The signal flow graph for a discrete system is shown in Fig. P11.13.

a) Write a set of state and output equations and put them into the matrix form

$$\mathbf{v}(n + 1) = \mathbf{A}\,\mathbf{v}(n) + \mathbf{B}\,x(n)$$

$$y(n) = \mathbf{C}\,\mathbf{v}(n) + \mathbf{D}\,x(n)$$

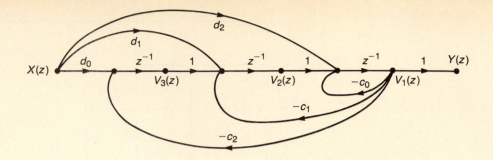

that is,

$$\mathbf{v}(n+1) = \begin{bmatrix} & & \\ & & \\ & & \end{bmatrix} \mathbf{v}(n) + \begin{bmatrix} \\ \\ \end{bmatrix} x(n)$$

$$y(n) = \begin{bmatrix} & \\ & \end{bmatrix} \mathbf{v}(n) + \begin{bmatrix} \\ \end{bmatrix} x(n)$$

b) Determine the transfer function

$$H(z) = Y(z)/X(z).$$

11.14 In the signal flow graph shown in Fig. P11.14, a and α are constants.

a) Find the transfer function $H(z) = Y(z)/X(z)$.

b) Is the system causal?

c) For what range of values of a and α is the system stable?

d) For $a = 1$, show by using a sketch what happens to the system poles as α varies in the range 0 to π. Label the pole locations when $\alpha = \pi/4$.

e) Determine the unit sample response for $a = 1$ and $\alpha = \pi/4$. Can you think of an application for this system?

11.15 A nonrecursive filter has the transfer function $H(z) = 1 - 0.5z^{-4}$.

a) Find the values of the lattice filter parameters $k_1, \ldots, k_M$ and draw the system diagram.

b) Repeat part (a) for

$$H(z) = 1 + 0.5z^{-2} - 0.6z^{-4}.$$

11.16 The process of inverse filtering or deconvolution is very useful in radar, sonar, and seismic problems for removing undesirable components in a time series. The undesirable components may be caused by the medium through which the signal passes. In Fig. P11.16 $g(n)$ represents the unit sample response of the medium and $h(n)$ represents the unit sample response of the filter designed to recover the signal $x(n)$. We want the recovered signal $y(n)$ to be equal to $x(n)$.

As a first-order approximation, assume that $g(0) = 1$, $g(1) = a$, and $g(n) = 0$ for $n \geq 2$.

a) Find $H(z)$, the transfer function of the filter that will make $y(n) = x(n)$.

b) Draw a realization for this filter.

11.17 The system shown in Fig. P11.17(a) has the unit sample response

$$h_1(n) = \begin{cases} a^n, & n \geq 0 \\ 0, & n < 0. \end{cases}$$

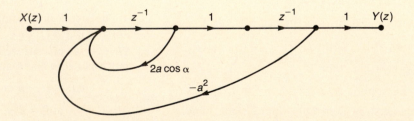

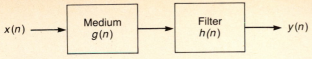

FIGURE P11.16

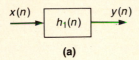

(a)

(b)

FIGURE P11.17

Another system is to be cascaded with this system so that for any input $x(n)$ the output $y'(n)$ of Fig. P11.17(b) of the cascaded system is equal to $x(n)$. Find the unit sample response $h_2(n)$ of the second system.

11.18 A discrete system is described by the state and output equations

$$\mathbf{v}(n+1) = \begin{bmatrix} 0 & 1 \\ -1 & a \end{bmatrix} \mathbf{v}(n) + \begin{bmatrix} 0 \\ 1 \end{bmatrix} x(n)$$

$$= \mathbf{A}\,\mathbf{v}(n) + \mathbf{B}\,x(n)$$

$$y(n) = [1 \quad 0]\,\mathbf{v}(n).$$

We want to estimate the shape of the initial condition response from simply knowing the characteristic roots and thus avoiding tedious paper and pencil calculations. Determine the approximate form of $y_{IC}(n)$ for the following values of a: $a = 1$, $a = -1$, $a = 0$, $a = 2$, and $a = -2$. Be as specific as you can in describing the response.

11.19 The discrete system of Problem 11.18 is modified by making the system input $x(n)$ a function of the states $v_1(n)$ and $v_2(n)$. That is, feedback is added so that the input to the system is now given by $x(n) = -f_1 v_1(n) - f_2 v_2(n) + r(n)$, or in matrix form, $x(n) = -\mathbf{F}\mathbf{v}(n) + r(n)$, where the feedback gain matrix is $\mathbf{F} = [f_1 \quad f_2]$ and $r(n)$ is a reference input.

a) Use $a = 1$ in the state equation of Problem 11.18 and rewrite the system equation as $\mathbf{v}(n+1) = \mathbf{A}'\mathbf{v}(n) + \mathbf{B}'r(n)$ where $\mathbf{A}'$ and $\mathbf{B}'$ are

the original $\mathbf{A}$ and $\mathbf{B}$ matrices that have been modified by feedback, $x(n) = -\mathbf{F}\mathbf{v}(n) + r(n)$. A primary purpose of a feedback law such as this is to change the system's characteristic roots so that the response is "more to our liking."

b) Suppose that characteristic roots of $z_1 = z_2 = 0$ are desired. Find the required values of f_1 and f_2 and sketch the shape of $y_{IC}(n)$.

c) Repeat part (b) for characteristic roots of $z_{1,2} = 0.60 \pm j0.45$.

11.20 An LTI system is described by the state equation of Eq. 11.247, i.e., $\mathbf{v}(n+1) = \mathbf{A}\mathbf{v}(n) + \mathbf{B}\mathbf{x}(n)$ where $\mathbf{v}(n)$ is the state vector, $\mathbf{x}(n)$ is the input vector, and $\mathbf{A}$ and $\mathbf{B}$ are matrices.

a) Find the system's characteristic equation.

b) The system is modified by adding state feedback and a reference input according to the law $\mathbf{x}(n) = -\mathbf{F}\mathbf{v}(n) + \mathbf{r}(n)$ where $\mathbf{F}$ is called the feedback gain matrix and $\mathbf{r}(n)$ is a vector of reference inputs. Find an expression for the system's characteristic equation.

c) Find the characteristic roots of a system described by

$$\mathbf{v}(n+1) = \begin{bmatrix} 1 & 0.632 \\ 0 & 0.368 \end{bmatrix} \mathbf{v}(n) + \begin{bmatrix} 0.368 \\ 0.632 \end{bmatrix} x(n)$$

$$y(n) = [1 \quad 0]\,\mathbf{v}(n).$$

d) The system is modified by adding state feedback and a reference input, i.e., $x(n) = -\mathbf{F}\mathbf{v}(n) + r(n)$. Find the elements of the feedback matrix $\mathbf{F}$ such that both characteristic roots will be located at $z = 0$.

e) With the gains found in part (d) find $y(n)$ if the input is the unit step sequence $r(n) = u(n)$. Let all initial conditions be zero and give $y(n)$ for $n = 0, 1, 2, 3, \ldots$. What do you observe about this response?

Extension

11.21 Up to this point, we have written a system's state equations from the transfer function $H(z)$. Let's turn the process around and draw an SFG from the state equations and then, using Mason's Gain Rule, compute the system's transfer function $H(z)$. Consider the state equations $v_1(n+1) = v_2(n)$, $v_2(n+1) = -v_1(n) + v_2(n) + x(n)$, and the output equation $y(n) = v_1(n)$.

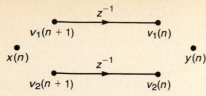

FIGURE P11.21

a) Draw an SFG for this system. Hint: See Fig. P11.21 for a systematic way to organize this procedure.

b) Use Mason's Gain Rule (MGR) to find the transfer function $H(z) = Y(z)/X(z)$.

c) Determine an analytical expression for the unit sample response of this system.

11.22 The state and output equations for a multiple-input, multiple-output system are

$$\mathbf{v}(n + 1) = \mathbf{A} \, \mathbf{v}(n) + \mathbf{B} \, \mathbf{x}(n) \qquad (P11.1)$$

and

$$\mathbf{y}(n) = \mathbf{C} \, \mathbf{v}(n) + \mathbf{D} \, \mathbf{x}(n). \qquad (P11.2)$$

Up to this point, we have used the transfer function $H(z)$ to define the ratio of the z-transform of the single system output $y(n)$ to the z-transform of the single system input $x(n)$, i.e.,

$$H(z) = \frac{Y(z)}{X(z)}. \qquad (P11.3)$$

But here we are dealing with a number of outputs and inputs denoted by the vectors $\mathbf{y}(n)$ and $\mathbf{x}(n)$, respectively. All of the possible output-input transfer functions can be represented by the transfer function matrix $\mathbf{H}(z)$ where

$$\mathbf{Y}(z) = \mathbf{H}(z)\mathbf{X}(z). \qquad (P11.4)$$

a) Start with Eqs. P11.1 and P11.2 and find the expression for $\mathbf{H}(z)$ in Eq. P11.4. Your answer will be in terms of the $\mathbf{A}, \mathbf{B}, \mathbf{C}$, and $\mathbf{D}$ matrices.

b) A multivariable (multiple-input, multiple-output) feedback control system is described by

$$\mathbf{v}(n + 1) = \begin{bmatrix} 1 & 0 & 0 \\ 0 & 0.9 & 0 \\ 0 & 0 & 0.8 \end{bmatrix} \mathbf{v}(n) + \begin{bmatrix} 0.1 & 0 \\ 0.01 & 0.01 \\ 0 & 0.2 \end{bmatrix} \mathbf{x}(n)$$

and

$$\mathbf{y}(n) = \begin{bmatrix} 1 & -1 & 0 \\ 1 & 0 & 1 \end{bmatrix} \mathbf{v}(n).$$

Use the results of part (a) to find the expressions for the entries of the matrix $\mathbf{H}(z) = \mathbf{C}[(z\mathbf{I} - \mathbf{A})^{-1}\mathbf{B}] + \mathbf{D}$ to find the transfer function matrix for this system.

11.23 Consider the system of Problem 11.22(b).

a) Draw a signal flow graph that represents the system.

b) Use Mason's Gain Rule to compute the transfer function for every combination of input and output. That is, complete the four-element transfer function matrix below.

$$\begin{bmatrix} Y_1(z) \\ Y_2(z) \end{bmatrix} = \begin{bmatrix} H_{11}(z) & H_{12}(z) \\ H_{21}(z) & H_{22}(z) \end{bmatrix} \begin{bmatrix} X_1(z) \\ X_2(z) \end{bmatrix}$$

11.24 An analog system is described by the continuous-time state equation

$$\dot{\mathbf{v}}(t) = \begin{bmatrix} 0 & 1 \\ -2 & -3 \end{bmatrix} \mathbf{v}(t) + \begin{bmatrix} 0 \\ 1 \end{bmatrix} x(t)$$

and the input to the system is piecewise constant, i.e., $x(t) = x(nT), nT \le t < nT + T$. With the aid of Appendix G show that the system can be described by

$$\mathbf{v}(n + 1) = \begin{bmatrix} 0.601 & 0.233 \\ -0.466 & -0.098 \end{bmatrix} \mathbf{v}(n) + \begin{bmatrix} 0.200 \\ 0.233 \end{bmatrix} x(n)$$

if $T = 1$ sec.

11.25 Repeat Problem 11.24 for the continuous-time system described by

$$\dot{\mathbf{v}}(t) = \begin{bmatrix} 0 & 1 \\ 0 & -1 \end{bmatrix} \mathbf{v}(t) + \begin{bmatrix} 0 \\ 1 \end{bmatrix} x(t)$$

For $T = 1$ show that the state difference equation is

$$\mathbf{v}(n + 1) = \begin{bmatrix} 1 & 0.632 \\ 0 & 0.368 \end{bmatrix} \mathbf{v}(n) + \begin{bmatrix} 0.368 \\ 0.632 \end{bmatrix} x(n).$$

11.26 The signal flow graphs that we constructed in this chapter did not include nodes to represent the initial conditions. It is, however, easy and often useful to represent the system's initial conditions on the flow graph.

a) Find the unilateral z-transform of the scalar difference equation $v(n + 1) = av(n) + bx(n)$

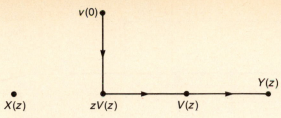

$v(0)$

$X(z)$ $zV(z)$ $V(z)$ $Y(z)$

FIGURE P11.26

and complete the SFG of Fig. P11.26. The output $y(n)$ is equal to $v(n)$.

b) Find the transfer function $H(z) = \dfrac{Y(z)}{X(z)}$ with $v(0) = 0$ and the transmission gain $T(z) = \dfrac{Y(z)}{v(0)}$ with $x(n) = 0$.

c) Use the SFG and the result of part (b) to find the total response $y(n)$ if $x(n) = (\alpha)^n \cdot u(n)$. One term in your answer should be kept in terms of the general initial condition $v(0)$.

11.27 Given that $Y_3(z) = 1 + 0.5z^{-1} + 0.2z^{-2} - 0.5z^{-3}$ as in Example 11.7.

a) Show that the lattice filter parameters k_1, k_2, and k_3 can be found by solving Eq. 11.82 for $Y_2(z)$ and $Y_1(z)$ and "picking out" the appropriate coefficients.

b) Comment on the relative merits of the approach in part (a) compared with the solution of Eq. 11.93 as in Example 11.7. Include consideration of the possibility of finding the k_i, $i = 1, 2, \ldots, M$ by use of a computer program.

11.28 Starting with Eq. 11.93 write the pseudocode, or draw a flowchart, which would be appropriate to find the lattice filter parameters of a filter of order M.

11.29 It is an easy matter to connect already designed filters in cascade or in parallel to create a new filter with different characteristics. For simplicity, let's consider as our original system a second-order, 1-dB ripple, Chebyshev lowpass filter that has the transfer function (from Table 10.9)

$$H(z) = \frac{Y(z)}{X(z)} = \frac{0.983(z + 1)^2}{3.201z^2 + 0.206z + 1.005}.$$

a) Find the gain of the frequency response at $\theta = 0$, $\theta = \pi/2$, and $\theta = 3\pi/4$ for the cascade connection of two of these filters as in Figure P11.29. Give your results in both M and M_{dB} vs. θ and make a sketch of M_{dB} vs. θ.

b) Write the difference equation that relates $y'(n)$ to $x(n)$.

11.30 A linear discrete system can be modeled by the signal flow graph of Fig. P11.30.

a) Find the transfer function $H(z) = Y(z)/X(z)$.

b) Write state and output equations for this system and put them in matrix form. Hint: It may be most convenient to write the state equations in the form $\mathbf{Tv}(n + 1) = \mathbf{P}_1 \mathbf{v}(n) + \mathbf{P}_2 x(n)$ and then manipulate them to the form $\mathbf{v}(n + 1) = \mathbf{Av}(n) + \mathbf{B}x(n)$.

11.31 An LTI system has the transfer function

$$H(z) = Y(z)/X(z) = \frac{4z^2}{z^3 + z^2 + 0.25z - 0.5}.$$

a) Find a set of state and output equations that represent the system and write these in matrix form.

b) If $y(0) = y(-1) = y(-2) = 0$ and $x(n) = (1/2)^n u(n)$, use an iterative procedure to find the values of the states $\mathbf{v}(n)$ and $y(n)$ for $n = 1$, 2, 3, 4. Hint: Determine the derived initial

FIGURE P11.29

$x(n)$ $y'(n)$

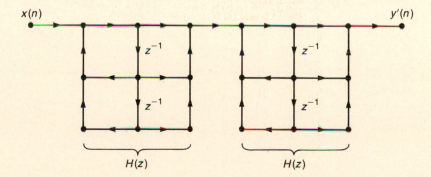

$H(z)$ $H(z)$

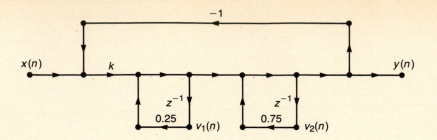

conditions $y(1)$ and $y(2)$ and solve three linear algebraic equations involving $y(0)$, $y(1)$, and $y(2)$ for the value of $\mathbf{v}(0)$, the state vector at $n = 0$.

c) Find $Y(z)$ for the input of part (b) and use long division to verify the results for $y(n)$ found above.

11.32 A system is characterized by the state equations $\mathbf{v}(n + 1) = \mathbf{A}\mathbf{v}(n) + \mathbf{B}\mathbf{x}(n)$. The purpose of this problem is to consider whether the system satisfies the definition of linearity given in Chapter Two.

a) Write the expression for the forced response $\mathbf{v}_F(n)$ in terms of $\mathbf{A}$, $\mathbf{B}$, and the input $\mathbf{x}(n)$.

b) Show that the system forced response relationship of part (a) satisfies the linearity test of Chapter Two.

c) Write an expression for the total response $\mathbf{v}(n) = \mathbf{v}_{IC}(n) + \mathbf{v}_F(n)$ in terms of $\mathbf{A}$, $\mathbf{B}$, $\mathbf{x}(n)$, and $\mathbf{v}(0)$, the initial value of $\mathbf{v}(n)$.

d) Does the total response relationship of part (c) satisfy the linearity test of Chapter Two? If not, why not?

e) Is the system linear or nonlinear? Explain.

Integrated Review

11.33 The unit sample response of an LTI system is given by

$$h(n) = \begin{cases} (0.5)^n + 2^n \cos(n\pi/2 - \pi/2), & n \ge 0 \\ 0, & n < 0 \end{cases}$$

a) Find the system's transfer function $H(z)$. Express this in the form $H(z) = N(z)/D(z)$ where $N(z)$ and $D(z)$ are polynomials in positive powers of z.

b) Find a difference equation that describes the system if $y(n)$ is the system output and $x(n)$ is the input.

c) Find the values of the system's unit sample response from the difference equation in (b) for $n = 0, 1, 2, 3$. Compare with the values found by letting $n = 0, 1, 2, 3$ in the given expression for $h(n)$.

d) Draw the system diagram in the form of Fig. 11.1(a).

e) Write state and output equations for the system.

f) Determine the steady-state output for the input $x(n) = 2 \cos(\pi n/3 + 1)$.

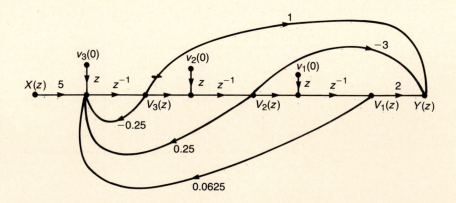

11.34 A signal flow graph for a discrete system is shown in Fig. P11.34 with initial conditions included as in Problem 11.26.

a) Write state and output equations for the system and put them in matrix form.

b) The z-transform of the system's initial condition response is given by $\mathbf{V}_{IC}(z) = z(z\mathbf{I} - \mathbf{A})^{-1}\mathbf{v}(0)$. This can be written as $\mathbf{V}_{IC}(z) = \boldsymbol{\Phi}(z)\mathbf{v}(0)$ where $\boldsymbol{\Phi}(z) = z(z\mathbf{I} - \mathbf{A})^{-1}$, that is,

$$\begin{bmatrix} V_1(z) \\ V_2(z) \\ V_3(z) \end{bmatrix}_{IC} = \begin{bmatrix} \phi_{11}(z) & \phi_{12}(z) & \phi_{13}(z) \\ \phi_{21}(z) & \phi_{22}(z) & \phi_{23}(z) \\ \phi_{31}(z) & \phi_{32}(z) & \phi_{33}(z) \end{bmatrix} \begin{bmatrix} v_1(0) \\ v_2(0) \\ v_3(0) \end{bmatrix}$$

From this last relationship and the signal flow graph it can be seen that a general entry of the matrix $\boldsymbol{\Phi}(z)$, say $\phi_{ij}(z)$, can be interpreted as a transmission gain from one of the initial condition nodes to one of the state nodes. Thus, $\phi_{ij}(z)$ can be found by using Mason's Gain Rule. What is the appropriate relationship for $\phi_{ij}(z)$?

c) Use the relationship of part (b) to find the entries $\phi_{12}(z)$, $\phi_{11}(z)$, $\phi_{21}(z)$, and $\phi_{32}(z)$.

d) Evaluate the matrix $z(z\mathbf{I} - \mathbf{A})^{-1}$ and compare the appropriate entries with the results found in part (c).

11.35 The desired frequency response characteristic of an ideal double-bandstop filter is shown in Fig. P11.35(a). We want to develop a design procedure to approximate this frequency response characteristic. As building blocks you may use ideal LP, HP, BP, and BS filters. Show how the desired frequency response characteristic can be obtained by the following:

a) A cascade combination of filters as in Fig. P11.35(b).

b) A parallel combination of filters as in Fig. P11.35(c).

In both cases, sketch the frequency response characteristics of any filter you use.

11.36 An LTI system is described by the difference equation $y(n) + 0.25y(n-2) = x(n) + 4x(n-2)$. Fill in the items in Fig. P11.36 with the quantities listed below:

a) System transfer function and a pole-zero plot.

b) An analytic expression for the unit sample response.

c) Frequency response function and a sketch of its magnitude.

d) A system diagram.

e) State equations.

FIGURE P11.35

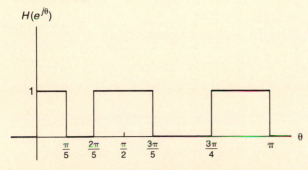

(a) Ideal frequency response characteristic

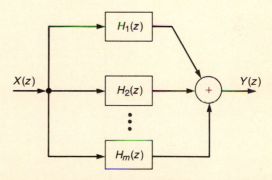

$Y(z) = H(z)X(z) = [H_1(z) + H_2(z) + \ldots + H_m(z)]X(z)$

(c) A parallel connection

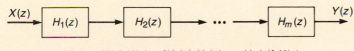

$Y(z) = H(z)X(z) = [H_1(z)H_2(z)\ldots H_m(z)]X(z)$

(b) A cascade connection

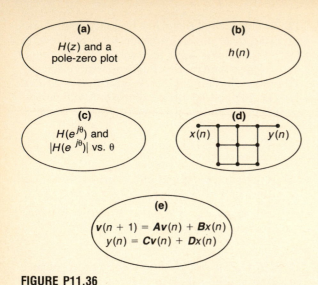

FIGURE P11.36

11.37 Repeat Problem 11.36 for the system characterized by the difference equation

$$y(n) = x(n) - 2.5x(n - 1) + x(n - 2).$$

11.38 A system is described by the state equations

$$\begin{bmatrix} v_1(n + 1) \\ v_2(n + 1) \end{bmatrix} = \begin{bmatrix} 0 & 1 \\ -1 & -1 \end{bmatrix} \begin{bmatrix} v_1(n) \\ v_2(n) \end{bmatrix} + \begin{bmatrix} 0 \\ 1 \end{bmatrix} x(n)$$

or $\mathbf{v}(n + 1) = \mathbf{A}\mathbf{v}(n) + \mathbf{B}x(n)$, and the output is given by $y(n) = v_2(n + 1)$.

a) Draw a signal flow graph for the system.

b) Find the transfer function $H(z) = Y(z)/X(z)$.

c) Find the poles of the system.

d) Find the eigenvalues of the matrix $\mathbf{A}$. How are these related to the poles of the system?

REFERENCES AND OTHER SOURCES OF INFORMATION

Arya, V. K., and J. K. Aggarwal, Eds. 1982. *Deconvolution of Seismic Data.* Benchmark Papers in Electrical Engineering and Computer Science. Stroudsburg, Pa.: Hutchinson Ross Publishing Company.

Bellanger, M. 1984. *Digital Processing of Signals—Theory and Practice.* Chichester, England: John Wiley and Sons. (Originally published under the title *Traitment Numerique Du Signal—Theorie Et Pratique.* Paris: Masson.)

Crochiere, R. E., and A. V. Oppenheim. 1975. "Analysis of Linear Digital Networks." *Proc. of the IEEE* 63 (4): 581–595.

Freeny, S. L. 1975. "Special-Purpose Hardware for Digital Filtering." *Proc. of the IEEE* 63 (4): 633–648.

Lorens, C. S. 1964. *Flowgraphs.* New York: McGraw-Hill.

Mason, S. J. 1952. "On the Logic of Feedback." Sc.D. Thesis. M.I.T. Department of Electrical Engineering.

Mason, S. J. 1953. "Feedback Theory: Some Properties of Signal Flow Graphs." *Proc. IRE* 41 (9): 1144–1156.

Mason, S. J. 1956. "Feedback Theory: Further Properties of Signal Flow Graphs." *Proc. IRE* 44 (7): 920–926.

Mitra, S. K., P. S. Kamat, and D. C. Huey. 1977. "Cascaded Lattice Realization of Digital Filters." *International Journal of Circuit Theory and Applications* 5: 3–11.

Markel, J. D., and A. H. Gray, Jr. 1976. *Linear Prediction of Speech.* Berlin: Springer Verlag.

Nagle, H. T., Jr., and V. P. Nelson. 1981. "Digital Filter Implementation on 16-Bit Microprocessors." *IEEE Micro.* (February): 23–41.

Orfanidis, S. J. 1985. *Optimum Signal Processing—An Introduction.* New York: Macmillan.

Papoulis, A. 1977. *Signal Analysis.* New York: McGraw-Hill.

Shannon, C. E. 1942. "The Theory and Design of Linear Differential Equation Machines." *OSRD Report 411* (January).

Ziolkowski, A. 1984. *Deconvolution.* Boston: International Human Resources Development Corporation.

APPENDIX A

Complex Numbers

Introduction

The two roots of the quadratic equation

$$ax^2 + bx + c = 0 \tag{A.1}$$

can be obtained from the quadratic formula as

$$x_{1,2} = \frac{-b \pm \sqrt{b^2 - 4ac}}{2a}. \tag{A.2}$$

If, for example, we have

$$2x^2 - 5x - 7 = 0 \tag{A.3}$$

the roots are

$$x_{1,2} = \frac{5 \pm \sqrt{25 + 56}}{4}$$

$$= 3.5 \text{ and } -1 \tag{A.4}$$

which is perfectly straightforward. But if we solve the equation

$$x^2 + 4x + 13 = 0$$

in the same way we get

$$x_{1,2} = \frac{-4 \pm \sqrt{16 - 52}}{2}$$

$$= \frac{-4 \pm \sqrt{-36}}{2}. \tag{A.5}$$

This poses a problem since $\sqrt{-36}$ cannot be represented by an ordinary number, for there is no real number whose square is a negative quantity. We can, however, write

$$\sqrt{-36} = \sqrt{-1 \cdot 36}$$

$$= \sqrt{-1}\sqrt{36}$$

$$= \sqrt{-1} \cdot 6 \tag{A.6}$$

and if we let the letter $j^\dagger$ stand for $\sqrt{-1}$, Eq. A.6 can be written as $j6$, and from Eq. A.5 we can write the two roots as

$$x_{1,2} = \frac{-4 \pm j6}{2} = -2 \pm j3. \qquad (A.7)$$

The root x_1 in Eq. A.7 consists of the two separate terms -2 and $j3$ while the other root is composed of -2 and $-j3$. The combination $x_1 = -2 + j3$ is called a *complex number*[‡] with -2 called the *real part* of x_1 and 3 called the *imaginary part* of x_1. Notice that the imaginary part of x_1 is simply 3 and not $j3$. And, of course, for the complex number $x_2 = -2 - j3$ the real part is -2 and the imaginary part is -3.

Graphical Representation of a Complex Number

We can represent a complex number $\mathbf{Z} = a + jb$ as a point in the real-imaginary coordinate system of Fig. A.1(a). The coordinates of this point are a and b with a representing the real part and b the imaginary part. The complex number $\mathbf{Z} = a + jb$ can also be considered to be the sum of the vector a and the vector jb as in Fig. A.1(b) where we see that the vector b

FIGURE A.1

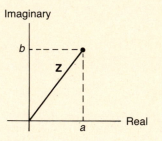

(a) Z as a point in the complex plane

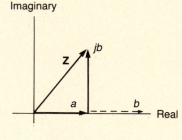

(b) Z $= a + jb$

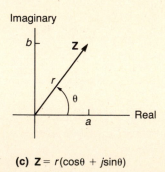

(c) Z $= r(\cos\theta + j\sin\theta)$

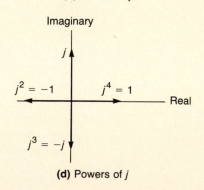

(d) Powers of j

[†] Some prefer the letter i but we have been using j for so many years that to change at this late date would cause severe psychological problems.
[‡] Professor Richard W. Hamming has suggested that the expression "numbers of a different kind" be used instead of complex numbers.

that is in line with and drawn from the tip of the vector a is given a counterclockwise rotation of $\pi/2$ radians when multiplied by j. Figure A.1(b) is known as an *Argand diagram*. A third way to represent the complex number **Z** is shown in Fig. A.1(c) where the vector of length r makes an angle of θ radians with respect to the positive real axis. Notice that Fig. A.1(c) can be related to Fig. A.1(b) through the trigonometric relation

$$r(\cos\theta + j\sin\theta) = a + jb \qquad (A.8)$$

where

$$r\cos\theta = a, \; r\sin\theta = b, \; r = (a^2 + b^2)^{1/2} \text{ and } \theta = \tan^{-1}(b/a). \qquad (A.9)$$

Powers of *j*

With $j = \sqrt{-1}$ we see that

$$j^2 = \sqrt{-1}\sqrt{-1} = -1$$

$$j^3 = j^2 \cdot j = -j$$

$$j^4 = j^3 \cdot j = (-j)(j) = -j^2 = 1$$

$$j^5 = j^4 \cdot j = 1 \cdot j = j \qquad (A.10)$$

and we are back where we started. This pattern is illustrated in Fig. A.1(d) where we see that each multiplication by j produces a counterclockwise progression of $\pi/2$ radians.

Exponential Form of a Complex Number

The exponential form is a very useful way to express the complex number illustrated in Fig. A.1(c). From calculus we can write a power series for the following functions:

$$\cos\theta = 1 - \frac{\theta^2}{2!} + \frac{\theta^4}{4!} - \frac{\theta^6}{6!} + \cdots \qquad (A.11)$$

$$\sin\theta = \theta - \frac{\theta^3}{3!} + \frac{\theta^5}{5!} - \cdots \qquad (A.12)$$

$$e^{j\theta} = 1 + j\theta + \frac{(j\theta)^2}{2!} + \frac{(j\theta)^3}{3!} + \cdots$$

$$= 1 + j\theta - \frac{\theta^2}{2!} - j\frac{\theta^3}{3!} + \frac{\theta^4}{4!} - \cdots. \qquad (A.13)$$

Adding Eq. A.11 and j times Eq. A.12 we have

$$\cos\theta + j\sin\theta = 1 + j\theta - \frac{\theta^2}{2!} - j\frac{\theta^3}{3!} + \frac{\theta^4}{4!} - \cdots \qquad (A.14)$$

and we notice that this is identical to Eq. A.13, the series expansion of $e^{j\theta}$. Thus, we have the *Euler relation* (identity)

$$\cos \theta + j \sin \theta = e^{j\theta}. \tag{A.15}$$

In general, multiplying by the positive real number r gives

$$r(\cos \theta + j \sin \theta) = re^{j\theta} \tag{A.16}$$

and comparing this with Eq. A.8 we can describe the complex number of Fig. A.1(c) as

$$\mathbf{Z} = re^{j\theta}. \tag{A.17}$$

This form of the complex number $\mathbf{Z}$ is known as the *complex exponential* or simply the exponential form where r is the amplitude or magnitude and θ is the phase in radians. In summary, we have three ways of expressing a complex number. They are:

$$\mathbf{Z} = a + jb \qquad \text{rectangular form} \qquad \text{(Fig. A.1(b))}$$
$$\mathbf{Z} = r(\cos \theta + j \sin \theta) \quad \text{polar form} \qquad \text{(Fig. A.1(c))}$$
$$\mathbf{Z} = re^{j\theta} \qquad \text{exponential form} \qquad \text{(Fig. A.1(c)).} \tag{A.18}$$

Properties of Complex Conjugate Numbers

The complex conjugate of

$$\mathbf{Z} = a + jb \tag{A.19}$$

is found by substituting $-j$ everywhere for j giving

$$\mathbf{Z}^* = a - jb \tag{A.20}$$

where the * (star) denotes the complex conjugate. For the polar form $\mathbf{Z} = r(\cos \theta + j \sin \theta)$ the complex conjugate is $\mathbf{Z}^* = r(\cos \theta - j \sin \theta)$ and for the exponential $\mathbf{Z} = re^{j\theta}$, $\mathbf{Z}^* = re^{-j\theta}$. Notice that in the rectangular form

$$\mathbf{Z}\,\mathbf{Z}^* = (a + jb)(a - jb)$$
$$= a^2 + b^2 \tag{A.21}$$

while in the exponential form

$$\mathbf{Z}\,\mathbf{Z}^* = re^{j\theta}\,re^{-j\theta}$$
$$= r^2 \tag{A.22}$$

and consequently

$$\mathbf{Z}\,\mathbf{Z}^* = |\mathbf{Z}|^2. \tag{A.23}$$

In other words, a complex number multiplied by its conjugate yields the square of its magnitude, where the magnitude is $\sqrt{a^2 + b^2}$ in the rectangular form and r in the exponential form.

Addition and Subtraction of Complex Numbers

Complex numbers are added or subtracted in the rectangular form. If $\mathbf{X} = 4 + j5$ and $\mathbf{Y} = 6 - j7$ then the sum is

$$\mathbf{X} + \mathbf{Y} = 4 + j5 + 6 - j7 \tag{A.24}$$

and treating the real and imaginary parts separately we have

$$\mathbf{X} + \mathbf{Y} = (4 + 6) + j(5 - 7)$$

$$= 10 - j2. \tag{A.25}$$

In a similar way we have the difference

$$\mathbf{X} - \mathbf{Y} = 4 + j5 - (6 - j7)$$

$$= (4 - 6) + j(5 + 7)$$

$$= -2 + j12 \tag{A.26}$$

and

$$\mathbf{Y} - \mathbf{X} = 6 - j7 - (4 + j5)$$

$$= (6 - 4) + j(-7 - 5)$$

$$= 2 - j12. \tag{A.27}$$

It is helpful to show these manipulations graphically as in Fig. A.2(a) where vectors for $\mathbf{X}$, $\mathbf{Y}$, and the sum $\mathbf{X} + \mathbf{Y}$ have been drawn using "head-to-tail" addition. To show the difference $\mathbf{X} - \mathbf{Y}$ the $\mathbf{Y}$ vector is reversed in direction and the head-to-tail addition of $\mathbf{X}$ and $(-\mathbf{Y})$ is given in Fig. A.2(b). Figure A.2(c) shows the same procedure for $\mathbf{Y} - \mathbf{X}$.

FIGURE A.2

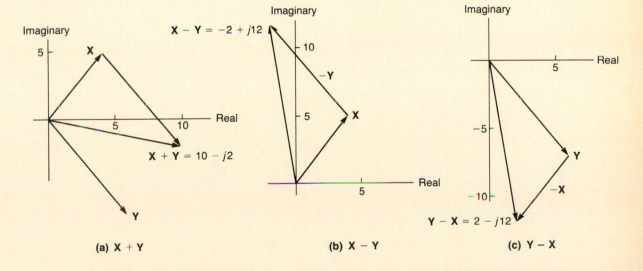

(a) $\mathbf{X} + \mathbf{Y}$ (b) $\mathbf{X} - \mathbf{Y}$ (c) $\mathbf{Y} - \mathbf{X}$

Multiplication and Division of Complex Numbers

These operations are most easily performed with the complex numbers expressed in exponential form. From algebra we recall that when exponentials are multiplied the magnitudes are multiplied and the exponents are added in the manner

$$(a_1 e^{\alpha_1})(a_2 e^{\alpha_2}) = a_1 a_2 e^{(\alpha_1 + \alpha_2)}. \tag{A.28}$$

If, for example, $\mathbf{X} = 5e^{j\pi/6}$ and $\mathbf{Y} = 7e^{-j\pi/12}$ the product is

$$\mathbf{X}\,\mathbf{Y} = (5e^{j\pi/6})(7e^{-j\pi/12})$$

$$= (5)(7)e^{j(\pi/6 - \pi/12)}$$

$$= 35e^{j\pi/12}. \tag{A.29}$$

A graphical interpretation of this is shown in Figs. A.3(a) and (b) where the vector $\mathbf{X}$ can be considered to be changed in length by a factor equal to the magnitude of $\mathbf{Y}$, which is 7, and rotated in phase in a clockwise (minus sign on the phase) direction by $\pi/12$, the magnitude of the phase of $\mathbf{Y}$.

Complex numbers also can, of course, be multiplied when expressed in the rectangular form as we now demonstrate. For $\mathbf{X} = 4.33 + j2.5$ and $\mathbf{Y} = 6.76 - j1.81$ the product is

$$\mathbf{X}\,\mathbf{Y} = (4.33 + j2.5)(6.76 - j1.81)$$

$$= 29.27 - j7.84 + j16.90 + 4.53. \tag{A.30}$$

FIGURE A.3

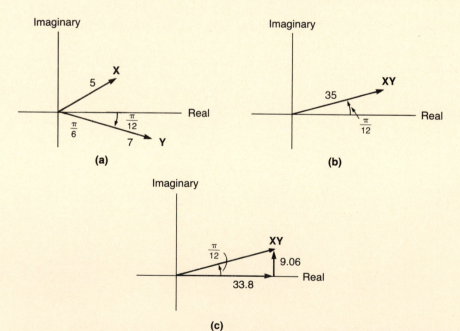

(a)

(b)

(c)

Collecting real and imaginary parts separately gives us

$$\mathbf{X\,Y} = 33.80 + j9.06 \qquad (A.31)$$

that can be put into the exponential form

$$\mathbf{X\,Y} = 34.99e^{j0.26} \approx 35e^{j\pi/12} \qquad (A.32)$$

which agrees with Eq. A.29. When converting a complex number from rectangular to exponential form, care must be taken to get the angle θ of $re^{j\theta}$ in the proper quadrant. To help avoid mistakes, sketch $a + jb$ in the real-imaginary plane as in Fig. A.3(c) and the proper quadrant can easily be verified.

Again from algebra we recall the rule for dividing exponentials, namely

$$a_1e^{\alpha_1}/a_2e^{\alpha_2} = (a_1/a_2)e^{(\alpha_1-\alpha_2)} \qquad (A.33)$$

and for $\mathbf{X} = 5e^{j\pi/6}$ and $\mathbf{Y} = 7e^{-j\pi/12}$ the quotient $\mathbf{Y/X}$ is

$$\frac{\mathbf{Y}}{\mathbf{X}} = \frac{7e^{-j\pi/12}}{5e^{j\pi/6}}$$

$$= \frac{7}{5}e^{j(-\pi/12-\pi/6)}$$

$$= 1.4e^{-j(\pi/4)}. \qquad (A.34)$$

A graphical interpretation of this is shown in Figs. A.4(a) and (b) where the vector $\mathbf{Y}$ can be considered to be changed in length by a factor equal to the reciprocal of the magnitude of $\mathbf{X}$, i.e., 1/5, and rotated in phase in a clockwise direction where $\pi/6$, the phase of $\mathbf{X}$, is subtracted from the phase of $\mathbf{Y}$.

As in multiplication, complex numbers can be divided when expressed in rectangular form as we now demonstrate. For $\mathbf{X} = 4.33 + j2.5$ and $\mathbf{Y} = 6.76 - j1.81$ the quotient $\mathbf{Y/X}$ is

$$\frac{\mathbf{Y}}{\mathbf{X}} = \frac{6.76 - j1.81}{4.33 + j2.5} \qquad (A.35)$$

FIGURE A.4

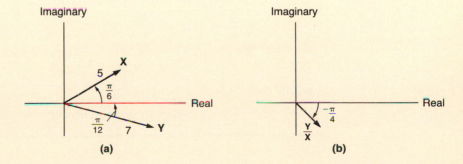

(a) (b)

and one way to proceed is to multiply the numerator and denominator of Eq. A.35 by $4.33 - j2.5$, the complex conjugate of the denominator giving

$$\frac{Y}{X} = \frac{6.76 - j1.81}{4.33 + j2.5} \cdot \frac{4.33 - j2.5}{4.33 - j2.5}$$

$$= \frac{29.27 - j16.9 - j7.84 - 4.53}{(4.33)^2 - j^2(2.5)^2}. \tag{A.36}$$

Collecting real and imaginary numbers in the numerator and recognizing that $j^2 = -1$ in the denominator we have

$$\frac{Y}{X} = \frac{24.74 - j24.74}{25}$$

$$= 0.99 - j0.99. \tag{A.37}$$

Notice that $0.99 - j0.99 = 1.4e^{-j(\pi/4)}$ as in Eq. A.34. Multiplying and dividing complex numbers expressed in rectangular form is lots of work and if given

$$Q = \frac{(2.5 + j4.33)(5 - j5)}{(-10 + j17.32)} \tag{A.38}$$

the best procedure is to place all the components into exponential form as

$$Q = \frac{(5e^{j\pi/3})(5\sqrt{2}e^{-j\pi/4})}{20e^{j2\pi/3}}$$

$$= \frac{5 \cdot 5\sqrt{2}}{20} e^{j(\pi/3 - \pi/4 - 2\pi/3)}$$

$$= 1.77e^{j(-7\pi/12)}. \tag{A.39}$$

A general rule may be stated for the complex number

$$\mathbf{Z} = \frac{(N_1 e^{j\alpha_1})(N_2 e^{j\alpha_2}) \cdots}{(D_1 e^{j\beta_1})(D_2 e^{j\beta_2}) \cdots}$$

$$= Me^{jP} \tag{A.40}$$

The amplitude is

$$M = N_1 N_2 \cdots / D_1 D_2 \cdots \tag{A.41}$$

and the phase is

$$P = (\alpha_1 + \alpha_2 + \cdots) - (\beta_1 + \beta_2 + \cdots). \tag{A.42}$$

Powers of Complex Numbers

If we have

$$\mathbf{Y} = \mathbf{X}^N \tag{A.43}$$

with $\mathbf{X} = re^{j\theta}$ we simply use the multiplication rule to form the product

$$\mathbf{Y} = \overbrace{(re^{j\theta})(re^{j\theta})\cdots(re^{j\theta})}^{N \text{ terms}}$$

$$= r^N e^{jN\theta}. \tag{A.44}$$

For example, with $\mathbf{X} = 2e^{j\pi/20}$ and $\mathbf{Y} = \mathbf{X}^6$ we have

$$\mathbf{Y} = (2e^{j\pi/20})^6$$

$$= 64e^{j6\pi/20}. \tag{A.45}$$

This general result is known as *De Moivre's Theorem* and it says that to raise a complex number $re^{j\theta}$ to any power N, we raise the magnitude r to the power N and multiply the phase θ by N. That is

$$(re^{j\theta})^N = r^N e^{jN\theta}. \tag{A.46}$$

Roots of Complex Numbers

We can exploit De Moivre's Theorem to find the roots of complex numbers by using N as a fractional power. For instance, if $\mathbf{X} = 4e^{j\pi/3}$ we have by raising both sides to the 1/2 power

$$\mathbf{X}^{1/2} = (4e^{j\pi/3})^{1/2}$$

$$= (4)^{1/2}e^{j\pi/6} = 2e^{j\pi/6}. \tag{A.47}$$

But this is only one root; there must be two roots that when squared will produce the original $\mathbf{X}$. We find the other root by noticing that the original complex number $\mathbf{X}$ could also be written $4e^{j(\pi/3+2\pi)}$ and applying De Moivre's Theorem again we get

$$\mathbf{X}^{1/2} = (4e^{j7\pi/3})^{1/2}$$

$$= 2e^{j7\pi/6}. \tag{A.48}$$

Thus, the two roots of $4e^{j\pi/3}$ are $2e^{j\pi/6}$ and $2e^{j7\pi/6}$.

Moving ahead to finding the cube root of a complex number, suppose that we have

$$\mathbf{X} = 8e^{j2\pi/3} \tag{A.49}$$

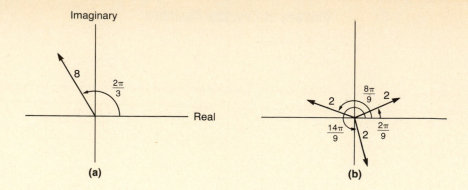

(a) (b)

as in Fig. A.5(a). Now the complex number X can be written as $8e^{j2\pi/3}$, $8e^{j(2\pi/3+2\pi)}$, $8e^{j(2\pi/3+4\pi)}$, and so forth. Applying De Moivre's Theorem to each of these gives

$$X^{1/3} = 8^{1/3}e^{j2\pi/9}, \; X^{1/3} = 8^{1/3}e^{j(2\pi/3+2\pi)/3}, \; \text{and} \; X^{1/3} = 8^{1/3}e^{j(2\pi/3+4\pi)/3}$$

or

$$X^{1/3} = 2e^{j2\pi/9}, \; X^{1/3} = 2e^{j8\pi/9}, \; \text{and} \; X^{1/3} = 2e^{j14\pi/9}.$$

Check:

$$(X^{1/3})^3 = 8e^{j2\pi/3}, \; (X^{1/3})^3 = 8e^{j8\pi/3} = 8e^{j2\pi/3}, \; \text{and}$$
$$(X^{1/3})^3 = 8e^{j14\pi/3} = 8e^{j2\pi/3} \tag{A.50}$$

The three roots of $X = 8e^{j2\pi/3}$ are shown in Fig. A.5(b).

A general rule for finding the N roots of a complex number $Z = re^{j\theta}$ may be stated as

$$Z^{1/N} = (r)^{1/N}e^{j(\theta+k2\pi)/N}, \; k = 0, 1, \dots, N-1. \tag{A.51}$$

Keep in mind that r must be a positive number so that if we wanted to find the cube root of $-8e^{j2\pi/3}$, for example, we'd first write this as $8e^{j(\pi+2\pi/3)} = 8e^{j(5\pi/3)}$.

Euler Identities

From the Euler relation

$$e^{j\theta} = \cos\theta + j\sin\theta \tag{A.52}$$

we can write the complex conjugate

$$e^{-j\theta} = \cos\theta - j\sin\theta. \tag{A.53}$$

Adding Eqs. A.52 and A.53 gives

$$e^{j\theta} + e^{-j\theta} = 2\cos\theta \qquad (A.54)$$

while subtracting Eq. A.53 from Eq. A.52 produces

$$e^{j\theta} - e^{-j\theta} = 2j\sin\theta. \qquad (A.55)$$

Thus, the cosine and sine formulas can be written in terms of the complex exponentials $e^{j\theta}$ and $e^{-j\theta}$ as

$$\cos\theta = \frac{e^{j\theta} + e^{-j\theta}}{2} \quad \text{and} \quad \sin\theta = \frac{e^{j\theta} - e^{-j\theta}}{2j}. \qquad (A.56)$$

An important result: For $\theta = \pi$ in Eq. A.52 we obtain

$$e^{j\pi} = \cos\pi + j\sin\pi \qquad (A.57)$$

or

$$e^{j\pi} = -1. \qquad (A.58)$$

Logarithm of a Complex Number

For the complex number in exponential form

$$\mathbf{Z} = re^{j\theta} \qquad (A.59)$$

we can write

$$\ln \mathbf{Z} = \ln[re^{j\theta}]$$

$$= \ln r + j\theta \qquad (A.60)$$

where ln denotes the *natural logarithm,* or log to the base e, and we have used the properties of logarithms

$$\ln[ab] = \ln a + \ln b \qquad (A.61)$$

and

$$\ln e^{\alpha} = \alpha. \qquad (A.62)$$

Thus, for

$$\mathbf{Z} = 8e^{j2\pi/3} \qquad (A.63)$$

the logarithm is

$$\ln \mathbf{Z} = \ln 8 + j2\pi/3$$

$$= 2.08 + j2\pi/3. \qquad (A.64)$$

As another example, the result in Eq. A.58 can be written more generally as

$$-1 = e^{j(\pi + k2\pi)}, \qquad k = 0, 1, 2, \ldots \tag{A.65}$$

and the logarithm is then found to be

$$\ln(-1) = j(\pi + k2\pi), \qquad k = 0, 1, 2, \ldots. \tag{A.66}$$

APPENDIX B

Fourier Series

Exponential Series

A *continuous-time periodic function* $x(t)$ with period T_0 can be written as the sum of an infinite number of complex exponentials as

$$x(t) = \sum_{n=-\infty}^{n=+\infty} \mathbf{X}_n e^{j2\pi n f_0 t} \tag{B.1}$$

where

$$\mathbf{X}_n = \frac{1}{T_0} \int_{t_0}^{t_0+T_0} x(t) e^{-j2\pi n f_0 t}\, dt, \qquad n = 0, \pm 1, \pm 2, \cdots \tag{B.2}$$

and f_0 is called the *fundamental frequency* of the periodic waveform $x(t)$ while nf_0 is called the nth harmonic. The period of the fundamental is $T_0 = 1/f_0$ which is also the period of $x(t)$. The $\mathbf{X}_n$ of Eq. B.2 are the *Fourier coefficients*, complex numbers that can be described in terms of their magnitude and phase as

$$\mathbf{X}_n = |\mathbf{X}_n| e^{j\angle \mathbf{X}_n}. \tag{B.3}$$

This allows us to write Eq. B.1 in the form

$$x(t) = \sum_{n=-\infty}^{n=+\infty} |\mathbf{X}_n| e^{j\angle \mathbf{X}_n} e^{j2\pi n f_0 t} \tag{B.4}$$

where the Fourier coefficients also satisfy the symmetry relation that

X_{-n} is the complex conjugate of X_n, i.e.,

$$X_{-n} = X_n{}^*$$ (B.5)

which means that

$$|X_{-n}| = |X_n|$$ (B.6)

and

$$\angle X_{-n} = -\angle X_n.$$ (B.7)

Notice that the coefficient for $n = 0$ that comes from Eq. B.2 is the real number

$$X_0 = \frac{1}{T_0} \int_{t_0}^{t_0+T_0} x(t)\, dt$$ (B.8)

which is the *average value* of the periodic waveform $x(t)$ because it represents the area under the $x(t)$ curve over one period divided by the duration of the period T_0.

Cosine Series

Equation B.4 can be written in three parts as

$$x(t) = \sum_{n=-\infty}^{n=-1} |X_n| e^{j\angle X_n} e^{j2\pi n f_0 t} + X_0 + \sum_{n=1}^{n=\infty} |X_n| e^{j\angle X_n} e^{j2\pi n f_0 t}$$ (B.9)

where the signs on n in the first term can be reversed to give

$$\sum_{n=1}^{n=\infty} |X_{-n}| e^{j\angle X_{-n}} e^{-j2\pi n f_0 t}.$$ (B.10)

But from Eqs. B.6 and B.7 we know that

$$|X_{-n}| = |X_n| \quad \text{and} \quad \angle X_{-n} = -\angle X_n$$ (B.11)

and, consequently Eq. B.10 becomes

$$\sum_{n=1}^{n=\infty} |X_n| e^{-j\angle X_n} e^{-j2\pi n f_0 t}.$$ (B.12)

Replacing the first term in Eq. B.9 with Eq. B.12 we have for the periodic function $x(t)$

$$x(t) = \sum_{n=1}^{n=\infty} |X_n| e^{-j\angle X_n} e^{-j2\pi n f_0 t} + X_0 + \sum_{n=1}^{n=\infty} |X_n| e^{j\angle X_n} e^{j2\pi n f_0 t}.$$ (B.13)

Using the Euler relation

$$e^{j\theta} + e^{-j\theta} = 2 \cos \theta$$ (B.14)

Eq. B.13 can be written as

$$x(t) = X_0 + 2 \sum_{n=1}^{n=\infty} |\mathbf{X}_n| \cos(2\pi n f_0 t + \underline{/\mathbf{X}_n}). \qquad (B.15)$$

The X_0 term is the same as Eq. B.8 and is sometimes referred to as the *dc* (or zero frequency) component.

Sine-Cosine Series

Although the exponential form of the Fourier Series of Eqs. B.1 or B.4 and the cosine form of Eq. B.15 are both very widely used, some prefer to describe the periodic waveform $x(t)$ as

$$x(t) = X_0 + \sum_{n=1}^{n=\infty} A_n \cos(2\pi n f_0 t) + \sum_{n=1}^{n=\infty} B_n \sin(2\pi n f_0 t). \qquad (B.16)$$

The constant term (average value) is still found from

$$X_0 = \frac{1}{T_0} \int_{t_0}^{t_0+T_0} x(t) \, dt \qquad (B.17)$$

with the coefficients of the cosine term being

$$A_n = \frac{2}{T_0} \int_{t_0}^{t_0+T_0} x(t) \cos(2\pi n f_0 t) \, dt \qquad (B.18)$$

and the corresponding coefficients for the sine terms are

$$B_n = \frac{2}{T_0} \int_{t_0}^{t_0+T_0} x(t) \sin(2\pi n f_0 t) \, dt. \qquad (B.19)$$

Using the Euler relation

$$e^{-j2\pi n f_0 t} = \cos(2\pi n f_0 t) - j \sin(2\pi n f_0 t) \qquad (B.20)$$

we can write Eq. B.2 in the form

$$\mathbf{X}_n = \frac{1}{T_0} \int_{t_0}^{t_0+T_0} x(t)\{\cos(2\pi n f_0 t) - j \sin(2\pi n f_0 t)\} \, dt. \qquad (B.21)$$

Separating Eq. B.21 into real and imaginary parts we get

$$\mathbf{X}_n = \frac{1}{T_0} \int_{t_0}^{t_0+T_0} x(t) \cos(2\pi n f_0 t) \, dt - j \frac{1}{T_0} \int_{t_0}^{t_0+T_0} x(t) \sin(2\pi n f_0 t) \, dt$$

$$(B.22)$$

and using Eqs. B.18 and B.19 we have

$$\mathbf{X}_n = \frac{1}{2} A_n - \frac{1}{2} j B_n$$

$$= \frac{1}{2}(A_n - jB_n) \qquad \text{(B.23)}$$

or

$$A_n = 2 \operatorname{Re}[\mathbf{X}_n] \quad \text{and} \quad B_n = -2 \operatorname{Im}[\mathbf{X}_n]. \qquad \text{(B.24)}$$

Some Symmetry Rules

If $x(t)$ is an *even function*, i.e., $x(t) = x(-t)$ as illustrated in Fig. B.1, there will be no sine terms in the sine-cosine series of Eq. B.16, that is

$$B_n = 0, \qquad n = 1, 2, \ldots . \qquad \text{(B.25)}$$

This can be seen by using $x(t)$ as an even function in Eq. B.19 where

$$B_n = \frac{2}{T_0} \int_{t_0}^{t_0+T_0} \underbrace{x(t)}_{\text{even}} \underbrace{\sin(2\pi n f_0 t)}_{\text{odd}} dt \ .$$

$$\underbrace{\qquad\qquad\qquad\qquad}_{\text{even} \times \text{odd} = \text{odd}}$$

$$= \text{integral over one period of an odd function}$$

$$= 0. \qquad \text{(B.26)}$$

Similarly, for an *odd function*, $x(t) = -x(-t)$ as shown in Fig. B.2, there will be no constant term and no cosine term. That is,

$$X_0 = 0 \quad \text{and} \quad A_n = 0, \qquad n = 1, 2, \ldots . \qquad \text{(B.27)}$$

From Eq. B.17 with $x(t)$ an odd function we have

$$X_0 = \frac{1}{T_0} \int_{t_0}^{t_0+T_0} \underbrace{x(t)}_{\text{odd}} dt$$

$$= \text{integral over one period of an odd function}$$

$$= 0 \qquad \text{(B.28)}$$

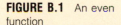

FIGURE B.1 An even function

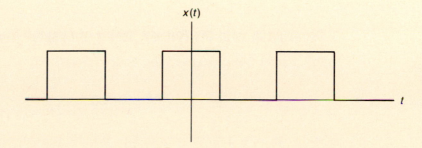

$x(t)$

t

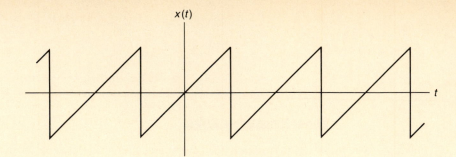

$x(t)$

and from Eq. B.18

$$A_n = \frac{2}{T_0} \int_{t_0}^{t_0 + T_0} \underbrace{\underbrace{x(t)}_{\text{odd}} \underbrace{\cos(2\pi n f_0 t)}_{\text{even}}}_{\text{odd}} \, dt$$

= integral over one period of an odd function

= 0. (B.29)

Dirichlet Conditions

The conditions under which it is possible to write the Fourier Series as
discussed are known as the *Dirichlet conditions*. They require that in
each period the function:

1. must have a finite number of discontinuities,
2. must possess a finite number of maxima or minima, and
3. must be absolutely integrable, that is

$$\int_{t_0}^{t_0 + T_0} |x(t)| \, dt < \infty. \tag{B.30}$$

It's very hard to imagine a physically realizable signal which doesn't meet
these conditions.

Comparison with the Fourier Series of Chapter Nine

In Chapter Nine we used the Fourier Series pair

$$H(e^{j\theta}) = \sum_{n=-\infty}^{n=+\infty} h(n)e^{-jn\theta} \longleftrightarrow h(n) = \frac{1}{2\pi} \int_{\theta_0}^{\theta_0 + 2\pi} H(e^{j\theta})e^{jn\theta} \, d\theta \tag{B.31}$$

and with $\omega_0 = 2\pi f_0$ the pair of Eqs. B.1 and B.2 can be written in terms of

ω_0 rather than f_0 as

$$x(t) = \sum_{n=-\infty}^{n=+\infty} \mathbf{X}_n e^{jn\omega_0 t} \longleftrightarrow \mathbf{X}_n = \frac{1}{T_0} \int_{t_0}^{t_0+T_0} x(t) e^{-jn\omega_0 t} \, dt. \qquad \text{(B.32)}$$

Notice the similarity between these two pairs with the major difference between them being the signs of the complex exponentials $e^{\pm jn\theta}$ and $e^{\pm jn\omega_0 t}$.

APPENDIX C

Laplace Transform

Introduction

The following should be regarded as being sufficient to meet the Laplace transform requirements of Chapter Ten.

Definition

The *unilateral* or *one-sided Laplace transform* of a function $f(t)$ is defined to be

$$\mathcal{L}[f(t)] = \int_0^{\infty} f(t) e^{-st} \, dt \qquad \text{(C.1)}$$

where s is a complex variable that is independent of t. From this definition we can build up a table of transform pairs, as was done for z-transforms in Chapter Six. As a matter of notation, capital letters are used to represent transformed variables—for example, $\mathcal{L}[f(t)]$ is written as $F(s)$.

Pairs

Here we develop a few transform pairs.

a) *Real Exponentials*

Suppose we want to find the Laplace transform of $f(t) = Ae^{at} \cdot u(t)$ where

$$u(t) = \begin{cases} 0, & t < 0 \\ 1, & t \geq 0 \end{cases} \qquad \text{(C.2)}$$

is the unit step function in the same manner that $u(n)$ is the unit step sequence in the discrete-time domain. As in Chapter Two, we are using $u(t)$ to turn the function Ae^{at} "on" for $t \geq 0$ and "off" for $t < 0$. Then, using the defining integral of Eq. C.1 we have

$$\mathcal{L}[Ae^{at} \cdot u(t)] = \int_0^\infty Ae^{at}e^{-st}\,dt = \int_0^\infty Ae^{(a-s)t}\,dt$$

$$= \frac{Ae^{(a-s)t}}{(a-s)}\bigg|_0^\infty = \frac{A}{a-s}[e^{(a-s)\infty} - e^{(a-s)0}] \qquad (C.3)$$

and if we assume that a is real, and that s may be chosen so that $a - \text{Re}[s] < 0,^\dagger$ it follows that $e^{(a-s)\infty} = 0$ and $e^{(a-s)0} = 1$.

$$\mathcal{L}[Ae^{at}] = \frac{A}{a-s}\{0 - 1\}$$

$$= A/(s-a). \qquad (C.4)$$

This is pair number 1 in Table C.1.

b) *Step Function*

We have just shown that

$$\mathcal{L}[Ae^{at} \cdot u(t)] = A/(s-a) \qquad (C.5)$$

and if we set $a = 0$ we have

$$\mathcal{L}[A \cdot u(t)] = A/s \qquad (C.6)$$

the Laplace transform of the step function $f(t) = A \cdot u(t)$. See pair number 2 in Table C.1.

c) *Complex Exponential*

For $f(t) = Ae^{at}e^{j\omega t} \cdot u(t) = Ae^{(a+j\omega)t} \cdot u(t)$, we simply replace a with $a + j\omega$ in pair number 1 and get

$$F(s) = A/(s - a - j\omega) \qquad (C.7)$$

which is pair number 4.

d) *General Oscillatory Function*

For $f(t) = Ae^{at}\cos(\omega t) \cdot u(t)$ we can use the Euler relation to write

$$f(t) = Ae^{at}\left[\frac{e^{j\omega t} + e^{-j\omega t}}{2}\right]u(t)$$

$^\dagger s$ is a complex variable, so $e^{a-s} = e^a e^{-s} = e^a e^{-\text{Re}[s]}e^{-j\text{Im}[s]}$, and $e^{(a-s)\infty} = e^{(a-\text{Re}[s])\infty}e^{-j\text{Im}[s]\infty}$. The second exponential has a magnitude of 1, hence if $a - \text{Re}[s] < 0$, or $a < \text{Re}[s]$, $e^{(a-s)\infty} \to 0$. The region $\text{Re}[s] > a$ is called the *region of convergence* because, for these values of s, the exponential $e^{(a-s)\infty}$ converges to zero. Notice that we are using $e^{(a-s)\infty}$ as shorthand notation for $\lim_{t\to\infty} e^{(a-s)t}$.

$$= \frac{A}{2}[e^{(a+j\omega)t} + e^{(a-j\omega)t}]u(t). \tag{C.8}$$

Thus, from pair number 4

$$F(s) = \frac{A}{2}\left[\frac{1}{s - a - j\omega} + \frac{1}{s - a + j\omega}\right]$$

$$= \frac{A(s - a)}{(s - a)^2 + \omega^2} \tag{C.9}$$

This is pair number 5.

e) *Cosine Wave*

Letting $a = 0$ in the general oscillatory function of part (d) gives us

$$f(t) = A \cos(\omega t) \cdot u(t)$$

and

$$F(s) = \frac{As}{s^2 + \omega^2} \tag{C.10}$$

See pair number 6 in Table C.1.

f) *Sine Wave*

Using pair number 4 with $a = 0$ and the Euler identity we have

$$f(t) = A\left[\frac{e^{j\omega t} - e^{-j\omega t}}{2j}\right]u(t) \longleftrightarrow F(s) = \frac{A}{2j}\left[\frac{1}{s - j\omega} - \frac{1}{s + j\omega}\right] \tag{C.11}$$

or

$$f(t) = A \sin(\omega t) \cdot u(t) \longleftrightarrow F(s) = \frac{A\omega}{s^2 + \omega^2} \tag{C.12}$$

which is pair number 7.

g) *Unit Impulse Function*

The unit impulse function is defined implicitly by its property (sifting)

$$\int_{-\infty}^{\infty} \delta(t - t_0)f(t)dt = f(t_0) \tag{C.13}$$

that is, the unit impulse function is defined in terms of its area. One representation of such an unusual function is as the limit of a very tall and very narrow pulse $p(t)$ having unit area as shown in Fig. C.1, that is,

$$\delta(t - t_0) = \lim_{\Delta \to 0} p(t). \tag{C.14}$$

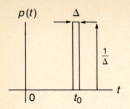

FIGURE C.1 A unit pulse $p(t)$.

Using this representation in Eq. C.13 leads to the product function shown in Fig. C.2(a) and we see that the value of the integral is

$$(f(t_0)/\Delta) \times \Delta = f(t_0). \tag{C.15}$$

As shorthand we generally represent a unit impulse as shown in Fig. C.2(b) where the magnitude (1 in this case) is taken to mean the area of the impulse.

$\delta(t)$ is simply the unit impulse function at $t = 0$. Its Laplace transform is

$$\mathscr{L}[\delta(t)] = \int_0^\infty \delta(t)e^{-st}\, dt \tag{C.16}$$

and using Eq. C.13 with $f(t) = e^{-st}$ we have

$$\mathscr{L}[\delta(t)] = e^{-s(0)} = 1. \tag{C.17}$$

This result is generalized to $f(t) = A\delta(t)$ rather than simply $\delta(t)$ for impulse functions other than the unit impulse function. See pair number 3.

Table C.1 summarizes the important Laplace transform pairs and several important properties follow the table.

FIGURE C.2(a)

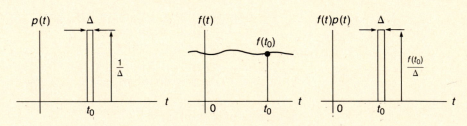

(a) Sifting property of impulse function

FIGURE C.2(b)

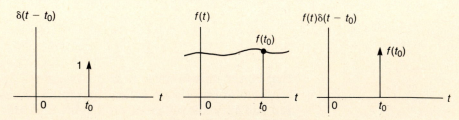

(b) Shorthand representation of impulse function and the sifting property

TABLE C.1 LAPLACE TRANSFORM PAIRS

$f(t)$	$\mathcal{L}[f(t)] = F(s)$
1. $Ae^{at} \cdot u(t)$	$A/(s - a)$
2. $A \cdot u(t)$	A/s
3. $A\delta(t)$	A
4. $Ae^{(a+j\omega)} \cdot u(t)$	$A/(s - a - j\omega)$
5. $Ae^{at} \cos(\omega t) \cdot u(t)$	$\dfrac{A(s - a)}{(s - a)^2 + \omega^2}$
6. $A \cos(\omega t) \cdot u(t)$	$\dfrac{As}{s^2 + \omega^2}$
7. $A \sin(\omega t) \cdot u(t)$	$\dfrac{A\omega}{s^2 + \omega^2}$
8. $Ae^{at} \cos(\omega t + \alpha) \cdot u(t)$	$\dfrac{\dfrac{A}{2}e^{j\alpha}}{s - a - j\omega} + \dfrac{\dfrac{A}{2}e^{-j\alpha}}{s - a + j\omega}$ $= \dfrac{A[\cos \alpha(s - a) - \omega \sin \alpha]}{(s - a)^2 + \omega^2}$
9. $At \cdot u(t)$	A/s^2

Laplace Transform Properties

Property 1 (Linearity): $\mathcal{L}[af(t) + bg(t)] = aF(s) + bG(s)$ (a and b are constants)

Property 2 (Derivative): $\mathcal{L}[df(t)/dt] = sF(s) - f(0)$

Property 3 (nth derivative): $\mathcal{L}[d^nf/dt^n] = s^nF(s) - s^{n-1}f(0) - s^{n-2}df/dt|_{t=0} - \cdots - sd^{n-2}f/dt^{n-2}|_{t=0} - d^{n-1}f/dt^{n-1}|_{t=0}$

Property 4 (Integration): $\mathcal{L}\left[\displaystyle\int_0^t f(\tau)d\tau\right] = F(s)/s$

Property 5 (Shifting): $\mathcal{L}[f(t - a) \cdot u(t - a)] = e^{-as}F(s)$

Transfer Function

For continuous-time (analog) systems, the transfer function relating the output and input signals is defined by

$$\text{system transfer function} = \frac{\text{Laplace transform of output}}{\text{Laplace transform of input}} \qquad (C.18)$$

or

$$H(s) = \frac{Y(s)}{X(s)} \qquad (C.19)$$

with all initial conditions set to zero. The system transfer function can be determined from the system differential equation or from the system's unit impulse response $h(t)$. For instance, a second-order Butterworth analog filter can be described by the differential equation

$$\frac{d^2y(t)}{dt^2} + \sqrt{2}\frac{dy(t)}{dt} + y(t) = x(t) \tag{C.20}$$

or by the filter's unit impulse response

$$h(t) = \sqrt{2}e^{-0.707t}\cos(0.707t - \pi/2), \qquad t \geq 0. \tag{C.21}$$

To find the transfer function from the differential equation we simply take the Laplace transform of Eq. C.20 setting all initial conditions to zero and then form the ratio of $Y(s)/X(s)$ giving

$$s^2Y(s) + \sqrt{2}sY(s) + Y(s) = X(s) \tag{C.22}$$

or

$$H(s) = \frac{Y(s)}{X(s)} = \frac{1}{s^2 + \sqrt{2}s + 1}. \tag{C.23}$$

Alternatively, from the unit impulse response $h(t)$ of Eq. C.21 we use pair number 8 to find

$$H(s) = \mathscr{L}[\sqrt{2}e^{-0.707t}\cos(0.707t - \pi/2)]$$

$$= \frac{0.707e^{-j\pi/2}}{s + 0.707 - j0.707} + \frac{0.707e^{j\pi/2}}{s + 0.707 + j0.707}$$

$$= \frac{1}{s^2 + \sqrt{2}s + 1} \tag{C.24}$$

as before.

Partial Fraction Expansion and Inverse Transform

Suppose that we want to find the unit step response of the second-order Butterworth filter described by the transfer function

$$H(s) = \frac{Y(s)}{X(s)} = \frac{1}{s^2 + \sqrt{2}s + 1}. \tag{C.25}$$

For the input of $x(t) = u(t)$ we have the transformed output of

$$Y(s) = H(s) \cdot X(s)$$

$$= \frac{1}{s^2 + \sqrt{2}s + 1} \cdot \frac{1}{s} \tag{C.26}$$

where $X(s) = 1/s$ from pair number 2 in Table C.1. As with z-transforms we expand $Y(s)$ in partial fractions to match the forms given in Table C.1. In this case, we expand $Y(s)$ rather than $Y(z)/z$ in the z-transform case.

$$Y(s) = \frac{1}{(s^2 + \sqrt{2}s + 1)s} = \frac{C_1}{s + 0.707 - j0.707} +$$
$$\frac{C_1{}^*}{s + 0.707 + j0.707} + \frac{C_2}{s} \qquad \text{(C.27)}$$

and after evaluating C_1, $C_1{}^*$, and C_2 in the usual way we have

$$Y(s) = \frac{0.707e^{-j5\pi/4}}{s + 0.707 - j0.707} + \frac{0.707e^{j5\pi/4}}{s + 0.707 + j0.707} + \frac{1}{s}. \qquad \text{(C.28)}$$

Then, using pairs number 2 and number 8 from Table C.1, the unit step response of a second-order Butterworth filter is given by the inverse transform of Eq. C.28, namely

$$y(t) = 1.41e^{-0.707t}\cos(0.707t - 5\pi/4) + 1, \qquad t \geq 0. \qquad \text{(C.29)}$$

APPENDIX D

Frequency Response of Continuous-Time (Analog) Systems

The linear, time-invariant (LTI) system represented in Fig. D.1 can be modeled in several ways, one of which is by the unit impulse response $h(t)$. As for discrete systems, when the system input is $x(t) = \delta(t)$, a unit impulse function, the system output $y(t)$ is defined as $h(t)$,[†] the unit impulse response. That is,

$$x(t) = \delta(t) \xrightarrow{\text{produces}} y(t) = h(t). \qquad \text{(D.1)}$$

From the continuous-time equivalent of discrete convolution we can de-

---

[†]From a Laplace transform point of view $Y(s) = H(s) \cdot X(s)$ where $H(s)$ is the system transfer function. Then, if $x(t) = \delta(t)$, $X(s) = 1$, and $Y(s) = H(s) \cdot 1$ and $y(t) = h(t)$, the system's unit impulse response.

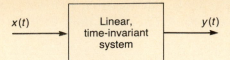

scribe the output $y(t)$ due to any input $x(t)$ by the convolution integral[†]

$$y(t) = \int_{-\infty}^{\infty} h(\tau)x(t-\tau)\, d\tau. \tag{D.2}$$

For a complex exponential input such as $x(t) = e^{j\omega t}$ we have

$$y(t) = \int_{-\infty}^{\infty} h(\tau)e^{j\omega(t-\tau)}\, d\tau$$

$$= \int_{-\infty}^{\infty} h(\tau)e^{j\omega t}e^{-j\omega\tau}\, d\tau. \tag{D.3}$$

But we are integrating with respect to τ making it possible to factor out $e^{j\omega t}$ giving

$$y(t) = e^{j\omega t}\int_{-\infty}^{\infty} h(\tau)e^{-j\omega\tau}\, d\tau. \tag{D.4}$$

If the system is causal and stable

$$h(t) = 0, \qquad t < 0 \tag{D.5}$$

and

$$\lim_{t\to\infty} h(t) \longrightarrow 0. \tag{D.6}$$

Then the steady-state output is

$$y_{ss}(t) = e^{j\omega t}\int_{0}^{\infty} h(\tau)e^{-j\omega\tau}\, d\tau \tag{D.7}$$

or

$$y_{ss}(t) = e^{j\omega t}H(j\omega) \tag{D.8}$$

where the system eigenvalue $H(j\omega)$ for the eigenfunction $e^{j\omega t}$ is defined as

$$H(j\omega) = \int_{0}^{\infty} h(\tau)e^{-j\omega\tau}\, d\tau.\text{[‡]} \tag{D.9}$$

For the input $x(t) = e^{-j\omega t}$ we could follow the same procedure to get

$$y_{ss}(t) = e^{-j\omega t}H(-j\omega). \tag{D.10}$$

[†]We can also use the convolution integral and the sifting property (see Appendix C) of the unit impulse function to define a system's unit impulse response as

$$h(t) = \int_{-\infty}^{\infty} \delta(t-\tau)h(\tau)\, d\tau.$$

[‡]Notice that $\mathcal{L}[h(t)] = \int_{0}^{\infty} h(\tau)e^{-s\tau}\, d\tau = H(s)$ and $\int_{0}^{\infty} h(\tau)e^{-j\omega\tau}\, d\tau = H(s)|_{s=j\omega} = H(j\omega)$.

For a sinusoidal input signal

$$x(t) = \cos \omega t = \frac{e^{j\omega t} + e^{-j\omega t}}{2} \tag{D.11}$$

we can apply superposition to obtain

$$y_{ss}(t) = \frac{e^{j\omega t}}{2} H(j\omega) + \frac{e^{-j\omega t}}{2} H(-j\omega). \tag{D.12}$$

It is easily shown that $H(j\omega)$ and $H(-j\omega)$ are complex conjugates and we can then define

$$H(j\omega) = Me^{jP} \quad \text{and} \quad H(-j\omega) = Me^{-jP} \tag{D.13}$$

which when substituted into Eq. D.12 produces with the help of the Euler identity

$$y_{ss}(t) = \frac{e^{j\omega t}}{2} Me^{jP} + \frac{e^{-j\omega t}}{2} Me^{-jP}$$

$$= M \cos(\omega t + P). \tag{D.14}$$

Thus, as with discrete-time systems, the input sinusoid is altered in amplitude by the magnitude M and changed in phase by P radians as it passes through the linear system. Again, this result could be called the "sinusoidal steady-state formula" for continuous-time systems and is more generally written for a stable LTI system as

$$\boxed{x(t) = X \cos(\omega t + \gamma) \xrightarrow{\text{produces}} y_{ss}(t) = XM \cos(\omega t + \gamma + P)} \tag{D.15}$$

where $M = |H(j\omega)|$ and $P = \angle H(j\omega)$ and the eigenvalue $H(j\omega)$ is known as the *frequency response* or *frequency response function*. Consider, for example, a causal LTI system described by the unit impulse response

$$h(t) = e^{-t} \cdot u(t). \tag{D.16}$$

From Eq. D.9, the frequency response $H(j\omega)$ is

$$H(j\omega) = \int_0^\infty h(\tau) e^{-j\omega\tau} \, d\tau$$

$$= \int_0^\infty e^{-\tau} e^{-j\omega\tau} \, d\tau$$

$$= \int_0^\infty e^{-(1+j\omega)\tau} \, d\tau$$

$$= -\frac{e^{-(1+j\omega)\tau}}{1 + j\omega} \Big|_0^\infty$$

$$= \frac{1}{1 + j\omega}. \tag{D.17}$$

Writing the frequency response in terms of its magnitude and phase gives

$$H(j\omega) = \frac{1}{1 + j\omega}$$

$$= \frac{1}{(1 + \omega^2)^{1/2}} e^{-j\tan^{-1}\omega}$$

$$= Me^{jP}. \qquad (D.18)$$

The magnitude and phase plots for this linear system are given in Fig. D.2.

Example D.1. This example illustrates the use of the sinusoidal steady-state formula.

The system described by $h(t) = e^{-t} \cdot u(t)$ is subjected to the following inputs:

a) $x(t) = 10 \cos(0.1t)$.
b) $x(t) = 10 \cos(1.0t)$.
c) $x(t) = 10 \cos(10t)$.
d) $x(t) = 10 \cos(100t)$. $\qquad (D.19)$

For each input find the steady-state output $y_{ss}(t)$.

Solution: For all cases $M = 1/(1 + \omega^2)^{1/2}$ and $P = -\tan^{-1}\omega$

a) $M = \dfrac{1}{(1 + 0.01)^{1/2}} = 0.995$ and $P = -\tan^{-1}(0.1) = -0.1$ rad

$$y_{ss}(t) = 9.95 \cos(0.1t - 0.1). \qquad (D.20)$$

b) $M = \dfrac{1}{(1 + 1)^{1/2}} = 0.707$ and $P = -\tan^{-1}(1) = -0.785$

$$y_{ss}(t) = 7.07 \cos(t - 0.785). \qquad (D.21)$$

c) $M = \dfrac{1}{(1 + 100)^{1/2}} = 0.0995$ and $P = -\tan^{-1}(10) = -1.471$

$$y_{ss}(t) = 0.995 \cos(10t - 1.471). \qquad (D.22)$$

d) $M = \dfrac{1}{(1 + 10^4)^{1/2}} = 0.010$ and $P = -\tan^{-1}(100) = -1.561$

$$y_{ss}(t) = 0.10 \cos(100t - 1.561). \qquad (D.23)$$

Comment: This system, described by $h(t) = e^{-t} \cdot u(t)$ or by $H(j\omega) = 1/(1 + j\omega)$ could be used as a lowpass filter because it passes low frequencies ($\omega = 0.1$ and $\omega = 1$) much more readily than high frequencies ($\omega = 10$ and $\omega = 100$) as indicated by the significantly smaller magnitudes for the frequency response at the higher frequencies.

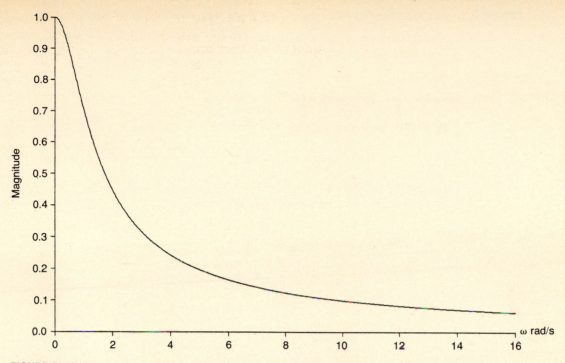

FIGURE D.2(a)   Frequency response magnitude for a first-order system

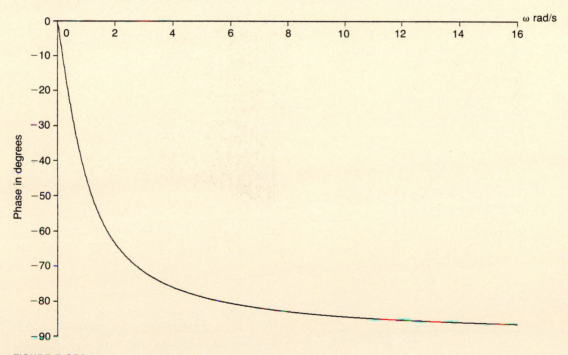

FIGURE D.2(b)   Frequency response phase for a first-order system

Example D.2. This example illustrates calculation of the frequency response function.

Find the frequency response function $H(j\omega)$ for the second-order linear continuous-time system described by

$$h(t) = 2\,e^{-t}\cos(2t)\cdot u(t). \tag{D.24}$$

In this case, determine $H(j\omega)$ from $H(s)|_{s=j\omega}$.

Solution: From pair number 8 in Table C.1 of Appendix C

$$\mathcal{L}[Ae^{at}\cos(\omega t + \alpha)\cdot u(t)] = \frac{A[\cos\alpha(s-a) - \omega\sin\alpha]}{(s-a)^2 + \omega^2} \tag{D.25}$$

and from Eq. D.24 $A = 2$, $a = -1$, $\omega = 2$, and $\alpha = 0$. Substituting these data into Eq. D.25 gives the transfer function

$$H(s) = \frac{2(s+1)}{(s+1)^2 + 2^2}$$

$$= \frac{2(s+1)}{s^2 + 2s + 5}. \tag{D.26}$$

FIGURE D.3(a) Frequency response magnitude for a second-order system

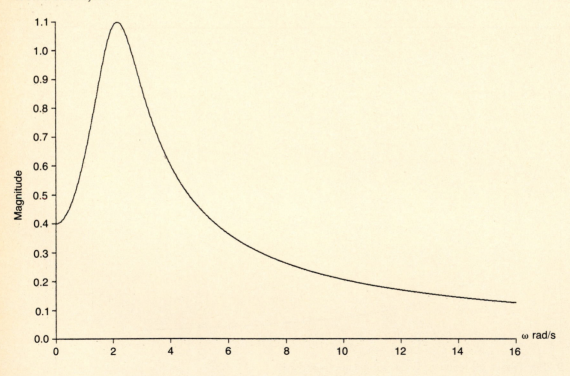

APPENDIX D

Thus, the frequency response is

$$H(j\omega) = H(s)|_{s=j\omega}$$

$$= \frac{2(1 + j\omega)}{5 - \omega^2 + j2\omega} \tag{D.27}$$

with its magnitude given by

$$|H(j\omega)| = M = \frac{2(1 + \omega^2)^{1/2}}{[(5 - \omega^2)^2 + 4\omega^2]^{1/2}} \tag{D.28}$$

and the phase by

$$\angle H(j\omega) = P = \tan^{-1}(\omega) - \tan^{-1}\left(\frac{2\omega}{5 - \omega^2}\right). \tag{D.29}$$

The magnitude and phase plots are given in Fig. D.3.

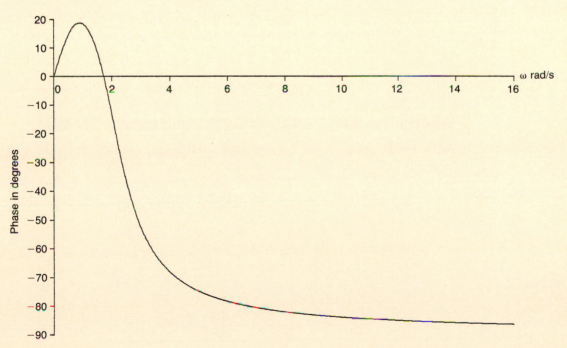

FIGURE D.3(b) Frequency response phase for a second-order system

A Summary of Fourier Pairs

In this appendix, four sets of Fourier pairs that are used extensively in engineering and other scientific applications are summarized and discussed. These pairs are considered in terms of time t and frequency f although other variables can, of course, be used depending upon the application. Four categories of signals or sequences, continuous (periodic and nonperiodic) and discrete (periodic and nonperiodic), are treated from both the "time" and "frequency" domain point of view.

Continuous-Time (Periodic) and Discrete-Frequency (Nonperiodic)

This is usually referred to as the Fourier Series representation of a continuous-time periodic signal with the pair given by

$$x(t) = \sum_{n=-\infty}^{n=+\infty} \mathbf{X}_n e^{j2\pi f_0 t} \longleftrightarrow \mathbf{X}_n = \frac{1}{T_0} \int_{t_0}^{t_0+T_0} x(t) e^{-j2\pi n f_0 t} \, dt \qquad (E.1)$$

where f_0 is the fundamental frequency, nf_0 is the nth harmonic frequency, and $T_0 = \dfrac{1}{f_0}$ is the period of $x(t)$. Figure E.1 shows a periodic continuous-time signal $x(t)$ and its associated discrete-frequency components $\mathbf{X}_n$.

Discrete-Time (Nonperiodic) and Continuous-Frequency (Periodic)

We used this form of the Fourier Series to design nonrecursive filters in Chapter Nine with the general form of the pair given by

FIGURE E.1

$$x(n) = \frac{1}{2\pi} \int_{\theta_0}^{\theta_0+2\pi} X(e^{j\theta}) e^{jn\theta} \, d\theta \longleftrightarrow X(e^{j\theta}) = \sum_{n=-\infty}^{n=+\infty} x(n) e^{-jn\theta}. \qquad (E.2)$$

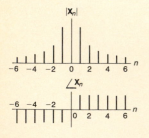

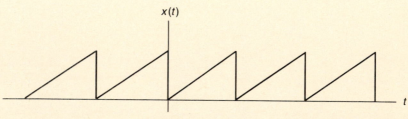

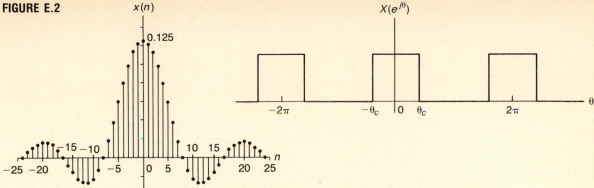

where $X(e^{j\theta})$ is the (discrete-time) Fourier Transform of the nonperiodic sequence $x(n)$. When designing filters we used $H(e^{j\theta})$ to denote the frequency response instead of $X(e^{j\theta})$ with $h(n)$ being the unit sample response of the filter. The filter coefficients b_n were found from $b_n = h(n)$. Figure E.2 shows a nonperiodic sequence $x(n)$ and its associated continuous-frequency transform $X(e^{j\theta})$.

Continuous-Time (Nonperiodic) and Continuous-Frequency (Nonperiodic)

This pair was not discussed in the text but it is known generally as the Fourier Transform pair, namely

$$x(t) = \int_{-\infty}^{\infty} X(f)e^{j2\pi ft}\, df \longleftrightarrow X(f) = \int_{-\infty}^{\infty} x(t)e^{-j2\pi ft}\, dt. \qquad (E.3)$$

Figure E.3 shows a nonperiodic continuous-time signal $x(t)$ and its associated nonperiodic continuous-frequency transform $X(f)$.

Discrete-Time (Periodic) and Discrete-Frequency (Periodic)

This pair was developed in Chapter Seven and is called the Discrete Fourier Transform (or Discrete Fourier Series) with the process described by

$$x(n) = \frac{1}{N} \sum_{k=0}^{N-1} X(k)e^{j(2\pi/N)nk} \longleftrightarrow X(k) = \sum_{n=0}^{N-1} x(n)e^{-j(2\pi/N)nk}$$

$$n = 0, 1, \ldots, N-1 \qquad\qquad k = 0, 1, \ldots, N-1 \qquad (E.4)$$

FIGURE E.3

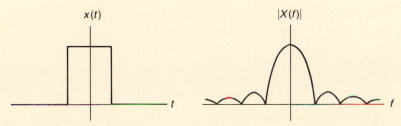

where N is the period of each sequence. When the sequence $x(n)$ is obtained by sampling an analog signal Eq. E.4 is often written as

$$x(nT) = \frac{1}{N} \sum_{k=0}^{N-1} X(k\Delta f)e^{j(2\pi/N)nk} \longleftrightarrow X(k\Delta f) = \sum_{n=0}^{N-1} x(nT)e^{-j(2\pi/N)nk}$$

$$n = 0, 1, \ldots, N-1 \qquad\qquad k = 0, 1, \ldots, N-1 \quad (E.5)$$

where T is the interval between time samples and Δf is the frequency spacing of the DFT. From Chapter Seven we also know that the record length is

$$T_0 = NT = 1/\Delta f \tag{E.6}$$

and Fig. E.4 shows a periodic sequence $x(nT)$ and its associated periodic discrete-frequency transform $X(k\Delta f)$. To approximate the continuous Fourier Transform $X(f)$ of Eq. E.3 by the Discrete Fourier Transform of Eq. E.5 it can be shown that it is necessary to multiply the DFT by T giving

$$X(f) \approx TX(k\Delta f) = T \sum_{n=0}^{N-1} x(nT)e^{-j(2\pi/N)nk}. \tag{E.7}$$

FIGURE E.4

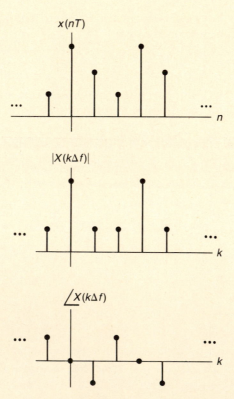

APPENDIX E

APPENDIX F

Matrices and Determinants

Definitions

A *matrix* is a rectangular array of numbers or functions such as

$$\mathbf{A} = \begin{bmatrix} a_{11} & a_{12} & a_{13} \\ a_{21} & a_{22} & a_{23} \end{bmatrix}, \quad \mathbf{B} = \begin{bmatrix} -1 & 2 \\ 3 & -4 \\ 5 & 6 \end{bmatrix},$$

$$\mathbf{y} = \begin{bmatrix} y_1 \\ y_2 \\ y_3 \end{bmatrix}, \quad \mathbf{\Phi}(z) = \begin{bmatrix} \phi_{11}(z) & \phi_{12}(z) \\ \phi_{21}(z) & \phi_{22}(z) \end{bmatrix}, \quad \text{and}$$

$$\mathbf{F} = [f_1 \quad f_2 \quad f_3 \quad f_4]. \tag{F.1}$$

The individual elements in a matrix (for example, a_{21} in the matrix $\mathbf{A}$ above) are identified by their subscripts. Thus, a_{21} is the element in the second row and first column of $\mathbf{A}$. In general, a_{ij} is the element in the ith row and jth column of $\mathbf{A}$. If the matrix has only a single row or a single column, only one subscript is needed.

The dimension of a matrix is written $m \times n$ and read "m by n," where m denotes the number of rows and n the number of columns. Thus, in Eq. F.1 $\mathbf{A}$ is 2×3, $\mathbf{B}$ is 3×2, $\mathbf{y}$ is 3×1, $\mathbf{\Phi}(z)$ is 2×2, and $\mathbf{F}$ is 1×4.

Special Matrices

Square matrix—A matrix of dimension $m \times m$. For example, $\mathbf{\Phi}(z)$ in Eq. F.1.

Row matrix—A $1 \times n$ matrix, for example $\mathbf{F}$ in Eq. F.1. It is often called a *row vector*.

Column matrix—An $m \times 1$ matrix, for example $\mathbf{y}$ above. It is often called a column vector or simply a vector.

Scalar—1×1 matrix.

Null matrix—Any matrix in which all elements are zero. It is written $\mathbf{0}$.

Diagonal matrix—A square matrix having $a_{ij} = 0$ for $i \neq j$. For example,

$$\mathbf{F} = \begin{bmatrix} f_{11} & 0 & 0 \\ 0 & f_{22} & 0 \\ 0 & 0 & f_{33} \end{bmatrix} \quad \text{or} \quad \mathbf{F} = \begin{bmatrix} f_{11} & & \bigcirc \\ & f_{22} & \\ \bigcirc & & f_{33} \end{bmatrix}. \quad \text{(F.2)}$$

Identity matrix—A diagonal matrix with all diagonal elements equal to unity. For example,

$$\mathbf{I} = \begin{bmatrix} 1 & 0 & 0 & 0 \\ 0 & 1 & 0 & 0 \\ 0 & 0 & 1 & 0 \\ 0 & 0 & 0 & 1 \end{bmatrix} \quad \text{or} \quad \mathbf{I} = \begin{bmatrix} 1 & & & \bigcirc \\ & 1 & & \\ & & 1 & \\ \bigcirc & & & 1 \end{bmatrix}. \quad \text{(F.3)}$$

Symmetrical matrix—A square matrix where $a_{ij} = a_{ji}$. For example,

$$\mathbf{A} = \begin{bmatrix} 1 & -2 & 3 \\ -2 & 4 & 5 \\ 3 & 5 & 6 \end{bmatrix}. \quad \text{(F.4)}$$

Elements of Matrix Algebra

a) *Equality*—$\mathbf{C} = \mathbf{D}$ means that corresponding elements of $\mathbf{C}$ and $\mathbf{D}$ are equal, that is, $c_{ij} = d_{ij}$ for all i, j. It is evident that $\mathbf{C}$ and $\mathbf{D}$ must have the same dimensions.

b) *Addition*—$\mathbf{E} = \mathbf{F} + \mathbf{G}$ means that $e_{ij} = f_{ij} + g_{ij}$ for all i, j. (It follows that if $\mathbf{E} = \mathbf{F} + \mathbf{G}$ then $\mathbf{E} = \mathbf{G} + \mathbf{F}$.) Again the matrices must have the same dimensions. Thus, for

$$\mathbf{F} = \begin{bmatrix} 1 & 2 \\ 3 & 4 \end{bmatrix} \quad \text{and} \quad \mathbf{G} = \begin{bmatrix} 5 & 6 \\ 7 & 8 \end{bmatrix}, \quad \mathbf{E} = \mathbf{F} + \mathbf{G} = \begin{bmatrix} 6 & 8 \\ 10 & 12 \end{bmatrix}. \quad \text{(F.5)}$$

c) *The Negative of a Matrix*—$\mathbf{B} = -\mathbf{A}$ means that $b_{ij} = -a_{ij}$ for all i, j. We treat the subtraction $\mathbf{K} - \mathbf{L}$ as the *addition* of $-\mathbf{L}$ to $\mathbf{K}$.

d) *Transpose of a Matrix*—$\mathbf{W} = \mathbf{Z}^T$ means that $w_{ij} = z_{ji}$ for all i, j. That is, the rows of $\mathbf{W}$ equal the columns of $\mathbf{Z}$ and vice versa. Thus, for

$$\mathbf{Z} = \begin{bmatrix} 1 & 2 \\ 3 & 4 \end{bmatrix} \quad \text{then} \quad \mathbf{W} = \mathbf{Z}^T = \begin{bmatrix} 1 & 3 \\ 2 & 4 \end{bmatrix}. \quad \text{(F.6)}$$

e) *Multiplication by a Scalar*—$\mathbf{Y} = k\mathbf{A}$ means that $y_{ij} = ka_{ij}$ for all i, j. Thus, for $k = 2$ and

$$\mathbf{A} = \begin{bmatrix} 1 & 2 \\ 3 & 4 \end{bmatrix}, \quad \mathbf{Y} = 2\mathbf{A} = 2\begin{bmatrix} 1 & 2 \\ 3 & 4 \end{bmatrix} = \begin{bmatrix} 2 & 4 \\ 6 & 8 \end{bmatrix}. \quad \text{(F.7)}$$

f) *Multiplication of Two Matrices*—$\mathbf{F} = \mathbf{CD}$ means that

$$f_{ij} = \sum_{k=1}^{p} c_{ik} \, d_{kj} \quad \text{for all } i, j. \tag{F.8}$$

$\mathbf{C}$ is $m \times p$, $\mathbf{D}$ is $p \times n$, and $\mathbf{F} = m \times n$. The following example illustrates the process:

$$\begin{bmatrix} 1 & 2 & 3 \\ 4 & 5 & 6 \end{bmatrix} \begin{bmatrix} 5 & 6 \\ 7 & 8 \\ 9 & 10 \end{bmatrix} = \begin{bmatrix} (1)(5) + (2)(7) + (3)(9) & (1)(6) + (2)(8) + (3)(10) \\ (4)(5) + (5)(7) + (6)(9) & (4)(6) + (5)(8) + (6)(10) \end{bmatrix}$$

$$= \begin{bmatrix} 46 & 52 \\ 109 & 124 \end{bmatrix}. \tag{F.9}$$

Note that $\mathbf{C}$ must have as many columns as $\mathbf{D}$ has rows; otherwise the product is undefined. Also, $\mathbf{CD} \neq \mathbf{DC}$, in general, and so the order of matrix products must be preserved. In describing the product $\mathbf{CD}$ we say that $\mathbf{D}$ is premultiplied by $\mathbf{C}$, or that $\mathbf{C}$ is postmultiplied by $\mathbf{D}$.

The Determinant of a Matrix

Unlike a matrix, which is an array, the determinant of a square matrix is a scalar. Thus, the value of a 2×2 determinant is defined as

$$|\mathbf{A}| = \begin{vmatrix} a_{11} & a_{12} \\ a_{21} & a_{22} \end{vmatrix} = a_{11}a_{22} - a_{12}a_{21}. \tag{F.10}$$

Next we list some properties of determinants that permit us to reduce any $n \times n$ determinant to a 2×2 determinant, whose value can be computed by Eq. F.10.

a) A common factor of any row (or column) may be factored out of the determinant.

b) Replacing the elements of one row by the product of a constant α times any other row plus the row itself does not alter the value of the determinant.

c) Columns may be treated similarly.

d) Any determinant can be expanded by the elements of any row, for example, the ith, as follows:

$$|\mathbf{A}| = \Delta = \begin{vmatrix} a_{11} & a_{12} & \cdots & a_{1n} \\ a_{21} & a_{22} & \cdots & a_{2n} \\ & \vdots & & \\ a_{n1} & a_{n2} & \cdots & a_{nn} \end{vmatrix} = a_{i1}(-1)^{i+1}\Delta_{i1} + a_{i2}(-1)^{i+2}\Delta_{i2} + $$
$$\cdots + a_{in}(-1)^{i+n}\Delta_{in} \tag{F.11}$$

where Δ_{ij} is the determinant remaining after the ith row and the jth column have been struck out of the determinant Δ.

e) A determinant can be similarly expanded by the elements of any column.

A convenient procedure is to apply properties (a), (b), and (c) until there is only one nonzero element in some row or column. Then we expand by that row or column, thereby reducing the order of the determinant by one. This procedure can be repeated until we are left with a 2×2 determinant whose value we can write down by inspection.

An alternative is to simply use Eq. F.11 to find the determinant of

$$
\mathbf{B} = \begin{bmatrix} 0 & 5 & 0 & -1 \\ 3 & 1 & -6 & -2 \\ 4 & 0 & -3 & 1 \\ 7 & -5 & 1 & 0 \end{bmatrix}. \tag{F.12}
$$

To minimize the number of terms, we expand about the row or column having the largest number of zeros. In this case the first row is the best choice. We have

$$
|\mathbf{B}| = 0 \cdot \Delta_{11} + 5(-1)^{(2+1)} \begin{vmatrix} 3 & -6 & -2 \\ 4 & -3 & 1 \\ 7 & 1 & 0 \end{vmatrix} + 0 \cdot \Delta_{13}
$$

$$
+ (-1) \cdot (-1)^{(4+1)} \begin{vmatrix} 3 & 1 & -6 \\ 4 & 0 & -3 \\ 7 & -5 & 1 \end{vmatrix}
$$

$$
= -5 \begin{vmatrix} 3 & -6 & -2 \\ 4 & -3 & 1 \\ 7 & 1 & 0 \end{vmatrix} + \begin{vmatrix} 3 & 1 & -6 \\ 4 & 0 & -3 \\ 7 & -5 & 1 \end{vmatrix}. \tag{F.13}
$$

Expanding the first determinant about the third column and the second determinant about the second row we obtain

$$
|\mathbf{B}| = -5 \times \left\{ (-2) \times (-1)^4 \begin{vmatrix} 4 & -3 \\ 7 & 1 \end{vmatrix} + 1(-1)^5 \begin{vmatrix} 3 & -6 \\ 7 & 1 \end{vmatrix} + 0 \right\}
$$

$$
+ \left\{ 4 \times (-1)^3 \begin{vmatrix} 1 & -6 \\ -5 & 1 \end{vmatrix} + (-3) \times (-1)^5 \begin{vmatrix} 3 & 1 \\ 7 & -5 \end{vmatrix} \right\}
$$

$$
= -5\{(-2)(1)[4 + 21] + (-1)[3 + 42]\}
$$

$$
+ (-4)[1 - 30] + 3[-15 - 7]
$$

$$
= -5[-50 - 45] + -4(-29) + 3(-22) = 525. \tag{F.14}
$$

The Minors and Cofactors of a Matrix

The *minor* M_{ij} of a square matrix $\mathbf{A}$ is the determinant of $\mathbf{A}$ after the ith row and jth column have been struck out. For example,

$$\text{If } \mathbf{A} = \begin{bmatrix} 1 & 2 & 3 \\ 4 & 5 & 6 \\ 7 & 8 & 9 \end{bmatrix} \text{ then } M_{12} = \begin{vmatrix} 1 & 2 & 3 \\ 4 & 5 & 6 \\ 7 & 8 & 9 \end{vmatrix} = \begin{vmatrix} 4 & 6 \\ 7 & 9 \end{vmatrix} = -6. \quad \text{(F.15)}$$

The *cofactor* c_{ij} of a square matrix $\mathbf{A}$ is the *signed minor* of $\mathbf{A}$, which is defined by

$$c_{ij} = (-1)^{i+j} M_{ij}. \quad \text{(F.16)}$$

The *matrix of cofactors* $\mathbf{C}$ of a square matrix $\mathbf{A}$ is the matrix formed by the cofactors of $\mathbf{A}$. Consequently, for $\mathbf{A}$ as in Eq. F.15 the matrix of cofactors $\mathbf{C}$ of the square matrix $\mathbf{A}$ is

$$\mathbf{C} = \begin{bmatrix} (-1)^2(-3) & (-1)^3(-6) & (-1)^4(-3) \\ (-1)^3(-6) & (-1)^4(-12) & (-1)^5(-6) \\ (-1)^4(-3) & (-1)^5(-6) & (-1)^6(-3) \end{bmatrix} = \begin{bmatrix} -3 & 6 & -3 \\ 6 & -12 & 6 \\ -3 & 6 & -3 \end{bmatrix}. \quad \text{(F.17)}$$

The Adjoint of a Matrix

The **adjoint** of a square matrix $\mathbf{A}$, denoted by **adj A**, is the transpose of the matrix of cofactors of $\mathbf{A}$. That is

$$\text{adj } \mathbf{A} = \mathbf{C}^T \quad \text{(F.18)}$$

where $\mathbf{C}$ is the matrix of cofactors of $\mathbf{A}$.

The Inverse of a Matrix

The inverse of a matrix $\mathbf{A}$, denoted by $\mathbf{A}^{-1}$, is defined by

$$\mathbf{A}\mathbf{A}^{-1} = \mathbf{A}^{-1}\mathbf{A} = \mathbf{I} \quad \text{(F.19)}$$

where $\mathbf{I}$ is the identity matrix. An inverse exists only if $\mathbf{A}$ is square and $|\mathbf{A}| \neq 0$.

There are several methods available for hand or machine calculation of the matrix inverse. One of the more useful methods for matrices of small dimensions is

$$\mathbf{A}^{-1} = \frac{\text{adj } \mathbf{A}}{|\mathbf{A}|}. \quad \text{(F.20)}$$

To illustrate the procedure indicated by Eq. F.20 we find the inverse of the matrix

$$\mathbf{A} = \begin{bmatrix} 1 & 2 \\ 3 & 4 \end{bmatrix}. \quad \text{(F.21)}$$

First, we calculate the matrix of cofactors $\mathbf{C}$ by using Eq. F.16 to obtain

$$\mathbf{C} = \begin{bmatrix} 4 & -3 \\ -2 & 1 \end{bmatrix} \quad \text{(F.22)}$$

and then from Eq. F.18 the adjoint of $\mathbf{A}$ is

$$\mathbf{adj\ A} = \mathbf{C}^T$$

$$= \begin{bmatrix} 4 & -2 \\ -3 & 1 \end{bmatrix}. \tag{F.23}$$

The determinant of $\mathbf{A}$ is

$$|\mathbf{A}| = 4 - 6 = -2 \tag{F.24}$$

and from Eq. F.20 the inverse of $\mathbf{A}$ is

$$\mathbf{A}^{-1} = \begin{bmatrix} -2 & 1 \\ \dfrac{3}{2} & -\dfrac{1}{2} \end{bmatrix}. \tag{F.25}$$

As a check we form

$$\mathbf{A\ A}^{-1} = \begin{bmatrix} 1 & 2 \\ 3 & 4 \end{bmatrix} \begin{bmatrix} -2 & 1 \\ \dfrac{3}{2} & -\dfrac{1}{2} \end{bmatrix}$$

$$= \begin{bmatrix} 1 & 0 \\ 0 & 1 \end{bmatrix}$$

$$= \mathbf{I}. \tag{F.26}$$

It is also easily verified that $\mathbf{A}^{-1}\mathbf{A} = \mathbf{I}$ so the result is correct.

Solution of Linear Algebraic Equations by Matrix Inverse

Given a set of linear algebraic equations where the number of equations equals the number of unknowns, namely

$$\mathbf{A\ x} = \mathbf{b}. \tag{F.27}$$

To solve for the vector $\mathbf{x}$, assuming that $|\mathbf{A}| \neq 0$, we premultiply both sides by the inverse of $\mathbf{A}$ to obtain

$$\mathbf{A}^{-1}\mathbf{A\ x} = \mathbf{A}^{-1}\mathbf{b}. \tag{F.28}$$

But $\mathbf{A}^{-1}\mathbf{A} = \mathbf{I}$ and $\mathbf{I\ x} = \mathbf{x}$ so the solution is given by

$$\mathbf{x} = \mathbf{A}^{-1}\mathbf{b}, \qquad |\mathbf{A}| \neq 0. \tag{F.29}$$

To illustrate the procedure indicated by Eq. F.29 let's solve the equations below for x_1, x_2, and x_3.

$$x_1 + 1.5x_2 - x_3 = 1$$

$$-2x_2 + 3x_3 = 5$$

$$-3.5x_1 + 2.5x_3 = 4. \tag{F.30}$$

First, putting Eq. F.30 in matrix notation gives us

$$\begin{bmatrix} 1 & 1.5 & -1 \\ 0 & -2 & 3 \\ -3.5 & 0 & 2.5 \end{bmatrix} \mathbf{x} = \begin{bmatrix} 1 \\ 5 \\ 4 \end{bmatrix} \quad \text{where } \mathbf{x} = \begin{bmatrix} x_1 \\ x_2 \\ x_3 \end{bmatrix}. \tag{F.31}$$

Next, the matrix of cofactors is

$$\mathbf{C} = \begin{bmatrix} -5 & -10.5 & -7 \\ -3.75 & -1 & -5.25 \\ 2.5 & -3 & -2 \end{bmatrix} \tag{F.32}$$

and the determinant of $\mathbf{A}$ is

$$|\mathbf{A}| = \begin{vmatrix} 1 & 1.5 & -1 \\ 0 & -2 & 3 \\ -3.5 & 0 & 2.5 \end{vmatrix} = \begin{vmatrix} 1 & 1.5 & -1 \\ 0 & -2 & 3 \\ 0 & 5.25 & -1 \end{vmatrix} \tag{F.33}$$

which is obtained by adding 3.5 times the first row to the third row. Thus, expanding by the first column we find that the determinant is

$$|\mathbf{A}| = \begin{vmatrix} -2 & 3 \\ 5.25 & -1 \end{vmatrix} = 2 - 15.75 = -13.75. \tag{F.34}$$

Finally, using Eq. F.20 we have

$$\mathbf{x} = \frac{\mathbf{C}^T}{|\mathbf{A}|}\mathbf{b} = \frac{-1}{13.75} \begin{bmatrix} -5 & -3.75 & 2.5 \\ -10.5 & -1 & -3 \\ -7 & -5.25 & -2 \end{bmatrix} \begin{bmatrix} 1 \\ 5 \\ 4 \end{bmatrix} = \begin{bmatrix} 1 \\ 2 \\ 3 \end{bmatrix}. \tag{F.35}$$

As a check notice that

$$\mathbf{A} \begin{bmatrix} 1 \\ 2 \\ 3 \end{bmatrix} = \begin{bmatrix} 1 & 1.5 & -1 \\ 0 & -2 & 3 \\ -3.5 & 0 & 2.5 \end{bmatrix} \begin{bmatrix} 1 \\ 2 \\ 3 \end{bmatrix} = \begin{bmatrix} 1 \\ 5 \\ 4 \end{bmatrix}. \tag{F.36}$$

APPENDIX G

Continuous-Time System with a Piecewise Constant Input

In this appendix we show how difference equations can arise when a continuous-time system is subjected to inputs that are piecewise constant. These inputs arise from the sample and hold process and the resulting difference equations characterize the system at the sampling instants only, i.e., at $t = 0, T, 2T, \ldots$. Our starting point is the matrix state equation for an LTI continuous-time system with a scalar input $x(t)$

$$\dot{\mathbf{v}}(t) = \mathbf{F}\mathbf{v}(t) + \mathbf{G}x(t) \text{ with the initial conditions } \mathbf{v}(0). \tag{G.1}$$

Taking the Laplace transform of Eq. G.1 gives

$$s\mathbf{V}(s) - \mathbf{v}(0) = \mathbf{F}\mathbf{V}(s) + \mathbf{G}X(s). \tag{G.2}$$

Multiplying the first term on the left of Eq. G.2 by the identity matrix $\mathbf{I}$ and collecting the coefficients of $\mathbf{V}(s)$ produces

$$[s\mathbf{I} - \mathbf{F}]\mathbf{V}(s) = \mathbf{v}(0) + \mathbf{G}X(s). \tag{G.3}$$

To solve for $\mathbf{V}(s)$ we premultiply Eq. G.3 by the inverse of the square matrix $[s\mathbf{I} - \mathbf{F}]$ which gives

$$\mathbf{V}(s) = [s\mathbf{I} - \mathbf{F}]^{-1} \mathbf{v}(0) + [s\mathbf{I} - \mathbf{F}]^{-1} \mathbf{G}X(s). \tag{G.4}$$

It is common practice to use the definition

$$\mathbf{\Phi}(s) = [s\mathbf{I} - \mathbf{F}]^{-1} \tag{G.5}$$

which allows us to write Eq. G.4 in the more compact form

$$\mathbf{V}(s) = \mathbf{\Phi}(s)\mathbf{v}(0) + \mathbf{\Phi}(s)\mathbf{G}X(s). \tag{G.6}$$

Taking the inverse Laplace transform produces the solution

$$\mathbf{v}(t) = \mathcal{L}^{-1}\{\mathbf{V}(s)\} = \mathcal{L}^{-1}\{\mathbf{\Phi}(s)\mathbf{v}(0)\} + \mathcal{L}^{-1}\{\mathbf{\Phi}(s)\mathbf{G}X(s)\} \tag{G.7}$$

that can be written as

$$\mathbf{v}(t) = \boldsymbol{\phi}(t)\mathbf{v}(0) + \int_0^t \boldsymbol{\phi}(t - \tau)\mathbf{G}x(\tau)\, d\tau. \tag{G.8}$$

The initial time 0 is an arbitrary reference time, so we can express this result more generally using t_0 as the reference. Doing this gives

$$\mathbf{v}(t) = \boldsymbol{\phi}(t - t_0)\mathbf{v}(t_0) + \int_{t_0}^{t} \boldsymbol{\phi}(t - \tau)\mathbf{G}x(\tau)\, d\tau \qquad (G.9)$$

where $\boldsymbol{\phi}(t - t_0)$ is called the state transition matrix. The first term in Eq. G.9 is the initial condition response, due to $\mathbf{v}(t_0)$, while the second term is the forced response, due to $x(t)$.

Digital Control

A typical arrangement for a digitally controlled system was shown in Fig. 11.20. Now if we assume that the analog-to-digital converter samples its input signals every T seconds, i.e., at $t = 0, T, 2T, \ldots, nT, nT + T, \ldots$, and that the output of the digital-to-analog converter is piecewise constant over a period of time shown in Fig. 11.21 then we can describe the input to the plant as

$$x(t) = x(nT), \qquad nT \leq t < nT + T. \qquad (G.10)$$

Then, using Eq. G.9 we set $t_0 = nT$ and $t = nT + T$ yielding

$$\mathbf{v}([n + 1]T) = \boldsymbol{\phi}(T)\mathbf{v}(nT) + \int_{nT}^{[n+1]T} \boldsymbol{\phi}([n + 1]T - \tau)\mathbf{G}x(\tau)\, d\tau. \quad (G.11)$$

But $x(\tau) = x(nT)$, $nT \leq \tau < (n + 1)T$ and thus

$$\mathbf{v}(n + 1) = \boldsymbol{\phi}(T)\mathbf{v}(n) + \left[\int_{nT}^{[n+1]T} \boldsymbol{\phi}([n + 1]T - \tau)\mathbf{G}\, d\tau \right] x(n) \quad (G.12)$$

where we have also dropped the explicit dependence on T in arguments of $\mathbf{v}(\ )$ and $x(\ )$.
But

$$\int_{nT}^{nT+T} \boldsymbol{\phi}([n + 1]T - \tau)\mathbf{G}\, d\tau \qquad (G.13)$$

is the same regardless of the values of n and we'll define this as

$$\boldsymbol{\Delta}(T) = \int_{0}^{T} \boldsymbol{\phi}(T - \tau)\mathbf{G}\, d\tau. \qquad (G.14)$$

Thus, the result is

$$\mathbf{v}(n + 1) = \boldsymbol{\phi}(T)\mathbf{v}(n) + \boldsymbol{\Delta}(T)x(n) \qquad (G.15)$$

which describes the continuous system at the sampling instants only when the system's input $x(t)$ is piecewise constant as in Eq. G.10.

This result can be generalized to the situation where there are several inputs represented by the vector

$$\mathbf{x}(t) = \mathbf{x}(nT), \; nT \leq t < (n + 1)T. \qquad (G.16)$$

Following the same derivation yields the result

$$\mathbf{v}(n + 1) = \boldsymbol{\phi}(T)\mathbf{v}(n) + \boldsymbol{\Delta}(T)\mathbf{x}(n). \qquad (G.17)$$

The only difference is that $\boldsymbol{\Delta}(T)$ in Eq. G.17 is a matrix given by

$$\boldsymbol{\Delta}(T) = \int_0^T \boldsymbol{\phi}(T - \tau)\mathbf{G} \, d\tau \qquad (G.18)$$

whereas $\boldsymbol{\Delta}(T)$ in Eq. G.14 is a column vector.

Answers to Selected Problems

Chapter 2

2.2 $x_1(n) = \delta(n + 1) + 2\delta(n) - \delta(n - 1) + 0.5\delta(n - 2) - 2\delta(n - 3)$

$x_2(n) = 2\delta(n + 3) - \delta(n + 2) + 3\delta(n + 1) + 4\delta(n) - 0.5\delta(n - 1) - 2\delta(n - 2) - \delta(n - 3) + 2\delta(n - 4)$

a) $2\delta(n + 3) - \delta(n + 2) + 4\delta(n + 1) + 6\delta(n) - 1.5\delta(n - 1) - 1.5\delta(n - 2) - 3\delta(n - 3) + 2\delta(n - 4)$

b) $2\delta(n + 1) + 4\delta(n) - 2\delta(n - 1) + \delta(n - 2) - 4\delta(n - 3)$

c) $-6\delta(n + 3) + 3\delta(n + 2) - 9\delta(n + 1) - 12\delta(n) + 1.5\delta(n - 1) + 6\delta(n - 2) + 3\delta(n - 3) - 6\delta(n - 4)$

d) $-6\delta(n + 3) + 3\delta(n + 2) - 7\delta(n + 1) - 8\delta(n) - 0.5\delta(n - 1) + 7\delta(n - 2) - \delta(n - 3) - 6\delta(n - 4)$

e) $\alpha_1\delta(n + 1) + 2\alpha_1\delta(n) - \alpha_1\delta(n - 1) + 0.5\alpha_1\delta(n - 2) - 2\alpha_1\delta(n - 3)$

f) $3\delta(n + 1) + 8\delta(n) + 0.5\delta(n - 1) - \delta(n - 2) + 2\delta(n - 3)$

2.5 $y(n) = 3\delta(n - 1) + 6\delta(n - 2) + 9\delta(n - 3) + 12\delta(n - 4) + 15\delta(n - 5) + 18\delta(n - 6) + 9\delta(n - 7)$

a) $3\delta(n - 4) + 6\delta(n - 5) + 9\delta(n - 6) + 12\delta(n - 7) + 15\delta(n - 8) + 18\delta(n - 9) + 9\delta(n - 10)$

b) $3\delta(n + 1) + 6\delta(n) + 9\delta(n - 1) + 12\delta(n - 2) + 15\delta(n - 3) + 18\delta(n - 4) + 9\delta(n - 5)$

c) $3\delta(-n - 1) + 6\delta(-n - 2) + 9\delta(-n - 3) + 12\delta(-n - 4) + 15\delta(-n - 5) + 18\delta(-n - 6) + 9\delta(-n - 7)$

d) $3\delta(2 - n) + 6\delta(1 - n) + 9\delta(n) + 12\delta(-1 - n) + 15\delta(-2 - n) + 18\delta(-3 - n) + 9\delta(-4 - n)$

2.6 a) Periodic with period 16
   b) Not periodic
   c) Not periodic
   d) Periodic with period 4

2.8 $f_s > 600$ Hz

2.11 a) Linear
   b) Time-invariant

2.13 a) Nonlinear
   b) Time-invariant

2.15 a) Linear
   b) Time-invariant

2.17 a) Causal
   b) Noncausal
   c) Noncausal

2.19 Nonlinear

2.21 a) Nonlinear
   b) Time-varying

2.22 a) $\frac{A}{3}\delta(n - 1) + \frac{2A}{3}\delta(n - 2) + A\delta(n - 3)$

   b) $\frac{A}{3}n[u(n) - u(n - 4)] + \frac{A}{3}(n - 4)[u(n - 4) - u(n - 8)]$

   c) $\frac{A}{3}n[u(n) - u(n - 4)] + \frac{A}{3}(n - 4)[u(n - 4) - u(n - 8)] + \cdots + \frac{A}{3}(n - 4[N - 1]) [u(n - 4[N - 1]) - u(n - 4N)]$

2.25 $a_0 = [1/T^2 + 5/T + 6], \quad a_1 = -2/T^2 - 5/T, \quad a_2 = 1/T^2$

2.26 a) $y(nT) = y([n - 1]T) + Tx([n - 1]T)$ or $y(n) = y(n - 1) + Tx(n - 1)$

   b) $y(1) = 0, \quad y(2) = T^2, \quad y(3) = 3T^2, \quad y(4) = 6T^2, \quad y(5) = 10T^2$; Exact values of integral are $y(nT) = (nT)^2/2$.

2.28 a) Linear
   b) Time-invariant

2.29 a) $\phi = 0.393$ rad, $\quad A_a = 10.00$
   b) $\phi = -0.522$ rad, $\quad A_b = 9.991 \approx 10$

Chapter 3

3.2 a) $y(n) = [1 + R/200]y(n - 1) + x(n)$
   b) $11,007.53
   c) $y(N) = \alpha^N A - (1 - \alpha^N)X/(1 - \alpha), \quad \alpha \neq 1$; $A =$ initial amount in account, $X =$ amount withdrawn every six months, $\alpha = [1 + R/200]$
   d) $768.76

3.3 a) $y(n + 1) = y(n) + 0.01Py(n) + x(n)$;
P = annual rate of return in percent;
$363,888.50
b) $y(n + 1) = y(n) + 0.01Py(n) - 10^{-4}RPy(n) + x(n)$;
R = tax rate in percent; $224,307.06

3.7 a) $y(n) = y(n - 1) + 7y(n - 2) + 2x(n) + 5x(n - 1) - 3x(n - 2)$
b) $y(n) = -9y(n - 1) + 4y(n - 3) + 2x(n - 1) + x(n - 3)$

3.8

n	0	1	2	3	4
$y(n)$	0	0	15	18.75	21.55

3.10 a) Stable
b) Stable
c) Unstable
d) Unstable
e) Unstable

3.12 a) Unstable
b) Unstable
c) Stable
d) Stable

3.14 a) $y(n) = [1.118(0.707)^n \cos(n\pi/4 + 1.107) + 1.733 \sin(n\pi/3)]u(n)$
b) $y(0) = 0.5$, $y(1) = 1.25$, $y(2) = 1.0$, $y(3) = -0.375$

3.16 a) $y(n) = [80 + 20n + (500/3)(5^n) - (560/3)(2^n)]u(n)$
b) $y(0) = 60$, $y(1) = 560$, $y(2) = 3540$, $y(3) = 19,480$

3.17 a) $y(n) = \left[1 + 0.5\sqrt{2}\left(\dfrac{\sqrt{2}}{2}\right)^n \cos(n\pi/4 - 3\pi/4)\right]u(n)$

3.22 a) 1.4142
b) 15.6677, 1.4142
c) $y(n - 1)/2$
d) No

3.24 a) b_ks do not enter into characteristic equation.
b) No, b_ks don't affect characteristic equation, hence no effect on stability.
c) Stable

3.30 a) $y(1) = \alpha$, $y(2) = \alpha^2 + \beta$, $y(3) = \alpha^3 + 2\alpha\beta$, $y(4) = \alpha^4 + 3\alpha^2\beta + \beta^2$
b) $y(0) = 0$, $y(1) = 1$, $y(2) = 1$, $y(3) = 4$

3.32 a) $F(n) = (1 + P/200)F(n - 1) - E/2$
b) $F(n) = \alpha^N F_0 - (E/2)\dfrac{1 - \alpha^N}{1 - \alpha}$,
$\alpha = (1 + P/200)$

c) $F_0 = 3.23E$

3.35 a) $y(L) = \alpha^L Y - P\left[\dfrac{1 - \alpha^L}{1 - \alpha}\right]$,
$\alpha = (1 + r/100)$
b) $P = (\alpha^L Y)(1 - \alpha)/(1 - \alpha^L)$
c) $253.35
d) $L = (\ln P - \ln [(1 - \alpha)Y + P])/\ln[\alpha]$
e) 89 months

Chapter 4

4.1 a) $e^{jn\pi/4} [0.765e^{j1.18}]$
b) $e^{-jn\pi/4} [0.765e^{-j1.18}]$
c) $7.65 \cos(n\pi/4 + 1.18)$

4.3 $0.631 \sin(n\pi/2 - 1.11)$

4.5 a) $f_s > 200$ kHz
b) $0.1\pi \leq \theta \leq 0.5\pi$
c) Magnitude of 0 in interval $0.1\pi \leq \theta \leq 0.5\pi$ and 1 elsewhere for $0 \leq \theta \leq \pi$

4.7 a) $2.778e^{j0}$
b) $0.610e^{j0}$
c) $0.842e^{-j0.569}$

4.9 a) $4e^{j0}$
b) $4e^{-j1.571}$
c) $4e^{-j3.393}$
d) $|H(e^{j\theta})| = 4$ in all cases—an all-pass filter

4.11 a) $-10 \cos(4n\pi/5 - \pi/2 - 4\pi/15) + 7.0 \cos(9n\pi/10 + 3\pi/8 - 9\pi/30)$
b) Highpass filter

4.17 a) $(1/4)e^{j2\theta} + (1/2)e^{j\theta} + 1 + (1/2)e^{-j\theta} + (1/4)e^{-j2\theta} = 2 \cos(2\theta) + \cos \theta + 1$
b) $e^{-j2\theta} [2 \cos(2\theta) + \cos \theta + 1]$
c) $|H_c(e^{j\theta})| = |H_{nc}(e^{j\theta})|$, $\angle H_c(e^{j\theta}) = -2\theta + \angle H_{nc}(e^{j\theta})$

4.18 a) $\pi/3 \leq \theta \leq 3\pi/4$
b) $\pi/4 \leq \theta \leq \pi$

4.19 a) $\dfrac{2X}{T} \sin(\omega T/2) \cos(n\omega T + \pi/2 - \omega T/2)$
b) $-X\omega \sin(n\omega T)$
c) For small T, the output approximates the derivative of the input.
d) $X_s(2/T) \sin(\theta/2) \cos(n\theta + \pi/2 - \theta/2) + X_N(2/T) \sin(5\theta) \cos(10n\theta + \pi/2 - 5\theta)$
e) Noise component amplified relative to signal component

4.20 a) $[T/(2 \tan \theta/2)]e^{-j\pi/2}$
b) $(1.21)(AT) \sin(n\pi/4)$ = scaled integral of input

Chapter 5

Note: Many of the problems in this chapter require sketches, therefore, only a few complete answers are provided.

5.3 a) Less than 1 kHz
  b) 0 Hz, 125 Hz, 250 Hz, 500 Hz

5.6 a) Double zero at $z = 0$, zeros at $z = \pm 1$; poles at $z = 0.707e^{\pm j\pi/4}$, $0.707e^{\pm j3\pi/4}$
  c) Bandpass of sorts

5.9 All-pass characteristic, i.e., M = constant for all θ

5.14 a) Zeros at $z = 1.05e^{j0}$, $1.05e^{\pm j\pi/4}$, $1.05e^{\pm j\pi/2}$, $1.05e^{\pm j3\pi/4}$, $1.05e^{j\pi}$; Poles at $z = 0$ (eight of them)
  c) $24.77 \cos(n3\pi/8 + 0.297)$
  d) $y(n) = x(n) - 1.477x(n - 8)$

5.15 a) Bandpass, recursive, $y(n) = -1.273y(n - 1) - 0.81y(n - 2) + x(n) - x(n - 2)$
  b) Lowpass, recursive, $y(n) = 0.7y(n - 1) + x(n) + 0.7x(n - 1)$
  c) Highpass, recursive, $y(n) = -0.7y(n - 1) - 0.7x(n - 1) + x(n)$
  d) Bandstop, recursive, $y(n) = 0.49y(n - 2) + x(n) - 1.70x(n - 1) + 1.44x(n - 2)$

5.16 a) Zeros: 0, 0, $\pm j1$; poles: $0.707e^{\pm j\pi/4}$, $0.707e^{\pm j3\pi/4}$
  c) $y_{ss}(n) = 1.003 \cos(n\pi/4 + \alpha_1 - \pi/4) + 0.272 \cos(n\pi + \alpha_3)$
  d) $y(n) = -0.25y(n - 4) + x(n) + x(n - 2)$

Chapter 6

6.1 a) Zeros at $z = -1$, $\pm j1$; poles at $z = 0.5$, ± 2
  b) Unstable
  c) ROC—all values of z such that $2 < |z|$

6.3 a) Zeros at $z = 0.4$, -0.2; poles at $z = \pm 0.5$
  b) Stable
  c) $0.88e^{j0.18}$

6.5 a) Zeros at $z = 0$, $\pm j1$; poles at $z = -0.5$, $\pm j0.5$
  b) Stable
  c) $[2.5(-0.5)^n + 2.12(0.5)^n \cos(n\pi/2 - 3\pi/4)] u(n)$
  d) Unit sample response

6.7 a) $[5(-0.5)^n + 4.47(0.707)^n \cos(n3\pi/4 + 2.68)] u(n)$

  b) $[n + 2] u(n)$

6.9 a) $0.5[(-1)^n + 1] u(n)$
  b) $y(n) = \begin{cases} 1, & n \text{ even} \\ 0, & n \text{ odd} \end{cases}$

6.11 a) $\dfrac{0.5z(z + 1)}{z^2 - z + 0.5}$
  b) $1.58(0.707)^n \cos(n\pi/4 - 1.25) u(n)$

6.12 a) $[-3(2)^n + (-1)] u(-n - 1)$
  b) $-3(2)^n u(-n - 1) - 1(-1)^n u(n)$
  c) $[3(2)^n - 1(-1)^n] u(n)$

6.17 a) $(1/N) \sum_{\ell=0}^{N-1} z^{-\ell}$
  b) $(1/5)(1 + z^{-1} + z^{-2} + z^{-3} + z^{-4})$

6.19 $(a^n/\sin \alpha) \sin([n + 1]\alpha) u(n)$

6.21 $[-500n - 5.55 \times 10^4 + 5.555 \times 10^4(1.01)^n] u(n)$

6.23 $[14.14 \cos(\pi n/2 - \pi/4) + 10] u(n)$

6.25 $[0.5n + 1.5] u(n)$

6.28 a) $4/[(1 - 0.5z^{-1})(1 + 0.5z^{-1})]$
  b) $C_1 = 2$, $C_2 = 2$
  c) $[2(0.5)^n + 2(-0.5)^n] u(n)$

6.33 $[z(z - 0.5)]/[(z - 0.33)(z - 0.25)]$

6.35 a) $(z^6 - 1)/z^6$
  b) Zeros at $z = 1e^{jm2\pi/6}$, $m = 0, 1, \ldots, 5$, 6 poles at $z = 0$
  e) $\delta(n) - \delta(n - 12)$

6.38 a) $23.1 \cos(2\pi n T/3 - 7\pi/6)$
  b) Zeros at $z = 0$, $1e^{\pm j\pi/2}$, poles at $z = -0.5$, $0.707e^{\pm j3\pi/4}$
  c) $y(n) = -1.5y(n - 1) - y(n - 2) - 0.25y(n - 3) + x(n) + x(n - 2)$
  d) $[5(-0.5)^n + 4.48(0.707)^n \cos(n3\pi/4 - 3.6)] u(n)$

6.39 a) $3/(z^2 - 0.25z - 0.125)$
  b) No finite zeros, poles at $z = 1/2$, $-1/4$
  c) $[16(-1/4)^n - 40(1/2)^n + 24(1)^n] u(n)$
  d) $y(0) = 0$, $y(1) = 0$, $y(2) = 15$, $y(3) = 75/4$

6.42 $a = 0.905$, $k = 1.819$, $\alpha = \pi/2$

6.44 $Az^{-l}X(z^{-1})X(z)$

6.46 a) $H(z) = (z^2 + 4)/(z^2 + 0.25)$, zeros at $z = \pm j2$, poles at $z = \pm j0.5$
  b) $16\delta(n) - 15(0.5)^n \cos(n\pi/2) u(n)$
  c) $(e^{j2\theta} + 4)/(e^{j2\theta} + 0.25)$

6.47 a) $[(1/4)(z^3 + z^2 + z + 1)]/z^3$
  b) Zeros at $z = -1$, $\pm j1$, 3 poles at $z = 0$
  c)

θ	0	$\pi/4$	$\pi/2$	$3\pi/4$	π
$|H(e^{j\theta})|$	1	0.66	0	0.653	0.271

6.49 $2z^{-2}X(z) - z^{-1}dX(z)/dz$

6.50 a) $[6(0.6)^n - 5(0.5)^n]\, u(n)$

Chapter 7

7.1 a) 6
b) 7
c) 4
d) 5

7.3 a) $X_p(k) = -j30$ for $k = 1$; $+j30$ for $k = 5$;
$X_p(k) = 0$ otherwise
b) $X_p(k) = 80$ for $k = 3$ and for $k = 17$;
$X_p(k) = 0$ otherwise
c) $X_p(k) = 35$ for $k = 5$ and for $k = 9$;
$X_p(k) = 0$ otherwise

7.5 a)

k	0	1	2	3	4
$X_p(k)$	10	$3e^{j0.7\pi}$	$0.726e^{j0.9\pi}$	$X_p^*(2)$	$X_p^*(1)$

b)

k	0	1	2	3	4	5
$X_p(k)$	3	4	0	-5	0	4

7.7 $2.5 + 10\cos(2\pi n/8) + 5\cos(\pi n)$

7.9 a) i) 5
ii) 9
b) i) $\Delta f = 50$ Hz, $X_p(k) = 5/2$ for $k = 2$ and 3; $X_p(k) = 0$ otherwise
ii) $\Delta f = 50$ Hz, $X_p(k) = 9/2$ for $k = 2$ and 7; $X_p(k) = 0$ otherwise

7.11

k	0	1	2	3	4	5
$DFS[x_p(n) \circledast r_p(n)]$	0.0	6.0	0.0	0.0	0.0	6.0

7.13 a) $T_{max} = 0.002$, $N_{min} = 1000$, $T_{0\,min} = 2.0$
b) $T = 0.002$, $N = 1024$, $T_0 = 2.048$

7.15 a) 4 Hz
b) 1024 Hz
c) 1024 Hz

7.17

k	0	1	2	3	4
$X_p(k)$	10	$3.08e^{j0.7\pi}$	$0.73e^{j0.9\pi}$	$X_p^*(2)$	$X_p^*(1)$

7.19 a)

n	<0	0	1	2	3	4	>4
$x_1(n) * x_2(n)$	0	-2	-7	3	8	-4	0

b)

n	0	1	2
$x_1(n) \circledast x_2(n)$	6	-11	3

c)

p	<-2	-2	-1	0	1	2	>2
$R_{x_1x_2}(p)$	0	4	-4	-9	5	2	0

d)

p	<-2	-2	-1	0	1	2	>2
$R_{x_1x_1}(p)$	0	-2	-3	14	-3	-2	0

e)

p	0	1	2
$\widetilde{R}_{x_1x_1}(p)$	14	-5	-5

7.22 0.50

7.23 a)

n	0	1	2	3	4	5	6	7
$x_1(n) * x_2(n)$	1	3/2	1/2	0	0	0	0	3/2
$x_1(n) \circledast x_2(n)$	2	3/2	1/2	0	0	0	1/2	3/2

n	8	9	10	11	12	13	14
$x_1(n) * x_2(n)$	1	0	0	0	0	0	1/2

b) i)

n	-7	-6	-5	-4	-3	-2	-1	0
$R_{xh}(p)$	1/2	1/2	0	0	0	0	1/2	2

n	1	2	3	4	5	6	7
$R_{xh}(p)$	1	0	0	0	0	1/2	1

ii)

n	0	1	2	3	4	5	6	7
$\widetilde{R}_{xh}(p)$	2	3/2	1/2	0	0	0	1/2	3/2

7.25 a)

n	0	1	2	3	4	5
$x_1(n) * x_2(n)$	3	8	1	-1	2	-1
$x_1(n) \circledast x_2(n)$	5	7	1	-1		

b) Use zero padding to form sequences of length 7

7.27 a)

n	0	1	2	3	4	5	6
$x_1(n) * x_2(n)$	−2	2	−1	0	−3	−2	6
$x_1(n) \circledast x_2(n)$	−5	0	5	0			

  b) Form 7-point sequences by zero padding $x_1(n)$ and $x_2(n)$

7.29

n	0	1	2	3
$y(n)$	−2	4	−2	0

7.31 a) 2
  b) 0
  c) 0
  d) 4

7.34 a)

n	0	1	2	3	4	5	6	7	8	9
$x_1(n) * x_2(n)$	0	0	2	1	−1	−13	1	15	2	10

n	10	11	12	13	14	15	16	17	18
$x_1(n) * x_2(n)$	3	0	−8	2	−8	3	0	0	0

  b) 19 points

7.35 a)

p	−9	−8	−7	−6	−5	−4	−3	−2	−1
$R_{x_1 x_2}(p)$	−1	0	2	12	8	3	−2	−14	−1

p	0	1	2	3	4	5	6	7	8	9
$R_{x_1 x_2}(p)$	1	−1	−5	13	−6	0	0	0	0	0

7.37 a)

p	0	1	2	3	4	5
$\widetilde{R}_{x_1 x_2}(p)$	3	18	−1	8	−3	−13

  b)

p	−4	−3	−2	−1	0	1	2
$R_{x_1 x_2}(p)$	4	8	−3	−13	3	18	−5

7.41 a) $Y(mN + k) = X(k), k = 0, 1, \ldots, N − 1,$ $m = 0, 1$

7.44 b) $5 + 0.824 \cos(2\pi n/3 − 0.904)$

7.53 a)

n	0	1	2	3	4	5	6
$x_1(n) \circledast x_2(n)$	6	3	6	10	14	12	9

  b)

n	0	1	2	3	4	5	6	7
$x_1(n) * x_2(n)$	1	3	6	10	14	12	9	5

  c) Different—use 8 points in circular convolution to yield the same results.

7.54 a) $0.5 + e^{−j2.5\theta} \cos(2.5\theta)$
  b) $1 + 0.5e^{−j\pi k}, k = 0, 1, \ldots, 9$
  c)

k	0	1	2	3	4	...	7	8	9
$H(k)$	1.5	0.5	1.5	0.5	1.5	...	0.5	1.5	0.5

  d) $H(k) = H(e^{j2\pi k/10})$

Chapter 8

8.1 a) $X_{m+1}(p) = X_m(p) + W_N^r X_m(q); X_{m+1}(q) = X_m(p) + W_N^{(r+N/2)} X_m(q)$
  b) $A = W_N^r; B = −1$

8.4 a) 60,000 real multiplies
  b) 65,536 real multiplies

8.5 a) 5
  b) 17
  c) $N = 2^\gamma$, Number multiplies = $N\left[\dfrac{\gamma}{2} − 1 + \left(\dfrac{1}{2}\right)^\gamma\right]$

8.7 a) 2 Hz
  b) 1024 Hz
  c) i) 5120
    ii) 5120
    iii) 3072
  d) 5

8.11 a) 2500 Hz
  b) Spectrum has lines at ± 1250 Hz, ± 750 Hz

8.15 a) 10,500
  b) 10,080
  c) 3,002,500
  d) 29,696

8.17 a) 21,420
  b) 23,460
  c) 2,083,350
  d) 20,480

Chapter 9

9.1 a) $H(j\omega) = \begin{cases} 1, & 0 \le f \le 100 \text{ kHz} \\ 0, & \text{otherwise} \end{cases}$;

$H(e^{j\theta}) = \begin{cases} 1, & 0 \le \theta \le 0.2\pi \\ 0, & 0.2\pi < \theta \le \pi \end{cases}$

b) $h_{LP}(n) = (1/\pi n) \sin(0.2\pi n)$

9.3 a) $H(z) = 0.106 - 0.318z^{-2} + 0.5z^{-3} - 0.318z^{-4} + 0.106z^{-6}$

b) $H(z) = 0.008 - 0.245z^{-2} + 0.5z^{-3} - 0.245z^{-4} + 0.008z^{-6}$

9.5 $h(n) = \dfrac{1}{\pi n}\left[0.8 \sin n\theta_c + 0.1 \sin\left(\left[\dfrac{\pi + \theta_c}{2}\right]n\right)\right]$

9.7 b) $H(e^{j\theta}) = \begin{cases} 1, & 0.4\pi \le \theta \le 0.5\pi \\ 0, & 0 \le \theta < 0.4\pi,\ 0.5\pi < \theta \le \pi \end{cases}$

c) 41

d) $h_{BP}(n) = \left[2\cos(0.45\pi n)\right]\left[\dfrac{1}{\pi n}\sin(0.05\pi n)\right]$

n	0	± 1	± 2
$h_{BP}(n)$	0.1	0.0156	-0.0936

e)

n	0	± 1	± 2
$h_{BP}(n)$	0.1	0.0155	-0.0914

9.11 a) $h_{HP}(n) = \begin{cases} (-1)^n \times \dfrac{1}{\pi n}\sin(n3\pi/4), \\ \quad n = \pm 1, \pm 2, \ldots \\ 3/4, \quad n = 0 \end{cases}$

9.13 a) $h_{BP}(n) = [2\cos(n2\pi/3)]\left[\dfrac{1}{\pi n}\sin(n\pi/6)\right]$

b) $M = |-0.276\cos(2\theta) - 0.318\cos(\theta) + 0.333|,\ P = 0$

9.15 a) $0 \le f < 20$ kHz

b)

n	0, 4	1, 3	2
$h_{HP}(n)$	0.00748	-0.163	0.6

c) $H(e^{j0.4\pi}) = 0.713e^{-j0.8\pi}$

9.17 a) $H(e^{j\theta}) = \begin{cases} 0, & 0.12\pi \le \theta \le 0.3\pi \\ 1, & \text{elsewhere in the interval} \\ & 0 \le \theta \le \pi \end{cases}$

b) $h_{BS}(0) = 1 - 2(0.09) = 0.82$

$h_{BS}(n) = \left[-\dfrac{2}{\pi n}\cos(0.2\pi n)\right][\sin(0.09\pi n)],$
$n = \pm 1, \pm 2, \ldots$

9.20 c)

n	0, 14	1, 13	2, 12	3, 11
$h(n)$	-0.0295	-0.0530	-0.0476	-0.0037
$\hat{h}(n)$	-0.0024	-0.0068	-0.0120	-0.0016

n	4, 10	5, 9	6, 8	7
$h(n)$	0.0724	0.1591	0.2277	0.2537
$\hat{h}(n)$	0.0465	0.1316	0.2172	0.2537

9.21

n	0, 14	1, 13	2, 12	3, 11
a) $h(n)$	-0.0138	-0.0243	-0.0274	-0.0008
b) $h(n)$	-0.0033	-0.0129	-0.0256	-0.0195

n	4, 10	5, 9	6, 8	7
a) $h(n)$	0.0636	0.1502	0.2251	0.2547
b) $h(n)$	0.0338	0.1368	0.2449	0.2916

9.29 b) $h(n) = \dfrac{1}{\pi n}[\cos(n\theta_\ell) - \cos(n\theta_u)]$

c)

n	0	± 1	± 2
$h(n)$	0	± 0.069	± 0.113

d)

n	0	1	2	3	4
$\hat{h}(n)$	0	-0.0345	0	0.0345	0

9.37 a) $h(n) = \dfrac{1}{\pi n}\sin(\pi n/2),\quad n = 0, \pm 1, \pm 2, \ldots, \pm 30$

b) $y(n) = h(0)\,x(n) + h(1)\,x(n-1) + \cdots + h(60)\,x(n-60)$

9.38 a) $\pi/4$

b)

n	0, 4	1, 3	2
$h(n)$	0.5	0.707	$\pi/4$

c) $H(z) = 0.5 + 0.707z^{-1} + 0.785z^{-2} + 0.707z^{-3} + 0.5z^{-4}$

d) $y_{ss}(n) \approx 25.1 \sin(n\pi/6 - \pi/3)$

Chapter 10

10.1 $y_{ss}(t) = 3.44\cos(t - 1.11)$

10.4 $H(s) = \dfrac{10^3 s}{s^2 + 50s + 10^4}$

10.5 a) $\omega_\ell = \dfrac{1}{2}\left\{-\alpha_1 + \sqrt{\alpha_1{}^2 + 4\alpha_2}\right\}$ and

$\omega_u = \dfrac{1}{2}\left\{\alpha_1 + \sqrt{\alpha_1{}^2 + 4\alpha_2}\right\}$

b) $\omega = \sqrt{\alpha_2}$

10.8 a) $H_{LP}(s) =$

$$\frac{27(10^9)}{s^3 + 6(10^3)s^2 + 18(10^6)s + 27(10^9)}$$

b) $H_{HP}(s) = \dfrac{0.983s^2}{s^2 + 6.255(10^4)s + 35.791(10^8)}$

c) $H_{LP}(s) =$

$$\frac{2126(s^2 + 7.504 \times 10^8)}{s^3 + 1.558(10^4)s^2 + 2.409(10^8)s + 1.620(10^{12})}$$

d) $H_{BS}(s) = \dfrac{s^2 + 14{,}400\pi^2}{s^2 + 20\pi s + 14{,}400\pi^2}$

10.9 a) $H_{BP}(z) = \dfrac{0.211(z^2 - 1)}{z^2 + 1.160z + 0.579}$

b) $H_{HP}(z) = \dfrac{76.539(z - 1)^2}{53.981z^2 - 105.765z + 164.823}$

c) $H_{BS}(z) = \dfrac{0.888(z^2 + 1)}{z^2 + 0.776}$

10.13 The constants a, b, and c must all have the same algebraic sign.

10.16 a) $H_{LP}(s) = \dfrac{10^{12}}{s^3 + 2(10^4)s^2 + 2(10^8)s + 10^{12}}$

10.18 b) $H_{LP_p}(s) = \dfrac{1}{s^3 + 2s^2 + 2s + 1}$

10.22 a) Butterworth

b) $\omega_{LP_p} = \dfrac{\omega_{BP}{}^2 - 3.553(10^8)}{6912\,\omega_{BP}}$

c) $H_{LP_p}(s) = \dfrac{1}{s^2 + 1.41s + 1}$

d) $H_{BP}(s) =$

$$\frac{4.78(10^7)s^2}{s^4 + 9.77(10^3)s^3 + 7.58(10^8)s^2 + 3.47(10^{12})s + 1.26(10^{17})}$$

10.23 a) 0.5-dB ripple Chebyshev

b) $\omega_{LP_p} = \dfrac{\omega_{BP}{}^2 - 3.548(10^8)}{2576\,\omega_{BP}}$

c) $H_{LP_p}(s) = \dfrac{1.431}{s^2 + 1.425s + 1.516}$

d) $H_{BP}(s) = \dfrac{9.497(10^6)s^2}{s^4 + 3.671(10^3)s^3 + 7.197(10^8)s^2 + 1.303(10^{12})s + 1.259(10^{17})}$

10.24 $H_{BP}(z) =$

$$\frac{0.00434(z + 1)^2(z - 1)^2}{z^4 - 3.538z^3 + 4.941z^2 - 3.208z + 0.823}$$

10.25 See Problem 10.24

10.26 See Problem 10.24

10.30 $H_{HP}(z) = \dfrac{0.282(z - 1)^2}{1.667z^2 + 4.605z + 4.026}$

10.31 a) $H_{HP}(z) =$

$$\frac{k(z^3 - 3z^2 + 3z - 1)}{z^3 - 0.475z^2 + 0.279z - 0.0497}; \text{ To}$$

make $H(z)\big|_{z=-1} = 1$, $k = 0.226$

10.39 a) $H_{HP}(z) =$

$$\frac{2.112(z - 1)^3}{1.584z^3 - 5.645z^2 + 6.805z - 2.792}$$

Chapter 11

11.2 a) Unstable because of characteristic root at $z = 2$

b) $\mathbf{v}(1) = [-2 \quad 0 \quad 2]^T$ and $y(1) = -2$
$\mathbf{v}(2) = [0 \quad 2 \quad 7]^T$ and $y(2) = 2$
$\mathbf{v}(3) = [2 \quad 7 \quad 19.5]^T$ and $y(3) = 9$

11.3 b)

$$\mathbf{v}(n + 1) = \begin{bmatrix} -0.5 & 0 & 0 \\ -1.5 & 0.9 & -0.81 \\ 0 & 1 & 0 \end{bmatrix} \mathbf{v}(n) + \begin{bmatrix} 10 \\ 10 \\ 0 \end{bmatrix} x(n)$$

$$y(n) = \begin{bmatrix} -1.5 & 2.31 & -0.81 \end{bmatrix} \mathbf{v}(n) + 10x(n)$$

11.6 a) $H_1(z) = \dfrac{z - 1}{z^2 - z + 1}$; $H_2(z) = \dfrac{1}{z^2 - z + 1}$

b) $\mathbf{v}(n + 1) = \mathbf{A}\,\mathbf{v}(n) + \mathbf{B}\,x(n)$ and $y(n) = \mathbf{C}\,\mathbf{v}(n) + \mathbf{D}\,x(n)$

where $\mathbf{A} = \begin{bmatrix} 0 & 1 \\ -1 & 1 \end{bmatrix}$, $\mathbf{B} = \begin{bmatrix} 1 & 0 \\ 0 & 1 \end{bmatrix}$,

$\mathbf{C} = \begin{bmatrix} 1 & 0 \end{bmatrix}$, and $\mathbf{D} = 0$

c) $y(n) = [-(2/3)(1/2)^n + (4/7)(-1/2)^n + 1.818\cos(1.047n - 1.519)]u(n)$

11.9 b) $H(z) = \dfrac{z^2 + 1.8z + 0.81}{z^2 - 1.8z + 0.81}$

c) Zeros: $z_{1,2} = -0.9$, Poles: $z_{1,2} = 0.9$

d) $h(n) = \delta(n) + 3.6n(0.9)^n u(n)$

11.13 a) $\mathbf{A} = \begin{bmatrix} -c_0 & 1 & 0 \\ -c_1 & 0 & 1 \\ -c_2 & 0 & 0 \end{bmatrix}$, $\mathbf{B} = \begin{bmatrix} d_2 \\ d_1 \\ d_0 \end{bmatrix}$,

$\mathbf{C} = \begin{bmatrix} 1 & 0 & 0 \end{bmatrix}$, and $\mathbf{D} = 0$

b) $Y(z)/X(z) = (d_2z^2 + d_1z + d_0)/(z^3 + c_0z^2 + c_1z + c_2)$

11.14 a) $H(z) = Y(z)/X(z) = \dfrac{1}{z^2 - z\,2a\cos\alpha + a^2}$

b) Yes

c) $a < 1$ and any value of α

e) $h(n) = \delta(n) + 1.41\cos(\pi n/4 - 3\pi/4)\,u(n)$

11.15 a) $k_1 = 0$, $k_2 = 0$, $k_3 = 0$, and $k_4 = -0.5$

b) $k_1 = 0$, $k_2 = 1.25$, $k_3 = 0$, and $k_4 = -0.6$

11.17 $h_2(n) = \delta(n) - a\delta(n - 1)$

11.19 a) $\mathbf{A}' = \begin{bmatrix} 0 & 1 \\ -1 - k_1 & 1 - k_2 \end{bmatrix}$, $\mathbf{B}' = \begin{bmatrix} 0 \\ 1 \end{bmatrix}$

b) $k_1 = -1$ and $k_2 = 1$

c) $k_1 = -0.4375$ and $k_2 = -0.2$

11.21 b) $H(z) = Y(z)/X(z) = \dfrac{1}{z^2 - z + 1}$

c) $h(n) = \delta(n) + \dfrac{2}{\sqrt{3}} \cos(\pi n/3 - 5\pi/6) \, u(n)$

11.26 b) $H(z) = \dfrac{b}{z - a}$ and $T(z) = \dfrac{z}{z - a}$

c) $y(n) = \left[\left(\dfrac{b}{\alpha - a} \right) \alpha^n + \left(\dfrac{-b}{\alpha - a} \right) a^n + v(0) a^n \right] u(n)$

11.29 a)

θ	0	$\pi/2$	$3\pi/4$
M	0.891	0.891	0.106
M_{dB}	-1	-1	-19.5

b) $10.246y(n) + 1.318y(n - 1) + 6.476y(n - 2) + 0.414y(n - 3) + 1.010y(n - 4) = 0.966x(n) + 3.864x(n - 1) + 5.796x(n - 2) + 3.864x(n - 3) + 0.966x(n - 4)$

11.31 a) There are several correct sets of state and output equations.

b) The derived initial conditions are $y(0) = 0$, $y(1) = 4$, and $y(2) = -2$. For the state and output equations

$$\mathbf{v}(n + 1) = \begin{bmatrix} -1 & -0.25 & 0.5 \\ 1 & 0 & 0 \\ 0 & 1 & 0 \end{bmatrix} \mathbf{v}(n) + \begin{bmatrix} 1 \\ 0 \\ 0 \end{bmatrix} x(n)$$

$$y(n) = \begin{bmatrix} 3 & -0.25 & 0.5 \end{bmatrix} \mathbf{v}(n) + x(n)$$

the state vector at $n = 0$ is

$$\mathbf{v}(0) = \begin{bmatrix} -0.2875 \\ -0.0530 \\ -0.2995 \end{bmatrix}$$

11.33 a) From Table 6.1

$$H(z) = \frac{z}{z - 0.5} + \frac{z[-2\cos(-\pi)]}{z^2 + 4}$$

$$= \frac{z^3 + 2z^2 + 3z}{z^3 - 0.5z^2 + 4z - 2}$$

b) $y(n) - 0.5y(n - 1) + 4y(n - 2) - 2y(n - 3) = x(n) + 2x(n - 1) + 3x(n - 2)$

c) $y(0) = h(0) = 1$, $y(1) = h(1) = 2.5$, $y(2) = h(2) = 0.25$, and $y(3) = h(3) = -7.875$

e) One acceptable answer is the following:

$$\mathbf{v}(n + 1) = \begin{bmatrix} 0.5 & -4 & 2 \\ 1 & 0 & 0 \\ 0 & 1 & 0 \end{bmatrix} \mathbf{v}(n) + \begin{bmatrix} 1 \\ 0 \\ 0 \end{bmatrix} x(n)$$

$$y(n) = \begin{bmatrix} 2.5 & -1 & 2 \end{bmatrix} \mathbf{v}(n) + x(n)$$

f) No steady-state solution—system is unstable

11.36 a) $H(z) = \dfrac{z^2 + 4}{z^2 + 0.25}$

b) $h(n) = 16\delta(n) - [15(-0.5)^n \cos(n\pi/2)] u(n)$

c) $H(e^{j\theta}) = \dfrac{1 + 4e^{-j2\theta}}{1 + 0.25e^{-j2\theta}}$

Index

Transfer functions, $H(z)$ (*continued*)
    from system diagram using MGR, 743–744
    from unit sample response, 297–299
    poles and zeros of, 300–302
    stability
        anticausal system, 346–348
        causal, 302–303, 346–348

Unit sample (impulse) response $h(n)$, 90–102
    for cascade connection, 122–125
    for finite impulse response (FIR) system, 91–92, 98
    for infinite impulse response (IIR) system, 96–98
    for parallel connection, 125–127
Unit sample (impulse) sequence
    definition, 22
    DFT of, 385
    z-transform of, 285–286
Unit step sequence, 23
Unstable, 60

von Hann window, 467–474, 561

Windows
    Bartlett, 561
    Hamming, 467–473, 561–566
    rectangular, 450, 466–467, 558–561
    use in Fourier Series design, 558–565
    use in spectrum analysis, 459–474
    von Hann, 467–474, 561

Zero padding, 425–427, 432–434, 439–446
Zeros
    definition, 254
    effect on frequency response, 262
    of a transfer function, 300–302

z-Transforms
    convolution relationship, 292–296
    definition, 283
    final-value theorem, 331–332, 353, 358 (Problem 6.32)
    initial-value theorem, 331, 353, 357 (Problems 6.31, 6.34)
    inverse transforms
        from definition, 305–306
        from inversion formula, 348–349
        from long division, 306–307
        notation, 284
        from partial fraction expansion (PFE), 307–318, 357 (Problems 6.27–6.29)
    derivation of pairs for right-sided sequences, 285–288
    of periodogram spectral estimate, 448, 454–455
    poles
        effect on time response, 326–329
        nonrepeated (distinct), 308–312
        repeated (multiple), 312–314
    of power spectrum, 459
    properties
        derivatives in z, 290–291, 355 (Problem 6.14)
        linearity, 288–289
        shifting, 289–290
    region of convergence (ROC), 286–288, 342–348, 352–353
    sinusoidal steady-state formula, derivation of, 334–337
    solution of difference equations, 318–326, 756–760
    stability
        and region of convergence, 346–348
        anticausal system, 346–348
        causal system, 302–303, 346–348
    tables of pairs and properties, 352–353
    transfer function, 296–302
    unilateral, shifting property, 318–322
    of unit sample response, 297–298
    zeros, 329–330

Circular convolution, $\quad \text{DFT}[x_1(n) \circledast x_2(n)] = X_1(k) \cdot X_2(k)$

Linear convolution and circular convolution

$$x_1(n) * x_2(n) = x_3(n) = x_3'(n) = x_1'(n) \circledast x_2'(n)$$

Linear correlation, $\quad R_{x_1 x_2}(p) = \sum_{m=-\infty}^{m=+\infty} x_1(m) x_2(p + m)$

Circular correlation, $\quad \tilde{R}_{x_1 x_2}(p) = \sum_{m=0}^{N-1} x_1(m) x_2(p \oplus m), \; p = 0, 1, \ldots, N - 1$

Circular correlation by DFTs, $\quad \text{DFT}[\tilde{R}_{x_1 x_2}(p)] = X_1^*(k) \cdot X_2(k)$

Periodogram spectral estimate

$$S_N(k) = \frac{1}{N} |X(k)|^2 = \frac{1}{N} X^*(k) X(k), \qquad k = 0, 1, \ldots, N - 1$$

Power spectrum z-transform, $S_N(z) = H(z) H^*(z^{-1})$

Hamming window, $\quad w(n) = 0.54 - 0.46 \cos\left(\frac{2\pi n}{N-1}\right), \quad 0 \le n \le N - 1$

von Hann window, $\quad w(n) = 0.50 - 0.50 \cos\left(\frac{2\pi n}{N-1}\right), \quad 0 \le n \le N - 1$

Fast Fourier Transforms

Weighting factor W_N, butterfly, Decomposition-In-Time (DIT), Decomposition-In-Frequency (DIF), Fast Convolution to obtain linear convolution or linear correlation